FORMAL SERVICE SCHOOL COURSES

CREDIT AND ADVANCED STANDING BY EXAMINATION

1968 Edition

A GUIDE TO THE EVALUATION OF EDUCATIONAL EXPERIENCES IN THE ARMED SERVICES

FORMAL SERVICE SCHOOL COURSES

CREDIT AND ADVANCED STANDING
BY EXAMINATION

Cornelius P. Turner, Editor

American Council on Education
Washington, D.C.

FOREWORD

THIS NATION IS CONCERNED about the educational needs of all its people—not only those who attend our formal educational institutions, but also those who are striving to advance themselves educationally outside of formal school situations. The needs of these adults have created special problems. They require different instructional materials, new teaching techniques, and effective methods of evaluation.

Although educators are by profession convinced that the best and quickest way to acquire an education is through completion of formal schooling, they are well aware that is not the only way. There are many media through which an individual, by his own efforts, can raise his educational level beyond that of his last formal schooling. For his educational or vocational ambitions to materialize, however, he often needs to have his educational competence evaluated and recognized by appropriate authorities.

The Armed Forces of the United States provide military personnel with a great variety of educational opportunities through formal service school training programs and off-duty educational activities. Since before World War II the American Council on Education, in cooperation with other national educational organizations, has been interested in the development and evaluation of the off-duty educational programs as well as the evaluation of the formal service training courses. In response to a need expressed by civilian educational institutions throughout the country the Council, in 1945, established its Commission on Accreditation of Service Experiences as an agency to assist institutions by providing continuing evaluations of military educational programs in terms of academic credit.

This GUIDE is one example of the Commission's service to educational institutions. It provides a sound appraisal of the various training programs. It also describes two national testing programs through which adults have an effective method for the evaluation of their achievements at specific educational levels.

The Council deeply appreciates the financial support for publication of the GUIDE provided by the Department of Defense and the Veterans Administration; the encouragement and assistance given by the American Association of Collegiate Registrars and Admissions Officers, the American Association of Junior Colleges, and the College Entrance Examination Board in the preparation of the manuscript; and the cooperation of hundreds of educators who have evaluated the many programs. It is hoped that institutions of higher education will find the 1968 GUIDE helpful in the admission and placement of veterans through the evaluation of service school training programs as well as in the admission and placement of those adults who qualify through the GED Testing Program and the College-Level Examination Program.

LOGAN WILSON, *President*
American Council on Education

April 1968

ACKNOWLEDGMENTS

The publication of this 1968 GUIDE is the result of the coordinated efforts of educators, organizations, and agencies to help veterans and service personnel of the Armed Forces of the United States to achieve their educational and vocational ambitions through an evaluation of their formal military educational experiences.

During the past twenty-three years, hundreds of leading educators, serving as consultants to the Commission, have contributed generously of their time in appraising service school training programs in terms of academic credit.

The Department of Defense and the Veterans Administration provided equally the financial support for the preparation, printing, and distribution of the publication.

The American Association of Collegiate Registrars and Admissions Officers, the American Association of Junior Colleges, and the College Entrance Examination Board, through their officials, have been of great assistance in the planning and preparation of the 1968 GUIDE.

The members and staff of the Commission on Accreditation of Service Experiences wish to express our appreciation to those educators, organizations, and agencies for the support given to this publication. Special acknowledgment is also given to the Commission's Advisory Committee whose members are listed below:

J. DOUGLAS CONNER, *Chairman*
Executive Secretary, American Association of Collegiate Registrars and Admissions Officers

EDMUND J. GLEAZER, JR.
Executive Director, American Association of Junior Colleges

ROBERT E. MAHN
Registrar, Ohio University

CHARLES W. McLANE
Director of Admissions and Registrar, University of Missouri

N. M. PARKHURST, *Vice-Chairman*
Registrar, Purdue University

ALFRED THOMAS, JR.
Registrar and Director of Admissions, Arizona State University

CLYDE VROMAN
Director of Admissions, University of Michigan

AMERICAN ASSOCIATION OF COLLEGIATE REGISTRARS AND ADMISSIONS OFFICERS

The American Association of Collegiate Registrars and Admissions Officers passed the following resolution at its 52nd Annual Meeting in Phoenix, Arizona:

> AACRAO expresses its appreciation for past services to the American Council on Education and its Commission on Accreditation of Service Experiences, and respectfully requests that the American Council on Education and the Commission act promptly to prepare a new edition of its publication, A GUIDE TO THE EVALUATION OF EDUCATIONAL EXPERIENCES IN THE ARMED SERVICES in order to provide maximum assistance to members of AACRAO in the placement of veterans and service personnel in educational programs offered by the institutions which we represent.

The Association, as an instigating force in the production of the 1968 edition, participated actively through the efforts of individual members who served on the Advisory Committee established to assist the Commission on Accreditation of Service Experiences in developing plans for the new GUIDE.

The Advisory Committee recommends the 1968 edition to the members of AACRAO with the hope that this GUIDE will be utilized to full advantage and that institutions which have not already done so will adopt policies appropriate to their particular needs for the proper educational placement of veterans.

> J. DOUGLAS CONNER, *Executive Secretary,*
> *American Association of Collegiate*
> *Registrars and Admissions Officers,*
> *and Advisory Committee Chairman*

April 1968

CONTENTS

INTRODUCTION

THIS EDITION OF THE GUIDE has been prepared at the request of the American Association of Collegiate Registrars and Admissions Officers. Anticipating hundreds of thousands of veterans enrolling in colleges and universities through the assistance provided by the Veterans Readjustment Benefits Act of 1966, and with the expectation that many would apply for academic credit for their military educational experiences, AACRAO requested the American Council on Education, through its Commission on Accreditation of Service Experiences, to revise and bring up to date its publication, A GUIDE TO THE EVALUATION OF EDUCATIONAL EXPERIENCES IN THE ARMED SERVICES, last issued in 1954.

The Commission approved the request of AACRAO and authorized the preparation of a new edition of the GUIDE for distribution in September 1968. The preparation, printing, and distribution of the publication was financed equally by the Department of Defense and the Veterans Administration.

Two previous editions of the GUIDE have been published. Immediately after World War II, in 1946, the first edition was issued to assist educational institutions in evaluating the military educational experiences of veteran students of that war. The extension of the World War II G.I. Bill, which included veterans of the Korean conflict and the subsequent enrollment of many veterans in colleges and universities, created a need for a second edition in 1954.

Since 1954, the introduction of new military tactics and weapons has caused rapid changes in service training programs resulting in new or revised recommendations for academic credit. This 1968 edition includes all the formal resident service school programs given from 1954 through February 1968 for which syllabi were provided to the Commission by the Air Force, Army, Coast Guard, Marine Corps, Navy, and the Department of Defense. In the preparation of this edition, 8,814 formal service school syllabi were analyzed, evaluated, and prepared for inclusion as exhibits.

The credit recommendations, prepared by the Commission on Accreditation of Service Experiences, are a guide to assist college officials in determining the amount and type of credit which they may consider granting to enrolled students for their military educational experiences. The formal service school courses have been evaluated by civilian educators, experts in the academic areas concerned, who serve as consultants to the Commission.

The Commission members as well as college and university officials have always held that academic credit for military educational experiences should never be granted as a reward for military service. Such credit should be granted only for valid educational experiences and on a basis of sound appraisal by civilian educators. The granting of credit for military training should be considered on the same basis as that followed in accepting transfer credit from another institution.

RECOMMENDATIONS OF ADVISORY COMMITTEE

The preparation of the planned new GUIDE required the advice and counsel of those who would use it. To assist the staff in policy matters, the Commission appointed an Advisory Committee with the membership representing AACRAO and the American Association of Junior Colleges. This committee, acting either in full session, in executive session, or through its chairman, provided advice and counsel throughout preparation of the 1968 GUIDE. The committee recommendations concerning policy were approved by the full commission. Those recommendations which resulted in changes of policy from previous editions of the GUIDE are described below.

Level of Credit Recommendations

The 1968 GUIDE includes credit recommendations at the *collegiate level* only. Previous editions of the GUIDE had listed credit recommendations at the baccalaureate, terminal junior college, and high school levels. The term *collegiate level* includes both baccalaureate and terminal junior college recommendations. However, those training programs which are of the nature of terminal junior college courses are designated in the 1968 GUIDE as *technical and vocational in nature*. All other recommendations listed are at the *baccalaureate level*.

For those high-level training programs which have been evaluated by the Commission at the *graduate and baccalaureate levels,* a credit recommendation at the *graduate level* has been added. In each exhibit for these courses, a statement explains that the evaluation was made by graduate school deans and professors selected by the president of the Council of Graduate Schools in the United States.

The 1968 GUIDE does not include any credit recommendations at the secondary school level. However, the Commission will provide credit recommendations at the high school level to appropriate officials of high schools or state departments of education upon written request. Today, throughout the country, high school equivalency certificates are issued on the basis of the General Educational Development (GED) tests; there have been few requests during the last several years for the recommendations of this Commission for service school training programs at the high school level. Therefore, recommendations at this level are not included in this GUIDE.

Preparation of Exhibits and Index

Previous editions of the GUIDE had included detailed descriptions of the subjects taught at service schools and explanatory statements concerning credit recommendations. Because of the many years of satisfactory experience that college officials have had in using the Commission's recommendations, and in view of the great numbers of training programs to be included in the 1968 GUIDE, it was the consensus of the committee members that each exhibit should: correctly identify the training program by title, length, location of training; and include only brief statements on the objectives of the course, the instructional program, and the credit recommendations. However, college officials desiring a detailed description of any course may send their request to the Commission.

Committee members also recommended that a separate index be compiled for each service rather than list all courses in one general section. Therefore, there are six indexes: Air Force, Army, Coast Guard, Marine Corps, Navy, and Department of Defense.

Distribution of 1968 GUIDE

Two copies of the publication have been distributed without charge to each institution of higher education listed in the *Education Directory, 1966–67; Part 3, Higher Education* issued by the U.S. Office of Education: one copy addressed to the president, the other to the director of admissions. Additional copies may be purchased from the Publications Division, American Council on Education.

Statement on the College-Level Examination Program

And last, the Advisory Committee recommended that because thousands of service personnel on active duty take the CLEP General Examinations, and because the CLEP Program has been evaluated by the Commission on Accreditation of Service Experiences, a statement on the College-Level Examination Program of the College Entrance Examination Board be included for the information of admissions officers. With the support of the College Entrance Examination Board and the GED Testing Service, Part II, "Credit and Advanced Standing by Examination," has been added to this edition.

DIRECTIONS FOR USING THE 1968 GUIDE

Organization

The GUIDE has three major divisions: Part I, "Formal Service School Courses," Part II, "Credit and Advanced Standing by Examination," and an Index.

Part I has seven sections: Air Force, Army, Coast Guard, Marine Corps, Navy, Department of Defense, and Addenda. Each of the first six sections includes the exhibits of courses given by that service or by the Department of Defense. The exhibits are listed alphabetically by the first course title in the exhibit. Many exhibits contain the titles of more than one course. The titles appearing in parentheses are previous titles of the first course listed when the instructional contents have not been changed sufficiently to alter the credit recommendation. In other exhibits, course titles are numbered. In some cases, the titles may be identical but they are numbered because the instruction varied significantly as the course was given at different times, resulting in changes in credit recommendations. In other cases, the numbered course titles represent similar or related programs which could be grouped together.

The seventh section, the Addenda, contains exhibits of courses for which information was received too late to be included in the main sections of Part I and also other courses which, subsequent to printing deadlines, required evaluation by consultants or extensive revision of exhibits in light of new syllabi provided by the respective services. The Addenda includes courses given by the Air Force, Army, Marine Corps, and Navy.

Part II describes two national testing programs through which military personnel on active duty in the Armed Forces of the United States may receive a different type of appraisal of their educational achievements. Both programs are also available to veterans and civilian adults.

The GED Testing Program has been used for many years by secondary school authorities to determine the issuance of high school equivalency certificates to adults who have not graduated from high school and by college admissions officers to fulfill entrance requirements of such adults. The College-Level Examination Program (CLEP) provides an opportunity to adults, qualified for admission to college by graduation from high school or through successful achievement on the GED tests, to begin their degree program at an advanced level.

The Index is given in six sections listed under the name of each service and the Department of Defense. Each course described in the Addenda is indexed under the service giving the program. Inversions of course titles have been inserted to assist officials in locating programs.

How to Find Specific Courses in Part I

In order to locate a specific course, the college official must obtain from the veteran or serviceman on active duty *all* of the following *exact* information: (1) *full and correct title of course completed;* (2) *location where training was given;* (3) *length of course in weeks;* (4) *exact dates of attendance;* and (5) *the service which gave the course.* The applicant should be required to verify the fact that he has completed formal service school training by submitting official records. The types of official records for verification of training which should be required and their sources are described on page xvi.

When *all* of the *exact* information is available, the college official should consult the Index of the service giving the course for the page reference. It should be noted that there will be many cases when a member of one service will have completed a service school program given by another service. The title, however, will be indexed under the service giving the course.

When it is not possible to determine the full and correct title of a course from information given on official records, college officials should refer such cases to the Commission for assistance as described on page xviii. (Official records use abbreviations of course titles in many cases, and they are sometimes difficult to decipher.)

Caution Statements

College officials should exercise great care in correctly identifying the course which an applicant has completed. To assist officials, a *caution statement* has been inserted in many exhibits following the item, *Credit recommendation, collegiate level.* Two examples will illustrate the reason for the caution statement and the necessity for requiring students to identify the course exactly through submission of official records:

One exhibit on page 113 lists nine related service school courses, all with the title "Weapons Control Systems Mechanic." The only means of differentiating among the courses, and therefore among the credit recommendations, is by the identifying material in parentheses following the course title. The course, "Weapons Control Systems Mechanic (MG-3, 10, 13 Data Flow)," carries a recommendation of six semester hours in electricity and electronics at the freshman or sophomore levels and credit in electrical laboratory on the basis of demonstrated skills and/or institutional examinations. This course includes extensive study of electronic theory as well as training in the repair of complicated electronic equipment. A second course, "Weapons Control Systems Mechanic (MG-3, MG-10 Data Flow)," carries a recommendation that credit in electricity and electronics and electrical laboratory be granted only on the basis of demonstrated skills and/or institutional examinations. The second course, twelve weeks longer than the first, does not include instruction in electronic theory, but is devoted solely to repair of electronic equipment.

In an exhibit on page 51 two other courses with identical titles, "Flight Facilities Equipment Repairman (TACAN)," carry two quite different recommendations. The thirty-week course receives three semester hours at the freshman or sophomore level as an elective in electricity and electronics as well as additional credit in electrical laboratory on the basis of demonstrated skills and/or institutional examinations. The seventeen-week course receives credit only in electricity and electrical laboratory on the basis of demonstrated skills and/or institutional examinations.

Official Records for Verification of Training

Those students who make application for credit for their service school training should be required to submit official records. The official records listed below are those which have been issued by the various services to veterans who were discharged prior to 1950, those who were discharged after January 1, 1950, and the records which service personnel on active duty may be required to submit.

FOR VETERANS*

DISCHARGED PRIOR TO 1950:
Air Force—Separation Qualification Record or transcript of in-service training from the General Services Administration, National Personnel Records Center (Military Personnel Records), 9700 Page Boulevard, St. Louis, Missouri 63132.

---

*If the appropriate entry concerning the completion of a service school course has not been recorded on the separation record, college officials may wish to permit the veteran to use as evidence the official diploma or certificate issued by the service school itself.

Army—Separation Qualification Record or transcript of in-service training from the General Services Administration, National Personnel Records Center (Military Personnel Records), 9700 Page Boulevard, St. Louis, Missouri 63132.

Coast Guard—Notice of Separation from the United States Naval Service or a transcript of in-service training from the General Services Administration, National Personnel Records Center (Military Personnel Records), 9700 Page Boulevard, St. Louis, Missouri 63132.

Marine Corps—USMC Report of Separation or a transcript of in-service training from the Commandant of the Marine Corps (Code DGK), Headquarters United States Marine Corps, Washington, D.C. 20380.

Navy—Notice of Separation from the United States Naval Service (commissioned or warrant officers may submit instead the Officer's Qualification Record Jacket or a certified copy thereof) or a transcript of in-service training from the Bureau of Naval Personnel (Code Pers E), Department of the Navy, Washington, D.C. 20370.

SEPARATED AFTER JANUARY 1, 1950:
DD Form 214—Armed Forces of the United States Report of Transfer or Discharge—or a transcript of in-service training from the appropriate service as listed above.

FOR SERVICE PERSONNEL ON ACTIVE DUTY
Certificates or diplomas from service schools completed and/or in-service training as certified on DD Form 295—Application for the Evaluation of Educational Experiences During Military Service.

TYPES OF TRAINING PROGRAMS EVALUATED

Part I contains only those service school programs conducted on a formal school basis and listed by the appropriate service in their catalogs as formal resident training. These courses are conducted for a specific period of time with a prescribed course of instruction, in a classroom situation, and with qualified instructors. Successful completion of a formal service school is determined on the basis of oral and/or written examinations. In order to qualify for evaluation, formal resident service school training programs must be given on a full-time basis of not less than three weeks duration with a minimum of thirty clock hours of academic instruction per week or, if the total training period is less than three weeks in length, the course must include a minimum of ninety clock hours of academic instruction within that period of time. The Commission also evaluates training conducted for National Guard and Reserve personnel (not on extended active duty status) when the training meets the same requirements.

The Commission does not evaluate informal on-the-job training, service jobs or billets, training programs conducted by contract with educational institutions and industry, training programs conducted overseas, service extension programs, training conducted prior to Pearl Harbor, foreign service school training, military training conducted primarily for civilians, ROTC training, service academy training, or training programs which carry a security classification.

CREDIT FOR MILITARY SERVICE, INCLUDING BASIC OR RECRUIT TRAINING

With the establishment of the six-month Reserve Training Programs by the services, as authorized by the Reserve Forces Act of 1955 (PL 305), the Commission received many requests from educational institutions for a recommendation on this training. The Commission, at its May 1957 meeting, appointed a special committee to study this training program, to review the recommendations with regard to basic and recruit training, and to prepare recommendations to the full Commission membership. The Commission accepted the recommendations of the special committee and established the following policy in 1957 as the credit recommendation for military service including completion of the six-month Reserve Training Programs and/or basic or recruit training:

I. *Secondary School*

The Commission recommends no high school credit for military service per se, including basic or recruit training. It is recommended, however, that the physical education experiences during military service of six months or more be accepted in lieu of the mandatory high school requirement of physical education or hygiene and health education.

II. *College*

1. *For military service—six months to one full year:*

   a. The Commission recommends that six months to one full year of military service, including the completion of basic or recruit training, be accepted as meeting the requirements in military science at the freshman level, only at those institutions which normally allow credit for collegiate level courses in this area.

   b. The Commission recommends no credit in physical education or in hygiene and health education if the applicant has completed one year or less of military service.

2. *For military service—over one year:*

   a. The Commission recommends that over one year of military service, including the completion of basic or recruit training, be accepted as meeting the requirements in military science at the freshman and sophomore levels, only at those institutions which normally allow credit for collegiate level courses in this area.

   b. The Commission recommends that the veteran's total military service experiences in the areas of physical education or hygiene and health education be considered as meeting the physical education or hygiene and health education requirements on the freshman and sophomore levels, provided the applicant's military service was of more than one year's duration, only at those institutions which normally allow credit for collegiate level courses in these areas.

COMMISSION'S ADVISORY SERVICE

Since its establishment in 1945, the Commission has provided a continuing advisory service to assist colleges, universities, state departments of education, high schools, civil service commissions, and employers in the evaluation of educational experiences of military personnel. Publication of the GUIDE has been a part of that service. Although the GUIDE is helpful, there are many occasions when the assistance of the Commission is needed.

For example, no edition of the GUIDE can include all training programs since it is not possible in many cases for the services to provide the Commission with the syllabi of instruction. After an edition of the GUIDE has been published, military training programs continue to be revised and new ones added. However, the Commission, through arrangements with the services, continues to receive copies of these revised and new programs of instruction. These are placed on file, and recommendations for these programs are provided upon request. In addition, it is difficult, many times, to identify from official records the exact course which an enrolled student may have completed. *Therefore, if enrolled students have completed formal service school training which cannot be located or identified in the* GUIDE, *college officials should write to the Commission.* The Commission will attempt to identify the exact programs or secure the programs of instruction from the appropriate service.

When requesting assistance in the evaluation of a service school program, it is essential that the Commission be provided with all information possible. For this purpose, college officials are asked to reproduce and use the form printed on page xix. The student should be required to fill out the form accurately and completely using no abbreviations. The Commission assumes that the college official will have required verification from official military records that the student completed the course. When it appears that the official military records would be helpful to the Commission, *copies* should be made and sent together with the completed evaluation form. *Do not send original records.*

It is the policy of the Commission that its advisory service by correspondence will provide credit recommendations for formal service school training only upon the direct request of an appropriate official of an educational institution, agency, or employer from which the applicant wishes to receive recognition for his educational achievements. Credit recommendations will not be provided by correspondence to individual veterans or service personnel on active duty.

REQUEST FOR EVALUATION OF SERVICE SCHOOL TRAINING

The applicant for credit must fill out one evaluation form for. each service school course completed. **A form should not be filled out unless the entire course was completed.** College officials are responsible for verifying from official records that the student completed the course, and for submitting the forms to the Commission.

Civilian Institution _____

Name of Student _____

_____   _____   _____
Status (Freshman, Sophomore, etc.)   Service (Army, Air Force, etc.)   Rank or Rating

Course Identification Information:

1. Name of service school attended ...._____

2. Specific location of service school ...._____

3. *Exact* course title (do not abbreviate) ...._____

4. Official course number, if available ...._____

5. Service giving the course ...._____

6. a) For Army courses, by which branch given,
   i.e., Signal Corps, Ordnance, etc. ...._____

   b) For Navy courses, specify aviation service
   or other naval service ...._____

7. Length of course (*in weeks*) ...._____

8. Dates of attendance (month, day, year) .... From: _____ To: _____

9. Was course for commissioned officers, warrant officers,
   aviation cadets, officer candidates, or enlisted men? ..._____

10. Some indication of subjects studied ...._____

_____

_____

11. Air Force AFSC or SSN number; Army or Marine
    Corps MOS number; or Navy or Coast Guard
    rating assigned at completion of course ...._____

12. Other information which may be of help in
    identifying the course ...._____

_____

(Use other side of form if necessary)

_____
Signature of Applicant

PART I

FORMAL SERVICE SCHOOL COURSES

AIR FORCE
ARMY
COAST GUARD
MARINE CORPS
NAVY
DEPARTMENT OF DEFENSE
ADDENDA

AIR FORCE

AIR FORCE

A-1A Oxygen-Nitrogen Generating Plant
Location: Chanute AFB, Ill.
Length: 7 weeks.
Objectives: To train airmen in the installation, testing, and overhaul of oxygen-nitrogen plants.
Instruction: Operation and maintenance of plant; trouble detection and repair of plant.
Credit recommendation, collegiate level: This course is technical and vocational in nature. Credit in gas generating plant maintenance on the basis of demonstrated skills and/or institutional examinations.

1. A-12D Autopilot
2. Automatic Astro Compass, Type MD-1 (F&O)
3. E-4 (A-12) Autopilot
4. E-6 Autopilot and N-1 Compass
5. Field and Organizational Maintenance, PB-10 Autopilot
6. MB-2 Autopilot, F-84F
7. MB-5 Autopilot Repairman, F-101B
8. MC-1 Autopilot and N-1 Compass (KC-135)
9. Auto Flight Control System, F-100D/F
10. Operation and Maintenance of MD-1 Astro Compass Test Equipment
11. A-14 Autopilot and N-1, MD-1 Compasses
12. N-1 and MD-1 Compasses, AN/AJA-1 Computer and A-14 Autopilot
13. B-52H, A-14 Autopilot, AN/AJN-8 HVRS and MD-1 Astro Compass

Locations: Amarillo AFB, Tex.; Chanute AFB, Ill.; Sheppard AFB, Tex.
Length: *Courses 1 through 9,* 4–7 weeks; *Courses 10 through 13,* 10–15 weeks.
Objectives: To provide instrument repairmen and aircraft electrical repairmen and technicians with technical training to enable them to perform organizational and field maintenance on the automatic pilots and/or compasses specified in the titles.
Instruction: Familiarization with the compass and/or autopilot system, construction features, operation, maintenance, inspection, malfunction analysis, and test equipment.
Credit recommendation, collegiate level: These courses are technical and vocational in nature. Credit in electrical instrument repair shop on the basis of demonstrated skills and/or institutional examinations.

AFK Supply Management
Locations: Amarillo AFB, Tex.; Lowry AFB, Colo.
Length: 4 weeks.
Objectives: To train officers and airmen to operate and manage a nuclear ordnance commodity system.
Instruction: Supplies and equipment; accounting procedures; fire program; war-support planning; inspection; handling and storage.

Credit recommendation, collegiate level: No credit because of the limited technical nature of this course.

AN/ALQ-T4 F&O Maintenance
Location: Keesler AFB, Miss.
Length: 9 weeks.
Objectives: To provide airmen with supplemental training in the organizational and field maintenance of the AN/ALQ-T4(V)2.
Instruction: Master scan generator—electronic emission and terminology; trainer characteristics and numbering system; analysis of the signal generation group; station simulator operation, calibration, and maintenance; analysis of comparator, summation and termination, modulation and holding, frequency power supply, programmer, and time and event printer; analysis of electronic warfare equipment simulators, and auxiliary equipment; mission programming and trainer maintenance.
Credit recommendation, collegiate level: Credit in electrical laboratory on the basis of demonstrated skills and/or institutional examinations.

AN/ASN-7 Automatic Navigational Computer (F&O Maintenance of Automatic Navigation Computer)
Location: Chanute AFB, Ill.
Length: 3–4 weeks.
Objectives: To train airmen to perform organizational and field maintenance of the automatic navigation computer system.
Instruction: Operation of the system; functional testing of components and circuits; line and shop inspection; system troubleshooting.
Credit recommendation, collegiate level: This course is technical and vocational in nature. Credit in electrical shop on the basis of demonstrated skills and/or institutional examinations.

AN/GMD-2 (Rawinsonde) Field and Organizational Maintenance
Location: Chanute AFB, Ill.
Length: 5 weeks.
Objectives: To train weather equipment repairmen and technicians in the maintenance of the equipment specified.
Instruction: System analysis, operational adjustments, preventive maintenance, and repair of the Rawin set, AN/GMD-2.
Credit recommendation, collegiate level: No credit because of the limited technical nature of the course.

AN/MSQ-35 Radar Bomb Scoring Central F/O

Location: Keesler AFB, Miss.

Length: 19 weeks.

Objectives: To train Strategic Air Command airmen in the operation and maintenance of AN/MSQ35 bomb scoring central and associated equipment.

Instruction: AN/MSQ-35 introduction; acquisition radar (transmitter and receiver groups); presentation group; tracking radar transmitter, receiver, and indicators; tracking radar data channel; IFF/SFF and television systems; computer principles and computer track mode; ballistics computations group; plotting and recording group.

Credit recommendation, collegiate level: Credit in electrical laboratory on the basis of demonstrated skills and/or institutional examinations.

AN/TRC-87 F&O Maintenance

Location: Keesler AFB, Miss.

Length: 3 weeks.

Objectives: To train airmen in the field and organizational repair of the communications equipment specified.

Instruction: Solid state devices; block and circuit analysis of the manual and automatic transmitters and receivers; auxiliary equipment; system operation; preventive maintenance; alignment; trouble analysis.

Credit recommendation, collegiate level: No credit because of the brevity and limited technical nature of the course.

1. ATC Instructor Training
2. ATC Instructor Training (Navigator)
3. Navigator Instructor Training
   (Instructor Training for Aircraft Observer Schools)
4. Marksmanship Instructor
   (Small Arms Marksmanship Instructor)
   (Marksmanship Instructor (Rifle and Pistol))
5. Technical Instructor

Locations: *Course 1,* Randolph AFB, Tex.; *Courses 2 and 3,* Ellington, Harlingen, and James Connally AFB's, Tex., Mather AFB, Calif.; *Course 4,* Lackland AFB, Tex.; *Course 5,* Amarillo AFB, Tex., Chanute AFB, Ill., Francis E. Warren AFB, Wyo., Keesler AFB, Miss., Lackland AFB, Tex., Lowry AFB, Colo., Parks AFB, Calif., Randolph AFB, Tex., Scott AFB, Ill., Sheppard AFB, Tex.

Length: *Course 1:* 4 weeks; *Courses 2 and 3:* 6 weeks; *Course 4:* 11–12 weeks; *Course 5:* 8 weeks.

Objectives: To train personnel, technically qualified in a subject area, to instruct others in that area.

Instruction: All of *Course 1* and the academic phase of *Courses 2 through 5* comprise instructor fundamentals, including principles of learning, oral and written communication, methods and techniques of instruction, evaluation and measurement of student achievement, and practice teaching procedures. The remainder of training is devoted in *Courses 2 and 3* to instructor flight training, in *Course 4* to rifle and pistol marksmanship training, and in *Course 5* to supervised practice training in the technical specialty.

Credit recommendation, collegiate level: *Courses 1 through 5:* 2 semester hours in instructional methods.

Academic Instructor

Location: Maxwell AFB, Ala.

Length: 6 weeks.

Objectives: To increase the effectiveness of selected Air Force instructor personnel.

Instruction: Administration; educational philosophy and psychology; communication techniques; methodology, including practice teaching exercises; educational evaluation.

Credit recommendation, collegiate level: 3 semester hours in instructional methods.

1. Accountant
2. Accountant

Location: Sheppard AFB, Tex.

Length: *Course 1,* 3 weeks; *Course 2,* 12 weeks.

Objectives: To train officers in civilian and Air Force accounting procedures.

Instruction: *Course 1:* Commercial and Air Force accounting procedures. *Course 2* is a more intensive course. Generally, the prerequisite is the completion of fundamentals of accounting at the baccalaureate level. The course includes commercial, Air Force, and specialized accounting systems.

Credit recommendation, collegiate level: CAUTION: *These courses vary in length and recommendation. Require exact identification of course by title and length. Course 1:* 3 semester hours in government accounting. *Course 2:* 3 semester hours in cost accounting, and 3 semester hours in government accounting.

Accounting and Finance Automated Materiel System (Accounting and Finance Applications of Base Supply Computers (UNIVAC 1050 II))

Location: Sheppard AFB, Tex.

Length: 3 weeks.

Objectives: To train accounting specialists and supervisors for duty at installations using base supply computers.

Instruction: Automated materiel system interfaced with supply system; accounting and finance internal records and related listings; categories and sources of inventory; local procurement transactions; military standard requisitioning and issue procedures; refund and reimbursement transactions; adjustments, system failure, and recovery; practical application to the materiel system.

Credit recommendation, collegiate level: 2 semester hours in procurement and inventory accounting records in the field of data processing.

Accounting and Finance Officer

Location: Sheppard AFB, Tex.

Length: 15–19 weeks.

Objectives: To train officers to organize and coordinate Air Force accounting activities.

Instruction: Introduction to accounting and finance; accounting and finance systems; civilian and military pay; travel; commercial services and materiel; paying and collecting; accounts control; management.

Credit recommendation, collegiate level: 3 semester

hours in general accounting, and 2 semester hours in cost accounting.

1. Accounting and Finance Specialist
2. Accounting and Finance Specialist

Location: Sheppard AFB, Tex.

Length: *Course 1*, 16 weeks; *Course 2*, 27 weeks.

Objectives: To train airmen in selected phases of accounting procedure.

Instruction: *Course 1:* Accounting principles; general ledger controls and subsidiaries; commercial services; travel; military pay; accounts control. *Course 2:* Accounting principles; inventory accounting (monetary); appropriation accounting; expense and general ledger; stock funds; military pay; travel; commercial services; paying and collecting; accounting and finance systems.

Credit recommendation, collegiate level: CAUTION: *These courses vary in length and recommendation. Require exact identification of course by title and length. Course 1:* 3 semester hours in elementary accounting, and 2 semester hours in general business practice. *Course 2:* 3 semester hours in elementary accounting, and 3 semester hours in general business practice.

Accounting and Finance Supervisor

Location: Sheppard AFB, Tex.

Length: 19 weeks.

Objectives: To provide advanced training for accounting and finance personnel.

Instruction: Air Force and commercial accounting principles; accounting and finance activities; appropriation and financial inventory accounting; expense and general ledger systems; stock funds; civilian and military pay procedures; travel, commercial services, paying and collecting, and accounts control procedures.

Credit recommendation, collegiate level: 3 semester hours in cost accounting, and 4 semester hours in finance and disbursing.

Accounting and Finance Supervisor (Disbursement Accounting)

Location: Sheppard AFB, Tex.

Length: 10 weeks.

Objectives: To prepare airmen to perform supervisory-level duties connected with the disbursement function of accounting and finance activities.

Instruction: Civilian pay; travel; military pay; paying and collecting; management, administration, and supervisory responsibilities.

Credit recommendation, collegiate level: 2 semester hours in disbursement accounting.

Accounting Specialist

Location: Sheppard AFB, Tex.

Length: 15 weeks.

Objectives: To train airmen in elementary accounting procedures.

Instruction: Elementary accounting; inventory accounting (monetary); Air Force accounting procedures; Air Force stock funds and nonappropriated funds.

Credit recommendation, collegiate level: 3 semester hours in elementary accounting.

Accounting Technician

Location: Sheppard AFB, Tex.

Length: 16–18 weeks.

Objectives: To train airmen in advanced accounting and budget procedures.

Instruction: Review of accounting fundamentals; specialized accounting systems; Air Force accounting system and budgeting; accounting for Air Force stock funds.

Credit recommendation, collegiate level: 3 semester hours in cost accounting.

Administrative Specialist
(Administrative Clerk)

Locations: Amarillo AFB, Tex.; Francis E. Warren AFB, Wyo.

Length: 8–15 weeks.

Objectives: To provide basic administrative clerical training for airmen.

Instruction: Typing; office practices; publications and forms; correspondence; orders; mail processing; files maintenance and disposition.

Credit recommendation, collegiate level: Credit in typing on the basis of institutional examination. At the technical and vocational level, credit in general office procedures on the basis of demonstrated skills and/or institutional examinations.

Advanced Aerospace Photo Intelligence

Location: Sheppard AFB, Tex.

Length: 5 weeks.

Objectives: To train intelligence personnel to interpret, process, retrieve, and disseminate intelligence information.

Instruction: Reconnaissance systems; physical factors in photo interpretation; applications of automatic and electronic data processing systems to intelligence; photogrammetry; microscale photo interpretation.

Credit recommendation, collegiate level: 2 semester hours in photo intelligence methods.

Advanced Air Traffic Control Officer

Location: Keesler AFB, Miss.

Length: 10 weeks.

Objectives: To train officers in the planning and directing of air traffic control activities.

Instruction: Duties and responsibilities of an Air Traffic Control staff officer; navigational aids; plans, programs, and budgets; air traffic control planning exercises.

Credit recommendation, collegiate level: 3 semester hours in air traffic control management.

Advanced Base Procurement Management

Location: Lowry AFB, Colo.

Length: 4 weeks.

Objectives: To train officers in procurement management techniques.

Instruction: Office management; procurement policy decisions; human relations; contract and labor law related to procurement; value engineering and analysis; negotiation and cost reduction techniques.

Credit recommendation, collegiate level: 2 semester hours in procurement management.

Advanced Observer Aircraft Performance Engineer (Basic Observer Aircraft Performance Engineer Training)

Location: Mather AFB, Calif.

Length: 28–36 weeks.

Objectives: To qualify graduates of the primary basic observer courses as aircraft performance engineers.

Instruction: Administration and aircraft general; performance fundamentals; engines and associated systems; aircraft systems; performance curves; performance problems and operations; physiological training; officer training.

Credit recommendation, collegiate level: Credit in aeronautical engineering on the basis of demonstrated skills and/or institutional examinations.

1. Advanced Observer, Tactical Reconnaissance and Bombardment Training (Advanced Observer, Strategic Reconnaissance and Bombardment Training)
2. Advanced Observer Strategic Bombardment

Location: Mather AFB, Calif.

Length: 20–25 weeks.

Objectives: To train graduates of the primary basic observer course as aircraft observer, navigator-bombardiers.

Instruction: K-system bombing; K-System reconnaissance; atomic, biological, and chemical warfare; physiological training.

Credit recommendation, collegiate level: No credit as courses are military in nature.

Advanced Pilot Training, Multi-Engine B-25 (Advanced Pilot Training, Multi-Engine T-29) (Advanced Pilot Multi-Engine TB-50 Training)

Locations: James Connally AFB, Tex.; Mather AFB, Calif.

Length: 10 weeks.

Objectives: To provide officers with advanced training in the aircraft indicated in title.

Instruction: Flying training; aircraft systems; aircraft instruments and procedures.

Credit recommendation, collegiate level: No credit because of the specialized nature of these courses.

1. Aerial Photographer
2. Aerial Photographer

Location: Lowry AFB, Colo.

Length: *Course 1*, 19 weeks; *Course 2*, 29 weeks.

Objectives: To train airmen to install, inspect, and operate aircraft cameras and related equipment in aircraft.

Instruction: *Courses 1 and 2:* Fundamentals of photography; aerial photography; reconnaissance cameras; oblique and night photography; in addition *Course 2* includes principles of electricity; AC and vacuum tubes; oscilloscopes; power supplies; wave-shaping circuits; motors, generators, and servomechanisms.

Credit recommendation, collegiate level: CAUTION: *These courses vary slightly in title, length, and recommendation. Require exact identification by title and length. Course 1:* 3 semester hours in aerial photography. *Course 2:* 3 semester hours in aerial photography, 2 semester hours in electricity and electronics, and credit in electrical laboratory on the basis of demonstrated skills and/or institutional examinations.

1. Aeromedical Evacuation Technician
2. Apprentice Aeromedical Evacuation Specialist

Locations: Brooks AFB, Tex.; Gunter AFB, Ala.

Length: 5–8 weeks.

Objectives: To train airmen to perform routine aeromedical evacuation procedures.

Instruction: Aviation medicine, including aeronautical sciences, clinical and military medicine, and surgery; altitude physiology; flight nursing; preventive medicine.

Credit recommendation, collegiate level: For each course, credit in first aid and hygiene on the basis of institutional examination.

Aeromedical Specialist (Apprentice Aeromedical Specialist)

Locations: Brooks AFB, Tex.; Gunter AFB, Ala.

Length: 7–9 weeks.

Objectives: To train airmen in routine, supervised, inflight medical care of personnel.

Instruction: Aviation medicine; otorhinolaryngology; internal and military medicine; neuropsychiatry; ophthalmology; surgery; flight nursing; preventive medicine.

Credit recommendation, collegiate level: 2 semester hours in hygiene and first aid.

Aeromedical Technician

Locations: Gunter AFB, Ala.; Brooks AFB, Tex.

Length: 8–11 weeks.

Objectives: To provide advanced technical- and supervisory-level training for aeromedical specialists.

Instruction: Air evacuation; aviation physiology; anatomy and physiology; otorhinolaryngology; ophthalmology; medicine; pharmacy; psychiatry; surgery; radiology and radiobiology; flight nursing; preventive medicine; clinical dentistry; medical administration.

Credit recommendation, collegiate level: 2 semester hours in first aid and hygiene.

Aerospace Ground Equipment Repair Technician
(Aircraft Ground Equipment Repair Technician)
(Aircraft and Missile Ground Support Equipment
Repair Technician)

Location: Chanute AFB, Ill.

Length: 11–12 weeks.

Objectives: To train airmen as technicians and supervisors in aerospace ground equipment.

Instruction: Electrical and electronic circuits and components; generator sets; pressurizing equipment; hydraulic support equipment; ground heaters; equipment coolers.

Credit recommendation, collegiate level: 2 semester hours in shop management, and credit in electricity and electrical laboratory on the basis of demonstrated skills and/or institutional examinations.

Aerospace Ground Equipment Repairman
(Aircraft Ground Equipment Repairman)
(Aircraft and Missile Ground Support Equipment
Repairman)
(Ground Powered and Support Equipment
Repairman)

Locations: Chanute AFB, Ill.; Francis E. Warren AFB, Wyo.

Length: 19–25 weeks.

Objectives: To train airmen to inspect, repair, adjust, and troubleshoot aircraft ground equipment.

Instruction: Electrical fundamenals; DC and AC electrical equipment; gasoline and diesel engines; compressors; equipment coolers.

Credit recommendation, collegiate level: Credit in electricity and electrical laboratory on the basis of demonstrated skills and/or institutional examinations.

1. **Aerospace Munitions Officer**
2. **Aerospace Munitions Officer, Conventional**
   Munitions Refresher

Location: Lowry AFB, Colo.

Length: *Course 1, 23–24 weeks; Course 2, 4 weeks.*

Objectives: *Course 1:* To train officers in the principles of management of aerospace munitions activities. *Course 2:* To provide aerospace munitions officers with refresher training on non-nuclear weapons.

Instruction: *Course 1:* DC and AC electricity; tubes and transistors; explosive airmunitions; chemical and biological airmunitions; supply, storage, and handling of airmunitions, nuclear weapons, missiles, and rockets; aerospace munitions maintenance squadron operations; aircraft weapons release systems and weapons loading; aerospace munitions management functions. *Course 2:* Explosive, chemical, biological, and pyrotechnic airmunitions; supply, storage, handling, and loading of conventional airmunitions.

Credit recommendation, collegiate level: *Course 1:* 3 semester hours in maintenance management, and credit in electricity and electrical laboratory on the basis of demonstrated skills and/or institutional examinations. *Course 2:* No credit as the course is military in nature.

Aerospace Munitions Staff Officer

Location: Lowry AFB, Colo.

Length: 13 weeks.

Objectives: To train officers in current and proposed U.S. and foreign aerospace munitions and their employment.

Instruction: Air Force doctrine, organization, and command operations; written and oral communication; maintenance management; conference leadership; briefing and problem-solving techniques; domestic and foreign munitions, including aircraft guns, chemical and biological agents and delivery systems, aerial mines, nuclear and non-nuclear weapons principles, munitions employment and logistics, tactical and strategic missiles, re-entry vehicles, and warheads; theoretical staff planning problems; current fighter and bomber avionics equipment.

Credit recommendation, collegiate level: 2 semester hours in principles of management, and credit in oral and written communication on the basis of institutional examination.

1. **Aerospace Photographic Systems Repairman**
   (Photographic Repairman)
   (Camera Repairman)
2. **Photographic Repairman**

Location: Lowry AFB, Colo.

Length: 22–35 weeks.

Objectives: To train airmen in organizational and field maintenance of ground and airborne cameras and accessories, motion picture equipment, and photographic laboratory equipment.

Instruction: *Course 1:* Fundamentals of DC and AC; reactive circuits; principles of vacuum tubes and transistors; power supplies; amplifiers and oscillators; maintenance of reconnaissance aerospace photographic equipment; *Course 2:* DC electricity; AC electricity; power supplies; maintenance of reconnaissance aerospace photographic equipment.

Credit recommendation, collegiate level: CAUTION: *These courses vary slightly in title, length, and recommendation. Course 2 is 30 weeks in length and was given during 1958. Require exact identification by year that course was given. Course 1:* 3 semester hours at freshman or sophomore level as an elective in electricity and electronics, and credit in repair of electronic photographic equipment on the basis of demonstrated skills and/or institutional examinations. *Course 2:* 2 semester hours at freshman or sophomore level as an elective in electricity and electronics, and credit in repair of electronic photographic equipment on the basis of demonstrated skills and/or institutional examinations.

1. **Air Command and Staff College**
2. **Command and Staff College**
   (Command and Staff School)
3. **Command and Staff Course**

Location: Maxwell AFB, Ala.

Length: *Courses 1 and 2, 38–40 weeks; Course 3, 43* weeks.

Objectives: To train captains and majors in command and staff tasks required to implement air strategy and execute missions of the Air Force; to develop doctrine, strategy, and tactics; military, national, and international affairs; command and staff management.

Instruction: Factors contributing to national power, staff organization, staff planning, command, military doctrine, scientific and technological developments, and the application and appraisal of current strategy and employment concepts.

The thesis program—the major portion of the Air Command and Staff College students' research activity —complements the lecture, reading, and seminar parts of the curriculum. Each student elects a problem dealing with the command and staff behavior in planning and executing the employment of aerospace forces, and in acquiring and programming the development of world resources.

Credit recommendation, collegiate level: CAUTION: *These courses vary slightly in title, length, and recommendation. Require exact identification of course by title and length. Courses 1 and 2:* For each course, 6 semester hours in business organization and management, 2 semester hours in political science, 3 semester hours in international relations, and credit in written and oral communication by institutional examination. *Course 3:* 6 semester hours in business organization and management, and 3 semester hours in political science and international relations.

Credit recommendation, graduate level: *Course 1:* In 1963 the Executive Committee of the Council of Graduate Schools in the United States requested the Commission on Accreditation of Service Experiences of the American Council on Education to evaluate high-level training programs of the Armed Forces to determine what aspects of these programs might be regarded as graduate-level caliber.

Upon invitation of the Commander of Air University, the Commission secured the services of professors —nominated by the President of the Council of Graduate Schools in the United States—from three graduate schools to serve as consultants. They visited the Air Command and Staff College in November 1963 to study and appraise the library facilities, the instructional program, faculty qualifications, examination program, and the thesis and research work required of the students.

As a result of the consultants' evaluations, the Commission on Accreditation recommends that a graduate of the Air Command and Staff College be allowed a transfer of credit up to 6 hours in a 1-year M.A. program in the field of Public Administration or in another such field as the thesis may properly fall.

It is further recommended that such transfer of credit be allowed only after an appraisal of the applicant's thesis. It is recommended that the applicant be required to submit a copy of his thesis for study by the graduate school, since it will provide an indication of the extent and depth of his reading, seminar, and research work during the course of instruction.

1. **Air Defense Artillery Director (SAGE)**
2. **Assistant Air Defense Artillery Director (SAGE)**
   Location: Keesler AFB, Miss.
   Length: 5–6 weeks.
   Objectives: *Course 1* trains Army officers, *Course 2* trains Army enlisted personnel, for work in a SAGE Direction Center in the positions specified in the titles.
   Instruction: Air defense fundamentals, including weapons, radars, SAGE computers and data processing;

SAGE Direction Center organization, functions, and displays; air defense artillery direction, including Army air defense command posts and director and assistant director positions.

Credit recommendation, collegiate level: No credit as the courses are military in nature.

Air Electronics Maintenance for Armament Systems Officer

Location: Keesler AFB, Miss.
Length: 6 weeks.
Objectives: To familiarize SAC armament systems officers with aircraft electronic subsystems to enable them to supervise related maintenance activities.
Instruction: Aircraft communications, electronic navigation and warfare principles; technical order and supply procedures; maintenance of aircraft electronic subsystems.
Credit recommendation, collegiate level: No credit because of the limited technical nature of the course.

Air Electronics Officer, Fighter Aircraft

Location: Keesler AFB, Miss.
Length: 17 weeks.
Objectives: To train officers in fighter aircraft communications and electronic equipment.
Instruction: Electronic principles, including measurement instruments; review of vacuum tubes and power supplies; voltage regulators; audio, video, and RF amplifiers; oscillators; modulators; receivers; special circuits; microwave techniques; special equipment; organization and management training, including management principles, career systems, training programs, administrative and technical publications, and inspection, maintenance, and supply management.
Credit recommendation, collegiate level: 2 semester hours at the freshman or sophomore level as an elective in electricity and electronics, 2 semester hours in shop management, and credit in electrical laboratory on the basis of demonstrated skills and/or institutional examinations.

Air Freight Specialist

Location: Sheppard AFB, Tex.
Length: 7–9 weeks.
Objectives: To train airmen in receiving, processing, and handling air freight shipments.
Instruction: Air transportation fundamentals; cargo and mail processing; load planning and weight and balance; aircraft loading and off-loading.
Credit recommendation, collegiate level: 2 semester hours in transportation.

1. **Air Intelligence Airman**
2. **Intelligence Operations Specialist**
3. **Photo Interpretation Specialist**
   Locations: Lowry AFB, Colo.; Sheppard AFB, Tex.
   Length: *Course 1,* 15–16 weeks; *Course 2,* 10–11 weeks; *Course 3,* 12–19 weeks.

Objectives: To train airmen in air intelligence methods and procedures.

Instruction: *Course 1:* Fundamentals of intelligence; maps; charts; fundamentals of photo intelligence; photogrammetry; tactical photo interpretation; operational weapons systems; industries; data processing and multisensors; specialized Air Force or Navy intelligence training; mission activities. *Course 2:* Fundamentals of air intelligence; charts; photo-radar; target development; weapons employment planning; foreign air defense capabilities; combat mission planning and reporting. *Course 3:* Introduction to photo intelligence; photo metrics; graphics and evaluation; military equipment and installations; surface transportation; industries; target analysis; bomb damage assessment; radar fundamentals.

Credit recommendation, collegiate level: *Course 1 and 3:* 4 semester hours in photographic interpretation for each course. *Course 2:* 3 semester hours in intelligence methods.

1. Air Intelligence Officer
2. Intelligence Officer
3. Intelligence Photo-Radar Officer
4. Air Intelligence Officer
5. Intelligence Photo-Radar Officer

Locations: Lowry AFB, Colo.; Sheppard AFB, Tex.

Length: *Course 1,* 28 weeks; *Course 2,* 12 weeks; *Course 3,* 31 weeks; *Course 4,* 12 weeks; *Course 5,* 10 weeks.

Objectives: *Course 1:* To train officers of *all* services to perform the combined duties of *Course 2* (operational intelligence activities) and *Course 3* (producing intelligence from direct and indirect aerial and aerospace photography). *Course 4:* To provide officers with initial and/or update training in air intelligence. *Course 5:* To train officers in the fundamentals of photo interpretation.

Instruction: *Course 1:* Fundamentals of intelligence; maps; charts; fundamentals of photographic intelligence; photogrammetry; tactical photo interpretation; operational weapons systems; surface transportation; industries; photo intelligence reporting exercise; basic radar mission planning and bombing; data processing and multisenors; radar prediction; conventional and nuclear weapons employment; mission activities; operational problems. *Course 2:* Air intelligence processes; maps, charts, and photo-radar interpretation; the Communist threat; targeting and weapons employment planning; combat mission activities. *Course 3:* Photo-radar intelligence; photogrammetry; interpretation of air warfare, weapons systems, basic and end products industries, and surface transportation; bomb damage assessment; target materials and prediction analysis; weapons employment planning; indirect bomb damage assessment; radar fundamentals; mission analysis; reconnaissance; target prediction and simulation; bombing and mission planning. *Course 4* is a special course which covers the same subjects as *Course 2. Course 5* is also a special course which covers certain phases of *Course 3*—photo intelligence, photogrammetry, aerospace weapons systems, surface transportation and reporting, and advanced aerospace photo intelligence.

Credit recommendation, collegiate level: CAUTION: *These courses vary in length and recommendation. Require exact identification by title and length. Course 1:* 6 semester hours in photographic interpretation and intelligence methods. *Courses 2 and 4:* 3 semester hours in intelligence methods for each course. *Course 3:* 6 semester hours in photographic interpretation. *Course 5:* 2 semester hours in photographic interpretation.

1. Air Launch Missile Guidance Mechanic (AGM-28A/B)
   (Air Launch Guidance Mechanic (AGM-28A/B))
   (AGM Guidance Mechanic (AGM-28A/B))
   (GAM Guidance Mechanic (GAM-77))
2. GAM Guidance Mechanic, GAM-77
   (Guidance Systems Mechanic, GAM-77)
3. Missile Guidance and Control Specialist (AGM-28A/B)

Location: Chanute AFB, Ill.

Length: *Course 1,* 42–44 weeks; *Course 2,* 30–33 weeks; *Course 3,* 36 weeks.

Objectives: To train airmen in the operation, maintenance, inspection, and repair of the guidance control system and the guidance control checkout equipment indicated in the title.

Instruction: *Course 1:* DC and AC; reactive circuits; principles of vacuum tubes and transistors; special purpose tubes; amplifiers and oscillators; motors and servomechanisms; multivibrators and sweep circuits; microwave principles; receiver principles; wave-shaping circuits. *Course 2:* DC and AC; reactive circuits; vacuum tubes and transistors; special purpose tubes; amplifiers and oscillators; motors and servomechanisms; multivibrators and sweep circuits. *Course 3:* DC and AC; solid state devices; vacuum tubes; amplifiers.

Credit recommendation, collegiate level: CAUTION: *These courses vary slightly in title, length, and recommendation. Require exact identification by title and length. Course 1:* 6 semester hours at freshman or sophomore level as an elective in electricity and electronics, and credit in electrical laboratory on the basis of demonstrated skills and/or institutional examinations. *Course 2:* 4 semester hours at freshman or sophomore level as an elective in electricity and electronics, and credit in electrical laboratory on the basis of demonstrated skills and/or institutional examinations. *Course 3:* 3 semester hours at freshman or sophomore level as an elective in electricity and electronics, and credit in electrical laboratory on the basis of demonstrated skills and/or institutional examinations.

1. Air Launch Missile Guidance Technician (AGM-28A/B)
2. Air Launch Missile Analyst Technician (AGM-28A/B)

Location: Chanute AFB, Ill.

Length: 8–13 weeks.

Objectives: To train airmen in the advanced diagnostic troubleshooting and field maintenance of the AGM-28A/B guided missile guidance and control system.

Instruction: Advanced electronics principles; guidance system analysis; flight control.

Credit recommendation, collegiate level: Credit in electrical laboratory on the basis of demonstrated skills and/or institutional examinations.

Air Launch Missile Safety Officer

Location: Lowry AFB, Colo.

Length: 3 weeks.

Objectives: To train airmen and civilian personnel as missile safety officers.

Instruction: Safety education; missile fundamentals; explosive and nuclear safety; accident prevention; personnel protection.

Credit recommendation, collegiate level: 2 semester hours in safety education.

Air Launch Missile Safety Technician

Location: Lowry AFB, Colo.

Length: 3 weeks.

Objectives: To train airmen and civilians as missile safety technicians.

Instruction: Evolution of missile safety; psychology of safety and human relations; safety education; environmental safety requirements; explosive and nuclear safety in missile assembly; personnel protection.

Credit recommendation, collegiate level: 2 semester hours in safety management.

Air Passenger Specialist
(Air Passenger and Operations Specialist)

Locations: Keesler AFB, Miss.; Sheppard AFB, Tex.

Length: 6–8 weeks.

Objectives: To train airmen to process and schedule military and civilian personnel for travel by air.

Instruction: Customer service; terminal service; passenger processing; load planning; military air transportation.

Credit recommendation, collegiate level: 2 semester hours in transportation.

1. Air Policeman
(Air Policeman (Basic Air Police Course))
(Air Police (Basic))
2. Air Police Officer
3. Air Police (NCO)
(Air Police Supervisor)

Locations: Parks AFB, Calif.; Lackland AFB, Tex.

Length: 4–13 weeks.

Objectives: *Course 1:* To train airmen in the use of police weapons, tactical ground operations, security, law enforcement and corrections. *Courses 2 and 3:* To train officers to manage security and law enforcement programs.

Instruction: *Courses 1, 2, and 3:* Law enforcement and correction; physical apprehension and restraining techniques; internal security; weapons and field training; in addition *Courses 2 and 3* include planning and scheduling of law enforcement and security activities.

Credit recommendation, collegiate level: These courses are technical and vocational in nature. Credit in police methods on the basis of demonstrated skills and/or institutional examinations.

Air Rescue Specialist—Medical

Location: Gunter AFB, Ala.

Length: 4 weeks.

Objectives: To train airmen in fundamental emergency medical treatment.

Instruction: Aviation medicine; clinical dentistry; medical laboratory; medical passive defense; anatomy and physiology; medicine; surgery; preventive medicine; nursing; training and logistics.

Credit recommendation, collegiate level: Credit in first aid on the basis of institutional examinations.

Air Surveillance (SAGE)

Location: Keesler AFB, Miss.

Length: 6–8 weeks.

Objectives: To train officers and airmen in the duties of the air surveillance officer or technician in a SAGE direction center.

Instruction: SAGE familiarization; digital information displays; computer positional training; weapons familiarization; SAGE system training program.

Credit recommendation, collegiate level: No credit because of the specialized nature of this course.

1. Air Traffic Control Officer
2. Air Traffic Control Technician
3. Air Route Control and Approach Control
Operator
(Apprentice Air Traffic Control Operator)

Location: Keesler AFB, Miss.

Length: 11–18 weeks.

Objectives: To train officers and airmen in the control of aircraft traffic.

Instruction: Weather; air-navigation aids; airport traffic control; conventional and/or radar approach control.

Credit recommendation, collegiate level: Credit, for each course, in air navigation or meteorology on the basis of demonstrated skills and/or institutional examinations.

Air Traffic Control Operator
(Air Traffic Control Operator (Radar))
(Air Traffic Control Operator (Non-Radar))

Location: Keesler AFB, Miss.

Length: 18–23 weeks.

Objectives: To train airmen and Army personnel in the control of aircraft traffic.

Instruction: Weather; air-navigation aids; airport traffic control; conventional and/or radar approach control.

Credit recommendation, collegiate level: Credit in navigation or meteorology on the basis of demonstrated skills and/or institutional examinations.

1. Air Traffic Control Radar Repairman
2. Air Traffic Control Radar Repairman, AN/CPN-4
   (Air Traffic Control Radar Repairman,
   AN/CPN-18, AN/FPN-16)
   (Air Traffic Control Radar Repairman
   AN/MPN-1)
3. Air Traffic Control Radar Repairman, AN/CPN-4
   (Air Traffic Control Radar Repairman,
   AN/FPN-16 and AN/CPN-18)
   (Air Traffic Control Radar Repairman,
   AN/MPN-1)
4. Air Traffic Control Radar Repairman, AN/TPN-12

Location: Keesler AFB, Miss.

Length: *Course 1,* 45–46 weeks; *Course 2,* 23–38 weeks; *Course 3,* 12–16 weeks; *Course 4,* 5 weeks.

Objectives: To train airmen in the principles of operation, maintenance, and repair of air traffic control radar and asociated communications and identification equipment.

Instruction: *Course 1:* DC and AC; reactive circuits; vacuum tubes and transistors; special purpose tubes; amplifiers and oscillators; special circuits; motors and servomechanisms; multivibrators and sweep circuits; microwave principles. *Course 2:* DC and AC; electron tubes and power supplies; amplifiers and oscillators; special circuits; radar microwave propagation. *Courses 3 and 4:* Transmitting and receiving systems; antenna systems; maintenance.

Credit recommendation, collegiate level: CAUTION: *These courses vary slightly in title, length, and recommendation. Require exact identification of course by title and length. Course 1:* 6 semester hours at freshman or sophomore level as an elective in electricity and electronics, and credit in electrical laboratory on the basis of demonstrated skills and/or institutional examinations. *Course 2:* 4 semester hours at freshman or sophomore level as an elective in electricity and electronics, and credit in electrical laboratory on the basis of demonstrated skills and/or institutional examinations. *Courses 3 and 4:* Credit in electrical laboratory, for each course, on the basis of demonstrated skills and/or institutional examinations.

1. Air Traffic Control Radar Technician
2. Air Traffic Control Radar Technician
   (Air Traffic Control Radar Maintenance
   Technician)
3. Air Traffic Control Radar Maintenance Technician

Location: Keesler AFB, Miss.

Length: *Course 1,* 39 weeks; *Course 2,* 33–34 weeks; *Course 3,* 23 weeks.

Objectives: To train airmen in the theory of operation, maintenance, and installation of air traffic control radars and associated equipment.

Instruction: *Course 1:* DC and AC; vacuum tubes and solid state devices; power supplies; oscillators; principles of electronic digital data processing; transmitter and receiver systems; test equipment; antenna systems; training and maintenance management. *Course 2:* DC and AC; advanced electronic circuits, transmitters and receivers; synchroscope and oscilloscope; test equipment; antenna systems; search-indicating and precision-indicating systems; remoting systems. *Course 3:* Search-indicating system and precision-indicating system; transmitting and receiving system; system troubleshooting.

Credit recommendation, collegiate level: CAUTION: *These courses vary slightly in title, length, and recommendation. Require exact identification by title and length. Course 1:* 2 semester hours in shop management, 3 semester hours as an elective in electricity and electronics, and credit in electrical laboratory on the basis of demonstrated skills and/or institutional examinations. *Course 2:* 2 semester hours at freshman or sophomore level as an elective in electricity and electronics, and credit in electrical laboratory on the basis of demonstrated skills and/or institutional examinations. *Course 3:* Credit in electrical laboratory on the basis of demonstrated skills and/or institutional examinations.

Air War College
(War College)

Location: Maxwell AFB, Ala.

Length: 43 weeks.

Objectives: To prepare senior officers for high command and staff duty by developing in them a sound understanding of military strategy in support of national security policy in order to assure the most effective development and employment of aerospace power.

Instruction: Bases of international relations; elements of power; current world conflict; current U.S. military strategy and major economic and political factors affecting it; political and military objectives and their inter-relationships; U.S. strategy for the future; national security forum. The curriculum for 1966–67 covers the same overall areas of study as in previous years but with more modification than previously of the academic content toward a greater emphasis on the military implications and strategic consequences of the problems studied.

The thesis program, the major portion of the Air War College students' research activity, complements the lecture, reading, and seminar parts of the curriculum. Each student selects a problem dealing with some aspect of national defense for detailed research and analysis.

Credit recommendation, collegiate level: CAUTION: *The collegiate recommendation may vary slightly according to the academic year of attendance at the Air War College. Academic years 1954–55 through 1965–66:* 6 semester hours in social science survey, 6 semester hours in political science (including international relations), 3 semester hours in recent history, 3 semester hours in economics, and 3 semester hours in business organization and management (planning and leadership). In addition, for *academic years 1963–64 through 1965–66:* Credit in oral and written communication on the basis of institutional examination. For *academic year 1966–67:* 6 semester hours in political science (including international relations), 9 semester hours in business organization and management (planning and leadership), 3 semester hours in social science survey, and credit in oral and written communication on the basis of institutional examination.

Credit recommendation, graduate level: In 1963 the Executive Committee of the Council of Graduate Schools in the United States requested the Commission on Accreditation of Service Experiences of the American Council on Education to evaluate high-level training programs of the Armed Forces to determine what, if any aspects of these programs might be regarded as graduate-level caliber.

Upon invitation of the Commander of Air University, the Commission secured the services of professors, nominated by the President of the Council of Graduate Schools in the United States from three graduate schools, to serve as consultants. They visited the Air War College in November 1963 to study and appraise the library facilities, the instructional program, faculty qualifications, examinations program, and the thesis and research work required of the students.

As a result of the consultants' evaluations, the Commission on Accreditation recommends that a graduate of the Air War College be allowed a transfer of credit up to 6 hours in a one-year M.A. program in the field of international relations, or in such other field as the thesis may properly fall.

It is further recommended that such transfer of credit be allowed only after an appraisal of the applicants' educational achievements. In this connection, since the thesis is an integral part of his program, it is recommended that the applicant be required to submit a copy for study by the graduate school as it will provide an indication of the extent and depth of his reading, seminar, and research work during the course of instruction.

Air Weapons

Location: Maxwell AFB, Ala.

Length: 7 weeks.

Objectives: To train command and staff officers to plan for weapons employment by scientific selection of weapons systems.

Instruction: Fundamentals of probability; ordnance, nuclear, biological, and chemical weapons and their employment; situation exercises; operational factors (delivery); logistics, weapons, and targets.

Credit recommendation, collegiate level: No credit as the course is military in nature.

Airborne ECM Operator
(Airborne Electronic Countermeasures Specialist)

Location: Keesler AFB, Miss.

Length: 16 weeks.

Objectives: To train airmen to operate and maintain airborne reconnaissance and electronic countermeasures jamming equipment and to analyze results of countermeasures operations.

Instruction: Electronic principles; electronic countermeasures search and analysis equipment; reconnaissance flights; electronic countermeasures jamming equipment and jamming flights.

Credit recommendation, collegiate level: 2 semester hours at the freshman or sophomore level as an elective in electronics, and credit in electrical laboratory on the basis of demonstrated skills and/or institutional examinations.

Airborne Electronic Navigation Equipment Repairman (Shoran)
(Aircraft Electronic Navigation Equipment Repairman (Shoran))
(Airborne Shoran Equipment Repairman)

Location: Keesler AFB, Miss.

Length: 27–30 weeks.

Objectives: To train airmen to maintain and repair airborne shoran systems and related test equipment.

Instruction: Direct and alternating current, electron tubes and power supplies, amplifiers and oscillators, special circuits, and radar microwave propagation comprise the first phase of training. The remainder of the course deals with shoran navigation equipment and K-4 bombing position computer analysis and maintenance.

Credit recommendation, collegiate level: CAUTION: *Courses in electronic navigation equipment repair vary in title, length, and recommendation. Require exact identification of course by full title and length.* 4 semester hours at the freshman or sophomore level as an elective in electricity and electronics, and credit in electrical laboratory on the basis of demonstrated skills and/or institutional examinations.

Airborne Radio Repairman

Location: Keesler AFB, Miss.

Length: 31 weeks.

Objectives: To train airmen to tune, operate, and maintain, and to assist in the installation and repair of, airborne radio and related navigational equipment.

Instruction: DC and AC; electron tubes and amplifiers; oscillators and modulators; transient circuits; radar microwave propagation.

Credit recommendation, collegiate level: 3 semester hours at freshman or sophomore level as an elective in electricity and electronics, and credit in electrical laboratory on the basis of demonstrated skills and/or institutional examinations.

Airborne Weather Equipment Technician

Location: Chanute AFB, Ill.

Length: 5 weeks.

Objectives: To train airmen in the maintenance and repair of airborne weather equipment.

Instruction: Introduction to airborne weather equipment; circuit analysis of Radiosonde receptor AN/AMR-1 and Radiosonde dispenser AN/AME-1; alignment and calibration of airborne weather equipment.

Credit recommendation, collegiate level: No credit because of the limited technical nature of the course.

Aircraft and Missile Ground Support Equipment Repairman (Ballistic Missiles)

Location: Sheppard AFB, Tex.

Length: 19 weeks.

Objectives: To train airmen as ground support ballistic missile repairmen.

Instruction: Missile fundamentals; electrical equipment maintenance; hydraulic, pneumatic, and engine maintenance; weapon system familiarization; mobile handling equipment; service and launch area equipment.

Credit recommendation, collegiate level: This course is technical and vocational in nature. Credit in electrical shop on the basis of demonstrated skills and/or institutional examinations.

1. Aircraft Control and Warning Operator (SAGE)
2. Aircraft Control and Warning Operator (Semiautomatic 412L)
3. Aircraft Control and Warning Operator
4. Aircraft Control and Warning Operator (Manual)

Location: Keesler AFB, Miss.

Length: 6–17 weeks.

Objectives: To train airmen to operate aircraft control and warning systems.

Instruction: *Course 1:* SAGE familiarization; radar mapping; manual data input; tracking; height finding, intercept control. *Course 2:* Surveillance, movement, and identifications; height, jammer tracker, and weapons operations; integrated 412L operations. *Courses 3 and 4:* ACW fundamentals; basic operations; procedures and simulated operations.

Credit recommendation, collegiate level: These courses are technical and vocational in nature. Credit in aircraft control operations on the basis of demonstrated skills and/or institutional examinations.

Aircraft Control and Warning Radar Officer

Location: Keesler AFB, Miss.

Length: 12 weeks.

Objectives: To provide training in ground electronics equipment.

Instruction: Direct current; alternating current; electron tubes and amplifiers; transmitters and receivers; transient circuits; microwave propagation.

Credit recommendation, collegiate level: Credit in electricity and electronics on basis of institutional examination.

1. Aircraft Control and Warning Radar Repairman
2. Aircraft Control and Warning Radar Repairman
3. Aircraft Control and Warning Radar Repairman (AN/CPS-1, AN/CPS-4, AN/CPS-5, IFF)
4. Aircraft Control and Warning Radar Repairman (AN/CPS-6B, AN/FPS-6) (Aircraft Control and Warning Radar Repairman (AN/CPS-6B, IFF))
5. Aircraft Control and Warning Radar Repairman (AN/FPS-3, AN/FPS-6) (Aircraft Control and Warning Radar Repairman (AN/FPS-3, AN/FPS-6, IFF))
6. Aircraft Control and Warning Radar Repairman (AN/FPS-4, AN/FPS-8) (Aircraft Control and Warning Radar Repairman (AN/FPS-4, AN/FPS-8, IFF))
7. Aircraft Control and Warning Radar Repairman (AN/FPS-6, AN/FPS-20)
8. Aircraft Control and Warning Radar Repairman (AN/FPS-18, AN/FST-1, AN/FSA-10, AN/FSW-1)
9. Aircraft Control and Warning Radar Repairman (AN/TPS-1D, AN/TPS-10D) (Aircraft Control and Warning Radar Repairman (AN/TPS-1D, AN/TPS-10D, IFF))

Location: Keesler AFB, Miss.

Length: *Course 1,* 17 weeks; *Course 2, 39–45 weeks; Courses 3 through 9, 28–39.*

Objectives: To provide airmen with skills for operation and maintenance of aircraft control and warning radar equipment.

Instruction: *Course 1:* Analysis and maintenance of aircraft control and warning equipment. *Course 2:* Direct and alternating current circuits; reactive circuits; vacuum tubes and transistors; amplifiers and oscillators; motors and servomechanisms; multivibrators and sweep circuits; microwave principles. *Courses 3 through 9:* Direct and alternating current circuits; electron tubes and power supplies; amplifiers and oscillators; special circuits; radar microwave propagation.

Credit recommendation, collegiate level: CAUTION: *Courses 1 and 2 vary slightly in title, length, and recommendation from Courses 3 through 9. Require exact identification of courses by title and length. Course 1:* This course is technical and vocational in nature. Credit in mechanical shop on the basis of demonstrated skills and/or institutional examinations. *Course 2:* 6 semester hours at freshman or sophomore level as an elective in electricity and electronics, and credit in electrical laboratory on the basis of demonstrated skills and/or institutional examinations. *Courses 3 through 9:* 3 semester hours at freshman or sophomore level as an elective in electricity and electronics, and credit in electrical laboratory on the basis of demonstrated skills and/or institutional examinations.

1. Aircraft Control and Warning Radar Technician (Aircraft Control and Warning Radar Maintenance Technician)
2. Aircraft Control and Warning Radar Maintenance Technician

Location: Keelser AFB, Miss.

Length: *Course 1, 34–40 weeks; Course 2, 19 weeks.*

Objectives: *Course 1:* To provide advanced training in the operation and maintenance of aircraft control and warning radar and associated equipment. *Course 2:* To train technicians to inspect, troubleshoot, repair, and install aircraft control and warning radar equipment.

Instruction: *Course 1:* Advanced electronic circuits; radar system circuits; test equipment and measurement principles; organization and management; transmitter and RF systems; receiver, indicating, and identification systems. *Course 2:* Analysis and maintenance of AN/KPS-8, AN/TPS-10D, AN/FPS-3, and Mark X IFF.

Credit recommendation, collegiate level: CAUTION: *These courses vary slightly in title, length, and recommendation. Require exact identification of course by title and length. Course 1:* 3 semester hours in business organization and management, 3 semester hours at freshman or sophomore level as an elective in electronics, and credit in electrical laboratory on the basis of demonstrated skills and/or institutional examinations. *Course 2:* This course is technical and vocational in nature. Credit in electrical shop on the basis of demonstrated skills and/or institutional examinations.

Aircraft ECM Repairman (Ground Equipment)

Location: Keesler AFB, Miss.

Length: 6 weeks.

Objectives: To train airmen to maintain and repair specific electronic countermeasures equipment.

Instruction: Operation and maintenance of communications receiver, recorder systems, Tektronix 545 oscilloscope, AN/SLA-2 pulse analyzer, CM-72, Dumont 321-A and 297 cameras, AN/SLR-2 receiver and brush recorder.

Credit recommendation, collegiate level: No credit because of the specialized nature of the course.

Aircraft Early Warning Radar Maintenance Technician

Location: Keesler AFB, Miss.

Length: 38 weeks.

Objectives: To train airmen in the maintenance, techniques, and circuit theory of aircraft early warning radar equipment.

Instruction: Basic electronics; DC and AC; transformers; motor principles; special purpose tubes; electronic measuring instruments; shop supervision and management; shop practices.

Credit recommendation, collegiate level: CAUTION: *Aircraft early warning radar maintenance technician courses vary in title, length, and recommendation. Require exact identification of course by title and length.* 2 semester hours in shop management, 2 semester hours as an elective in electricity and electronics, and credit in electrical laboratory on the basis of demonstrated skills and/or institutional examinations.

---

1. Aircraft Early Warning Radar Repairman
2. Aircraft Early Warning Radar Repairman
   (Airborne Early Warning Radar Repairman
   (AN/APS-20E))
   (Airborne Early Warning Radar Repairman
   (AN/APS-45))
3. Aircraft Early Warning Radar Repairman

Location: Keesler AFB, Miss.

Length: *Course 1,* 42–45 weeks; *Course 2,* 27–38 weeks; *Course 3,* 17 weeks.

Objectives: *Courses 1 and 2:* To train airmen in the fundamentals of electronics, operation, and maintenance of aircraft early warning radar equipment. *Course 3:* To train Navy personnel in the operation and maintenance of AN/APS-45 and AN/APS-20E radar equipment.

Instruction: *Courses 1 and 2:* Direct and alternating current; electron tubes and power supplies; amplifiers and oscillators; special circuits; radar microwave principles; in addition *Course 1* includes motors and servomechanisms; multivibrators, and sweep circuits. *Course 3:* Maintenance and repair of equipment.

Credit recommendation, collegiate level: CAUTION: *These courses vary slightly in title, length, and recommendation. Require exact identification of course by title and length. Course 1:* 4 semester hours at freshman or sophomore level as an elective in electronics, and credit in electrical laboratory on the basis of demonstrated skills and/or institutional examination. *Course 2:* 3 semester hours at freshman or sophomore level as an elective in electronics, and credit in electrical laboratory on the basis of demonstrated skills and/or institutional examinations. *Course 3:* This course is technical and vocational in nature. Credit in electrical shop on the basis of demonstrated skills and/or institutional examinations.

Aircraft Electrical Repair Technician (Aircraft and Missile Electrical Repair Technician)

Location: Chanute AFB, Ill.

Length: 14–16 weeks.

Objectives: To provide advanced electricity and electronics training for aircraft electrical repairmen.

Instruction: Advanced DC and AC principles; electronic circuits and testers; transistors and reactors; power, control, and warning systems.

Credit recommendation, collegiate level: 2 semester hours as an elective in electricity and electronics, and credit in electrical laboratory on the basis of demonstrated skills and/or institutional examinations.

Aircraft Electrical Repairman (Aircraft and Missile Electrical Repairman)

Locations: Chanute AFB, Ill.; Sheppard AFB, Tex.

Length: 17–19 weeks.

Objectives: To train airmen to repair and maintain aircraft electrical systems and components.

Instruction: Basic mechanics; electronic principles; DC power and motor systems; AC power systems; control and warning systems; inspection and maintenance.

Credit recommendation, collegiate level: 2 semester hours at the freshman or sophomore level as an elective in electricity, and credit in electrical laboratory on the basis of demonstrated skills and/or institutional examinations.

1. Aircraft Electrical Repairman, B-52
2. Aircraft Electrical Repairman, B-52G
3. Aircraft Electrical Repairman, B-52H
4. Aircraft Electrical Repairman, C-130A
5. Aircraft Electrical Repairman, F-101A
6. Aircraft Electrical Repairman (F-101B)
7. Aircraft Electrical Repairman, F-102A
8. Aircraft Electrical Repairman, F-104
9. KC-135 Aircraft Electrical Repairman
   (Aircraft Electrical Repairman, KC-135)

Locations: Amarillo AFB, Tex.; Chanute AFB, Ill.; Sheppard AFB, Tex.

Length: *Courses 1, 2, and 3,* 6 weeks; *Courses 4 through 7,* 3 weeks; *Courses 8 and 9,* 4 weeks.

Objectives: To train aircraft electrical repairmen or technicians to maintain and repair electrical systems of specific aircraft.

Instruction: Aircraft familiarization; location and function of electrical and related systems and components; inspection, maintenance and repair, including removal and replacement of defective and worn parts.

Credit recommendation, collegiate level: These courses are technical and vocational in nature. Credit in aircraft electrical repair shop on the basis of demonstrated skills and/or institutional examinations.

Aircraft Electrician Gunner, B-36

Location: Lowry AFB, Colo.

Length: 8 weeks.

Objectives: To train airmen as aerial gunners of B-36 aircraft.

Instruction: Operation, inspection, and techniques of aerial gunnery.

Credit recommendation, collegiate level: No credit because course is military in nature.

Aircraft Electronic Navigation Equipment Maintenance Technician
(Airborne Electronic Navigation Equipment Maintenance Technician)

Location: Keesler AFB, Miss.

Length: 19–41 weeks.

Objectives: To provide airmen with advanced technical training in the installation, inspection, and maintenance of airborne electronic communication and navigation equipment.

Instruction: The first phase includes problem solving, aircraft electronic principles and functional circuits, test equipment, troubleshooting logic, and shop supervision. The second phase of the course comprises advanced analysis and repair of aircraft electronic navigation equipment, including instrument landing, TACAN, IFF, Doppler, aircraft search radar, aircraft beacon, loran, and shoran systems, and radar shop practices.

Credit recommendation, collegiate level: 2 semester hours in shop management, and credit in electrical laboratory on the basis of demonstrated skills and/or institutional examinations.

Aircraft Electronic Navigation Equipment Repairman
(Aircraft Electronic Navigation Equipment Repairman (General))
(Airborne Electronic Navigation Equipment Repairman)
(Aircraft Electronic Navigation Equipment Repairman (Navigation))

Location: Keesler AFB, Miss.

Length: 28–40 weeks.

Objectives: To train airmen to maintain and repair aircraft electronic and radio navigation equipment.

Instruction: The first phase is electronics training which includes DC and AC electricity, electron tubes and power supplies, amplifiers and oscillators, special circuits, motors and servomechanisms, multivibrators and sweep circuits, and radar microwave propagation. The second phase deals with special equipment.

Credit recommendation, collegiate level: CAUTION: *Courses in electronic navigation equipment repair vary in title, length, and recommendation. Require exact identification of course by full title and length.* 6 semester hours as an elective at the freshman or sophomore level in electricity and electronics, and credit in electrical laboratory on the basis of demonstrated skills and/or institutional examinations.

Aircraft Electronic Navigation Equipment Repairman (AN/APN-105/131 Doppler, F-105)
(AN/APN-105/131 Doppler Maintenance)

Location: Keesler AFB, Miss.

Length: 15 weeks.

Objectives: To train airmen in the maintenance and repair of the Doppler radar navigation system specified.

Instruction: Navigation and Doppler principles; functional analysis of APN-131 systems, RT/antenna and modulator, tracker, and present position and course computers; maintenance and repair.

Credit recommendation, collegiate level: Credit in electrical laboratory on the basis of demonstrated skills and/or institutional examinations.

Aircraft Electronic Navigation Equipment Repairman (Doppler Supplement)
(Aircraft Electronic Navigation Equipment Repairman (AN/APN-82 and AN/APN-89))
(Aircraft Electronic Navigation Equipment Repairman (AN/APN-82))

Location: Keesler AFB, Miss.

Length: 12 weeks.

Objectives: To provide airmen with advanced specialized training in aircraft electronic navigation equipment named in the course titles.

Instruction: Doppler navigation system principles; functional analysis of the system; circuit analysis, adjustment and unit troubleshooting of transmitter, antenna, receiver, frequency tracker, wind-memory amplifier and computer; computer alignment and system maintenance techniques.

Credit recommendation, collegiate level: CAUTION: *Courses in electronic navigation equipment repair vary in title, length, and recommendation. Require exact identification of course by full title and length.* Credit in electricity and electrical laboratory on the basis of demonstrated skills and/or institutional examinations.

Aircraft Electronic Navigation Equipment Repairman (TACAN Supplement)

Location: Keesler AFB, Miss.

Length: 3–6 weeks.

Objectives: To provide airmen with supplemental training on the airborne TACAN receiver-transmitter and associated test equipment and simulators.

Instruction: Bench testing, adjustment, signal, block diagram, and circuit analysis of AN/ARN-2; functional and trouble analysis of beacon simulator; maintenance procedures and troubleshooting techniques for AN/ARN-21.

Credit recommendation, collegiate level: CAUTION: *Courses in electronic navigation equipment repair vary in title, length, and recommendation. Require exact identification of course by full title and length.* No credit because of the brevity and nature of the course.

Aircraft Electronic Navigation Equipment Technician

Location: Keesler AFB, Miss.

Length: 43 weeks.

Objectives: To train airmen in the installation, operation, and maintenance of aircraft electronic navigation and associated equipment.

Instruction: Applied mathematics; analysis of DC and AC circuits; vacuum tubes and solid state devices; power supplies and oscillators; principles of electronic digital data processing; analysis of functional circuits of transmitter, RF, receiver, indicator, and servo systems; test equipment, administration and publications; training and maintenance management.

Credit recommendation, collegiate level: 2 semester hours in shop management, 3 semester hours at the freshman or sophomore level as an elective in electricity and electronics, and credit in electrical laboratory on the basis of demonstrated skills and/or institutional examinations.

1. Aircraft Environmental Systems Repairman (Mechanical Accessories and Equipment Repairman)
2. Aircraft Environmental Systems Repair Technician (Mechanical Accessories and Equipment Repair Technician)
3. KC-135 Mechanical Accessories and Equipment Repairman
4. Mechanical Accessories and Equipment Repairman, C-130A
5. Mechanical Accessories and Equipment Repairman, B-52

Locations: Chanute AFB, Ill.; Sheppard AFB, Tex.

Length: *Course 1,* 16–17 weeks; *Course 2,* 9–13 weeks; *Courses 3, 4, and 5,* 3 weeks.

Objectives: *Course 1:* To train airmen in the organizational and field maintenance of aircraft mechanical accessories and equipment. *Course 2:* To provide advanced training for mechanical accessories and equipment repairmen and qualify them for supervisory positions. *Courses 3, 4, and 5:* To provide qualified repairmen with additional training on the aircraft specified in the course titles.

Instruction: *Course 1:* Electrical principles as applied to aircraft mechanical accessories and equipment; aircraft combustion heater, fire extinguishing, and oxygen installations; air conditioning, pressurization, and pneumatics systems. *Course 2:* Electrical and electronic circuits; air conditioning and anti-icing systems; pressurization, pneumatics, oxygen, and fire extinguishing systems; administration and maintenance management training. *Courses 3, 4, and 5:* Familiarization with the structures, ground handling, and servicing of the specified aircraft; air conditioning, pressurization, anti-icing, defrosting, fire extinguishing, utility, oxygen, and pneumatic equipment systems.

Credit recommendation, collegiate level: *Courses 1 and 2:* For each course, credit in electricity and electrical laboratory on the basis of demonstrated skills and/or institutional examinations. *Courses 3, 4 and 5:* No credit because of the brevity and limited technical nature of the courses.

Aircraft Fuel System Mechanic

Location: Chanute AFB, Ill.

Length: 11–13 weeks.

Objectives: To train airmen in the maintenance of aircraft fuel systems.

Instruction: Operating principles of fuel systems and system components; removal and installation procedures of fuel cells; aircraft fuel tanks and maintenance procedures; wet-wing repair and inspection.

Credit recommendation, collegiate level: This course is technical and vocational in nature. Credit in aircraft fuel systems repair shop on the basis of demonstrated skills and/or institutional examinations.

Aircraft Fuel System Technician

Location: Chanute AFB, Ill.

Length: 7–9 weeks.

Objectives: To train airmen to analyze, install, repair, and supervise maintenance of aircraft fuel systems.

Instruction: Fuel system management and trouble analysis; fuel cell maintenance; component overhaul and checkout; integral tank maintenance.

Credit recommendation, collegiate level: This course is technical and vocational in nature. Credit in aircraft fuel systems maintenance on the basis of demonstrated skills and/or institutional examinations.

1. Aircraft Hydraulic Repairman, B-52G (Aircraft Hydraulic Repairman, B-52)
2. Aircraft Hydraulic Repairman, C-130A
3. Aircraft Hydraulic Repairman, F-100D/F
4. Aircraft Hydraulic Repairman, F-102A
5. KC-135 Aircraft Hydraulic Repairman (KC-135 Aircraft Repairman, Hydraulic)

Locations: Amarillo AFB, Tex.; Chanute AFB, Ill.; Sheppard AFB, Tex.

Length: 3–4 weeks.

Objectives: To provide aircraft hydraulic repairmen with supplemental training on the aircraft specified.

Instruction: Aircraft familiarization; operation, servicing, inspection, and troubleshooting of the hydraulic systems.

Credit recommendation, collegiate level: No credit because of the brevity and limited technical nature of the courses.

Aircraft Inertial and Radar Navigation Systems Repairman

Location: Keesler AFB, Miss.
Length: 40 weeks.
Objectives: To train airmen in the operation, organizational maintenance, and repair of inertial and radar navigation equipment including altimeter, Doppler, inertial, and computer systems.
Instruction: DC and AC; reactive circuits; principles of vacuum tubes and transistors; tubes and solid state devices; amplifiers and oscillators; detection and discrimination; motors and servomechanisms; multivibrators and sweep circuits; microwave principles.
Credit recommendation, collegiate level: 6 semester hours at freshman or sophomore level as an elective in electricity and electronics, and credit in electrical laboratory on the basis of demonstrated skills and/or institutional examinations.

Aircraft Inertial and Radar Navigation Systems Repairman (AN/APN-89/99/108 Doppler)

Location: Keesler AFB, Miss.
Length: 12 weeks.
Objectives: To train airmen to install, inspect, and repair Doppler navigation radar systems.
Instruction: Doppler principles and functional and circuit analysis; navigational computer and specialized equipment for computer maintenance; alignment, maintenance procedures, and troubleshooting techniques for AN/APN-81/82/89A/99A/108.
Credit recommendation, collegiate level: Credit in electrical laboratory on the basis of demonstrated skills and/or institutional examinations.

1. **Aircraft Landing Control Operator**
   (Apprentice Aircraft Landing Control Operator)
   (Aircraft Landing Control Technician)
2. **Control Tower Operator**
   (Control Tower Technician)
   Location: Keesler AFB, Miss.
   Length: 11–18 weeks.
   Objectives: To train airmen in the duties of a control tower operator and in the control of aircraft traffic on airfields.
   Instruction: Weather, navigational aids; civil air regulation; airport traffic control; air route traffic control.
   Credit recommendation, collegiate level: These courses are technical and vocational in nature. Credit in airport control tower operation on the basis of demonstrated skills and/or institutional examinations.

1. **Aircraft Loadmaster**
2. **Aircraft Loadmaster (Transportation of Guided Missiles by Air)**
   Location: Sheppard AFB, Tex.
   Length: 4–9 weeks.
   Objectives: To train airmen in aircraft loading and unloading procedures.
   Instruction: *Course 1:* Military air transportation; weight and balance; load planning; aircraft loading; airdrop. *Course 2:* Aircraft loading systems; Air Force guided missiles; missile loading.
   Credit recommendation, collegiate level: No credit because of the specialized nature of these courses.

Aircraft Maintenance Indoctrination (SAC)

Location: Chanute AFB, Ill.
Length: 5–6 weeks.
Objectives: To indoctrinate SAC officers, recently designated to assume positions in aircraft and/or armament electronics maintenance career fields, in the correct principles and concepts of SAC maintenance procedures.
Instruction: SAC aircraft maintenance; supply classification, property responsibility and unit manning document; aircraft records and reports.
Credit recommendation, collegiate level: 2 semester hours in shop management.

1. **Aircraft Maintenance Staff Officer**
   (Aircraft Maintenance Management Officer)
2. **Aircraft Maintenance Management Officer**
   (Aircraft Maintenance Officer)
3. **Aircraft Maintenance Officer**
4. **Aircraft Maintenance Officer**
   Location: Chanute AFB, Ill.
   Length: *Course 1,* 5–6 weeks; *Course 2,* 8–9 weeks; *Course 3,* 30–32 weeks; *Course 4,* 35 weeks.
   Objectives: To train aircraft maintenance management officers in the principles and concepts of management, personal relations, and maintenance organization.
   Instruction: *Courses 1 and 2:* Maintenance policies and concepts; statistics; material management; maintenance control; quality control; personnel administration. *Course 2:* Consists of the same subject matter as *Course 1* but in greater depth. *Course 3:* Management and leadership; management systems; maintenance procedures; maintenance problem solving; classification and supply; aircraft electricity and instruments; aircraft systems; weight and balance, and power plants. *Course 4:* Administration and management; maintenance; electrical, electronic, and instrument systems; aircraft systems; weight and balance, and power plants.
   Credit recommendation, collegiate level: CAUTION: *These courses vary slightly in title, length, and recommendation. Require exact identification of course by title and length.* Course 1: 3 semester hours in shop management. *Course 2:* 4 semester hours in shop management. *Course 3:* 6 semester hours in business organization and management, 2 semester hours in personnel management, and credit in electricity, electrical laboratory, and aircraft maintenance shop on the basis of demonstrated skills and/or institutional examinations. *Course 4:* 3 semester hours in business organiza-

tion and management, 2 semester hours in personnel management, 2 semester hours at freshman or sophomore level as an elective in electricity, and credit in electrical laboratory and aircraft maintenance shop on the basis of demonstrated skills and/or institutional examinations.

1. Aircraft Maintenance Technician
2. Aircraft Maintenance Technician
3. Aircraft Maintenance Technician, Jet Engine Aircraft
   (Aircraft Maintenance Technician, Jet Engine Type Aircraft)
4. Aircraft Maintenance Technician, Jet Engine Type Aircraft
5. Aircraft Maintenance Technician, Reciprocating Engine Aircraft
   (Aircraft Maintenance Technician, Reciprocating Engine Type Aircraft)
6. Aircraft Maintenance Technician, Reciprocating Engine

Location: Sheppard AFB, Tex.

Length: *Course 1,* 18 weeks; *Course 2,* 16 weeks; *Courses 3 and 5,* 14–16 weeks; *Courses 4 and 6,* 4 weeks.

Objectives: *Courses 1, 2, 3, and 5:* To train airmen in the maintenance of jet and/or reciprocating engine type aircraft. *Courses 4 and 6:* To familiarize airmen with the electrical and utility systems of the aircraft.

Instruction: *Course 1:* Electrical systems; Air Force supply system; aircraft systems; reciprocating engine type aircraft; jet aircraft. *Courses 2, 3, and 5:* Maintenance management; aircraft electrical systems; hudraulic or pneudralic systems; flight control systems; utility and fuel systems. *Courses 4 and 6:* Electrical systems; utility systems; instruments and technical orders.

Credit recommendation, collegiate level: CAUTION: *These courses vary slightly in title, length, and recommendation. Require exact identification by title and length. Course 1:* Credit in electricity and electrical laboratory on the basis of demonstrated skills and/or institutional examinations. *Courses 2, 3, and 5:* For each course, 2 semester hours in shop management, and credit in electricity and electrical laboratory on the basis of demonstrated skills and/or institutional examinations. *Courses 4 and 6:* These courses are technical and vocational in nature. Credit in electrical shop on the basis of demonstrated skills and/or institutional examinations.

1. Aircraft Mechanic, B-52
2. Aircraft Mechanic, B-52G
3. Aircraft Mechanic, C-130
4. Aircraft Mechanic, C-130A
5. Aircraft Mechanic, F-100D
6. Aircraft Mechanic, F-101A
7. Aircraft Mechanic, F-101B
8. Aircraft Mechanic, F-102A
9. Aircraft Mechanic, F-104
10. F-106 Aircraft Mechanic
11. KC-135 Aircraft Mechanic
12. Aircraft Mechanic, T-33A

Locations: Amarillo AFB, Tex.; Chanute AFB, Ill.; Sheppard AFB, Tex.

Length: 4–9 weeks.

Objectives: To provide transition training, on the aircraft specified, for qualified aircraft mechanics and/or instructor personnel.

Instruction: Familiarization with the aircraft, including identification, location, and function of system components; operational checks; servicing; troubleshooting; replacement of components; minor repairs and adjustments.

Credit recommendation, collegiate level: These courses are technical and vocational in nature. Credit in aircraft systems repair shop on the basis of demonstrated skills and/or institutional examinations.

1. Aircraft Mechanic, Reciprocating Engine Aircraft
   (Aircraft Mechanic, Reciprocating Engine Types)
   (Aircraft Mechanic, Reciprocating, One or Two Engines)
   (Aircraft Mechanic, Reciprocating, One and Two Engines)
   (Aircraft Mechanic, Reciprocating, Over Two Engines)
2. Reciprocating Engine Mechanic
   (Aircraft Reciprocating Engine Mechanic)
3. Reciprocating Engine Technician
4. Reciprocating Engine Technician

Locations: Chanute AFB, Ill., Sheppard AFB, Tex.

Length: *Courses 1 and 2,* 14–18 weeks; *Course 3,* 14 weeks; *Course 4,* 12 weeks.

Objectives: *Course 1:* To train airmen in aircraft systems maintenance. *Course 2:* To train airmen in the maintenance of aircraft reciprocating engines. *Courses 3 and 4:* To provide reciprocating engine mechanics with advanced supervisory-level training.

Instruction: *Course 1:* Fundamentals of aircraft mechanics; power plant and basic conditioning; airframes and flight controls; electrical, hydraulic, landing gear, and utility systems; aircraft inspection and maintenance. *Course 2:* Fundamentals of aircraft mechanics; basic engines and engine systems; power package and engine maintenance; engine conditioning. *Course 3:* Maintenance management; technical publications; supply procedures; inspection system and forms; reciprocating engine systems; engine and accessory inspection and maintenance; power package disassembly, buildup, removal, and installation; Nacelle testing; engine conditioning. *Course 4* superseded *Course 3* in August 1965 and covers the same general subject areas but with less emphasis on management training.

Credit recommendation, collegiate level: CAUTION: *These courses vary in title, length, and recommendation. Require exact identification of course by title and length. Note that Courses 3 and 4 vary in recommendation only according to length and dates given. Courses 1, 2, and 4* are technical and vocational in nature. *Course 1:* Credit in aircraft systems repair shop on the basis of demonstrated skills and/or institutional examinations. *Courses 2 and 4:* Credit in aircraft reciprocating engine repair shop on the basis of demonstrated skills and/or institutional examinations. *Course 3:* 2 semester hours in shop management. At the technical and vocational level, credit in aircraft reciprocating engine repair shop on the basis of demonstrated skills and/or institutional examinations.

1. Aircraft Observer Technical Upgrading
   (Aircraft Observer Technical-Upgrading,
   AN/APQ-24)
2. Aircraft Observer Upgrading Training to AFSC
   1521P

Locations: Ellington AFB, Tex.; Harlingen AFB,
Tex.; James Connally AFB, Tex.; Mather AFB, Calif.

Length: *Course 1:* 24–25 weeks; *Course 2:* Varies in
length in accordance with the previous training of the
individual.

Objectives: To qualify officers possessing one or more
aircraft observer AFSC's as navigator-bombardiers.

Instruction: *Courses 1 and 2:* Flying training subjects; celestial navigation; navigation flight missions;
radar flight missions; dead reckoning; bombing; radar;
in addition *Course 2* offers observer fundamentals;
weather; observer electronics.

Credit recommendation, collegiate level: *Course 1:* 5
semester hours in navigation. *Course 2:* Credit in navigation, electricity, and electronics on the basis of demonstrated skills and/or institutional examinations.

Aircraft Observer Training-Pilot

Location: James Connally AFB, Tex.

Length: 24–27 weeks.

Objectives: To train rated pilots to bomb and to navigate utilizing an applicable radar set.

Instruction: Flying training subjects; dead reckoning;
weather; celestial sunlines; celestial night; grid navigation; radar navigation; bombing.

Credit recommendation, collegiate level: 4 semester
hours in navigation.

1. Aircraft Pneudraulic Repairman
   (Aircraft and Missile Pneudraulic Repairman)
   (Aircraft and Missile Hydraulic Repairman)
   (Aircraft Hydraulic Repairman)
2. Aircraft Pneudraulic Repair Technician
   (Aircraft and Missile Pneudraulic Repair
   Technician)
   (Aircraft and Missile Hydraulic Technician)
   (Aircraft Hydraulic Technician)

Locations: Amarillo AFB, Tex.; Chanute AFB, Ill.;
Sheppard AFB, Tex.

Length: *Course 1,* 13–17 weeks; *Course 2,* 8–10
weeks.

Objectives: *Course 1:* To train airmen in the operation and maintenance of aircraft pneudraulic and/or
hydraulic units and related ground support equipment. *Course 2:* To provide advanced training for
qualified repairmen.

Instruction: *Course 1:* Operation, disassembly, inspection, test, adjustment and repair of pneumatic
and/or hydraulic units; normal and emergency operation of aircraft and missile pneudraulic or hydraulic
systems; maintenance of hydraulic jacks and test stand;
inspection of aircraft pneudraulic and allied systems.
Course 2: Application of pneumatic and/or hydraulic
theory; pneumatic and/or hydraulic components; system operational analysis, inspection, malfunction analysis, adjustment, and repair; control systems and related
test equipment.

Credit recommendation, collegiate level: These
courses are technical and vocational in nature. Credit

in aircraft hydraulic and pneudraulic systems repair on
the basis of demonstrated skills and/or institutional
examinations.

1. Aircraft Propeller Repairman
2. Aircraft Propeller Technician

Locations: Chanute AFB, Ill.; Sheppard AFB, Tex.

Length: *Course 1,* 17–19 weeks; *Course 2,* 9–13
weeks.

Objectives: *Course 1:* To train airmen in aircraft
propeller maintenance. *Course 2:* To provide aircraft
propeller repairmen with advanced propeller maintenance training.

Instruction: *Course 1:* Fundamentals of aircraft mechanics; propeller fundamentals; Curtiss electric propeller and controls; turbolectric propellers; Hamilton
propellers and turbo-propellers; operation, inspection
and maintenance of propellers. *Course 2* includes some
management training and covers the repair and maintenance of the same equipment as *Course 1* with emphasis given to analyzing technical problems and determining corrective action.

Credit recommendation, collegiate level: These
courses are technical and vocational in nature. Credit
in aircraft propeller maintenance on the basis of demonstrated skills and/or institutional examinations.

1. Aircraft Radio Maintenance Technician
2. Aircraft Radio Maintenance Technician
   (Airborne Radio Maintenance Technician)

Locations: Keesler AFB, Miss.; Scott AFB, Ill.

Length: *Course 1,* 33–39 weeks; *Course 2,* 19–23
weeks.

Objectives: To provide aircraft radio repairmen with
advanced special equipment training.

Instruction: *Course 1:* Problem solving in basic electronics; analysis of DC and AC circuits; vacuum tubes
and solid state devices; analysis of functional circuits of
transmitter, RF, receiver, indicator, and servo systems;
shop supervision; administration; training and maintenance management; test equipment and maintenance
of special equipment. *Course 2:* Liaison and command
equipment; IFF and navigation equipment; communications equipment maintenance.

Credit recommendation, collegiate level: CAUTION:
*These courses vary in length and recommendation. Re-
quire exact identification by title and length. Course 1:*
3 semester hours at the freshman or sophomore level as
an elective in electricity and electronics, 3 semester
hours in maintenance management, and credit in
electrical laboratory on the basis of demonstrated skills
and/or institutional examinations. *Course 2:* Credit in
electrical laboratory on the basis of demonstrated skills
and/or institutional examinations.

1. Aircraft Radio Repairman
2. Aircraft Radio Repairman
3. Aircraft Radio Repairman (Communications)
4. Aircraft Radio Repairman (Navigational)
5. Aircraft Radio Repairman (Navigational)
6. Aircraft Radio Repairman (General)
7. Aircraft Radio Repairman (General)
8. Ground Radio Repairman

Locations: *Courses 1, 3, 4, and 6:* Keesler AFB, Miss.; *Courses 2, 5, 7, and 8:* Scott AFB, Ill.

Length: *Courses 1, 2, 3, 4, and 8,* 31–33 weeks; *Courses 5, 6, and 7,* 26–28 weeks.

Objectives: *Courses 1 through 7:* To train airmen to install, maintain, and repair airborne communications and related navigational equipment. *Course 8:* To train airmen to install, maintain, and repair ground communications and related navigational equipment.

Instruction: *Course 1:* DC and AC; electron tubes and power supplies; amplifiers and oscillators; transmitter principles; antennas and tuners; receivers; tuning system principles. *Courses 2, 3, 4, 6, and 8:* Basic electronics; electron tubes and circuit applications; radio transmitters and receivers; pulse techniques. *Courses 5 and 7:* Operation, tuning, adjustment, and organizational and field maintenance of aircraft radio equipment.

Credit recommendation, collegiate level: CAUTION: *These courses vary slightly in title, location, and recommendation. Require exact identification by title and location. Course 1:* 6 semester hours at the freshman or sophomore level as an elective in electricity and electronics, and credit in electrical laboratory on the basis of demonstrated skills and/or institutional examinations. *Courses 2, 3, 4, 6, and 8:* For each course, 4 semester hours at the freshman or sophomore level as an elective in electricity and electronics, and credit in electrical laboratory on the basis of demonstrated skills and/or institutional examinations. *Courses 5 and 7:* For each course, credit in electrical laboratory on the basis of demonstrated skills and/or institutional examinations.

1. Aircraft Radio Repairman (Command)
2. Aircraft Radio Repairman (Command)

Locations: *Course 1:* Scott AFB, Ill.; *Course 2:* Keesler AFB, Miss.

Length: *Course 1,* 20 weeks; *Course 2,* 25 weeks.

Objectives: To train airmen to operate, maintain, and repair airborne command communications equipment and related test equipment.

Instruction: *Courses 1 and 2:* Aircraft command radio and associated equipment; UHF command equipment; VHF command equipment; maintenance; in addition *Course 2* includes electricity and magnetism; AC; vacuum tubes, power supplies, and voltage regulators; amplifiers and oscillators; modulation, detection, and receiver kit construction; special circuits; microwaves; high-frequency energy and synchros.

Credit recommendation, collegiate level: CAUTION: *These courses vary slightly in length, recommendation, and location. Require exact identification by location and length. Course 1:* Credit in electrical laboratory on the basis of demonstrated skills and/or institutional examinations. *Course 2:* 4 semester hours at freshman or sophomore level as an elective in electricity and electronics, and credit in electrical laboratory on the basis of demonstrated skills and/or institutional examinations.

Aircraft Radio Repairman (Data Link Supplement)

Location: Keesler AFB, Miss.

Length: 10–12 weeks.

Objectives: To train airmen in the maintenance and repair of airborne data link systems.

Instruction: Principles of Boolean algebra and binary counting; data processing circuitry and symbology; semiconductor theory and application; functional and failure analysis; performance testing and maintenance of AN/ARR-60/61 using specialized test equipment.

Credit recommendation, collegiate level: Credit in electrical laboratory on the basis of demonstrated skills and/or institutional examinations.

Aircraft Structural Sealing, B-52

Location: Amarillo AFB, Tex.

Length: 3 weeks.

Objectives: To train airframe repairmen in aircraft sealing procedures as applicable to the B-52.

Instruction: Aircraft familiarization and seal plane analysis; sealants and sealing requirements; body fuel cavity sealant repair; removal sealing and replacement.

Credit recommendation, collegiate level: No credit because of the brevity and specialized nature of the course.

Aircrew Egress Systems Repairman

Locations: Amarillo AFB, Tex.; Chanute AFB, Ill.

Length: 10–12 weeks.

Objectives: To train airmen to operate, inspect, and repair aircrew egress systems and associated equipment.

Instruction: Publications and maintenance requirements; aircraft hardward and tools; safetying devices and procedures; principles of electricity, pneudraulics, mechanical devices, ballistics and rocketry, and aerospace ground equipment; egress systems maintenance, including seat and canopy operation and adjustment, electrical and pneumatic canopy system, upward, rotational, and downward ejection seat systems, escape hatch familiarization, and jettison procedures.

Credit recommendation, collegiate level: This course is technical and vocational in nature. Credit in electrical shop on the basis of demonstrated skills and/or institutional examinations.

Airframe Repair, C-141

Location: Amarillo AFB, Tex.

Length: 3 weeks.

Objectives: To train airframe repairmen in the structural repair of the C-141 aircraft.

Instruction: Aircraft familiarization; repair of bonded honeycomb assemblies; radomes, fasteners, and inserts; corrosion, solvents and finishes; aircraft balancing and symmetry checks.

Credit recommendation, collegiate level: No credit because of the brevity and specialized nature of the course.

Airframe Repairman

Location: Amarillo AFB, Tex.

Length: 16–18 weeks.

Objectives: To train airmen in the structural repair of the airframe and metal components of aircraft.

Instruction: Aircraft familiarization and safety; repair equipment; layout of repairs; metal cutting and forming equipment; riveting; corrosion control; repair of fiberglass structures; fabrication of cable and tubing assemblies, thermo-dimpling; repair of aluminum, steel, magnesium, and titanium structures.

Credit recommendation, collegiate level: This course is technical and vocational in nature. Credit in metal shop on the basis of demonstrated skills and/or institutional examinations.

Airframe Titanium Repair

Location: Amarillo AFB, Tex.

Length: 3 weeks.

Objectives: To train airframe repairmen in titanium repair.

Instruction: Identification and inspection of titanium; preparation of titanium for repair and fabrication; forming titanium; assembly and final inspection of repaired parts.

Credit recommendation, collegiate level: No credit because of the brevity and specialized nature of the course.

Airplane and Engine Mechanic, Liaison Types

Location: Gary AFB, Tex.

Length: 13 weeks.

Objectives: To train Army personnel in the operation, inspection, and maintenance of liaison airplanes, engines, and related equipment.

Instruction: Liaison aircraft and systems; airplane repair; power plants and related equipment; inspection and maintenance.

Credit recommendation, collegiate level: This course is technical and vocational in nature. Credit in aircraft engine repair shop on the basis of demonstrated skills and/or institutional examinations.

All Relay Central Office Equipment Specialist

Location: Sheppard AFB, Tex.

Length: 8 weeks.

Objectives: To train installation maintenance personnel as all relay central office equipment specialists.

Instruction: Installation of relays and linefinder; guard and selector circuits; connector circuit and wiring diagram; auxiliary circuits; intra- and inter-office wiring; trouble location.

Credit recommendation, collegiate level: This course is technical and vocational in nature. Credit in central office equipment maintenance on the basis of demonstrated skills and/or institutional examinations.

Ammunition Officer (Munitions)
(Ammunition Officer)

Location: Lowry AFB, Colo.

Length: 8–12 weeks.

Objectives: To train officers to manage ammunitions activities and plan for defense of installations against attack.

Instruction: Air armament management; ammunition general (explosive); chemical and biological agents, munitions, and protective measures; supply, storage, handling, and disposal of ammunition and explosives; nuclear weapons; biological warfare.

Credit recommendation, collegiate level: 2 semester hours in supply management.

Analyst Technician, GAM-77
(Missile Systems Analyst/Technician, GAM-77)

Location: Chanute AFB, Ill.

Length: 18 weeks.

Objectives: To train airmen in the operation, checkout, and adjustment of the GAM-77 missile systems.

Instruction: Missile familiarization; missile subsystems; flight control; guidance; combined systems run.

Credit recommendation, collegiate level: Credit in electrical laboratory on the basis of demonstrated skills and/or institutional examinations.

Antenna Installation and Maintenance

Location: Sheppard AFB, Tex.

Length: 10 weeks.

Objectives: To train U.S. Army personnel in antenna installation and maintenance.

Instruction: Antenna fundamentals; installation plans and specifications for antenna construction; installation of rhombic, delta match, and discone antenna; antenna tower assembly and erection; hazard lighting; lightning protection; elementary surveying.

Credit recommendation, collegiate level: This course is technical and vocational in nature. Credit in antenna installation and maintenance on the basis of demonstrated skills and/or institutional examinations.

1. Atomic Energy, Phase I (Electrical)
2. Atomic Energy, Phase I

Location: Keesler AFB, Miss.

Length: *Course 1*, 12 weeks; *Course 2*, 18 weeks.

Objectives: To train airmen in the electrical principles fundamental to the field of atomic energy.

Instruction: *Courses 1 and 2:* Electricity; magnetism; alternating current; vacuum tubes; power supplies, voltage regulators, amplifiers, oscillators, modulation, and detection; in addition *Course 2* includes application of electrical fundamentals to radar equipment.

Credit recommendation, collegiate level: CAUTION: *These courses vary in title, length, and recommendation. Require exact identification of course by title and length. Course 1:* 3 semester hours in basic electronics (electricity). *Course 2:* 3 semester hours in basic electronics (electricity), and credit in electrical laboratory on the basis of demonstrated skills and/or institutional examinations.

Atomic Weapons Officer

Location: Lowry AFB, Colo.

Length: 30 weeks.

Objectives: To train officers to maintain, repair, and assemble atomic weapons components and to command atomic weapons units.

Instruction: Introduction to theory and basic application of electricity; AC principles; vacuum tubes and power supplies; vacuum tube amplifiers; oscillator circuits; receiver and transmitter circuits; special electronic circuits; microwave energy generation, transmission and propagation.

Credit recommendation, collegiate level: 6 semester hours at the freshman or sophomore level as an elective in the areas of electricity and electronics, and credit in electrical laboratory on the basis of demonstrated skills and/or institutional examination.

Auditing Data Processing Systems

Location: Sheppard AFB, Tex.

Length: 3 weeks.

Objectives: To familiarize auditing personnel with the techniques of auditing data processing systems.

Instruction: Introduction to automatic data processing and equipment; the auditor's role in systems development; audit of automatic data processing.

Credit recommendation, collegiate level: No credit because of the brevity and limited technical nature of the course.

Auditor

Location: Sheppard AFB, Tex.

Length: 15 weeks.

Objectives: To train officers to audit internal accounts and contracts and to coordinate audit activities.

Instruction: Organization and management; cost accounting; time and material contracts; commercial and internal audit procedures; non-appropriated funds; Accounting and Finance Division of the Financial Management System; Air Force stock and industrial funds; machine accounting.

Credit recommendation, collegiate level: 4 semester hours in general accounting, and 4 semester hours in auditing.

Automated Systems Program Designer
(Management Support Systems)

Location: Sheppard AFB, Tex.

Length: 9 weeks.

Objectives: To train airmen in the skills and knowledge necessary to perform the duties of an automated systems program designer.

Instruction: Introduction to punched card equipment; electronic data processing; programming a punched card oriented computer; programming a tape oriented computer; COBOL; automatic data processing systems.

Credit recommendation, collegiate level: 3 semester hours in computer operations in the field of data processing.

Automated Systems Programming Technician
(Management Support Systems)

Location: Sheppard AFB, Tex.

Length: 7 weeks.

Objectives: To train airmen in the theory and operating principles of computers.

Instruction: Introduction to data processing; symbolic programming; flow charting; storage media; input/output directives; COBOL programming.

Credit recommendation, collegiate level: 2 semester hours in computer programming in the field of data processing.

Automatic Central Office Equipment Technician
(Kellogg K-60)

Location: Sheppard AFB, Tex.

Length: 15 weeks.

Objectives: To train airmen to repair and maintain ballistic missile communications system, Kellogg K-60 (SM-65).

Instruction: Fundamentals of electricity and K1A1 key telephone units; direct line and SASS; type K-60 dial telephone switching system.

Credit recommendation, collegiate level: Credit in electricity and electrical laboratory on the basis of demonstrated skills and/or institutional examinations.

1. Automatic Flight Control Systems Specialist (Tanker/Cargo/Utility/Bomber, Except B-58)
2. Automatic Flight Control Systems Specialist (Fighters and B-58)
3. Flight Control/Autopilot Systems Repairman (Other)
4. Flight Control/Autopilot Systems Repairman (B-58)
5. Flight Control/Autopilot Systems Repairman
6. Automatic Flight Control Systems Specialist (Bomber)
7. Automatic Flight Control Systems Specialist (B-58)
8. Automatic Flight Control Systems Specialist (Other)
9. Automatic Flight Control Systems Specialist
10. Automatic Flight Control Systems Specialist
11. Flight Control/Autopilot Systems Repairman
12. Autopilot/Compass Systems Repairman

Locations: Chanute AFB, Ill.; Amarillo AFB, Tex.

Length: *Courses 1, 2, 3, and 10, 31–36 weeks; Courses 4 through 9, 20–30 weeks; Courses 11 and 12, 18–20 weeks.*

Objectives: To train airmen to inspect, maintain, and repair automatic flight control systems and related subassemblies and components.

Instruction: *Courses 1, 2, 3, and 10:* DC and AC circuits; solid state devices; vacuum tubes; oscillators; wave-shaping circuits; special circuitry. *Courses 4 through 9:* DC and AC; reactive circuits; vacuum tubes and transistors; amplifiers and oscillators; motors and servomechanisms. *Courses 11 and 12:* DC and AC, electron theory and electromagnetism; electrical circuits and components; amplifiers and oscillators.

Credit recommendation, collegiate level: CAUTION: *These courses vary slightly in title, length, and recommendation. Require exact identification of course by* *title and length. Courses 1, 2, 3, and 10:* 4 semester hours in electricity and electronics, and credit in electrical laboratory and electrical instrument repair on the basis of demonstrated skills and/or institutional examinations. *Courses 4 through 9:* 3 semester hours in electricity and electronics, and credit in electrical laboratory and electrical instrument repair on the basis of demonstrated skills and/or institutional examinations. *Courses 11 and 12:* 2 semester hours in electricity and electronics, and credit in electrical laboratory and electrical instrument repair on the basis of demonstrated skills and/or institutional examinations.

Automatic Flight Control Systems Technician (Bomber/Tanker)
(Automatic Flight Control Systems Technician (Bomber))
(Automatic Flight Control Systems Technician (Fighter and B-58))
(Automatic Flight Control Systems Technician)
(Flight Control/Autopilot Systems Repair Technician (Other))
(Flight Control/Autopilot Systems Repair Technician)

Locations: Chanute AFB, Ill.; Amarillo AFB, Tex.
Length: 14–17 weeks.
Objectives: To provide airmen with advanced technical training in organizational and field maintenance of automatic flight control systems.
Instruction: Review of electron theory; DC and AC circuits analysis; vacuum tubes and solid state devices; amplifiers and oscillators; polarity and phase sensitive devices; wave-shaping circuitry.
Credit recommendation, collegiate level: 2 semester hours as an elective in electronics, and credit in electrical laboratory and electrical instrument repair on the basis of demonstrated skills and/or institutional examinations.

Automatic Teletype and Electronic Switching Systems Repairman
(Electronic Communications and Cryptographic Systems Equipment Repairman (Automatic Teletype))

Location: Sheppard AFB, Tex.
Length: 35–36 weeks.
Objectives: To provide airmen with basic training in the maintenance of Plan 55 automatic teletype switching equipment.
Instruction: DC and AC circuits; solid state devices and vacuum tubes; electromechanical equipment, including Model 28 transmitter-distributor (LBXD), Model 28 typing reperforator (LPR), and Model 28 multimagnetic reperforator (LARP) operation and adjustments; relays and rotary switches; manual and automatic switching; patching and test equipment; maintenance of receiving and cross office components; Plan 55, system maintenance.
Credit recommendation, collegiate level: 3 semester hours at the freshman or sophomore level as an elective in electricity and electronics, and credit in electrical laboratory on the basis of demonstrated skills and/or institutional examinations.

1. **Automatic Tracking Radar Technician (Radar Equipment)**
2. **Automatic Tracking Radar Technician (Automatic Tracking Radar Equipment)**
   (Automatic Tracking Radar Technician)
3. **Automatic Tracking Radar Technician**

Location: Keesler AFB, Miss.
Length: *Course 1,* 40 weeks; *Course 2,* 35 weeks; *Course 3,* 19–24 weeks.
Objectives: To train airmen in the theory of operation, maintenance, and installation of automatic tracking radar and associated equipment.
Instruction: *Course 1:* DC and AC circuits; vacuum tubes; solid state devices; power supplies; oscillators; principles of electronic digital data processing; transmitter and RF system circuits; receiver system circuits; indicator and servo system circuits. *Course 2:* DC and AC; transmitter and RF system circuits; synchroscope and oscilloscope; servos and resolvers. *Course 3:* Circuit analysis; testing; troubleshooting and repair.
Credit recommendation, collegiate level: CAUTION: *These courses vary slightly in title, length, and recommendation. Require exact identification by title and length. Course 1:* 4 semester hours at freshman or sophomore level as an elective in electricity and electronics, and credit in electrical laboratory on the basis of demonstrated skills and/or institutional examinations. *Course 2:* 3 semester hours at freshman or sophomore level as an elective in electricity and electronics, and credit in electrical laboratory on the basis of demonstrated skills and/or institutional examinations. *Course 3:* This course is technical and vocational in nature. Credit in electrical shop on the basis of demonstrated skills and/or institutional examinations.

Automotive Repairman
(Automotive Mechanic)

Locations: Chanute AFB, Ill.; Francis E. Warren AFB, Wyo.
Length: 13–17 weeks.
Objectives: To train airmen in the maintenance of automotive vehicles and materials handling equipment.
Instruction: Tools; engines; automotive electrical units; fuel systems; power trains; steering; brakes; dump trucks; material handling vehicles; engine change; vehicle tune-up, wheel and frame alignment; use of dynamometer and headlight tester.
Credit recommendation, collegiate level: These courses are technical and vocational in nature. Credit in auto repair shop on the basis of demonstrated skills and/or institutional examinations.

Automotive Shop Management

Location: Chanute AFB, Ill.
Length: 8 weeks.
Objectives: To train airmen to supervise shop activities.
Instruction: Shop organization; supply functions; shop layout; inspection and production control operations; administration, supervision, and training.
Credit recommendation, collegiate level: 3 semester hours in supply management.

Aviation Cadet Pre-Flight (Pilot and Navigator)
(Aviation Cadet Pre-Flight (Pilot))
(Preflight Training for Aviation Cadets)
  Location: Lackland AFB, Tex.
  Length: 12 weeks.
  Objectives: To provide preflight cadets with knowledge and training necessary for assignment at flying training bases.
  Instruction: Basic military education; leadership training; Air Force familiarization.
  Credit recommendation, collegiate level: No credit because of the specialized nature of this course.

Aviation Fuel Monitoring Specialist
  Location: Amarillo AFB, Tex.
  Length: 3 weeks.
  Objectives: To train airmen to sample and test aviation fuels.
  Instruction: Metric system and analytical balance; quality control; solids content of aviation fuels; fuels systems icing inhibitor content of jet fuel test; free water content of jet fuels (Hydrokit method); solids determination of demineralized water (distillation method); determination of pH; determination of chlorides ppm.
  Credit recommendation, collegiate level: This course is technical and vocational in nature. Credit in aviation fuel testing on the basis of demonstrated skills and/or institutional examinations.

1. Avionics Officer (AGM-28A)
2. Armament Systems Officer (GAM-77)
  Location: Chanute AFB, Ill.
  Length: 3–4 weeks.
  Objectives: To familiarize officers with the operation and maintenance of AGM-28A or GAM-77 missile systems.
  Instruction: *Courses 1 and 2:* Maintenance and subsystems familiarization; electronic systems and ground supporting equipment.
  Credit recommendation, collegiate level: No credit because of the brevity and specialized nature of the courses.

Avionics Officer (Bomber)
(Armaments Systems Officer, Bomber)
  Location: Lowry AFB, Colo.
  Length: 28–35 weeks.
  Objectives: To train officers in the management of aviation electronics activities.
  Instruction: Maintenance management; DC electricity; AC principles and circuitry; electron tubes; amplifiers; waveforming; transmission; solid state principles and circuits; computers and servomechanisms; radar. Application of electronic training to bomber radar, navigation, weapons, and defensive fire control systems.
  Credit recommendation, collegiate level: 3 semester hours at the freshman or sophomore level as an elective in electricity and electronics, 2 semester hours in shop management, and credit in electrical laboratory

on the basis of demonstrated skills and/or institutional examinations.

Avionics Officer (Fighter)
(Armament Systems Officer, Fighter)
  Location: Lowry AFB, Colo.
  Length: 24–36 weeks.
  Objectives: To train officers to manage aviation electronics units.
  Instruction: Maintenance management, DC and AC electricity, electron tubes, amplifiers, wave-forming, solid state principles and circuits, computers and servomechanisms, transmission, radar, and applied management. The remainder of the course familiarizes the officer with nuclear weapons; planning, organizing, and directing of aviation electronics systems; and maintenance of fire control and weapons control systems.
  Credit recommendation, collegiate level: 3 semester hours as an elective in electricity and electronics, 2 semester hours in shop management, and credit in electrical laboratory on the basis of demonstrated skills and/or institutional examinations.

Avionics Officer (Other)
(Air Electronics Officer)
  Location: Keesler AFB, Miss.
  Length: 39–41 weeks.
  Objectives: To train officers to supervise units responsible for the maintenance of airborne communications and navigation electronic equipment.
  Instruction: DC and AC electricity; electron tubes and power supplies; amplifiers; oscillators; transmitters; receivers; higher frequency techniques; transistors; special circuits and computers; airborne communications-electronics maintenance management; C-E programming; search radar and radar navigation systems.
  Credit recommendation, collegiate level: 6 semester hours as an elective in electricity and electronics, 3 semester hours in shop management, and credit in electrical laboratory on the basis of demonstrated skills and/or institutional examinations.

Avionics Staff Officer
(Avionics Munitions Staff Officer)
(Armament Officer)
(Advanced Armament Officer)
  Location: Lowry AFB, Colo.
  Length: 10–18 weeks.
  Objectives: To train officers to employ air weapons.
  Instruction: Weapons orientation and employment; aircraft guns and explosive munitions; nuclear weapons; turret systems; chemical and biological warfare; fire control systems; guided missiles and bomb-navigation systems.
  Credit recommendation, collegiate level: No credit as the course is military in nature.

1. B-52, C-135, and KC-135 Fuel System Repairman and Wet Wing Sealing
2. B-52G Fuel System Repairman and Wet Wing Sealing
3. KC-135 Fuel System Repairman and Wet Wing Sealing

Location: Chanute AFB, Ill.

Length: 3–7 weeks.

Objectives: To train airmen in the maintenance of the aircraft fuel systems indicated in title.

Instruction: Construction of integral tanks; maintenance methods and procedures; leak detection; fuel systems operation; body tank inspection and maintenance.

Credit recommendation, collegiate level: These courses are technical and vocational in nature. Credit in aircraft fuel systems maintenance on the basis of demonstrated skills and/or institutional examinations.

B-58 Ground Support Equipment, Field and Organizational Maintenance

Location: Chanute AFB, Ill.

Length: 6 weeks.

Objectives: To train airmen in the field and organizational maintenance of air-conditioners, hydraulic test stands, and gas turbine compressors applicable to B-58 aircraft.

Instruction: Fundamentals of refrigeration; B-58 equipment coolers; gas turbine compressors; B-58 hydraulic test stand.

Credit recommendation, collegiate level: This course is technical and vocational in nature. Credit in refrigeration and air conditioning maintenance on the basis of demonstrated skills and/or institutional examinations.

BMEWS Surveillance Officer

Location: Keesler AFB, Miss.

Length: 3 weeks.

Objectives: To train officers as surveillance officers at ballistic missile early warning system sites.

Instruction: System orientation; description of the system and its function.

Credit recommendation, collegiate level: No credit because of the limited technical nature of this course.

1. Baker
2. Baking
3. Aleutian DEW Line Baker

Locations: Francis E. Warren AFB, Wyo.; Keesler AFB, Miss.

Length: *Course 1,* 17 weeks; *Course 2,* 12 weeks; *Course 3,* 4 weeks.

Objectives: *Courses 1 and 2:* To train airmen in garrison and field baking. *Course 3:* To train airmen cooks to perform both as cooks and bakers on Aleutian DEW Line assignment.

Instruction: Small quantity baking, pastry and bread baking.

Credit recommendation, collegiate level: These courses are technical and vocational in nature. Credit in baking on the basis of institutional examination.

Ballistic Missile Analyst Specialist (HGM-16F) (Ballistic Missile Analyst Specialist (SM-65F))

Location: Sheppard AFB, Tex.

Length: 19 weeks.

Objectives: To train airmen to checkout missile systems.

Instruction: Introduction to the weapon system; propellant storage and transfer; pneumatics; hydraulics; propulsion; propellant utilization; inertial guidance; flight control; re-entry vehicle; launch control of missile systems; composite checkout.

Credit recommendation, collegiate level: Credit in electrical laboratory on the basis of demonstrated skills and/or institutional examinations.

Ballistic Missile Analyst Specialist (PGM-16D) (Ballistic Missile Analyst Specialist (SM-65D))

Location: Sheppard AFB, Tex.

Length: 18 weeks.

Objectives: To train airmen in the operational and maintenance activities at the launch site and missile assembly and maintenance shops.

Instruction: APCHE; launch control; airframe and erection system; electrical, propulsion, and hydraulic systems; flight control; re-entry vehicle systems.

Credit recommendation, collegiate level: Credit in electrical laboratory on the basis of demonstrated skills and/or institutional examinations.

Ballistic Missile Analyst Specialist (PGM-16E) (Ballistic Missile Analyst Specialist (HGM-25A)) (Ballistic Missile Analyst Specialist (SM-68A)) (Ballistic Missile Analyst Specialist (SM-65E))

Location: Sheppard AFB, Tex.

Length: 16–18 weeks.

Objectives: To train airmen in the operation, analysis, inspection, checkout, and the interrelationship of missile subsystems and associated equipment.

Instruction: Propellant storage; hydraulic system; flight control system; launch control of missile systems; composite checkout missile system using electrical checkout vehicle.

Credit recommendation, collegiate level: CAUTION: *Ballistic missile analyst courses vary slightly in title, length, and recommendation. Require exact identification of course by title and length.* Credit in electricity and electrical laboratory on the basis of demonstrated skills and/or institutional examinations.

Ballistic Missile Analyst Technician (SM-65F)

Location: Sheppard AFB, Tex.

Length: 24 weeks.

Objectives: To train airmen as missile systems analyst technicians.

Instruction: Weapon system 107A-1; mobile APCHE; launch control; propellants storage and transfer and pneumatics; hydraulics propulsion and propellant utilization system; inertial guidance; autopilot; composite checkout.

Credit recommendation, collegiate level: Credit in

electrical laboratory on the basis of demonstrated skills and/or institutional examinations.

Ballistic Missile Checkout Equipment Specialist (HGM-25A)
(Ballistic Missile Checkout Equipment Specialist (SM-68A))
(Ballistic Missile Checkout Equipment Specialist (SM-68B))
(Ballistic Missile Checkout Equipment Specialist (SM-65 E&F))

Location: Sheppard AFB, Tex.

Length: 10–17 weeks.

Objectives: To train airmen to operate, inspect, and maintain missile test equipment.

Instruction: Weapon system familiarization; maintenance concepts; circuit analysis; troubleshooting, inspection, and servicing.

Credit recommendation, collegiate level: CAUTION: *Ballistic missile checkout equipment courses vary slightly in title, length, and recommendation. Require exact identification of course by title and length.* These courses are technical and vocational in nature. Credit in mechanical shop on the basis of demonstrated skills and/or institutional examinations.

Ballistic Missile Checkout Equipment Specialist (SM-65D)

Location: Sheppard AFB, Tex.

Length: 14–17 weeks.

Objectives: To train airmen as ballistic missile checkout equipment specialists.

Instruction: Missile orientation; operation, inspection, and maintenance of launch control system equipment, automatic programmed checkout equipment, and semiautomatic test equipment.

Credit recommendation, collegiate level: Credit in electrical laboratory on the basis of demonstrated skills and/or institutional examinations.

Ballistic Missile Checkout Equipment Specialist, WS-133A
(Ballistic Missile Checkout Equipment Specialist, SM-80)

Location: Chanute AFB, Ill.

Length: 35–43 weeks.

Objectives: To train airmen to operate, maintain, inspect, and repair test equipment associated with the ballistic missile.

Instruction: DC and AC; reactive circuits; vacuum tubes and transistors; tubes and solid state devices; amplifiers and oscillators; motors and servomechanisms; multivibrators and sweep circuits.

Credit recommendation, collegiate level: 4 semester hours at the freshman or sophomore level as an elective in electricity and electronics and credit in electrical laboratory on the basis of demonstrated skills and/or institutional examinations.

Ballistic Missile Checkout Equipment Specialist/ Technician

Location: Sheppard AFB, Tex.

Length: 13 weeks.

Objectives: To train airmen to perform maintenance on checkout equipment.

Instruction: Theory of operation; circuit analysis of special circuits; launch control monitoring and checkout system; missile systems fault locator; propellant transfer system; rocket engine test set.

Credit recommendation, collegiate level: Credit in electrical laboratory on the basis of demonstrated skills and/or institutional examinations.

Ballistic Missile Checkout Equipment Technician, SM-80

Location: Chanute AFB, Ill.

Length: 25 weeks.

Objectives: To train airmen as ballistic missile checkout equipment technicians on the SM-80.

Instruction: Theory of operation; system analysis alignment; calibration verification; adjustments and maintenance; equipment function correlation; circuit analysis; digital techniques and numbering systems.

Credit recommendation, collegiate level: Credit in electrical laboratory on the basis of demonstrated skills and/or institutional examinations.

Ballistic Missile Control Mechanic (HGM-25A)
(Ballistic Missile Control Mechanic (SM-68A))

Location: Sheppard AFB, Tex.

Length: 9 weeks.

Objectives: To train airmen to operate, inspect, and maintain the ballistic missile control system indicated in title.

Instruction: Weapon system and flight control system familiarization; flight control system checker circuit analysis and maintenance.

Credit recommendation, collegiate level: CAUTION: *Ballistic missile mechanic courses vary slightly in title, length, and recommendation. Require exact identification by title and length.* Credit in electrical laboratory on the basis of demonstrated skills and/or institutional examinations.

Ballistic Missile Inertial Guidance Mechanic (LGM-25C)
(Ballistic Missile Inertial Guidance Mechanic (SM-68B))

Location: Sheppard AFB, Tex.

Length: 8 weeks.

Objectives: To train airmen in the inspection, operation, and maintenance of the inertial guidance system.

Instruction: Introduction to weapon system; stabilization subsystem; missile guidance computer subsystem; associated guidance equipment.

Credit recommendation, collegiate level: Credit in electrical laboratory on the basis of demonstrated skills and/or institutional examinations.

Ballistic Missile Inertial Guidance Mechanic (SM-65 E&F)

Location: Sheppard AFB, Tex.

Length: 10 weeks.

Objectives: To train airmen in the checkout and maintenance of the ballistic missile inertial guidance system.

Instruction: Introduction and analysis of the missile guidance system; alignment group; countdown group; installation and calibration of IGS equipment.

Credit recommendation, collegiate level: Credit in electrical laboratory on the basis of demonstrated skills and/or institutional examinations.

Ballistic Missile Inertial Guidance Mechanic/ Technician (SM-68B)

Location: Sheppard AFB, Tex.

Length: 15 weeks.

Objectives: To train airmen mechanics as ballistic missile inertial guidance mechanics.

Instruction: Stabilization subsystem; missile guidance computer subsystem; associated guidance equipment.

Credit recommendation, collegiate level: Credit in electrical laboratory on the basis of demonstrated skills and/or institutional examinations.

Ballistic Missile Inertial Guidance Technician/ Mechanic (SM-65F) (Guidance System Technician/Mechanic (SM-65F))

Location: Sheppard AFB, Tex.

Length: 16 weeks.

Objectives: To train airmen as guidance system technician-mechanics.

Instruction: Introduction to weapon system and inertial guidance system; missile guidance set; alignment group countdown group; inertial guidance system equipment; installation and maintenance.

Credit recommendation, collegiate level: Credit in electrical laboratory on the basis of demonstrated skills and/or institutional examinations.

Ballistic Missile Inventory Management and Comlognet Procedures (Ballistic Missile Inventory Management Procedures Log Bal Net Operations)

Location: Amarillo AFB, Tex.

Length: 4 weeks.

Objectives: To enable airmen to function as a special traveling team trained in supply procedures peculiar to the operational ballistic missile supply organization.

Instruction: Ballistic missile inventory management procedures; teletypewriting, message coordination, and card punch operation; programming and AFW supply operations.

Credit recommendation, collegiate level: No credit because of the limited technical nature of this course

Ballistic Missile Launch Equipment Repairman (SM-65 E&F)

Location: Sheppard AFB, Tex.

Length: 18 weeks.

Objectives: To train airmen to operate, maintain, test, and troubleshoot ballistic launch equipment.

Instruction: Introduction to weapons systems; electromechanical relay checkout unit; launch control system maintenance.

Credit recommendation, collegiate level: Credit in electrical laboratory on the basis of demonstrated skills and/or institutional examinations.

Ballistic Missile Launch Equipment Repairman/ Technician, SM-68B

Location: Sheppard AFB, Tex.

Length: 11–13 weeks.

Objectives: To train airmen to perform maintenance on launch equipment.

Instruction: Theory of operation and circuit analysis; adjustment, troubleshooting, and repair of the launch control set and flight control system; hazard sensing and damage control system.

Credit recommendation, collegiate level: CAUTION: *Missile launch equipment repairman/technician courses vary slightly in title, length, and recommendation. Require exact identification by title and length.* This course is technical and vocational in nature. Credit in electrical shop on the basis of demonstrated skills and/or institutional examinations.

Ballistic Missile Launch Equipment Technician, SM-80

Location: Chanute AFB, Ill.

Length: 18 weeks.

Objectives: To train airmen as ballistic missile launch equipment technicians on SM-80 launch equipment.

Instruction: Guidance and control system; SCN data processing equipment; missile targeting and alignment set; programmer group; guidance and control coupler; integrated systems maintenance; strategic missile support base maintenance.

Credit recommendation, collegiate level: Credit in electrical laboratory on the basis of demonstrated skills and/or institutional examinations.

1. Ballistic Missile Radio Guidance Mechanic (SM-68A)
2. Ballistic Missile Radio Guidance Mechanic (SM-65D)

Location: Sheppard AFB, Tex.

Length: *Course 1,* 20 weeks; *Course 2,* 7 weeks.

Objectives: To train airmen to operate, inspect, and maintain guidance systems.

Instruction: *Course 1:* Inspection, troubleshooting, and maintenance of guidance system; ground guidance radar data flow and operational procedures; missile guidance set. *Course 2:* Radio inertial guidance operation; semiautomatic test equipment operation.

Credit recommendation, collegiate level: Credit, for each course, in electrical laboratory on the basis of demonstrated skills and/or institutional examinations.

Ballistic Missile Safety

Location: Chanute AFB, Ill.
Length: 4 weeks.
Objectives: To train airmen in ballistic missile safety surveillance duties including familiarization with constructional features of launch emplacements.
Instruction: Missile terminology; constructional features; missile safety; monitoring of hazardous missile operations.
Credit recommendation, collegiate level: 2 semester hours in safety management.

Bandsman Supervisor

Location: Bolling AFB, Washington, D.C.
Length: 11–12 months.
Objectives: To provide advanced training in band conducting for airmen.
Instruction: Elementary and advanced conducting; instrumental instruction (both on major and required secondary instrument); music theory; solfeggio; arranging and analysis; performing in, and conducting of, dance band, glee club, concert and marching band, and ensembles; public speaking; administration; supply; management; leadership.
Credit recommendation, collegiate level: This course is at the professional level. Credit in the subjects listed on the basis of demonstrated skills and/or institutional examinations.

Base Civil Engineer
(Basic Installations Engineering Officer)

Location: Wright-Patterson AFB, Ohio.
Length: 8–9 weeks.
Objectives: To indoctrinate officers in policies and procedures for the management of base-level civil engineering activities.
Instruction: Functions of the Air Force civil engineer; maintenance methods and control; engineering contracts; fiscal budgeting; programming for operations and maintenance; supervisory management; installations planning; real estate; military construction programs; fire and crash rescue; nuclear defense planning; arctic construction techniques.
Credit recommendation, collegiate level: 3 semester hours in business organization and management.

Basic Course in Medical Service Administration
(Basic Course in Medical Administration)

Location: Gunter AFB, Ala.
Length: *Phase I,* 8 weeks; *Phase II,* 7 weeks; or 15 weeks.
Objectives: To train recently commissioned Medical Service Corps officers to perform basic Air Force Medical Service administrative and staff duties.

Instruction: Basic officer skills, including career seminars, Medical Service orientation, supervising and counseling, military comportment, and command; management of medical unit functional areas, including administrative services, business office, patient care, plans and operations, and registrar; disaster planning and control.
Credit recommendation, collegiate level: *This course has been given in two phases of 8 and 7 weeks each and also as a 15-week course. Completion of Phase I:* 3 semester hours in medical administration. *Completion of both phases or the 15-week course:* 6 semester hours in medical administration.

Basic Observer Navigator Training

Locations: Harlingen AFB, Tex.; James Connally AFB, Tex.; Ellington AFB, Tex.
Length: 14 weeks.
Objectives: To qualify aviation cadets and nonrated officers as aircraft observers and navigators.
Instruction: Flying training subjects; celestial navigation; polar navigation; pressure pattern; radar.
Credit recommendation, collegiate level: Credit in navigation on the basis of demonstrated skills and/or institutional examinations.

1. Basic Observer Reconnaissance Training RB-57/66
2. Basic Observer Reconnaissance BORB-36/47/52
3. Basic Observer B-36, B-47, and B-52 Training

Locations: James Connally AFB, Tex.; Mather AFB, Calif.
Length: 24, 26, and 36 weeks.
Objectives: To train graduates of the Primary Observer Course to perform special reconnaissance missions, and to plan and fly each phase of photo-reconnaissance missions.
Instruction: Flying training subjects; air navigation techniques; instruments; weather; celestial and polar navigation; pressure pattern; bombing; reconnaissance; radar.
Credit recommendation, collegiate level: Credit, for each course, in navigation on the basis of demonstrated skills and/or institutional examinations.

Basic Orientation Course for Officers of the Medical Service

Location: Gunter AFB, Ala.
Length: 3–4 weeks.
Objectives: To provide personnel processing and basic orientation for Medical Service officers.
Instruction: Basic medical orientation; medicine and surgery; medical administration; military dentistry; nursing service; personnel administrative processing; preventive medicine; radiobiology; training and logistics; veterinary service.
Credit recommendation, collegiate level: 2 semester hours in medical administration.

Basic Pilot Instructor, Multi-Engine Conventional

Locations: Goodfellow AFB. Tex.; Reese AFB, Tex.; Vance AFB, Okla.

Length: 6 weeks. *Note*—Since flying training is dependent upon weather and other factors, the length of the course may vary.

Objectives: To train rated Air Force pilots to teach basic multi-engine pilot trainees to fly the TB-25 aircraft.

Instruction: Engineering for instructor pilots, techniques of flight instruction, principles of learning, training aids, curricula materials, tests and measurement; lesson planning, practice briefing, navigational flight training; and operation of link-type P-3 instrument trainer comprise the academic phase of the course. Flying training includes contact, formation, instruments, and navigation teaching techniques.

Credit recommendation, collegiate level: Credit in instructional methods on the basis of institutional examination.

1. Basic Pilot Training
   (Basic Pilot Training, Single Engine Jet)
2. Basic Pilot Training, Multi-Engine

Locations: Greenville AFB, Miss.; Laredo AFB, Tex.; Bryan AFB, Tex.; Webb AFB, Tex.; Reese AFB, Tex.; Goodfellow AFB, Tex.; Vance AFB, Okla.; Craig AFB, Ala.

Length: 4–5 weeks.

Objectives: To train aviation cadets and officers in the principles of instrument and visual flying.

Instruction: Flying training; navigation, flight operations; survival training; weapons training; officer training.

Credit recommendation, collegiate level: No credit because of the specialized nature of these courses.

Bomb Navigation Systems (Flight Line Mechanic)

Location: Lowry AFB, Colo.

Length: 15 weeks.

Objectives: To train airmen to perform organizational flight-line maintenance on the MA-2/ASB-4 bomb-navigation system.

Instruction: Fundamentals; bombing and navigation computer; radar data presentation set; high-speed bombing radar and systems maintenance.

Credit recommendation, collegiate level: This course is technical and vocational in nature. Credit in electrical instrument repair on the basis of demonstrated skills and/or institutional examinations.

Bomb-Navigation Systems Mechanic (B-52C/D: ASB-15 System)
(Bomb-Navigation Systems Mechanic (ASB-15 System))
(Bomb-Navigation Systems Mechanic (ASB-15))

Location: Lowry AFB, Colo.

Length: 42–43 weeks.

Objectives: To train airmen to inspect, align, troubleshoot, and isolate malfunctions of major components and subassemblies of the ASB-15 bomb-navigation system.

Instruction: DC and AC; reactive circuits; vacuum tubes and solid state devices; amplifiers and oscillators; circuit analysis; detection and discrimination; microwave operation; multivibrators; sweep and logic circuits; introduction to bomb-navigation system; navigation and bombing problems.

Credit recommendation, collegiate level: CAUTION: *Bomb-navigation system mechanic courses vary slightly in title, length, and recommendation. Require exact identification by title and length.* 4 semester hours at freshman or sophomore level as an elective in electricity and electronics, and credit in electrical laboratory on the basis of demonstrated skills and/or institutional examinations.

1. Bomb Navigation Systems Mechanic (B-52E, F, G, H: ASB-4A/9A/16 Systems)
   (Bomb Navigation Systems Mechanic (ASB-4A/9A/16 Systems))
   (Bomb Navigation Systems Mechanic (ASB-4/4A/9/9A/16 Systems))
2. (Bomb Navigation Systems Mechanic (ASB-4/4A/9/9A/16 Systems))
3. Bomb Navigation Systems Mechanic (ASB-4 and ASB-9 Systems)
   (Bomb Navigation Systems Mechanic (ASB-4 Systems))
4. Bomb Navigation Systems Mechanic (MA-2 System)

Location: Lowry AFB, Colo.

Length: *Course 1,* 40 weeks; *Course 2,* 42 weeks; *Course 3,* 26 weeks; *Course 4,* 24 weeks.

Objectives: To train airmen in the fundamentals of electronics, use of test equipment, circuit diagrams, and data flow required to accomplish system inspections, alignments, and repairs of the bomb-navigation systems indicated in the title.

Instruction: *Courses 1 through 4:* Fundamentals of DC and AC; vacuum tubes and power supplies; amplifiers, transmitter, and receivers. *Course 1* also includes reactive circuits; circuit analysis; detection and discrimination; microwave operation; multivibrators; sweep and logic circuits. *Course 2* also includes reactive circuits; special purpose tubes; oscillators; special circuits; motors and servomechanisms; multivibrators and sweep circuits; microwave principles. *Course 3* also includes reactive circuits; special purpose tubes.

Credit recommendation, collegiate level: CAUTION: *These courses vary slightly in title, length, and recommendation. Require exact identification of course by title and length. Course 1:* 4 semester hours at freshman or sophomore level as an elective in electricity and electronics, and credit in electrical laboratory on the basis of demonstrated skills and/or institutional examinations. *Course 2:* 6 semester hours at freshman or sophomore level as an elective in electricity and electronics, and credit in electrical laboratory on the basis of demonstrated skills and/or institutional examinations. *Course 3:* 3 semester hours at freshman or sophomore level as an elective in electricity and electronics, and credit in electrical laboratory on the basis of demonstrated skills and/or institutional examinations. *Course 4:* 2 semester hours at freshman or sophomore level as an elective in electricity and electronics, and credit in electrical laboratory on the basis of demonstrated skills and/or institutional examinations.

Bomb Navigation Systems Mechanic (K-5 Series)

Location: Lowry AFB, Colo.

Length: 35 weeks.

Objectives: To train airmen to perform organizational and field maintenance on the K-5 bomb-navigation system.

Instruction: Fundamentals of DC and AC; vacuum tubes and power supply circuits; amplifier and oscillator principles; nonsinusoidal generators; radar circuitry; servosystems; radar transmitting and receiving; radar stabilization and synchronizing chains; computer tracking, sighting, bombing, and navigational chains; optics; organizational maintenance and associated equipment.

Credit recommendation, collegiate level: 3 semester hours at the freshman or sophomore level as an elective in electricity and electronics, and credit in electrical laboratory based on deomonstrated skills and/or institutional examinations.

1. **Bomb Navigation Systems Mechanic (MA-6A and MA-7A Systems)**
2. **Bomb Navigation Systems Mechanic (MA-6A, MA-7A Systems)**
3. **Bomb Navigation System Mechanic (MA-6A, MA-7A System)**
   (Bomb Navigation System Mechanic (K, MA-6A, MA-7A Systems))
4. **Bomb Navigation System Mechanic (K, MA-6A, MA-7A Systems)**
   (Bomb Navigation System Mechanic (K Series))
   (K-Series System Mechanic)

Location: Lowry AFB, Colo.

Length: *Course 1,* 37 weeks; *Course 2,* 30–32 weeks; *Course 3,* 24 weeks; *Course 4,* 20–24 weeks.

Objectives: To train airmen to isolate unit malfunctions and to perform organizational maintenance in bomb-navigation system assemblies.

Instruction: *Course 1:* DC and AC; reactive circuits; vacuum tubes and solid state devices; amplifiers and oscillators; circuit analysis; detection and discrimination; microwave operation; multivibrators, sweep and logic circuits. *Course 2:* DC and AC; reactive circuits; principles of vacuum tubes and transistors; amplifiers and radar. *Course 3:* Principles of electricity; principles of operation of electronic components. *Course 4:* Familiarization with the bombing-navigational system; test, inspection, and maintenance of the system.

Credit recommendation, collegiate level: CAUTION: *These courses vary slightly in title, length, and recommendation. Require exact identification of course by title and length. Note that the title for the Bomb Navigation System Mechanic (K, MA-6A, MA-7A System) is listed as a former title for Course 3 and is the title for Course 4. Credit recommendations for these two courses of identical title can be determined only by the date of attendance. Course 4 was given prior to February 1958. Course 3 was given after October 1958. Course 1:* 4 semester hours at freshman or sophomore level as an elective in electricity and electronics, and credit in electrical laboratory on the basis of demonstrated skills and/or institutional examinations. *Course 2:* 3 semester hours at freshman or sophomore level as an elective in electricity and electronics, and credit in electrical laboratory on the basis of demonstrated skills and/or institutional examinations. *Course 3:* 2 semester hours at freshman or sophomore level as an elective in electricity and electronics, and credit in electrical laboratory on the basis of demonstrated skills and/or institutional examinations. *Course 4:* This course is technical and vocational in nature. Credit in electrical shop on the basis of demonstrated skills and/or institutional examinations.

Bomb-Navigation Systems Mechanic (MA-6A, MA-7A, Systems) Televised

Location: Lowry AFB, Colo.

Length: 27 weeks.

Objectives: To train airmen as apprentice bomb-navigation system mechanics by means of closed circuit television instruction.

Instruction: DC and AC; vacuum tubes and amplification; radar and servo systems; system theory and operational adjustments; after installation checks and adjustments; malfunction analysis.

Credit recommendation, collegiate level: CAUTION: *Bomb-navigation system mechanic courses vary slightly in title, length, and recommendation. Require exact identification by title and length.* 2 semester hours at freshman or sophomore level as an elective in electricity, and credit in electrical laboratory on the basis of demonstrated skills and/or institutional examinations.

Bomb Navigation Systems Technician (ASB-4A/9A/16 Systems)
(Bomb Navigation Systems Technician) (ASB-4/4A/9/9A/16))
(Bomb Navigation Systems Technician (ASB-4 and ASB-9 Systems))
(Bomb Navigation Systems Technician (ASB-4 Systems))

Location: Lowry AFB, Colo.

Length: 22–34 weeks.

Objectives: To train airmen to analyze and isolate system malfunctions and to repair systems components and assemblies.

Instruction: Electronic principles; bench maintenance procedures; inspection, analysis, and repair; circuit analysis; special test equipment.

Credit recommendation, collegiate level: Credit in electricity and electrical laboratory on the basis of demonstrated skills and/or institutional examinations.

1. **Bomb Navigation Systems Technician (MA-6A, 7A Radar and ICE)**
   (Bomb Navigation Systems Technician (MA-6A, MA-7A Radar and Interconnect))
   (K-Series Radar and Interconnection Equipment Technician)
2. **Bomb Navigation Systems Technician (K, MA-6A, MA-7A Radar and Interconnect)**
   (Bomb Navigation Systems Technician (K, MA-6A, MA-7A Series Radar Interconnects))

Location: Lowry AFB, Colo.

Length: *Course 1,* 26 and 32 weeks; *Course 2,* 27 weeks.

Objectives: To train airmen to inspect, test, and maintain the bomb-navigation systems indicated in title.

Instruction: *Course 1:* Fundamentals of DC and AC; tubes, power supplies, and voltage regulators; amplifiers and oscillators; sweep generators and receiver principles; fundamentals of transmission, synchros, and cathode ray tubes. *Course 2:* DC and AC; vacuum tubes; equipment circuit analysis.

Credit recommendation, collegiate level: CAUTION: *Bomb-navigation systems technician courses vary in credit recommendation. Require complete identification by title and length. Note that titles vary only by name of equipment following title in the parentheses. Course 1:* 3 semester hours at freshman or sophomore level as an elective in electricity and electronics, and credit in electrical laboratory on the basis of demonstrated skills and/or institutional examinations. *Course 2:* 2 semester hours at freshman or sophomore level as an elective in electronics, and credit in electrical laboratory on the basis of demonstrated skills and/or institutional examinations.

1. Bomb Navigation Systems Technician (MA-6A and MA-7A Systems)
2. Bomb Navigation Systems Technician (MA-6A and MA-7A Computer and Stab and Optics)
    (Bomb Navigation Systems Technician (MA-6A, MA-7A Computer))
    (Bomb Navigation Systems Technician (K, MA-6A, MA-7A Computer))
    (Bomb Navigation Systems Technician (K, MA-6A, MA-7A Series Stabilization and Optics))
    (Bomb Navigation Systems Technician (K-Series Computer))
    (K-Series Computer Technician)
    (K-Series Stabilization and Optics Technician)
3. Bomb Navigation Systems Technician (K, MA-6A, MA-7A Systems)
    (Bomb Navigation Systems Technician (K Series Flight Line))
4. K-Series Computer Technician

Location: Lowry AFB, Colo.

Length: *Course 1,* 28–37 weeks; *Course 2,* 22–32 weeks; *Course 3,* 22 weeks; *Course 4,* 19 weeks.

Objectives: To train airmen to check the operation, to analyze malfunctions, and to dissassemble and repair computer components.

Instruction: *Course 1:* DC and AC; analysis and application of electron tube; electronic circuit analysis; *Course 2:* DC and AC; tubes and amplifiers; principles of synchros and gyroscopes; *Courses 3 and 4:* Use of test equipment; maintenance and repair.

Credit recommendation, collegiate level: CAUTION: *Bomb Navigation systems technician courses vary in credit recommendation. Require complete identification by title and length. Note that titles vary only by name of equipment following title in the parentheses. Course 1:* 3 semester hours at freshman or sophomore level as an elective in electricity and electronics, and credit in electrical laboratory on the basis of demonstrated skills and/or institutional examinations. *Course 2:* 2 semester hours at freshman or sophomore level as an elective in electricity and electronics, and credit in electrical laboratory on the basis of demonstrated skills and/or institutional examinations. *Courses 3 and 4:* Credit in electricity and electrical laboratory on the basis of demonstrated skills and/or institutional examinations.

Bonded Honeycomb and Structural Sealing (B-52/KC-135)
(Bonded Honeycomb and Structural Sealing, B-52 (Repair of Bonded Honeycomb Structures))
(Repair of Bonded and Brazed Honeycomb Structures, B-58)
(Repair of Bonded Honeycomb Structures)

Location: Amarillo AFB, Tex.

Length: 3–4 weeks.

Objectives: To train airmen to repair bonded honeycomb assemblies, control surface balancing, and structural sealing.

Instruction: Aircraft familiarization; bonded honeycomb structure repair; bonded metal structure repair; rebalancing of control surfaces; structural sealing.

Credit recommendation, collegiate level: These courses are technical and vocational in nature. Credit in aircraft repair on the basis of demonstrated skills and/or institutional examinations.

1. Budget Officer
2. Budget Specialist

Location: Sheppard AFB, Tex.

Length: *Course 1,* 10–11 weeks; *Course 2,* 8 weeks.

Objectives: *Course 1* trains officers, and *Course 2* trains airmen, in budget procedures and administration of financial plans.

Instruction: *Course 1:* Fundamentals of Air Force budgeting, government fiscal procedures, Air Force accounting and finance activities; developing estimates of requirements; bogey and single submission concepts; financial plans; personal and nonpersonal services; supplies, materials and equipment; transportation; subsistence; medical facilities; preparation of budget estimates and financial plans; financial management and administration. *Course 2* includes, in less detail, the same general subject areas as *Course 1.*

Credit recommendation, collegiate level: *Course 1:* 6 semester hours in finance and budget planning. *Course 2:* 4 semester hours in finance and budget planning.

COBOL Programming

Location: Sheppard AFB, Tex.

Length: 3 weeks.

Objectives: To train officers and airmen in COBOL programming techniques.

Instruction: Magnetic tape; introduction to COBOL; program and data organization; language structure; reference format; data, procedures, environment, and identification divisions; COBOL compiler programming applications.

Credit recommendation, collegiate level: 2 semester hours in computing science: computer operation.

1. Cable Splicing Specialist
    (Cable Splicing Specialist (General))
    (Cable Splicer)
2. Cable Splicing Specialist (General)
    (Cable Splicing Specialist/Supervisor (General))

Locations: Sheppard AFB, Tex.; Francis E. Warren AFB, Wyo.

Length: *Course 1,* 11–15 weeks; *Course 2,* 8 weeks.

Objectives: To provide airmen with basic training in the installation and maintenance of cable systems.

Instruction: Cable splicing; cable sealing; cable system testing, troubleshooting, and repair.

Credit recommendation, collegiate level: These courses are technical and vocational in nature. Credit in metal shop on the basis of demonstrated skills and/or institutional examinations.

Calibration and Maintenance of the Shaw-Estes Test Stand

Location: Chanute AFB, Ill.

Length: 3 weeks.

Objectives: To train airmen to adjust, troubleshoot, and maintain the Shaw-Estes test stand.

Instruction: Review of electrical principles; constructional details; preventive maintenance; operation, test, and adjustment of the thrust indicator, load cell, strobotach, tailpipe pyrometer, and vibration meter.

Credit recommendation, collegiate level: This course is technical and vocational in nature. Credit in electrical shop on the basis of demonstrated skills and/or institutional examinations.

Central Heating Plant Specialist

Location: Sheppard AFB, Tex.

Length: 7 weeks.

Objectives: To train airmen in the operation and maintenance of central heating plants.

Instruction: Fuel burning equipment and basic electricity; fuels and combustion principles; hot water heating systems; boilers, steam heating systems, and auxiliary equipment; water treatment and corrosion control.

Credit recommendation, collegiate level: No credit because of the limited vocational nature of the course.

Channel and Technical Control Operator
(Channel and Technical Control Operator (Channel Technical Control Center))

Location: Keesler AFB, Miss.

Length: 14 weeks.

Objectives: To train airmen in the operation and maintenance of channel and technical control equipment.

Instruction: Electronic fundamentals; radiotelegraph; radiotelephone; frequency propagation and spectrum; telephone, telegraph, and teletype circuits and systems.

Credit recommendation, collegiate level: Credit in electricity and electrical laboratory on basis of demonstrated skills and/or institutional examinations.

Chaplain Services Specialist

Locations: Amarillo AFB, Tex.; Lackland AFB, Tex.; Francis E. Warren AFB, Wyo.

Length: 8–11 weeks.

Objectives: To train airmen as chaplain services specialists.

Instruction: Typewriting; report preparation; records management; supply management; chaplain fund accounting.

Credit recommendation, collegiate level: Credit in typing on the basis of institutional examination.

1. Chaplain Services Supervisor
2. Chaplain Services (Specialist) Supervisor

Location: Francis E. Warren AFB, Wyo.

Length: 4–6 weeks.

Objectives: To train chaplain services specialists to manage chaplain services activities.

Instruction: Management and correspondence; supply, funds, and reports; chaplain activities and public relations.

Credit recommendation, collegiate level: No credit because of the specialized nature of these courses.

Civil Engineer Inspector

Location: Sheppard AFB, Tex.

Length: 6 weeks.

Objectives: To train airmen to inspect minor construction and modification projects undertaken by contractors.

Instruction: Inspector responsibilities and management methods; blueprints, plans and specifications interpretation; contracts; building construction and inspection; utility systems inspection, including plumbing, sewer, fire alarm, sprinkler, electrical distribution, and refrigeration systems; roads and grounds inspection.

Credit recommendation, collegiate level: This course is technical and vocational in nature. Credit in building construction inspection on the basis of institutional examination.

Clinical Laboratory Officer

Location: Gunter AFB, Ala.

Length: 16 weeks.

Objectives: To train clinical laboratory officers in the techniques and administrative methods applied in medical clinical laboratories.

Instruction: Medical orientation; bacteriology; parasitology; mycology; basal metabolism; blood grouping and transfusions; clinical chemistry; hematology; histological technique; urinalysis; virology.

Credit recommendation, collegiate level: 6 semester hours in advanced clinical laboratory techniques.

Color Photo Processes

Location: Lowry AFB, Colo.

Length: 8–9 weeks.

Objectives: To train airmen in color photo processing.

Instruction: Photo analysis; color sensitometry; principles of color photography; printing techniques; reversal and negative color printing; slide production.

Credit recommendation, collegiate level: This course is technical and vocational in nature. Credit in color photo processing on the basis of demonstrated skills and/or institutional examinations.

Combative Measures Instructor Training

Location: Fairchild AFB, Wash.

Length: 5 weeks.

Objectives: To qualify officers and airmen as instructors in judo and hand-to-hand combative measures.

Instruction: Code of conduct training; instructional methods, including the learning process, evaluation, audio-visual aids, lecture preparation, and oral communication; basic judo techniques; air police and aircrew self-defense techniques.

Credit recommendation, collegiate level: Credit in instructional methods on the basis of institutional examination.

Command and Control System Computer Programmer
(Weapon Support Systems Computer Programmer)

Location: Keesler AFB, Miss.

Length: 15–16 weeks.

Objectives: To train officers in the fundamentals of programming.

Instruction: Computer principles; basic programming; peripheral equipment programming; symbolic programming and program assembly; control, maintenance, and operational programs; advanced programming techniques and developments.

Credit recommendation, collegiate level: 5 semester hours in computer programming in the field of computing science.

Commissary Operation
(Commissary NCO)
(Commissary NCOIC)
(Commissary Officer)

Location: Amarillo AFB, Tex.

Length: 3–4 weeks.

Objectives: To train officers and airmen in the management of a commissary.

Instruction: Organization and subsistence handling; personnel management; operations and general accounting procedures; on-the-job training; warehousing and storage; inventory procedures; pricing procedures.

Credit recommendation, collegiate level: 2 semester hours in store management.

Communications Center Specialist

Locations: Sheppard AFB, Tex.; Francis E. Warren AFB, Wyo.

Length: 11–13 weeks.

Objectives: To train airmen to operate switchboard, teletype, and facsimile equipment and to process and distribute incoming and outgoing messages received at communications centers.

Instruction: Teletypewriting; teletypewriter tape reading; message-handling procedures; communication center operation.

Credit recommendation, collegiate level: Credit in typing on the basis of institutional examination.

Communications-Electronics Staff Officer
(Communications-Electronics Officer)

Location: Keesler AFB, Miss.

Length: 25–34 weeks.

Objectives: To train officers to formulate communications-electronics policies and procedures and to direct communications-electronics programs.

Instruction: Principles of telephone, teletype, radio, radar, and related power equipment; operational plans and orders; maintenance procedures; programming and budgeting.

Credit recommendation, collegiate level: 3 semester hours in management principles and 3 semester hours in radio engineering.

Communications Officer

Locations: Keesler AFB, Miss.; Scott AFB, Ill.

Length: 43–45 weeks.

Objectives: To train officers in the fundamental concepts of electronics and management of communications units, including construction, operation, maintenance, and repair of ground communications equipment and systems.

Instruction: Principles of DC and AC; power supplies; oscillators and special circuits; transmitters and receivers; higher-frequency techniques; radar and computer principles; C-E administration and programming; base communications; telephone; teletype; facsimile; HF transmitter facilities; radio relay facilities; cryptography; air traffic control system; electronic warfare.

Credit recommendation, collegiate level: 3 semester hours in personnel and supply management, 8 semester hours at the freshman or sophomore level as an elective in electricity and electronics, and credit in electrical laboratory on the basis of demonstrated skills and/or institutional examinations.

Complete Denture Prosthetics

Locations: Gunter AFB, Ala.; Sheppard AFB, Tex.

Length: 6–7 weeks.

Objectives: To provide advanced dental laboratory airmen with training in the fundamentals of complete denture construction.

Instruction: Dental administration and prosthetic dentistry, including complete denture fabrication, dental materials, duplication, rebase, repairs, immediate dentures, special techniques, and dental laboratory.

Credit recommendation, collegiate level: Credit in dental laboratory technology on the basis of institutional examination.

Computer Operation

Location: Sheppard AFB, Tex.

Length: 3 weeks.

Objectives: To train airmen to operate the Burroughs 263 computer system and any general purpose digital computer.

Instruction: Computer concepts and components; numbering systems; flow charting; basic programming; applied computer operation.

Credit recommendation, collegiate level: 2 semester hours in computer operation in the field of data processing.

Computer Principles

Location: Keesler AFB, Miss.

Length: 5–6 weeks.

Objectives: To provide airmen with training in computer principles prerequisite to career specialization.

Instruction: Principles of computer circuits; digital techniques; programming principles.

Credit recommendation, collegiate level: 3 semester hours in computer principles in the field of data processing.

Computer Programming

Location: Sheppard AFB, Tex.

Length: 7 weeks.

Objectives: To train officers and airmen in the techniques and applications of computer programming.

Instruction: Theory and operating principles of computers; symbolic and input/output programming; utility programs and subroutines; numbering systems; flow charting; advanced programming techniques.

Credit recommendation, collegiate level: 4 semester hours in computer programming in the field of computing science.

Contract Administration

Location: Amarillo AFB, Tex.

Length: 5 weeks.

Objectives: To train procurement personnel in the principles of government contracting, the basis for administration of contracts, and contract cost.

Instruction: Basic principles of government contract law; fixed-price contracts; cost reimbursement contracts; fixed-price incentive fee and cost-plus incentive fee contracts; contract provisions, modifications, and charges; responsibility for supplies; federal, state, and local taxes; claims; accounting principles; administrative techniques.

Credit recommendation, collegiate level: 3 semester hours in the principles of contracting.

Control Room Instrumentation, Jet Engine Test Facility

Location: Chanute AFB, Ill.

Length: 3 weeks.

Objectives: To train key maintenance and instructor personnel in jet engine test facility control room instrumentation.

Instruction: Construction, operation, circuit analysis, maintenance, and calibration of the pyrometer potentiometer, thrust indicator, and load cell; operation, test, and adjustment of strobotach, tailpipe pyrometer, and vibration meter.

Credit recommendation, collegiate level: No credit because of the brevity and limited technical nature of the course.

1. **Control Systems Analyst (GAM-77)**
2. **Control Systems Analyst (GAM-72)**
3. **Control Systems Analyst (TM-76A)**
4. **Control Mechanic/Technician (GAM-77)**
   (Control Systems Mechanic/Technician (GAM-77))
5. **Control System Mechanic/Technician (SM-68)**
6. **Control System Technician/Mechanic (SM-65F)**

Locations: Amarillo AFB, Tex.; Chanute AFB, Ill.; Lowry AFB, Colo.; Sheppard AFB, Tex.

Length: *Course 1,* 23 weeks; *Course 2,* 15 weeks; *Courses 3 through 6,* 12–19 weeks.

Objectives: To train airmen in the maintenance and theory of control systems indicated in title.

Instruction: *Courses 1 and 2:* Direct and alternating current fundamentals; vacuum tubes and transistors; in addition *Course 1* includes fundamental electronic circuits. *Courses 3 through 6:* Control system familiarization; control system analysis; test and ground support equipment.

Credit recommendation, collegiate level: CAUTION: *These courses vary only slightly in title, length, and recommendation. Require exact identification of course by full title and length. Course 1:* 3 semester hours at the freshman or sophomore level as an elective in electricity and electronics, and credit in electrical laboratory on the basis of demonstrated skills and/or institutional examinations. *Course 2:* 2 semester hours at the freshman or sophomore level as an elective in electricity and electronics, and credit in electrical laboratory on the basis of demonstrated skills and/or institutional examinations. *Courses 3 through 6:* Credit, for each course, in electricity and electrical laboratory on the basis of demonstrated skills and/or institutional examinations.

1. Controls Systems Mechanic
2. Controls Systems Mechanic, GAM-72
3. Control Systems Mechanic (SM-65, 68)
4. Control Systems Mechanic (TM-61C)
5. Tactical Missile Control Mechanic
     (MGM-13A/CGM-IBB)
     (Tactical Missile Control Mechanic (TM-76A/B))
6. Control Systems Mechanic, IM-99A
     (Control Systems Mechanic, IM-99B)
7. GAM Control Mechanic, GAM-77

Locations: Lowry AFB, Colo.; Amarillo AFB, Tex.; Chanute AFB, Ill.; Sheppard AFB, Tex.
Length: 22–23 weeks.
Objectives: To train airmen to operate, maintain, inspect, and repair missile control systems.
Instruction: *Courses 1 through 7:* Electrical fundamentals; vacuum tubes; alternating current circuitry; special circuits; amplification, waveshaping; oscilloscope construction; in addition *Courses 6 and 7* include motors and servos; multivibrators and sweep circuits; microwave principles.
Credit recommendation, collegiate level: CAUTION: *These courses vary only slightly in title, length, and recommendation. Require exact identification of course by title and length. Courses 1 through 5:* For each course, 3 semester hours at the freshman or sophomore level as an elective in electronics, and credit in electrical laboratory on the basis of demonstrated skills and/or institutional examinations. *Courses 6 and 7:* For each course, 4 semester hours at the freshman or sophomore level as an elective in electronics, and credit in electrical laboratory on the basis of demonstrated skills and/or institutional examinations.

Conventional Weapons Application
(Weapons Effects)

Location: Lowry AFB, Colo.
Length: 4 weeks.
Objectives: To train intelligence officers in the elements of targeting and weaponry germane to the Southeast Asian environment.
Instruction: Targets, including photometrics, structural analysis, vulnerability, bomb damage assessment, and target indicators; weapons types, new developments, effects, and operational factors; weapons selection and planning procedures.
Credit recommendation, collegiate level: No credit as the course is military in nature.

Cook
(Cooking)

Locations: Keesler AFB, Miss.; Amarillo AFB, Tex.; Sheppard AFB, Tex.; Scott AFB, Ill.
Length: 12 weeks.
Objectives: To train airmen to prepare, cook, and serve food.
Instruction: Preparation and service of food in unit, consolidated field, and inflight kitchens; emergency rations; subsistence supplies; use and care of food service equipment.
Credit recommendation, collegiate level: This course is technical and vocational in nature. Credit in cooking on the basis of demonstrated skills and/or institutional examinations.

1. Corrosion Control Specialist
2. Corrosion Control
   Location: Sheppard AFB, Tex.
   Length: 7–8 weeks.
   Objectives: To train Air Force personnel in the causes and characteristics of corrosion.
   Instruction: Causes and characteristics of the corrosion process; identification of corrosion products; corrosion product removal by mechanical and chemical means; application of protective coatings; corrosion control inspection and nondestructive test methods.
   Credit recommendation, collegiate level: These courses are technical and vocational in nature. Credit in metal shop (corrosion control) on the basis of demonstrated skills and/or institutional examinations.

Crown and Fixed Partial Denture Prosthetics
(Crown and Bridge Dental Prosthetics)

Locations: Gunter AFB, Ala.; Sheppard AFB, Tex.
Length: 5–7 weeks.
Objectives: To train advanced dental laboratory airmen in the fundamentals of crown, inlay, and fixed partial denture construction.
Instruction: Dental administration and prosthetic dentistry, including theory of crown and bridge fabrication, crown and fixed partial denture construction, specialized techniques, and dental laboratory.
Credit recommendation, collegiate level: Credit in dental laboratory technology on the basis of institutional examination.

1. Cryogenic Fluids Production Specialist
   (Gas Generating Plant Operator)
2. Cryogenic Fluids Production Specialist Technician
   (Gas Generator Plant Operator/Technician)
3. Field Analysis of Cryogenic Liquids and Gases
   Locations: Chanute AFB, Ill.; Francis E. Warren AFB. Wyo.
   Length: *Courses 1 and 2,* 4–19 weeks; *Course 3,* 3 weeks.
   Objectives: *Courses 1 and 2:* To train airmen to operate and perform operator maintenance on oxygen-nitrogen generating plants and related equipment which produce liquid or gaseous oxygen or nitrogen. *Course 3:* To train airmen to test ballistic missile cryogenic liquids for compliance with military specifications.
   Instruction: *Courses 1 and 2:* Cryogenic fluids production; operation and maintenance of air processing equipment; operation and maintenance of air separator, and cryotainers. *Course 3:* Field analysis of cryogenic liquids and gases.
   Credit recommendation, collegiate level: These courses are technical and vocational in nature. Credit in oxygen or nitrogen plant operation on the basis of demonstrated skills and/or institutional examinations.

1. Cryptographic Equipment Repairman,
   Electro-Mechanical
   (Cryptographic Equipment Electro-Mechanical Repairman)
2. TSEC/KW-22 Cryptographic Equipment Maintenance
3. Cryptographic Equipment Maintenance TSEC/KW-26

Locations: Sheppard AFB, Tex.; Lackland AFB, Tex.
Length: *Course 1, 6–8 weeks; Courses 2 and 3, 10–12 weeks.*
Objectives: To train airmen to test, maintain, and repair cryptographic equipment.
Instruction: Installation; repair, system operation and corrective maintenance.
Credit recommendation, collegiate level: These courses are technical and vocational in nature. Credit in cryptographic machine repair on the basis of demonstrated skills and/or institutional examinations.

Cryptographic Operator

Location: Scott AFB, Ill.
Length: 8 weeks.
Objectives: To train airmen in the operation of cryptographic systems.
Instruction: Security and communications; crypto systems; cryptographic center operation.
Credit recommendation, collegiate level: This course is technical and vocation in nature. Credit in cryptographic machine operation on the basis of institutional examination.

1. Data Automation Officer
2. Electronic Data Processing Officer

Location: Sheppard AFB, Tex.
Length: *Course 1, 11 weeks; Course 2, 8 weeks.*
Objectives: To train officers in the principles of managing electronic data processing activities.
Instruction: *Course 1:* Punched card equipment; introduction to electronic data processing; programming punched card oriented and tape oriented computers; introduction to COBOL; automatic data processing systems; management of a data processing installation. *Course 2:* Introduction to electronic data processing; programming methodology; electronic data processing systems, selected machines, and installation management.
Credit recommendation, collegiate level: *Course 1:* 5 semester hours in data processing: computer programming and management. *Course 2:* 3 semester hours in computer programming and management in the field of data processing.

Data Processing Machine Operator

Location: Sheppard AFB, Tex.
Length: 11 weeks.
Objectives: To train airmen in computer operation and basic programming.
Instruction: Operation of the Burroughs 263 computer system; basic programming; operation of punched card accounting machines, including card punches, sorters, reproducing punches, alphabetical interpreters, accounting machines, and collators; control panel wiring; minor adjustments of mechanical and electrical parts.
Credit recommendation, collegiate level: CAUTION: *Courses in data processing machine operation vary in title, length, and recommendation. Require exact identification by full title and length.* 4 semester hours in unit record and computer operation in the field of data processing.

1. Data Processing Machine Operator
   (Punched Card)
   (Machine Accountant)
2. Data Processing Machine Operator
   (Punched Card)

Locations: Lowry AFB, Colo.; Sheppard AFB, Tex.
Length: *Course 1, 11–12 weeks; Course 2, 6 weeks.*
Objectives: *Course 1:* To train airmen in the techniques of control panel wiring and operation of electrical accounting machines. *Course 2:* To provide basic training for airmen in the operation of electrical accounting machines.
Instruction: *Course 1:* Basic operation and wiring of electrical accounting machines; operation of the reproducing punch (type 514), the alphabetic collator (type 089), the accounting machine (type 407), and the calculating punch (type 602A). *Course 2* covers operation of the same equipment in less detail and includes an introduction to selected basic data processing machines.
Credit recommendation, collegiate level: CAUTION: *Courses in data processing machine operation vary in title, length, and recommendation. Require exact identification by full title and length.* These courses are technical and vocational in nature. Credit in electrical accounting machine operation on the basis of demonstrated skills.

Data Processing Machine Supervisor

Location: Sheppard AFB, Tex.
Length: 12 weeks.
Objectives: To provide data processing machine operators with advanced, supervisory-level training.
Instruction: Advanced operation and wiring of selected data processing machines; Burroughs 263 computer system; principles of computer operation and programming; data systems analysis and design; management principles of a data processing activity.
Credit recommendation, collegiate level: 4 semester hours in computer operation in the field of data processing.

Data Processing Machine Supervisor (Punched Card) (Machine Accounting Supervisor)

Location: Sheppard AFB, Tex.
Length: 12–14 weeks.
Objectives: To provide advanced training for airmen in the wiring and operation of selected data processing (or electrical accounting) machines and in the management of a machine accounting unit.

Instruction: Operation and wiring of selected data processing (or electrical accounting) machines; Adjutant General's office circuit and collator; type-407 IBM accounting machine; principles of the calculating punch, IBM type-602; functions of management and on-the-job training programs; Air Force mechanized reporting.

Credit recommendation, collegiate level: 2 semester hours in office management. At the technical and vocational level, credit in electrical accounting machine operation on the basis of demonstrated skills.

1. Data Processing (SAGE)
2. Data Processing (SAGE)

Location: Keesler AFB, Miss.

Length: 6–8 weeks.

Objectives: To train airmen as mapping, height, or manual data technicians or supervisors in SAGE direction centers.

Instruction: SAGE organizational and functional concepts; communications; symbology interpretation; equipment and procedures relative to technician and supervisor positions.

Credit recommendation, collegiate level: No credit because of the specialized nature of the courses.

Data Services Specialist

Location: Sheppard AFB, Tex.

Length: 8 weeks.

Objectives: To train airmen in the functions and techniques of data services.

Instruction: Collecting, interpreting, auditing, coding, processing, and controlling of data input-output; routine data systems administrative duties; statistics organization.

Credit recommendation, collegiate level: No credit because of the specialized nature of the course.

1. Data Systems Analysis and Design
2. Data Systems Analysis and Design

Location: Sheppard AFB, Tex.

Length: 4–5 weeks.

Objectives: *Course 1* trains officers, *Course 2* trains airmen, in the techniques of data systems analysis and design.

Instruction: Data systems concepts; survey and analysis of the present system resources; electronic data processing equipment—evolution, input, output, storage media, components, and processing methods; introduction to computer programming; design of proposed system.

Credit recommendation, collegiate level: 2 semester hours in computer systems in the field of data processing.

Data Systems and Statistics Officer

Location: Sheppard AFB, Tex.

Length: 11 weeks.

Objectives: To train officers to manage data systems and statistics activities.

Instruction: Basic data processing machines; accounting machine, type 407; reporting systems; management of a data systems and statistics activity; electronic data processing; data systems analysis and design.

Credit recommendation, collegiate level: 3 semester hours in unit record and computer management in the field of data processing.

Defense Missile Checkout Equipment Technician (IM-99B)
(Missile Test Equipment Technician (Guidance) (IM-99B))

Location: Chanute AFB, Ill.

Length: 26 weeks.

Objectives: To train airmen to perform detailed maintenance on the guidance section of the functional checkout set.

Instruction: Portable and microwave support calibration equipment; operation and maintenance of the mobile inspection unit and command system test equipment; target seeker test equipment; functional checkout step analysis.

Credit recommendation, collegiate level: CAUTION: *Missile test equipment technician courses vary slightly in title, length, and recommendation. Require exact identification by title and length. Note that titles vary by name of equipment in the parentheses following the title.* Credit in electrical laboratory on the basis of demonstrated skills and/or institutional examinations.

Defense Missile Control Mechanic/Technician, IM-99B

Location: Chanute AFB, Ill.

Length: 16 weeks.

Objectives: To train airmen to inspect and repair flight control systems and to operate associated ground equipment.

Instruction: IM-99B familiarization; APU and coordinate converter systems; flight control system; mobile inspection unit operation; missile testing and troubleshooting.

Credit recommendation, collegiate level: This course is technical and vocational in nature. Credit in mechanical shop on the basis of demonstrated skills and/or institutional examinations.

1. Defense Missile Guidance Mechanic, IM-99A
2. Defense Missile Guidance Mechanic, IM-99B

Location: Chanute AFB, Ill.

Length: *Course 1,* 28 weeks; *Course 2,* 35 weeks.

Objectives: To train airmen in the operation, maintenance, and repair of the IM-99A or IM-99B guidance system.

Instruction: DC and AC; reactive circuits; principles of vacuum tubes and transistors; special purpose tubes; amplifiers and oscillators; motors and servomechanisms; multivibrators and sweep circuits; microwave principles.

Credit recommendation, collegiate level: For each course, 6 semester hours at the freshman or sophomore level as an elective in electricity and electronics, and credit in electrical laboratory on the basis of demonstrated skills and/or institutional examinations.

Defense Missile Guidance Mechanic/Technician, IM-99B

Location: Chanute AFB, Ill.
Length: 18 weeks.
Objectives: To train airmen to perform operational tests on, and maintenance of, the IM-99B guidance system.
Instruction: General familiarization; mobile inspection unit; command system; fuze system; guidance transponder; target seeker; trouble isolation.
Credit recommendation, collegiate level: This course is technical and vocational in nature. Credit in electrical and mechanical shop on the basis of demonstrated skills and/or institutional examinations.

Defense Missile Guidance Technician (Gar-1/2/11)
(Guidance Systems Technician (GAR-1/2/11))
(Guidance Systems Technician (GAR-1/2))
(Guidance Systems Technician (GAR-1))

Location: Lowry AFB, Colo.
Length: 13–26 weeks.
Objectives: To train airmen in the use of system test sets, circuits, and data flow required to maintain GAR guidance system equipment.
Instruction: Electronic principles; isolation and repair of malfunctions; calibration of missile and checkout console components.
Credit recommendation, collegiate level: CAUTION: *Guidance systems technicians courses vary slightly in title, length, and recommendation. Require exact identification of course by title and length.* Credit in electricity and electrical laboratory on the basis of demonstrated skills and/or institutional examinations.

1. **Defense Sensor Interpretation and Applications Training (DSIAT) (Airmen)**
2. **Defense Sensor Interpretation and Applications Training (DSIAT) (Officer)**

Location: Offutt AFB, Neb.
Length: *Course 1,* 11 weeks; *Course 2,* 12 weeks.
Objectives: To train officers and airmen in all facets of photographic interpretation.
Instruction: Reconnaissance; exploitation equipment; sensors; photo processing quality control standards; photogrammetry.
Credit recommendation, collegiate level: 2 semester hours in photographic intelligence.

Defensive FCS (Fire Control System) Mechanic (MD-7, AN/ASG-21 Turrets)
(Defensive Fire Control System Mechanic (MD-7, AN/ASG-21))

Location: Lowry AFB, Colo.
Length: 36 weeks.
Objectives: To train airmen to maintain defensive fire control system equipment.
Instruction: DC and AC; reactive circuits; vacuum tubes and transistors; amplifiers and oscillators; special circuits; motors and servomechanisms; multivibrators; microwave principles; data flow; test set operation and auxiliary equipment.
Credit recommendation, collegiate level: CAUTION: *Courses in fire control vary slightly in title, length, and credit recommendation. Note that titles vary only by name of equipment in the parentheses following the title. Require exact identification of course by full title and length.* 4 semester hours at the freshman or sophomore level as an elective in electricity and electronics, and credit in electrical laboratory on the basis of demonstrated skills and/or institutional examinations.

1. **Defensive Fire Control Systems Mechanic (A-3A, MD-9, ASG-15 Turrets)**
   (Defensive Fire Control Systems Mechanic (A-3A, MD-9, ASG-15 Fire Control Systems))
2. **Turret Systems Mechanic (A3A, MD-9, ASG-15 Turrets)**
3. **Turret Systems Mechanic (A3A/MD-9 Turrets)**
   (Turret Systems Mechanic (B-52, A-3A))

Location: Lowry AFB, Colo.
Length: *Course 1,* 38–40 weeks; *Course 2,* 33–36 weeks; *Course 3,* 23–28 weeks.
Objectives: To train airmen in the maintenance of defensive fire control systems.
Instruction: *Course 1:* DC and AC; reactive circuits; vacuum tubes and solid state devices; amplifiers and oscillators; circuit analysis; detection and discrimination; microwave operation; multivibrators; sweep and logic circuits; data flow and functional loop analysis; isolation of unit malfunctions; turret system maintenance. *Course 2:* DC and AC; reactive circuits; vacuum tubes and transistors; amplifiers and radar; data flow; checks and adjustments; troubleshooting. *Course 3:* Use and application of test equipment; data flow; radar checks; turret checks; troubleshooting.
Credit recommendation, collegiate level: CAUTION: *Courses in fire control systems vary only slightly in title, length, and recommendation. Note that titles vary only by name of equipment in the parentheses following the title. Require exact identification of course by full title and length. Course 1:* 4 semester hours at the freshman or sophomore level as an elective in electricity and electronics, and credit in electrical laboratory on the basis of demonstrated skills and/or institutional examinations. *Course 2:* 3 semester hours at the freshman or sophomore level as an elective in electricity and electonics, and credit in electrical laboratory on the basis of demonstrated skills and/or institutional examinations. *Course 3:* Credit in electronics and electrical laboratory on the basis of demonstrated skills and/or institutional examinations.

1. Defensive Fire Control Systems Mechanic
   (MD-1, MD-1A, MD-4 & A5)
2. Gunlaying Systems Mechanic, B-47
3. Gunlaying Systems Mechanic, B-36
4. Turret System Mechanic, B-36
5. Turret Systems Mechanic (A5, MD-1 & A, MD-4)
6. Turret Systems Mechanic (A5, MD-1 & A, MD-4)
   (Turret Systems Mechanic (MD-1, MD-4, A-5))

Location: Lowry AFB, Colo.

Length: *Course 1,* 32–35 weeks; *Course 2,* 26 weeks; *Course 3,* 28 weeks; *Course 4,* 22 weeks; *Course 5,* 28–29 weeks; *Course 6,* 18–19 weeks.

Objectives: To train airmen in the operation, inspection, organizational maintenance, and repair of defensive fire control systems.

Instruction: *Courses 1, 5, and 6:* Data flow of the fire control system; system checkout; radar loop test and adjustment; computing, turret drive, and firing loop; test and adjustment; system harmonization; system troubleshooting; in additon *Course 1* includes DC and AC; reactive circuits; vacuum tubes and solid state devices; amplifiers and oscillators; circuit analysis; detection and discrimination; microwave operation; multivibrators; sweep and logic circuits; in addition *Course 5* includes DC; AC; reactive circuits; vacuum tubes and transistors; amplifiers and radar. *Courses 2, 3, and 4:* Fundamentals of electricity; fundamentals of AC; vacuum and gas-filled tubes; power supplies; voltage regulators; amplifiers; oscillators; sweep generators; oscilloscope; selsyns and servomechanisms; turret drive, firing, computing, and radar systems; system interconnection, trouble shooting, harmonization, and inspections.

Credit recommendation, collegiate level: CAUTION: *These courses vary only slightly in title, length, and credit recommendation. Note that some titles vary only by name of equipment in the parentheses following the title. Require exact identification of course by full title and length. Course 1:* 4 semester hours at the freshman or sophomore level as an elective in electricity and electronics, and credit in electrical laboratory on the basis of demonstrated skills and/or institutional examinations. *Courses 2 through 5:* For each course, 3 semester hours at the freshman or sophomore level as an elective in electricity and electronics, and credit in electrical laboratory on the basis of demonstrated skills and/or institutional examinations. *Course 6:* Credit in electronics and electrical laboratory on the basis of demonstrated skills and/or institutional examinations.

Defensive Fire Control Systems Technician
       (A-3A, MD-9, ASG-15 Turrets)
(Defensive Fire Control Systems Technician
       (A-3A, MD-9, ASG-15 Fire Control Systems))
(Turret Systems Technician A-3A, MD-9, ASG-15
       Turrets)

Location: Lowry AFB, Colo.

Length: 23–26 weeks.

Objectives: To train airmen in the maintenance and analysis of MD-9 and ASG-15 fire control systems, including the alignment and harmonization of the radar, turret drive, and computing systems.

Instruction: Turret drive system component analysis and amplifier testing; computing system analysis, testing and subassembly maintenance; radar power

supplies, frequency converter, and modulator analysis; system dynamics inspection; use of special testers.

Credit recommendation, collegiate level: CAUTION: *Courses in fire systems control vary only slightly in title, length, and credit recommendation. Note that titles vary only by name of equipment in the parentheses following the title. Require exact identification of course by full title and length.* Credit in electronics and electrical laboratory on the basis of demonstrated skills and/or institutional examinations.

Defensive System Trainer Specialist (AN/ALQ-T4 (V))

Location: Keesler AFB, Miss.

Length: 12 weeks.

Objectives: To train airmen to operate and maintain the AN/ALQ-T4 trainer.

Instruction: Review of electronic principles; theory of circuit operation; data flow analysis; programming procedures; alignment and checkout procedures, and use of test equipment; troubleshooting and repair.

Credit recommendation, collegiate level: Credit in electrical laboratory on the basis of demonstrated skills and/or institutional examinations.

1. Dental Laboratory Specialist
   (Apprentice Dental Laboratory Specialist)
2. Dental Laboratory Technician

Locations: Gunter AFB, Ala.; Sheppard AFB, Tex.

Length: *Course 1,* 21–26 weeks; *Course 2,* 16 weeks.

Objectives: *Course 1:* To train airmen in basic dental laboratory techniques and routine procedures. *Course 2:* To provide advanced training for dental laboratory specialists.

Instruction: *Course 1:* Dental anatomy, materials, and administration; surgery and preventive medicine; fabrication of complete dentures, removable partial dentures, inlays, crowns, and fixed, partial dentures; reline, duplication, and repair of dentures. *Course 2* provides advanced training in the same areas of instruction.

Credit recommendation, collegiate level: For each course, credit in dental laboratory technology on the basis of institutional examination.

Dental Specialist
(Apprentice Dental Specialist)

Locations: Gunter AFB, Ala.; Sheppard AFB, Tex.

Length: 8–14 weeks.

Objectives: To train airmen as subprofessional dental assistants in support of dental clinic treatment.

Instruction: Dental and medical administration; medical laboratory; preventive medicine; clinical dentistry, including dento-oral anatomy, oral pathology, dental materials, instruments and instrument cabinet arrangement, instrument maintenance, operating room procedures, oral surgery, and preventive dentistry.

Credit recommendation, collegiate level: Credit in dental technology on the basis of institutional examination.

Dental Technician
(Dental Technician, Advanced)

Locations: Gunter AFB, Ala.; Sheppard AFB, Tex.

Length: 8–12 weeks.

Objectives: To provide dental specialists with advanced training in dental clinic procedures and supervision.

Instruction: Dental and medical administration; medical laboratory; pharmacy; preventive medicine; prosthetic dentistry; radiology; surgery; anatomy and physiology; clinical dentistry, including dental anatomy, materials, radiography, emergency dentistry, head and neck anatomy, maintenance of dental equipment, operating room procedures, oral pathology, and preventive dentistry.

Credit recommendation, collegiate level: Credit in dental technology on the basis of institutional examination.

1. ## Depot Overhaul of the AN/ASH-4 Light and Time Recorder and AN/UVM-1 Test Set
2. ## F&O Maintenance of the AN/ASH-4 Light and Time Recording Set

Location: Lowry AFB, Colo.

Length: 3–4 weeks.

Objectives: To train photographic repairmen to install and overhaul the AN/ASH-4 light and time recording set.

Instruction: Installation and operation; power, control, and signal circuits; troubleshooting; overhaul procedures.

Credit recommendation, collegiate level: These courses are technical and vocational in nature. Credit in electrical shop on the basis of demonstrated skills and/or institutional examinations.

Dial Central Office Equipment Mechanic/Technician (SM-68)

Location: Sheppard AFB, Tex.

Length: 3–4 weeks.

Objectives: To train airmen to repair and maintain ballistic missile communications system Stromberg-Carlson (SM-68).

Instruction: Console circuits; relay adjustments and pallet circuits; power and supervisory circuits; test desk operation.

Credit recommendation, collegiate level: This course is technical and vocational in nature. Credit in electrical shop on the basis of demonstrated skills and/or institutional examinations.

Dial Central Office Equipment Specialist

Locations: Sheppard AFB, Tex.; Francis E. Warren AFB, Wyo.

Length: 16 weeks.

Objectives: To qualify airmen for assignment as dial central office equipment specialists.

Instruction: Electrical fundamentals; circuit analysis; relay and switch adjustment; maintenance of a complete dial exchange.

Credit recommendation, collegiate level: CAUTION: *Dial central office equipment courses vary only slightly in title and length. Require exact identification by full title and length.* Credit in electricity and electrical laboratory on the basis of demonstrated skills and/or institutional examinations.

Dial Central Office Equipment Specialist, SM-68B

Location: Sheppard AFB, Tex.

Length: 6 weeks.

Objectives: To train airmen to be dial central office equipment specialists SM-68B.

Instruction: Communication panel and console circuits; conference nets; miscellaneous circuits; power and test equipment; radio access equipment.

Credit recommendation, collegiate level: CAUTION: *Dial central office equipment courses vary only slightly in title and length. Require exact identification by full title and length.* This course is technical and vocational in nature. Credit in electrical or radio shop on the basis of demonstrated skills and/or institutional examinations.

Diet Supervisor

Location: Gunter AFB, Ala.; Sheppard AFB, Tex.

Length: 4–5 weeks.

Objectives: To train airmen in the management of food service departments at Air Force medical treatment facilities.

Instruction: Food service administration; food production and service; food service sanitation; nutrition and diet therapy.

Credit recommendation, collegiate level: 2 semester hours in food service management.

1. ## Disaster Control Specialist (Disaster Control Instructor)
2. ## Disaster Control Specialist (Disaster Preparedness Specialist)
3. ## Disaster Control Instructor
4. ## Passive Defense Instructor
5. ## Disaster Control Specialist (Disaster Preparedness Specialist)

Location: Lowry AFB, Colo.

Length: *Course 1, 15–17 weeks; Course 2, 10 weeks; Courses 3 and 4, 6–7 weeks; Course 5, 8 weeks.*

Objectives: To train airmen in disaster control measures and qualify them to conduct disaster control training programs.

Instruction: *Course 1:* Weapons effects (nuclear, chemical, and biological); individual and collective protection; decontamination; biological, chemical, and radiological monitoring; disaster control planning and operations; instructor training—fundamental and applied, including effective speaking, use of the library, research and outlining, and lesson planning and presentation. *Courses 2, 3, and 4* cover the same general areas, weapons effects, protection, detection, decontamination, and instructor training, as *Course 1. Course 5* also covers the same areas but does not include instructor training.

Credit recommendation, collegiate level: CAUTION: *Identical titles differ in recommendation according to course length. Require identification of a course by title and exact length. Course 1:* Credit in instructional methods, speech, and protective service occupations on the basis of institutional examination. *Courses 2, 3, and 4:* Credit in instructional methods and protective service occupations on the basis of institutional examination. *Course 5.* Credit in protective service occupations on the basis of institutional examination.

Disaster Preparedness Officer
(Disaster Control Officer)
(Passive Defense Officer)
Location: Lowry AFB, Colo.
Length: 4–6 weeks.
Objectives: To train officers in management of overall disaster control or preparedness activities.
Instruction: Effects of chemical, biological, and nuclear weapons; protection, detection, and decontamination; weapons systems accidents; domestic emergencies; limited and total war operations.
Credit recommendation, collegiate level: No credit because of the brevity and limited technical nature of the course.

Disbursement Accounting Specialist
Location: Sheppard AFB, Tex.
Length: 11 weeks.
Objectives: To train airmen in disbursement accounting.
Instruction: Principles of accounting and finance; maintenance of disbursement and collection records and files pertaining to pay and travel; processing of payrolls and travel vouchers for payment; preparation of posting media to record appropriations; expense and general ledger data; manual procedures; principles of typical mechanized equipment.
Credit recommendation, collegiate level: 3 semester hours in general business practice, and credit in accounting and finance on the basis of institutional examination.

Disbursing Clerk
Location: Lowry AFB, Colo.
Length: 10 weeks.
Objectives: To train airmen in disbursement procedures.
Instruction: Military pay and maintenance of military pay records; travel allowances; payment of commercial accounts; accounting for public funds; basic principles of disbursement accounting.
Credit recommendation, collegiate level: 3 semester hours in general business practice.

1. Disbursing Officer
2. Disbursing Officer
Location: Sheppard AFB, Tex.
Length: *Course 1,* 13 weeks; *Course 2,* 3 weeks.
Objectives: *Course 1:* To train officers in the management and operation of financial services. *Course 2:* To provide officers, fully qualified in accounting, with familiarization training in the operations of a finance office.

Instruction: *Course 1:* Disbursing procedures; military pay; travel allowances; commercial accounts; accounting for public funds; finance office management. *Course 2* surveys the same areas covered in detail by the longer course.
Credit recommendation, collegiate level: CAUTION: *These courses vary in length and credit recommendation. Require exact identification of course by title and length. Course 1:* 4 semester hours in finance and disbursing. *Course 2:* No credit because of the nature and brevity of the course.

Disbursing Supervisor
Location: Lowry AFB, Colo.
Length: 13 weeks.
Objectives: To train airmen in advanced disbursing procedures and finance office management.
Instruction: Disbursing procedures; military pay; travel allowances; commercial accounts; accounting for public funds; finance office management.
Credit recommendation, collegiate level: 4 semester hours in disbursing and finance.

1. Disposal Management
2. Disposal Specialist
Location: Amarillo AFB, Tex.
Length: 3 weeks.
Objectives: *Course 1* trains officers and *Course 2* trains airmen in the handling and disposal of surplus Air Force property.
Instruction: Classification, recording and storing of incoming materials; base redistribution of property; marketing of property by spot and sealed bids and negotiated sales.
Credit recommendation, collegiate level: 2 semester hours in supply management for each course.

ECM Maintenance for Armament Systems Officer
Location: Keesler AFB, Miss.
Length: 6 weeks.
Objectives: To train officers to perform supervisory duties related to the maintenance of aircraft electronic countermeasures systems.
Instruction: ECM principles; technical orders and supply procedures; maintenance of chaff dispenser, and ECM receiver and transmitter sets.
Credit recommendation, collegiate level: No credit because of the limited technical nature of the course.

1. Electrical Power Production Repairman/Technician (SM-68)
2. Electrical Power Production Specialist/Technician, SM-68B
3. Electrical Power Production Technician/Specialist (SM-65F)
Location: Sheppard AFB, Tex.
Length: 8 weeks.
Objectives: To train airmen in the operation and maintenance of electrical power production facilities at Air Force missile installations.

Instruction: Weapon system familiarization; engine principles and operation; maintenance of auxiliary equipment; electrical system and switchgear maintenance; generating equipment operation and maintenance.

Credit recommendation, collegiate level: These courses are technical and vocational in nature. Credit in electrical shop on the basis of demonstrated skills and/or institutional examinations.

Electrical Power Production System Maintenance (LGM-25)

Location: Sheppard AFB, Tex.

Length: 3 weeks.

Objectives: To train electrical power production specialists and technicians on power production equipment at LGM-25 missile installations.

Instruction: Maintenance data collection system; interphase of weapon system components related to power production equipment; voltage regulator; unit operation and troubleshooting.

Credit recommendation, collegiate level: This course is technical and vocational in nature. Credit in electrical shop on the basis of demonstrated skills and/or institutional examinations.

1. Electrical Power Production Technician
2. Electrical Power Production Operator
3. Electrical Power Production Repairman
4. Electrical Power Production Specialist
5. Electrical Power Production, Aleutian DEW Line (Power Production Specialist (DEW Line))

Locations: Sheppard AFB, Tex.; Francis E. Warren AFB, Wyo.

Length: *Course 1,* 9–10 weeks; *Course 2,* 12–15 weeks; *Course 3,* 8 weeks; *Course 4,* 18–19 weeks; *Course 5,* 6 weeks.

Objectives: *Course 1:* To provide supervisory training for airmen in the electrical power production field. *Courses 2 through 5:* To train airmen in the operation and maintenance of electrical power production equipment.

Instruction: *Course 1:* Military and commercial publications relative to electrical power production; maintenance policies and management; installation blueprints and plans; precision measurement and maintenance of generating system components; switchgear arrangements and related wiring diagrams; generator set operation and malfunction analysis. *Courses 2 through 5:* Selected generator sets in the 100 to 650 kilowatt range; power production fundamentals; operating principles and maintenance of generator set equipment including diesel engines, generators, exciters, and switchgear components; power plant auxiliary and controlling equipment.

Credit recommendation, collegiate level: CAUTION: *These courses vary in title, length, and recommendation. Require exact identification of course by title and length. Course 1:* 2 semester hours in shop management. *Courses 2 through 5 are technical and vocational in nature.* Credit in electrical shop on the basis of demonstrated skills and/or institutional examinations.

Electrical Standards Console

Location: Lowry AFB, Colo.

Length: 3–4 weeks.

Objectives: To train airmen to calibrate and use the electrical standards console.

Instruction: DC ratio calibration system and circuit analysis; calibration of standard cells, DC power supplies, standard resistors, voltage and current dividers; AC ratio calibration system and circuit analysis; AC-DC/DC comparator circuit analysis; calibration of standard capacitors, inductors, and AC power supplies.

Credit recommendation, collegiate level: Credit in electrical laboratory on the basis of demonstrated skills and/or institutional examinations.

Electrical Systems Maintenance, LGM-25

Location: Sheppard AFB, Tex.

Length: 5 weeks.

Objectives: To train electricians in the maintenance of Titan II missile facility electric power distribution system.

Instruction: Launch silo, control center, portal, tunnel, and decontamination area power distribution systems; fire protection, warning, air conditioning, water, and waste systems and controls; silo and portal elevators—troubleshooting and repair; DC power supply; motor generator sets circuit analysis.

Credit recommendation, collegiate level: This course is technical and vocational in nature. Credit in electrical shop on the basis of demonstrated skills and/or institutional examinations.

Electrician

Locations: Francis E. Warren AFB, Wyo.; Sheppard AFB, Tex.

Length: 10–14 weeks.

Objectives: To train airmen in fundamental electrical installation, maintenance, and repair procedures.

Instruction: Elementary electricity; installation and maintenance of exterior electrical power distribution systems; interior utility systems; utility equipment; special purpose systems for airfield light, fire detection, floodlighting, equipment control, and remote monitoring.

Credit recommendation, collegiate level: This course is technical and vocational in nature. Credit in electrical shop on the basis of demonstrated skills and/or institutional examinations.

1. Electrician, SM-80
2. Electrician, WS-133A, B, A-M (Electrician, WS-133B)

Location: Chanute AFB, Ill.

Length: *Course 1,* 5 weeks; *Course 2,* 6–7 weeks.

Objectives: To train airmen to perform electrical maintenance work on ground operations and real property installed equipment at missile launch facilities.

Instruction: Weapon system familiarization; application of electrical principles to launch and launch control electrical systems; strategic missile support base maintenance.

Credit recommendation, collegiate level: These courses are technical and vocational in nature. Credit in electrical shop on the basis of demonstrated skills and/or institutional examinations.

Electrician/Electrical Technician, SM-68B

Location: Sheppard AFB, Tex.
Length: 10 weeks.
Objectives: To train airmen in the maintenance and repair of selected electrical systems at strategic missile facilities.
Instruction: Weapon system familiarization and safety; launch silo, control center, portal, tunnel and decontamination area power distribution systems; servicing and repair of motor control centers and facility power control board; heating, ventilating, air conditioning, lighting, fire protection, and warning systems maintenance and repair.
Credit recommendation, collegiate level: Credit in electricity and electrical laboratory on the basis of demonstrated skills and/or institutional examinations.

1. Electrician/Supervisor (SM-68)
2. Electrician/Supervisor (SM-65F)
3. Electrician/Supervisor (Facility) (SM-65)
   Location: Sheppard AFB, Tex.
   Length: 13 weeks.
   Objectives: To provide airmen electricians with technical training in specified ballistic missile installations electrical systems and components.
   Instruction: Weapons system familiarization; electron theory; DC and AC circuits; magnetism and electromagnetism; circuit analysis; electrical and electronic test equipment; installation motor control centers and power distribution systems.
   Credit recommendation, collegiate level: For each course, 2 semester hours at the freshman or sophomore level as an elective in electricity, and credit in electrical laboratory on the basis of demonstrated skills and/or institutional examinations.

Electroencephalographic Specialist

Location: Lackland AFB, Tex.
Length: 9 weeks.
Objectives: To train airmen to operate electroencephalographic equipment and perform related duties.
Instruction: Principles of anatomy, physiology, and pathology; neuropsychiatric diseases and disorders; electroencephalographic equipment and laboratory procedures; EEG specialist's duties, including patient management, use of electrodes and localization, apparatus calibration, recording techniques, analysis and correction of extraneous potentials, recognizing satisfactory tracings, and preventive maintenance.
Credit recommendation, collegiate level: This course is technical and vocational in nature. Credit in electroencephalographic equipment operation on the basis of demonstrated skills and/or institutional examinations.

Electronic Communications and Cryptographic Equipment Systems Repairman
(Electronic Communications and Cryptographic Systems Equipment Repairman (Ciphony))
(Electronic Communications and Cryptographic Systems Equipment Repairman (Encrypted Tel-Data Fax))
(Electronic Communications and Cryptographic Equipment Repairman (Data and Facsimile))
(Electronic Communications and Cryptographic Systems Equipment Repairman (Encrypted Teletype))
(Electronic Communications and Cryptographic Equipment Repairman (Ciphony))

Location: Lackland AFB, Tex.
Length: 20–41 weeks.
Objectives: To train airmen to maintain and repair cryptographic, ciphony, or encrypted teletype data facsimile equipment.
Instruction: The electronics portion of these courses includes basic electronic principles; series, parallel, series-parallel, and bridge resistive circuits; reactive circuits and use of the oscilloscope; transistor circuits; electron tubes and circuits; and pulse techniques. The remainder of the course is special equipment training.
Credit recommendation, collegiate level: 3 semester hours at the freshman or sophomore level as an elective in electricity and electronics, and credit in electrical laboratory on the basis of demonstrated skills and/or institutional examinations.

1. Electronic Computer Repairman (AN/FSA-21/412L)
   (Electronic Digital Computer Repairman (An/FSA-21/412L))
2. Electronic Computer Repairman (DPC/465L)
   (Electronic Digital Computer Repairman (DPC/465L))
3. Electronic Computer Repairman (Display Equipment/412L)
   (Electronic Digital Computer Repairman (Display Equipment/412L))
4. Electronic Computer Repairman (Display Equip/465L)
   (Electronic Digital Computer Repairman (Display Equip/465L))
5. Electronic Computer Repairman (EDTCC/465L)
   (Electronic Digital Computer Repairman (EDTCC/465L))
6. Electronic Computer Repairman (SAGE-AN/FSQ-7)
   (Electronic Digital Computer Repairman (SAGE-AN/FSQ-7))
7. Electronic Digital Data Processing Repairman (Data Processing Equipment/412L)
8. Electronic Digital Data Processing Repairman (Input-Output/465L Concentrator)
9. Electronic Digital Data Processing Repairman (Input-Output 465L RCC Ancillary)
   Location: Keesler AFB, Miss.
   Length: 35–48 weeks.
   Objectives: To train airmen in the repair and maintenance of the computer equipment systems and components specified.
   Instruction: DC and AC; reactive circuits; vacuum

tubes and transistors; special purpose tubes and solid state devices; amplifiers and oscillators; motors and servomechanisms; multivibrators; sweep and computer circuits; digital techniques; application of electricity and electronics training to the special equipment specified in the course titles.

Credit recommendation, collegiate level: For each course, 4 semester hours at the freshman or sophomore level as an elective in electricity and electronics, and credit in electrical laboratory on the basis of demonstrated skills and/or institutional examinations.

Electronic Digital Computer Repairman (HGM-25A) (Electronic Digital Data Processing Repairman (Ballistic Missile Guidance Computer) (SM-68A))

Location: Sheppard AFB, Tex.
Length: 18 weeks.
Objectives: To train airmen in the operation, inspection, and maintenance of computers and associated aerospace ground equipment.
Instruction: Computer fundamentals; power supplies; number systems; control section; arithmetic section; electronic test set and magnetic drum; magnetic cores; digital-to-digital converters; simulator verifier; ground guidance system.
Credit recommendation, collegiate level: Credit in electrical laboratory on the basis of demonstrated skills and/or institutional examinations.

Electronic Digital Data Processing Equipment Maintenance Technician (AN/FSQ-7 Systems Technician)

Location: Keesler AFB, Miss.
Length: 15 weeks.
Objectives: To provide AN/FSQ-7 computer maintenance specialists with advanced training.
Instruction: Computer logic and logic circuit analysis; memory and computer control devices; theory of operation of the line printer, card reader, card recorder, tape system, card punch, computer entry punch, AN/FSQ-7 display system, and the manual data input element; use of test equipment; maintenance recording and reporting.
Credit recommendation, collegiate level: 4 semester hours in computer operation in the field of data processing.

Electronic Digital Data Processing Equipment Repairman (Ballistic Missile Guidance Computer) (SM-65-D)

Location: Keesler AFB, Miss.
Length: 38 weeks.
Objectives: To train airmen in electronic and computer fundamentals and their application to the operation, maintenance, and repair of ground guidance digital computers.
Instruction: DC and AC; reactive circuits; vacuum tubes and transistors; special purpose tubes; amplifiers and oscillators; motors and servomechanisms; multivi-

brators and sweep circuits; computer circuits; digital techniques; program, memory, and arithmetic units; inputs, outputs, simulator, and printer; computer checks and troubleshooting; test console; computer and package troubleshooting.

Credit recommendation, collegiate level: 6 semester hours at the freshman or sophomore level as an elective in electricity and electronics and credit in electrical laboratory on the basis of demonstrated skills and/or institutional examinations.

Electronic Digital Data Processing Equipment Repairman, Central Computer (416L-AN/FSQ-7)

Location: Keesler AFB, Miss.
Length: 19 weeks.
Objectives: To train airmen as central computer repairmen.
Instruction: Computer fundamentals; electronic chemical devices; shop practice; programming principles; test equipment; instruction analysis; memory; control; drum system; maintenance methods.
Credit recommendation, collegiate level: Credit in electrical laboratory on the basis of demonstrated skills and/or institutional examinations.

Electronic Digital Data Processing Specialist/ Technician (SM-68)

Location: Sheppard AFB, Tex.
Length: 25 weeks.
Objectives: To train airmen in the maintenance and repair of the WS 107A-2 guidance computer.
Instruction: Weapon system familiarization; computer fundamentals; power supplies; control section; arithmetic section; magnetic drum; electronic circuit test set; magnetic cores; digital-to-digital converter; weapon system integration.
Credit recommendation, collegiate level: Credit in electrical laboratory on the basis of demonstrated skills and/or institutional examinations.

Electronic Fuel Control Repair Technician

Location: Chanute AFB, Ill.
Length: 14 weeks.
Objectives: To provide advanced training for electronic fuel control repairmen.
Instruction: Administration and management, including technical publications, shop organization, utilization of personnel, and the airman training program; electrical theory; controlling and protective devices and test equipment; aircraft electrical power; electronics theory; integrated electronic control system operation and test equipment; fuel system component installation and repair; engine operation malfunction analysis.
Credit recommendation, collegiate level: This course is technical and vocational in nature. Credit in electrical shop and aircraft electronic fuel control systems repair shop on the basis of demonstrated skills and/or institutional examinations.

Electronic Fuel Control Repairman

Location: Chanute AFB, Ill.

Length: 19 weeks.

Objectives: To train airmen to maintain and repair aircraft electronic fuel control systems and components.

Instruction: Maintenance practices; basic electrical theory, circuits and measuring devices; aircraft power sources and wiring diagrams; electronic fundamentals; test equipment; F-86D fuel system; integrated electronic control system operation, testing and repair, engine starting, operation, and shutdown; fuel control system inspection.

Credit recommendation, collegiate level: This course is technical and vocational in nature. Credit in electrical shop and aircraft electronic fuel control systems repair shop on the basis of demonstrated skills and/or institutional examinations.

1. Electronic Intercept Operations/Analysis Specialist
(Electronic Intercept Operations Specialist (Interim))
2. Electronic Intercept Operations Specialist

Location: Keesler AFB, Miss.

Length: *Course 1,* 24–25 weeks; *Course 2,* 13 weeks.

Objectives: To train airmen in the operational principles of electronic intercept equipment and in the maintenance and analysis of electronic intercept logs.

Instruction: *Course 1:* Direct and alternating current; reactive circuits; principles of vacuum tubes and transistors; special purpose tubes; basic radio and radar principles; special equipment and techniques, including electronic intercept identification and analysis, operation of an intercept station, and signal analysis and intercept data processing. Except for a brief survey of electronic principles and terminology, *Course 2* deals entirely with special electronic intercept equipment and techniques.

Credit recommendation, collegiate level: CAUTION: *These courses vary in title, length, and recommendation. Require exact identification of course by full title and length. Course 1:* 3 semester hours at the freshman or sophomore level as an elective in electricity and electronics, and credit in electrical laboratory on the basis of demonstrated skills, and/or institutional examinations. *Course 2:* Credit in electricity, electronics, and electrical laboratory on the basis of demonstrated skills and/or institutional examinations.

Electronic Test Equipment Calibration and Repair (Tektronix)

Location: Lowry AFB, Colo.

Length: 3 weeks.

Objectives: To train airmen to develop systematic troubleshooting and malfunction elimination techniques and to calibrate Tektronix test equipment.

Instruction: Oscilloscopes and their uses; pulse techniques; time domain reflectometry; circuit analysis and calibration of the TEK 545 or 545A oscilloscope and TEK-type plug-ins.

Credit recommendation, collegiate level: No credit because of the brevity and specialized nature of the course.

Electronic Warfare Countermeasures Specialist (Aircraft Control and Warning Operator (ECCM Operator))
(ECCM Operator)

Location: Keesler AFB, Miss.

Length: 16 weeks.

Objectives: To train airmen as A-J console operators at long-range radar sites and/or SAGE direction centers.

Instruction: DC, AC, and reactive circuits; vacuum tubes; meter movements; measuring instruments; amplifiers; oscillators; modulation circuits; basic radar systems; basic electronic countermeasures; electronic counter-countermeasures; semiautomatic ground environment systems.

Credit recommendation, collegiate level: 3 semester hours at the freshman or sophomore level as an elective in electricity and electronics, and credit in electrical laboratory on the basis of demonstrated skills and/or institutional examinations.

Electronic Warfare Officer (Navigator, ECM)
(ECM Officer)
(Basic Observer Electronic Countermeasures)

Locations: Mather AFB, Calif.; Keesler AFB, Miss.

Length: 28–40 weeks.

Objectives: To train officer navigators in the preflight inspection and inflight operation and maintenance of specialized electronic countermeasures equipment.

Instruction: Electricity and magnetism; alternating current, semiconductors and power supplies; amplifiers, oscillators and wave-shaping circuits; transmission and reception; microwave principles; radar systems analysis; special electronic warfare systems and their applications.

Credit recommendation, collegiate level: 3 semester hours at the freshman or sophomore level as an elective in electricity and electronics, and credit in electrical laboratory on the basis of demonstrated skills and/or institutional examinations.

Electronic Warfare Officer Upgrade Training (B-58) (B-58 Bomber Defense Officer)

Locations: Mather AFB, Calif.; Keesler AFB, Miss.

Length: 4–6 weeks.

Objectives: To familiarize officers with B-58 aircraft operations.

Instruction: B-58 weapons system; communications procedures; active defense system; defensive electronic countermeasures systems; operating procedures and tactics.

Credit recommendation, collegiate level: No credit as the course is military in nature.

1. Electronic Warfare Repairman
2. Aircraft ECM Repairman (Jamming Equipment)
   (Aircraft Electronic Countermeasures Repairman
   (Jamming Equipment))
3. Aircraft Electronic Countermeasures Repairman
   (Surveillance Equipment)
   (Aircraft ECM Repairman (Surveillance
   Equipment))
   (Aircraft ECM Repairman (Reconnaissance
   (Equipment))
   (Aircraft ECM Repairman (Recon Equipment))
   (Aircraft Electronic Countermeasures Repairman
   (Reconnaissance Equipment))

Location: Keesler AFB, Miss.

Length: *Course 1,* 39 weeks; *Course 2,* 27–31 weeks; *Course 3,* 28–34 weeks.

Objectives: To train airmen to maintain airborne electronic warfare equipment.

Instruction: The electronics fundamentals phase of the courses includes DC, AC, and reactive circuits; principles of vacuum tubes and transistors; special purpose tubes and solid state devices; amplifiers and oscillators; amplitude and frequency modulation; detection; Doppler principles; transmission lines; schematic interpretation and troubleshooting; saturable reactors and magnetic amplifiers; motors, servo-mechanisms, multivibrators, sweep circuits, and microwave principles. The remainder of each course applies the electronics training to special equipment.

Credit recommendation, collegiate level: For each course, 6 semester hours at the freshman or sophomore level as an elective in electricity and electronics, and credit in electrical laboratory on the basis of demonstrated skills and/or institutional examinations.

1. Electronic Warfare Technician
2. Aircraft ECM Maintenance Technician
   (Electronics Countermeasures Maintenance
   Technician)

Location: Keesler AFB, Miss.

Length: *Course 1,* 40 weeks; *Course 2,* 17–36 weeks.

Objectives: To provide airmen with advanced technical training in the operational maintenance and repair of electronic countermeasures equipment.

Instruction: *Course 1:* Applied mathematics; analysis of DC and AC circuits; vacuum tubes and solid state devices; power supplies and oscillators; principles of electronic digital data processing; transmitter and RF systems circuits; receiver, indicator, and servo systems circuits; application of electronic training to electronic warfare equipment; administrative, training, and maintenance management. *Course 2:* For airmen qualified as electronic countermeasures repairmen; includes a review of electronics with concentration on the advanced technical equipment training and shop management practices.

Credit recommendation, collegiate level: CAUTION: *These courses vary in title, length, and recommendation. Require exact identification by title and length. Course 1:* 2 semester hours at the freshman or sophomore level as an elective in electricity and electronics, 2 semester hours in shop management, and credit in electrical laboratory on the basis of demonstrated skills and/or institutional examinations. *Course 2:* 2 semester hours in shop management, and credit in electrical laboratory on the basis of demonstrated skills and/or institutional examinations.

Electronic Warfare Training (Specialized F-4 Pilot)

Location: Nellis AFB, Nev.

Length: 4 weeks.

Objectives: To train pilots in the principles of radar and the operation and use of F-4 electronic warfare equipment.

Instruction: Radar analysis; radar equipment; radar order of battle analysis; equipment operation and techniques; audio analysis; trainer missions.

Credit recommendation, collegiate level: No credit as the course is military in nature.

Electronics Computer Maintenance Officer

Location: Keesler AFB, Miss.

Length: 46 weeks.

Objectives: To train officers in overall electronic computer maintenance management.

Instruction: Electronic fundamentals; computer principles, including functional and circuit analysis; principles of radio and radar; computer mathematics; computer programming; input-output equipment; central computer systems; drum, disc, and magnetic core storage systems; test equipment; analysis and corrective maintenance; computer maintenance management; computer applications in defense, tactical, and data processing systems.

Credit recommendation, collegiate level: 6 semester hours in computer principles in the field of data processing, 2 semester hours in maintenance management, 4 semester hours at the freshman or sophomore level as an elective in electricity and electronics, and credit in electrical laboratory on the basis of demonstrated skills and/or institutional examinations.

Engine Analyzer, Sperry Maintenance

Location: Chanute AFB, Ill.

Length: 4 weeks.

Objectives: To train airmen in the operation and maintenance of the Sperry engine analyzer.

Instruction: Description, location, and installation of all engine analyzer components; engine analyzer circuits; troubleshooting and repair.

Credit recommendation, collegiate level: This course is technical and vocational in nature. Credit in electrical shop on the basis of demonstrated skills and/or institutional examinations.

Engineering Entomology Specialist

Location: Sheppard AFB, Tex.

Length: 7 weeks.

Objectives: To train airmen in the fundamentals of insect and rodent control.

Instruction: Collection and identification of specimens; determination of control measures; types and uses of treatment solutions; operation and maintenance of insecticide dispersal equipment; entomology operations safety, publications, and records.

Credit recommendation, collegiate level: This course is vocational in nature. Credit in insect and pest control on the basis of demonstrated skills and/or institutional examinations.

Experimental Test Pilot Course
(USAF Flight Test School)
(USAF Experimental Flight Test School)
　　Location: Edwards AFB, Calif.
　　Length: 24–36 weeks.
　　Objectives: To train pilots to conduct flight tests on experimental production-type aircraft.
　　Instruction: Refresher course in calculus, graphical and analytical interpretation of the differential, physics, mechanics, dynamics, and aerodynamics; test flying techniques; data reduction for airplane performance; handling characteristics of airplanes.
　　Credit recommendation, collegiate level: Credit in aeronautics including aerodynamics on the basis of institutional examination.

Explosive Safety Training
　　Location: Lowry AFB, Colo.
　　Length: 3 weeks.
　　Objectives: To train airmen in the theory and handling of aerospace explosives.
　　Instruction: Chemical and biological aerospace munitions and protective measures; pyrotechnics, small arms, and aircraft guns; fire protection; disposal of aerospace munitions; safety programs.
　　Credit recommendation, collegiate level: No credit as the course is military in nature.

F-104 Flight Control Specialist
　　Location: Chanute AFB, Ill.
　　Length: 5 weeks.
　　Objectives: To qualify autopilot-compass systems repairmen to perform organizational and field maintenance in the F-104 flight control system.
　　Instruction: Aircraft familiarization; aerodynamics and gyroscope principles; operation of flight control system; inspection and maintenance.
　　Credit recommendation, collegiate level: This course is technical and vocational in nature. Credit in electrical instrument repair shop on the basis of demonstrated skills and/or institutional examinations.

1. **F-111 Computer Programmer Test Stations Technician**
2. **F-111 Indicator and Controls Test Stations Technician**
3. **F-111 Radar and Controls Test Stations Technician**
4. **F-111 Communications Guidance Test Stations Technician**
　　Location: Lowry AFB, Colo.
　　Length: 13–28 weeks.
　　Objectives: To train airmen to perform maintenance on the aerospace ground equipment specified.
　　Instruction: Theory, operation, inspection, and maintenance of pertinent aerospace ground equipment recommendation data for the purpose of performing maintenance on applicable line replaceable units, test stations, and peculiar support aerospace ground equipment; ground safety; technical publications; corrosion control; security; maintenance management.

Credit recommendation, collegiate level: For each course, credit in electrical laboratory on the basis of demonstrated skills and/or institutional examinations.

F-111 Navigation and Test Stations Technician
　　Location: Lowry AFB, Colo.
　　Length: 8 weeks.
　　Objectives: To train airmen to operate, inspect, and maintain AGERD 6818 and IFF test equipment group for the purpose of maintaining line replacement units, test stations, and AGE.
　　Instruction: Operation, maintenance and calibration of AGERD 6818; test stations and support AGE; IFF test equipment group; shop performance.
　　Credit recommendation, collegiate level: This course is technical and vocational in nature. Credit in electrical shop on the basis of demonstrated skills and/or institutional examinations.

F-111 Penetration Aids Test Stations Technician
　　Location: Lowry AFB, Colo.
　　Length: 18–21 weeks.
　　Objectives: To train airmen to operate, inspect, and maintain AGERD 6811 and AGERD 6812.
　　Instruction: Infrared receiver set familiarization; operation, analysis, and maintenance of AGERD 6811 and 6812; radar homing and warning system familiarization and circuit analysis.
　　Credit recommendation, collegiate level: Credit in electricity and electrical laboratory on the basis of demonstrated skills and/or institutional examinations.

F-111A Weapons System Training
　　Location: Cannon AFB, N. Mex.
　　Length: 8–9 weeks.
　　Objectives: To train rated pilots in the principles of radar and its employment and in the operation and use of F-111A avionic systems.
　　Instruction: F-111A navigation, bombing, and weapons systems; radar air-combat techniques and electronic countermeasures; F-111A avionics systems operation (simulator).
　　Credit recommendation, collegiate level: No credit as the course is military in nature.

F&O Maintenance AN/GMQ-10A Transmissometer,
AN/GMQ-13 Rotating Beam Ceilometer
　　Location: Chanute AFB, Ill.
　　Length: 5 weeks.
　　Objectives: To train weather equipment technicians in the field and organizational maintenance of the equipment specified.
　　Instruction: Analysis, operation, adjustment, and repair of the AN/GMQ-10A transmissometer and AN/GMQ-13 rotating beam ceilometer.
　　Credit recommendation, collegiate level: No credit because of the limited technical nature of the course.

FORTRAN Programming

Location: Sheppard AFB, Tex.

Length: 3 weeks.

Objectives: To train officers and airmen in FORTRAN programming techniques.

Instruction: Coding conventions; constants, variables, and subscripts; control and end statements; input-output and specification statements; subroutines related to FORTRAN programming language.

Credit recommendation, collegiate level: 2 semester hours in computer programming in the field of computing science.

1. Fabric, Leather, and Rubber Products Repairman
2. Fabric and Leather Worker

Location: Chanute AFB, Ill.

Length: 12–18 weeks.

Objectives: To train airmen to inspect, repair, and fabricate leather, rubber, and fabric equipment and to dope aircraft control surfaces.

Instruction: Inspection, repair, and fabrication of protective covers and flight-line equipment, airplane upholstery, flying clothing, and aircrew protective and survival equipment; fabrication, installation, and doping of fabric covers on airplane surfaces.

Credit recommendation, collegiate level: These courses are technical and vocational in nature. Credit in fabric maintenance and repair on the basis of demonstrated skills and/or institutional examinations.

Field and Organizational Maintenance, T56-A-1A Engine

Location: Sheppard AFB, Tex.

Length: 4 weeks.

Objectives: To train jet engine mechanics to maintain and repair the T56-A-1A engine.

Instruction: T-56 engine inspection, disassembly, and assembly; operating principles and adjustment of engine and engine systems; T-56 operational checks, trouble analysis and storage.

Credit recommendation, collegiate level: This course is technical and vocational in nature. Credit in jet engine repair shop on the basis of demonstrated skills and/or institutional examinations.

Field and Organizational Maintenance, TSEC/KL-7 (F&O Maintenance KL-7)

Location: Sheppard AFB, Tex.

Length: 3 weeks.

Objectives: To train airmen to install, adjust, and maintain KL-7 equipment.

Instruction: Mechanical operation; adjustment and preventive maintenance; circuit analysis; troubleshooting.

Credit recommendation, collegiate level: This course is technical and vocational in nature. Credit in electrical shop on the basis of demonstrated skills and/or institutional examinations.

Fighter Gunnery Instructor

Location: Nellis AFB, Nev.

Length: 11 weeks. *Note*—since flying training is dependent upon weather and other factors the actual length of the course may vary.

Objectives: To train pilots as gunnery instructors.

Instruction: The course is divided into a flight gunnery training phase and an academic phase. The latter consists of harmonization; aerial attack; film assessing; sights; ground attack; training equipment and fighter weapons; principles of instruction; flying safety; field trips.

Credit recommendation, collegiate level: No credit as the course is military in nature.

Fighter Weapons Instructors

Location: Luke AFB, Ariz.

Length: 15 weeks. *Note*—since flying training is dependent upon weather and other factors, the actual length of the course may vary.

Objectives: To train selected pilots as fighter weapons instructors.

Instruction: Academic instruction includes aerial attack; gun camera film assessing; sights; ground attack; fighter and special weapons; techniques of instruction and practice teaching. The remainder of the course is flying training.

Credit recommendation, collegiate level: Credit in instructional methods on the basis of institutional examination.

Film Cutting Specialist

Location: Lowry AFB, Colo.

Length: 8–9 weeks.

Objectives: To train airmen to edit silent and sound motion picture films.

Instruction: Fundamental editing procedures; elementary and advanced editing techniques; editing sound film.

Credit recommendation, collegiate level: This course is technical and vocational in nature. Credit in film editing on the basis of demonstrated skills and/or institutional examinations.

1. Finance Supervisor
2. Finance Supervisor
3. Finance Specialist
4. Finance Specialist

Location: Sheppard AFB, Tex.

Length: *Course 1,* 13 weeks; *Course 2,* 5 weeks; *Course 3,* 11 weeks; *Course 4,* 4 weeks.

Objectives: To train airmen to compute and maintain records for military pay, travel allowances, and commercial accounts.

Instruction: *Course 1:* Disbursement procedures; military pay; travel allowance; commercial accounts; accounting for public funds; finance office management. *Course 2:* Finance procedures; military pay; travel allowance; commercial accounts; disbursements and collections. *Course 3:* Military pay; travel allowances; commercial accounts; accounting for public funds. *Course 4:* Military pay.

Credit recommendation, collegiate level: CAUTION: *These courses vary slightly in title, length, and recommendation. Require exact identification of course by title and length. Course 1: 4 semester hours in disbursing and finance. Course 2: 2 semester hours in disbursing and finance. Course 3: 3 semester hours in disbursing and finance. Course 4: No credit because of the brevity and nature of the course.*

1. Fire Control Systems Mechanic (AN/ASG-14 System)
2. Fire Control Systems Mechanic (AN/ASG-14 System)

Location: Lowry AFB, Colo.
Length: *Course 1,* 26 weeks; *Course 2,* 12 weeks.
Objectives: To train airmen to install, maintain, and repair AN/ASG-14 fire control systems.
Instruction: *Courses 1 and 2:* ASG-14 radar transmitter and receiver circuits; ASG-14 radar ECM operation indicator; ASG-14 optical gunsight system; ASG-14 IR sight; in addition *Course 1* includes fundamentals of electricity; fundamentals of AC; vacuum and gas-filled tubes; amplifiers, oscillators, and sweep circuits; oscilloscope and radar principles.
Credit recommendation, collegiate level: CAUTION: *Courses in fire control systems vary only slightly in title, length, and recommendation. Require exact identification by full title and length. Note that titles vary mainly by name of equipment in the parentheses following the title. Course 1:* 3 semester hours at the freshman or sophomore level as an elective in electronics, and credit in electrical laboratory on the basis of demonstrated skills and/or institutional examinations. *Course 2:* Credit in electricity and electrical laboratory on the basis of demonstrated skills and/or institutional examinations.

1. Fire Control Systems Mechanic (ASG-19 System)
2. Weapon Control Systems Mechanic (ASG-19 System)
3. Weapon Control Systems Mechanic (ASG-19 System)
4. Offensive Fire Control Systems Mechanic (ASG-19 System)
5. Offensive Fire Control Systems Mechanic (ASG-19 System)

Location: Lowry AFB, Colo.
Length: *Course 1,* 40 weeks; *Course 2,* 37 weeks; *Course 3,* 35 weeks; *Course 4,* 36–38 weeks; *Course 5,* 19 weeks.
Objectives: To train airmen to trace data flow and troubleshoot, maintain, and repair ASG-19 fire control systems.
Instruction: *Courses 1 and 2:* DC and AC; reactive circuits; vacuum tubes and transistors; special purpose tubes; amplifiers and oscillators; special circuits; motors and servomechanisms; multivibrators and sweep circuits; microwave principles; air-to-air search display; acquisition; track and antenna positioning; navigation and bombing modes; attack and display subsystems; bombing computer. *Course 3:* DC and AC; reactive circuits; vacuum tubes and transistors; amplifiers and oscillators; amplifiers and radar; air-to-air search dis-

play; acquisition, track, and antenna positioning; navigation and bombing modes; attack and display subsystem; bombing computer. *Course 4* includes all of *Course 3* with the addition of special circuits; microwave operation; multivibrators; sweep and logic circuits. *Course 5:* Air-to-air search display; acquisition, track, and antenna positioning; navigation and bombing modes; attack and display subsystem; bombing computer.

Credit recommendation, collegiate level: CAUTION: *Courses in fire and weapon control systems vary only slightly in title, length, and recommendation. Note that titles vary mainly by name of equipment in the parentheses following the title. Require exact identification by full title and length. Courses 1 and 2:* For each course, 6 semester hours at the freshman or sophomore level as an elective in electricty and electronics, and credit in electrical laboratory on the basis of demonstrated skills and/or institutional examinations. *Course 3:* 3 semester hours at the freshman or sophomore level as an elective in electricity and electronics, and credit in electrical laboratory on the basis of demonstrated skills and/or institutional examinations. *Course 4:* 4 semester hours at the freshman or sophomore level as an elective in electricity and electronics and credit in electrical laboratory on the basis of demonstrated skills and/or institutional examinations. *Course 5:* Credit in electronics and electrical laboratory on the basis of demonstrated skills and/or institutional examinations.

1. Fire Control Systems Mechanic (MA-3, ASG-17 Systems)
    (Offensive Fire Control Systems Mechanic (MA-3, ASG-17 Systems))
    (Offensive Fire Control Systems Mechanic (MA-1, 2, 3, GBR Sight Systems))
    (Offensive Fire Control Systems Mechanic (MA-1, MA-2, MA-3 Systems))
2. Offensive Fire Control Systems Mechanic (MA-1, MA-2, MA-3)
    (Offensive Fire Control Systems Mechanic (MA-1, MA-2, and MA-3 Systems))
    (Sighting Systems Mechanic)

Location: Lowry AFB, Colo.
Length: *Course 1,* 29–37 weeks; *Course 2,* 23–26 weeks.
Objectives: To train airmen to analyze, maintain, repair, and install fire control systems.
Instruction: *Course 1:* Direct and alternating current; reactive circuits; vacuum tubes and transistors; special purpose tubes; amplifiers and oscillators; special circuits; motors and servomechanisms; multivibrators and sweep circuits; microwave principles. *Course 2:* Fundamentals of electricity; fundamentals of alternating current; vacuum tubes and power supplies; amplifiers; oscillators; sweep generators; radar principles.
Credit recommendation, collegiate level: CAUTION: *Courses in fire control systems vary only slightly in title, length, and recommendation. Require exact identification by full title and length. Note that titles vary mainly by name of equipment in the parentheses following the title. Course 1:* 6 semester hours at the freshman or sophomore level as an elective in electricity and electronics, and credit in electrical laboratory on the basis of demonstrated skills and/or institution-

al examinations. *Course 2:* 3 semester hours at the freshman or sophomore level as an elective in electricity and electronics, and credit in electrical laboratory on the basis of demonstrated skills and/or institutional examinations.

Fire Control Systems Mechanic (MA-7 System)

Location: Lowry AFB, Colo.

Length: 32 weeks.

Objectives: To train airmen to operate, analyze, and maintain MA-7 fire control systems as installed in the F-101 aircraft.

Instruction: Fundamentals of electricity and alternating current; vacuum tubes and power supplies; amplifiers, oscillators, and sweep generators; radar principles.

Credit recommendation, collegiate level: CAUTION: *Courses in fire control systems vary only slightly in title, length, and recommendation. Require exact identification by full title and length. Note that titles vary mainly by name of equipment in the parentheses following the title.* 3 semester hours at the freshman or sophomore level as an elective in electronics, and credit in electrical laboratory on the basis of demonstrated skills and/or institutional examinations.

Fire Control Systems Mechanic (MA-10 System)

Location: Lowry AFB, Colo.

Length: 32 weeks.

Objectives: To train airmen as fire control systems mechanics.

Instruction: Fundamentals of electricity and alternating current; vacuum tubes and power supplies; amplifiers, oscillators, and sweep generators; radar principles.

Credit recommendation, collegiate level: CAUTION: *Courses in fire control systems vary only slightly in title, length, and recommendation. Require exact identification by full title and length. Note that titles vary mainly by name of equipment in the parentheses following the title.* 3 semester hours at the freshman or sophomore level as an elective in electricity, and credit in electrical laboratory on the basis of demonstrated skills and/or institutional examinations.

Fire Control Systems Technician (MA-10, ASG-14 System)

Location: Lowry AFB, Colo.

Length: 11 weeks.

Objectives: To train airmen to analyze, service, and troubleshoot MA-10 and ASG-14 fire control systems.

Instruction: Transistors; radar transmitter circuits; radar receiver, computer, indicator, ECM, and test panel circuits; AN/ASG-14 optical gunsight system; AN/ASG-14 infrared sight system.

Credit recommendation, collegiate level: CAUTION: *Courses in fire control systems vary only slightly in title, length, and recommendation. Note that titles vary mainly by name of equipment in the parentheses following the title. Require exact identification by full title and length.* Credit in electronics and electrical

laboratory on the basis of demonstrated skills and/or institutional examinations.

1. Fire Protection Supervisor (Fire Fighting Supervisor)
2. Fire Protection Specialist (Fire Protection Fundamentals) (Firefighter)

Locations: Chanute AFB, Ill.; Greenville AFB, Miss.; Lowry AFB, Colo.

Length: *Course 1,* 4–8 weeks; *Course 2,* 8–10 weeks.

Objectives: *Course 1:* To train airmen to plan fire-fighting operations, and to supervise fire-fighting personnel. *Course 2:* To train airmen to extinguish aircraft and structural fires, to rescue personnel and to administer emergency first aid.

Instruction: *Course 1:* Fire department administration; fire prevention; fire protection; fire fighting. *Course 2:* Principles and theory of combustion, control, and extinguishment; operation and maintenance of fire-fighting equipment; fire suppression and rescue operations.

Credit recommendation, collegiate level: No credit because of the specialized nature of these courses.

Flak Intelligence Officer

Locations: Lowry AFB, Colo.; Sheppard AFB, Tex.

Length: 6 weeks.

Objectives: To train officers in advanced principles and techniques of intelligence on enemy ground defenses against aircraft.

Instruction: Antiaircraft artillery materiel and gunnery; firing demonstrations; construction of the fire unit analyzer; employment of antiaircraft artillery and surface-to-air missiles; USAF operational capabilities; applied flak analysis and intelligence.

Credit recommendation, collegiate level: No credit as the course is military in nature.

Flight Control System Analyst SM-62

Location: Amarillo AFB, Tex.

Length: 6 weeks.

Objectives: To train airmen as flight control system analysts for the SM-62 missile.

Instruction: Missile familiarization; use and operation of analyzers, test equipment, and ground support equipment; functional and data flow analysis of flight control system components.

Credit recommendation, collegiate level: Credit in electronics and electrical laboratory on the basis of demonstrated skills and/or institutional examinations.

Flight Engineer Specialist (Flight Engineer Technician)

Locations: Chanute AFB, Ill.; Sheppard AFB, Tex.

Length: 12–14 weeks.

Objectives: To train airmen as flight engineer technicians emphasizing knowledge of aircraft weight and balance, flight plans, and flight logs.

Instruction: Aerodynamics; construction and use of charts and graphs; weight, balance, and take-off performance; cruise and mission planning; engine performance; fuel consumption.

Credit recommendation, collegiate level: 3 semester hours in aerodynamics.

1. Flight Facilities Equipment Repairman
2. Flight Facilities Equipment Repairman
3. Flight Facilities Equipment Repairman (Ranges and Beacons)
4. Flight Facilities Equipment Repairman (Ranges and Beacons)
5. Flight Facilities Equipment Repairman (ILS)
6. Flight Facilities Equipment Repairman (ILS)
7. Flight Facilities Equipment Repairman (TACAN)
8. Flight Facilities Equipment Repairman (TACAN)

Locations: Keesler AFB, Miss.; Scott AFB, Ill.

Length: *Course 1,* 37–39 weeks; *Course 2,* 36 weeks; *Courses 3, 5, and 7,* 28–30 weeks; *Courses 4, 6, and 8,* 14–17 weeks.

Objectives: To train airmen to perform organizational maintenance, performance testing, adjustment, and repair of equipment indicated in title.

Instruction: *Course 1:* DC and AC; reactive circuits; vacuum tubes and transistors; special purpose tubes; amplifiers and oscillators; special circuits; motors and servomechanisms; multivibrators and sweep circuits; microwave principles. *Course 2:* DC and AC; electron tubes and power supplies; amplifiers and oscillators; special circuits; transmitters. *Courses 3, 5, and 7:* DC and AC; electron tubes and power supplies; amplifiers and oscillators; special circuits. *Courses 4, 6, and 8:* Repair of low-frequency radio range equipment.

Credit recommendation, collegiate level: CAUTION: *These courses vary only slightly in title, length, and recommendation. Require exact identification of course by full title and length. Course 1:* 6 semester hours at the freshman or sophomore level as an elective in electricity and electronics, and credit in electrical laboratory on the basis of demonstrated skills and/or institutional examinations. *Course 2:* 4 semester hours at the freshman or sophomore level as an elective in electricity and electronics, and credit in electrical laboratory on the basis of demonstrated skills and/or institutional examinations. *Courses 3, 5, and 7:* For each course, 3 semester hours at the freshman or sophomore level as an elective in electricity and electronics, and credit in electrical laboratory on the basis of demonstrated skills and/or institutional examinations. *Courses 4, 6, and 8:* For each course, credit in electricity and electrical laboratory on the basis of demonstrated skills and/or institutional examinations.

1. Flight Facilities Equipment Technician
2. Flight Facilities Equipment Maintenance Technician

Location: Keesler AFB, Miss.

Length: *Course 1,* 38 weeks; *Course 2,* 32 weeks.

Objectives: To train airmen in the operation, maintenance, and installation of flight facilities and associated equipment.

Instruction: *Course 1:* DC and AC circuits; vacuum tubes and solid state devices; power supplies and oscillators; principles of electronic digital data processing; analysis of functional circuits of transmitter, RF, receiver, indicator, and servo systems. *Course 2:* Fundamentals of DC and AC; circuit analysis; oscillators; wave propagation.

Credit recommendation, collegiate level: *Course 1:* 2 semester hours in shop management, 6 semester hours at the freshman or sophomore level as an elective in electricity and electronics, and credit in electrical laboratory on the basis of demonstrated skills and/or institutional examinations. *Course 2:* 2 semester hours in shop management, and credit in electricity and electrical laboratory on the basis of demonstrated skills and/or institutional examinations.

Flight Nurse

Locations: Brooks AFB, Tex.; Gunter AFB, Ala.

Length: 5–6 weeks.

Objectives: To train registered nurses of the Air Force, Air Force Reserve, Air National Guard, Army, Navy, and allied countries in the techniques of inflight nursing care and procedures required in the event of an aircraft emergency.

Instruction: Aeromedical indoctrination; aviation medicine; flight nursing; review of basic nursing content in surgery, psychiatry, preventive and internal medicine, radiobiology, neurology, and ophthalmology.

Credit recommendation, collegiate level: No credit because of the prerequisites and review nature of the course.

1. Flight Simulator Fundamentals
2. Flight Simulator Specialist
3. Flight Simulator Specialist

Locations: Chanute AFB, Ill.; Keesler AFB, Miss.

Length: *Course 1,* 25 weeks; *Course 2,* 35–36 weeks; *Course 3,* 23 weeks.

Objectives: *Course 1:* To provide airmen with skills necessary for on-the-job maintenance training in flight simulators. *Courses 2 and 3:* To train airmen in the maintenance and repair of flight simulators.

Instruction: *Course 1:* Electricity and magnetism; alternating current; vacuum tubes; power supplies; voltage regulators; amplifiers and oscillators; synchros; servosystems; transients; special circuits. *Course 2:* DC and AC; reactive circuits; vacuum tubes and transients; amplifiers and oscillators. *Course 3:* DC and AC; electron tubes; amplifiers and oscillators; servosystems.

Credit recommendation, collegiate level: CAUTION: *These courses vary only slightly in title, length, and recommendation. Require exact identification by title and length. Course 1:* 4 semester hours at the freshman or sophomore level as an elective in electricity and electronics, and credit in electrical laboratory on the basis of demonstrated skills and/or institutional examinations. *Course 2:* 3 semester hours at the freshman or sophomore level as an elective in electricity and electronics, and credit in electrical laboratory on the basis of demonstrated skills and/or institutional examinations. *Course 3:* 2 semester hours at the freshman or sophomore level as an elective in electricity and electronics, and credit in electrical laboratory on the basis of demonstrated skills and/or institutional examinations.

1. Flight Simulator Technician
2. Flight Simulator Technician

Location: Chanute AFB, Ill.

Length: *Course 1,* 21 and 36 weeks; *Course 2,* 21 weeks.

Objectives: To train airmen for supervision of flight simulator activities, system analysis, installation, and repair of flight simulators.

Instruction: *Course 1:* DC and AC; advanced simulator circuits; amplifiers and servomechanisms; solid state theory and devices. *Course 2:* Advanced electronics; simulator computing devices; special components and techniques; solid state devices.

Credit recommendation, collegiate level: CAUTION: *Courses 1 and 2 vary in length and credit recommendation. Course 2 was given only between October 1965 and February 1966. Require exact identification of course by date. Course 1:* 3 semester hours at the freshman or sophomore level as an elective in electricity and electronics, and credit in electrical laboratory on the basis of demonstrated skills and/or institutional examinations. *Course 2:* 2 semester hours at the freshman or sophomore level as an elective in electricity and electronics, and credit in electrical laboratory on the basis of demonstrated skills and/or institutional examinations.

Flight Training Devices Instructor Operator

Location: Chanute AFB, Ill.

Length: 8 weeks.

Objectives: To train airmen as flight training instructors on instrument trainers.

Instruction: Instructor operator fundamentals; instrument flying procedures; instrument landing procedures.

Credit recommendation, collegiate level: No credit because of the specialized nature of the course.

Foreign Service Institute Resident Language Course (1964)

Location: Foreign Service Institute, Arlington, Va.

Length: 16–44 weeks.

Objectives: To provide practical skills in foreign languages including the ability to understand and speak the language for living, travel, social, representational, and professional purposes, and to provide understanding of the related culture.

Instruction: 20–30 hours per week in systematic drills and guided conversations under the tutelage of a native speaker of the language and a linguist; 10–20 hours per week in outside study including language topics; reading of current foreign language newspapers, periodicals, documentary material, and literature in various professional fields; area studies.

EXPLANATORY STATEMENT: The language courses given at the Foreign Service Institute were evaluated for the first time by the Commission in August, 1964. Prior to that time the Commission's policy provided only for the evaluation of educational programs given directly by the Armed Forces. However, the Commission had received a number of requests from civilian educational institutions asking for credit recommendations for courses taken by members of the Armed Forces who had been assigned to the Foreign Service

Institute rather than to a language school established by the Department of Defense.

The majority of military enrollments at the Foreign Service Institute have been Air Force personnel, although some Army, Marine Corps, and Navy officers and enlisted men have attended. Therefore, in order to provide them with an opportunity to receive recognition of their language training, the Commission amended its policy in order to evaluate the resident language courses given at the Foreign Service Institute in Arlington, Virginia. (The Commission's policy does not provide for the evaluation of the Foreign Service Institute's intensive, advanced courses given at the overseas centers in Beirut, Tangier, Taichung, or Tokyo. Also not included in the evaluation were Foreign Service Institute part-time programs available at approximately 220 overseas posts in over 60 different languages.)

At the time that the group of linguistic scientists who acted as consultants to the Commission evaluated the resident language courses at the Foreign Service Institute, 35 languages or dialects were being taught. These courses varied from 16 to 44 weeks in length. It will be noted that there is sometimes a variation in the amount of credit recommended for courses of the same length but in different languages. The variations are based upon the relative difficulty of the language studied.

The chart below lists the languages given by the Foreign Service Institute under three such groupings:

A. The least difficult languages for the English-speaking learner include: French, German, Italian, Portuguese, Rumanian, Spanish and Swahili.

B. Languages of greater difficulty, but with alphabetical writing systems which may be learned concurrently without appreciably affecting the progress in learning the spoken language, include: Bulgarian, Burmese, Cambodian, Czech, Finnish, Greek, Hausa, Hebrew, Hindi/Urdu, Hungarian, Igbo, Indonesian, Lingala, Persian, Polish, Rundi, Russian, Serbo-Croatian, Thai, Twi, Turkish, Vietnamese, and Yoruba.

C. The more difficult languages, in which the reading problem is complicated, include: Amharic, Arabic, Chinese, Japanese, and Korean.

Credit recommendation, collegiate level: CAUTION: *Before granting credit to an applicant, the accrediting official should obtain a certified Language Training Report (Form DS-651) for the individual from the Foreign Service Institute, Department of State, 1400 Key Boulevard, Arlington, Virginia 22209.*

COURSE	LENGTH (WEEKS)	BACCALAUREATE SEMESTER HOURS
1. Amharic	44	27
2. Arabic	24	18
3. Arabic	44	27
4. Bulgarian	24	18
5. Bulgarian	44	24
6. Burmese	24	18
7. Burmese	44	24
8. Cambodian	24	18
9. Cambodian	44	24
10. Chinese (Mandarin)	24	18
11. Chinese (Mandarin)	44	27
12. Czech	24	18
13. Czech	44	24
14. Finnish	24	18
15. Finnish	44	24
16. French	16	12

COURSE	LENGTH (WEEKS)	BACCALAUREATE SEMESTER HOURS
17. French	24	15
18. German	16	12
19. German	24	15
20. Greek	24	18
21. Greek	44	24
22. Hausa	19	15
23. Hebrew	24	18
24. Hebrew	44	24
25. Hindi/Urdu	24	18
26. Hindi/Urdu	44	24
27. Hungarian	24	18
28. Hungarian	44	24
29. Igbo	16	12
30. Indonesian	24	18
31. Indonesian	44	24
32. Italian	16	12
33. Italian	24	15
34. Japanese	24	18
35. Japanese	44	27
36. Korean	24	18
37. Korean	44	27
38. Lingala	16	12
39. Persian	24	18
40. Persian	44	24
41. Polish	24	18
42. Polish	44	24
43. Portuguese	16	12
44. Portuguese	24	15
45. Rumanian	24	15
46. Rumanian	44	21
47. Rundi	16	12
48. Russian	24	18
49. Russian	44	24
50. Serbo-Croatian	24	18
51. Serbo-Croatian	44	24
52. Spanish	16	12
53. Spanish	24	15
54. Swahili	32	18
55. Thai	24	18
56. Thai	44	24
57. Turkish	24	18
58. Turkish	44	24
59. Twi	16	12
60. Vietnamese	16	12
61. Vietnamese	20	15
62. Vietnamese	24	18
63. Vietnamese	44	24
64. Yoruba	16	12

Freight Traffic Specialist

Location: Sheppard AFB, Tex.
Length: 9 weeks.
Objectives: To train airmen to manage commercial and military freight traffic.
Instruction: Traffic management; shipping and receiving procedures; bill of lading procedures; household goods.
Credit recommendation, collegiate level: 3 semester hours in traffic operations.

---

1. **Front End Alignment, Operation, and Maintenance**
2. **Wheel Alignment Equipment, Operation, and Maintenance**

Location: Chanute AFB, Ill.
Length: 3 weeks.
Objectives: To train airmen in wheel alignment.
Instruction: Steering systems and alignment; alignment equipment; standard, independent, and torsion bar suspension systems; wheel balancing and use of visualiner; correction of steering malfunctions.
Credit recommendation, collegiate level: No credit because of the brevity and nature of the courses.

Fuel Cell Repair (B-52 and KC-135)

Location: Chanute AFB, Ill.
Length: 3 weeks.
Objectives: To train airmen to repair and maintain aircraft fuel cells.
Instruction: Procedures for repair and maintenance of fuel cells in B-52 and KC-135 aircraft including identification, construction, treating, and storage of fuel cells.
Credit recommendation, collegiate level: No credit because of the brevity and limited technical nature of the course.

Fuel Specialist (Missile Liquid Fuel Propellant)
(Fuel Specialist (Missile Liquid Fuel Propellant) (LGM-25))
(Fuel Specialist (Unconventional Fuels))
(Fuel Specialist (Unconventional Fuels) (SM-68B))
(Fuel Specialist (Nonconventional) (SM-68B))
(Fuel Specialist (SM-68B))
(Fuel Specialist)

Locations: Amarillo AFB, Tex.; Chanute AFB, Ill.
Length: 4–13 weeks.
Objectives: To train airmen in the receiving, handling, transferring, and storage of propellants, gases, and unconventional fuels.
Instruction: Propellant familiarization; propellant quality control and disposal; propellant storage; transport equipment.
Credit recommendation, collegiate level: These courses are technical and vocational in nature. Credit in fuel system maintenance on the basis of demonstrated skills and/or institutional examinations.

Fuel Specialist (Petroleum Fuels)
(Fuel Specialist (Conventional Fuels))
(Fuel Specialist, Conventional Fuel)
(Fuel Supply Specialist, Conventional Fuel)
(Petroleum Supply Specialist)

Location: Amarillo AFB, Tex.
Length: 8–13 weeks.
Objectives: To train airmen to receive, store, and issue petroleum products; to control quantity and quality; to operate refueling tractors and trailers.
Instruction: Petroleum characteristics, safety, and technical publications; bulk storage and dispensing systems; vehicle operation; flight-line products.

Credit recommendation, collegiate level: These courses are technical and vocational in nature. Credit in petroleum products handling on the basis of demonstrated skills and/or institutional examinations.

Fuel Supply Specialist, IM-99

Location: Chanute AFB, Ill.
Length: 3 weeks.
Objectives: To train airmen to receive, store, transfer, and dispose of liquid rocket fuels and oxidizers.
Instruction: Missile familiarization; propellants and compressed gases; propellant handling, transfer, and servicing.
Credit recommendation, collegiate level: No credit because of the limited technical nature of the course.

Fuels Officer (Petroleum Fuels)
(Fuels Officer (Conventional Fuels))
(Fuel Supply Officer)

Location: Amarillo AFB, Tex.
Length: 5–6 weeks.
Objectives: To train officers in the handling, accounting, storage, and dispensing of fuels.
Instruction: Characteristics of petroleum products; accounting procedures; quantity and quality control; receiving, storing, and dispensing systems; vehicle inspection and maintenance; fueling and defueling of aircraft; tank cleaning.
Credit recommendation, collegiate level: 2 semester hours in handling and storage of petroleum products.

Fundamentals of Missile Engine Maintenance

Location: Chanute AFB, Ill.
Length: 10 weeks.
Objectives: To provide airmen with specific skills necessary for entry into missile engine mechanic courses.
Instruction: Missile maintenance fundamentals; missile systems; missile engine systems; aerospace ground equipment.
Credit recommendation, collegiate level: This course is technical and vocational in nature. Credit in mechanical shop on the basis of demonstrated skills and/or institutional examinations.

Fundamentals of Missile Maintenance

Location: Sheppard AFB, Tex.
Length: 12 weeks.
Objectives: To train airmen in the fundamental subjects common to selected ballistic missile career fields.
Instruction: AC-DC fundamentals; missile inspection and maintenance systems; use and care of tools and meters; analysis of missile electrical circuits; pneudraulic systems; motors and generators; air-conditioners and air compressors.
Credit recommendation, collegiate level: Credit in electricity and electrical laboratory on the basis of demonstrated skills and/or institutional examinations.

GAM-83 Pilot Ground Trainer Operator/ Maintenance

Location: Chanute AFB, Ill.
Length: 4 weeks.
Objectives: To train airmen to repair and maintain the GAM-83 pilot ground trainer.
Instruction: Installation; theory and operation of computer and recorder systems; testing, troubleshooting, and repair; visual system; operational procedures; inspection and preventive maintenance.
Credit recommendation, collegiate level: Credit in electrical laboratory on the basis of demonstrated skills and/or institutional examinations.

GAR-3A/4A F&O Maintenance Technician

Location: Lowry AFB, Colo.
Length: 12 weeks.
Objectives: To train airmen as maintenance technicians on the GAR-3A/4A missile systems.
Instruction: GAR-3A/4A missile system; checkout console functions; antenna and AFC functions; range tracking functions; control and power functions; console power function; WSEM system.
Credit recommendation, collegiate level: This course is technical and vocational in nature. Credit in electrical shop on the basis of demonstrated skills and/or institutional examinations.

G. C. A. Radar Officer

Location: Keesler AFB, Miss.
Length: 12 weeks.
Objectives: To provide generalized training for officers on ground electronics equipment and in the management of ground electronics activities.
Instruction: Introduction to ground electronic equipment; transmit-receiver system; indicating system; administration; applied management; supply procedures.
Credit recommendation, collegiate level: 2 semester hours in maintenance management, and credit in electrical laboratory on the basis of demonstrated skills and/or institutional examinations.

General Accounting Specialist

Location: Sheppard AFB, Tex.
Length: 12 weeks.
Objectives: To train airmen in accounting principles.
Instruction: Introduction to accounting; appropriation accounting; Air Force general ledger and expense systems; materiel and commercial services; stock funds; mechanized procedures.
Credit recommendation, collegiate level: 3 semester hours in elementary accounting.

General Maintenance Mechanic
(Building Maintenance Mechanic)

Location: Sheppard AFB, Tex.
Length: 6 weeks.
Objectives: To train airmen in the maintenance of repair of Air Force buildings.

Instruction: Building maintenance, including hand and power tools, painting, plumbing, and concrete and masonry repair; electrical maintenance, including fundamentals of electricity, wiring diagrams, and building electrical circuits and units; major and small appliance repair.

Credit recommendation, collegiate level: This course is technical and vocational in nature. Credit in electrical and mechanical shop on the basis of demonstrated skills and/or institutional examinations.

General Safety Specialist
(Ground Safety Specialist)

Location: Chanute AFB, Ill.

Length: 8–10 weeks.

Objectives: To train airmen to conduct safety programs; survey areas and activities for accident hazards; analyze accident statistical data; and provide safety supervision during hazardous operations.

Instruction: Human factors and safety education; physical and chemical safety; industrial hygiene and industrial safety; motor vehicle and traffic safety; off-duty safety.

Credit recommendation, collegiate level: 3 semester hours in industrial safety.

1. Ground Communications Equipment Repairman (Heavy)
2. Ground Communications Equipment Repairman (Heavy) Receivers
3. Ground Communications Equipment Repairman (Heavy) Receivers
4. Ground Communications Equipment Repairman (Heavy) Transmitters
5. Ground Communications Equipment Repairman (Heavy) Transmitters

Locations: Keesler AFB, Miss.; Scott AFB, Ill.

Length: *Course 1,* 32–34 weeks; *Course 2,* 28 weeks; *Course 3,* 15 weeks; *Course 4,* 32 weeks; *Course 5,* 18–22 weeks.

Objectives: To train airmen to install, maintain, and repair selected ground radio equipment.

Instruction: *Course 1:* Direct current; alternating current; reactive circuits; vacuum tubes and transistors; special purpose tubes; amplifiers and oscillators; motors and servomechanisms. *Courses 2 and 4:* Direct and alternating current; electric tubes and power supplies; amplifiers and oscillators; special circuits. *Course 3:* Ground radio receiving communications and equipment. *Course 5:* Ground radio transmitting equipment.

Credit recommendation, collegiate level: CAUTION: *Courses in ground communications equipment repair vary in credit recommendation. Require complete identification by title and length. Note that titles vary only by name of equipment following title in the parentheses. Course 1:* 4 semester hours at the freshman or sophomore level as an elective in electricity and electronics, and credit in electrical laboratory on the basis of demonstrated skills and/or institutional examinations. *Courses 2 and 4:* For each course, 3 semester hours at the freshman or sophomore level as an elective in electricity and electronics, and credit in electrical laboratory on the basis of demonstrated skills and/or institutional examination. *Courses 3 and 5:* For each course, credit in electricity and electrical laboratory on the basis of demonstrated skills and/or institutional examinations.

Ground Communications Equipment Repairman (Light)

Location: Keesler AFB, Miss.

Length: 32–38 weeks.

Objectives: To train airmen to operate, adjust, maintain, and repair selected ground radio communications equipment.

Instruction: Direct current; alternating current; reactive circuits; vacuum tubes and transistors; amplifiers and oscillators; reactive circuits.

Credit recommendation, collegiate level: CAUTION: *Courses in ground communications equipment repair vary in credit recommendation. Require complete identification by title and length. Note that titles vary only by name of equipment following title in the parentheses.* 4 semester hours at the freshman or sophomore level as an elective in electronics, and credit in electrical laboratory on the basis of demonstrated skills and/or institutional examinations.

1. Ground Communications Equipment Repairman (VHF-UHF)
2. Ground Communications Equipment Repairman (HF)

Locations: Keesler AFB, Miss.; Scott AFB, Ill.

Length: 20–27 weeks.

Objectives: To train airmen to install, maintain, and repair low-powered ground radio equipment.

Instruction: Ground communications equipment; ground radio transmitting and receiving equipment; point-to-point and mobile communications systems.

Credit recommendation, collegiate level: CAUTION: *Courses in ground communications equipment repairman vary in credit recommendation. Require complete identification by title and length. Note that titles vary only by name of equipment following title in the parentheses.* Credit in electronics and electrical laboratory on the basis of demonstrated skills and/or institutional examinations.

Ground Communications Equipment Technician (TDDL)
(Ground Communications Equipment Technician (Light) (TDDL Equipment))

Location: Keesler AFB, Miss.

Length: 10 weeks.

Objectives: To train airmen in the theory, operation, and maintenance of the AN/GKA(V) flight control group and AN/FRT-49 amplifier.

Instruction: Fundamentals of TDDL, simulator and multiplexers; central monitor and systems maintenance, AN/FRT-49.

Credit recommendation, collegiate level: Credit in electricity and electrical laboratory on the basis of demonstrated skills and/or institutional examinations.

Ground ECM Specialist

Location: Keesler AFB, Miss.

Length: 29–33 weeks.

Objectives: To train airmen in the maintenance and repair of ground electronic countermeasures equipment.

Instruction: DC and AC electricity; electron tubes and power supplies; amplifiers and oscillators; special circuits; radar microwave propagation; special equipment training.

Credit recommendation, collegiate level: 6 semester hours at the freshman or sophomore level as an elective in electricity and electronics, and credit in electrical laboratory on the basis of demonstrated skills and/or institutional examinations.

1. Ground Electronics Officer (ECCM)
2. Ground Electronics Officer (Ground Electronics Officer (Electronics))
3. Ground Electronics Officer

Location: Keesler AFB, Miss.

Length: *Course 1,* 45 weeks; *Course 2,* 43–51 weeks; *Course 3,* 20 weeks.

Objectives: To train officers to supervise units responsible for the maintenance of ground radar equipment.

Instruction: *Courses 1 and 2:* The first phase comprises electronics training, including direct and alternating current, electron tubes and power supplies, amplifiers and oscillators, transmitters and receivers, special circuits and computer principles, and microwave techniques. The second phase of *Courses 1 and 2* applies the electronics training to special electronic ground equipment and provides officers with communications electronics organization and administration training. *Course 3* is similar to the second phase of the first two courses, dealing only with special equipment and providing officer management training.

Credit recommendation, collegiate level: CAUTION: *These courses vary in length and recommendation. Require exact identification of course by full title and length. Courses 1 and 2:* For each course, 6 semester hours as an elective in electricity and electronics, 2 semester hours in shop management, and credit in electrical laboratory on the basis of demonstrated skills and/or institutional examinations. *Course 3:* 2 semester hours in shop management, and credit in electrical laboratory on the basis of demonstrated skills and/or institutional examinations.

Ground Equipment Maintenance Officer

Locations: Chanute AFB, Ill.; Francis E. Warren AFB, Wyo.

Length: 9–10 weeks.

Objectives: To familiarize officers with the technical maintenance of motorized ground equipment and vehicle components.

Instruction: Air Force maintenance policies; ground equipment and components; manpower management; maintenance shop organization, operation, and supply; personnel management and training programs; supervision, inspection, and production control operations.

Credit recommendation, collegiate level: 4 semester hours in shop management.

1. Ground Radio Communication Equipment Repairman (WS-133A/B)
2. Ground Radio Communication Equipment Repairman (WS-133B)
3. Ground Radio Communication Equipment Repairman (WS-133A/A-M) (Ground Radio Communication Equipment Repairman, WS-133A)
4. Ground Radio Communications Technician (KWT-655B)

Locations: Chanute AFB, Ill.; Keesler AFB, Miss.

Length: *Course 1,* 31 weeks; *Courses 2, 3, and 4,* 5–8 weeks.

Objectives: To train airmen to operate, install, inspect, and repair ground radio communications equipment.

Instruction: *Course 1:* Principles of DC and AC; reactive circuits; vacuum tubes and transistors; special purpose tubes; amplifiers and oscillators; special circuits; motors and servomechanisms; multivibrators and sweep circuits; microwave principles. *Courses 2 and 3:* Weapon system familiarization; launch facility security system; UHF command radio system; MF radio subsystem or voice reporting system. *Course 4:* KWT-6 principles and application; KWT-6 systems adjustment.

Credit recommendation, collegiate level: CAUTION: *Courses in ground communications equipment repair vary in credit recommendation. Require complete identification by title and length. Note that titles vary only by name of equipment following title in the parentheses. Course 1:* 6 semester hours at the freshman or sophomore level as an elective in electronics, and credit in electrical laboratory on the basis of demonstrated skills and/or institutional examinations. *Courses 2, 3, and 4:* These courses are technical and vocational in nature. Credit in radio repair on the basis of demonstrated skills and/or institutional examinations.

1. Ground Radio Communications Equipment Repairman
2. Ground Radio Communications Equipment Repairman

Location: Keesler AFB, Miss.

Length: *Course 1,* 37–40 weeks; *Course 2,* 25 weeks.

Objectives: To train airmen to operate, install, inspect, maintain, and repair ground radio communications equipment.

Instruction: *Course 1:* DC and AC circuits; reactive circuits; vacuum tubes; transistors; tubes and solid state devices. *Courses 1 and 2:* Amplifiers and oscillators; detection and discrimination; motors and servomechanisms; multivibrators; sweep circuits; microwave principles.

Credit recommendation, collegiate level: *Course 1:* 6 semester hours at the freshman or sophomore level as an elective in electricity and electronics, and credit in electrical laboratory on the basis of demonstrated skills and/or institutional examinations. *Course 2:* 3 semester hours at the freshman or sophomore level as an elective in electricity and electronics, and credit in electrical laboratory on the basis of demonstrated skills and/or institutional examinations.

Ground Radio Communications Equipment
Repairman, CIM-10B
Ground Communications Equipment Repairman,
CIM-10B)
Ground Communication Equipment Repairman
(Light), CIM-10B)
Ground Communication Equipment Repairman
(Light), IM-99B)

Location: Chanute AFB, Ill.
Length: 13–18 weeks.
Objectives: To train airmen to maintain and repair the weapon system ground communication equipment indicated in title.
Instruction: Prelaunch acquisition system translator group; video prelaunch command distribution system; status simulators; status multiplexers; selector and comparators.
Credit recommendation, collegiate level: CAUTION: *Courses in ground communications equipment repair vary in credit recommendation. Require complete identification by title and length. Note that titles vary only by name of equipment following title in the parentheses.* Credit in electronics and electrical laboratory on the basis of demonstrated skills and/or institutional examinations.

Ground Radio Communications Equipment
Repairman (Long Haul Communications
G/A and P/P)
(Ground Communications Repairman (Heavy)
(SSB))

Location: Keesler AFB, Miss.
Length: 5 weeks.
Objectives: To train airmen to be ground radio communications equipment repairmen.
Instruction: Familiarization and analysis of SSB system; transmitter and receiver site equipment operation and troubleshooting.
Credit recommendation, collegiate level: CAUTION: *Courses in ground communications equipment repair vary in credit recommendation. Require complete identification by title and length. Note that titles vary only by name of equipment following title in the parentheses.* These courses are technical and vocational in nature. Credit in radio repair on the basis of demonstrated skills and/or institutional examinations.

Ground Radio Communications Equipment
Repairman (SLFCS)

Location: Keesler AFB, Miss.
Length: 4 weeks.
Objectives: To train airmen to perform field and organizational maintenance of ground communications equipment.
Instruction: 487-L receiving system; operation, installation, testing, and troubleshooting on the demodulator data converter, receiver group, page printer, modulator, and associated test equipment.
Credit recommendation, collegiate level: This course is technical and vocational in nature. Credit in electrical shop on the basis of demonstrated skills and/or institutional examinations.

1. Ground Radio Communications Equipment
Technician
2. Ground Communications Equipment Technician
(Light)
(Ground Communications Equipment
Maintenance Technician (Light))
3. Ground Communications Equipment
Maintenance Technician (Heavy)

Location: Keesler AFB, Miss.
Length: 31–42 weeks.
Objectives: To train airmen to operate, maintain, and install ground radio communication and associated equipment.
Instruction: *Course 1:* Applied mathematics; DC and AC circuits; vacuum tubes and solid state devices; power supplies and oscillators; electronic digital data processing; transmitter circuits and RF systems; receiver system circuits; indicator circuits; servo systems. *Course 2:* Electronic principles; maintenance principles; communications transmitters and receivers. *Course 3:* Electrical concepts; receivers and transmitters; single side band.
Credit recommendation, collegiate level: CAUTION: *Courses in ground radio equipment repair vary in credit recommendation. Require complete identification by title and length. Note that titles vary only by name of equipment following title in the parentheses. Course 1:* 2 semester hours in shop management, 4 semester hours at the freshman or sophomore level in electricity and electronics, and credit in electrical or radio laboratory on the basis of demonstrated skills and/or institutional examinations. *Courses 2 and 3:* For each course, 2 semester hours in shop management, 2 semester hours at the freshman or sophomore level as an elective in electricity and electronics, and credit in electrical or radio laboratory on the basis of demonstrated skills and/or institutional examinations.

Ground Radio Maintenance Technician Fixed
Stations, Communications Systems

Location: Scott AFB, Ill.
Length: 19 weeks.
Objectives: To train airmen in advanced installation, maintenance, and repair of ground radio equipment.
Instruction: Administrative maintenance practices; test equipment; advanced radio equipment maintenance techniques; multiplex and associated equipment; single side band equipment and associated power amplifier; radio relay system.
Credit recommendation, collegiate level: Credit in electrical laboratory on the basis of demonstrated skills and/or institutional examinations.

1. Ground Radio Maintenance Technician,
Navigational Aids, Communications
Systems
2. Ground Radio Maintenance Technician

Location: Scott AFB, Ill.
Length: 19 weeks.
Objectives: To train airmen to maintain and repair ground communications equipment.
Instruction: Administrative maintenance practices; electronic test equipment; UHF communications

equipment; transmission lines and antennas; radio direction finding systems.

Credit recommendation, collegiate level: Credit in electrical laboratory on the basis of demonstrated skills and/or institutional examinations.

1. Ground Radio Officer
2. Ground Radio Officer

Location: Scott AFB, Ill.

Length: *Course 1,* 13 weeks; *Course 2,* 19 weeks.

Objectives: To train officer graduates of the USAF ROTC program, who will command or manage Air Force activities, in the installation, maintenance, and management of ground radio communications equipment and systems.

Instruction: *Courses 1 and 2:* Organization and management; radio communications equipment; communications. In addition *Course 2* includes batteries and meters; motors and generators; transformers; rectifiers; diode and triode tubes; amplifiers and oscillators; converters and mixers; transmitters.

Credit recommendation, collegiate level: CAUTION: *These courses vary slightly in title, length, and recommendation. Require exact identification by title and length. Course 1:* Credit in electrical laboratory on the basis of demonstrated skills and/or institutional examinations. *Course 2:* 2 semester hours at freshman or sophomore level as an elective in electricity, and credit in electrical laboratory on the basis of demonstrated skills and/or institutional examinations.

1. Ground Radio Operator
2. Airborne Radio Operator

Location: Keesler AFB, Miss.

Length: 15–19 weeks.

Objectives: To train airmen in the operation and tuning of radio receivers and transmitters, and in international Morse code and communication procedures.

Instruction: *Courses 1 and 2:* International Morse code; radio fundamentals; ground or airborne radio equipment; radiotelegraph procedure; simulated ground or flight communications. In addition *Course 1* includes typewriting.

Credit recommendation, collegiate level: *Course 1:* Credit in typing on the basis of institutional examination. At the technical level, credit in radio operation on the basis of demonstrated skills and/or institutional examinations. *Course 2:* This course is technical and vocational in nature. Credit in radio operation on the basis of demonstrated skills and/or institutional examinations.

1. Ground Support Air Conditioner (B-58)
2. MA-1 and MA-3 Air Conditioners, F&O Maintenance

Location: Chanute AFB, Ill.

Length: 3 weeks.

Objectives: To train maintenance and/or instructor personnel in the field and organizational maintenance of the air conditioning equipment specified.

Instruction: Basic refrigeration principles; refrigeration system and cycle; air conditioner and drive system; air flow, heating, and electrical systems; preventive maintenance, operation, and troubleshooting.

Credit recommendation, collegiate level: These courses are technical and vocational in nature. Credit in air conditioning equipment repair on the basis of demonstrated skills and/or institutional examinations.

Ground Weather Equipment Operator

Location: Chanute AFB, Ill.

Length: 19 weeks.

Objectives: To train airmen to use electronic and non-electronic weather recording equipment and to process, interpret, and encode the weather data obtained.

Instruction: Elementary meteorology and weather observations; weather equipment; rawinsonde evaluation; equipment laboratory.

Credit recommendation, collegiate level: 3 semester hours in meteorology.

Ground Weather Observing Procedures

Location: Chanute AFB, Ill.

Length: 8 weeks.

Objectives: To provide supplemental training for weather observers in observing, recording, and encoding weather phenomena, and plotting weather maps and charts.

Instruction: Surface weather observations and equipment; plotting weather maps and charts; weather station operation.

Credit recommendation, collegiate level: 2 semester hours in meteorology.

Guidance and Control Officer (RIGS) (HGM-25A)
(Guidance and Control Officer (RIGS) (SM-68A))
(Guidance Control Officer (RIGS) (SM-68))

Location: Sheppard AFB, Tex.

Length: 15 weeks.

Objectives: To train officers in the operation, maintenance, and applicable logistics of the missile ground-guidance system specified.

Instruction: Missile system familiarization; ground-guidance radar data flow and operation; ground-guidance operational procedures; ground-guidance console and unit check procedures; ground-guidance simplified maintenance; missile guidance set and guided missile test set data flow, operation, and maintenance; computer fundamentals; central computer and simulator-verifier; computer input-output, peripheral equipment, and aerospace ground equipment.

Credit recommendation, collegiate level: 2 semester hours in computer principles in the field of data processing.

Guidance Control Officer (Computer) (SM-68)

Location: Sheppard AFB, Tex.

Length: 7 weeks.

Objectives: To train officers, from related career fields, in the operation and maintenance of the WS-107A-2 Guidance Computer.

Instruction: Orientation; functional description; operating and maintenance procedures.

Credit recommendation, collegiate level: Credit in electrical laboratory on the basis of demonstrated skills and/or institutional examinations.

Guidance Control Officer (SM-65)

Location: Keesler AFB, Miss.

Length: 17 weeks.

Objectives: To provide officers with a detailed knowledge of the AN/URW-12 guidance system.

Instruction: Guidance system and special circuits; AN/GSQ-33 computer and associated equipment; transmitter and receiver group; antenna system; rate data and checkout equipment; track data and checkout equipment.

Credit recommendation, collegiate level: Credit in electrical laboratory on the basis of demonstrated skills and/or institutional examinations.

Guidance System Technician (SM-68)

Location: Sheppard AFB, Tex.

Length: 32 weeks.

Objectives: To train airmen in the maintenance and repair of the WS 107A-2 guidance subsystem, with the exception of the computer.

Instruction: Ground-guidance radar data flow and operation; ground-guidance operational procedures; console and unit check procedures; missile guidance set and guided missile test set periodic inspections.

Credit recommendation, collegiate level: This course is technical and vocational in nature. Credit in mechanical shop on the basis of demonstrated skills and/or institutional examinations.

1. Guidance Systems Analyst (TM-76A)
2. Guidance Systems Analyst (TM-76A)
3. Guidance Systems Analyst (GAM-63 Missile D/A)
4. Guidance Systems Analyst (SM-62)

Locations: Amarillo AFB, Tex.; Lowry AFB, Colo.

Length: *Course 1,* 25 weeks; *Courses 2 and 3,* 19–24 weeks; *Course 4,* 19 weeks.

Objectives: To train airmen in the operation and maintenance of the guidance system indicated in title.

Instruction: *Course 1:* Principles of DC and AC; electronic fundamentals. *Courses 2 and 3:* Basic electricity; basic electronics. *Course 4:* Familiarization and analysis of SM-62.

Credit recommendation, collegiate level: CAUTION: *These courses vary slightly in title, length, and recommendation. Require exact identification by title and length. Course 1:* 2 semester hours at the freshman or sophomore level as an elective in electricity and electronics, and credit in electrical laboratory on the basis of demonstrated skills and/or institutional examina-

tions. *Courses 2 and 3:* For each course, credit in electricity and electrical laboratory on the basis of demonstrated skills and/or institutional examinations. *Course 4:* Credit in electrical laboratory on the basis of demonstrated skills and/or institutional examinations.

1. Guidance Systems Mechanic (Ballistic Missile Inertial)
2. Guidance Systems Mechanic (TM-61)
3. Guidance Systems Mechanic (TM-61C)
4. Guidance Systems Mechanic (SM-65, 68)
5. Guidance Systems Mechanic

Locations: Lowry AFB, Colo.; Sheppard AFB, Tex.

Length: 16–26 weeks.

Objectives: To train airmen to install, operate, maintain, and inspect the guided missile guidance system and associated test equipment indicated in title.

Instruction: Fundamentals of electricity; alternating currents; vacuum tubes; guidance and control circuits; amplifiers and oscillators.

Credit recommendation, collegiate level: CAUTION: *Guidance systems mechanics courses vary slightly in title, length, and recommendation. Require exact identification by title and length.* 3 semester hours at the freshman or sophomore level as an elective in electricity and electronics, and credit in electrical laboratory on the basis of demonstrated skills and/or institutional examinations.

Guidance Systems Mechanic/Technician, GAM-77

Location: Chanute AFB, Ill.

Length: 18 weeks.

Objectives: To train airmen maintenance personnel in the theory, operation, and maintenance of the GAM-77 guidance system and associated ground support equipment.

Instruction: GAM-77A fundamentals; guidance system; Verdan computer; maintenance; circuit analysis; alignment and calibration.

Credit recommendation, collegiate level: Credit in electrical laboratory on the basis of demonstrated skills and/or institutional examinations.

Guidance Systems Officer (Surface-to-Surface) (TM-61C)
(Guidance Systems Officer)
(Pilotless Aircraft Guidance and Control Officer)

Location: Lowry AFB, Colo.

Length: 26–32 weeks.

Objectives: To train officers in the operation, maintenance, and inspection of the guidance and control systems of specific pilotless aircraft.

Instruction: Fundamentals of electricity; alternating current; vacuum and gas-filled tubes; amplifiers and oscillators; principles of receiving and transmission; superheterodyne receiver and sweep circuits.

Credit recommendation, collegiate level: 3 semester hours at the freshman or sophomore level as an elective in radio and electronics, and credit in electrical laboratory on the basis of demonstrated skills and/or institutional examinations.

Guided Missile Operations Staff Officer, IM-99

Location: Chanute AFB, Ill.

Length: 4 weeks.

Objectives: To train officers in all areas of the Bomarc weapon system and the relationship of SAGE in the tactical employment of the weapon system.

Instruction: Semiautomatic ground environment familiarization; IM-99A and IM-99B weapon system.

Credit recommendation, collegiate level: No credit as the course is military in nature.

Gunnery Trainer Specialist
(Gunnery Trainer Specialist (APG-T1, T1A))
(Gunnery Trainer Specialist (AN/APG-T1, T1A))

Locations: Lowry AFB, Colo.; Chanute AFB, Ill.

Length: 25–34 weeks.

Objectives: To train airmen to install, operate, maintain, and repair gunnery trainers and associated electronic test equipment.

Instruction: Fundamentals of DC and AC; vacuum and gas-filled tubes; power supplies and voltage regulators; amplifiers, oscillators, and sweep generators.

Credit recommendation, collegiate level: 3 semester hours at the freshman or sophomore level as an elective in electricity and electronics, and credit in electrical laboratory on the basis of demonstrated skills and/or institutional examinations.

1. Hamilton Standard Propeller, C-119 Installation
2. Field and Organizational Maintenance A6341FN-D1 Propeller
3. Field and Organizational Maintenance of 34G60 Propeller

Locations: Chanute AFB, Ill.; Sheppard AFB, Tex.

Length: 3–4 weeks.

Objectives: To train aircraft propeller repairmen to maintain and repair the propeller and system specified in the title.

Instruction: Theory of propeller and systems operation; propeller removal, installation, inspection, maintenance, and balancing; trouble analysis; adjustment.

Credit recommendation, collegiate level: These courses are technical and vocational in nature. Credit in aircraft propeller maintenance on the basis of demonstrated skills and/or institutional examinations.

Heating Plant Management and Supervision

Location: Sheppard AFB, Tex.

Length: 4 weeks.

Objectives: To train heating specialists in the principles of heating plant supervision.

Instruction: Air Force publications; systems supervision and management; fuels, combustion principles, and operational efficiency; water treatment; corrosion control.

Credit recommendation, collegiate level: No credit because of the brevity and limited vocational nature of the course.

Heating Specialist

Location: Francis E. Warren AFB, Wyo.

Length: 11 weeks.

Objectives: To train airmen in the operation and maintenance of heating equipment.

Instruction: Operation and maintenance of warm air, hot water, and steam heating systems, including lubrication of moving parts, inspection and cleaning of burners, and valve adjustment.

Credit recommendation, collegiate level: No credit because of the limited vocational nature of the course.

1. Helicopter Instructor Training (H-43B)
2. Helicopter Pilot Instructor Training (H-19/H-21)

Location: Stead AFB, Nev.

Length: *Course 1,* 7 weeks; *Course 2,* 5 weeks. *Note—* since flying training is dependent upon weather and other factors, the length of the courses may vary.

Objectives: To qualify rated helicopter pilots to instruct helicopter pilot trainees.

Instruction: Transition, instrument and operational training instruction techniques comprise the flying training phase. The academic phase includes fundamentals of instruction, psychology of learning, methods of instruction, lesson planning, evaluation, practice teaching, and helicopter engineering and operations.

Credit recommendation, collegiate level: For each course, credit in instructional methods on the basis of institutional examination.

Helicopter Maintenance Officer

Location: Sheppard AFB, Tex.

Length: 3 weeks.

Objectives: To train officers in the theory and practice of helicopter maintenance.

Instruction: Construction features and general service requirements of single and dual rotor-type helicopters; history of helicopter development; and aircraft inspection system.

Credit recommendation, collegiate level: No credit because of the brevity and limited technical nature of the course.

1. Helicopter Mechanic (Aircraft Mechanic, Rotary Wing)
2. Helicopter Mechanic, CH-3C
3. Helicopter Mechanic, HH-43B (Helicopter Mechanic, H-43B)
4. Helicopter Mechanic, UH-1F

Locations: Gary AFB, Tex.; Sheppard AFB, Tex.

Length: *Course 1,* 15–19 weeks; *Courses 2 and 3,* 6 weeks; *Course 4,* 4 weeks.

Objectives: *Course 1:* To train airmen in the fundamentals of mechanics with emphasis on the maintenance and inspection of helicopter aircraft. *Courses 2, 3, and 4:* To provide mechanics with supplemental training on the helicopters specified in the title.

Instruction: *Course 1:* Fundamentals for helicopter mechanics; fuel, electrical, instrument, and hydraulic systems; inspection and maintenance of engine, transmission, rotor, and flight control systems. *Courses 2, 3,* *and 4:* Identification, location, and function of helicopter systems and components; partial disassembly and inspection of engine; replacement of accessories; troubleshooting; engine change and buildup; preparation of engines for storage.

Credit recommendation, collegiate level: *These courses are technical and vocational in nature.* Credit in helicopter repair shop on the basis of demonstrated skills and/or institutional examinations.

Identification/Air Tactics (SAGE)

Location: Keesler AFB, Miss.
Length: 8 weeks.
Objectives: To train officers and airmen as identification or air tactics technicians for SAGE direction centers.
Instruction: SAGE system fundamentals, identification, and air tactics branch operation; air surveillance branch and weapons branch familiarization.
Credit recommendation, collegiate level: No credit because of the limited technical nature of the course.

Industrial Photo Interpretation and Bomb Damage Assessment

Location: Sheppard AFB, Tex.
Length: 6 weeks.
Objectives: To train airmen in the interpretation of surface transportation and industrial installations and in the assessment of non-nuclear bomb damage from aerial photography.
Instruction: Surface transportation; basic industries; end products industries; bomb damage assessment.
Credit recommendation, collegiate level: Credit in photographic interpretation on the basis of institutional examination.

1. **Inflight Refueling Systems Repairman (Inflight Refueling Specialist)**
2. **Inflight Refueling Specialist**
3. **KC-135 Inflight Refueling Specialist**
4. **AF/S32R-2 Refueler, F&O Maintenance**

Locations: Chanute AFB, Ill.; Sheppard AFB, Tex.
Length: *Courses 1 and 2,* 8–12 weeks; *Course 3,* 4 weeks; *Course 4,* 3 weeks.
Objectives: *Courses 1 and 2:* To train airmen in the operation, assembly, and repair of the probe-drogue and/or boom-type refueling systems and controls. *Course 3:* To train maintenance and instructor personnel on the KC-135 aircraft inflight refueling system. *Course 4:* To train airmen on the AF/S32-R-2 refueler.
Instruction: *Courses 1 and 2:* Fundamentals; inflight refueling general maintenance; aerial refueling systems operation and repair. *Course 3:* Aerial refueling systems; maintenance and inspection. *Course 4:* Field and organizational maintenance of the AF/S32R-2 refueler.
Credit recommendation, collegiate level: These courses are technical and vocational in nature. Credit in electrical and mechanical shop on the basis of demonstrated skills and/or institutional examinations.

1. **Inside Plant, Installation**
2. **Outside Plant, Installation**

Location: Sheppard AFB, Tex.
Length: *Course 1,* 4–6 weeks; *Course 2,* 10 weeks.
Objectives: *Course 1:* To train airmen and civilians to install inside plant equipment. *Course 2:* To train airmen in antenna fundamentals and construction.
Instruction: *Course 1:* Use of symbols and technical orders; installation, support, and maintenance of cables; wiring and connections; dismantling and recovery. *Course 2:* Cable and antenna fundamentals; installation of rhombic, delta, and discone antennas; antenna construction.
Credit recommendation, collegiate level: These courses are technical and vocational in nature. Credit in cable and antenna installation on the basis of demonstrated skills and/or institutional examinations.

Instructional Programmer

Location: Lackland AFB, Tex.
Length: 5 weeks.
Objectives: To train airmen in the techniques and application of instructional systems programming.
Instruction: Covert and overt behavior; instructional program writing; stimulus-response inventory and teaching points; terminal frames; diagnostic examinations; use of panels and media; chaining theory of learning; developmental testing; adjunct method of programming; editing; instructional systems concept.
Credit recommendation, collegiate level: 2 semester hours in instructional programming in the field of teacher education.

Instructor Interceptor, Jet (F-86D/L)

Location: Perrin AFB, Tex.
Length: 20 weeks. *Note—*since flying training is dependent upon weather and other factors, the actual length of the course may vary.
Objectives: To qualify jet pilots as instructors and to qualify supervisors who are required to fly primary mission aircraft as *alert-ready* in the F-86D/L.
Instruction: The course concentrates on flight training, including navigation, weather, instruments, synthetic trainer, F-86D engineering, airborne interception, conversion techniques, applied tactics, and flight simulator training.
Credit recommendation, collegiate level: No credit as the course is military in nature.

Instructor Management Training

Location: Greenville AFB, Miss.
Length: 4 weeks.
Objectives: To train management airmen to instruct courses in management at their respective bases.
Instruction: Methods and techniques of instruction, including speech, training aids, interviewing and counseling, course organization, evaluation and measurement, and a conference laboratory. The remainder of the course is devoted to practice and graded management conferences.
Credit recommendation, collegiate level: Credit in

instructional methods on the basis of institutional examination.

1. Instrument Pilot Instructor Training (T-39/T-38)
   (Instrument Pilot Instructor Training (T-38/T-39))
   (Instrument Pilot Instructor Training (T-39))
   (Instrument Pilot Instructor Training (T-38))
2. Instrument Pilot Instructor Training (T-33)
   (USAF Instrument Pilot Instructor Training (Jet))
   (USAF Instrument Pilot Instructor School (Jet))
3. Instrument Pilot Instructor Training (T-29)
   (USAF Instrument Pilot Instructor Training (Reciprocating))
   (USAF Instrument Pilot Instructor School (Reciprocating Engine))

Locations: James Connally AFB, Tex.; Moody AFB, Ga.; Randolph AFB, Tex.

Length: *Course 1, 6–8 weeks; Courses 2–3, 8–10 weeks. Note*—since flying training is dependent upon weather and other factors the length of the courses may vary.

Objectives: To train rated pilots as instrument flight instructors on aircraft indicated in the course titles.

Instruction: The courses consist of two phases—the first is flying training, which develops instrument proficiency and instrument instruction techniques—the second is academic training, which includes fundamentals of instruction, practice teaching, flight instruments and navigational aids, regulations and publications, computer and flight planning, and weather.

Credit recommendation, collegiate level: For each course, credit in instructional methods on the basis of institutional examination.

1. Instrument Pilot Training (C-47)
2. Instrument Pilot (Jet)

Locations: Keesler AFB, Miss.; Moody AFB, Ga.; Perrin AFB, Tex.; Randolph AFB, Tex.; Tyndall AFB, Fla.

Length: 6 weeks.

Objectives: To qualify pilots to operate C-47 aircraft or jet aircraft under instrument conditions.

Instruction: Flying training; instruments and instrument procedures; navigation aids; weather.

Credit recommendation, collegiate level: No credit because of the specialized nature of this course.

1. Instrument Repairman
2. Instrument Repair Technician

Location: Chanute AFB, Ill.

Length: *Course 1, 17–19 weeks; Course 2, 11–16 weeks.*

Objectives: *Course 1:* To train airmen to maintain and repair instruments and instrument systems necessary for the operation and navigation of aircraft. *Course 2:* To provide qualified instrument repairmen with advanced training.

Instruction: *Course 1:* Electrical and maintenance fundamentals; instrument repair techniques; engine, flight, and navigation instruments. *Course 2* provides advanced training in electrical and instrument mainte-

nance, and administration and management techniques.

Credit recommendation, collegiate level: For each course, credit in electricity and electrical laboratory on the basis of demonstrated skills and/or institutional examinations.

Instrument Trainer Instructor-Operator

Location: Chanute AFB, Ill.

Length: 8–10 weeks.

Objectives: To train Strategic Air Command airmen to operate instrument trainers.

Instruction: Basic instrument flying procedures; low- and medium-frequency radio range procedures; advanced instrument flying procedures; instrument landing procedures and practice.

Credit recommendation, collegiate level: Credit in instrument navigation on the basis of institutional examination.

1. Instrument Trainer Specialist
2. Instrument Trainer Specialist (C-11)
   (Electronic Instrument Trainer Specialist)
   (Electronic Instrument Trainer Specialist (C-11 Type))
3. Instrument Trainer Specialist (P)
   (Instrument Trainer Specialist (P&Z))
   (Electronic Instrument Trainer Specialist (P&Z))
   (Electronic Instrument Trainer Specialist (Z&P Types))

Location: Chanute AFB, Ill.

Length: *Course 1, 37 weeks; Course 2, 31–34 weeks; Course 3, 27–30 weeks.*

Objectives: To train airmen to install, operate, maintain, and repair instrument trainer equipment.

Instruction: Electronic principles, including direct and alternating current, reactive circuits and use of the oscilloscope, vacuum tubes, transistors, and special purpose tubes, amplifiers, oscillators, motors and servomechanisms. The remainder of the courses consists of aerodynamics principles and instrument flying techniques, instrument trainer components and computing systems, flight and engine systems, instrument trainer operation, and radio aids systems.

Credit recommendation, collegiate level: For each course, 3 semester hours at the freshman or sophomore level as an elective in electricity and electronics, and credit in electrical laboratory on the basis of demonstrated skills and/or institutional examinations.

1. Instrumentation Mechanic
2. Instrumentation Mechanic

Location: Lowry AFB, Colo.

Length: *Course 1, 30–35 weeks; Course 2, 19 weeks.*

Objectives: To train airmen in the assembly, installation, and maintenance of mechanical, electrical, and electronic equipment used in measuring the performance of guided missile systems.

Instruction: *Course 1:* Electronic principles, including direct and alternating current, reactive circuits, principles of vacuum tubes and transistors, amplifiers and radar. The second phase of the course covers special equipment training in instrumentation fundamentals, airborne telemetry systems and components, telemetry receiving and recording, demultiplexing and graphic recording, visual instrumentation and maintenance procedures. *Course 2* comprises only the special equipment training phase.

Credit recommendation, collegiate level: CAUTION: *These courses vary in length and recommendation. Require exact identification of course by title and length. Course 1:* 3 semester hours at the freshman or sophomore level as an elective in electricity and electronics, and credit in electrical laboratory on the basis of demonstrated skills and/or institutional examinations. *Course 2:* Credit in electrical laboratory on the basis of demonstrated skills and/or institutional examinations.

Intelligence Area Studies (SEA)

Location: Lowry AFB, Colo.
Length: 4 weeks.
Objectives: To train officers in the physical and cultural patterns of Southeast Asia and in the application of multisensor reconnaissance to that environment.
Instruction: Area physical and cultural patterns, including characteristics of villages and urban centers, Communist insurgent activity, and psychological orientation; multisensor reconnaissance, including high resolution radar theory and interpretation, infrared theory and metrics, and panoramic metrics; mission planning.
Credit recommendation, collegiate level: Credit in photographic interpretation on the basis of institutional examination.

1. Intelligence Operations Technician
2. Intelligence Operations Technician

Location: Sheppard AFB, Tex.
Length: *Course 1,* 10 weeks; *Course 2,* 4 weeks.
Objectives: *Course 1:* To provide advanced training for airmen in intelligence techniques and photo interpretation methods. *Course 2:* To train Air National Guard and Air Force Reserve personnel in intelligence fundamentals and tactical employment.
Instruction: *Course 1:* Air Intelligence; charts and photo-radar; target development; weapons employment planning; foreign air defense capabilities; combat survival; combat mission planning and reporting. *Course 2:* Fundamentals of air intelligence and combat mission activities.
Credit recommendation, collegiate level: CAUTION: *These courses vary in length and recommendation. Require exact identification of course by title and length. Course 1:* 3 semester hours in intelligence methods. *Course 2:* No credit because of the brevity and specialized nature of the course.

Intercept Direction (SAGE)

Location: Keesler AFB, Miss.
Length: 6–8 weeks.
Objectives: To train officers as intercept directors and airmen as intercept director technicians at a semi-

automatic ground environmental system direction center.
Instruction: Positional training and battle-simulation positional training; weapons room familiarization; computer processing familiarization.
Credit recommendation, collegiate level: No credit because of the limited technical nature of the course.

Intercept Operator (Preparatory)
(Non-Morse Intercept Operator Preparatory)

Location: Keesler AFB, Miss.
Length: 13–14 weeks.
Objectives: This is a basic course designed to train airmen in international Morse code, typewriting, and intercept operating procedures.
Instruction: Touch typing; transcription of international Morse code; operation of radio receivers and associated equipment.
Credit recommendation, collegiate level: Credit in typing on the basis of institutional examination. At the vocational level, credit in radio operation on the basis of demonstrated skills and/or institutional examinations.

Interceptor Pilot Instructor Training (F-102)

Location: Perrin AFB, Tex.
Length: 8–10 weeks. *Note*—since flying training is dependent upon weather and other factors, the length of the course may vary.
Objectives: To qualify interceptor pilots as instructors for the interceptor phase of pilot training courses.
Instruction: Flying training includes simulator transition and familiarization; interceptor target and checkout; instrument continuation; simulator radar intercept training; radar intercept training; applied tactics; simulator console operation. The academic training phase covers survival and personal equipment; engineering; airborne interception; NORAD doctrine and weapons familiarization.
Credit recommendation, collegiate level: No credit because of the specialized nature of the course.

1. Inventory Management Specialist
2. Supply Records Specialist
3. Inventory Management Supervisor
(Supply Records Supervisor)

Locations: Amarillo AFB, Tex.; Francis E. Warren AFB, Wyo.
Length: *Courses 1 and 2,* 9–11 weeks; *Course 3,* 5–7 weeks.
Objectives: *Courses 1 and 2:* To train airmen in manual and mechanized procedures for property control in a base supply operation. *Course 3:* To provide advanced technical training for inventory management specialists which will enable them to supervise personnel and operations.
Instruction: *Courses 1 and 2:* Organization and supply publications; property accounting and stock control; requisitioning, receipt, and shipment; redistribution, adjustments, and document control; manual and mechanized inventory control procedures. *Note—Course*

2, prior to 1958, included typing instruction and dealt largely with preparation and maintenance of supply records, supply publications, and model supply training. *Course 3:* Logistics systems and publications research; personnel management; inventory management; supplies and equipment management.

Credit recommendation, collegiate level: CAUTION: *Course 2 varies in recommendation according to the year attended. Require exact identification by the title and year attended. Courses 1 and 2:* For each course, credit in property accounting on the basis of institutional examination; for *Course 2* prior to 1958, credit also in typing on the basis of institutional examination. *Course 3:* 3 semester hours in supply management.

1. J-57 Jet Engine (Without Afterburner) F&O
    Maintenance (B-52)
2. J-57 Jet Engine (W/O Afterburner) F&O
    Maintenance
    (J-57 Engine, Field and Organizational
    Maintenance (KC-35))
3. J-57 Jet Engine (W/O Afterburner)
    Organizational Maintenance
4. J-57 Jet Engine, Organizational Maintenance
    (KC-135)

Location: Chanute AFB, Ill.
Length: *Courses 1 and 2,* 5–6 weeks; *Courses 3 and 4,* 3 weeks.
Objectives: To train jet engine mechanics to perform field maintenance on the J-57 jet engine without afterburner.
Instruction: *Courses 1 and 2:* Engine inspection, disassembly, assembly, installation, operational checkout, and block test. *Courses 3 and 4:* Engine inspection, operational checkout, malfunction analysis, removal and installation.
Credit recommendation, collegiate level: These courses are technical and vocational in nature. Credit in jet engine repair shop on the basis of demonstrated skills and/or institutional examinations.

J57-P-23 Jet Engine Field Maintenance (F-102)
Location: Amarillo AFB, Tex.
Length: 4 weeks.
Objectives: To provide transition training for jet engine mechanics and technicians in the maintenance of the J57-P-23 engine.
Instruction: Engine familiarization; assembly and disassembly; inspection; test; storage.
Credit recommendation, collegiate level: This course is technical and vocational in nature. Credit in jet engine maintenance on the basis of demonstrated skills and/or institutional examinations.

1. J-79 Engine F&O Maintenance and Controls
    (B-58)
2. J-79 Engine, Organizational Maintenance (F-104)
3. J-79 Engine F&O Maintenance (F-104)
4. J-79 Engine, F&O Maintenance and Control
    System (F-104)
5. J-79 Engine, Organizational Maintenance and
    Control System, F-104

Location: Chanute AFB, Ill.
Length: 3–8 weeks.
Objectives: To train jet engine mechanics and technicians in the maintenance of the J-79 engine and systems as installed in the F-104 or B-58 aircraft.
Instruction: Engine and systems familiarization; engine operation, adjustment, removal, repair, and installation; engine control system and rigging procedure; engine troubleshooting and system adjustments.
Credit recommendation, collegiate level: These courses are technical and vocational in nature. Credit in jet engine repair shop on the basis of demonstrated skills and/or institutional examinations.

J79-15 Engine Systems and Engine Run-Up
Location: Chanute AFB, Ill.
Length: 3 weeks.
Objectives: To train jet engine mechanics to operate an M37-T6 engine test stand.
Instruction: Engine systems; M37-T6 test stand familiarization; engine installation and pre-start inspection; engine operation troubleshooting.
Credit recommendation, collegiate level: No credit because of the brevity and limited technical nature of the course.

JEFM J79-15 Engine
Location: Chanute AFB, Ill.
Length: 3 weeks.
Objectives: To train jet engine mechanics in J79-15 engine field maintenance.
Instruction: Disassembly and assembly of the engine; cleaning, inspection, and repair procedures; ground safety; field and organizational maintenance.
Credit recommendation, collegiate level: This course is technical and vocational in nature. Credit in jet engine repair shop on the basis of demonstrated skills and/or institutional examinations.

JOVIAL Programming
Location: Sheppard AFB, Tex.
Length: 4 weeks.
Objectives: To train officers and airmen in the techniques of JOVIAL programming.
Instruction: Coding conventions; types and uses of constants; assignment and exchange statements; decision-making and compound statements; modifiers, indexing, subscripts, subroutines, strings, and arrays as related to JOVIAL programming.
Credit recommendation, collegiate level: 2 semester hours in computing science: computer programming.

1. Jet Aircraft Mechanic
2. Aircraft Maintenance Specialist, Jet Aircraft One and Two Engines
   (Jet Aircraft Mechanic, One and Two Engines)
   (Aircraft Mechanic, Jet Fighter)
   (Aircraft Mechanic, Jet, One Engine)
3. Aircraft Mechanic (Jet Bomber, Two Engines)
   (Aircraft Mechanic (Jet, Two Engines))
4. Aircraft Mechanic (Jet, Over Two Engines)
   (Aircraft Mechanic, Jet Bomber, Over Two Engines)
5. Aircraft Maintenance Specialist, Turbo-Prop Aircraft
   (Aircraft Mechanic, Turbo-Prop Aircraft)
   (Aircraft Mechanic, Turbo-Prop Aircraft (C-130 and C-133))
   (Aircraft Mechanic, Jet Aircraft Over Two Engines)

Locations: Amarillo AFB, Tex.; Chanute AFB, Ill.; Sheppard AFB, Tex.

Length: 11–17 weeks.

Objectives: To train airmen in the fundamentals of aircraft mechanics with emphasis on the inspection and maintenance of the aircraft specified in the titles.

Instruction: Fundamentals for mechanics, including regulations, technical publications, tools and maintenance materials, aircraft and technical fundamentals; airframe and power plant; aircraft systems, including ground handling, electrical, instrument, utility, landing gear, hydraulic or pneudraulic, flight control, fuel, and engine systems; aircraft inspection and maintenance.

Credit recommendation, collegiate level: These courses are technical and vocational in nature. Credit in aircraft repair shop on the basis of demonstrated skills and/or institutional examinations.

1. Jet Engine Analyzer-IRD Maintenance
2. Jet Engine Analyzer-IRD Operator

Location: Chanute AFB, Ill.

Length: 3 weeks.

Objectives: To train jet engine mechanics in the maintenance and/or operation of IRD jet engine analyzer equipment.

Instruction: *Courses 1 and 2:* Description, location, and installation of all engine analyzer components; analyzer troubleshooting and repair. *Course 1* includes a review of electronic fundamentals and electronic circuits related to engine analyzer circuits. *Course 2* includes a review of all jet engine systems for pattern wave forms and meter indications.

Credit recommendation, collegiate level: No credit because of the brevity and limited technical nature of the courses.

1. Jet Engine Block Test and Vibration Analyzer
2. Jet Engine Conditioning and Vibration Analyzer (Sperry)
3. Jet Engine Block Test Mechanic
   (Aircraft Jet Engine Block Test Mechanic)

Location: Chanute AFB, Ill.

Length: 4–6 weeks.

Objectives: To train jet engine mechanics in jet engine test requirements and use of testing equipment.

Instruction: Familiarization with jet engine vibration analyzer and operating principles, Sperry, Shaw-Estes, or Universal semi-portable test facility; functional and performance testing; malfunction analysis; engine evaluation and conditioning.

Credit recommendation, collegiate level: No credit because of the limited technical nature of the courses.

1. Jet Engine Mechanic
2. Jet Engine Technician
3. Jet Engine Mechanic
4. Jet Engine Familiarization

Locations: Amarillo AFB, Tex.; Chanute AFB, Ill.; Sheppard AFB, Tex.

Length: *Courses 1 and 2,* 10–16 weeks; *Course 3,* 5 weeks; *Course 4,* 3 weeks.

Objectives: *Course 1:* To train airmen in the maintenance of aircraft jet engines. *Course 2:* To provide supervisory and advanced-level training for jet engine mechanics. *Courses 3 and 4:* To familiarize aircraft mechanics with jet engines.

Instruction: *Course 1:* Fundamentals for mechanics; operation of engines, engine systems, and components; inspection, adjustment, maintenance, and repair of jet engines. *Course 2:* Maintenance management and supervision; Air Force publications and maintenance forms; electrical fundamentals; engine repair and systems operation, test, and trouble analysis; turbo-prop engines and recent developments. *Courses 3 and 4:* Jet engine operation; inspection, maintenance, and repair of jet engine systems, components, and accessories; engine repair and assembly.

Credit recommendation, collegiate level: CAUTION: *Courses in jet engine repair vary in length and recommendation. Require exact identification of course by title and length. Courses 1, 3, and 4 are technical and vocational in nature. Credit in jet engine repair shop on the basis of demonstrated skills and/or institutional examinations. Course 2:* 2 semester hours in shop management. At the technical and vocational level, credit in jet engine repair shop on the basis of demonstrated skills and/or institutional examinations.

1. Jet Engine Mechanic, T-58
2. Jet Engine Technician, (Repair, Build-Up and Installation) GAM-72
3. Jet Engine Mechanic (GAM-77)
4. Jet Engine Mechanic, (J-85 Engine Repair, Build-Up and Installation) GAM-72
5. Jet Engine Mechanic, J75 Engine Minor Overhaul and Testing
6. Jet Engine Mechanic (J57 Engine Minor Overhaul and Testing)

Locations: Amarillo AFB, Tex.; Chanute AFB, Ill.; Sheppard AFB, Tex.

Length: 3–5 weeks.

Objectives: To provide qualified maintenance personnel with supplemental training on the engines specified in the course titles.

Instruction: Engine inspection, disassembly, repair, and reassembly; engine and engine systems operational checks; troubleshooting of the engine and engine systems; engine testing after overhaul.

Credit recommendation, collegiate level: No credit

because of the brevity and limited technical nature of the courses.

Jet Engine Vibration Analyzer Maintenance (Sperry)

Location: Chanute AFB, Ill.

Length: 3 weeks.

Objectives: To train airmen in the maintenance of the Sperry jet engine analyzer equipment.

Instruction: Review of electronic principles; troubleshooting analyzer circuits; installation, maintenance, and calibration of the analyzer.

Credit recommendation, collegiate level: This course is technical and vocational in nature. Credit in electrical shop on the basis of demonstrated skills and/or institutional examinations.

Jet Engine Vibration Analyzer Operator (Sperry)

Location: Chanute AFB, Ill.

Length: 3 weeks.

Objectives: To train airmen in the maintenance of the Sperry jet engine analyzer equipment.

Instruction: Description, installation, application, maintenance, and calibration of Sperry jet engine analyzer equipment.

Credit recommendation, collegiate level: This course is technical and vocational in nature. Credit in mechanical shop on the basis of demonstrated skills and/or institutional examinations.

Jet Qualification Training (T-33)
(Jet Qualification Training)
(Jet Qualification Course)

Locations: Craig AFB, Ala.; Randolph AFB, Tex.

Length: 4–7 weeks.

Objectives: To provide initial jet qualification training in the T-33 aircraft for rated pilots prior to their entry into advanced fighter training courses or administrative flying of jet type aircraft.

Instruction: Flying training; jet flight planning; instrument operation and procedures; weather; T-33 engineering; aviation physiology.

Credit recommendation, collegiate level: No credit because of the specialized nature of the course.

Joy Helium Compressor F&O

Location: Chanute AFB, Ill.

Length: 3 weeks.

Objectives: To train airmen to perform field and organizational maintenance on the Joy helium compressor.

Instruction: Operation, troubleshooting, and maintenance of compressor.

Credit recommendation, collegiate level: This course is technical and vocational in nature. Credit in mechanical shop on the basis of demonstrated skills and/or institutional examinations.

Laboratory Animal Technician

Location: Brooks AFB, Tex.

Length: 8 weeks.

Objectives: To train noncommissioned officers and airmen in the management, care, and handling of laboratory animals.

Instruction: Veterinary medicine, including anatomy, clinical laboratory, necropsy, nutrition, aseptic technique surgery, laboratory animal diseases, and pharmacology; laboratory management; practice training.

Credit recommendation, collegiate level: Credit in veterinary laboratory technology on the basis of institutional examination.

Laundry Machine Operator

Location: Keesler AFB, Miss.

Length: 4 weeks.

Objectives: To train airmen to operate power driven laundry machines.

Instruction: Techniques of proper laundering; ironing; assorting and identification of clothing and equipment.

Credit recommendation, collegiate level: No credit because of the limited vocational nature of this course.

Liquid Fuel System Specialist/Technician, SM-65
(Liquid Fuel System Specialist/Technician, SM-68A)
(Liquid Fuel System Maintenance Specialist/ Technician, SM-68A)
(Liquid Fuel System Maintenance Specialist/ Technician, SM-68B)
(Liquid Fuel System Maintenance Specialist/ Technician)
(Liquid Fuel System Maintenance Technician (Conventional Fuel))

Locations: Amarillo AFB, Tex.; Chanute AFB, Ill.

Length: 6–13 weeks.

Objectives: To train airmen to inspect, troubleshoot, and maintain liquid fuel systems.

Instruction: Operation of propellant systems; loading and unloading procedures; component cleaning, inspecting, and packaging; system troubleshooting and safety procedures.

Credit recommendation, collegiate level: CAUTION. *These courses vary slightly in title, length, and recommendation. Require exact identification of course by title and length.* These courses are technical and vocational in nature. Credit in liquid fuel systems maintenance on the basis of demonstrated skills and/or institutional examinations.

Liquid Fuel Systems Maintenance Specialist (Conventional Fuel)
(Petroleum Systems Maintenance Specialist)

Location: Amarillo AFB, Tex.

Length: 7–10 weeks.

Objectives: To train airmen to inspect, maintain, replace, and modify liquid fuel systems.

Instruction: Maintenance fundamentals; mechanical ystems; hydrant systems.

Credit recommendation, collegiate level: This course is technical and vocational in nature. Credit in liquid uel systems maintenance on the basis of demonstrated kills and/or institutional examinations.

Liquid Fuel Systems Maintenance Specialist (HGM-16F)
Liquid Fuel Systems Maintenance Specialist (SM-65F))

Location: Chanute AFB, Ill.

Length: 6–15 weeks.

Objectives: To train airmen in the maintenance of quid fuel systems of the HGM-16F or SM-65F ballis-c missile.

Instruction: Operating principles; constructional fea-ures; inspection, maintenance, troubleshooting, and esting of the propellant transfer systems; safety pre-autions.

Credit recommendation, collegiate level: This course s technical and vocational in nature. Credit in liquid uel systems maintenance on the basis of demonstrated kills and/or institutional examinations.

. Liquid Fuel Systems Maintenance Specialist (LGM-25C)
. Liquid Fuel Systems Maintenance Specialist, SM-65 and 68
. Liquid Fuel Systems Maintenance Specialist (SM-68B) (Titan II)
. Liquid Fuel Systems Maintenance Specialist (SM-68B)
. Liquid Fuel Systems Maintenance Specialist (SM-68A)
. Liquid Fuel Systems Maintenance Specialist (HGM-25)

Location: Chanute AFB, Ill.

Length: 6–16 weeks.

Objectives: To train airmen as liquid fuel systems pecialists.

Instruction: Weapon system familiarization; charac-eristics of weapon systems propellants; component esting; operation and maintenance of system compo-ents; troubleshooting and repair of propellant system; reapon system safety.

Credit recommendation, collegiate level: All of the ourses are technical and vocational in nature. Credit n liquid fuel systems maintenance on the basis of emonstrated skills and/or institutional examinations.

Liquid Fuel Systems Maintenance Specialist (PGM-16D/E)
Liquid Fuel Systems Maintenance Specialist (SM-65D and SM-65E))
Liquid Fuel Systems Maintenance Specialist (SM-65E))
Liquid Fuel Systems Maintenance Specialist (SM-65D))

Location: Chanute AFB, Ill.

Length: 8–16 weeks.

Objectives: To train airmen in the maintenance of liquid fuel systems associated with the ballistic missiles indicated in title.

Instruction: Familiarization of operating principles; constructional features; inspection and testing; mainte-nance and repair of compressors, storage tanks, vacu-um pumps, and other components of propellant sys-tems.

Credit recommendation, collegiate level: This course is technical and vocational in nature. Credit in liquid fuel systems maintenance on the basis of demonstrated skills and/or institutional examinations.

Liquid Oxygen Generation Plant Operation and Maintenance (25 Ton/D)

Location: Chanute AFB, Ill.

Length: 10 weeks.

Objectives: To train airmen in the operation and maintenance of the 25 ton/day liquid oxygen plant.

Instruction: Erection, assembly, operation, checkout, troubleshooting, and repair of oxygen-nitrogen genera-tor; diesel engine operation and maintenance.

Credit recommendation, collegiate level: This course is technical and vocational in nature. Credit in liquid fuel systems maintenance on the basis of demonstrated skills and/or institutional examinations.

M37-T1 Test Stand, Maintenance and Calibration

Location: Chanute AFB, Ill.

Length: 3 weeks.

Objectives: To train airmen in the maintenance and calibration of the M37-T1 aircraft engine test stand.

Instruction: Operating instructions; inspection, maintenance, and lubrication; calibration and adjust-ment; trouble analysis.

Credit recommendation, collegiate level: No credit because of the brevity of this course.

1. MA-2/ASB-4 Bomb Navigation Systems (Analyst Supervisor)
2. MA-2/ASB-4 Bomb Navigation Systems (Radar and Computer Technician)

Location: Lowry AFB, Colo.

Length: 20–22 weeks.

Objectives: To train airmen to operate and maintain the MA-2/ASB-4 bombing navigation computer.

Instruction: Fundamentals of the MA-2/ASB-4; bombing computer; navigation computer; radar data presentation set; high-speed bombing radar and system maintenance.

Credit recommendation, collegiate level: Credit in electrical laboratory on the basis of demonstrated skills and/or institutional examinations.

MB-2 Towing Tractor, Field and Organizational Maintenance

Location: Chanute AFB, Ill.

Length: 4 weeks.

Objectives: To train airmen to operate, test, and repair the components and systems of the MB-2 towing tractor.

Instruction: Operation of MB-2 aircraft towing tractor; engine system; injection system; transmission and drives; hydraulic steering system; winterization system.

Credit recommendation, collegiate level: This course is technical and vocational in nature. Credit in tractor operation and maintenance on the basis of demonstrated skills and/or institutional examinations.

1. Machinist
2. Machinist
   Location: Chanute AFB, Ill.
   Length: *Course 1,* 15–20 weeks; *Course 2,* 6 weeks.
   Objectives: *Course 1:* To train airmen to perform general equipment maintenance as apprentice machinists on Air Force weapons. *Course 2:* To provide advanced training in design and fabrication of tools, dies, jigs, and fixtures required to maintain Air Force weapons systems and general ground support equipment.
   Instruction: *Course 1:* Preparatory shop and introductory lathe work; special applications to lathe work; lathe threading, milling, fitting, and rework practices; contour machine and shaper work; heat treating and precision grinding. *Course 2:* General shop principles; special machining operations; tool design and fabrication practices.
   Credit recommendation, collegiate level: These courses are technical and vocational in nature. *Course 1:* Credit in machine shop on the basis of demonstrated skills and/or institutional examinations. *Course 2:* Credit in tool and die making on the basis of demonstrated skills and/or institutional examinations.

Maintenance Analysis
(Maintenance Engineering Production Analysis)
   Location: Chanute AFB, Ill.
   Length: 6–8 weeks.
   Objectives: To train officers and airmen in statistical data analysis of maintenance production.
   Instruction: Practical methematics and statistical methods; work measurement techniques; analysis of maintenance data.
   Credit recommendation, collegiate level: 3 semester hours in statistical analysis.

Maintenance Analysis Specialist
(Aircraft and Missile Maintenance Analysis
         Specialist)
   Location: Chanute AFB, Ill.
   Length: 6–13 weeks.
   Objectives: To train airmen in the techniques of analysis of aircraft and missile maintenance data.
   Instruction: Statistical methods, including practical mathematics, graphic techniques, measures of central tendency, dispersion, control charts, and introduction to correlation; maintenance analysis, including man-hour accounting system, man-hour utilization, forecasting maintenance capabilities, maintenance data collection system, and analysis of maintenance effort.

Credit recommendation, collegiate level: 4 semester hours in statistical analysis.

Maintenance Analysis Technician
   Location: Chanute AFB, Ill.
   Length: 6–8 weeks.
   Objectives: To train airmen in analytical methods used in data collection, assembly, and analysis.
   Instruction: Data collection and processing techniques; identifying and forecasting maintenance trends and problems; analysis reports and presentations.
   Credit recommendation, collegiate level: 3 semester hours in elementary statistical methods and practice.

1. Maintenance Management
2. Consolidated Maintenance Management (ADC)
3. Consolidated Maintenance Management (TAC)
   Location: Chanute AFB, Ill.
   Length: 3–4 weeks.
   Objectives: To train officers in maintenance organization programs and procedures.
   Instruction: Functions of management; management data collection; man-hour reporting; maintenance and materiel control.
   Credit recommendation, collegiate level: For each course, 2 semester hours in maintenance management.

Maintenance of A/S 48A-1 Wheel Mover
   Location: Chanute AFB, Ill.
   Length: 3 weeks.
   Objectives: To train airmen in the repair and maintenance of the A/S 48A-1 wheel mover.
   Instruction: Familiarization with equipment; hookup and unhook procedures; unit operation without load; hydraulic system theory; repair of vehicle systems and components, remote electrical and hydraulic control; electrical systems, vehicle running gear, and hydraulic transmissions and clutch assembly.
   Credit recommendation, collegiate level: No credit because of the brevity and limited technical nature of the course.

Maintenance of Survival and Aircrew Protective
         Equipment (Fabric, Leather, and Rubber)
(Maintenance of Survival and Aircrew Protective
         Equipment (Fabric and Leather))
   Location: Chanute AFB, Ill.
   Length: 3–4 weeks.
   Objectives: To train airmen in the maintenance of survival and aircrew protective equipment.
   Instruction: Sewing machine operation; inspection repair, and alteration of flying clothing and equipment; partial-pressure suits; tent and tarpaulin repair
   Credit recommendation, collegiate level: This course is technical and vocational in nature. Credit in sewing and fabric maintenance on the basis of demonstrated skills and/or institutional examinations.

1. Maintenance Scheduling Specialist
2. Workload Control
3. Materiel Control

Location: Chanute AFB, Ill.

Length: *Course 1, 8–10 weeks; Courses 2 and 3, 3* weeks.

Objectives: To train airmen in Air Force methods of maintenance scheduling, workload, or materiel control.

Instruction: *Course 1:* Maintenance control fundamentals; scheduling and controlling aircraft; missile and aerospace support equipment maintenance and facilities; dispatch of specialists and equipment; controlling maintenance by authorizing and assigning jobs, priorities, and completion times; determining materiel requirements and scheduling the movement of aircraft, missiles, and aerospace ground equipment through all phases of maintenance. *Course 2:* Maintenance management functions; work order processing; preparation and utilization of maintenance schedules and monthly maintenance plans. *Course 3:* Stock levels and supply procedures; man-hour and materiel requirements; work order fundamentals; parts routing; engineering data; technical orders, supply publications and researching.

Credit recommendation, collegiate level: *Course 1:* 6 semester hours in maintenance management. *Courses 2 and 3:* No credit because of the brevity and limited technical nature of the courses.

1. Management Analysis Officer
2. Management Analysis Officer
3. Management Analysis Officer

Locations: Lowry AFB, Colo.; Sheppard AFB, Tex.

Length: *Courses 1 and 3:* 10–11 weeks; *Course 2,* 6 weeks.

Objectives: *Courses 1 and 3:* To train officers in the concepts and techniques of analysis for management. *Course 2:* To provide advanced training for management analysis officers.

Instruction: *Course 1,* taught prior to July 1964: Preparation for analysis, including organization, data processing, graphic and tabular presentation, office machines, and oral briefing; managerial statistics, including frequency distribution, measures of central tendency and variability, sampling, statistical inference, simple linear correlation and regression, factors and standards; financial analysis, including non-appropriated case study, Air Force budget process, appropriation accounting, and proprietary financial analysis and case study; applied management analysis, including war plans and peacetime programs, program development and application, management evaluation systems, mission analysis and case study. *Course 2,* taught from July 1964 to January 1967, covered the same general areas omitting the financial analysis phase. The training was at a more advanced level and the officers participated in seminars on the individual subjects throughout the course. *Course 3,* effective January 1967: Preparation for analysis; analytic techniques of management science, including statistics and operations research techniques; introduction to data automation; resource management and analysis, including program and systems analysis case studies, reliability and mission capability case studies.

Credit recommendation, collegiate level: CAUTION: *These courses vary in recommendation according to the dates attended. Require exact identification of the*

course by title, length, and dates attended. Course 1: 1 semester hour in oral and written communication, 5 semester hours in financial analysis, and 3 semester hours in applied management analysis. Course 2: 1 semester hour in oral and written communication, 2 semester hours in managerial statistics, and 3 semester hours in management control systems. Course 3: 5 semester hours in applied management analysis and 4 semester hours in management control systems.

**Management Analysis Specialist
(Management Analysis Technician)**

Location: Sheppard AFB, Tex.

Length: 9–10 weeks.

Objectives: To train airmen in the concepts and techniques of analysis for management.

Instruction: Preparation for analysis, including organization, data processing, graphic and tabular presentation, office machines, and oral briefing; managerial statistics, including frequency distribution, measures of central tendency and variability; sampling, statistical inference, simple linear correlation and regression, factors, and standards; financial analysis, including non-appropriated case study, Air Force budget process, appropriation accounting, and proprietary financial analysis and case study; applied management analysis, including war plans and peacetime programs, program development and application, management evaluation systems, and mission analysis and case study.

Credit recommendation, collegiate level: 1 semester hour in oral and written communication, 5 semester hours in financial analysis, and 3 semester hours in applied management analysis.

Management Engineering Officer

Location: Lowry AFB, Colo.

Length: 10 weeks.

Objectives: To train officers in Air Force procedures for development and application of manpower standards.

Instruction: Basic definitions; organizational analysis; manpower allocation system; work center description; statistics; operations analysis; human relations; time study; work sampling; operational audit; predetermined time systems; USAF management systems; major command activities.

Credit recommendation, collegiate level: 3 semester hours in statistics and 3 semester hours in business organization and management.

Management Engineering Specialist

Location: Lowry AFB, Colo.

Length: 8 weeks.

Objectives: To train airmen in methods of developing and using work center manpower standards.

Instruction: Organization analysis; manpower allocation system; basic mathematics and statistics; work center description and layout analysis; flow process charting; work sampling; leveling and allowance factors and time study; operational audit; correlation and regression; human relations; computation of work center manpower standard.

Credit recommendation, collegiate level: 3 semester hours in statistics.

Manpower Management Officer

Location: Scott AFB, Ill.

Length: 7 weeks.

Objectives: To train officers to administer base-level manpower management programs.

Instruction: Base policies and organization; human relations; conference leadership; executive development; problem solving; management engineering, including work simplification methods, work measurement, Air Force and industrial organization, mission analysis, organization structure, manpower management, and management engineering laboratories.

Credit recommendation, collegiate level: 3 semester hours in manpower management methods.

Manpower Management Technician (Management Technician)

Location: Soctt AFB, Ill.

Length: 6–8 weeks.

Objectives: To train airmen in the techniques involved in analysis of management activities.

Instruction: Manpower management fundamentals and Air Force organization; management engineering techniques; management training program.

Credit recommendation, collegiate level: 3 semester hours in management analysis and 2 semester hours in principles of personnel management.

Manual Central Office Equipment Specialist (Central Office Equipment Specialist (Manual)) (Automatic Central Office Equipment Repairman) (Central Office Equipment Mechanic)

Location: Sheppard AFB, Tex.

Length: 13–26 weeks.

Objectives: To train airmen to install and maintain manual central office telephone exchange equipment.

Instruction: Manual telephone systems; line testing and central office maintenance; electrical fundamentals; local and common battery switchboards; telephone fundamentals.

Credit recommendation, collegiate level: This course is technical and vocational in nature. Credit in electrical shop or telephone maintenance on the basis of demonstrated skills and/or institutional examinations.

1. Materiel Facilities Specialist (Warehousing Specialist)
2. Warehousing Supervisor

Locations: Amarillo AFB, Tex.; Francis E. Warren AFB, Wyo.

Length: *Course 1,* 7–9; *Course 2,* 6–7 weeks.

Objectives: *Course 1:* To train airmen in storage and inventory procedures. *Course 2:* To provide specialists with training in warehouse management.

Instruction: *Course 1:* Storage principles; stock locator systems; property accounting and disposition; technical and supply publications; fire prevention and safety. *Course 2:* Planning and scheduling of warehousing activities; supervision and on-the-job training of warehousing personnel; inspection and evaluation of warehousing activities; technical warehousing functions.

Credit recommendation, collegiate level: *Course 1:* Credit in property accounting on the basis of institutional examination. *Course 2:* 3 semester hours in supply management.

Meat Cutting

Location: Keesler AFB, Miss.

Length: 8 weeks.

Objectives: To train airmen in the techniques of cutting and processing meats.

Instruction: Fundamentals of meat cutting; cutting and processing of beef, veal, lamb, pork, poultry, seafood, and meat products.

Credit recommendation, collegiate level: This course is technical and vocational in nature. Credit in meat cutting on the basis of demonstrated skills.

Mechanical Instrument Trainer Specialist

Location: Chanute AFB, Ill.

Length: 17 weeks.

Objectives: To train airmen to repair AN-T-18 and C-8 instrument flying and landing trainers.

Instruction: Electricity and electronics principles; AN-T-18 instrument trainer principles and maintenance; construction, theory, and maintenance of C-8 trainer units and assemblies; operation and flying of C-8 and AN-T-18 instrument trainers.

Credit recommendation, collegiate level: Credit in electricity and electrical laboratory on the basis of demonstrated skills and/or institutional examinations.

Medical Administrative Specialist (Apprentice Medical Administrative Specialist)

Locations: Gunter AFB, Ala.; Sheppard AFB, Tex.

Length: 6–9 weeks.

Objectives: To train airmen to perform basic medical administrative functions.

Instruction: Typing forms and correspondence; Medical Service organization; administrative services; general administration and financial management; legal medicine; materiel procedures; registrar's office; aviation, preventive, veterinary, and disaster medicine; dental service; interpersonal and public relations.

Credit recommendation, collegiate level: 2 semester hours in general office procedures, and credit in typing on the basis of institutional examination.

1. Medical Administrative Supervisor
2. Medical Administrative Supervisor
3. Medical Administrative Supervisor

Locations: Gunter AFB, Ala.; Sheppard AFB, Tex.

Length: *Course 1,* 12 weeks; *Course 2,* 8 weeks; *Course 3,* 6 weeks.

Objectives: To provide supervisory-level training for medical administrative specialists.

Instruction: *Course 1:* Basic medical orientation; medical administration, including personnel and general administration, medical materiel service, registrar's service, and military law; anatomy; physiology; surgery; preventive medicine; radiobiology; training and logistics, including leadership and training management, logistics, food service, and field training. *Course 2* covers the same general subject areas as *Course 1* in somewhat less detail and includes oral and written communication training. *Course 3:* Administrative services and unit command; administrative support professional services; hospital business office functions; financial management; effective speaking and its application.

Credit recommendation, collegiate level: CAUTION: *These courses vary in recommendation according to their length. Require exact identification by title and length. Course 1:* 5 semester hours in medical administration. *Course 2:* 3 semester hours in medical administration. *Course 3:* 2 semester hours in medical administration.

1. Medical Equipment Repairman
   (Apprentice Medical Equipment Repairman)
   (Apprentice Medical Equipment Repair)
2. Medical Equipment Repair
3. Medical Equipment Repair Technician

Locations: Gunter AFB, Ala.; Sheppard AFB, Tex.

Length: *Courses 1 and 2,* 15–20 weeks; *Course 3,* 30 weeks.

Objectives: To train airmen in the installation, repair, and maintenance of medical equipment.

Instruction: *Courses 1 and 2:* Safety; use and care of hand and power tools; electrical and electronic fundamentals, including direct and alternating current circuits, schematic interpretation, vacuum tubes, and solid state devices; maintenance of electronic complex, and gas related medical equipment, X-ray equipment, and dental equipment; supply and maintenance shop organization and procedures. *Course 3* covers the same basic areas of instruction with emphasis on electricity and electronics training.

Credit recommendation, collegiate level: CAUTION: *These courses vary in length and recommendation. Require exact identification of a course by full title and length. Courses 1 and 2:* For each course, 2 semester hours at the freshman or sophomore level as an elective in electricity. At the technical level, credit in medical equipment maintenance based on demonstrated skills and/or institutional examinations. *Course 3:* 3 semester hours at the freshman or sophomore level as an elective in electricity and electronics. At the technical level, credit in medical equipment maintenance based on demonstrated skills and/or institutional examinations.

Medical Helper
(Basic Medical)

Locations: Greenville AFB, Miss.; Lackland AFB, Tex.; Sheppard AFB, Tex.

Length: 4–8 weeks.

Objectives: To provide airmen with basic medical instruction and pretechnical preparation for training in a specific medical field.

Instruction: Fundamentals of USAF Medical Service; anatomy and physiology; basic hospital procedures; emergency medical treatment; mass casualty care.

Credit recommendation, collegiate level: No credit because of the brevity and limited technical nature of the course.

1. Medical Laboratory Specialist (Phase I)
2. Medical Laboratory Specialist (Phase II)
   (Hospital Laboratory Training)
3. Apprentice Medical Laboratory Specialist
   (Medical Laboratory Specialist)

Locations: Gunter AFB, Ala.; Sheppard AFB, Tex.

Length: *Course 1,* 14–17 weeks; *Course 2,* 36 weeks; *Course 3,* 19–21 weeks.

Objectives: To train airmen in routine clinical laboratory procedures.

Instruction: *Course 1:* Introductory chemistry; urinalysis; clinical chemistry; microscopy; bacteriology; parasitology; histological techniques; preventive medicine; hematology; serology; medical materiel; disaster medicine. *Course 2* is the continuation and hospital laboratory training phase of *Course 1.* Students are assigned to USAF hospital clinical laboratories for practical training in urinalysis, hematology, blood banking, serology, clinical chemistry, bacteriology, and parasitology. *Course 3* covers the same general subject areas as *Course 1.*

Credit recommendation, collegiate level: CAUTION: *These courses vary in title, length, and recommendation. Require exact identification by full title and length. The recommendation for Courses 1 and 2 applies beginning September 1960 and requires successful completion of both phases. No direct academic credit is recommended for either phase considered separately. Courses 1 and 2:* 30 semester hours applied to a *major* in medical technology or 10 semester hours applied to a *minor* in either chemistry or biology. *Course 3:* In preparation for a nonscientific degree, 5 semester hours in basic science. In preparation for a scientific degree, 2 semester hours in biology or chemistry in a student's minor.

Medical Laboratory Technician

Location: Gunter AFB, Ala.

Length: 25 weeks.

Objectives: To train medical laboratory specialists in advanced laboratory techniques.

Instruction: Anatomy and physiology; pharmacy; preventive medicine; medical laboratory, including bacteriology, blood grouping and transfusions, basal metabolism, clinical chemistry, hematology, histological technique, parasitology, serology, virology, urinalysis, electrocardiography, and laboratory administration.

Credit recommendation, collegiate level: 10 semester hours in basic science if a student is preparing for a nonscientific degree. In preparation for a scientific degree, 5 semester hours in biology or chemistry applied to a science minor.

1. Medical Materiel Specialist
(Apprentice Medical Materiel Specialist)
2. Medical Materiel Supervisor
Locations: Gunter AFB, Ala.; Sheppard AFB, Tex.
Length: 6–10 weeks.
Objectives: To train airmen in medical supply procedures.
Instruction: Basic medical orientation; general principles and organization of medical supply; medical materiel procurement, issue, control, and maintenance; special materiel procedures; training and logistics.
Credit recommendation, collegiate level: 3 semester hours in supply management for each course.

Medical Officer Flight Familiarization Training (T-37)
(Medical Officer Flight Familiarization Training (T-33))
Location: Randolph AFB, Tex.
Length: 5–6 weeks. *Note*—since flying training is dependent upon weather and other factors, the actual length of a course may vary.
Objectives: To familiarize medical officers with flying and related academic subjects so that they can understand the physiological and psychological stresses encountered by pilots and student pilots.
Instruction: Flying training includes flight indoctrination, instrument trainer, navigation, and contact, instrument and formation flying. Academic training includes applied aerodynamics, aircraft engineering, instrument procedures and radio aids, navigation and flight planning, weather, safety, and aviation physiology.
Credit recommendation, collegiate level: No credit because of the brevity and specialized nature of the course.

Medical Service Specialist
(Apprentice Medical Service Specialist)
Locations: Gunter AFB, Ala.; Sheppard AFB, Tex.
Length: 9–13 weeks.
Objectives: To train airmen to assist medical officers in the examination and treatment of patients and to perform routine dispensary and clinical duties.
Instruction: Aeromedical evacuation; anatomy and physiology; medical administration, laboratory, and passive defense; medicine; nursing; ophthalmology; otorhinolaryngology; pharmacy; preventive medicine; psychiatry; radiology; surgery; training and logistics.
Credit recommendation, collegiate level: 2 semester hours in physiology and hygiene.

Medical Service Technician
Locations: Gunter AFB, Ala.; Sheppard AFB, Tex.
Length: 17–19 weeks.

Objectives: To train airmen in high-level technical and supervisory medical skills connected with the immediate care and treatment of patients.
Instruction: Anatomy and physiology; medicine; surgery; psychiatry; pharmacy; psychiatric, surgical, and general nursing; preventive medicine; veterinary services; medical administration; disaster medicine; dental services; medical laboratory; radiology.
Credit recommendation, collegiate level: 2 semester hours in elementary anatomy, 2 semester hours in elementary physiology, and 1 semester hour in preventive medicine.

Medical Supply Officer
Location: Gunter AFB, Ala.
Length: 7 weeks.
Objectives: To train officers of the Medical Service Corps to perform the duties of a base and unit medical supply officer.
Instruction: Dental and medical administration; medical materiel, including general principles and organization of medical supply, materiel requirements, procurement, storage, issues, controls, maintenance, and identification, special materiel services, organizational supply activities, and instructional tours.
Credit recommendation, collegiate level: 3 semester hours in supply management.

1. Metals Processing Specialist
(Welder)
2. Heat Treatment and Electroplating of Metals
(Heat Treatment of Ferrous and Non-Ferrous Metals)
3. Welding of A-286 Alloy Metal (J-79 Engine)
Location: Chanute AFB, Ill.
Length: *Course 1,* 15–19 weeks; *Course 2,* 4–5 weeks; *Course 3,* 3 weeks.
Objectives: *Course 1:* To train airmen in the operation and maintenance of welding equipment used in the repair and maintenance of aircraft, jet engine parts, and ground support equipment. *Courses 2 and 3:* To train metals processing specialists in the characteristics of specific metals and techniques of heat treating or welding.
Instruction: *Course 1:* Introductory gas welding; welding fabrication; gas welding and heat treating applications; metallic arc and resistance welding; gas shielded welding; aircraft and jet engine repair procedures. *Course 2:* Annealing, normalizing, hardening and tempering of alloy steels; solution heat treatment and annealing of aluminum alloys; heat treatment of copper, nickel, and magnesium alloys; properties of miscellaneous metals. *Course 3:* Welding characteristics and welding of A-286 alloy; chromoloy welding; L-605, incoloy T, and N-155 material welding; repair of heat-treated and aged A-286 and tempered chromoloy materials.
Credit recommendation, collegiate level: These courses are technical and vocational in nature. Credit in welding shop on the basis of demonstrated skills and/or institutional examinations.

Military Aspects of Sanitary and Industrial Hygiene Engineering

Location: Gunter AFB, Ala.

Length: 8 weeks.

Objectives: To train officer engineers in aerospace medicine and radiological health.

Instruction: Personnel and medical administration; nuclear medicine; disaster medicine; entomology; aviation medicine training; industrial and sanitary engineering. *Note*—76 hours radiological health instruction conducted by the U.S. Public Health Service is not available for evaluation and is not included in the course description or considered in the recommendation.

Credit recommendation, collegiate level: 2 semester hours in community sanitation.

Military Training Instructor

Location: Lackland AFB, Tex.

Length: 4–9 weeks.

Objectives: To qualify airmen to conduct military training activities.

Instruction: Principles, methods, and techniques of instruction; practice teaching; evaluation; early identification program; drill and ceremonies.

Credit recommendation, collegiate level: 2 semester hours in instructional methods.

Missile and Facility Pneudraulic Technician (SM-65F)

Location: Sheppard AFB, Tex.

Length: 12–15 weeks.

Objectives: To train airmen in the operation and maintenance of the Atlas "F" series hydraulic and pneumatic systems, components, and associated servicing and test equipment.

Instruction: Introduction to weapons systems; hydraulic pumping units; airborne hydraulic systems; propellant transfer and pneumatic systems.

Credit recommendation, collegiate level: This course is technical and vocational in nature. Credit in mechanical shop on the basis of demonstrated skills and/or institutional examinations.

Missile Combat Crew (CGM-13B, Launch)

Location: Lowry AFB, Colo.

Length: 12 weeks–officers; 9 weeks–airmen.

Objectives: To train Air Force personnel as CGM-13B combat launch crews.

Instruction: *Officers only:* CGM-13B weapon system; CGM-13B launch equipment. *Officers and airmen:* CGM-13B missile operation No. 1 and No. 2.

Credit recommendation, collegiate level: No credit as the course is military in nature.

Missile Control Communications Systems Repairman
(Telephone Switching Equipment Specialist (Combat Operations Support))

Location: Sheppard AFB, Tex.

Length: 28–33 weeks.

Objectives: To train airmen to operate and maintain missile control communications systems.

Instruction: Electronic fundamentals; circuit analysis; standard test equipment; soldering techniques; principles of telephony; circuit analysis and maintenance of ground telephone equipment; Titan I and/or Titan II control communications systems maintenance.

Credit recommendation, collegiate level: 3 semester hours at the freshman or sophomore level as an elective in electricity and electronics, and credit in electrical laboratory on the basis of demonstrated skills and/or institutional examinations.

Missile Electrical Repairman/Technician, SM-68

Location: Sheppard AFB, Tex.

Length: 14 weeks.

Objectives: To train airmen as missile electrical repairmen/technicians on SM-68 missile electrical systems and associated checkout and test equipment.

Instruction: Operation and maintenance of the missileborne and engine electrical system; operation and maintenance of the accessory supply system ground operational equipment; integrated maintenance of the missileborne and ground operational equipment.

Credit recommendation, collegiate level: Credit in electrical laboratory on the basis of demonstrated skills and/or institutional examinations.

1. Missile Electrical Specialist (LGM-25)
2. Missile Electrical Specialist (SM-68B)
3. Missile Electrical Specialist (SM-68A)
4. Missile Electrical Specialist (SM-65D)
5. Missile Electrical Specialist (SM-65 E&F)

Location: Sheppard AFB, Tex.

Length: *Course 1,* 17 weeks; *Courses 2, 3, and 4,* 6–10 weeks; *Course 5,* 3 weeks.

Objectives: To train airmen to operate and maintain missile electrical systems and associated ground equipment.

Instruction: *Course 1:* Principles of electricity; principles of mechanics; motors, generators, and malfunction analysis; electronics and rocket engines. *Courses 2, 3, and 4:* Missile familiarization; operation and maintenance of the electrical system; ground equipment. *Course 5:* Introduction to the missile; missile electrical system.

Credit recommendation, collegiate level: CAUTION: *These courses vary slightly in title, length, and recommendation. Require exact identification by title and length. Course 1:* Credit in electricity and electrical laboratory on the basis of demonstrated skills and/or institutional examinations. *Courses 2 through 5:* Credit in electrical laboratory on the basis of demonstrated skills and/or institutional examinations.

Missile Electrical Specialist/Technician, SM-68B

Location: Sheppard AFB, Tex.

Length: 7 weeks.

Objectives: To train airmen to maintain the missile electrical system and associated test equipment.

Instruction: Missile familiarization; electrical system; electrical equipment; operating ground equipment; installation exercise test set.

Credit recommendation, collegiate level: Credit in electrical laboratory on the basis of demonstrated skills and/or institutional examinations.

1. Missile Electronic Equipment Specialist, AGM-28A/B
2. Missile Checkout Equipment Repairman, AGM-28A/B
   (Air Launch Missile Checkout Equipment Repairman (AGM-28A/B))
3. Air Launch Missile Checkout Equipment Repairman (AGM-28A/B)
   (AGM Checkout Equipment Repairman (AGM-28A))
   (GAM Checkout Equipment Repairman (GAM-77))

Location: Chanute AFB, Ill.

Length: *Course 1,* 27 weeks; *Course 2,* 35 weeks; *Course 3,* 28–39 weeks.

Objectives: To train maintenance personnel in the alignment, calibration, and repair of AGM-28A/B and/or GAM-77 special test equipment.

Instruction: *Courses 1, 2, and 3:* DC and AC circuits; motors and servomechanisms; reactive circuits; vacuum tubes and transistors. *Courses 1 and 2* also include tubes and solid state devices; amplifiers and oscillators; in addition *Course 3* includes multivibrators and sweep circuits; detection and discrimination.

Credit recommendation, collegiate level: *Course 1:* 2 semester hours at the freshman or sophomore level as an elective in electricity and electronics, and credit in electrical laboratory on the basis of demonstrated skills and/or institutional examinations. *Course 2:* 3 semester hours at the freshman or sophomore level as an elective in electricity and electronics, and credit in electrical laboratory on the basis of demonstrated skills and/or institutional examinations. *Course 3:* 4 semester hours at the freshman or sophomore level as an elective in electricity and electronics, and credit in electrical laboratory on the basis of demonstrated skills and/or institutional examinations.

1. Missile Electronic Equipment Specialist (LGM-25)
2. Missile Guidance and Control Specialist (LGM-25)

Location: Sheppard AFB, Tex.

Length: 29 and 36 weeks.

Objectives: To train airmen as missile electronic equipment specialists or missile guidance and control specialists.

Instruction: Fundamentals of AC and DC; solid state devices; vacuum tubes; signal generation; timing and control; inspection, maintenance, and checkout.

Credit recommendation, collegiate level: For each course, 3 semester hours at the freshman or sophomore level as an elective in electricity and electronics, and credit in electrical laboratory on the basis of demonstrated skills and/or institutional examinations.

1. Missile Electronic Equipment Specialist, WS-133A
2. Missile Electronic Equipment Specialist, WS-133B
3. Missile Checkout Equipment Repairman, WS-133B
4. Ballistic Missile Checkout Equipment Specialist, WS-133B
5. Missile Electronic Equipment Technician, WS-133A-M

Location: Chanute AFB, Ill.

Length: *Courses 1 through 4,* 38–44 weeks; *Course 5,* 6–7 weeks.

Objectives: To train airmen to operate, maintain, and inspect missile launch equipment, standard test equipment, and special test equipment.

Instruction: *Courses 1 through 4:* DC and AC; solid state devices; vacuum tubes and power supplies; amplifiers and oscillators; isolation and correction of launch equipment. *Course 5:* Application and analysis of electronic principles; circuit theory and testing; launch and test equipment.

Credit recommendation, collegiate level: *Courses 1 through 4:* 3 semester hours at the freshman or sophomore level as an elective in electricity and electronics and credit in electrical laboratory on the basis of demonstrated skills and/or institutional examinations. *Course 5:* Credit in electrical laboratory on the basis of demonstrated skills and/or institutional examinations.

1. Missile Engine Mechanic (LGM-25)
2. Missile Engine Mechanic (SM-68B)
3. Missile Engine Mechanic (HGM-25A)
   (Missile Engine Mechanic (SM-68A))
4. Missile Engine Mechanic (SM-65 E/F)
5. Missile Engine Mechanic
6. Missile Engine Mechanic
7. Missile Engine Mechanic (SM-65D)
8. Missile Engine Mechanic (SM-65D)
9. Missile Engine Mechanic (IM-99)

Locations: Chanute AFB, Ill.; Sheppard AFB, Tex.

Length: *Course 1,* 19–20 weeks; *Courses 2 through 7,* 6–14 weeks; *Courses 8 and 9,* 3–4 weeks.

Objectives: To train airmen in the responsibilities and skills of missile engine mechanics.

Instruction: *Course 1:* Fundamentals of AC and DC; principles of mechanics; motors, generators, and malfunction analysis; electronics and rocket engines. *Courses 2 through 7:* General familiarization; propellants and safety; engine familiarization and maintenance; ground equipment maintenance. *Course 8:* Launch control. *Course 9:* Missile familiarization; propellants and compressed gases; rocket engine construction, maintenance, testing, and operation.

Credit recommendation, collegiate level: *Course 1:* Credit in electricity and electrical laboratory on the basis of demonstrated skills and/or institutional examinations. *Courses 2 through 9:* These courses are technical and vocational in nature. Credit in electrical and mechanical shop on the basis of demonstrated skills and/or institutional examinations.

1. Missile Engine Mechanic/Technician (SM-65F)
   (Missile Engine Mechanic/Technician (SM-65))
2. Missile Engine Mechanic/Technician (SM-68)
   Locations: Chanute AFB, Ill.; Sheppard AFB, Tex.
   Length: 12–14 weeks.
   Objectives: To train airmen in the operation, checkout, troubleshooting, and repair of the missile engine systems, subsystems, and components.
   Instruction: Weapon system familiarization; engine systems; component and system checkout; engine handling and maintenance; ground support equipment.
   Credit recommendation, collegiate level: These courses are technical and vocational in nature. Credit in electrical and mechanical shop on the basis of demonstrated skills and/or institutional examinations.

Missile Engine Mechanic/Technician, SM-68B

Location: Sheppard AFB, Tex.
Length: 12 weeks.
Objectives: To train airmen in the handling, operation, and maintenance of the Stage I and Stage II liquid rocket engine.
Instruction: Propellants and safety; engine familiarization and safety; silo and ground equipment maintenance.
Credit recommendation, collegiate level: This course is technical and vocational in nature. Credit in mechanical shop on the basis of demonstrated skills and/or institutional examinations.

1. Missile Facilities Specialist/Technician (SM-65F)
2. Missile Facilities Specialist/Technician (SM-68B)
   Location: Sheppard AFB, Tex.
   Length: 14–15 weeks.
   Objectives: To train airmen as missile facilities specialist-technicians.
   Instruction: *Course 1:* Launch installation system; heating, ventilation, and air cooling system; power distribution system; pneumatic and hydraulic systems; fluid storage facilities; propellant transfer system. *Course 2:* Propellant and cryogenic transfer; pneumatic systems; missile lift and suspension system; launch installation utilities; miscellaneous systems and launch control.
   Credit recommendation, collegiate level: These courses are technical and vocational in nature. Credit in mechanical shop on the basis of demonstrated skills and/or institutional examinations.

1. Missile Facilities Specialist, WS-133A
   (Missile Facilities Specialist, SM-80)
2. Missile Facilities Specialist, LGM-25
3. Missile Facilities Specialist, LGM-25C
   (Missile Facilities Specialist, SM-68B)
4. Missile Facilities Specialist, LGM-25
5. Missile Facilities Specialist, HGM-16F
   (Missile Facilities Specialist (SM-65E/F))
   (Missile Facilities Specialist, SM-65F)
6. Missile Facilities Specialist, HGM-25A
   (Missile Facilities Specialist, SM-68A)
7. Missile Facilities Specialist, SM-65D
8. Missile Facilities Specialist, SM-65D&E
9. Missile Facilities Specialist, IM-99B
10. Missile Facilities Specialist, CGM-13B AGE
    CREW
    Locations: Chanute AFB, Ill.; Sheppard AFB, Tex.
    Length: *Courses 1 and 2,* 21–25 weeks; *Courses 3 through 10,* 8–14 weeks.
    Objectives: To train airmen to inspect, maintain, and repair missile ground support equipment.
    Instruction: *Courses 1 and 2:* Fundamentals of electricity; principles of mechanics; missile fundamentals; motors, generators, and malfunction analysis; pneudraulic system; launch control facility. *Courses 3 through 10:* Weapon system familiarization; handling and maintenance; launch area equipment.
    Credit recommendation, collegiate level: CAUTION: *These courses vary slightly in title, length, and recommendation. Require exact identification by title and length. Courses 1 and 2:* For each course, credit in electricity and electrical laboratory on the basis of demonstrated skills and/or institutional examinations. *Courses 3 through 10:* For each course, credit in electrical laboratory on the basis of demonstrated skills and/or institutional examinations.

Missile Facilities Technician, SM-80

Location: Chanute AFB, Ill.
Length: 9 weeks.
Objectives: To familiarize airmen with the WS-133A general operational and maintenance characteristics, and all non-electric component requirements, performed at the launch facility and the support base.
Instruction: WS-133A familiarization; launch facility; launch control facility.
Credit recommendation, collegiate level: This course is technical and vocational in nature. Credit in mechanical shop on the basis of demonstrated skills and/or institutional examinations.

Missile Facility Water Treatment

Location: Sheppard AFB, Tex.
Length: 5 weeks.
Objectives: To provide supplemental training for water and waste processing specialists in the operation and maintenance of water processing and treatment equipment at missile sites.
Instruction: Basic chemistry; testing water for specific impurities; missile facilities water treatment equipment and treatment procedures.
Credit recommendation, collegiate level: 2 semester hours in water purification.

Missile Ground Support Equipment Repair Technician/Repairman (SM-65F)

Location: Sheppard AFB, Tex.

Length: 20 weeks.

Objectives: To train airmen to operate, inspect, checkout, and service selected missile systems.

Instruction: Propellant and cryogenic transfer; pneumatic systems; missile lift and suspension system; launch installation utilities; miscellaneous systems and equipment; silo electrical system and launch control.

Credit recommendation, collegiate level: This course is technical and vocational in nature. Credit in mechanical shop on the basis of demonstrated skills and/or institutional examinations.

1. Missile Guidance and Control Specialist
   (CGM-13B, FCC)
2. Missile Guidance and Control Specialist (AGM/
   AIM) TAC
   (Missile Guidance and Control Specialist (AIM))
   (Defense Missile Guidance Mechanic-Falcon
   (AIM))
   (Defense Missile Guidance Mechanic (GARS))
   (Guidance Systems Mechanic (GARS))
   (Guidance Systems Mechanic (GAR-1/2/3)
3. Guidance Systems Mechanic (GAR-1)
4. Guidance Systems Mechanic (GAR 1)
5. Guidance Systems Mechanic (GAR-3)
6. Guidance Systems Mechanic (GAM-63 Missile)
   (Guidance Systems Analyst (GAM-63 Missile))
7. Defense Missile Guidance Mechanic (GAR)

Location: Lowry AFB, Colo.

Length: *Courses 1 and 7,* 10 weeks; *Course 2,* 25–30 weeks; *Course 3,* 20 weeks; *Courses 4 and 5,* 22–24 weeks; *Course 6,* 19–20 weeks.

Objectives: To train airmen in the operation, maintenance, inspection, and repair of the guidance system used in the AIM or GARS.

Instruction: *Courses 2 and 3:* DC and AC; reactive circuits; principles of vacuum tubes and transistors; amplifiers and oscillators; radar. *Courses 4, 5, and 6:* DC and AC; resonance; vacuum tubes and power supplies; amplifiers and wave-shaping circuits. *Courses 1 and 7:* Missile system familiarization; console checkout.

Credit recommendation, collegiate level: CAUTION: *These courses vary slightly in title, length, and recommendation. Require exact identification by title and length. Courses 2 and 3:* For each course, 3 semester hours at the freshman or sophomore level as an elective in electricity and electronics, and credit in electrical laboratory on the basis of demonstrated skills and/or institutional examinations. *Courses 4, 5, and 6:* For each course, 2 semester hours at the freshman or sophomore level as an elective in electricity and electronics, and credit in electrical laboratory on the basis of demonstrated skills and/or institutional examinations. *Courses 1 and 7:* These courses are technical and vocational in nature. Credit in electrical and mechanical shop on the basis of demonstrated skills and/or institutional examinations.

1. Missile Guidance and Control Specialist
   (CGM-13B, GEMS)
2. Missile Guidance and Control Specialist
   (CGM-13B, GEMS)
   (Tactical Missile Guidance Mechanic (CGM-13B
   GEMS))
   (Tactical Missile Guidance Mechanic (MACE,
   CGM-13B/GEMS))
   (Tactical Missile Guidance Mechanic (MACE,
   MGM-13C/GEMS))
   (Tactical Missile Guidance Mechanic (TM-76B/
   GEMS))

Location: Lowry AFB, Colo.

Length: *Course 1,* 28–30 weeks; *Course 2,* 33–49 weeks.

Objectives: To train airmen in the operation, maintenance, and repair of the inertial guidance system modules and the guidance equipment maintenance set.

Instruction: *Courses 1 and 2:* Guidance system principles; operation, checkout and troubleshooting; operation and use of applicable test equipment and ground support equipment. In addition *Course 2* includes DC and AC; reactive circuits; vacuum tubes and solid state devices; amplifiers and oscillators; circuit analysis.

Credit recommendation, collegiate level: CAUTION: *These courses vary slightly in title, length, and recommendation. Require exact identification by title and length. Course 1:* Credit in electrical laboratory on the basis of demonstrated skills and/or institutional examinations. *Course 2:* 3 semester hours at the freshman or sophomore level as an elective in electricity and electronics, and credit in electrical laboratory on the basis of demonstrated skills and/or institutional examinations.

Missile Guidance and Control Specialist (CGM-13B,
   GSC)
Tactical Missile Guidance Mechanic (CGM-13B)
(Tactical Missile Guidance Mechanic (CGM-13C))
(Tactical Missile Guidance Mechanic (MACE, MGM-
   13C))
(Tactical Missile Guidance Mechanic (TM-76B/
   GSC))
(Tactical Missile Guidance Mechanic and Checkout-
   Equipment Repairman (TM-76B/GEMS))
(Guidance Systems Mechanic (TM-76B))

Location: Lowry AFB, Colo.

Length: 28–36 weeks.

Objectives: To train airmen in the maintenance of missile inertial guidance systems and guidance system checker.

Instruction: DC and AC; reactive circuits; principles of vacuum tubes and transistors; amplifiers and oscillators; circuit analysis.

Credit recommendation, collegiate level: CAUTION: *These courses vary slightly in title, length, and recommendation. Require exact identification by title and length.* 3 semester hours at the freshman or sophomore level as an elective in electricity and electronics, and credit in electrical laboratory on the basis of demonstrated skills and/or institutional examinations.

Missile Hydraulic Repairman/Technician (SM-68)

Location: Sheppard AFB, Tex.

Length: 8 weeks.

Objectives: To train airmen to operate, inspect, and repair missile hydraulic systems.

Instruction: Weapon system familiarization; operation, inspection, and maintenance of missile, portal, and auxiliary hydraulic systems; missile launcher system; antenna protecting and elevating set.

Credit recommendation, collegiate level: This course is technical and vocational in nature. Credit in mechanical shop on the basis of demonstrated skills and/or institutional examinations.

1. Missile Launch Equipment Repairman, WS-133A
   (Missile Launch Equipment Repairman, WS-133B)
   (Ballistic Missile Launch Equipment Repairman, WS-133A)
   (Ballistic Missile Launch Equipment Repairman, WS-133B)
   (Ballistic Missile Launch Equipment Repairman, SM-80)
2. Ballistic Missile Launch Equipment Repairman (SM-68A)
   (Ballistic Missile Launch Equipment Repairman (SM-68B))

Locations: Chanute AFB, Ill.; Sheppard AFB, Tex.

Length: *Course 1, 31–38 weeks; Course 2, 9–12 weeks.*

Objectives: To train airmen in the operation, maintenance, and inspection of missile launch equipment.

Instruction: *Course 1:* DC and AC; motors and servomechanisms; reactive circuits; vacuum tubes and transistors; special purpose tubes; amplifiers and oscillators; multivibrators and sweep circuits. *Course 2:* Familiarization, analysis, and checkout of the launch control set and flight systems.

Credit recommendation, collegiate level: CAUTION: *Missile launch equipment repairmen courses vary slightly in title, length, and recommendation. Require exact identification by title and length. Course 1:* 3 semester hours at the freshman or sophomore level as an elective in electricity and electronics, and credit in electrical laboratory on the basis of demonstrated skills and/or institutional examinations. *Course 2:* This course is technical and vocational in nature. Credit in electrical shop on the basis of demonstrated skills and/or institutional examinations.

1. Missile Launch/Missile Officer (LGM-25)
2. Missile Launch/Missile Officer (Titan II/LGM-25)
   (Missile Launch/Missile Officer (Titan II))
3. Missile Launch/Missile Officer (Titan I, HTM-25B)
4. Missile Launch/Missile Officer (Atlas HGM-16F)
5. Missile Launch/Missile Officer (Atlas PGM-16E)
6. Guided Missile Operations Maintenance Officer (SM-68)
7. Missile Launch/Missile Officer (SM-68A)
8. Missile Launch/Missile Officer (SM-68B)
9. Missile Launch/Missile Officer (SM-65D)
10. Missile Launch/Missile Officer (SM-65E)
11. Missile Launch/Missile Officer (SM-65F)
12. Missile Launch/Missile Officer (Ballistic Missiles)
13. Missile Launch/Missile Officer (Ballistic Missiles)
    (Guided Missile Operations/Maintenance Officer (Ballistic Missiles))

Location: Sheppard AFB, Tex.

Length: *Course 1, 14 weeks; Courses 2 through 12, 6–9 weeks; Course 13, 10–12 weeks.*

Objectives: To train officers in the operation and maintenance of the weapon system indicated in title.

Instruction: *Course 1:* Weapon system familiarization; electrical/electronic principles; facility systems; missile systems; launch control and checkout. *Courses 2 through 12:* Weapon system familiarization; facilities systems; missile systems; maintenance and inspection; launch procedures. *Course 13:* Weapon system introduction; missile electrical systems; electronics for missiles; launch complex systems; guidance and controls.

Credit recommendation, collegiate level: CAUTION: *These courses vary slightly in title, length, and recommendation. Require exact identification by full title and length. Courses 1 through 12:* Credit in electrical laboratory on the basis of demonstrated skills and/or institutional examination. *Course 13:* 2 semester hours at the freshman or sophomore level as an elective in electricity and electronics, and credit in electrical laboratory on the basis of demonstrated skills and/or institutional examinations.

1. Missile Launch Officer (CGM-13B)
2. Missile Launch Officer (MGM-13A)
3. Missile Launch Officer (MACE, MGM-13B)
4. Missile Launch Officer (MACE, MGM-13C)
5. Missile Launch Officer (TM-76A)
6. Missile Launch Officer (TM-76B)
7. Guided Missile Operations Officer (TM-76A)
8. Guided Missile Operations Officer (TM-76B)

Location: Lowry AFB, Colo.

Length: 13–20 weeks.

Objectives: To train officers in the operation and supervision of tactical missile launch activities.

Instruction: DC and AC; electron tubes; amplifiers and oscillators; transmission.

Credit recommendation, collegiate level: CAUTION: *Missile launch officer courses vary slightly in title, length, and recommendation. Require exact identification.* For each course, 2 semester hours at the freshman or sophomore level as an elective in electricity and electronics, and credit in electrical laboratory on the basis of demonstrated skills and/or institutional examinations.

Missile Launch Officer, WS-133A-M
(Missile Launch Officer, WS-133A)
(Missile Launch Officer, WS-133B)
(Missile Launch Officer, SM-80)

Location: Chanute AFB, Ill.

Length: 3–5 weeks.

Objectives: To train officers as missile launch officers on missile combat crews.

Instruction: Training to receive, verify, and initiate launch commands; inhibit launch command signals; initiate and evaluate test and calibrate signals; monitor and interpret launch site security violations and ground support equipment displays; perform minor operator maintenance on launch control center equipment.

Credit recommendation, collegiate level: CAUTION: *Missile launch officer courses vary slightly in title, length, and recommendation. Require exact identification by title and length.* No credit as the course is military in nature.

1. Missile Maintenance Mechanic/Technician, SM-68
2. Missile Mechanic/Maintenance Technician, SM-68B
3. Missile Mechanic/Maintenance Technician, IM-99B

Locations: Chanute AFB, Ill.; Sheppard AFB, Tex.

Length: *Course 1,* 14 weeks; *Course 2,* 6 weeks; *Course 3,* 9 weeks.

Objectives: To train mechanics in the skills necessary for missile maintenance.

Instruction: Missile operational checks; engine, fuel, electrical, hydraulic, pressurization, and temperature control systems; safety instruction.

Credit recommendation, collegiate level: These courses are technical and vocational in nature. Credit in mechanical shop on the basis of demonstrated skills and/or institutional examinations.

Missile Maintenance Technician, SM-62

Location: Amarillo AFB, Tex.

Length: 9 weeks.

Objectives: To train airmen in the operation, servicing, and maintenance of missiles and launch support equipment.

Instruction: Inspection, removal, and replacement of airframe assemblies; launch and support equipment; flight control; guidance and consoles; power plant; pre-operational and operational procedures.

Credit recommendation, collegiate level: This course is technical and vocational in nature. Credit in mechanical shop on the basis of demonstrated skills and/or institutional examinations.

Missile Mechanic (AGM-28A/B)
(Missile Mechanic (GAM-77))
(Missile Mechanic (TM-61A/C))
(Missile Mechanic (Ballistic))
(Missile Specialist (TM-61C))

Locations: Chanute AFB, Ill.; Lowry AFB, Colo.; Sheppard AFB, Tex.

Length: 17–23 weeks.

Objectives: To train airmen in the maintenance of the missile indicated in title.

Instruction: Missile familiarization; assembly and disassembly; transportation, handling, and replacement; missile systems; inspection and repair.

Credit recommendation, collegiate level: CAUTION: *Missile mechanic courses vary slightly in title, length, and recommendation. Require exact identification by title and length.* These courses are technical and vocational in nature. Credit in electrical and mechanical shop on the basis of demonstrated skills and/or institutional examinations.

1. Missile Mechanic (CGM-13B, LCH PREP)
2. Missile Mechanic (WS-133B)
3. Missile Mechanic (WS-133A/A-M)
   (Missile Mechanic, WS-133A)
   (Missile Mechanic, SM-80)

Locations: Chanute AFB, Ill.; Lowry AFB, Colo.

Length: 11–24 weeks.

Objectives: To train airmen in the inspection and maintenance of missile systems and associated equipment.

Instruction: Missile fundamentals; electrical fundamentals; electrical maintenance; missile handling; aerospace ground equipment; launch site maintenance.

Credit recommendation, collegiate level: CAUTION: *Missile mechanic courses vary slightly in title, length, and recommendation. Require exact identification of course by title and length.* Credit in electricity and electrical laboratory on the basis of demonstrated skills and/or institutional examinations.

1. Missile Mechanic (CGM-13B, MMC)
   (Missile Mechanic (CGM-13B))
   (Missile Mechanic (CGM-13C))
   (Missile Mechanic (MGM-13B))
   (Missile Mechanic (MGM-13C))
   (Missile Mechanic (MACE, MGM-13B))
   (Missile Mechanic (MACE, MGM-13C))
   (Missile Mechanical Tactical (TM-76B))
   (Missile Mechanical Tactical (TM-76A))
2. Missile Mechanic (TM-76A/B)
   (Missile Mechanic (TM-76A))
   (Missile Mechanic (TM-76))
   (Missile Mechanic Tactical (TM-76A/B))
   (Missile Specialist (TM-76A))

Location: Lowry AFB, Colo.

Length: *Course 1,* 19–24 weeks; *Course 2,* 17–24 weeks.

Objectives: To train airmen in the installation, transport, assembly, disassembly, inspection, servicing, and operation of the missile indicated in title.

Instruction: *Course 1:* Weapon system orientation; basic electricity; aerodynamics; hydraulics; checkout procedures; maintenance training. *Course 2:* Fundamentals of missiles; support equipment; launch area procedures; checkout and maintenance.

Credit recommendation, collegiate level: CAUTION: *Missile mechanic courses vary slightly in title, length, and recommendation. Require exact identification of course by title and length. Course 1:* Credit in electricity, electronics and electrical laboratory on the basis of demonstrated skills and/or institutional examinations. *Course 2:* This course is technical and vocational in nature. Credit in electrical and mechanical shop on the basis of demonstrated skills and/or institutional examinations.

1. Missile Mechanic (LGM-25)
2. Missile Mechanic (LGM-25C)
    (Missile Mechanic (SM-68B))
    Location: Sheppard AFB, Tex.
    Length: *Course 1,* 18 weeks; *Course 2,* 6 weeks.
    Objectives: To train airmen in the handling, installation, and inspection of the missile systems indicated in title.
    Instruction: *Course 1:* Principles of mechanics; fundamentals of AC and DC; motors, generators, and malfunction analysis; electronics and rocket engines; operation and function, installation and removal of missile systems. *Course 2:* Operation, function, and maintenance of missile systems; missile handling equipment; missile installation and removal.
    Credit recommendation, collegiate level: CAUTION: *Missile mechanic courses vary slightly in title, length, and recommendation. Require exact identification by title and length. Course 1:* Credit in electricity and electrical laboratory on the basis of demonstrated skills and/or institutional examinations. *Course 2:* This course is technical and vocational in nature. Credit in electrical and mechanical shop on the basis of demonstrated skills and/or institutional examinations.

1. Missile Mechanic (PGM-16E and HGM-16F)
    (Missile Mechanic (SM-65E/F))
2. Missile Mechanic (HGM-25A)
    (Missile Mechanic (SM-68A))
3. Missile Mechanic (SM-65D)
4. Missile Mechanic (GAM-72)
    Locations: Amarillo AFB, Tex.; Sheppard AFB, Tex.
    Length: 6–12 weeks.
    Objectives: To train airmen in the inspection and maintenance of missile systems and associated equipment.
    Instruction: Operation, inspection, and maintenance of missile systems; installation, ground handling, and transportation of missiles; operation of launch systems.
    Credit recommendation, collegiate level: CAUTION: *Missile mechanic courses vary slightly in title, length, and recommendation. Require exact identification by title and length.* These courses are technical and vocational in nature. Credit in electrical and mechanical shop on the basis of demonstrated skills and/or institutional examinations.

1. Missile Officer (TM-76A)
2. Missile Officer (TM-76B)
    (Missile Maintenance Officer (TM-76B))
3. Guided Missile Maintenance Officer (TM-76A)
4. Missile Officer (CGM-13B)
    Location: Lowry AFB, Colo.
    Length: *Courses 1 and 2,* 27 weeks; *Course 3,* 25 weeks; *Course 4,* 6 weeks.

Objectives: To train officers to supervise missile maintenance activities.
Instruction: *Courses 1 and 2:* DC and AC; electron tubes; amplifiers; wave forming; transmission; radar. *Course 3:* Fundamentals of DC and AC; vacuum tubes; amplifiers and oscillators; wave shaping. *Course 4:* Maintenance equipment; guidance system checkout and maintenance; test equipment.
Credit recommendation, collegiate level: CAUTION: *Missile officer courses vary slightly in title, length, and recommendation. Require exact identification by title and length. Courses 1 and 2:* 3 semester hours at the freshman or sophomore level as an elective in electricity and electronics, and credit in electrical laboratory on the basis of demonstrated skills and/or institutional examinations. *Course 3:* 2 semester hours at the freshman or sophomore level as an elective in electricity and electronics, and credit in electrical laboratory on the basis of demonstrated skills and/or institutional examinations. *Course 4:* This course is technical and vocational in nature. Credit in electrical shop on the basis of demonstrated skills and/or institutional examinations.

1. Missile Officer, WS-133A
    (Missile Officer, WS-133A-M)
2. Missile Officer, SM-80
    Location: Chanute AFB, Ill.
    Length: 7–15 weeks.
    Objectives: To train officers as supervisors of missile maintenance and targeting and alignment activities.
    Instruction: *Course 1:* Electronic fundamentals; missile fundamentals; missile facility system; missile alignment; Air Force management; maintenance management. *Course 2:* Familiarization, launch control, and launch facilities; missile targeting and alignment.
    Credit recommendation, collegiate level: CAUTION: *Missile officer courses vary slightly in title, length, and recommendation. Require exact identification by title and length. Course 1:* 2 semester hours in shop management, and credit in electricity and electrical laboratory on the basis of demonstrated skills and/or institutional examinations. *Course 2:* 2 semester hours in shop management.

1. Missile Officer, WS-133B
2. Missile Officer, WS-133B
    Location: Chanute AFB, Ill.
    Length: *Course 1,* 13–15 weeks; *Course 2,* 8 weeks.
    Objectives: To train officers in maintenance responsibilities and targeting and alignment tasks associated with the WS-133B weapon system.
    Instruction: *Course 1:* Electronic fundamentals; missile fundamentals; facility system and alignment; Air Force and maintenance management. *Course 2:* Weapon system orientation; launch facility equipment and maintenance sequences; missile alignment; missile maintenance management.
    Credit recommendation, collegiate level: CAUTION: *Missile officer courses vary slightly in title, length, and recommendation. Require exact identification of course by title and length. Course 1:* 2 semester hours in shop management, and credit in electricity and electrical laboratory on the basis of demonstrated skills and/or

institutional examinations. *Course 2:* 2 semester hours in shop management, and credit in electrical laboratory on the basis of demonstrated skills and/or institutional examinations.

1. Missile Pneudraulic Repairman (LGM-25)
2. Missile Pneudraulic Repairman (LGM-25C)
   (Missile Pneudraulic Repairman (SM-68B))
3. Missile Pneudraulic Repairman (WS-133A, B, A-M)
   (Missile Pneudraulic Repairman (WS-133A))
4. Missile Pneudraulic Repairman (HGM-25A)
   (Missile Pneudraulic Repairman (SM-68A))
5. Missile Pneudraulic Repairman (PGM-16D)
   (Missile Pneudraulic Repairman (SM-65D))
6. Missile Pneudraulic Repairman (SM-65 E&F)
7. Missile Pneudraulic Repairman (SM-65F)

Locations: Chanute AFB, Ill.; Sheppard AFB, Tex.
Length: *Course 1,* 18 weeks; *Courses 2 through 7,* 3–12 weeks.
Objectives: To train airmen in the operation and maintenance of pneumatic systems, components, and associated servicing and test equipment.
Instruction: *Course 1:* Fundamentals of AC and DC; principles of mechanics; motors, generators, and malfunction analysis; electronics and rocket engines. *Courses 2 through 7:* Familiarization; inspection; checkout; handling; troubleshooting; adjustment and alignment.
Credit recommendation, collegiate level: *Course 1:* Credit in electricity and electrical laboratory on the basis of demonstrated skills and/or institutional examinations. *Courses 2 through 7:* These courses are technical and vocational in nature. Credit in electrical and mechanical shop on the basis of demonstrated skills and/or institutional examinations.

Missile Safety Technician
Location: Chanute AFB, Ill.
Length: 15 weeks.
Objectives: To train safety personnel for missile safety surveillance duties at ballistic missile sites.
Instruction: Basic concepts of mathematics, physics, fluid mechanics, electricity, chemistry, and construction practices applicable to construction and operation of missile facilities; propulsion systems; industrial safety; industrial hygiene; safety management.
Credit recommendation, collegiate level: 3 semester hours in industrial safety management.

1. Missile Systems Analyst Specialist (AGM-28A/B)
2. Air Launch Missile Analyst Mechanic (AGM-28A/B)
3. GAM Analyst Mechanic, GAM-77

Location: Chanute AFB, Ill.
Length: *Course 1,* 27 weeks; *Course 2,* 36 weeks; *Course 3,* 38–41 weeks.
Objectives: To train airmen in the operation, checkout, alignment, and adjustment of the missile system indicated in title.
Instruction: *Courses 1 through 3:* DC and AC circuits; motors and servomechanisms; reactive circuits; vacuum tubes and transistors; tubes and solid state de-

vices; in addition *Course 2* includes amplifiers and oscillators; multivibrators and sweep circuits; detection and discrimination. *Course 3* provides additional instruction in special circuits and microwave principles.
Credit recommendation, collegiate level: *Course 1:* 3 semester hours at the freshman or sophomore level as an elective in electricity and electronics, and credit in electrical laboratory on the basis of demonstrated skills and/or institutional examinations. *Course 2:* 4 semester hours at the freshman or sophomore level as an elective in electricity and electronics, and credit in electrical laboratory on the basis of demonstrated skills and/or institutional examinations. *Course 3:* 6 semester hours at the freshman or sophomore level as an elective in electricity and electronics, and credit in electrical laboratory on the basis of demonstrated skills and/or institutional examinations.

1. Missile Systems Analyst Specialist (LGM-25)
2. Ballistic Missile Analyst Specialist (LGM-25C)
   (Ballistic Missile Analyst Specialist (SM-68B))

Location: Sheppard AFB, Tex.
Length: *Course 1,* 33 weeks; *Course 2,* 10 weeks.
Objectives: To train airmen in the operation, troubleshooting, and repair of missile systems.
Instruction: *Course 1:* DC and AC; solid state devices; vacuum tubes; test equipment and logic; special circuits; subsystems operation; functional analysis; operation and maintenance; checkout and troubleshooting. *Course 2:* Operational and functional analysis; launch control monitoring; checkout system; integrated job operations.
Credit recommendation, collegiate level: *Course 1:* 3 semester hours at the freshman or sophomore level as an elective in electricity and electronics and credit in electrical laboratory on the basis of demonstrated skills and/or institutional examinations. *Course 2:* Credit in electrical laboratory on the basis of demonstrated skills and/or institutional examinations.

1. Missile Systems Analyst Specialist, WS-133A
2. Missile Systems Analyst Specialist, WS-133A
   (Ballistic Missile Analyst Specialist, WS-133A)
   (Ballistic Missile Analyst Specialist, SM-80)

Location: Chanute AFB, Ill.
Length: *Course 1,* 18–20 weeks; *Course 2,* 35–38 weeks.
Objectives: To train airmen in the operation, inspection, checkout, and periodic maintenance on the SM-80 or WS-133A systems.
Instruction: *Course 1:* Support systems; guidance and control; maintenance; alignment. *Course 2:* DC and AC; motors and servomechanisms; reactive circuits; vacuum tubes and transistors; special purpose tubes; amplifiers and oscillators; multivibrators and sweep circuits.
Credit recommendation, collegiate level: CAUTION: *These courses vary slightly in title, length, and recommendation. Require exact identification of the course by title and length.* *Course 1:* Credit in electrical laboratory on the basis of demonstrated skills and/or institutional examinations. *Course 2:* 4 semester hours at the freshman or sophomore level as an elective in electricity and electronics, and credit in electrical laboratory on the basis of demonstrated skills and/or institutional examinations.

1. Missile Systems Analyst Specialist, WS-133B
2. Missile Systems Analyst Specialist, WS-133B
   (Ballistic Missile Analyst Specialist, WS-133B)
   Location: Chanute AFB, Ill.
   Length: *Course 1*, 20 weeks; *Course 2*, 37 weeks.
   Objectives: To train airmen to operate, inspect, checkout, and maintain the WS-133B system.
   Instruction: *Courses 1 and 2:* Assembly and installation of components; test equipment; inspection and maintenance. In addition *Course 2* includes DC and AC; reactive circuits; vacuum tubes and transistors; tubes and solid state devices; amplifiers and oscillators.
   Credit recommendation, collegiate level: *Course 1:* Credit in electrical laboratory on the basis of demonstrated skills and/or institutional examinations. *Course 2:* 4 semester hours at the freshman or sophomore level as an elective in electricity and electronics, and credit in electrical laboratory on the basis of demonstrated skills and/or institutional examinations.

1. Missile Systems Analyst/Technician SM-62
2. Missile Systems Analyst/Technician (SM68)
   Locations: Amarillo AFB, Tex.; Sheppard AFB, Tex.
   Length: 21–24 weeks.
   Objectives: To train airmen for assignment as missile systems analyst technicians.
   Instruction: Missile familiarization; electrical, hydraulic, and engine systems; guidance system; flight control system; missile systems checkout and analysis.
   Credit recommendation, collegiate level: CAUTION: *Missile system analyst technician courses vary slightly in title, length, and recommendation. Require exact identification by title and length.* These courses are technical and vocational in nature. Credit in electrical and mechanical shop on the basis of demonstrated skills and/or institutional examinations.

Missile Systems Analyst Technician (SM-65F)
   Location: Sheppard AFB, Tex.
   Length: 24 weeks.
   Objectives: To train airmen in the maintenance of missile systems.
   Instruction: Weapon system; mobile APCHE; launch control; propellants; hydraulics; inertial guidance; autopilot; composite checkout.
   Credit recommendation, collegiate level: Credit in electrical laboratory on the basis of demonstrated skills and/or institutional examinations.

1. Missile Systems Analyst Technician (TEAT)
   WS-133A-M
2. Missile Systems Analyst Technician WS-133A-M
   Location: Chanute AFB, Ill.
   Length: *Course 1*, 10 weeks; *Course 2*, 6 weeks.
   Objectives: To train airmen in the theory, operation, periodic maintenance, and inspection of the WS-133A-M weapon system electronic system.
   Instruction: Checkout procedures; adjustment; fault isolation; removal, replacement, and repair of missile, missile components, and aerospace ground equipment.

In addition *Course 1* includes logic, level signal flow, integrated system flow, and detailed system analysis.
   Credit recommendation, collegiate level: *Course 1:* Credit in electrical laboratory on the basis of demonstrated skills and/or institutional examinations. *Course 2:* This course is technical and vocational in nature. Credit in electrical shop on the basis of demonstrated skills and/or institutional examinations.

Missile Systems Cable Splicing Specialist
(Cable Splicing Specialist, Hardened Missile
      Systems)
(Cable Splicer Specialist (Hardened Missile
      Systems))
   Location: Sheppard AFB, Tex.
   Length: 6–8 weeks.
   Objectives: To train airmen in the installation and maintenance of cable systems.
   Instruction: Cable splicing fundamentals; installation and replacement of splice cases; replacement of cable sections; cable testing procedures; function, operation, and maintenance of pressurized cable systems.
   Credit recommendation, collegiate level: This course is technical and vocational in nature. Credit in cable splicing on the basis of demonstrated skills and/or institutional examinations.

Missile Systems Fundamentals
   Location: Sheppard AFB, Tex.
   Length: 19–22 weeks.
   Objectives: To train airmen in the fundamental subjects common to the ballistic missile career field.
   Instruction: DC and AC; reactive circuits; principles of vacuum tubes and transistors; vacuum tube amplifiers and oscillators; transistor circuits and computer principles.
   Credit recommendation, collegiate level: 3 semester hours at the freshman or sophomore level as an elective in electricity and electronics, and credit in electrical laboratory on the basis of demonstrated skills and/or institutional examinations.

1. Missile Technician (GAM-77)
2. Missile Technician (SM-80)
   Location: Chanute AFB, Ill.
   Length: *Course 1*, 4–6 weeks; *Course 2*, 7 weeks.
   Objectives: To train airmen in the principles of organization, operation, and maintenance of the GAM-77 or the WS-133A missile.
   Instruction: *Course 1:* Familiarization with the GAM-77 weapon system; electrical, temperature control, and pressurization systems; ground-handling and checkout equipment. *Course 2:* SM-80 systems and facilities; transportation and handling equipment maintenance; missile transportation and handling.
   Credit recommendation, collegiate level: These courses are technical and vocational in nature. Credit in mechanical shop on the basis of demonstrated skills and/or institutional examinations.

Missile Test Equipment Specialist (SM 65, 68)

Location: Sheppard AFB, Tex.

Length: 19 weeks.

Objectives: To train airmen as missile test equipment specialists.

Instruction: Fundamentals of electronics; test equipment; transistors; launch control system equipment; automatic programmed checkout equipment; semiautomatic component checkout equipment; guidance system test and checkout equipment.

Credit recommendation, collegiate level: Credit in electricity and electrical laboratory on the basis of demonstrated skills and/or institutional examinations.

Missile Test Equipment Technician (Control) IM-99B

Location: Chanute AFB, Ill.

Length: 20 weeks.

Objectives: To train airmen in the functional theory, operation, calibration, and maintenance of missile test equipment.

Instruction: Weapon support calibration equipment; computers; functional checkout sets; electronic launching equipment; auxiliary equipment and operational tests.

Credit recommendation, collegiate level: Credit in electrical laboratory on the basis of demonstrated skills and/or institutional examinations.

Missile Test Equipment Technician (GAM-77)

Location: Chanute AFB, Ill.

Length: 18 weeks.

Objectives: To train airmen in the alignment, calibration, and repair of GAM-77 special test equipment.

Instruction: Missile familiarization and maintenance; removal, repair, replacement, and test of assemblies, components, and units of test equipment; trouble analysis and repair of interconnecting wiring of test equipment.

Credit recommendation, collegiate level: CAUTION: *Missile test equipment technician courses vary in title, length, and recommendation. Require exact identification of course by title and length. Note that titles vary only by name of equipment in the parentheses following the title. This course is technical and vocational in nature, and credit in electrical and mechanical shop on the basis of demonstrated skills and/or institutional examinations.*

Missile Test Equipment Technician (Propulsion and Propellant) (SM-68)

Location: Sheppard AFB, Tex.

Length: 18 weeks.

Objectives: To train airmen to maintain propellant loading and pressurization system checkout equipment.

Instruction: Titan familiarization; missile and facility propellant loading and pressurization system; test equipment and chassis modular circuitry; circuit analysis; inspection and maintenance.

Credit recommendation, collegiate level: CAUTION: *Missile test equipment technician courses vary slightly in title, length, and recommendation. Require exact*

identification of course by title and length. Note that titles vary only by name of equipment in the parentheses following the title. This course is technical and vocational in nature. Credit in electrical and mechanical shop on the basis of demonstrated skills and/or institutional examinations.

Missile Test Equipment Technician/Specialist (Launch Control Systems) (SM-65F)

Location: Sheppard AFB, Tex.

Length: 15 weeks.

Objectives: To train airmen as missile test equipment technician-specialists.

Instruction: Introduction to weapon system; special electronic and logic systems; logic unit and launch signal responder; troubleshooting launch control system and associated equipment.

Credit recommendation, collegiate level: Credit in electrical laboratory on the basis of demonstrated skills and/or institutional examinations.

Missile Test Equipment Technician/Specialist (Programmed Checkout Equipment (SM-65F))

Location: Sheppard AFB, Tex.

Length: 13 weeks.

Objectives: To train airmen as missile test equipment technician-specialists.

Instruction: Introduction to weapon system; test equipment; special electronic and logic systems; MAPCHE; mechanical repair and adjustment.

Credit recommendation, collegiate level: Credit in electrical laboratory on the basis of demonstrated skills and/or institutional examinations.

Modern Weather Techniques

Location: Chanute AFB, Ill.

Length: 6–7 weeks.

Objectives: To train officers and supervision-level airmen in the latest developments in the field of meteorology and forecasting techniques.

Instruction: Central weather facilities; central weather facility methods; operational weather forecasting; weather presentation.

Credit recommendation, collegiate level: Credit in advanced weather forecasting techniques on the basis of institutional examination.

1. Morse Intercept Operator (Radio Intercept Operator)
2. Morse Intercept Operator

Location: Keesler AFB, Miss.

Length: *Course 1,* 23–26 weeks; *Course 2,* 10 weeks.

Objectives: To train airmen in international Morse code and in operation and tuning of selected radio intercept equipment.

Instruction: *Course 1:* International Morse code; typewriting; intercept and communications equipment;

traffic analysis; intercept operating procedures; simulated intercept operations. *Course 2:* International Morse code; intercept operating procedures; traffic analysis; simulated intercept operations.

Credit recommendation, collegiate level: *Course 1:* Credit in typing on the basis of institutional examination. At the technical and vocational level for *Courses 1 and 2,* credit in radio operation on the basis of demonstrated skills and/or institutional examinations.

Motor Transportation Supervisor

Location: Sheppard AFB, Tex.
Length: 6 weeks.
Objectives: To train airmen to manage motor transportation activities.
Instruction: Motor pool organization, management, and operations; development and operation of formal and on-the-job training programs.
Credit recommendation, collegiate level: This course is technical and vocational in nature. Credit in motor transportation on the basis of institutional examination.

1. Motor Vehicle Maintenance Officer
2. Motor Vehicle Maintenance Officer

Location: Chanute AFB, Ill.
Length: *Course 1,* 8–9 weeks; *Course 2,* 6 weeks.
Objectives: To train officers in motor vehicle shop maintenance.
Instruction: *Course 1:* Air Force maintenance system and shop safety; principles of vehicle components; job descriptions and manpower management; maintenance shop supply, operation, layout, and training programs; inspection and production control operations; forms processing and military correspondence. *Course 2* covers approximately the same general subject areas in less detail.
Credit recommendation, collegiate level: CAUTION: *These courses vary in length and recommendation. Require exact identification of course by title and length. Course 1:* 3 semester hours in supply management. *Course 2:* 2 semester hours in supply management.

Munitions Specialist

Location: Lowry AFB, Colo.
Length: 11–18 weeks.
Objectives: To train airmen in explosives, incendiary, and toxic munitions work.
Instruction: Introduction to munitions; general explosive ammunitions; bombs, fuzes, and assembly of conventional munitions; aircraft rockets, missiles, and components; chemical, biological, and pyrotechnic ammunition; liquid-propellant fuel storage; storage, handling, transportation, and destruction of ammunition and explosives.
Credit recommendation, collegiate level: No credit as the course is military in nature.

Navigation and Bombing Trainer Specialist (AN/APQ-T3)

Location: Lowry AFB, Colo.
Length: 29 weeks.
Objectives: To provide airmen with the skills for organizational maintenance of the AN/APQ-T3 radar trainer and OA/ADQ13-T1A simulator group.
Instruction: Fundamentals of DC and AC; vacuum tubes and power supply circuits; amplifier and oscillator principles; nonsinusoidal generators; radar circuitry; synchros and servomechanisms.
Credit recommendation, collegiate level: 3 semester hours at the freshman or sophomore level as an elective in electronics, and credit in electrical laboratory on the basis of demonstrated skills and/or institutional examinations.

1. Navigation and Bombing Trainer Specialist (AN/APQ-T10)
2. Navigation and Bombing Trainer Specialist (Navigation and Bombing Trainer Specialist (AN/APQ-T2A))

Locations: Lowry AFB, Colo.; Chanute AFB, Ill.
Length: *Course 1,* 33–35 weeks; *Course 2,* 27–32 weeks.
Objectives: To train airmen to perform organizational maintenance and repair on navigation and bombing trainer equipment.
Instruction: *Course 1:* DC and AC; reactive circuits; vacuum tubes and solid state devices; amplifiers and oscillators; detection and discrimination; microwave operation; multivibrators, sweep and logic circuits. *Course 2:* DC and AC; reactive circuits; principles of vacuum tubes and transistors; amplifiers and radar.
Credit recommendation, collegiate level: *Course 1:* 4 semester hours at the freshman or sophomore level as an elective in electricity and electronics, and credit in electrical laboratory on the basis of demonstrated skills and/or institutional examinations. *Course 2:* 3 semester hours at the freshman or sophomore level as an elective in electricity and electronics, and credit in electrical laboratory on the basis of demonstrated skills and/or institutional examinations.

1. Navigator-Bombardier Training (Navigator-Bombardier Training (ASQ-38)) (Navigator-Bombardier Training (ASQ-48))
2. Navigator-Bombardier Training (MA-6A/7A) (Advanced Navigator Radar Bombardment Training)
3. Advanced Navigator Reconnaissance Bombardment
4. Advanced Navigator Reconnaissance Bombardment (Advanced Observer Reconnaissance Bombardment)

Location: Mather AFB, Calif.
Length: *Course 1,* 20–28 weeks; *Course 2,* 28 weeks; *Course 3,* 8–22 weeks; *Course 4,* 21–42 weeks.
Objectives: To qualify navigators and officers to bomb, navigate, and perform aerial reconnaissance with the equipment that is most commonly installed in reconnaissance bombardment aircraft.

Instruction: *Course 1:* Flying training subjects; bomb-navigation system operations; weapons delivery training; reconnaissance. *Course 2:* Flying training subjects; electricity and magnetism; alternating current; vacuum tubes; basic radio; bomb-navigation system operations; weapons delivery training; reconnaissance. *Course 3:* Flying training subjects; dead reckoning; grid navigation; pressure differential; reconnaissance-bombardment training; electricity and magnetism; alternating current; vacuum tubes; basic radio. *Course 4:* Flying training subjects; dead reckoning; grid navigation; pressure pattern; low-level navigation.

Credit recommendation, collegiate level: CAUTION: *These courses vary slightly in title, length, and recommendation. Require exact identification of course by title and length. Note that Course 3 and Course 4 have identical titles and lengths. Course 3 was given during 1958. Course 4 was given during 1957. Require exact identification of these courses by year of attendance. The following credit recommendations apply only when credit has not been previously granted in the specific field. Course 1:* No credit as the course is military in nature. *Course 2:* 2 semester hours at the freshman or sophomore level as an elective in electricity, and credit in electrical laboratory on the basis of demonstrated skills and/or institutional examinations. *Course 3:* 4 semester hours in navigation, 2 semester hours at the freshman or sophomore level as an elective in electricity, and credit in electrical laboratory on the basis of demonstrated skills and/or institutional examinations. *Course 4:* 5 semester hours in navigation.

Navigator-Bombardier Upgrade Training (ASQ-38)
(Upgrading, B-52 Aircraft)
(Upgrading, B-52 Aircraft (AN/ASQ-38 Weapons Control System))
(Upgrading, B-52 Aircraft (AN/ASQ-38 Weapons Delivery System))
(B-52 Aircraft Upgrading)

Location: Mather AFB, Calif.
Length: 6–9 weeks.
Objectives: To train navigator-bombardiers on the weapons systems employed in B-52 aircraft.
Instruction: Radar systems familiarization; weapons control system theory; bombing and navigation computers theory; operating procedures and malfunction analysis.
Credit recommendation, collegiate level: No credit as the courses are military in nature.

Navigator-Bombardier Upgrade Training (ASQ-42)
(Upgrading, B-58 Aircraft)
(AN/ASQ-42 Weapons Control)

Location: Mather AFB, Calif.
Length: 5–7 weeks.
Objectives: To train navigator-bombardiers to navigate and bomb with the AN/ASQ-42 weapons control system.
Instruction: Weapon system orientation; sighting; bombing; radar; Doppler; heading and stabilization.
Credit recommendation, collegiate level: CAUTION: *Navigator-bombardier training courses vary slightly in title, length, and recommendation. Require exact identification by title and length.* No credit as the course is military in nature.

Navigator-Bombardier Upgrade Training (ASQ-48)

Location: Mather AFB, Calif.
Length: 7–8 weeks.
Objectives: To train navigator-bombardiers to bomb and navigate with the AN/ASQ-48 weapons control system.
Instruction: Computer system, radar system, operating procedures, and malfunction analysis of the AN/ASQ-48 weapons control system.
Credit recommendation, collegiate level: CAUTION: *Navigation-bombardier training courses vary slightly in title, length, and recommendation. Require exact identification by title and length.* No credit as the course is military in nature.

Navigator Radar Intercept
(Advanced Observer Intercept)
(Advanced Observer, Intercept Training)

Location: James Connally AFB, Tex.
Length: 16–21 weeks.
Objectives: To train aircraft observers qualified in radar intercepts for entry into all weather jet fighter crew training.
Instruction: Airborne intercept radar equipment; radar equipment malfunction analysis; interception technique; simulated flight missions; operational navigation technique; jet navigation.
Credit recommendation, collegiate level: Credit in navigation and electricity on the basis of institutional examination.

Navigator Reconnaissance Upgrade Training (RF-4C)

Location: Mather AFB, Calif.
Length: 4 weeks.
Objectives: To qualify rated navigators to enter the RF-4C Tactical Reconnaissance course.
Instruction: Reconnaissance procedures; radar; mission planning.
Credit recommendation, collegiate level: No credit as the course is military in nature.

1. Non-Destructive Inspection Specialist
2. Non-Destructive Inspection (T/A 455)

Location: Chanute AFB, Ill.
Length: 12–13 weeks.
Objectives: To train airmen in the nondestructive inspection of Air Force weapons and equipment.
Instruction: Preparation of metals and parts for inspection; procedures for nondestructive inspection of parts using magnetic particle liquid penetrant, ultrasonic, eddy current, conductivity meter, ultrasonic leak, and radiographic inspection methods; types, causes, and characteristics of discontinuities and defects; conditions requiring nondestructive inspection; interpretation of testing indications.
Credit recommendation, collegiate level: These courses are technical and vocational in nature. Credit in metals testing on the basis of demonstrated skills and/or institutional examinations.

Non-Destructive Testing of Aircraft and Related Equipment Components (Non-Destructive Testing)

Location: Chanute AFB, Ill.

Length: 3 weeks.

Objectives: To train airmen in the procedures and techniques used in performing nondestructive testing.

Instruction: Nondestructive testing; cleaning of aircraft parts; reapplication of protective coatings; inspection.

Credit recommendation, collegiate level: No credit because of the brevity and limited technical nature of this course.

Nuclear Measurement Technician

Location: Lowry AFB, Colo.

Length: 23–26 weeks.

Objectives: To train airmen to operate, analyze, and repair special nuclear laboratory instruments.

Instruction: DC and AC; vacuum tubes; amplifiers and oscillators; special circuits; test equipment and electronic construction techniques; basic physics and nuclear physics.

Credit recommendation, collegiate level: 4 semester hours at the freshman or sophomore level as an elective in electricity and electronics, and credit in electrical laboratory and in nuclear physics on the basis of demonstrated skills and/or institutional examinations.

Nuclear Technician

Location: Lowry AFB, Colo.

Length: *Channel A,* 23 weeks; *Channel B,* 28 weeks.

Objectives: To train airmen to analyze electrical and electronic equipment, to operate radiological detection devices, to inspect, assemble, and handle nuclear components, and to supervise subordinates in these tasks.

Instruction: Fundamentals of DC and AC; vacuum tubes and power supplies; amplifiers and oscillators; ionization detectors and sealer; servomechanisms; test equipment and electronic construction technique.

Credit recommendation, collegiate level: 3 semester hours at the freshman or sophomore level as an elective in electricity and electronics, and credit in electrical laboratory on the basis of demonstrated skills and/or institutional examinations.

Nuclear Weapons Mechanical Specialist

Location: Lowry AFB, Colo.

Length: 15 weeks.

Objectives: To train airmen to inspect, maintain, repair, assemble and disassemble nuclear weapons.

Instruction: Introduction to nuclear weapons; familiarization with, and maintenance of, nuclear weapons.

Credit recommendation, collegiate level: This course is technical and vocational in nature. Credit in electrical shop on the basis of demonstrated skills and/or institutional examinations.

1. Nuclear Weapons Officer
2. Nuclear Weapons Officer

Location: Lowry AFB, Colo.

Length: *Course 1,* 24–26 weeks; *Course 2,* 30 weeks.

Objectives: To train officers in maintenance and repair of nuclear weapons test equipment, and command of nuclear weapons units.

Instruction: *Course 1:* DC and AC electricity; electronic tubes; special circuits; munitions maintenance; supply, storage and handling of airmunitions; operational and organizational techniques. *Course 2:* Electricity and magnetism; alternating current; vacuum tubes; special electronics, including electronic counters, diode and triode limiters, switches and relays; nuclear weapons training.

Credit recommendation, collegiate level: CAUTION: *These courses vary in length and recommendation. Require exact indentification of course by title and length. Course 1:* 2 semester hours in maintenance management, 2 semester hours at the freshman or sophomore level as an elective in electricity and electronics, and credit in electrical laboratory on the basis of demonstrated skills and/or institutional examinations. *Course 2:* 4 semester hours at the freshman or sophomore level as an elective in electricity and electronics, and credit in electrical laboratory on the basis of demonstrated skills and/or institutional examinations.

1. Nuclear Weapons Specialist
2. Nuclear Weapons Specialist
   (Nuclear Weapons Specialist (Other))
3. Nuclear Weapons Specialist (Re-Entry Vehicle) (HGM-16F)
   (Nuclear Weapons Specialist (Re-Entry Vehicle) (SM-65F))
   (Nuclear Weapons Specialist (Re-Entry Vehicle) (SM-65E))
   (Nuclear Weapons Specialist (Re-Entry Vehicle) (SM-68B))

Location: Lowry AFB, Colo.

Length: *Course 1,* 15 weeks; *Course 2,* 27–29 weeks; *Course 3,* 6–8 weeks.

Objectives: *Courses 1 and 2:* To train airmen to assemble, maintain, inspect, and repair nuclear weapons, warheads, related components and test equipment. *Course 3:* To train airmen to assemble, inspect, repair, and package the re-entry vehicle indicated in title.

Instruction: *Courses 1 and 2:* DC and AC; reactive circuits; vacuum tubes and transistors; amplifiers and oscillators. *Course 3:* Weapon system orientation; electrical test equipment; launch site procedures.

Credit recommendation, collegiate level: CAUTION: *Nuclear weapons specialist courses vary slightly in title, length, and recommendation. Require exact identification by full title and length. Courses 1 and 2:* For each course, 3 semester hours at the freshman or sophomore level as an elective in electricity and electronics, and credit in electrical laboratory on the basis of demonstrated skills and/or institutional examinations. *Course 3:* Credit in electrical laboratory on the basis of demonstrated skills and/or institutional examinations.

1. **Nuclear Weapons Specialist (Re-Entry Vehicle, LGM-30, MK 11)**
2. **Nuclear Weapons Specialist (Re-Entry Vehicle) (LGM-30C, Mk11)**
3. **Nuclear Weapons Specialist (Re-Entry Vehicle) (LGM-30C) (MK11)**

Location: Lowry AFB, Colo.

Length: *Course 1,* 18 weeks; *Course 2,* 24 weeks; *Course 3,* 8 weeks.

Objectives: To train airmen in the repair and maintenance of nuclear weapons re-entry vehicles.

Instruction: *Courses 1 and 2:* Principles of AC and DC; semiconductor devices; safety; technical publications; maintenance management; nuclear weapons theory; weapon system, re-entry vehicle, and warhead operation; re-entry vehicle test set assembly, checkout, mating, and unmating; aerospace ground equipment. In addition, *Course 2* includes Boolean notation; digital techniques; symbolic logic; penetration aids. *Course 3:* Mathematics; solid state electronics; re-entry vehicle test set; re-entry vehicle assembly, checkout, mating, and unmating.

Credit recommendation, collegiate level: CAUTION: *Nuclear weapons specialist courses vary in title, length, and recommendation. Require exact identification by full title and length.* For each course, credit in electricity and electrical laboratory on the basis of demonstrated skills and/or institutional examinations.

1. **Nuclear Weapons Specialist (Re-Entry Vehicle, SM-80-MK5)**
2. **Nuclear Weapons Specialist (CGM-13B, LCH PREP)**

Location: Lowry AFB, Colo.

Length: *Course 1,* 6 weeks; *Course 2,* 3 weeks.

Objectives: *Course 1:* To train airmen to package, unpackage, inspect, assemble, and repair the SM-80-MK5 re-entry vehicle. *Course 2:* To train airmen in the nuclear weapon specialist duties on launch crews.

Instruction: *Course 1:* Re-entry vehicle orientation and operation; re-entry vehicle test set, assembly, and checkout; simulator test set; mating, unmating, and inspection. *Course 2:* Weapon system orientation; missile-nose replacement and recycle.

Credit recommendation, collegiate level: CAUTION: *Nuclear weapons specialist courses vary in title, length, and recommendation. Require exact identification of course by full title and length.* This course is technical and vocational in nature. Credit in electrical shop on the basis of demonstrated skills and/or institutional examinations.

Nuclear Weapons Specialist (Re-Entry Vehicles) (Weapons Fuzing System Specialist (Re-Entry Vehicles))

Location: Lowry AFB, Colo.

Length: 14–18 weeks.

Objectives: To train airmen as apprentice nuclear weapons specialists.

Instruction: Principles of DC and AC; nuclear weapon familiarization; assembly and disassembly; maintenance, test, and troubleshooting.

Credit recommendation, collegiate level: CAUTION: *Nuclear weapons specialist courses vary in title, length, and recommendation. Require exact identification by full title and length.* Credit in electricity and electrical laboratory on the basis of demonstrated skills and/or institutional examinations.

1. **Nursing Service Administration**
2. **Nursing Service Administration**

Location: Gunter AFB, Ala.

Length: 24 weeks.

Objectives: To provide Nurse Corps officers with administrative training.

Instruction: *Course 1:* Students begin this course by attending the first 4 weeks of the Technical Instructor course described separately in this guide. The course proper comprises oral and written communicative skills, disaster plans and programs, Air Medical Service mission and organization, personnel management, staff study seminar, and functional management of nursing services, including staffing, nursing supervision, coordination, research and evaluation, records, facility and financial planning, medical materiel, military law and forensic medicine, hospital accreditation, and supervisory staff visits. 6 weeks training time is devoted to practical applicatory experience. *Course 2:* Students begin this course by attending the 6-week Academic Instructor course described separately in this guide. The course proper is similar in content to *Course 1.*

Credit recommendation, collegiate level: *These courses vary only in the instructor training preceding the formal course. The recommendation applies only to the formal course content and does not include consideration of academic or technical instructor training.* For each course, 4 semester hours in nursing administration, 2 semester hours in personnel management, and credit in written and oral communication on the basis of institutional examination.

1. **O-11A, O-11B and O-6 Crash Fire Truck Maintenance**
2. **O-6 and R-2 Crash Rescue Trucks, Field and Organizational Maintenance**
3. **O-10 and O-11A Crash Fire Trucks, Field Maintenance**
4. **O-11A and O-11B Crash Fire Truck Field Maintenance**

Location: Chanute AFB, Ill.

Length: *Courses 1 and 2,* 5 weeks; *Courses 3 and 4,* 4 weeks.

Objectives: To train airmen in the operation, maintenance, and repair of crash fire trucks.

Instruction: Inspection and repair of engines and steering, dispensing, heating electrical systems; operational tests; and final adjustment of the assembled units.

Credit recommendation, collegiate level: No credit because of the brevity and nature of the courses.

Offensive Fire Control Systems Mechanic (MA-8 System)
(Fire Control Systems Mechanic (MA-8 System))
Location: Lowry AFB, Colo.
Length: 29–35 weeks.
Objectives: To train airmen as MA-8 systems fire control mechanics.
Instruction: DC and AC; reactive circuits; vacuum tubes and transistors; special purpose tubes; amplifiers and oscillators; special circuits; motors and servomechanisms; multivibrators and sweep circuits; microwave principles.
Credit recommendation, collegiate level: CAUTION: *Courses in fire control vary only slightly in title, length, and recommendation. Note that titles vary by name of equipment in the parentheses following the title. Require exact identification of course by full title and length.* 6 semester hours at the freshman or sophomore level as an elective in electricity and electronics, and credit in electrical laboratory on the basis of demonstrated skills and/or institutional examinations.

1. Offensive Fire Control Systems Mechanic (MA-10, ASG-14 Systems)
2. Fire Control Systems Mechanic (MA-10, ASG-14 Systems)
Location: Lowry AFB, Colo.
Length: *Course 1*, 28 weeks; *Course 2*, 34 weeks.
Objectives: To train airmen as fire control systems mechanics.
Instruction: *Courses 1 and 2:* DC and AC; reactive circuits; vacuum tubes and transistors; amplifiers and oscillators; special circuits; multivibrators and sweep circuits; microwave principles; in addition, *Course 1* includes special purpose tubes; motors and servomechanisms.
Credit recommendation, collegiate level: CAUTION: *Courses in fire control vary only slightly in title, length, and recommendation. Note that titles vary by name of equipment in the parentheses following the title. Require exact identification by full title and length. Course 1:* 4 semester hours at the freshman or sophomore level as an elective in electricity and electronics and credit in electrical laboratory on the basis of demonstrated skills and/or institutional examinations. *Course 2:* 6 semester hours at the freshman or sophomore level as an elective in electricity and electronics and credit in electrical laboratory on the basis of demonstrated skills and/or institutional examinations.

Offensive Fire Control Systems Technician (MA-3, ASG-17 Systems)
(Fire Control Systems Technician (MA-3, ASG-17 Systems))
(Fire Control Systems Technician (MA-1, -2, -3 GBR Sight System))
(Fire Control Systems Technician (MA-1, MA-2, MA-3 Systems))
(Sighting Systems Technician)
Location: Lowry AFB, Colo.
Length: 11–16 weeks.
Objectives: To train airmen to analyze, adjust, maintain, and repair fire control systems indicated in title.

Instruction: Radar operation and maintenance; gun-bomb-rocket sight systems; low-altitude bombing system operation.
Credit recommendation, collegiate level: CAUTION: *Courses in fire control vary only slightly in title, length, and recommendation. Require exact identification by full title and length.* Credit in electronics and electrical laboratory on the basis of demonstrated skills and/or institutional examinations.

1. Officer Candidate School
2. USAF Officer Candidate School
Location: Lackland AFB, Tex.
Length: 24–25 weeks.
Objectives: To prepare officer candidates to perform the duties and assume the responsibilities of commissioned officers in the Air Force.
Instruction: *Course 1:* Political geography; international affairs; Air Force organization and function; office duties and responsibilities; leadership and human relations; character guidance. *Course 2:* Administration; classification; supply; military management and justice; leadership; character guidance.
Credit recommendation, collegiate level: CAUTION: *These courses vary only slightly in title, length, and recommendation. Require exact identification by full title and length. Course 1:* 3 semester hours in political science, 3 semester hours in business organization and management, and credit in advanced military in accordance with the school's policy. *Course 2:* 3 semester hours in business organization and management, and credit in advanced military in accordance with the school's policy.

Officer Preflight Training (Pilot and Navigator)
(Officer Preflight (Pilot))
(Officer Preflight (Navigator))
(Officer Preflight Training Program)
Location: Lackland AFB, Tex.
Length: 4 weeks.
Objectives: To prepare AFROTC graduates for the responsibilities and duties of a United States Air Force officer.
Instruction: Officer responsibilities; drills and ceremonies; physical training processing; air science.
Credit recommendation, collegiate level: No credit because of the specialized nature of this course.

1. Officers Airborne Electronics Orientation
2. Officers Ground Electronics Orientation
Location: Keesler AFB, Miss.
Length: 4 weeks.
Objectives: To familiarize officers with current Air Force management policies and procedures and with electronics equipment function and maintenance.
Instruction: Administration and supply procedures; electronics equipment functions, capabilities, and maintenance requirements.
Credit recommendation, collegiate level: No credit because of the brevity and nature of the courses.

Officers Phase I, Atomic Energy

Location: Keesler AFB, Miss.

Length: 23 weeks.

Objectives: To train officers in the fundamental principles of electronics.

Instruction: Introduction to theory; direct and alternating current principles; vacuum tubes; power supplies; vacuum tube amplifier and oscillator circuits; receiver and transmitter circuits; special electronic circuits; microwave energy generation; transmission and propagation; application of electronic principles to radar equipment.

Credit recommendation, collegiate level: 6 semester hours at the freshman or sophomore level as an elective in electricity and electronics, credit in electrical laboratory on the basis of demonstrated skills and/or institutional examinations.

Operating Room Specialist

Locations: Gunter AFB, Ala.; Sheppard AFB, Tex.

Length: 10–12 weeks.

Objectives: To train airmen to perform operating room functions and to prepare patients for surgery.

Instruction: Anatomy and physiology; operating room techniques, including packs and supplies, surgical instruments, asepsis and sterilization, circulating and scrub duties, and patient preparation; diseases requiring surgery; operating room procedures; nursing care, including psychiatric and surgical nursing; disaster medicine; field training.

Credit recommendation, collegiate level: CAUTION: *This course varies in recommendation according to the date attended. Require exact identification by title and dates of attendance.* Until May 1960, 2 semester hours in physiology and hygiene. Effective May 1960, 3 semester hours in anatomy, physiology and hygiene.

Operation and Maintenance of UNIVAC 1218 Computer

Location: Chanute AFB, Ill.

Length: 10 weeks.

Objectives: To train airmen in the operation, programming, fault isolation, and maintenance of the computer specified.

Instruction: Computer operation; computer control, arithmetic, input-output and memory sections–logic analysis and operation.

Credit recommendation, collegiate level: 4 semester hours in computer operation in the field of data processing.

Operator and Operation Maintenance of AC Systems Tester, Model T-35

Location: Chanute AFB, Ill.

Length: 3 weeks.

Objectives: To provide airmen with lateral training in the operation and maintenance of the Model T-35 (Avtron) tester.

Instruction: Description and use of the tester; component operation; use of calibration equipment; panel checking; tester calibration; testing aircraft electrical power systems units; tester troubleshooting.

Credit recommendation, collegiate level: No credit because of the brevity and limited technical nature of the course.

1. Organizational Supply Supervisor
2. Organizational Supply Specialist
3. Organizational Supply Specialist
4. Special Organizational Supply

Locations: Amarillo AFB, Tex.; Francis E. Warren AFB, Wyo.

Length: *Course 1,* 6–7 weeks; *Course 2,* 8 weeks; *Course 3,* 9–11 weeks; *Course 4,* 5 weeks.

Objectives: To train airmen to secure, handle, store, account for, and issue supplies and equipment.

Instruction: *Course 1:* Supply publications and management; equipment management system and control; organizational property accounting. *Courses 2 and 3:* Supply publications; equipment management system and control; accounting procedures; in addition *Course 3* includes typing. *Course 4:* Supply publications; organizational property accounting; inventory.

Credit recommendation, collegiate level: CAUTION: *These courses vary slightly in title, length, and recommendation. Require exact identification by title and length. Courses 1, 2, and 4:* No credit because of the limited technical nature of these courses. *Course 3:* Credit in typing on the basis of institutional examination.

Orientation AN/FSQ-7, AN/FSQ-8

Location: Keesler AFB, Miss.

Length: 6 weeks.

Objectives: To familiarize communications-electronics officers with AN/FSQ-7,8 computers and the SAGE system.

Instruction: SAGE familiarization; basic computer instruction and miscellaneous apparatus; power supplies; marginal checking; input and output systems; maintenance and operational program.

Credit recommendation, collegiate level: No credit as the course is military in nature.

Outside Wire and Antenna Systems Installation and Maintenance Specialist
(Outside Wire and Antenna Systems Installation and Maintenance)
(Cable and Antenna Installation Specialist)

Locations: Francis E. Warren AFB, Wyo.; Sheppard AFB, Tex.

Length: 12–15 weeks.

Objectives: To train airmen to install and maintain outside wire and antenna systems.

Instruction: Pole climbing and outside wire fundamentals; pole line construction; cable installation; field wire and cable systems installation and maintenance; antenna supports and installation; antenna fabrication, installation, and maintenance.

Credit recommendation, collegiate level: This course

is technical and vocational in nature. Credit in wire and antenna systems installation and maintenance on the basis of demonstrated skills and/or institutional examinations.

Parachute Rigger

Location: Chanute AFB, Ill.

Length: 14–16 weeks.

Objectives: To train airmen in the construction, maintenance, and repair of parachutes.

Instruction: Sewing principles; sewing machine maintenance; principles of parachute packing; testing, maintenance, and repair; special parachutes.

Credit recommendation, collegiate level: This course is technical and vocational in nature. Credit in sewing and parachute maintenance on the basis of demonstrated skills and/or institutional examinations.

Passenger and Household Goods Specialist (Passenger Traffic Specialist)

Location: Sheppard AFB, Tex.

Length: 4–9 weeks.

Objectives: To train airmen in the techniques and responsibilities applicable to passenger traffic management.

Instruction: Passenger traffic procedures; special and group passenger movements; household goods; transportation modes; commercial traffic; travel itineraries.

Credit recommendation, collegiate level: 2 semester hours in transportation.

Pavements Maintenance Specialist

Location: Sheppard AFB, Tex.

Length: 3–6 weeks.

Objectives: To train airmen to construct and maintain pavements.

Instruction: Plans, specifications, and blueprints; tools and equipment; soil mechanics; drainage; concrete mixtures; pavement construction; maintenance.

Credit recommendation, collegiate level: No credit because of the specialized nature of this course.

Personnel Management and Data Systems

Location: Amarillo AFB, Tex.

Length: 3 weeks.

Objectives: To train personnel to be Consolidated Base Personnel Office managers and supervisors.

Instruction: Officer and airmen personnel data systems; CBPO unit responsibilites (interface); assignments; reenlistment and separation.

Credit recommendation, collegiate level: No credit because of the brevity and limited technical nature of the course.

---

1. Personnel Officer
2. Personnel Officer
3. Advanced Personnel Officer
4. Personnel Technician
5. Personnel Specialist
6. Personnel Specialist (Classification Specialist)
7. Personnel Services Officer
8. Personnel Affairs Specialist (Personnel Affairs)

Locations: Amarillo AFB, Tex.; Greenville AFB, Miss.; Lackland AFB, Tex.; Scott AFB, Ill.

Length: *Course 1,* 12–15 weeks; *Courses 2 and 3,* 8–9 weeks; *Course 4,* 8–11 weeks; *Courses 5 and 6,* 11–18 weeks; *Course 7,* 6 weeks; *Course 8,* 4 weeks.

Objectives: To train officers and airmen in all phases of classification and assignment procedures and advisory services to personnel.

Instruction: These courses are similar in content, but vary in intensity and scope of instruction—career programs; testing practices; administration; records and procedures; personnel accounting; interviewing; classification fundamentals; in addition *Courses 5 and 6* include typing, and *Courses 7 and 8* include educational counseling and personal affairs services.

Credit recommendation, collegiate level: CAUTION: *These courses vary slightly in title, length, and recommendation. Require exact identification by title and length. Note—Courses 5 and 6 have identical titles and lengths; Course 5 was given through 1955; Course 6 was given from 1957 to the present. Require exact identification of these courses by the year they were given. Course 1:* 6 semester hours in personnel classification. *Courses 2, 3, and 4:* 4 semester hours in personnel classification for each course. *Course 5:* This course is technical and vocational in nature. Credit in typing and office practice on the basis of institutional examination. *Course 6:* 2 semester hours in personnel classification and credit in typing on the basis of institutional examination. *Course 7:* 3 semester hours in applied sociology. *Course 8:* Credit in applied sociology on the basis of institutional examination.

Personnel Staff Officer

Location: Amarillo AFB, Tex.

Length: 4 weeks.

Objectives: To train experienced personnel officers in philosophy, concepts, and principles of Air Force personnel management systems, functions, and career development and personnel planning.

Instruction: Personnel data systems; personnel services management; budget and funds management; motivation and career development; human relations and management.

Credit recommendation, collegiate level: 2 semester hours in personnel management.

Petroleum Plants and Systems, Advanced Maintenance

Location: Amarillo AFB, Tex.

Length: 5 weeks.

Objectives: To train airmen to supervise maintenance of conventional liquid fuel systems and plants.

Instruction: Fuel characteristics; basic hydraulics;

roads, ground, and rail spurs; pipelines; storage tanks; systems design criteria; mechanical system; hydrant system.

Credit recommendation, collegiate level: This course is technical and vocational in nature. Credit in petroleum plants and systems maintenance on the basis of demonstrated skills and/or institutional examinations.

Petroleum Systems Maintenance Technician

Location: Amarillo AFB, Tex.

Length: 6 weeks.

Objectives: To train airmen in the inspection and maintenance of petroleum storage and dispensing systems and equipment.

Instruction: Familiarization with petroleum products; petroleum storage and dispensing system components; operating practices; mechanical system; hydrant system; hydraulic system; maintenance of inspection records.

Credit recommendation, collegiate level: This course is technical and vocational in nature. Credit in petroleum products handling on the basis of demonstrated skills and/or institutional examinations.

Petroleum Tank Cleaning Supervisor

Location: Amarillo AFB, Tex.

Length: 3 weeks.

Objectives: To train airmen to supervise petroleum tank cleaning operations.

Instruction: Tank construction features; tank types; tank accessories; safety precautions and devices; tank inspection; tank cleaning and sludge disposal procedures; return of tanks to service.

Credit recommendation, collegiate level: No credit because of specialized nature of this course.

Pharmacy Specialist
(Apprentice Pharmacy Specialist)

Locations: Gunter AFB, Ala.; Sheppard AFB, Tex.

Length: 12–18 weeks.

Objectives: To train airmen in Air Force pharmacy operation, the dispensing and compounding of drugs under supervision, and in the use and storage of drugs, chemicals, and biological products.

Instruction: Pharmaceutical chemistry; pharmaceutical calculations; general pharmacy processes and preparations; pharmacy laboratory; pharmacological drug classes; dispensing and compounding; Air Force pharmacy; physiology.

Credit recommendation, collegiate level: 2 semester hours in pharmaceutical mathematics, 2 semester hours in pharmaceutical chemistry, and 1 semester hour in pharmacology.

Pharmacy Technician

Locations: Gunter AFB, Ala.; Sheppard AFB, Tex.

Length: 16 weeks.

Objectives: To provide airmen with advanced pharmaceutical training.

Instruction: Pharmaceutical chemistry (organic, inorganic, and physiological); pharmaceutical calculations; pharmacology; pharmacy management and administration; anatomy and physiology; chemical, biological, and radiological weapons effects and field training; writing and public speaking.

Credit recommendation, collegiate level: 3 semester hours in pharmaceutical chemistry; 2 semester hours in pharmaceutical laboratory, and 1 semester hour in pharmaceutical mathematics.

Photo Interpretation Technician

Location: Sheppard AFB, Tex.

Length: 4 weeks.

Objectives: To familiarize airmen in the fundamentals of photo interpretation.

Instruction: Photo metrics; photo mission planning; use of maps and charts; interpretation of aerial photography; intelligence reporting.

Credit recommendation, collegiate level: Credit in photo interpretation on the basis of institutional examination.

1. Photographer
(Still Photographer)
2. Still Photographer
(Still Photographic Officer)
(Photo and Laboratory Technician)

Location: Lowry AFB, Colo.

Length: *Course 1,* 18 weeks; *Course 2,* 14–15 weeks.

Objectives: To train airmen and officers in the theories of photographic processes and in the operation of photographic equipment.

Instruction: *Course 1:* Fundamentals of photography; sensitized materials, optics and light; light sources and filtration; photographic reproduction; chemistry, quality control, and color; laboratory techniques; specialized mission techniques; administration, supply, and operating procedures. *Course 2:* Elementary principles of photography; camera operation and photographic copying; projection printing; laboratory procedures; airborne equipment.

Credit recommendation, collegiate level: CAUTION: *These courses vary only slightly in title, length, and recommendation. Require exact identification by title and length. Course 1:* 4 semester hours in photographic processing laboratory. *Course 2:* 3 semester hours in photographic processing laboratory.

Photomapping

Location: Aeronautical Chart and Information Center, St. Louis, Mo.

Length: 10 weeks.

Objectives: To train airmen to prepare military maps, charts, and sketches using drafting and plotting instruments.

Instruction: Introduction to cartography; map projections; vertical and trimetrogon photogrammetry; reproduction.

Credit recommendation, collegiate level: 4 semester hours in mapping and drafting.

Physical Therapy Specialist

Location: Sheppard AFB, Tex.

Length: 10 weeks.

Objectives: To train airmen to assist officers and perform basic physical therapy procedures.

Instruction: Introduction to the basic medical sciences, including psychology, psychiatry, physiology, anatomy, neurology, osteology, myology, arthrology, and orthopedics; hydrotherapy and radiation therapy; hot packs; paraffin, Hubbard, contrast, and whirlpool baths; cryotherapy; massage; electrotherapy; laboratory diathermy; exercise and rehabilitation.

Credit recommendation, collegiate level: 2 semester hours in anatomy and physiology, and credit in physical therapy techniques on the basis of institutional examination.

Physiological Training Officer

Locations: Brooks AFB, Tex.; Gunter AFB, Ala.

Length: 6–7 weeks.

Objectives: To train officers to carry out the Air Force Physiological Training Unit or Program.

Instruction: Aviation physiology; aviation medicine; physical examinations; neurology; preventive medicine; surgery; dentistry; training and logistics.

Credit recommendation, collegiate level: 3 semester hours in aviation physiology.

1. Physiological Training Specialist
(Apprentice Physiological Training Specialist)
2. Physiological Training Supervisor

Locations: Brooks AFB, Tex.; Gunter AFB, Ala.

Length: 5–7 weeks.

Objectives: *Course 1:* To train airmen to assist officers in the operation of physiological training units. *Course 2:* To train airmen in advanced practices and procedures of aviation physiology, the use of new equipment, and in the supervisory responsibilities of the Physiological Training Program.

Instruction: *Course 1:* Basic medical orientation; aviation physiology; practical physiological training; oxygen equipment; escape and parachute training; pressure suit training; chamber flights; medicine; surgery; otorhinolaryngology. *Course 2* covers the same general areas of instruction in a program of review and advanced training.

Credit recommendation, collegiate level: 3 semester hours in aviation physiology for each course.

1. Pilot Instructor Training (T-28)
2. Pilot Instructor Training (T-28)
3. Pilot Instructor Training (T-38)
4. Pilot Instructor Training (T-38)

Locations: Moody AFB, Ga.; Randolph AFB, Tex.

Length: *Courses 1 and 3,* 10 weeks; *Course 2,* 4 weeks; *Course 4,* 5–6 weeks. *Note*—since flying training is dependent upon weather and other factors, the length of a course may vary.

Objectives: *Courses 1 and 3:* To qualify rated Air Force pilots as instructors for undergraduate pilot training. *Courses 2 and 4:* To train qualified pilot instructors on the aircraft indicated in the course title.

Instruction: All the courses are divided into flying training and academic phases. Flying training covers flight indoctrination; contact, formation, navigation, and instrument flying. The academic phase of *Courses 1 and 3* includes principles of instruction; aircraft engineering; applied aerodynamics; flight planning; instrument procedures; radio aids. The academic training of *Course 4* is similar to *Courses 1 and 3* but does not include principles of instruction. *Course 2* covers only aircraft engineering in the academic phase.

Credit recommendation, collegiate level: CAUTION: *These courses vary in length and recommendation. Require exact identification of course by title and length. Courses 1 and 3:* For each course, credit in instructional methods on the basis of institutional examination. *Courses 2 and 4:* No credit because of the brevity and specialized nature of the courses.

1. Pilot Instructor Training (T-37)
2. Pilot Instructor Training (T-33)
(Pilot Instructor Training (Basic))
(Pilot Instructor Training-Basic Single-Engine (Jet))
3. Pilot Instructor Training, Primary (T-34/T-28)
4. Pilot Instructor Training, Basic Multi-Engine (T-28)

Locations: Craig AFB, Ala.; James Connally AFB, Tex.; Randolph AFB, Tex.; Williams AFB, Ariz.

Length: *Course 1,* 9–10 weeks; *Course 2,* 10–11 weeks; *Course 3,* 8 weeks; *Course 4,* 7 weeks. *Note*—since flying training is dependent upon weather conditions and other factors, the length of the courses may vary.

Objectives: To qualify rated Air Force pilots as instructors for undergraduate pilot training.

Instruction: Flying training includes flight line indoctrination; synthetic instrument trainer; techniques of instructing contact, instrument, formation, and navigation flying. Academic training covers principles of learning; aviation physiology; aircraft engineering; flight planning; applied aerodynamics; instrument procedures; radio aids.

Credit recommendation, collegiate level: For each course, credit in instructional methods on the basis of institutional examination.

Pilot Instructor Training (T-41)

Location: Petersen Field, Colo.

Length: 5 weeks. *Note*—since flying training is dependent upon weather and other factors, the actual length of a course may vary.

Objectives: To qualify rated Air Force pilots as instructors for the Pilot Indoctrination Program.

Instruction: The course is divided into flying training and academic phases. Flying training covers policies, procedures, contact, instrument, and navigation flying. The academic phase includes principles of instruction, aircraft systems (T-41C), applied aerodynamics, and flying safety.

Credit recommendation, collegiate level: Credit in instructional methods on the basis of institutional examination.

Pilotless Aircraft Control Systems Mechanic

Location: Lowry AFB, Colo.

Length: 18 weeks.

Objectives: To train airmen as apprentice pilotless aircraft control systems mechanics.

Instruction: Fundamentals of electricity; alternating current; vacuum and gas-filled tubes; voltage regulators; amplifiers and sweep generators; control systems circuits.

Credit recommendation, collegiate level: 3 semester hours at the freshman or sophomore level as an elective in electronics, and credit in electrical laboratory on the basis of demonstrated skills and/or institutional examinations.

Plumber
(Plumbing Specialist)

Locations: Francis E. Warren AFB, Wyo.; Sheppard AFB, Tex.

Length: 10–12 weeks.

Objectives: To train airmen to install and maintain pipe systems, plumbing fixtures, and steam operated equipment.

Instruction: Introduction to plumbing; water supply system; plumbing fixtures; maintenance of piping and components; maintenance of utility equipment; waste systems; sewer installation.

Credit recommendation, collegiate level: This course is technical and vocational in nature. Credit in plumbing on the basis of demonstrated skills and/or institutional examinations.

1. Plumbing System Maintenance (LGM-25)
(Plumber/Plumbing Supervision (SM-68B))
2. Plumber/Plumbing Supervisor (SM-65F)

Location: Sheppard AFB, Tex.

Length: 4–6 weeks.

Objectives: To train airmen to inspect, service, repair, and replace the plumbing equipment of missile installations.

Instruction: Water treatment; water supply system; water storage and distribution system; waste and drainage systems.

Credit recommendation, collegiate level: These courses are technical and vocational in nature. Credit in plumbing on the basis of demonstrated skills and/or institutional examinations.

Power Production, Operation and Maintenance
(SAGE)

Location: Sheppard AFB, Tex.

Length: 8 weeks.

Objectives: To train airmen to operate and maintain electrical power production facilities at SAGE installations.

Instruction: Operating principles and plant systems; diesel engine operation, maintenance and servicing; electrical systems maintenance; power system operation and maintenance.

Credit recommendation, collegiate level: This course

is technical and vocational in nature. Credit in electrical shop on the basis of demonstrated skills and/or institutional examinations.

1. Precision Measuring Equipment Specialist
(Electronics)
2. Precision Measuring Equipment Specialist
(Electronics)
3. Precision Measuring Equipment Specialist
4. Precision Measuring Equipment Specialist
5. Precision Measuring Equipment Technician

Location: Lowry AFB, Colo.

Length: *Course 1,* 20 weeks; *Courses 2 and 3,* 35 weeks; *Course 4,* 28 weeks; *Course 5,* 16–18 weeks.

Objectives: To train airmen and civilians to analyze and isolate malfunctions, and to modify, calibrate, and repair precision measuring equipment, using Air Force base standards.

Instruction: *Courses 1, 2, and 3:* Applied mathematics; DC and low-frequency AC measurement; wave-form analysis; frequency measurement; microwave measurement. In addition *Courses 2 and 3* include DC and AC circuit analysis; vacuum tubes and special circuit analysis; solid state electronics; nuclear radiation measurements; and physical measurement. *Course 4:* Applied mathematics; metrology; electronic circuits; voltage, current, and power measurement; resistance and impedance measurement; wave-form analysis; frequency, microwave, nuclear radiation, and physical measurement. *Course 5:* Fundamentals of calibration; voltage and current measuring equipment; frequency and RF measurement; radar test equipment; electromechanical and mechanical standards.

Credit recommendation, collegiate level: CAUTION: *These courses vary slightly in title, length, and recommendation. Require exact identification by title and length. Course 1:* Credit in electricity and electrical laboratory on the basis of demonstrated skills and/or institutional examinations. *Courses 2 and 3:* For each course, 4 semester hours at the freshman or sophomore level as an elective in electricity and electronics, and credit in electrical laboratory on the basis of demonstrated skills and/or institutional examinations. *Course 4:* 3 semester hours at the freshman or sophomore level as an elective in electricity and electronics, and credit in electrical laboratory on the basis of demonstrated skills and/or institutional examinations. *Course 5:* Credit in electrical laboratory on the basis of demonstrated skills and/or institutional examinations.

1. Precision Photographic Services Officer
2. Precision Photographic Processing Specialist
3. Precision Photographic Processing Technician
(Precision Photographic Processing Control
Technician)
(Precision Photographic Processing Control)
4. Precision Photographic Processing Techniques
(Precision Photographic Processing Specialist)

Location: Lowry AFB, Colo.

Length: *Courses 1 and 2,* 21–25 weeks; *Course 3,* 13 weeks; *Course 4,* 9–10 weeks.

Objectives: To train airmen and officers in the science of precision photographic processing.

Instruction: *Courses 1 and 2:* Fundamentals of photography; physics of photography; fundamentals of color photography; preview of mathematics; photographic science; statistical and mathematical functions; chemistry of the photographic process; kinetics of the photographic process; precision control techniques; photographic image evaluation; management and support of advanced photographic systems. *Course 3:* Statistical quality control; chemistry of the photographic processes; mechanics and kinetics of the photographic process; photographic image evaluation. *Course 4:* Sensitometric control procedures; principles of photographic chemistry; statistical and mathematical functions; precision equipment and evaluation procedures.

Credit recommendation, collegiate level: CAUTION: *These courses vary slightly in title, length, and recommendation. Require exact identification by title and length. Courses 1 and 2:* For each course, 5 semester hours in precision photographic processing laboratory, and credit in elementary statistics on the basis of institutional examination. *Course 3:* 3 semester hours in precision photographic processing laboratory. *Course 4:* 2 semester hours in precision photographic processing laboratory, and credit in elementary statistics on the basis of institutional examination.

1. **Preventive Medicine Specialist**
   (Apprentice Preventive Medicine Specialist)
2. **Preventive Medicine Technician**

Locations: Brooks AFB, Tex.; Gunter AFB, Ala.
Length: 10–16 weeks.
Objectives: *Course 1:* To train airmen in the fundamentals of preventive medicine. *Course 2:* To provide preventive medicine specialists with advanced, supervisory-level training.

Instruction: *Course 1:* Basic medical orientation; environmental sanitation; epidemiology; medical entomology; biostatistics; radiobiology; industrial hygiene; field medical training. *Course 2:* Bio-environmental engineering; basic mathematics and chemistry of water and sewage disposal; disaster medicine; epidemiology; medical entomology; nuclear medicine.

Credit recommendation, collegiate level: *Course 1:* 2 semester hours in elementary preventive medicine and 2 semester hours in sanitary bacteriology. *Course 2:* 2 semester hours in elementary preventive medicine and 3 semester hours in sanitary bacteriology.

Primary-Basic Navigator Upgrading
Location: Mather AFB, Calif.
Length: 26 weeks. *Note*—since flying training is dependent upon weather and other factors, the length of the course may vary.
Objectives: To upgrade World War II navigators to the standard levels of training in navigation and electronics required for all specialities in the aircraft observer career fields.
Instruction: Flying training subjects; dead reckoning; celestial fixes; loran; grid navigation; weather; pressure pattern; radar navigation; electricity and magnetism; AC; vacuum tubes.
Credit recommendation, collegiate level: CAUTION: *Primary-basic navigator (observer) upgrading courses vary slightly in title, length, and recommendation. Re-*

quire exact identification by title and length. 3 semester hours at the freshman or sophomore level as an elective in electricity and electronics, 3 semester hours in navigation, *provided no previous credit has been given in this field,* and credit in electrical laboratory on the basis of demonstrated skills and/or institutional examinations.

1. **Primary-Basic Observer Upgrading**
2. **Primary-Basic Observer Upgrading**

Locations: Ellington AFB, Tex.; Mather AFB, Calif.
Length: *Course 1,* 23 weeks; *Course 2,* 34 weeks.
Objectives: To upgrade rated observers and to train them in the fundamentals of all observer skills.
Instruction: *Courses 1 and 2:* Flying training; dead reckoning; map reading and radio; sunlines; celestial fixes; loran; grid navigation; pressure pattern; radar; weather; in addition, *Course 2* includes electricity and magnetism; alternating current; vacuum tubes; radio-loran; radar systems; amplifiers and oscillators.

Credit recommendation, collegiate level: CAUTION: *These courses vary slightly in length and recommendation. Require exact identification by title and length. Course 1:* 6 semester hours in navigation. *Course 2:* 6 semester hours in navigation, 3 semester hours in electricity and electronics, and credit in electrical laboratory on the basis of demonstrated skills and/or institutional examinations.

Prior Service Military Training
Location: Lackland AFB, Tex.
Length: 3 weeks.
Objectives: To classify and indoctrinate airmen for military service.
Instruction: Military law; squadron orientation; Air Force customs and courtesies; survival training, weapons and marksmanship; drills and ceremonies.
Credit recommendation, collegiate level: No credit as the course is military in nature.

1. **Procurement Officer**
   (Purchasing and Contracting Officer)
2. **Purchasing and Contracting Officer**

Locations: Amarillo AFB, Tex.; Francis E. Warren, AFB, Wyo.
Length: *Course 1,* 6–11 weeks; *Course 2,* 12 weeks.
Objectives: To train officers and civilian personnel in the principles and techniques of procuring at base, depot, and headquarters level.
Instruction: *Course 1:* Procurement procedures, including law, responsibilities, and ethics; bonds, insurance, and taxes; patents and copyrights; financial aids; methods of procurement; purchase requests; bids; types of contracts; contract administration; contract termination.
Credit recommendation, collegiate level: CAUTION: *These courses vary slightly in title, length, and recommendation. Require exact identification by title and length. Course 1:* 4 semester hours in principles of contract negotiation. *Course 2:* 6 semester hours in principles of contract negotiation.

1. Procurement Supervisor
2. Procurement Specialist

Location: Amarillo AFB, Tex.

Length: 6–7 weeks.

Objectives: To train airmen and civilians in procurement procedures.

Instruction: Procurement procedures; sources and negotiation; small purchases; formal advertising; kinds of contracts and administration.

Credit recommendation, collegiate level: 3 semester hours in procurement policies.

Production Control

Location: Chanute AFB, Ill.

Length: 12–14 weeks.

Objectives: To train airmen as production scheduling or materials estimating specialists.

Instruction: Production control fundamentals; material control fundamentals; estimating and researching work order requirements; utilization of maintenance production analysis; shop scheduling; aircraft scheduling.

Credit recommendation, collegiate level: 3 semester hours in business organization and management.

Programming Concepts

Location: Sheppard AFB, Tex.

Length: 3 weeks.

Objectives: To train airmen in the fundamentals of computer programming.

Instruction: Familiarization with typical data systems; components and functions of EDP equipment; basic computer programming.

Credit recommendation, collegiate level: Credit in programming concepts on the basis of institutional examination in the field of computer management.

Programming Specialist

Location: Sheppard AFB, Tex.

Length: 9 weeks.

Objectives: To train airmen in general computer programming.

Instruction: Theory and operating principles of computers; symbolic and input-output programming; utility programs; problem oriented language; flow charting; applications of programming procedures to actual card, magnetic tape, magnetic drum, and high speed printer problem situations.

Credit recommendation, collegiate level: 4 semester hours in computer programming in the field of computing science.

Propulsion Shop Management

Location: Chanute AFB, Ill.

Length: 3–4 weeks.

Objectives: To train airmen in propulsion shop management.

Instruction: Workload forecasting techniques; production planning; materiel and tool requirements; work scheduling; management appraisal; work planning and control evaluation.

Credit recommendation, collegiate level: 2 semester hours in shop management.

Protective Coating Specialist

Location: Sheppard AFB, Tex.

Length: 8 weeks.

Objectives: To train airmen in the causes and effects, treatment and protection of metal corrosion and of wood, masonry, and concrete deterioration.

Instruction: Introduction to corrosion control and nonmetal deterioration; material and equipment; corrosion control for metals; preparation and protection of wood, masonry, and concrete surfaces.

Credit recommendation, collegiate level: This course is technical and vocational in nature. Credit in corrosion control on the basis of demonstrated skills and/or institutional examinations.

Provost Marshal
(Air Police (Provost Marshal), Phase I)

Location: Lackland AFB, Tex.

Length: 3 weeks.

Objectives: To provide a refresher course for officers in basic military police methods.

Instruction: Duties of a provost marshal; corrections; military and martial law; law enforcement functions; traffic management; administrative security; administrative and command matters.

Credit recommendation, collegiate level: No credit because of the brevity and specialized nature of this course.

1. Psychiatric Ward Specialist
2. Psychiatric Ward Specialist

Locations: *Course 1*, Gunter AFB, Ala.; *Course 2*, Sheppard AFB, Tex.

Length: *Course 1*, 16 weeks; *Course 2*, 14 weeks.

Objectives: To train airmen to assist professional personnel in the care and treatment of patients in psychiatric wards.

Instruction: *Course 1:* Anatomy; physiology; medicine; surgery; general nursing; disaster medicine; medical materiel; pharmacy; psychiatric nursing. For the second half of the course students are sent on temporary assignment to Eglin AFB Psychiatric Service for clinical application of psychiatric nursing fundamentals. *Course 2:* Aeromedical evacuation; anatomy; physiology; preventive medicine; radiology; surgery; introduction to psychiatric nursing; pathological behavior; implementing nursing skills; psychotherapy; chemical and electroconvulsive somatic therapy; adjunct therapy; practical application of psychiatric nursing.

Credit recommendation, collegiate level: these courses are at the professional or preprofessional level. Credit in psychiatric nursing procedures on the basis of institutional examination.

Publications Functions—Supervisor

Location: Amarillo AFB, Tex.

Length: 3 weeks.

Objectives: To train noncommissioned officers in the supervision of publications systems.

Instruction: Publications systems; preparation, reproduction, distribution, and control of publications; files and maintenance; management and supervision.

Credit recommendation, collegiate level: No credit because of the brevity and limited technical nature of this course.

Quality Control—Materials and Processes

Location: Chanute AFB, Ill.

Length: 3 weeks.

Objectives: To provide training for Air Force personnel in the procedures and techniques of quality control of materials and processes.

Instruction: Types, uses, and characteristics of metals; heat treatment of metals; welding processes; chemical milling; industrial cleaning of metal surfaces; destructive and nondestructive testing methods.

Credit recommendation, collegiate level: This course is technical and vocational in nature. Credit in metals testing on the basis of demonstrated skills and/or institutional examinations.

Radar Equipment Air Maintenance Upgrading

Location: Mather AFB, Calif.

Length: 4–6 weeks.

Objectives: To train experienced aircraft navigator-bombardiers to analyze equipment malfunctions and perform corrective inflight maintenance.

Instruction: Training in the malfunction and maintenance of K-systems or MA-6A/7A systems.

Credit recommendation, collegiate level: This course is technical and vocational in nature. Credit in mechanical shop on the basis of demonstrated skills and/or institutional examinations.

Radar Intercept Officer Training

Location: James Connally AFB, Tex.

Length: 25 weeks.

Objectives: To qualify navigators as radar intercept officers.

Instruction: Electricity and magnetism; alternating current; vacuum tubes; basic radio.

Credit recommendation, collegiate level: 4 semester hours at the freshman or sophomore level as an elective in electricity, and credit in electrical laboratory on the basis of demonstrated skills and/or institutional examinations.

Radio Inertial Ground Guidance Familiarization (SM-65D)

Location: Keesler AFB, Miss.

Length: 3 weeks.

Objectives: To familiarize officer engineering personnel with the AN/URW-12 ground guidance system.

Instruction: Familiarization with guidance systems data flow; subsystem function and troubleshooting aspects; use of self-check equipment.

Credit recommendation, collegiate level: No credit because of the specialized nature of the course.

1. Radio Relay Equipment Repairman (AN/TRC)
2. Radio Relay Equipment Repairman (AN/TRC)

Locations: Keesler AFB, Miss.; Scott AFB, Ill.

Length: *Course 1,* 30 weeks; *Course 2,* 17–19 weeks.

Objectives: To train airmen to install, maintain, and repair UHF radio relay and associated terminal equipment.

Instruction: *Course 1:* DC and AC; electron tubes and power supplies; amplifiers and oscillators; special circuits. *Courses 1 and 2:* Radio relay transmitting and receiving equipment; radio relay systems.

Credit recommendation, collegiate level: CAUTION: *Courses in radio relay equipment repair vary in credit recommendation. Require complete identification by title and length. Note that titles may vary only by name of equipment in the parentheses following the title. Course 1:* 3 semester hours at the freshman or sophomore level as an elective in electricity and electronics, and credit in electrical laboratory on the basis of demonstrated skills and/or institutional examinations. *Course 2:* Credit in electrical laboratory on the basis of demonstrated skills and/or institutional examinations.

1. Radio Relay Equipment Repairman (Carrier and Antrac Equipment)
2. Radio Relay Equipment Repairman (Carrier and Antrac Equipment)
3. Radio Relay Equipment Repairman (Carrier)
4. Radio Relay Equipment Repairman (Carrier) (Carrier Repeater Mechanic Course)

Locations: Francis E. Warren AFB, Wyo.; Keesler AFB, Miss.; Scott AFB, Ill.

Length: *Course 1,* 36 weeks; *Course 2,* 34 weeks; *Course 3,* 30 weeks; *Course 4,* 16–25 weeks.

Objectives: To train airmen in the organizational maintenance and repair of carrier and/or antrac radio relay equipment.

Instruction: *Courses 1, 2, and 3:* Direct and alternating current; tubes and power supplies; amplifiers and oscillators; special circuits; telephone and telegraph principles; in addition, *Course 1* includes radar microwave propagation. *Course 4:* Construction and troubleshooting of basic electrical circuits; construction and troubleshooting of basic electronic tubes; long distance telephone and telegraph signals.

Credit recommendation, collegiate level: CAUTION: *Courses in radio relay equipment repair vary in credit recommendation. Require complete identification by title and length. Note that titles may vary only by name of equipment in the parentheses following the title. Course 1:* 4 semester hours at the freshman or sophomore level as an elective in electronics and electricity, and credit in electrical laboratory on the basis of demonstrated skills and/or institutional examinations. *Courses 2 and 3:* For each course, 3 semester hours at the freshman or sophomore level as an elective in electricity and electronics, and credit in electrical laboratory on the basis of demonstrated skills and/or institutional examinations. *Course 4:* This course is technical and vocational in nature. Credit in telephone repair on the basis of demonstrated skills and/or institutional examinations.

Radio Relay Equipment Repairman (EAME)
(Radio Relay Equipment Repairman)

Location: Keesler AFB, Miss.

Length: 31–38 weeks.

Objectives: To train airmen in the operation, maintenance, and repair of radio relay equipment.

Instruction: DC and AC circuits; solid state devices; vacuum tubes; oscillators and amplifiers; receiver principles; motors and servomechanisms; microwave principles; telegraph and telephone multiplexing; VHF-UHF communications; tactical radio relay and fixed-radio relay.

Credit recommendation, collegiate level: CAUTION: *Courses in radio relay equipment repair vary in credit recommendation. Require complete identification by title and length. Note that titles may vary only by name of equipment in the parentheses following the title.* 6 semester hours at the freshman or sophomore level as an elective in electricity and electronics, and credit in electrical laboratory on the basis of demonstrated skills and/or institutional examinations.

Radio Relay Equipment Repairman (FPTS)
(Radio Relay Equipment Repairman (FPTS)
(AN/FRC-39 and AN/FRC-39A))
(Ground Communications Equipment Repairman (Heavy) (FPTS))
(Ground Communications Equipment Repairman, FPTS (Heavy))

Location: Keesler AFB, Miss.

Length: 4–7 weeks.

Objectives: To train airmen in the repair, preventive maintenance, and theory of operation of radio relay equipment.

Instruction: System familiarization and function; performance testing; trouble analysis; equipment repair.

Credit recommendation, collegiate level: CAUTION: *Courses in ground communication and radio relay equipment repair vary in credit recommendation. Require complete identification by title and length. Note that titles may vary only by name of equipment in the parentheses following the title.* These courses are technical and vocational in nature. Credit in radio repair on the basis of demonstrated skills and/or institutional examinations.

1. Radio Relay Equipment Repairman (Microwave and Associated Relay Center Equipment)
2. Radio Relay Equipment Repairman (Microwave)
3. Radio Relay Equipment Repairman (Microwave)
4. Radio Relay Repairman (Microwave)

Locations: Keesler AFB, Miss.; Scott AFB, Ill.

Length: *Courses 1 and 2,* 32–36 weeks; *Courses 3 and 4,* 19–22 weeks.

Objectives: To train airmen in the operation, maintenance, and repair of microwave radio relay and associated equipment.

Instruction: *Courses 1 and 2:* Direct and alternating current; reactive circuits; vacuum tubes and transistors; special purpose tubes; amplifiers and oscillators; special circuits; motors and servomechanisms; multivibrators and sweep circuits. *Courses 3 and 4:* Introduction to microwave radio relay equipment CLR-6; terminal equipment CMT-4.

Credit recommendation, collegiate level: CAUTION: *Courses in radio relay equipment repair vary in credit recommendation. Require complete identification by title and length. Note that titles vary only by name of equipment in the parentheses following the title. Courses 1 and 2:* For each course, 4 semester hours at the freshman or sophomore level as an elective in electricity and electronics, and credit in electrical laboratory on the basis of demonstrated skills and/or institutional examinations. *Courses 3 and 4:* For each course, credit in electricity and electrical laboratory on the basis of demonstrated skills and/or institutional examinations.

1. Radio Relay Equipment Repairman (Relay Center Equipment)
2. Ground Communications Equipment Repairman (Relay Center)

Locations: Keesler AFB, Miss.; Scott AFB, Ill.

Length: *Course 1,* 28 weeks; *Course 2,* 17–18 weeks.

Objectives: To train airmen to install, maintain, and repair radio relay equipment.

Instruction: *Course 1:* Direct and alternating current; electron tubes and power supplies; amplifiers and oscillators; special circuits. *Course 2:* Ground communications terminal equipment; multiplex equipment; single-side-band terminal equipment; facsimile equipment.

Credit recommendation, collegiate level: CAUTION: *Courses in ground communications and radio relay equipment repair vary in credit recommendation. Require complete identification by title and length. Note that titles may vary only by name of equipment in the parentheses following the title. Course 1:* 4 semester hours at the freshman or sophomore level as an elective in electricity; and credit in electrical laboratory on the basis of demonstrated skills and/or institutional examinations. *Course 2:* This course is technical and vocational in nature. Credit in radio repair on the basis of demonstrated skills and/or institutional examinations.

Radio Relay Equipment Repairman (Wide-band)

Location: Keesler AFB, Miss.

Length: 12 weeks.

Objectives: To provide airmen with a knowledge of wide-band communication concepts, systems, and configurations.

Instruction: Wide-band communications systems; telephone and telegraph terminals; microwave transceivers; forward propagation tropospheric scatter equipment.

Credit recommendation, collegiate level: CAUTION: *Courses in radio relay equipment repair vary in credit* *recommendation. Require complete identification by title and length. Note that titles may vary only by name of equipment in the parentheses following the title.* Credit in electrical laboratory on the basis of demonstrated skills and/or institutional examinations.

1. Radio Relay Equipment Technician
2. Radio Relay Equipment Maintenance Technician

Location: Keesler AFB, Miss.

Length: 39–44 weeks.

Objectives: To train airmen in the operation, maintenance, and installation of radio relay and associated equipment.

Instruction: *Course 1:* Applied mathematics; DC and AC; vacuum tubes and solid state devices; power supplies; oscillators; principles of electronic digital data processing; transmitter and RF systems; receiver systems; indicator and servo systems; administration and publications; training and maintenance management. *Course 2:* Electronic concepts; basic circuits; advanced circuits; frequency modulation transmitter and receiver principles; management and supervision.

Credit recommendation, collegiate level: *Course 1:* 2 semester hours in shop management; 6 semester hours at the freshman or sophomore level as an elective in electricity and electronics, and credit in electrical laboratory on the basis of demonstrated skills and/or institutional examinations. *Course 2:* 2 semester hours in shop management, 3 semester hours at the freshman or sophomore level as an elective in electricity and electronics, and credit in electrical laboratory on the basis of demonstrated skills and/or institutional examinations.

Radiograph Interpreter

Location: Chanute AFB, Ill.

Length: 3 weeks.

Objectives: To train Air Force personnel in the procedures and techniques of producing radiographs.

Instruction: Radiographic theory; film exposure and processing; radiographic equipment; laboratory operation; interpretation of radiographs.

Credit recommendation, collegiate level: No credit because of the brevity and specialized nature of the course.

Radiology Specialist
(Apprentice Radiology Specialist)

Locations: Gunter AFB, Ala.; Sheppard AFB, Tex.

Length: 12–18 weeks.

Objectives: To train airmen to assist radiologists in examinations and therapy treatments and to operate radiographic and fluoroscopic equipment.

Instruction: Radiographic physics; anatomy and physiology; nursing; electrical and radiation protection; darkroom technique; radiographic positioning and technique; special procedures; field equipment and maintenance; therapy; dental radiology.

Credit recommendation, collegiate level: CAUTION: *This course varies in recommendation according to the year attended. Require identification of the course by*

the title and dates attended. Prior to January 1963, credit in anatomy and physiology on the basis of institutional examination. At the technical level, credit in X-ray technology on the basis of institutional examination. Effective January 1963, 2 semester hours in elementary anatomy and physiology. At the technical level, credit in X-ray technology on the basis of institutional examination.

Radiology Technician

Locations: Gunter AFB, Ala.; Sheppard AFB, Tex.

Length: 9–16 weeks.

Objectives: To provide advanced training for radiology personnel.

Instruction: Review of radiographic fundamentals and advanced studies in the areas of anatomy and physiology, radiographic techniques, special radiographic positions, special equipment and procedures, and radiation protection and administration.

Credit recommendation, collegiate level: 2 semester hours in elementary anatomy and physiology. At the technical level, credit in X-ray technology on the basis of institutional examination.

Ramjet Engine Mechanic, RJ-43, IM-99B

Location: Chanute AFB, Ill.

Length: 5 weeks.

Objectives: To train jet engine mechanics to install and maintain ramjet engines.

Instruction: Operation and maintenance of the ramjet test set; IM-99B weapon system; engine disassembly and assembly; high-pressure gases safety precautions.

Credit recommendation, collegiate level: This course is technical and vocational in nature. Credit in ramjet engine repair shop on the basis of demonstrated skills and/or institutional examinations.

Rawinsonde Operation

Location: Chanute AFB, Ill.

Length: 12 weeks.

Objectives: To train weather observers in the theory and practice of rawinsonde observation.

Instruction: Rawinsonde equipment; recorder record evaluation; charts evaluation; winds aloft evaluation; rawinsonde laboratory and evaluation.

Credit recommendation, collegiate level: 3 semester hours in meteorology.

Rawinsonde Procedures

Location: Chanute AFB, Ill.

Length: 4 weeks.

Objectives: To provide supplemental training for airmen in rawinsonde procedures.

Instruction: Theory and operation of rawinsonde equipment; recorder records; radiosonde charts; winds aloft computation and encoding.

Credit recommendation, collegiate level: Credit in meteorology on the basis of institutional examination.

1. Reciprocating Engine Conditioning with Analyzers
   (R2800 and Smaller)
2. Reciprocating Engine Conditioning with Analyzers
   (R3350)
3. Reciprocating Engine Conditioning with Analyzers
   (R4360)
4. Aircraft Reciprocating Engine Conditioning
5. Reciprocating Engine Mechanic, Engine Analyzer

Location: Sheppard AFB, Tex.

Length: 4–5 weeks.

Objectives: To train airmen in the conditioning of aircraft reciprocating engines and in the application of ignition and engine analyzers.

Instruction: Operating principles of reciprocating engines and systems; ignition and engine analyzers; engine operation, test, and adjustments utilizing analyzers and test equipment.

Credit recommendation, collegiate level: No credit because of the limited technical nature of the courses.

Recruiter
(USAF Recruiter)
(USAF Recruiting Course)

Location: Lackland AFB, Tex.

Length: 7–9 weeks.

Objectives: To train officers and airmen in the skill, knowledge, and techniques essential for Air Force recruiting salesmen.

Instruction: Selection criteria; publicity and community relations; speech and personal relations; salesmanship and sales management.

Credit recommendation, collegiate level: Credit in speech and public relations on the basis of demonstrated skills and/or institutional examinations.

1. Redistribution and Marketing Officer
2. Redistribution and Marketing Specialist
3. Redistribution and Marketing

Location: Amarillo AFB, Tex.

Length: 3–4 weeks.

Objectives: To train airmen and officers to perform duties in base redistribution and marketing activity.

Instruction: Procedures for receiving, storing, reporting, accounting for, and disposing of USAF excess and surplus property.

Credit recommendation, collegiate level: These courses are technical and vocational in nature. Credit in office practice on the basis of institutional examination.

Refresher Course in Hospital Administration
(Senior Hospital Administrator)

Location: Gunter AFB, Ala.

Length: 3 weeks.

Objectives: to provide a forum for the exchange of ideas and new materials between staff-level personnel and hospital administrators.

Instruction: Basic medical review; medical administration, including hospital administration, materiel, military law, and registrar sections.

Credit recommendation, collegiate level: No credit because of the brevity and nature of the course.

Refrigeration and Air Conditioning Specialist
(Refrigeration Specialist)
(Refrigeration Specialist (Refrigeration and Air Conditioning))
(Refrigeration Specialist (Equipment Cooling))
(Equipment Cooling Specialist)

Location: Sheppard AFB, Tex.

Length: 17–24 weeks.

Objectives: To train airmen in the operating principles of refrigeration and air-conditioning systems.

Instruction: Principles of refrigeration; refrigeration systems; air conditioning.

Credit recommendation, collegiate level: These courses are technical and vocational in nature. Credit in refrigeration and air-conditioning equipment maintenance on the basis of demonstrated skills and/or institutional examinations.

1. Refrigeration Specialist, WS-133B
2. Refrigeration Specialist, WS-133A
   (Refrigeration Specialist (SM-80))
3. Refrigeration Technician, SM-80
4. Refrigeration Supervisor/Technician (SM-65F)
5. Refrigeration Specialist/Supervisor (SM-68)
6. Equipment Cooling Specialist/Technician,
   SM-68B
7. Refrigeration and Air Conditioning Controls

Locations: Chanute AFB, Ill.; Sheppard AFB, Tex.

Length: 3–10 weeks.

Objectives: To train airmen in the operation and maintenance of refrigeration, air conditioning, and accessory equipment.

Instruction: *Courses 1 and 2:* Familiarization and controls; launch control facility; launch facility systems and maintenance; guidance and control cooling; support vehicle environmental systems. *Courses 3 and 4:* Facility system components and controls; facility system maintenance and operation. *Courses 5 and 6:* Operation and maintenance of control systems, chilled water and refrigerated air-conditioning system. *Course 7:* Pneumatic controls; electrical and electronic controls.

Credit recommendation, collegiate level: These courses are technical and vocational in nature. Credit in refrigeration and air-conditioning equipment maintenance on the basis of demonstrated skills and/or institutional examinations.

1. Removable Partial Denture Prosthetics
2. Chrome-Cobalt Dental Prosthetics

Locations: Gunter AFB, Ala.; Sheppard AFB, Tex.

Length: 6–7 weeks.

Objectives: To train dental laboratory airmen in the fundamentals of cast partial denture prosthetics using chrome-cobalt alloy.

Instruction: Dental administration and dental laboratory procedures, including cast partial frameworks, partial denture base, partial denture repairs and construction.

Credit recommendation, collegiate level: Credit in dental laboratory technology on the basis of institutional examination.

Rescue and Survival Technician–Medical

Locations: Gunter AFB, Ala.; Sheppard AFB, Tex.
Length: 4 weeks.
Objectives: To train airmen to perform emergency medical treatment.
Instruction: Anatomy and physiology; parenteral therapy; physical examination; treatment of hemorrhage, shock, wounds, infections, thermal injuries, fractures, dislocations, respiratory distress, head and spinal cord injuries; emergency delivery; poisonous agents; disaster medicine.
Credit recommendation, collegiate level: Credit in first aid on the basis of institutional examination.

Rocket Propulsion Technician (Interim)

Location: Chanute AFB, Ill.
Length: 5 weeks.
Objectives: To train airmen to perform organizational and field maintenance on liquid propellant rockets.
Instruction: Rocket propulsion introduction; liquid propellant rockets; storage and handling of propellants and gases; theoretical and mechanical aspects of liquid rockets.
Credit recommendation, collegiate level: This course is technical and vocational in nature. Credit in rocket propellant system repair on the basis of demonstrated skills and/or institutional examinations.

1. SAGE System Maintenance Management Officer
(SAGE Maintenance Control Officer)
2. SAGE Maintenance Control Technician

Location: Keesler AFB, Miss.
Length: 11–15 weeks.
Objectives: To train officers and airmen in the organization and operation of the SAGE system.
Instruction: Computer principles; central computer operation; computer drums and display system; function of SAGE subsystems; operational programs; SAGE maintenance control procedures.
Credit recommendation, collegiate level: No credit because of the specialized nature of the courses.

Safety Supervisor

Location: Chanute AFB, Ill.
Length: 3 weeks.
Objectives: To provide supervisory-level training for safety specialists and technicians.
Instruction: Philosophy of accident prevention; educating for safety; accident investigation and reporting; motor vehicle and traffic safety.
Credit recommendation, collegiate level: No credit

because of the brevity and limited technical nature of the course.

Senior Observer Technical Specialist Training

Location: Mather AFB, Calif.
Length: 40–48 weeks.
Objectives: To train officers in the policies, techniques, and developmental requirements of an observer's duties and staff responsibilities.
Instruction: Algebra; plane and spherical trigonometry; analytical geometry; differential and integral calculus; statistics; properties of matter; dynamics of translatory motion; dynamics of rotary motion; heat; sound and light; meteorology; cartography; molecular theory; equilibrium; electrostatics and magnetism; fundamentals of electricity; vacuum tubes; power supplies; amplifiers and oscillators; generators and servomechanisms; radar systems; aerodynamics; celestial navigation; aircraft performance engineering; pressure pattern and grid navigation; advanced navigational aids and techniques.
Credit recommendation, collegiate level: Credit in mathematics, physics, electronics, navigation, and meteorology on the basis of institutional examination.

1. Sensitometric and Densitometric Control Techniques
2. Sensitometric and Densitometric Equipment Operator

Location: Lowry AFB, Colo.
Length: 3–5 weeks.
Objectives: To train airmen and officers in sensitometric and densitometric equipment as applied to general photographic processes.
Instruction: Principles of sensitometric control; methods and measurement of exposure; logarithmic exposure progression; chemical mixing; transmission, density, and opacity; D log E curves.
Credit recommendation, collegiate level: Credit in photography on the basis of demonstrated skills and/or institutional examinations.

1. Sentry Dog Handler
(Sentry Dog Handler (Air Policeman))
2. Sentry Dog Replacement Course

Location: Lackland AFB, Tex.
Length: *Course 1*, 6–8 weeks; *Course 2*, 4 weeks.
Objectives: To train Air Policemen and dogs as effective sentry teams.
Instruction: *Course 1:* History and health of dogs; prevention of disease and first aid; obedience training; agitation; attack; detection; search and escort of apprehended personnel; transporting dogs; safety measures; simulated sentry post patrol. *Course 2* is for qualified sentry dog handlers and dogs with obedience training. Emphasis is on actual performance, and instruction consists of field, security, and apprehension training.
Credit recommendation, collegiate level: These courses are technical and vocational in nature. Credit in dog handling and care on the basis of demonstrated skills.

Single-Side-Band System Maintenance

Location: Keesler AFB, Miss.

Length: 16 weeks.

Objectives: To train airmen in the advanced theory of operation and maintenance of a single-side-band communications system.

Instruction: Communication relay center equipment; circuit analysis; transmitting and receiving equipment; troubleshooting and repair; testing of complete SSB system.

Credit recommendation, collegiate level: Credit in electrical laboratory on the basis of demonstrated skills and/or institutional examinations.

Site Development Specialist

Location: Sheppard AFB, Tex.

Length: 19 weeks.

Objectives: To train airmen in the development of site plans.

Instruction: Drafting fundamentals; construction drawing; site plans, material estimates, and facility drawings; fundamentals of surveying; transit adjustments and readings; traverse computations and direct level circuit; road layout and utilities drainage; civil engineering inspection responsibilities; inspection of building construction, utility systems, and roads and grounds.

Credit recommendation, collegiate level: 6 semester hours in construction engineering.

Small Arms Gunsmith Specialist

Location: Lowry AFB, Colo.

Length: 11 weeks.

Objectives: To train airmen in the maintenance of small arms.

Instruction: Use of tools; operation, disassembly, assembly, inspection, and overhaul of small arms; shop procedures.

Credit recommendation, collegiate level: This course is technical and vocational in nature. Credit in mechanical shop on the basis of demonstrated skills and/or institutional examinations.

Solid State Devices, F&O Maintenance

Location: Keesler AFB, Miss.

Length: 3 weeks.

Objectives: To train airmen in the principles and application of solid state devices.

Instruction: Introduction to transistors; basic transistor circuit configurations; transistor amplifiers and oscillators; transistor multivibrators and receivers.

Credit recommendation, collegiate level: This course is technical and vocational in nature. Credit in electrical shop on the basis of demonstrated skills and/or institutional examinations.

1. Special Electronics Equipment Specialist, "Q" System
2. Special Electronic Equipment Specialist

Location: Lowry AFB, Colo.

Length: 39-40 weeks.

Objectives: To train airmen to maintain and repair classified special electronic equipment.

Instruction: Electronics training includes fundamentals of DC and AC electricity; vacuum tubes; amplifiers and oscillators; transmitter and receiver principles; special circuits; construction of an oscilloscope kit; special electronic equipment systems.

Credit recommendation, collegiate level: For each course, 3 semester hours at the freshman or sophomore level as an elective in electricity and electronics, *and* credit in electrical laboratory on the basis of demonstrated skills and/or institutional examinations.

Special Investigators

Location: USAF Special Investigations School, Washington, D.C.

Length: 10 weeks.

Objectives: To train officers and airmen in current standard Office of Special Investigations procedures and policies which are to be followed when conducting investigations within the purview of the mission assigned to that office.

Instruction: Military law and pertinent legal rights and procedures; report writing; general and procurement investigations; counterintelligence and personnel investigations; investigative techniques.

Credit recommendation, collegiate level: 3 semester hours in intelligence or police methods.

Special Maintenance 618S-1 System
(Collins 18S-4 Radio Set)

Location: Scott AFB, Ill.

Length: 3-4 weeks.

Objectives: To train airmen to perform organizational and field maintenance on the Collins HF liaison transmitter-receiver and antenna coupler.

Instruction: Operation and function; circuit analysis; tuning and alignment; maintenance and repair.

Credit recommendation, collegiate level: No credit because of the brevity and limited technical nature of the course.

1. Special Training, AN/APN-59
2. Special Training, AN/APS-23A
3. Special Training, AN/APX-28
4. Special Training, AN/GKA-1 & 4 (F&O)
5. Special Training, AN/GPA-37 (F&O)
6. Special Training, AN/MSQ-1A (F&O)
7. Special Training on Airborne Radar Beacon AN/APN-69 (F&O)
8. Special Training on Airborne Radar Beacon AN/APN-69 (Depot)
9. Special Training on Antenna OA-492/APS-20B (Depot)
10. Special Training on Loran Receiver AN/APN-70
11. Special Course on Radar Set AN/ALT-7 and Pulse Generator O-207/ALA-7 (Depot)
12. Special Course AN/APX-25

Location: Keesler AFB, Miss.
Length: 3–17 weeks.
Objectives: To train airmen in the operation and analysis of specialized radar equipment.
Instruction: Specialized training above the basic level on the radar equipment indicated in title.
Credit recommendation, collegiate level: Credit in electrical laboratory on the basis of demonstrated skills and/or institutional examinations.

Special Training, AN/ARC-58 Single-Side-Band HF Radio Set
(Special Training, AN/ARC-21 HF Liaison Equipment)
(Special Radio Maintenance Technician AN/MRN-7 and AN/MRN-8 Instrument Landing System)
(Special Radio Maintenance Technician HF Liaison Equipment AN/ARC-21)
(Special Radio Maintenance Technician AN/TRC-24 Radio Set)

Locations: Keesler AFB, Miss.; Scott AFB, Ill.
Length: 4–6 weeks.
Objectives: To train airmen to perform inspection and maintenance on the equipment indicated in the title.
Instruction: Operation, alignment, trouble analysis, repair, and performance testing of the equipment indicated in the title.
Credit recommendation, collegiate level: No credit because of the limited technical nature of the courses.

1. Special Training, AN/FPS-7 (F&O)
2. Special Training AN/FPS-24 (F&O)
3. Special Training AN/FPS-26A (F&O)
4. Special Training AN/FPS-2F (F&O Maintenance)
5. AN/FPS-17 Operation and Monitoring

Location: Keesler AFB, Miss.
Length: 5–12 weeks.
Objectives: To train airmen in the operation and analysis of specialized radar equipment.
Instruction: Transmitters; receivers; characteristics and functions of radar equipment indicated in title.
Credit recommendation, collegiate level: For each course, credit in electrical laboratory on the basis of demonstrated skills and/or institutional examinations.

Special Training, AN/FST-2B and RAPPI (F&O)
(Special Training, AN/FST-2 and RAPPI)
(Special Training, AN/FST-2 (F&O))

Location: Keesler AFB, Miss.
Length: 16–18 weeks.
Objectives: To train airmen to operate, inspect, and maintain the equipment indicated in the title.
Instruction: Digital principles and circuitry; basic timing and fine grain data target conversion; input group and drum, semiautomatic height finder; system troubleshooting.
Credit recommendation, collegiate level: Credit in electrical laboratory on the basis of demonstrated skills and/or institutional examinations.

1. Special Training, AN/MRN-7A, AN/MRN-8A and Wilcox 492A Maintenance F&O
2. Special Training, AN/URN-3A Maintenance F&O

Location: Keesler AFB, Miss.
Length: 4 weeks.
Objectives: To provide maintenance personnel with supplemental training in the field and organizational maintenance of the radar equipment specified.
Instruction: System familiarization and function; arrangement of system components; block diagrams and circuit analysis; isolation of malfunctions; system inspection, repair, testing, alignment, and calibration.
Credit recommendation, collegiate level: No credit because of the brevity and limited technical nature of the courses.

1. Special Training on AN/ALT-6 Equipment (Depot)
2. Special Training on AN/ALT-6 Equipment (F&O)
3. Special Training on AN/ALT-8 (F&O)
4. Special Training on AN/APR-9B Equipment (Depot)
5. Special Training on AN/APS-42A
6. Special Training on AN/ASN-6 (F&O)
7. Special Training on AN/CPS-6B and Mark X IFF
8. Special Training on AN/FPN-13
9. Special Training on AN/FPS-8
10. Special Training on AN/FPS-6
11. Special Training on AN/FPS-6 (Army)

Location: Keesler AFB, Miss.
Length: 3–12 weeks.
Objectives: To provide specialized training for airmen (and Army personnel—Course 11) on selected radar equipment.
Instruction: Specialized training on the equipment indicated in title.
Credit recommendation, collegiate level: For each course, credit in electrical laboratory on the basis of demonstrated skills and/or institutional examinations.

Special Training on Radar Bombing Navigation System, AN/APQ-24A

Location: Keesler AFB, Miss.
Length: 14 weeks.
Objectives: To train airmen to perform organiza-

tional and field maintenance on radar bombing-navigation system AN/APQ-24A.

Instruction: Introduction to search radar; ground position indicator; troubleshooting.

Credit recommendation, collegiate level: Credit in electrical laboratory on the basis of demonstrated skills and/or institutional examinations.

Special Training on Shoran Equipment AN/APN-84 and Electronic Bombing Computer K-4

Location: Keesler AFB, Miss.

Length: 6 weeks.

Objectives: To train airmen to perform organizational and field maintenance on radio set AN/APN-84 and K-4 electronic bombing computer.

Instruction: Analysis, assembly, and disassembly of AN/APN-84 and bombing computer K-4.

Credit recommendation, collegiate level: Credit in electrical laboratory on the basis of demonstrated skills and/or institutional examinations.

Special Training on Shoran Equipment AN/APN-84, with K-4, AN/APN-3, with K-1A and AN/APA-54(A)

Location: Keesler AFB, Miss.

Length: 7 weeks.

Objectives: To train airmen to perform organizational and field maintenance on radar sets AN/APN-84 and AN/APN-3 and electronic bombing computers K-4 and K-1A.

Instruction: Analysis, inspection, and troubleshooting of equipment indicated in title.

Credit recommendation, collegiate level: Credit in electrical laboratory on the basis of demonstrated skills and/or institutional examinations.

Special Training, TACAN, TVOR, and ILS (F&O)

Location: Keesler AFB, Miss.

Length: 11 weeks.

Objectives: To train maintenance personnel as repairmen on TACAN, omni-range, and instrument landing systems.

Instruction: System familiarization and function; arrangement of systems components; block diagrams and circuit analysis; isolation of equipment malfunctions; inspection, repair, and testing.

Credit recommendation, collegiate level: Credit in electrical laboratory on the basis of demonstrated skills and/or institutional examinations.

Special Training, Wilcox 482 Omni-Range System Maintenance F&O

Location: Keesler AFB, Miss.

Length: 3 weeks.

Objectives: To train airmen to repair the Wilcox 482 omni-range system.

Instruction: Operational analysis of TVOR; power

supply and transmitter; reference and variable circuits; goniometer motor; voice and identification circuits; monitor system; flight check procedures; preventive maintenance and repair procedures.

Credit recommendation, collegiate level: No credit because of the brevity and limited technical nature of the course.

Special Vehicle Repairman (Special Vehicle Mechanic)

Locations: Chanute AFB, Ill.; Francis E. Warren AFB, Wyo.

Length: 15–28 weeks.

Objectives: To train airmen to maintain and repair aircraft-towing, fire-fighting, recovery and refueling vehicles.

Instruction: Repair of diesel and gasoline engines; engine electrical systems; power trains; brake and steering systems; automatic transmissions; aircraft-refueling vehicles; truck-mounted cranes; structural and crash fire and rescue trucks; recovery and towing tractor; engine tune-up.

Credit recommendation, collegiate level: This course is technical and vocational in nature. Credit in auto repair shop on the basis of demonstrated skills and/or institutional examinations.

1. Special Weapons Maintenance Technician
2. Special Weapons Maintenance Technician
3. Special Weapons Maintenance Technician

Location: Lowry AFB, Colo.

Length: *Course 1,* 31–39 weeks; *Course 2,* 14 weeks; *Course 3,* 25 weeks.

Objectives: To train airmen to inspect and maintain special weapons and associated equipment.

Instruction: *Course 1:* Fundamentals of AC and DC electricity; vacuum tubes; amplifiers; oscillators; special circuits; transistors; radio principles; oscilloscope kit construction. The remainder of *Course 1* is classified and is not available for evaluation. *Course 2:* Fundamentals of AC and DC electricity; vacuum tubes; nuclear physics; nucleonics fundamentals. *Course 3:* The electricity/electronics phase of this course is identical to that of *Course 1.* The remainder of *Course 3* covers nuclear physics, count rate meters, and collection equipment.

Credit recommendation, collegiate level: CAUTION: *These courses vary in length and recommendation. Require exact identification by title and length. Course 1:* 4 semester hours at the freshman or sophomore level as an elective in electricity and electronics, and credit in electrical laboratory on the basis of demonstrated skills and/or institutional examinations. *Course 2:* 3 semester hours in introductory atomic physics, 2 semester hours at the freshman or sophomore level as an elective in electricity and electronics, and credit in electrical laboratory on the basis of demonstrated skills and/or institutional examinations. *Course 3:* 3 semester hours at the freshman or sophomore level as an elective in electricity and electronics, and credit in introductory atomic physics and electrical laboratory on the basis of demonstrated skills and/or institutional examinations.

Specialized Communications and Electronics Training

Location: Keesler AFB, Miss.
Length: 16 weeks.
Objectives: To provide updated communications and electronics training for selected airmen.
Instruction: Electronic principles; transistors; transmitters and receivers; television; direction finding; telephone systems.
Credit recommendation, collegiate level: 3 semester hours at the freshman or sophomore level as an elective in electricity and electronics, and credit in electrical laboratory on the basis of demonstrated skills and/or institutional examinations.

Specialized Navigation/Electronic Warfare Training (B-52)

Location: Mather AFB, Calif.
Length: 12 weeks.
Objectives: To qualify navigators for admission to B-52 Combat Crew Training School.
Instruction: Fundamentals of radar; audio analysis; reconnaissance and active systems; defensive systems analysis; countermeasures application; simulator ALQ-T4 training.
Credit recommendation, collegiate level: No credit as the course is military in nature.

Squadron Officer School (Squadron Officer Course)

Location: Maxwell AFB, Ala.
Length: 10–14 weeks.
Objectives: To provide lieutenants and captains with a broad foundation for professional development and to increase their ability to perform duties normally assigned to company-grade officers.
Instruction: Communication of ideas through effective speaking and writing; Air Force organization; command and leadership; personnel; materiel; world affairs; human relations.
Credit recommendation, collegiate level: 3 semester hours in speech, and credit in political science on the basis of institutional examination.

Squadron Operations Center and Data Handling Equipment Repairman, IM-99B

Location: Chanute AFB, Ill.
Length: 16 weeks.
Objectives: To train airmen to maintain weapon system communication equipment and data handling and missile status display equipment.
Instruction: AN/GSA-28, prelaunch acquisition system translator; common power supply group; communications terminal; launcher status summarizer; launcher status multiplexer; squadron supervisor's station; interceptor missile squadron supervisory control equipment; shop and maintenance procedures.
Credit recommendation, collegiate level: Credit in electrical laboratory on the basis of demonstrated skills and/or institutional examinations.

Staff Aircraft Performance Officer (Staff Aircraft Performance Engineer)

Location: Mather AFB, Calif.
Length: 19–22 weeks.
Objectives: To provide officers with the technical knowledge necessary to administer the operational performance program of a tactical jet organization.
Instruction: Fundamental algebra and trigonometry; differential and integral calculus; fluid dynamics; aerodynamics theory; compressibility theory; theory of propulsion; turbo-jet engines and flight limits; take-off, climb, descent, approach, and landing; range; endurance; mission planning.
Credit recommendation, collegiate level: Credit in aerodynamics theory, calculus, and fluid dynamics on the basis of institutional examination.

1. Statistical Services Officer
2. Statistical Services Officer
3. Statistical Services Supervisor
4. Statistical Specialist

Locations: Lowry AFB, Colo.; Sheppard AFB, Tex.
Length: *Course 1,* 10–13 weeks; *Course 2,* 5 weeks; *Course 3,* 10 weeks; *Course 4,* 9–12 weeks.
Objectives: *Courses 1 and 3:* To train airmen and officers in the principles and techniques of managing statistical services activities. *Course 2:* To train officers and airmen in the principles and operation of electrical accounting machines and data processing systems. *Course 4:* To train airmen in the principles and techniques of statistical reporting and the processing of reports.
Instruction: *Course 1:* Introduction to statistical services; personnel accounting system; operations and materiel reporting system; accounting machines and/or data processing machines; management of statistical services activity. *Course 2:* Basic data processing machines; accounting machine, type 407; calculating punch, type 602A, flow charts. *Course 3:* Introduction to statistical services; statistical analysis and presentation; personnel reporting; materiel and operational statistics. *Course 4:* Statistical functions and reports control; accounting; personnel reporting; operations and materiel reporting.
Credit recommendation, collegiate level: CAUTION: *These courses vary slightly in title, length, and recommendation. Require exact identification by title and length. Course 1:* 3 semester hours in methods of statistical analysis and 2 semester hours in statistical office management. *Course 2:* This course is technical and vocational in nature. Credit in electrical accounting machine operation on the basis of demonstrated skills and/or institutional examinations. *Courses 3 and 4:* For each course, 3 semester hours in methods of statistical analysis.

Status Authentication Subsystem Maintenance, WS-133B

Location: Chanute AFB, Ill.
Length: 5 weeks.
Objectives: To train airmen to perform maintenance on the status authentication subsystem, WS-133B.
Instruction: Operation, circuit analysis, component

checkout, analysis and correction of malfunctions; cryptographic security procedures; safety.

Credit recommendation, collegiate level: Credit in electrical laboratory on the basis of demonstrated skills and/or institutional examinations.

Stock Control Technician

Location: Francis E. Warren AFB, Wyo.

Length: 4 weeks.

Objectives: To train supply records personnel as stock control technicians.

Instruction: Computation of stock levels and recorder points; stock balance reporting; local purchase procedures; requisition register.

Credit recommendation, collegiate level: No credit because of the limited technical nature of this course.

Structural Repair of High Performance Aircraft

Location: Amarillo AFB, Tex.

Length: 5–6 weeks.

Objectives: To train airframe repairmen in the structural repair of high-performance aircraft.

Instruction: Principles and techniques of designing structural repair; repair of wing skin, tapered, metal bonded, and sandwich constructions; sealing of aircraft structures; maintaining aerodynamic smoothness; thermo-dimpling; repair and fabrication of titanium parts; leveling and alignment of aircraft components; balancing of control surfaces.

Credit recommendation, collegiate level: This course is technical and vocational in nature. Credit in metal shop on the basis of demonstrated skills and/or institutional examinations.

Supply Computer System Specialist

Location: Amarillo AFB, Tex.

Length: 6 weeks.

Objectives: To train airmen in the operation of the 1050-II computer, peripheral, and PCAM support equipment.

Instruction: Standardized accounting; records management; program instructions; computer room operating procedures; computer performance; practical problems.

Credit recommendation, collegiate level: 3 semester hours in computer principles in the area of data processing.

Supply Inspection Technician

Location: Francis E. Warren AFB, Wyo.

Length: 7–8 weeks.

Objectives: To train warehouse personnel in the principles and techniques of inspection.

Instruction: Supply publications; inspection equipment; inspection of incoming and outgoing shipments; inspection of local purchase, central procurement, and stored items.

Credit recommendation, collegiate level: This course

is technical and vocational in nature. Credit in stock classification and inspection on the basis of demonstrated skills and/or institutional examinations.

1. **Supply Management Staff Officer
   (Supply Staff Officer)
   (Advanced Supply Officer)**
2. **Supply Services Officer**
3. **Supply Services Supervisor**
4. **Administrative Supervisor**

Locations: Amarillo AFB, Tex.; Francis E. Warren AFB, Wyo.; Lowry AFB, Colo.

Length: *Course 1,* 8–10 weeks; *Course 2,* 14 weeks; *Course 3,* 6 weeks; *Course 4,* 6–8 weeks.

Objectives: *Courses 1, 2, and 3:* To train officers and airmen in the management of supply and base services programs. *Course 4:* To train clerks, postal and stenographic specialists as supervisors in administrative or postal activities.

Instruction: *Course 1:* Management techniques; supply management and conversion procedures; inventory management; plans, programs, and requirements. *Course 2:* Supply policies; clothing sales store; exchange service; commissaries and food service; mortuary affairs. *Course 3:* Supply services management and administration; requisitioning, storage, merchandising, sales and issues; sales accounting and financial control. *Course 4:* Correspondence and directives; administrative responsibilities and supervision; postal activities.

Credit recommendation, collegiate level: *Course 1:* 4 semester hours in supply management. *Courses 2 and 4:* No credit because of the limited technical nature of the courses. *Course 3:* 2 semester hours in supply services management.

Supply Operations Officer
(Supply Officer)

Locations: Amarillo AFB, Tex.; Francis E. Warren AFB, Wyo.

Length: 9–12 weeks.

Objectives: To train officers to operate and manage supply activities.

Instruction: Item accounting and supplies management; stock control and requisitioning procedures; equipment management; budget and financial management.

Credit recommendation, collegiate level: 4 semester hours in supply management.

Survival Instructor Training

Locations: Fairchild AFB, Wash.; Stead AFB, Nev.

Length: 21–24 weeks.

Objectives: To qualify airmen as instructors in the techniques of global survival.

Instruction: Global geography, climatic, and vegetation variations; general principles and techniques of survival, including forestry, water survival, and air recovery; global techniques of survival, including fishing, trapping, snaring, hunting, plant life, firecraft, campsites, and survival medicine; evasion, resistance, and escape, including POW life, history, and exploration; special forces, guerrillas, Communism, and the Geneva Convention; survival teaching methods, including instructor effect on student learning, methods and techniques, lesson planning, training aids, and practice teaching. The foregoing subjects are taught in both the academic and field training phases of the course.

Credit recommendation, collegiate level: 2 semester hours in instructional methods, and 3 semester hours in survival techniques, including woodcraft and camp training, winter survival and recreation.

Survival Training
(Advanced Survival Training)
(USAF Combat Survival Training)
(Combat Survival Training Course)

Locations: Fairchild AFB, Wash.; Stead AFB, Nev.
Length: 3–4 weeks.
Objectives: To train Air Force and other military personnel in advanced survival techniques and related skills.
Instruction: Survival techniques and procedures; water survival; survival weapons; combative measures; travel and evasion; resistance training; counterinsurgency training; field training.
Credit recommendation, collegiate level: 2 semester hours in woodcraft and camp training or winter survival and recreation.

1. Survival Training and Personal Equipment Officer
2. Survival Training and Personal Equipment Officer
   (Survival Training and Equipment Officer)
3. Personal Equipment and Survival Training
   (Officer)
4. Protective Equipment Specialist
   (Personal Equipment Specialist)
   (Personal Equipment Specialist (General))
   (Survival Training and Personal Equipment
   Specialist)
5. Personal and Survival Equipment Training
   (Enlisted)
   (Personal Equipment and Survival Training
   (Enlisted))

Locations: Brooks AFB, Tex.; Chanute AFB, Ill.
Length: 3–15 weeks.
Objectives: *Course 1:* To train personal equipment officers in the physiological effects of altitude. *Courses 2 through 5:* To train officers and airmen in the operation, use, inspection, and maintenance of personal survival and emergency equipment.
Instruction: *Course 1:* Aeromedical indoctrination; aerospace medicine; physiology; instructor education. *Courses 2 through 5:* Emergency protective equipment; oxygen equipment; supply and personal equipment; special purpose clothing; survival procedures.
Credit recommendation, collegiate level: No credit because of the specialized nature of these courses.

TF-33 Turbofan Engine Maintenance
(B-52H Turbofan Engine, Field and Organizational Maintenance)

Location: Chanute AFB, Ill.
Length: 6–7 weeks.
Objectives: To train airmen to operate and maintain the TF-33 or the TF-33-P-7 engine.
Instruction: Engine familiarization; field and organizational maintenance; engine operation.
Credit recommendation, collegiate level: This course is technical and vocational in nature. Credit in aircraft engine repair on the basis of demonstrated skills and/or institutional examinations.

1. Tactical Missile Checkout Equipment Repairman
   (CGM-13B (TEMS))
   (Tactical Missile Checkout Equipment Repairman
   (MACE, MGM-13C/TEMS))
   (Tactical Missile Checkout Equipment Repairman
   (TM-76B TEMS))
   (Tactical Missile Checkout Equipment Repairman
   (TM-76A, TEMS))
   (Missile Test Equipment Specialist (TM-76B))
   (Missile Test Equipment Specialist (TM-76A))
2. Missile Electronic Equipment Specialist
   (CGM-13B, TEMS)
3. Tactical Missile Checkout Equipment Repairman
   (MGM-13B (TEMS))
   (Tactical Missile Checkout Equipment Repairman
   (TM-76A/TEMS))

Location: Lowry AFB, Colo.
Length: *Course 1,* 18 weeks; *Courses 2 and 3,* 23–31 weeks.
Objectives: To train airmen in the maintenance of operational and peculiar test equipment associated with the missile indicated in the title.
Instruction: *Course 1:* Operational concepts; circuit analysis; repair and calibration; test equipment. *Courses 2 and 3:* Specialized electronics including DC and AC, rectifiers, oscillators, and circuit analysis; weapon system familiarization, calibration and repair.
Credit recommendation, collegiate level: CAUTION: *These courses vary slightly in title, length, and recommendation. Require exact identification by full title and length. Courses 1, 2, and 3:* For each course, credit in electricity and electrical laboratory on the basis of demonstrated skills and/or institutional examinations.

1. Tactical Missile Guidance Mechanic (MGM-13A)
   (Tactical Missile Guidance Mechanic (TM-76A))
2. Tactical Missile Guidance Mechanic (TM-76A)
   (Guidance Systems Mechanic (TM-76A))

Location: Lowry AFB, Colo.
Length: *Course 1,* 35 weeks; *Course 2,* 37 weeks.
Objectives: To train airmen in the operation, maintenance, inspection, and repair of the missile guidance system and guidance checkout equipment.
Instruction: *Course 1:* DC and AC; reactive circuits; principles of vacuum tubes; special purpose tubes; amplifiers and oscillators; special circuits; motors and servomechanisms; multivibrators and sweep circuits; microwave principles. *Course 2* covers the same elements as *Course 1,* but in greater depth and intensity.

Credit recommendation, collegiate level: CAUTION: *These courses vary slightly in title, length, and recommendation. Require exact identification of course by title and length. Course 1:* 4 semester hours at the freshman or sophomore level as an elective in electricity and electronics, and credit in electrical laboratory on the basis of demonstrated skills and/or institutional examinations. *Course 2:* 6 semester hours at the freshman or sophomore level as an elective in electricity and electronics, and credit in electrical laboratory on the basis of demonstrated skills and/or institutional examinations.

1. Tactical Missile Launch Specialist (CGM-13B)
   (Tactical Missile Launch Specialist (MGM-13A))
   (Tactical Missile Launch Specialist (MGM-13B))
   (Tactical Missile Launch Specialist (MACE, MGM-13C))
   (Tactical Missile Launch Specialist (TM-76A))
   (Tactical Missile Launch Specialist (TM-76B))
   (Missile Systems Analyst Specialist (CGM-13B, LCH PREP))
   (Missile Systems Analyst Specialist (SM-65E))
   (Missile Systems Analyst Specialist (TM-76A))
   (Missile Systems Analyst Specialist (TM-76B))
   (Missile Systems Analyst Technician (TM-76B))
   (Missile Systems Analyst (SM-65, 68))
   (Guidance Systems Analyst (SM-65E))
2. Tactical Missile Launch Specialist (MGM-13A)
3. Missile Systems Analyst Specialist (CGM-13B, LCH PREP NCO)
   (Tactical Missile Launch Specialist (TM-76A))
   (Missile Systems Analyst Specialist (TM-76A))

Locations: Lowry AFB, Colo.; Sheppard AFB, Tex.
Length: *Course 1,* 20–30 weeks; *Course 2,* 14–16 weeks; *Course 3,* 10–12 weeks.
Objectives: To train airmen in missile system principles, and operational maintenance and checkout.
Instruction: *Course 1:* DC and AC; reactive circuits; vacuum tubes and solid state devices; amplifiers and oscillators. *Course 2:* DC and AC; reactive circuits; vacuum tubes and solid state devices. *Course 3:* Missile systems; support and test equipment; launch area checkout.
Credit recommendation, collegiate level: CAUTION: *These courses vary slightly in title, length, and recommendation. Require exact identification by full title and length. Course 1:* 3 semester hours at the freshman or sophomore level as an elective in electricity and electronics, and credit in electrical laboratory on the basis of demonstrated skills and/or institutional examinations. *Course 2:* 2 semester hours at the freshman or sophomore level as an elective in electricity and electronics, and credit in electrical laboratory on the basis of demonstrated skills and/or institutional examinations. *Course 3:* This course is technical and vocational in nature. Credit in electrical and mechanical shop on the basis of demonstrated skills and/or institutional examinations.

Tactical Reconnaissance Pilot, RF-101
(Tactical Reconnaissance Pilot)
Location: Shaw AFB, S.C.
Length: 16 weeks.

Objectives: To qualify rated officers as RF-101 tactical reconnaissance pilots.
Instruction: RF-101 MTD, flight simulator, transition, and reconnaissance training.
Credit recommendation, collegiate level: No credit because of the specialized nature of this course.

Tanker Aircrew, KC-97
Location: Randolph AFB, Tex.
Length: 10 weeks.
Objectives: To train aircrews in the procedures and techniques of KC-97 aerial refueling operations.
Instruction: Flying training; aviation physiology; survival; aircraft general and aircraft electrical; aerial refueling.
Credit recommendation, collegiate level: No credit as the course is military in nature.

TelAutograph Transcriber Equipment Repairman
Location: Sheppard AFB, Tex.
Length: 3 weeks.
Objectives: To train airmen to install, repair, and maintain TelAutograph transcriber equipment.
Instruction: Circuit operation and analysis; receiver and transmitter; TelAutograph installation and alignment; trouble analysis and corrective maintenance.
Credit recommendation, collegiate level: This course is technical and vocational in nature. Credit in electrical equipment repair on the basis of demonstrated skills and/or institutional examinations.

Telecommunications Systems Control Specialist/Attendant
Location: Keesler AFB, Miss.
Length: 29–34 weeks.
Objectives: To train airmen to check the quality of permanent or part-time circuits and to analyze the performance of radio and wire telecommunications circuits and equipment.
Instruction: Principles of DC and AC circuits; reactive circuits; vacuum tubes; transistors; tubes and solid state devices; amplifiers; oscillators; special circuits.
Credit recommendation, collegiate level: 4 semester hours at the freshman or sophomore level as an elective in electricity and electronics, and credit in electrical laboratory on the basis of demonstrated skills and/or institutional examinations.

Telephone Circuit Analysis
Location: Sheppard AFB, Tex.
Length: 3 weeks.
Objectives: To train officers and airmen in the techniques of telephone circuitry analysis.
Instruction: Principles of telephony; operation, circuitry, and wiring; optional features; connections and cabling.
Credit recommendation, collegiate level: This course is technical and vocational in nature. Credit in tele-

phone maintenance on the basis of demonstrated skills and/or institutional examinations.

Telephone Installer-Repairman

Location: Francis E. Warren AFB, Wyo.

Length: 10 weeks.

Objectives: To train airmen to install, replace, and maintain telephone and interoffice voice communications systems.

Instruction: Pole climbing and field wire systems; telephone repair; substation installation; interoffice and key telephone equipment.

Credit recommendation, collegiate level: This course is technical and vocational in nature. Credit in telephone systems repair on the basis of demonstrated skills and/or institutional examinations.

1. Telephone Switching Equipment Repairman, Electro/Mechanical (Other)
2. Telephone Equipment Installer-Repairman
3. Telephone Switching Equipment Repairman, Electro/Mechanical
(Telephone Switching Equipment Technician (Step-by-Step and X-Y Equipment))

Location: Sheppard AFB, Tex.

Length: *Course 1,* 14 weeks; *Course 2,* 19 weeks; *Course 3,* 28 and 30 weeks.

Objectives: To train airmen as telephone switching equipment repairmen.

Instruction: *Courses 1, 2, and 3:* DC circuits; AC circuits; reactive circuits; amplifiers and oscillators. In addition *Course 1* includes switching center principles; cable installation and relay adjustment; manual central office maintenance management. *Course 2* includes fundamentals and installation; Basic 1A1, 200G series 1A1, 1A2, and 6A key systems and intercomm. *Course 3* includes switching center principles; relay maintenance; cable installation; Strowger switch; step-by-step circuits; central office switching.

Credit recommendation, collegiate level: For each course, 2 semester hours at the freshman or sophomore level as an elective in electricity and electronics, and credit in telephone systems repair on the basis of demonstrated skills and/or institutional examinations.

Titan II Communications Equipment (F&O)

Location: Keesler AFB, Miss.

Length: 8 weeks.

Objectives: To provide airmen with maintenance training on Titan II communications equipment.

Instruction: Titan II systems and fundamentals principles; voice signaling system and radio network; intercomplex radio system.

Credit recommendation, collegiate level: Credit in electrical laboratory on the basis of demonstrated skills and/or institutional examinations.

Tow Reel Specialist

Location: Sheppard AFB, Tex.

Length: 8 weeks.

Objectives: To train airmen to operate, inspect, and maintain tow reels.

Instruction: Tools; technical orders; electrical and hydraulic systems; operation, inspection, and maintenance of tow targets and related equipment.

Credit recommendation, collegiate level: This course is technical and vocational in nature. Credit in aircraft repair on the basis of demonstrated skills and/or institutional examinations.

1. Tracking/Identification (SAGE)
2. Tracking (SAGE)

Location: Keesler AFB, Miss.

Length: 6–8 weeks.

Objectives: To train officers and airmen to perform duties as tracking supervisors and monitors.

Instruction: SAGE organizational and functional concepts; symbology interpretation; equipment operation.

Credit recommendation, collegiate level: No credit because of the specialized nature of the courses.

1. Transition Pilot Training (C-47)
2. Medium Bomb Course-Transition (B-47)
(Medium Bomb Course-Observer (B-47))
(USAF Aircrew Transition School (Medium Bomb Jet))
3. USAF Combat Flying School, Medium Transport (C-119) Transition
(USAF Advanced Flying School, Medium Transport (C-119) Aircrew Transition)
4. Medium Bombardment Conventional (B-29)

Locations: McConnell AFB, Kan.; Moody AFB, Ga.; Randolph AFB, Tex.; Keesler AFB, Miss.

Length: 4–13 weeks.

Objectives: To provide aircrews with transition or combat readiness training.

Instruction: Flying training; aircraft engineering; flight operations; weather.

Credit recommendation, collegiate level: No credit because of the specialized nature of the courses.

Transportation of Dangerous Cargo, Nuclear Weapons and Missiles
(Missile and Nuclear Weapons Transportation Safety)

Location: Sheppard AFB, Tex.

Length: 3 weeks.

Objectives: To provide supplemental training in the transportation of dangerous cargo, nuclear weapons, and missiles.

Instruction: Transportation of dangerous cargo and missiles; transportation of nuclear materials.

Credit recommendation, collegiate level: No credit because of the brevity and specialized nature of the courses.

1. Transportation Staff Officer
   (Transportation Officer)
2. Transportation Officer
   (Air Transportation Officer)
   (Surface Transportation Officer)
3. Air Transportation Officer
4. Surface Transportation Officer

   Location: Sheppard AFB, Tex.

   Length: *Course 1,* 12, 19, and 24 weeks; *Course 2,* 9, 10, 14 and 16 weeks; *Courses 3 and 4,* 3 weeks.

   Objectives: To train officers in the movement of materiel and personnel by air and/or water, rail, and land transportaion.

   Instruction: *Course 1:* Elements of transportation; principles of traffic management; economics of transportation; budget; plans, programs, and development; military air transportation; commercial transportation; Interstate Commerce Act. *Course 2:* Introduction to traffic management; movement of personnel and materiel; employment of aircraft; shipping and receiving; aircraft loading. *Course 3:* Movement of passengers and household goods; movement of freight. *Course 4:* Employment of airlift; air terminal operations; aircraft loading.

   Credit recommendation, collegiate level: CAUTION: *These courses vary slightly in title, length, and recommendation. Require exact identification by title and length. Course 1:* 6 semester hours in transportation management. *Course 2:* 3 semester hours in transportation management. *Courses 3 and 4:* No credit because of the brevity of the courses.

Turret System Gunner (A3A/MD-9 Turrets)
(Turret System Gunner, B-52 (A-3A))

Location: Lowry AFB, Colo.

Length: 8 weeks.

Objectives: To train airmen in the duties and responsibilities of an aerial gunner for bombardment aircraft.

Instruction: The operation, inspection, and maintenance of a gunner's equipment; principles and techniques of aerial gunnery.

Credit recommendation, collegiate level: No credit as the course is military in nature.

Turret Systems Gunner (B-36)
(Gunlaying System Mechanic Gunner, B-36)
(Flexible Gunnery Training Turret System Mechanic
   Gunner, B-36)
(Flexible Gunnery Training Gunlaying System
   Mechanic Gunner, B-36)

Location: Lowry AFB, Colo.

Length: 7–11 weeks.

Objectives: To train airmen as aerial gunners in heavy bombardment aircraft.

Instruction: The operation, inspection, and maintenance of gunner's equipment; principles and techniques of aerial gunnery.

Credit recommendation, collegiate level: No credit as the course is military in nature.

Turret Systems Gunner, B-66 (MD-1)

Location: Lowry AFB, Colo.

Length: 14 weeks.

Objectives: To train airmen as aerial gunners in B-66 aircraft.

Instruction: Operation, inspection, and techniques of aerial gunnery.

Credit recommendation, collegiate level: No credit as the course is military in nature.

Type 1A1 Keying Equipment Maintenance
(Key Telephone Systems Maintenance)

Location: Sheppard AFB, Tex.

Length: 4 weeks.

Objectives: To train airmen to construct, operate, maintain, and repair key telephone units and key telephone systems.

Instruction: Construction and operation of telephones; installation, analysis, and troubleshooting of key telephone systems.

Credit recommendation, collegiate level: This course is technical and vocational in nature. Credit in telephone system maintenance on the basis of demonstrated skills and/or institutional examinations.

1. USAF Advanced Flying School, Interceptor
   (T-33/F-86L)
2. USAF Advanced Flying School, Interceptor
   (T-33/F-86D/L)
3. USAF Advanced Flying School, Interceptor
   (F-89D)
4. USAF Advanced Flying School, Fighter (F-86)
5. USAF Advanced Flying School, Fighter (F-86F)
6. USAF Advanced Flying School, Fighter (T-33)
   Phase I
7. USAF Advanced Flying School, Fighter (F-100A)
   (Phase II)
8. USAF Combat Flying School (Interceptor)
   (F-94C)
9. USAF Combat Flying School (Interceptor)
   (T-33/F-89D)
10. USAF Combat Flying School (Interceptor)
    (T-33/F-94C)
11. USAF Combat Flying School, Light Bomb Jet
    (B-57)
12. USAF Advanced Interceptor Pilot Training
    F-86L
13. USAF Advanced Fighter Training (F-86F)
14. Advanced Fighter Training (T-33/F-86)
    (MAP/ANG)
15. All-Weather Interceptor, Jet (F-86D)
16. AFS Fighter, Jet (T-33)
17. AFS Fighter, Jet (F-100)
18. Combat Crew Training, Fighter (F-84E) Phase
    II
19. Combat Crew Training, Fighter (F-84 E/F)
20. Combat Crew Training Fighter (F-84F)
21. Combat Crew Training Fighter (T-33/F-84)
22. Fighter Course, Unit Conversion, F-100
23. Interceptor Course - F-86D/L
24. Interceptor Pilot Training
25. Interceptor Pilot Training (F-102)

   Locations: Laughlin AFB, Tex.; Luke AFB, Ariz.; Moody AFB, Ga.; Nellis AFB, Nev.; Perrin AFB, Tex.

Randolph AFB, Tex.; Tyndall AFB, Fla.; Williams AFB, Ariz.

Length: 6–22 weeks.

Objectives: To provide aircrews (aircraft commander, pilot, and observer) with advanced flying training for combat readiness.

Instruction: Flying training; crew training; systems and characteristics of the aircraft.

Credit recommendation, collegiate level: No credit because of the specialized nature of the courses.

1. **USAF Interceptor Weapons Instructor School (F-94C)**
2. **USAF Interceptor Weapons Instructor School (F-89D)**

Location: Moody AFB, Ga.

Length: 10–11 weeks. *Note*—since flying training is dependent upon weather and other factors, the actual length of the courses may vary.

Objectives: To train instructors in all phases of interceptor weapons employment.

Instruction: Flying training consists of interceptor target flying; day and night interceptor techniques, applied tactics, and rocketry; synthetic trainer and instruction techniques. Academic training includes teaching fundamentals and practice teaching; weather; fire control systems assessment procedures; rockets; targets; flying safety.

Credit recommendation, collegiate level: For each course, credit in instructional methods on the basis of institutional examination.

Undergraduate Navigator Training
(Primary-Basic Navigator Training)
(Primary-Basic Observer Cadet Training)

Locations: Ellington AFB, Tex.; Harlingen AFB, Tex.; James Connally AFB, Tex.; Mather AFB, Calif.

Length: 30–44 weeks.

Objectives: To qualify preflight graduates, nonrated officers, aviation cadets, and/or junior officers to navigate an aircraft utilizing all available navigational aids.

Instruction: Flight training; navigation fundamentals; navigator skills including celestial, grid, and radar navigation; in addition the course sometimes includes electricity and magnetism; alternating current; vacuum tubes; radio and loran; radar system.

Credit recommendation, collegiate level: CAUTION: *These courses are similar in content but vary in the intensity of instruction in specific areas each year. Therefore credit will be recommended according to the year the course was given. Require exact identification of course by year of attendance.* Courses given from *1954 through April 1957*, or from *November 1962 through February 1965:* 6 semester hours in navigation, 2 semester hours at the freshman or sophomore level as an elective in electricity, and credit in electrical laboratory on the basis of demonstrated skills and/or institutional examinations. Courses given from *September 1957 through March 1962*, or from *August 1965 through 1967:* 6 semester hours in navigation. For all courses given before *February 1965*, credit for advanced military in accordance with the school's policy.

1. **Undergraduate Pilot Training (T-41/T-37/T-38)**
2. **Undergraduate Pilot Training (T-41/T-37/T-33)**
   (Undergraduate Pilot Training (T-37/T-33))
3. **Undergraduate Pilot Training (T-37/T-38)**
4. **Primary Pilot Training (T-34/T-28)**
   (Primary Pilot Training (PA-18/T-6))
5. **Army Primary Pilot Training**

Locations: *Courses 1, 2, and 3:* Craig AFB, Ala.; Laredo AFB, Tex.; Laughlin AFB, Tex.; Moody AFB, Ga.; Randolph AFB, Tex.; Reese AFB, Tex.; Vance AFB, Okla.; Webb AFB, Tex.; Williams AFB, Ariz. *Course 4:* Bainbridge AFB, Ga.; Bartow AFB, Fla.; Columbus AFB, Miss.; Graham AFB, Fla.; Hondo AFB, Tex.; Malden AFB, Mo.; Marana AFB, Ariz.; Moore AFB, Tex.; Spence AFB, Ga.; Stallings AFB, N.C. *Course 5:* Edward Gary AFB, Tex.

Length: *Courses 1, 2 and 3*, 53–55 weeks; *Course 4*, 24 weeks; *Course 5*, 17 weeks.

Objectives: To qualify nonrated, junior, and/or Army officers to perform the duties and assume the responsibilities of a pilot.

Instruction: *Courses 1, 2, and 3:* Flying training subjects; aircraft engineering; instrument procedures and radio aids; principles of flight; flight instruments; navigation; applied aerodynamics; weather; reciprocating engines. *Courses 4 and 5:* These courses include the same subject matter as *Courses 1, 2, and 3*, but in less depth and intensity.

Credit recommendation, collegiate level: For each course, 3 semester hours in primary meteorology and navigation, and credit in advanced military at institutions which require such credit.

1. **Undergraduate Pilot Training Helicopter (T-28)**
2. **Undergraduate Pilot Training Helicopter (H-19/H-43B or H-19/CH-3C)**
   (Helicopter Pilot Training (H-1F/H-1F) (H-1F/CH-3) (H-1F/H-43))
   (Helicopter Pilot Training (H-19/H-43) (H-19/H-3))
   (Helicopter Pilot Training (H-19/H-43B) (H-19/CH-3C) or (H-19/CH-3C) (H-19/H-43B))
   (Helicopter Pilot Training (H-19/H-21/H-43B))
   (Helicopter Pilot Training (H-19/H-21))
   (Helicopter Pilot Training (H-13, H-19, and H-21))
3. **Helicopter Pilot Training (CH-3C)**

Locations: Randolph AFB, Tex.; Sheppard AFB, Tex.; Stead AFB, Nev.

Length: *Course 1*, 28 weeks; *Course 2*, 12–18 weeks; *Course 3*, 5–6 weeks.

Objectives: To provide airmen and officers with an understanding of the basic principles of flying the aircraft indicated in the titles which will enable them to gain proficiency in helicopter flying techniques to facilitate subsequent helicopter training.

Instruction: *Course 1:* Flying training subjects; aviation physiology; aircraft engineering; instrument procedures and radio aids; flight instruments; navigation; weather. *Course 2:* Flying training subjects; history, theory, and familiarization; engineering; operational training. *Course 3:* Flying training subjects; familiarization and engineering; operational training.

Credit recommendation, collegiate level: For each course, credit in helicopter pilot training on the basis of demonstrated skills and/or institutional examinations.

1. Unit Test Equipment (AN/ASQ-38)
2. Unit Test Equipment (AN/ASQ-48)

Location: Lowry AFB, Colo.

Length: *Course 1,* 7–10 weeks; *Course 2,* 4–5 weeks.

Objectives: To train bomb-navigation systems mechanics and technicians in the operation and repair of the unit test equipment specified.

Instruction: *Course 1:* AN/ASM-46 computer test set, terrain computer, and subassembly test set; radar data presentation set and test set; radar performance tester–circuitry, operation, and calibration; power supply and amplifier test sets; servo and electrical test sets. *Course 2:* AN/ASM-46 computer test set, terrain computer, and subassembly test set; electronic circuit plug-in test sets, AN/APM 160 and AN/APM 159.

Credit recommendation, collegiate level: For each course, credit in electrical laboratory on the basis of demonstrated skills and/or institutional examinations.

Upgrading B-66 Aircraft

Location: Mather AFB, Calif.

Length: 6 weeks.

Objectives: To qualify aircraft observer navigation-bombardiers to navigate and bomb using radar and to perform navigation and radar reconnaissance.

Instruction: K-5 system bombing; radar equipment; tactical radar operating procedures.

Credit recommendation, collegiate level: No credit as the course is military in nature.

Vehicle Diagnostic Test Equipment

Location: Chanute AFB, Ill.

Length: 6 weeks.

Objectives: To train airmen in the use of vehicle diagnostic test equipment.

Instruction: Vehicle starting and charging systems, engine systems, steering systems, wheel alignment, and use of related test equipment, including generator regulator tester, universal engine analyzers, and chassis dynamometer.

Credit recommendation, collegiate level: This course is technical and vocational in nature. Credit in automotive repair shop on the basis of demonstrated skills and/or institutional examinations.

Vehicle Maintenance Technician

Location: Francis E. Warren AFB, Wyo.

Length: 19 weeks.

Objectives: To train airmen to inspect, maintain, and repair construction, special purpose, and general equipment.

Instruction: Maintenance of power train units, engines and electrical equipment, including use of diagnostic and reconditioning equipment; inspection and maintenance of Air Force special purpose vehicles and construction equipment; technical inspections, on-the-job training, and shop supervision.

Credit recommendation, collegiate level: This course is technical and vocational in nature. Credit in automotive shop on the basis of demonstrated skills and/or institutional examinations.

1. Veterinary Specialist (Apprentice Veterinary Specialist)
2. Veterinary Technician

Locations: Gunter AFB, Ala.; Sheppard AFB, Tex.

Length: 10–15 weeks.

Objectives: To train airmen in food inspection procedures and veterinary support of combat operations.

Instruction: *Course 1:* Basic medical orientation; basic veterinary administration; introduction to zoonotic disease control and animal service; inspection of meat, poultry, fish, seafoods, dairy products, and eggs; fundamentals of food processing sanitation; inspection of fruits, vegetables, and canned and stored foods; principles of attribute inspection; disaster medicine. *Course 2* provides advanced training in the same areas covered by *Course 1.*

Credit recommendation, collegiate level: *Courses 1 and 2:* For each course, 3 semester hours in meat and dairy hygiene.

Water and Waste Processing Specialist

Location: Sheppard AFB, Tex.

Length: 12 weeks.

Objectives: To train airmen in water supply and treatment and waste processing methods.

Instruction: Introduction to water and waste treatment; characteristics of water supply, including electrical fundamentals, chemistry of water processing, chemical analysis of raw and treated water, water system filters, cation and anion exchangers, electrodialysis demineralization, and distillation; waste treatment; operation and maintenance of water and waste components; scale and corrosion control in water and waste treatment systems.

Credit recommendation, collegiate level: 3 semester hours in water purification.

1. Weapon Control Systems Mechanic (E-4, E-5, E-6 Systems)
(Weapons Control Systems Mechanic (E-4, 5, 6, Systems))
(E-4, E-5, and E-6 Series Systems Mechanic)
2. E-1 Series System Mechanic
3. Weapons Control Systems Technician (E-4, 5 and 6 Systems)
(Weapons Control Systems Technician (E-4, E-5, E-6 Systems))
(E-4, E-5, and E-6 Series System Technician)

Location: Lowry AFB, Colo.

Length: *Course 1,* 34–38 weeks; *Course 2,* 26 weeks *Course 3,* 14–18 weeks.

Objectives: *Courses 1 and 2:* To provide airmen with fundamental maintenance and repair training on th weapon control systems specified. *Course 3:* To provide qualified mechanics with advanced maintenance training on the weapon control systems specified.

Instruction: The first phase of *Courses 1 and 2* covers electrical fundamentals, direct and alternating current, reactive circuits, vacuum tubes and solid state devices, amplifiers, oscillators, oscilloscope and receiver principles; multivibrators, sweep and logic circuits, and radar system components, transmission, and fundamentals tie-in. The second phase of *Courses 1 and 2* and all of *Course 3* is devoted to special equipment training.

Credit recommendation, collegiate level: CAUTION: *Courses in weapons control systems repair vary only slightly in title, length, and recommendation. Require exact identification by full title and length. Courses 1 and 2:* For each course, 3 semester hours at the freshman or sophomore level as an elective in electricity and electronics, and credit in electrical laboratory on the basis of demonstrated skills and/or institutional examinations. *Course 3:* Credit in electronics and electrical laboratory on the basis of demonstrated skills and/or institutional examinations.

1. Weapon Control Systems Mechanic (F4, AMCS)
2. Weapon Control System Mechanic (F4, AMCS)
   (Weapon Control Systems Mechanic
   (AMCS-AERO-1A))
   (Offensive Fire Control Systems Mechanic
   (AMCS-AERO 1A))
3. Weapon Control Systems Mechanic
   (AMCS-AERO-1A)
   (Offensive Fire Control Systems Mechanic
   (AMCS-AERO-1A))

Location: Lowry AFB, Colo.

Length: *Course 1,* 32–33 weeks; *Course 2,* 34–37 weeks; *Course 3,* 15–16 weeks.

Objectives: To train airmen to troubleshoot, repair, calibrate, and align the weapon control system and to use associated test equipment.

Instruction: *Courses 1 and 2:* DC and AC; reactive circuits; vacuum tubes and transistors; amplifiers and oscillators; in addition *Course 2* includes special circuits; motors and servomechanisms; multivibrators. *Course 3:* Review of the fundamentals of electronics; analysis, maintenance, and repair of AMCS Aero 1A control system; use of associated test equipment.

Credit recommendation, collegiate level: CAUTION: *Courses in fire and weapons control vary only slightly in title, length, and credit recommendation. Note that titles vary by name of equipment in the parentheses following the title. Require exact identification of course by title and length. Course 1:* 3 semester hours at the freshman or sophomore level as an elective in electricity and electronics, and credit in electrical laboratory on the basis of demonstrated skills and/or institutional examinations. *Course 2:* 4 semester hours at the freshman or sophomore level as an elective in electricity and electronics, and credit in electrical laboratory on the basis of demonstrated skills and/or institutional examinations. *Course 3:* Credit in electricity and electrical laboratory on the basis of demonstrated skills and/or institutional examinations.

1. Weapon Control Systems Mechanic (MA-1, ASQ-25 Systems)
2. Weapon Control Systems Mechanic (MA-1, ASQ-25 Systems)
3. Weapon Control Systems Mechanic (MA-1, ASQ-25 Systems)

Location: Lowry AFB, Colo.

Length: *Course 1,* 41 weeks; *Course 2,* 37–39 weeks; *Course 3,* 33–34 weeks.

Objectives: To train airmen as apprentice weapon control systems mechanics.

Instruction: *Course 1:* DC and AC; vacuum tubes and transistors; reactive circuits; special purpose tubes; amplifiers and oscillators; special circuits; motors and servomechanisms; multivibrators and sweep circuits; microwave principles; weapons control system equipment training. *Courses 2 and 3* are similar in content to *Course 1* but vary in the amount of electricity and electronics training in proportion to their shorter lengths.

Credit recommendation, collegiate level: CAUTION: *Courses in weapon control systems vary only slightly in title, length, and recommendation. Note that the courses above vary in recommendation only according to length. Require exact identification by full title and length. Course 1:* 6 semester hours at the freshman or sophomore level as an elective in electricity and electronics and credit in electrical laboratory on the basis of demonstrated skills and/or institutional examinations. *Course 2:* 4 semester hours at the freshman or sophomore level as an elective in electricity and electronics, and credit in electrical laboratory on the basis of demonstrated skills and/or institutional examinations. *Course 3:* 3 semester hours at the freshman or sophomore level as an elective in electricity and electronics, and credit in electrical laboratory on the basis of demonstrated skills and/or institutional examinations.

1. Weapons Control Systems Mechanic (E9 System)
2. Weapons Control Systems Mechanic (E9, MG-12 System)
3. Weapons Control Systems Mechanic (E9, MG-12 System)
4. Fire Control Systems Mechanic (E9 Series)
5. Fire Control Systems Mechanic (E9 Series)

Location: Lowry AFB, Colo.

Length: *Courses 1, 2, and 5,* 42 weeks; *Course 3,* 23 weeks; *Course 4,* 20 weeks.

Objectives: To train airmen to analyze, install, maintain, and repair weapon control systems.

Instruction: *Courses 1 and 2:* Fundamentals of electricity and AC; vacuum tubes and power supplies; amplifiers, oscillators, and sweep generators; radar principles. *Courses 3, 4, and 5:* Introduction to the control system; intelligence gathering; antenna positioning; computing loop; system tie-in; in addition, *Course 5* includes fundamentals of DC and AC.

Credit recommendation, collegiate level: CAUTION: *Courses in fire and weapons control vary only slightly in title, length, and recommendation. Note that titles vary mainly by name of equipment in the parentheses following the title. Require exact identification by full title and length. Courses 1 and 2:* For each course, 3 semester hours at the freshman or sophomore level as an elective in electronics, and credit in electrical laboratory on the basis of demonstrated skills and/or institutional examinations. *Courses 3 and 4:* For each course, credit in electricity and electrical laboratory on the basis of demonstrated skills and/or institutional examinations. *Course 5:* 2 semester hours at the freshman or sophomore level as an elective in electricity, and credit in electrical laboratory on the basis of demonstrated skills and/or institutional examinations.

1. Weapons Control Systems Mechanic (MA-1 System)
2. Weapons Control Systems Mechanic (MA-1 System)
3. Weapons Control Systems Mechanic (MA-1 Systems)

Locations: Amarillo AFB, Tex.; Lowry AFB, Colo.

Length: *Courses 1 and 2,* 30 weeks; *Course 3,* 41–45 weeks.

Objectives: To train airmen as apprentice weapons control systems mechanics.

Instruction: *Course 1* given from May 1958 to May 1959: Fundamentals of AC and DC; vacuum tubes and power supplies; amplifiers, oscillators, and sweep generators; radar and servomechanism principles; transistors and gyros; special radar equipment training. *Course 2* given from May 1959 to April 1960: Electronic mathematics; electricity and magnetism; alternating current; electron tubes and power supplies; amplifiers and oscillators; transients and timing circuits; wave-shaping and radio circuits; microwaves; servo and computer devices. *Course 3* given April 1960 to May 1962: DC and AC; reactive circuits; vacuum tubes and transistors; special purpose tubes; amplifiers; oscillators; special circuits; motors and servomechanisms; multivibrators and sweep circuits; microwave principles; special equipment training.

Credit recommendation, collegiate level: CAUTION: *Courses in weapons control systems vary only slightly in title, length, and recommendation. Require exact identification by full title and length. In addition, the courses above vary in recommendation only according to length and dates of attendance. Require exact identification by full title, length, and dates attended. Course 1* given from May 1958 to May 1959: 3 semester hours at the freshman or sophomore level as an elective in electricity and electronics, and credit in electrical laboratory on the basis of demonstrated skills and/or institutional examinations. *Course 2* given from May 1959 to April 1960: 6 semester hours at the freshman or sophomore level as an elective in electricity and electronics. *Course 3* given from April 1960 to May 1962: 6 semester hours at the freshman or sophomore level as an elective in electricity and electronics, and credit in electrical laboratory on the basis of demonstrated skills and/or institutional examinations.

1. Weapons Control Systems Mechanic (MG-3, MG-10 Computer Controls)
2. Weapons Control Systems Mechanic (MG-13 Computer and Controls)

Location: Lowry AFB, Colo.

Length: 32–33 weeks.

Objectives: To train airmen in the maintenance of the aircraft weapons control system specified.

Instruction: *Courses 1 and 2:* Introduction to weapons control systems, radar, and computer functions; power generation and distribution; flight sensing, attack steering, timing and firing, parameter setting, armament controlling, and timed missile power functions, missile auxiliary and systems verification test set; attach display circuits; data link; tie-in of radar and computer systems; system self tests; field exercises.

Credit recommendation, collegiate level: CAUTION: *Weapons control systems repair courses vary only slightly in title, length, and recommendation. Require exact identification by full title and length.* For each course, credit in electrical laboratory on the basis of demonstrated skills and/or institutional examinations.

1. Weapons Control Systems Mechanic (MG-3, MG-10, MG-13 Computer Controls)
2. Weapons Control Systems Mechanic (MG-3, MG-10, MG-13 Computer and Controls)

Location: Lowry AFB, Colo.

Length: *Course 1,* 42–50 weeks; *Course 2,* 23 weeks.

Objectives: To train airmen as weapon control systems mechanics.

Instruction: *Course 1:* Fundamentals of electricity and AC; vacuum and gas-filled tubes; power supplies; voltage regulators; amplifiers, oscillators, and sweep generators; synchros, servomechanisms, and resolvers; basic mathematics; special equipment training. *Course 2:* Introduction to system and system tie-in; power generation and distribution; field exercises; computer functions; self tests; data link.

Credit recommendation, collegiate level: *Course 1:* 3 semester hours at the freshman or sophomore level as an elective in electricity and electronics, and credit in electrical laboratory on the basis of demonstrated skills and/or institutional examinations. *Course 2:* Credit in electrical laboratory on the basis of demonstrated skills and/or institutional examinations.

1. Weapons Control Systems Mechanic (MG-3, MG-10, MG-13 Radar)
   (Weapons Control Systems Mechanic (MG-10 Radar))
   (Fire Control Systems Mechanic, MG-10 Radar)
2. Weapons Control Systems Mechanic (MG-13 Radar)
   (Weapons Control Systems Mechanic (MG-3, MG-10 Radar))
   (Weapons Control Systems Mechanic (MG-3, MG-10, MG-13 Radar))

Location: Lowry AFB, Colo.

Length: *Course 1,* 40–58 weeks; *Course 2,* 20–28 weeks.

Objectives: To train airmen to analyze, maintain, and repair weapons control systems indicated in the title.

Instruction: *Course 1:* Fundamentals of electricity and AC; vacuum tubes and power supplies; amplifiers; oscillators; sweep generators; radar principles. *Course 2:* Introduction to system and system tie-in; power generation and distribution; antenna positioning; testing.

Credit recommendation, collegiate level: CAUTION *Courses in fire and weapons control vary only slightly in title, length, and recommendation. Note that title* *vary mainly by name of equipment in the parentheses following the title. Require exact identification by full title and length. Course 1:* 3 semester hours at the freshman or sophomore level as an elective in electronics, and credit in electrical laboratory on the basis of demonstrated skills and/or institutional examinations. *Course 2:* Credit in electricity and electrical laboratory on the basis of demonstrated skills and/or institutional examinations.

1. Weapons Control Systems Mechanic (MG-10, 13 Systems)
2. Weapons Control Systems Mechanic (MG-3, 10, 13 Systems)
3. Weapons Control Systems Mechanic (MG-3, 10, 13 Data Flow)
4. Weapons Control Systems Mechanic (MG-3, MG-10, MG-13 Data Flow)
5. Weapons Control Systems Mechanic (MG-3/10 Data Flow)
6. Weapons Control Systems Mechanic (MG-3/10 Data Flow)
7. Weapons Control Systems Mechanic (MG-3, MG-10 Data Flow)
8. Weapons Control Systems Mechanic (MG-13 Data Flow)
9. Fire Control Systems Mechanic (MG-10 Series Data Flow Specialist)
   (Fire Control Systems Mechanic (MG-10, Data Flow))

Location: Lowry AFB, Colo.

Length: *Course 1,* 32–34 weeks; *Course 2,* 29–31 weeks; *Course 3,* 31 weeks; *Course 4,* 43 weeks; *Course 5,* 46 weeks; *Course 6,* 38 weeks; *Course 7,* 31 weeks; *Course 8,* 43 weeks; *Course 9,* 36 weeks.

Objectives: To train airmen as apprentice weapons control systems mechanics.

Instruction: *Courses 1, 2, 3, 5, and 6:* DC and AC; reactive circuits; vacuum tubes and transistors; amplifiers and oscillators; special circuits; multivibrators and sweep circuits; microwave principles; in addition *Courses 3, 5, and 6* include special purpose tubes; multivibrators and sweep circuits. *Courses 4, 7, 8, and 9:* Adjustment, inspection, test and repair of the weapons control system indicated in title; in addition *Courses 4 and 9* include fundamentals of AC and DC.

Credit recommendation, collegiate level: CAUTION: *Courses in fire and weapons control vary only slightly in title, length, and recommendation. Note that titles vary mainly by name of equipment in the parentheses following the title. Require exact identification by full title and length. Courses 1 and 2:* For each course, 4 semester hours at the freshman or sophomore level as an elective in electricity and electronics, and credit in electrical laboratory on the basis of demonstrated skills and/or institutional examinations. *Courses 3, 5, and 6:* For each course 6 semester hours at the freshman or sophomore level as an elective in electricity and electronics, and credit in electrical laboratory on the basis of demonstrated skills and/or institutional examinations. *Courses 4 and 9:* For each course, 2 semester hours at the freshman or sophomore level as an elective in electricity and electronics, and credit in electrical laboratory on the basis of demonstrated skills and/or institutional examinations. *Courses 7 and 8:* For each course, credit in electricity, electronics and

electrical laboratory on the basis of demonstrated skills and/or institutional examinations.

Weapons Control Systems Mechanic (MG-12 System)

Location: Lowry AFB, Colo.

Length: 37–39 weeks.

Objectives: To train airmen as weapons control systems mechanics.

Instruction: Direct and alternating current; reactive circuits; vacuum tubes and solid state devices; amplifiers and oscillators; circuit analysis; microwave operation; multivibrators; sweep and logic circuits. The remainder of the course comprises special equipment training.

Credit recommendation, collegiate level: CAUTION: *Courses in weapons control systems repair vary slightly in title, length, and recommendation. Require exact identification of course by full title and length.* 4 semester hours at the freshman or sophomore level as an elective in electricity and electronics, and credit in electrical laboratory on the basis of demonstrated skills and/or institutional examinations.

Weapons Control System Technician (MG-3, MG-10 Radar)

Location: Lowry AFB, Colo.

Length: 25 weeks.

Objectives: To provide weapons control system mechanics with advanced training on the equipment specified.

Instruction: Publications and supervision; oscilloscopes, meters, and special devices; power meter and signal generators; dummy loads; antenna test sets; radar and computer functions; power generation and distribution; transmitting; receiver and receiver plumbing; focus, intensity, and range sweep channels; radar ranging functions; antenna positioning; missile servos; self tests; missile auxiliary test set and armament systems tester.

Credit recommendation, collegiate level: CAUTION: *Courses in weapons control systems repair vary only slightly in title, length, and recommendation. Require exact identification by full title and length.* Credit in electrical laboratory on the basis of demonstrated skills and/or institutional examinations.

Weapons Control Systems Technician (E-9 Systems)

Location: Lowry AFB, Colo.

Length: 21–26 weeks.

Objectives: To provide weapon control systems mechanics with advanced training.

Instruction: Service function and signal data recorder; transmitting, target detection, display, and radar ranging functions; antenna positioning; computer servo and attack steering functions; timing, firing, missile servo, and timed missile power functions; missile parameter, flight sensing, armament control, and optical steering and tracking functions; system tie-in and malfunction analysis; supervision, hazards, and publications. The 26-week course also includes standard test equipment training.

Credit recommendation, collegiate level: CAUTION: *Courses in weapons control systems repair vary only slightly in title, length, and recommendation. Require exact identification by full title and length.* Credit in electrical laboratory on the basis of demonstrated skills and/or institutional examinations.

1. **Weapons Control Systems Technician (MG-3, MG-10 Data Flow)**
2. **Weapons Control Systems, Technician (MG-13 Data Flow)**

Location: Lowry AFB, Colo.
Length: 29 weeks.
Objectives: To provide weapons control systems mechanics with advanced training on the systems specified.
Instruction: Fundamentals of AC and DC; power supplies; amplifiers; wave-shaping circuits; radar and servomechanism principles; power generation and distribution; transmitters; target display and detection; radar ranging; antenna positioning; missile servo and armament controlling function; attack steering; timing and firing function; timed missile power and parameter setting functions; flight sensing; computer and system self tests; data link functions; automatic flight control.
Credit recommendation, collegiate level: CAUTION: *Courses in weapons control systems repair vary only slightly in title, length, and recommendation. Require exact identification by full title and length.* For each course, credit in electrical laboratory on the basis of demonstrated skills and/or institutional examinations.

Weapons Control Systems Technician (MG-12 Systems)

Location: Lowry AFB, Colo.
Length: 26 weeks.
Objectives: To provide weapons control systems mechanics with advanced training on the system specified.
Instruction: Supervision; technical orders and forms; standard test equipment; intelligence gathering; antenna positioning; computers; optical steering and tracking function; fighter missile system; service function, nadar, and system tie-in.
Credit recommendation, collegiate level: CAUTION: *Courses in weapons control systems repair vary only slightly in title, length, and recommendation. Require exact identification by full title and length.* Credit in electrical laboratory on the basis of demonstrated skills and/or institutional examinations.

1. **Weapons Control Systems Technician (MG-13 Computer Controls)**
2. **Weapons Control Systems Technician (MG-3, MG-10 Computer Controls)**

Location: Lowry AFB, Colo.
Length: 32–38 weeks.
Objectives: To provide weapons control systems mechanics with advanced training on the equipment specified.
Instruction: Publications and supervision; oscillo-

scopes, meters, and impedance devices; radar and computer functions; power generation and distribution; attack steering; timing and firing; timed missile power; parameter setting; missile auxiliary and armament system test sets; flight sensing functions; computer self tests; signal generators, coders, and keyers; data link; automatic flight control systems.

Credit recommendation, collegiate level: CAUTION: *Courses in weapons control systems repair vary only slightly in title, length, and recommendation. Require exact identification by full title and length.* For each course, credit in electrical laboratory on the basis of demonstrated skills and/or institutional examinations.

Weapons Control Systems Technician (MG-13 Radar)

Location: Lowry AFB, Colo.
Length: 29 weeks.
Objectives: To provide weapons control systems mechanics with advanced training on the equipment specified.
Instruction: Publications and supervision; oscilloscope, meters, and special devices; power meter and signal generators; dummy loads; antenna test set; power generation and distribution; transmitter and radar ranging functions; target detection and display; antenna positioning; missile servos; radar; optical sight mode and tie-in.
Credit recommendation, collegiate level: CAUTION: *Courses in weapons control systems repair vary only slightly in title, length, and recommendation. Require exact identification by full title and length.* Credit in electrical laboratory on the basis of demonstrated skills and/or institutional examinations.

1. **Weapon Controller (412L System)**
2. **Weapon Controller (SAGE)**
3. **Weapon Controller (ECCM Operations Officer)**

Location: Keesler AFB, Miss.
Length: *Course 1,* 6–7 weeks; *Course 2,* 14 weeks; *Course 3,* 42–44 weeks.
Objectives: *Courses 1 and 2:* To train officers in the surveillance, identification, evaluation, assignment, and control function of air weapons control systems environment. *Course 3:* To train officers in the fundamentals of air defense.
Instruction: *Course 1:* 412L system familiarization; air surveillance and identification elements; situation projection, status and jam-track groups; weapons control. *Course 2:* Air defense; weapons controlling; air surveillance and identification. *Course 3:* Direct and alternating current; rectifiers, filters, and power supplies; amplifiers and oscillators; transmitters and receivers.
Credit recommendation, collegiate level: CAUTION: *These courses vary slightly in title, length, and recommendation. Require exact identification by full title and length. Courses 1 and 2:* No credit as the courses are military in nature. *Course 3:* 6 semester hours at the freshman or sophomore level as an elective in electronics, and credit in electrical laboratory on the basis of demonstrated skills and/or institutional examinations.

Weapons Controller Training
(Interceptor Controller Training)
(Interceptor Controllers)

Location: Tyndall AFB, Fla.

Length: 8–10 weeks.

Objectives: To train officers in interceptor controller fundamentals.

Instruction: Weapons; radar control techniques; ground central intercept techniques.

Credit recommendation, collegiate level: No credit as the course is military in nature.

Weapons Direction (SAGE)

Locations: Keesler AFB, Miss.; Richards-Gebauer AFB, Mo.

Length: 6–8 weeks.

Objectives: To train officers and airmen to operate director positions in semiautomatic ground environment direction centers.

Instruction: SAGE organizational and functional concepts; communications; symbology interpretation; equipment and procedures relative to director positions.

Credit recommendation, collegiate level: No credit as the course is military in nature.

1. Weapons Fusing Systems Specialist
2. Weapons Fuzing Systems Specialist (Electronic)
(Weapons Fusing System Specialist (Electronic))

Location: Lowry AFB, Colo.

Length: *Course 1, 36–43 weeks; Course 2, 27–30 weeks.*

Objectives: To train airmen to assemble, maintain, and repair weapons fusing systems components and test equipment.

Instruction: The first phase of both courses consists of electricity and electronics training, including, generally, electricity and magnetism, alternating current, vacuum tubes and power supplies, amplifiers, oscillators, modulation and detection, receiver principles, special circuits, and microwave principles. The remainder of both courses consists of special equipment training.

Credit recommendation, collegiate level: For each course, 4 semester hours at the freshman or sophomore level as an elective in electricity and electronics, and credit in electrical laboratory on the basis of demonstrated skills and/or institutional examinations.

Weapons Fuzing Systems Specialist (Electrical)

Location: Lowry AFB, Colo.

Length: 19 weeks.

Objectives: To train airmen to inspect, assemble, test, maintain, and repair weapons fuzing systems components and related test equipment.

Instruction: Electricity and magnetism; alternating current; vacuum tubes; volt meters; oscilloscope, transformers.

Credit recommendation, collegiate level: 2 semester hours at the freshman or sophomore level as an elective in electricity, and credit in electrical laboratory on the basis of demonstrated skills and/or institutional examinations.

1. Weapons Mechanic
2. Weapons Mechanic

Location: Lowry AFB, Colo.

Length: *Course 1, 33 weeks; Course 2, 16–29 weeks.*

Objectives: To train airmen to install, maintain, repair, and modify weapons and associated equipment.

Instruction: *Course 1:* Principles of electricity and electronics; weapons publications; hand tools; 20mm automatic guns; 50 caliber machine guns; associated armament equipment; bomber and fighter weapons systems; nuclear weapons; field training. *Course 2:* Electrical fundamentals; weapons publications; hand tools; launching systems on bombardment and fighter type aircraft; hand and shoulder weapons; 20mm automatic guns; malfunction laboratory; field training.

Credit recommendation, collegiate level: CAUTION: *Weapons mechanic courses vary only slightly in title, length, and recommendation. Require exact identification by full title and length. Course 1:* 2 semester hours at the freshman or sophomore level as an elective in electricity and electronics. At the technical and vocational level for *Courses 1 and 2,* credit in electrical and mechanical shop on the basis of demonstrated skills and/or institutional examinations for each course.

1. Weapons Mechanic (ADC)
2. Weapons Mechanic (SAC)
3. Weapons Mechanic (TAC)

Location: Lowry AFB, Colo.

Length: 12–18 weeks.

Objectives: To train airmen to inspect and maintain conventional and nuclear weapons.

Instruction: *Courses 1, 2 and 3:* Technical publications and forms; principles of AC and DC; airmunitions; M61A1 automatic gun. The remainder of each course deals with aircraft used in the Air Defense, Strategic Air, or Tactical Air Command. *Course 1:* F-101B weapons systems checkout, maintenance and loading. *Course 2:* B-52 conventional weapons systems inspection, maintenance, and loading. *Course 3:* Linkless feed system and gun pod; M39A2 automatic gun; F-100D weapons systems inspection, maintenance and loading.

Credit recommendation, collegiate level: CAUTION: *Weapons mechanic courses vary only slightly in title, length, and recommendation. Require exact identification by full title and length.* These courses are technical and vocational in nature. Credit in electrical and mechanical shop on the basis of demonstrated skills and/or institutional examinations.

1. Weapons Mechanic, Bomber
2. Weapons Mechanic, Fighter Bomber
3. Weapons Mechanic, Fighter Interceptor

Location: Lowry AFB, Colo.

Length: 13–17 weeks.

Objectives: To train airmen to maintain and repair

weapons and weapon systems on the type of aircraft specified.

Instruction: Air Force publications; hand tools; electrical fundamentals; base defense weapons; 20mm automatic guns; malfunction laboratory; associated armament equipment; bomber, fighter, or interceptor launching systems; field training; nuclear weapons.

Credit recommendation, collegiate level: CAUTION: *Weapons mechanic courses vary only slightly in title, length, and recommendation. Require exact identification by full title and length.* These courses are technical and vocational in nature. Credit in electrical and mechanical shop on the basis of demonstrated skills and/or institutional examinations.

Weapons Mechanic, GAM-72

Location: Amarillo AFB, Tex.
Length: 4–5 weeks.
Objectives: To provide weapons mechanics with supplemental training on the GAM-72 missile.
Instruction: GAM-72 structure and maintenance; ground support equipment; carrier, electrical, and launch gear systems; launch gear; carrier, missile, and package loading.
Credit recommendation, collegiate level: CAUTION: *Weapons mechanic courses vary only slightly in title, length, and recommendation. Require exact identification by full title and length.* This course is technical and vocational in nature. Credit in electrical and mechanical shop on the basis of demonstrated skills and/or institutional examinations.

Weather Equipment Refresher Training

Location: Chanute AFB, Ill.
Length: 12 weeks.
Objectives: To provide weather equipment technicians with additional electronic fundamentals and current weather equipment maintenance training.
Instruction: Review of electronic and radar fundamentals; block and circuit analysis, troubleshooting and preventive maintenance of AN/GMQ-13, AN/TMQ-11, AN/CPS-9, AN/APQ-13, and AN/GMQ-10.
Credit recommendation, collegiate level: No credit because of the specialized, review nature of the course.

Weather Equipment Repairman

Location: Chanute AFB, Ill.
Length: 31–33 weeks.
Objectives: To train airmen in the installation and maintenance of electrical, mechanical, and optical meteorological observing equipment.
Instruction: Direct and alternating current; electron tubes and power supplies; wave shaping and amplifiers; oscillators, transmitters, and receivers; circuit analysis; synchros, servomechanisms, and special circuits; radar and non-radar meteorological equipment, including visibility and storm detection, temperature, humidity, wind, and cloud height determining equipment.
Credit recommendation, collegiate level: 6 semester

hours at the freshman or sophomore level as an elective in electricity and electronics, and credit in electrical laboratory on the basis of demonstrated skills and/or institutional examinations.

Weather Equipment Superintendent

Location: Chanute AFB, Ill.
Length: 19–28 weeks.
Objectives: To train weather equipment technicians in management, siting, and maintenance of weather equipment.
Instruction: Electrical mathematics; advanced electronics; staff technical writing and administrative practices; radar and advanced electronics; current weather equipment; site surveying and installation of equipment.
Credit recommendation, collegiate level: 3 semester hours in business organization and management.

Weather Equipment Technician

Location: Chanute AFB, Ill.
Length: 43–45 weeks.
Objectives: To provide advanced training for meteorological equipment repair personnel.
Instruction: Fundamentals of direct and alternating current and magnetism; receivers and transmitters; wave-shaping circuits; synchros and microwaves; special radar and weather equipment training.
Credit recommendation, collegiate level: 4 semester hours at the freshman or sophomore level as an elective in electricity and electronics, and credit in electrical laboratory on the basis of demonstrated skills and/or institutional examinations.

1. Weather Forecaster Superintendent
2. Weather Superintendent

Location: Chanute AFB, Ill.
Length: *Course 1,* 35–37 weeks; *Course 2,* 10 weeks.
Objectives: To provide weather technicians with supplemental training to enable them to superintend technical activities of weather stations.
Instruction: *Course 1:* Mathematics; analysis; oceanography; physical and dynamic meteorology; climatological studies; operational weather; forecast studies; advanced forecasting. *Course 2:* Operational forecasting; general meteorology; weather station management; weather analysis and presentation.
Credit recommendation, collegiate level: For each course, credit in advanced weather forecasting techniques on the basis of institutional examination.

Weather Observer

Location: Chanute AFB, Ill.
Length: 16–22 weeks.
Objectives: To train airmen in the basic theory and practice of weather observation.

Instruction: Weather elements–theory and instrumentation; plotting weather maps and charts; surface weather observations; weather equipment operation; weather station operation.

Credit recommendation, collegiate level: 3 semester hours in meteorology.

Weather Observer Technician

Location: Chanute AFB, Ill.

Length: 16–25 weeks.

Objectives: To provide advanced, supervisory-level training for weather observers.

Instruction: Elementary mathematics; general meteorology and map analysis; operation and supervision of surface observing activities; electronic observations and equipment; office procedures; upper air observations; management; communication skills; OJT programs; supply and maintenance; data dissemination and chart preparation.

Credit recommendation, collegiate level: 3 semester hours in meteorology and 3 semester hours in business organization and management.

Weather Technician
(Weather Forecaster Technician)

Location: Chanute AFB, Ill.

Length: 32–44 weeks.

Objectives: To train weather observers in meteorological theory and forecasting practices.

Instruction: Mathematics; physics; air mass analysis; synoptic meteorology; climatology; introductory analysis; thermal consistency of analysis; prognostic charts and current weather laboratory; analysis and forecasting applications.

Credit recommendation, collegiate level: 17 semester hours in weather forecasting or meteorology.

Woodworker

Location: Francis E. Warren AFB, Wyo.

Length: 13 weeks.

Objectives: To train airmen to construct, modify, and repair wooden structures and woodwork furnishings.

Instruction: Introduction to woodworking; frame construction; finish construction; construction and woodworking modification and repair.

Credit recommendation, collegiate level: This course is technical and vocational in nature. Credit in woodworking shop on the basis of demonstrated skills and/or institutional examinations.

Work Control Specialist

Location: Sheppard AFB, Tex.

Length: 5 weeks.

Objectives: To train airmen in work control and scheduling.

Instruction: Control center management and supervision; work request processing; work order processing; planning procedures; scheduling fundamentals; planning the annual maintenance and repair program; preventive maintenance; service calls; data automation; control room operation.

Credit recommendation, collegiate level: 2 semester hours in maintenance management.

ARMY

ARMY

1. AAA Integrated Fire Control Maintenance
2. AAA Integrated Fire Control Maintenance Officer

Location: Air Defense School, Fort Bliss, Tex.

Length: *Course 1,* 30 weeks; *Course 2,* 31–34 weeks.

Objectives: To train officers and warrant officers in the technical operation, functions, characteristics, and maintenance of conventional AAA integrated fire control systems.

Instruction: *Course 1:* Basic electrical theory and use of test instruments, including series and parallel AC and DC circuits, inductance and reactance, capacitance, generator principles, transformers, and principles of DC motors; electronic circuits and devices used in radio transmitting and receiving equipment; adjustment, repair, and maintenance of radar and computer equipment; characteristics, capabilities, and limitations of acquisition and tracking radars; inspection and maintenance of power control systems. *Course 2:* This contains the same instruction as *Course 1* but includes more theory.

Credit recommendation, collegiate level: CAUTION: *These courses vary only slightly in title, length, and recommendation. Require exact identification of course by title and length. Course 1:* 3 semester hours at the freshman or sophomore level as an elective in electricity and electronics, and credit in electrical laboratory on the basis of demonstrated skills and/or institutional examinations. *Course 2:* 4 semester hours at the freshman or sophomore level as an elective in electricity and electronics, and credit in electrical laboratory on the basis of demonstrated skills and/or institutional examinations.

AAA Operations and Intelligence Noncommissioned Officer

Location: Antiaircraft Artillery and Guided Missile School, Fort Bliss, Tex.

Length: 14 weeks.

Objectives: To train enlisted personnel to assist operations and staff officers in antiaircraft artillery and surface-to-air missile operations and intelligence and to prepare operations and training material.

Instruction: Engineering drawing, including proficiency in the use of drawing equipment and basic drafting techniques necessary in the preparation of operation charts, graphs, and overlays; plane surveying, including position determination and azimuth determination; map and aerial photograph reading; familiarization with AAA gunnery and materiel; characteristics, capabilities, and techniques of operation of the Nike-Ajax system; AAA and SAM tactics.

Credit recommendation, collegiate level: Credit in plane surveying and engineering drawing on the basis of institutional examination.

ADPS (Fieldata) Auxiliary Equipment Repair

Location: Signal School, Fort Monmouth, N.J.

Length: 25–27 weeks.

Objectives: To train enlisted personnel to inspect, test, and repair fieldata stored program computer auxiliary equipment.

Instruction: Series and parallel circuits, DC power, magnetism and electromagnetism, AC, inductance, capacitance, AC and DC generators and motors, impedance, and differentiating and integrating circuits; semiconductors, transistors, and transistor circuits; basic fieldata circuits; operation and maintenance of the input-output converter; data processing keyboard equipment; high-speed paper tape reader punch and buffer unit; digital magnetic tape transports; high-speed line printer, buffer, and memory; card reader punch machine and buffer unit.

Credit recommendation, collegiate level: 3 semester hours at the freshman or sophomore level as an elective in electricity and electronics, and credit in electrical laboratory on the basis of demonstrated skills and/or institutional examinations.

1. ADPS (Fieldata) Console Operation
2. ADPS Console Operation

Location: Signal School, Fort Monmouth, N.J.

Length: 9 weeks.

Objectives: *Course 1:* To train enlisted personnel in the operation and operator maintenance of fieldata computers. *Course 2:* To train enlisted personnel in the operation and operator maintenance of digital computers and their peripheral equipment.

Instruction: *Course 1:* Operation of basic components; program control; paper tape input-output, magnetic tape, and printer operations; operation of an automatic data processing systems fieldata console; system operation. *Course 2:* Number systems; concept of the stored program; computer programming; paper tape and magnetic tape operations; assembly programs; program testing; computer operation.

Credit recommendation, collegiate level: CAUTION: *These courses vary in title and recommendation. Require exact identification of course by title. Course 1:* 3 semester hours in computer operation in the field of data processing. *Course 2:* 5 semester hours in computer operation in the field of data processing.

ADPS (Fieldata) Repair

Location: Signal School, Fort Monmouth, N.J.

Length: 36 weeks.

Objectives: To train enlisted personnel to inspect, test, and repair fieldata computers.

Instruction: Fundamental computer circuits; construction and analysis of a computer system; electrical fundamentals, including current and voltage, Ohm's law, series and parallel circuits, AC, motors, transformers, magnetism and electromagnetism, inductance, capacitance, impedance, and nonsinusoidal wave forms; transistor fundamentals; diagnostic analysis and repair of a central processor; input-output system; functional units, order codes and programming of the computer, and adjustment of the power supply; input-output converter; techniques required to program and operate a computer; familiarization with computer numbering systems.

Credit recommendation, collegiate level: 3 semester hours at the freshman or sophomore level as an elective in electricity and electronics, and credit in electrical laboratory on the basis of demonstrated skills and/or institutional examinations.

ADPS Plans and Operations Officer
(ADPS (Fieldata) Plans and Operations Officer)

Location: Signal School, Fort Monmouth, N.J.
Length: 11 weeks.
Objectives: To train commissioned officers in the planning and operation of automatic data processing systems.
Instruction: Principles of operation of an automatic data processing system; electronic principles of data transmission; characteristics, capabilities, and employment of tactical and fixed communications systems to support a data processing system; procedures and techniques of computer programming; ADP systems engineering; management of an automatic data processing system; analysis, system design, and computer programming and documentation.
Credit recommendation, collegiate level: 3 semester hours in principles of data processing.

ADPS Programming
(ADPS (Fieldata) Programming)

Location: Signal School, Fort Monmouth, N.J.
Length: 10–11 weeks.
Objectives: To train enlisted personnel in the principles and techniques of programming computers for an automatic data processing system.
Instruction: Operation of a data processing system; principles of programming; application of machine language and symbolic coding to programming operations; input-output equipment; advanced programming techniques; introduction to COBOL language; COBOL programming.
Credit recommendation, collegiate level: 5 semester hours in computer programming in the field of computing science.

AH-1G (Hueycobra) Helicopter Repair Transition

Location: Transportation School, Fort Eustis, Va.
Length: 3 weeks.
Objectives: To provide enlisted personnel with a working knowledge in organization, direct support and general support maintenance of the Hueycobra (AH-1G) helicopters.
Instruction: Hueycobra (AH-1G) tools and support equipment; main and tail rotor blades; weight and balance; armament systems; airframe and airframe maintenance; pylon system; tail rotor and tail rotor drive; power plant and related systems; flight control system; hydraulic systems.
Credit recommendation, collegiate level: This course is technical and vocational in nature. Credit in helicopter repair shop on the basis of demonstrated skills and/or institutional examinations.

AH-1G (Hueycobra) Pilot Transition/Gunnery

Location: Aviation School, Fort Rucker, Ala.
Length: 3–4 weeks.
Objectives: To qualify officers and warrant officers as gunnery pilots in the AH-1G Hueycobra helicopter.
Instruction: Gunner flight control training; transition flight training; night flight operations; Mini gun and 40mm range qualification; XM-19 and 2.75″ rocket qualification; principles of air-to-ground machine gun fire; armed helicopter employment fundamentals; aerial rockets; techniques of fire.
Credit recommendation, collegiate level: No credit as course is military in nature.

AN/MPQ-36 Radar Signal Simulator Maintenance
(15D2 Radar Signal Simulator Maintenance)

Location: Army Air Defense School, Fort Bliss, Tex.
Length: 7–10 weeks.
Objectives: To train enlisted personnel to operate, adjust, and maintain the 15D2 radar signal simulator of the AN/MPQ-36 radar signal simulator.
Instruction: Operator training and 15D2 or AN/MPQ-36 familiarization; circuits used in simulating targets for associated acquisition and tracking radars and in simulating electronic and reflection jamming effects; missile simulation; monitor circuits.
Credit recommendation, collegiate level: Credit in electrical laboratory on the basis of demonstrated skills and/or institutional examinations.

AN/MPQ-T1 Radar Signal Simulator Maintenance

Location: Army Air Defense School, Fort Bliss, Tex.
Length: 10–12 weeks.
Objectives: To train commissioned officers, warrant officers, and enlisted personnel to operate, adjust, and maintain the AN/MPQ-T1 radar signal simulator.
Instruction: Characteristics and operation of the AN/MPQ-T1, including power distribution, presentation circuits, and transistorized circuits; target, IFF, and ECM simulation circuits; chaff, clutter, and masking simulation circuits; missile simulation circuits, system tie-in and analysis, and alignment procedures.
Credit recommendation, collegiate level: Credit in electrical laboratory on the basis of demonstrated skills and/or institutional examinations.

AN/MPS-23 Radar Repair

Location: Army Air Defense School, Fort Bliss, Tex.
Length: 16 weeks.
Objectives: To train warrant officers and enlisted per-

sonnel to perform organizational and field maintenance on the AN/MPS-23 and AN/MPS-23A radar sets.

Instruction: AN/MPS-23 radar special circuits, power distribution, and antenna; programmer and transmitter; receiver, indicators, and testing function; IFF unit; theory of operation of the AN/MPS-23A radar sets and telephone communications.

Credit recommendation, collegiate level: Credit in electrical laboratory on the basis of demonstrated skills and/or institutional examinations.

AN/MSQ-28 Army Air Defense Command Post Controller

Location: Air Defense School, Fort Bliss, Tex.
Length: 3 weeks.
Objectives: To provide artillery officers and enlisted personnel with a working knowledge of the capabilities, limitations, and tactical operations of the AN/MSQ-28 Army Air Defense Command Post.
Instruction: Familiarization with the organization and operation and mission of Air Defense Command Post systems.
Credit recommendation, collegiate level: No credit as course is military in nature.

AN/TPQ-21 Hawk Guided Missile System Simulator Maintenance

Location: Air Defense School, Fort Bliss, Tex.
Length: 8–9 weeks.
Objectives: To train warrant officers and enlisted personnel in the operation, adjustments, and organizational maintenance of the AN/TPQ-21 Hawk guided missile system simulator.
Instruction: AC-DC control circuits power system; target position generator; polar integrators; troubleshooting; slant range follower and radial speed computer; error signals generator; simulator ROR logic circuits; countermeasures console; electronic tube assembly camera and clutter-generator; system analysis operation and maintenance.
Credit recommendation, collegiate level: Credit in electrical laboratory on the basis of demonstrated skills and/or institutional examinations.

AN/TRC-80 Operation (Pershing)

Location: Artillery and Missile School, Fort Sill, Okla.
Length: 9 weeks.
Objectives: To train enlisted personnel in the operation and maintenance of the AN/TRC-80 radio terminal set and associated equipment.
Instruction: Communication procedures and security; orientation to standard communication equipment and electronic warfare; operation and maintenance of AN/TRC-80 equipment, including a working knowledge of its power distribution, engine generator, antenna system, modulator-multiplier and demultiplexer-multiplexer units, transmit converter, power amplifier, and control panel.
Credit recommendation, collegiate level: This course is technical and vocational in nature. Credit in radio

operation and maintenance on the basis of demonstrated skills and/or institutional examinations.

AN/TSQ-38 and AN/MSQ-18 Coder-Decoder Group Maintenance
(AN/MSQ-18 Coder-Decoder Group Maintenance)
(AN/MSQ-18 Battery Terminal Equipment Maintenance)

Location: Air Defense School, Fort Bliss, Tex.
Length: 12–13 weeks.
Objectives: To train warrant officers and enlisted personnel in the function, operation, organizational maintenance, and inspection of the coder-decoder group for missile monitors.
Instruction: Orientation and basic theory; coordinate data set transmitter and receiver; coder-decoder group; operations central; ground-to-slant converter; system analysis.
Credit recommendation, collegiate level: Credit in electrical laboratory on the basis of demonstrated skills and/or institutional examinations.

AN/TSQ-51 System Maintenance

Location: Army Air Defense School, Fort Bliss, Tex.
Length: 33 weeks.
Objectives: To train warrant officers and enlisted personnel to perform organizational, direct support–general support maintenance on the air defense fire distribution system AN/TSQ-51.
Instruction: Digital computer fundamentals; console operations and system power supplies; theory and operation of the sweep and video portion and the symbol generation circuits of the display subsystems; introduction to programming; theory and operation of the computer power supplies and memory section; program control unit and arithmetic unit; input-output unit, and automatic data link unit; AN/TSQ-51 system program, diagnostics, and card repair.
Credit recommendation, collegiate level: 2 semester hours in digital logic in the field of computing science, and credit in electrical laboratory on the basis of demonstrated skills and/or institutional examinations.

1. Accounting (Basic)
2. Accounting (Intermediate)
3. Cost Accounting
4. Accounting (Advanced)
5. Accounting

Location: Finance School, Fort Benjamin Harrison, Ind.
Length: *Courses 1, 2, and 3,* 4 weeks; *Course 4,* 5 weeks; *Course 5,* 17 weeks.
Objectives: To train commissioned officers in accounting principles.
Instruction: *Course 1:* Basic accounting theory; working papers, and end-of-period adjustments; procedures related to negotiable instruments, manufacturing accounts, voucher systems, and alternative adjustments; accounts and financial statements; corporations. *Course 2:* Accounting cycle and records; working capital analysis; governmental and commercial budgetary ac-

counts; balance sheet accounts; statement of funds. *Course 3:* Elements of cost; job order cost accounting; process cost accounting; budgets; standards cost accounting. *Course 4:* Statement of affairs; branch office accounting; consolidated statements; auditing; assets and equities; comparative financial statements; analysis of income statement long-term financial conditions. *Course 5:* This course includes all of the instruction given in *Courses 1 through 4.*

Credit recommendation, collegiate level: CAUTION: *These courses vary only slightly in title, length, and recommendation. Require exact identification of course by title and length. Course 1:* 4 semester hours in basic accounting. *Course 2:* 4 semester hours in intermediate accounting. *Course 3:* 4 semester hours in cost accounting. *Course 4:* 5 semester hours in advanced accounting. *Course 5:* 4 semester hours in basic accounting, 4 semester hours in intermediate accounting, 4 semester hours in cost accounting, and 5 semester hours in advanced accounting.

Accounting Specialist

Location: Finance School, Fort Benjamin Harrison, Ind.

Length: 7–9 weeks.

Objectives: To train enlisted personnel at the finance career entry-level in the principles, policies, and procedures relative to examining, disbursing, and accounting for public funds.

Instruction: Fiscal code; general ledger chart of accounts; introduction to accounting; nonappropriated fund accounting; status of funds transactions; reimbursement transactions; analysis and reconciliation; military supply and introduction to stock fund; procurement and sales transactions; pay of military personnel; disbursing operations; concepts and principles of auditing; audit techniques and report; familiarization with internal control.

Credit recommendation, collegiate level: 4 semester hours in government accounting.

Adjutant/Adjutant General Officer Familiarization

Location: Adjutant General School, Fort Benjamin Harrison, Ind.

Length: 5 weeks.

Objectives: To familiarize officers with the organization, functions, duties, and responsibilities of the Adjutant General.

Instruction: Command and staff responsibilities, and relationships at all levels of command; roles and functions of the Adjutant General; organization of the division Adjutant General section; personnel and office management; administration of records and reports.

Credit recommendation, collegiate level: 2 semester hours in office management, *provided no previous credit has been granted in this field.*

Adjutant General Officer Advanced
(Adjutant General Officer Career)

Location: Adjutant General's School, Fort Benjamin Harrison, Ind.

Length: 24–38 weeks.

Objectives: To provide military education and branch training in the duties and responsibilities of Adjutant General's Corps officers.

Instruction: Military leadership; military justice; unit supply procedures; effective oral and written communication; management and manpower control; military pay, absences, personal affairs, casualty reporting, and separations; personnel management, including tests and measurements, interviewing and counseling, classification and distribution to training, assignment priorities and utilization requirements, career planning, evaluation system, allocation and distribution of personnel, and personnel records; postal service operations; familiarization with data processing equipment and operations; command and staff functions; administrative service functions and operations; nuclear weapons employment; organization, capabilities, and techniques of employment of Army division; combat and combat service support; supervision of special services.

Credit recommendation, collegiate level: 3 semester hours in business organization and management and 3 semester hours in personnel management.

Adjutant General Officer Basic
(Adjutant General Officer Orientation)

Location: Adjutant General School, Fort Benjamin Harrison, Ind.

Length: 5–10 weeks.

Objectives: To provide newly commissioned officers with basic branch training in the duties and responsibilities appropriate to their grade and expected service.

Instruction: Personnel management, including instruction in counseling and interviewing, tests and measurements, evaluation of personnel, personnel control devices, officer career planning, replacement operations, and personnel records; selection of board members, and appointment of investigating officers; procedures for filing various reports and handling absences, personal affairs, and separations; general knowledge of staff, combat, and combat support operations to determine personnel and administration requirements.

Credit recommendation, collegiate level: 2 semester hours in personnel management, and credit in advanced military at institutions which regularly offer such credit.

Advanced Air Drop Equipment Maintenance

Location: Quartermaster School, Fort Lee, Va.

Length: 6 weeks.

Objectives: To train enlisted personnel in the maintenance of airdrop equipment at organizational, field, and depot level.

Instruction: Patternmaking and blueprint heading; materials used in airdrop equipment repair; maintenance of sewing machines; section replacement; suspension line repair and replacement; personnel parachute and pack tray replacement and repair; repair of air items; airdrop equipment repair techniques.

Credit recommendation, collegiate level: This course is technical and vocational in nature. Credit in parachute rigging on the basis of demonstrated skills and/or institutional examinations.

Advanced Army Administration

Location: Adjutant General School, Fort Benjamin Harrison, Ind.

Length: 8 weeks.

Objectives: To train enlisted personnel to supervise administrative and clerical operations in a military headquarters or office.

Instruction: Administrative functions including communication distribution and control, publications management, records disposition and management, military correspondence, administration of military justice, and principles, functions, and techniques of management; office research and problems; oral and written communication; personnel management.

Credit recommendation, collegiate level: 3 semester hours in office management.

Advanced Bandsman (Bandmaster Preparatory)

Location: U.S. Naval School of Music, U.S. Naval Receiving Station, Washington, D.C.

Length: 20 weeks.

Objectives: To train warrant officers and enlisted personnel in advanced techniques of band conducting, leadership, organization, mission function, supply and administration; to qualify enlisted personnel for appointment as warrant officers.

Instruction: Command and leadership, administration and supply, instrumental techniques, piano, harmony and ear training, band arranging, conducting, the marching band, dance band style and techniques, band literature survey.

Credit recommendation, collegiate level: Institutions which offer a music degree curriculum should determine the amount of credit by institutional examination. The professional character of the training is similar in content and proficiency to courses in colleges or conservatories.

Advanced Chemical NCO
(Advanced Chemical NCO (Staff Specialist))
(Chemical Staff Supervision)

Location: Chemical Corps School, Fort McClellan, Ala.

Length: 8 weeks.

Objectives: To provide officers and enlisted personnel with a working knowledge in administration, staff procedures, and technical aspects of CBR operations.

Instruction: Logistics, CBR plans, training, and operations; biological weapons system; chemical weapons system; nuclear warfare and radiological defense.

Credit recommendation, collegiate level: No credit because of the limited technical nature of the course.

Advanced Geodetic Surveyor

Location: Engineer School, Fort Belvoir, Va.

Length: 19–20 weeks.

Objectives: To train engineer warrant officers and selected senior noncommissioned officers in advanced geodetic survey techniques and precise instrumentation related to high-order surveys.

Instruction: Mathematics; basic geodesy; map compiling; vertical control surveys; horizontal control; theodolite; surveys; geodometer; triangle computation; traverse computations; gravity; astronomic observations; azimuth; theodolite; latitudes.

Credit recommendation, collegiate level: 6 semester hours in geodesy and 4 semester hours in geodetic astronomy.

Advanced Information Specialist

Locations: Defense Information School, Fort Slocum, N.Y.; Fort Benjamin Harrison, Ind.

Length: 8 weeks.

Objectives: To train Armed Forces noncommissioned and petty officers in the information career field to plan, supervise, and coordinate the activities of an information office/section and an Armed Forces radio and television outlet.

Instruction: Information policies, objectives, and programs; community relations; news analysis and publicity techniques; editorial writing; magazine article research and development; copy editing; makeup and layout; oral communications; principles, policies, and procedures of releasing information for radio and television broadcast; introduction to international relations and government.

Credit recommendation, collegiate level: 3 semester hours in journalism, and credit in the area of social studies on the basis of institutional examination.

Advanced Machine Accounting

Location: Adjutant General School, Fort Benjamin Harrison, Ind.

Length: 4 weeks.

Objectives: To train enlisted personnel to supervise machine accounting specialists engaged in operating and wiring electrical accounting equipment and performing related duties in machine accounting activities.

Instruction: Types and care of electrical accounting machines; development of source documents for accounting machines, principles of coding, punch card design, types and construction of procedures; principles of planning, directing, and controlling a machine accounting section; familiarization with general management principles.

Credit recommendation, collegiate level: This course is technical and vocational in nature. Credit in electrical accounting machine operation on the basis of demonstrated skills and/or institutional examinations.

1. Advanced Nursing Administration
2. Advanced Nursing Administration
3. Military Nursing Advanced

Location: Medical Service School, Fort Sam Houston, Tex.

Length: *Course 1,* 27 weeks; *Course 2,* 23 weeks; *Course 3,* 22–23 weeks.

Objectives: To train Army Nurse Corps officers in administrative and supervisory principles as applied in the performance of professional nursing duties and responsibilities.

Instruction: *Course 1:* Personnel management; procedures for hospital plant planning and maintenance; administrative aspects of records and reports; medical and military law; medical supply procedures; hospital organization; techniques of written and oral communication; medical administration; management methods; emergency medical treatment procedures; organization and function of the field medical service; nursing service administration, including planning, organization, staffing, directing, and budgeting; counseling and guidance of nursing service personnel; instructional techniques in nursing; new developments in medicine; preventive medicine. *Courses 2 and 3:* These courses vary from *Course 1* in that they include less instruction in hospital organization and administration, instructional methods, and personnel management.

Credit recommendation, collegiate level: CAUTION: *These courses vary only slightly in title, length, and recommendation. Require exact identification of course by title and length. Course 1:* 6 semester hours in nursing administration, 3 semester hours in hospital management, 3 semester hours in personnel management, 2 semester hours in instructional methods, and credit in speech on the basis of institutional examination. *Courses 2 and 3:* For each course, 6 semester hours in nursing administration, 2 semester hours in hospital management, 2 semester hours in personnel management, and credit in instructional methods on the basis of institutional examination.

Advanced Personnel Management Enlisted

Location: Adjutant General School, Fort Benjamin Harrison, Ind.
Length: 5 weeks.
Objectives: To train enlisted supervisors in the Army personnel system and in the objectives of personnel management.
Instruction: Administrative functions; training as a function of supervision; principles and functions of personnel management; psychology and human behavior; leadership procedures and techniques; personnel records.
Credit recommendation, collegiate level: 2 semester hours in personnel management.

Aerial Surveillance Officer

Location: Intelligence School, Fort Holabird, Md.
Length: 18–22 weeks.
Objectives: To train commissioned officers in the organization and employment of all aerial reconnaissance and surveillance agencies from division to Army level; in the skills of all aspects of aerial surveillance, reconnaissance planning and operations, tactical multisensor imagery interpretation techniques; and in strategic imagery interpretation.
Instruction: Aerial surveillance organization, operations and planning; imagery interpretation techniques; military equipment identification; lines in communication analysis; functional analysis of basic industries; interpretation of radar, thermal, and high altitude photo-imagery; metrics; terrain; general military and intelligence subjects.
Credit recommendation, collegiate level: 6 semester hours in intelligence methods of imagery interpretation.

Air Base Construction

Location: Engineer School, Fort Belvoir, Va.
Length: 6 weeks.
Objectives: To train officers in the technical aspects of military airfield construction.
Instruction: Selection, layout, drainage, construction survey, grades, earthwork calculations, use of mass diagram, work estimates, and construction scheduling; use and evaluation of soil tests; design of airfield base; types, grades, composition, and characteristics of bituminous materials; types of bituminous surface treatments and pavements and methods of construction; selection of material and determination of mix proportions; stability tests; rigid pavement design and construction; requirements, plans, and layout for airfield buildings; principles of pit and quarry operations for the production of aggregates; operation and maintenance of surfacing and quarry machines.
Credit recommendation, collegiate level: 3 semester hours as an elective in engineering construction.

Air Defense Acquisition Radars Maintenance

Location: Army Air Defense School, Fort Bliss, Tex.
Length: 40 weeks.
Objectives: To train warrant officers and enlisted personnel in the operation, adjustment, and organizational maintenance of air defense acquisition radars, associated IFF equipment, and associated ECCM consoles.
Instruction: AC and DC circuits; inductance; capacitance; resonant circuits; transformers; three-phase power; diodes and rectifiers; filters voltage dividers, and potentiometers; triodes; multi-element tubes; amplifiers; oscillators; superheterodyne receiver; sweep generators; relays and control devices; synchros; servosystems; radar circuits associated with the AN/TPS-1G; low-power acquisition radar; IFF Mark X system; improved alternate battery acquisition radars and ECCM consoles; electronic section high-power acquisition radar; systems checkout; introduction to the AN/MPQ-T1 radar.
Credit recommendation, collegiate level: 3 semester hours at the freshman or sophomore level as an elective in electricity and electronics, and credit in electrical laboratory on the basis of demonstrated skills and/or institutional examinations.

1. Air Defense Artillery Automatic Weapons Repair
2. Air Defense Artillery Automatic Weapons Officer

Location: Army Air Defense School, Fort Bliss, Tex.
Length: 4–5 weeks.
Objectives: *Course 1:* To train enlisted personnel to perform organizational maintenance on unit small arms and air defense artillery automatic weapons. *Course 2:* To train battery- and field-grade officers in air defense artillery automatic weapons tactics, techniques, and materiel.

Instruction: *Course 1:* Characteristics and functioning of small arms and the M60 machine gun, cal .50 machine guns and M55 mount, and the twin 40-mm gun, self-propelled M42. *Course 2:* In addition to the preceding instruction this course contains tactics and techniques of air defense and the mission, organization, and operations of air defense automatic weapons units.

Credit recommendation, collegiate level: CAUTION: *These courses vary in title and recommendation. Require exact identification of course by title. Course 1:* This course is technical and vocational in nature. Credit in small arms repair on the basis of demonstrated skills and/or institutional examinations. *Course 2:* No credit as the course is military in nature.

Air Defense Artillery Field Grade Officer Refresher (Senior Air Defense Artillery Officer)

Location: Air Defense School, Fort Bliss, Tex.
Length: 3 weeks.
Objectives: To provide general officers and field-grade officers with a working knowledge of Army air defense systems.
Instruction: Familiarization with the characteristics, capabilities, limitations, operations, and tactics of the Nike-Hercules and Hawk missile systems.
Credit recommendation, collegiate level: No credit as courses are military in nature.

Air Defense Artillery Officer Mobilization Advanced
1. Phase II
2. Phase III

Location: Army Air Defense School, Fort Bliss, Tex.
Length: *Phase II,* 4 weeks; *Phase III,* 4 weeks.
Objectives: To train air defense artillery officers of the Reserve components not on extended active duty during peace time, and all components during mobilization, for branch command staff duties at battalion through brigade or comparable levels in both divisional and nondivisional units. *Note*—Reserve officers complete *Phase I* through service extension courses provided by the Department of the Army. These courses are not evaluated by the Commission.
Instruction: *Phase II:* Nike-Hercules system and the tactical duties required of a battery officer in a Nike-Hercules air defense artillery unit; purpose, description, characteristics and capabilities of the Hawk missile system, twin 40-mm gun, self-propelled M42, and cal .50 machine gun and M55 mount; tactics and techniques of the combined arms team. *Phase III:* Concepts and procedures for the employment of surface-to-air systems; planning, tactics, and techniques of employment of air defense weapons in a composite defense.
Credit recommendation, collegiate level: *Phases II and III:* No credit as these phases are military in nature.

Air Defense Electronic Warfare

Location: Air Defense School, Fort Bliss, Tex.
Length: 3 weeks.
Objectives: To familiarize officers with electronic countermeasures and the use of air defense radars.

Instruction: Jamming, target detection, and use of radars in electronic countermeasures; electronic warfare training devices and techniques.
Credit recommendation, collegiate level: No credit because of the limited technical nature of this course.

Air Defense Fire Distribution Systems Controller

Location: Air Defense School, Fort Bliss, Tex.
Length: 3–8 weeks.
Objectives: To train enlisted personnel in the functions and operating, and operator maintenance procedures, of missile monitor systems.
Instruction: Familiarization with the capabilities, limitations, and controller functions of fire distribution systems and radar tracking stations; orientation to air defense missile systems.
Credit recommendation, collegiate level: No credit as course is military in nature.

Air Defense Missile Maintenance Technician (Hawk) (Hawk Maintenance Supervision)

Location: Ordnance Guided Missile School, Redstone Arsenal, Ala.
Length: 40–46 weeks.
Objectives: To train warrant officers and enlisted personnel to supervise the maintenance of Hawk guided missile systems and associated equipment.
Instruction: Hawk missile system and test equipment; CW/pulse electronics console; battery control central; sweep and video circuitry; radar launcher and firing control circuitry; pulse acquisition and range only radars; parallax computing systems; continuous wave radars; transmitting and receiving systems; speedgate; launcher and test set; organizational maintenance; logistical support; Hawk system analysis.
Credit recommendation, collegiate level: 2 semester hours in maintenance management, and credit in electrical laboratory on the basis of demonstrated skills and/or institutional examinations.

1. Air Defense Officer Basic (Air Defense Officer Orientation)
2. Air Defense Missile Officer Basic (SAM Officer Basic)
3. Air Defense Artillery Officer Basic (AAA Officer Basic)

Location: Air Defense School, Fort Bliss, Tex.
Length: *Course 1,* 8–9 weeks; *Courses 2 and 3,* 9–12 weeks.
Objectives: To provide newly commissioned officers with branch training and orientation in air defense weapon systems.
Instruction: *Courses 1 and 2:* Characteristics and operation of the Nike-Ajax battery control area equipment, the Nike-Universal system, the Hercules system, and the Hawk system; integrated battery operations; air defense tactics. *Course 3:* The contents of this course when given prior to May 1967 include characteristics and employment of light, medium, and heavy antiaircraft artillery. When given after April 1967, the course includes command and staff procedures; nuclear

weapons fundamentals; combined arms operations; air defense tactics; Nike-Hercules, Hawk missile, and forward area weapons systems.

Credit recommendation, collegiate level: Credit in advanced military at institutions which regularly offer such credit.

Air Observer

Location: Aviation School, Fort Rucker, Ala.
Length: 8 weeks.
Objectives: To train officers for air observer duty.
Instruction: Aviation equipment and operations; camouflage; engineer reconnaissance technique; combat intelligence; fire support; tactical radio procedure and operation; surveillance; basic flight techniques; tactical maps and photos.
Credit recommendation, collegiate level: No credit as course is military in nature.

Airborne
(Airborne Qualification)

Location: Infantry School, Fort Benning, Ga.
Length: 3 weeks.
Objectives: To qualify personnel as parachute jumpers.
Instruction: Pre-jump procedures; methods of manipulation and control of parachute during descent; methods of landing; preflight and inflight orientation, including preparation of weapons and combat equipment for jumping; qualification jumps from aircraft in flight.
Credit recommendation, collegiate level: No credit as courses are military in nature.

1. **Airborne Infrared Repair (UAS-4)**
2. **(Airborne Infrared Repair (UAS-4))**
   (Airborne Infrared Repair (AN/UAS4))

Location: Combat Surveillance School, Fort Huachuca, Ariz.
Length: *Course 1,* 12 weeks; *Course 2,* 24 weeks.
Objectives: To train enlisted personnel to perform direct support and general support maintenance on the Airborne Infrared AN/UAS-4.
Instruction: *Course 1:* Basic infrared fundamentals; optic theory; preamplifiers; system block diagram; controls and indicators; preflight, inflight, and postflight checks; special circuitry; schematic analysis, alignment, and troubleshooting of all components. *Course 2:* In addition to the preceding instruction, this course contains series and parallel circuits, inductance, capacitance, AC fundamentals, oscilloscope, LP circuits, RLC circuits, and transformers theory, vacuum tube diodes, semiconductors, triode vacuum tubes, triode amplifiers, transistor circuits, tetrode-pentrode vacuum tubes, transistor amplifiers, rectifiers, oscillators, modulator principles and AM transmitters, receiver and receiver input circuits, superheterodyne receiver, and radar fundamentals.
Credit recommendation, collegiate level: CAUTION: *These courses vary in title, length, and recommendation. Require exact identification of course by title and*

length. Course 1: Credit in electrical laboratory on the basis of demonstrated skills and/or institutional examinations. *Course 2:* 3 semester hours at the freshman or sophomore level as an elective in electricity and electronics, and credit in electrical laboratory on the basis of demonstrated skills and/or institutional examinations.

Airborne Sensor Specialist

Location: Combat Surveillance School, Fort Huachuca, Ariz.
Length: 10–13 weeks.
Objectives: To train enlisted personnel in the operation and organizational maintenance of AN/APS-94, AN/UAS-4, AN/UAS-4A, KS-61 camera systems, and AN/ASN-64.
Instruction: Operation and organization maintenance of the AN/UAS-4 infrared surveillance system, AN/APS-94 radar surveillance system and its associated ground data link station, photographic surveillance system KS-61 camera, and Canadian Marconi Doppler navigation system; aerial observer training.
Credit recommendation, collegiate level: This course is technical and vocational in nature. Credit in operation and maintenance of cameras and camera equipment on the basis of demonstrated skills and/or institutional examinations.

Airbrake Repair

Location: Transportation School, Fort Eustis, Va.
Length: 10 weeks.
Objectives: To train enlisted personnel to dismantle, inspect, repair, and lubricate airbrake equipment and component parts on steam and diesel-electric locomotives, railway cars, and auxiliary railway mechanical equipment.
Instruction: Principles of operation, construction, and maintenance of rolling stock airbrake equipment, steam locomotive airbrake equipment, and diesel-electric locomotive equipment.
Credit recommendation, collegiate level: This course is technical and vocational in nature. Credit in airbrake repair shop on the basis of demonstrated skills and/or institutional examinations.

Aircraft Armament Repair

Location: Ordnance School, Aberdeen Proving Ground, Md.
Length: 17 weeks.
Objectives: To train enlisted personnel in the operation, construction, functioning, disassembly, assembly, inspection, testing, troubleshooting, and repair of aircraft weapons systems and their related ammunition.
Instruction: Basic electricity and electronics; operation, maintenance, and repair of MWO's, field expedients, and PM indicators of the 7.62mm machine gun M60C, the XM16, XM21, and XM27 series helicopter armament subsystems, and the M22/UH-1B helicopter armament subsystems; maintenance of tools and equipment.
Credit recommendation, collegiate level: Credit in

electricity, electronics, and electrical laboratory on the basis of demonstrated skills and/or institutional examinations.

Aircraft Carburetor Repair

Location: Transportation School, Fort Eustis, Va.
Length: 8–11 weeks.
Objectives: To train enlisted personnel to repair aircraft fuel systems and allied equipment.
Instruction: Precision tools and shop equipment; replacement and repair of tubing; use of gaskets and seals; types, construction, and principles of operation of aircraft carburetors; disassembly, repair, cleaning, reassembly, testing, and troubleshooting of fuel system components; removal, repair, installation, adjustment, inspection, preservation, and storage of aircraft carburetors.
Credit recommendation, collegiate level: This course is technical and vocational in nature. Credit in aircraft carburetor repair on the basis of demonstrated skills and/or institutional examinations.

Aircraft Component Repair (Entry)
(Aircraft Component Repair Helper (Entry))

Location: Transportation School, Fort Eustis, Va.
Length: 8–9 weeks.
Objectives: To provide enlisted personnel with the basic skills and knowledge required to repair aircraft components and systems.
Instruction: Aircraft fundamentals; structural repair procedures; aircraft hydraulics; instrument and electrical systems; engine repair.
Credit recommendation, collegiate level: These courses are technical and vocational in nature. Credit in mechanical and electrical shop on the basis of demonstrated skills and/or institutional examinations.

Aircraft Electrician

Location: Transportation School, Fort Eustis, Va.
Length: 12–19 weeks.
Objectives: To train enlisted personnel to repair aircraft electrical systems and electrical components.
Instruction: Principles of operation of combustion engines; electrical theory and application; basic troubleshooting techniques; electrical hand tools; maintenance, testing, and repair of aircraft electrical components and systems.
Credit recommendation, collegiate level: This course is technical and vocational in nature. Credit in electrical shop on the basis of demonstrated skills and/or institutional examinations.

Aircraft Engine Repair

Location: Transportation School, Fort Eustis, Va.
Length: 8–13 weeks.
Objectives: To train enlisted personnel to repair aircraft engines and allied equipment.
Instruction: Aircraft fundamentals; aircraft engines; electrical systems.

Credit recommendation, collegiate level: This course is technical and vocational in nature. Credit in mechanical and electrical shop on the basis of demonstrated skills and/or institutional examinations.

Aircraft Hydraulics Repair

Location: Transportation School, Fort Eustis, Va.
Length: 7–12 weeks.
Objectives: To train enlisted personnel to repair aircraft hydraulic systems and hydraulic components.
Instruction: Use and care of tools and shop equipment; purpose, types, principles of operation, troubleshooting, and repair of hydraulic systems and hydraulic system components.
Credit recommendation, collegiate level: This course is technical and vocational in nature. Credit in aircraft hydraulics repair on the basis of demonstrated skills and/or institutional examinations.

Aircraft Instrument and Electrical Systems Repair

Location: Transportation School, Fort Eustis, Va.
Length: 18 weeks.
Objectives: To train enlisted personnel to repair, overhaul, and rebuild Army aircraft instruments, electrical systems, and components.
Instruction: Elementary physics; fundamentals of electricity; principles of aircraft electrical systems; mechanical and electrical aircraft instruments and equipment.
Credit recommendation, collegiate level: This course is technical and vocational in nature. Credit in electrical shop on the basis of demonstrated skills and/or institutional examinations.

Aircraft Instrument Repair

Location: Transportation School, Fort Eustis, Va.
Length: 10–18 weeks.
Objectives: To train enlisted personnel to repair aircraft instruments.
Instruction: Operating principles of aircraft instrument electrical components; component system fault analysis; testing, maintenance, and repair procedures for aircraft mechanical, electrical, and gyroscopic instruments and remote indicating systems; field test and shop test equipment, repair equipment, and calibrating equipment; fundamentals of electricity.
Credit recommendation, collegiate level: This course is technical and vocational in nature. Credit in aircraft instrument repair on the basis of demonstrated skills and/or institutional examinations.

Aircraft Maintenance (Entry)

Location: Aviation School, Fort Rucker, Ala.
Length: 5–8 weeks.
Objectives: To provide enlisted personnel with basic fundamentals required in the operation of Army airfields and airstrips and in the servicing and maintenance of fixed-wing and rotary-wing aircraft.

Instruction: Fundamentals of aircraft mechanics and electrical systems.

Credit recommendation, collegiate level: This course is technical and vocational in nature. Credit in mechanical and electrical shop on the basis of demonstrated skills and/or institutional examinations.

Aircraft Maintenance Officer

Location: Transportation School, Fort Eustis, Va.
Length: 12–15 weeks.
Objectives: To train officers to coordinate and supervise field, depot, and organizational aircraft maintenance, including technical maintenance inspection of Army aircraft.
Instruction: Fundamentals of electricity; aircraft ground-handling and hydraulics; aircraft structural repair; aircraft electrical instruments; aircraft power plants; aircraft inspection; helicopter transmissions; helicopter rigging.
Credit recommendation, collegiate level: This course is technical and vocational in nature. Credit in mechanical and electrical shop on the basis of demonstrated skills and/or institutional examinations.

Aircraft Maintenance Supervisor
(Army Aviation Maintenance Management)

Location: Transportation School, Fort Eustis, Va.
Length: 5–8 weeks.
Objectives: To provide enlisted personnel with training in aviation maintenance and management production and quality control.
Instruction: General management subjects including personnel management, performance analysis, purchasing, and aircraft maintenance procedures; methods, problems, and techniques required in the technical inspection for each aircraft system.
Credit recommendation, collegiate level: 2 semester hours in shop management.

Aircraft Powertrain Repair

Location: Transportation School, Fort Eustis, Va.
Length: 7–16 weeks.
Objectives: To train enlisted personnel to repair aircraft powertrains and allied equipment.
Instruction: Precision tools and shop equipment; purpose and function of powertrain systems, including disassembly, inspection, repair and/or replacement of defective parts, reassembly, and troubleshooting of components.
Credit recommendation, collegiate level: This course is technical and vocational in nature. Credit in aircraft powertrain repair shop on the basis of demonstrated skills and/or institutional examinations.

Aircraft Rotor and Propeller Repair

Location: Transportation School, Fort Eustis, Va.
Length: 12–15 weeks.
Objectives: To train enlisted personnel to repair aircraft propellers, rotor blades, and allied equipment.

Instruction: Use and care of precision tools and shop equipment; repairing and rebuilding propellers and rotor blades by disassembly and repair of damaged areas; replacement or repair of defective parts and reassembly of components; inspection of propeller and rotor blade assemblies.

Credit recommendation, collegiate level: This course is technical and vocational in nature. Credit in aircraft propeller and rotor blade repair on the basis of demonstrated skills and/or institutional examinations.

Airframe Repair

Location: Transportation School, Fort Eustis, Va.
Length: 8–13 weeks.
Objectives: To train enlisted personnel to repair and rebuild aircraft structural members, sheet metal surfaces, and plastics.
Instruction: Airframe repair tools and equipment; aircraft structural metals; sheet metal layout procedures; repair of aircraft fiberglass and plastics; formation of aircraft parts; aircraft structural member repair; basic riveting.
Credit recommendation, collegiate level: This course is technical and vocational in nature. Credit in airframe structural repair shop on the basis of demonstrated skills and/or institutional examinations.

Airframe Welding

Location: Transportation School, Fort Eustis, Va.
Length: 6–7 weeks.
Objectives: To train enlisted personnel to repair airframes and aircraft components.
Instruction: Oxyacetylene cutting operations and welding equipment; welding on ferrous and nonferrous metals; operation of arc welding equipment; welding operations using tungsten inert and metal gas shielded arc welding equipment.
Credit recommendation, collegiate level: This course is technical and vocational in nature. Credit in welding on the basis of demonstrated skills and/or institutional examinations.

Airplane Maintenance

Location: Aviation School, Fort Rucker, Ala.
Length: 6 weeks.
Objectives: To train enlisted personnel in the maintenance of single- and multi-engine fixed-wing aircraft.
Instruction: Fundamentals of aircraft mechanical and electrical systems.
Credit recommendation, collegiate level: This course is technical and vocational in nature. Credit in mechanical and electrical shop on the basis of demonstrated skills and/or institutional examinations.

Ammunition and Missile Maintenance Officer
(Guided Missile and Special Weapons Staff Officer)
(Ordnance Staff Officer Guided Missile and Special Weapons)
(Ordnance Staff Officer Guided Missile and Nuclear Weapons)

Location: Missile and Munitions School, Redstone Arsenal, Ala.

Length: 11–19 weeks.

Objectives: To train senior-company and field-grade officers in maintenance and supply policies and in problems associated with guided missiles and nuclear weapons.

Instruction: Organization, employment, deployment, capabilities, and planning patterns for support and use of equipment; duties of staff officers associated with this materiel; new developments and techniques in guided missile and nuclear weapons materiel.

Credit recommendation, collegiate level: 6 semester hours in supply management.

Ammunition and Missile Maintenance Officer
(Transition)

Location: Missile and Munitions Center and School, Redstone Arsenal, Ala.

Length: 3 weeks.

Objectives: To train officers in conventional munitions service.

Instruction: Principles, classifications, function, storage, uses, security, safety precautions, and transportation of conventional ammunition items; conventional munitions organization, data control, logistics, and service and support functions.

Credit recommendation, collegiate level: No credit as this course is military in nature.

Ammunition Records

Locations: Missile and Munitions Center and School, Redstone Arsenal, Ala.; Ordnance School, Aberdeen Proving Ground, Md.

Length: 7 weeks.

Objectives: To train enlisted personnel in sources of information, maintenance and submission of records, documents, and reports used for movement, storage, and accounting of ammunition.

Instruction: Ammunition materiel; storage regulations; organization, types, and missions of ammunition installations; type, purpose, and preparation of forms, records, and reports; stock control procedures; operation and use of adding machines, calculators, and manual key punch machines; practical exercise in accounting and documentation procedures in ammunitions offices and installations.

Credit recommendation, collegiate level: This course is technical and vocational in nature. Credit in office records procedures on the basis of institutional examination.

1. Ammunition Renovation
2. Ammunition Storage
3. Ammunition (Entry)
(Ammunition Helper)

Locations: Ordnance School, Aberdeen Proving Ground, Md.; Missile and Munitions Center and School, Redstone Arsenal, Ala.

Length: 6–11 weeks.

Objectives: To train enlisted personnel in the receipt, storage, issuance, and maintenance of ammunition.

Instruction: Characteristics, identification, inspection, storage, handling, renovation, and transportation of ammunition; destruction and salvage operations.

Credit recommendation, collegiate level: No credit because of the limited technical nature of these courses.

1. Amphibian Engineer (Mechanic)
2. Amphibian Engineer (Repairman)

Location: Transportation School, Fort Eustis, Va.

Length: 4–7 weeks.

Objectives: To train enlisted personnel in the maintenance and repair of amphibious vehicles.

Instruction: Operation, inspection, repair, maintenance, and troubleshooting of electrical systems, fuel systems, high-speed diesel engines, hydraulic systems, and pneumatic systems.

Credit recommendation, collegiate level: These courses are technical and vocational in nature. Credit in mechanical and electrical shop on the basis of demonstrated skills and/or institutional examinations.

Amphibian Operator

Location: Transportation School, Fort Eustis, Va.

Length: 6 weeks.

Objectives: To train enlisted personnel in the operation of amphibious vehicles.

Instruction: Duties and responsibilities of operator and crewmen; vehicle instruments and controls; land driving; water operations; cargo handling, loads and loading; ship-to-shore operations.

Credit recommendation, collegiate level: No credit because of the limited technical nature of this course.

Amphibious Truckmaster

Location: Transportation School, Fort Eustis, Va.

Length: 15 weeks.

Objectives: To train enlisted personnel to supervise or to assist in supervising transport operations of a military organization equipped with amphibious wheel vehicles used to transport personnel and materiel over water and land areas.

Instruction: Map reading; elevation, relief, and visibility; angular measurements; instructional methods; organization and function of an amphibious unit; troubleshooting; organizational maintenance; convoy organization and operation; communications; nautical operations; inspections; vehicle recovery; cargo handling; supervision of land, beach, and water operations; planning and control of operations; assault and logistical over-the-beach operations.

Credit recommendation, collegiate level: This course is technical and vocational in nature. Credit in automotive repair on the basis of demonstrated skills and/or institutional examinations.

1. Antiaircraft Artillery Remote Control Repair (Basic)
2. Antiaircraft Artillery Remote Control Repair

Location: Ordnance School, Aberdeen Proving Ground, Md.

Length: 8–9 weeks.

Objectives: To train enlisted personnel to inspect, test, and perform depot and repair maintenance of light and heavy nonintegrated antiaircraft artillery remote control equipment.

Instruction: Fundamentals of electricity; principles of remote control systems; function and maintenance of the drive controllers and wiring sets; inspection and repair of oil gears; repair of indicator systems; characteristics, assembly, operation, and maintenance of power control units and fuze setters; operating principles and maintenance of the motor drive and torque amplifier.

Credit recommendation, collegiate level: Credit, for each course, in electricity and electrical shop on the basis of demonstrated skills and/or institutional examinations.

Area Communications Systems Operations

Location: Southeastern Signal School, Fort Gordon, Ga.

Length: 19 weeks.

Objectives: To train enlisted personnel to supervise, coordinate, and technically assist in the installation, operation, and maintenance of an integrated area communication system.

Instruction: Organization and employment of Army units; administration and logistics; tactical communications center operation; wire communication; radio communication; communication system planning.

Credit recommendation, collegiate level: 4 semester hours in business organization and management, and credit in wire and radio communications on the basis of institutional examination.

Area Signal Center Officer

Location: Southeastern Signal School, Fort Gordon, Ga.

Length: 5 weeks.

Objectives: To train Signal Corps company-grade officers in the installation, operation, and maintenance of an area signal center within an area communication center.

Instruction: Area signal center mission, company duties, and maintenance supervision; organization, characteristics, and deployment of an area signal center; signal center planning, installation, and operation; support mission in counterinsurgency and limited actions; division area signal center installation and operation in an offensive situation.

Credit recommendation, collegiate level: 3 semester hours in business organization and management.

Armament Maintenance and Repair Officer

Location: Ordnance School, Aberdeen Proving Ground, Md.

Length: 6–7 weeks.

Objectives: To familiarize commissioned officers and warrant officers in the organization and management of armament maintenance facilities.

Instruction: Construction, characteristics, and functioning of small arms, mortars, and recoilless weapons; inspections and maintenance procedures for field artillery materiel, antiaircraft materiel, turret artillery materiel, and observation and fire control instruments.

Credit recommendation, collegiate level: No credit because of the limited technical nature of the course.

Armament Maintenance (Entry)

Location: Ordnance School, Aberdeen Proving Ground, Md.

Length: 8 weeks.

Objectives: To train enlisted personnel to assist in performance of organization, field, and depot maintenance on armament materiel and similar equipment.

Instruction: Driving, cutting, holding and turning, power and heating tools; abrasives; measuring tools; metalworking, disassembly, assembly, and maintenance of small arms and artillery materiel.

Credit recommendation, collegiate level: This course is technical and vocational in nature. Credit in metal shop on the basis of demonstrated skills and/or institutional examinations.

Armament Maintenance Foreman

Location: Ordnance School, Aberdeen Proving Ground, Md.

Length: 8 weeks.

Objectives: To train enlisted personnel to organize armament maintenance facilities and supervise personnel engaged in armament maintenance and repair.

Instruction: Leadership fundamentals; instruction training, small arms, field artillery, antiaircraft artillery, and turret artillery materiel; shop organization; supply procedures; ordnance service management including work distribution and flow charts, motion economy, work count, and shop control techniques.

Credit recommendation, collegiate level: 2 semester hours in shop management.

1. Armor/Infantry Officer Career
2. Infantry/Armor Officer Career

Locations: Armor School, Fort Knox, Ky.; Infantry School, Fort Benning, Ga.

Length: 35–36 weeks.

Objectives: To train armor and infantry officers in the duties and responsibilities of commanders and staff officers of armor, armor cavalry, and infantry units in the employment of combined arms.

Instruction: *Courses 1 and 2:* Tactical employment of combined arm forces in offensive and defensive operations; capabilities, limitations, and employment of the combat support elements; organization and employment of air cavalry troops, armored cavalry squadrons, and armored cavalry regiments; organization, mission, and tactical employment of field artillery; organization and employment of engineer operations; nuclear weapons employment, and target analysis procedures; Army financial management; logistical staff planning; techniques of planning and conducting combat operations; administration of legal matters; communication equipment and procedures; maintenance management; characteristics, techniques, and principles of tank gunnery. *Course 2:* In addition to the preceding instruction this course contains 53 hours in the electives program in which students elect further instruction from one of the following areas: international affairs, management, scientific and technical military arts, communicative arts, and general studies.

Credit recommendation, collegiate level: *Courses 1 and 2:* 6 semester hours in business organization and management for each course. *Course 2:* Additional credit for courses completed in the electives program on the basis of institutional examination.

Armor Maintenance Officer
(Armor Maintenance and Motor Transport)
(Armor Motor Officer)

Location: Armor School, Fort Knox, Ky.
Length: 14–15 weeks.
Objectives: To train officers in organizational maintenance in armor units.
Instruction: Principles of operation, construction, disassembly, and assembly of engines and fuel systems; diagnosing, locating, and correcting engine, electrical, air-fuel, cooling and lubrication systems; maintenance of electrical units and circuits; construction, functioning, and maintenance of wheeled vehicle power train and chassis units; supervision of light- and medium-gun tank maintenance; administrative operation of maintenance.
Credit recommendation, collegiate level: These courses are technical and vocational in nature. Credit in automotive maintenance on the basis of demonstrated skills and/or institutional examinations.

Armor Noncommissioned Officer
(Armor Advanced Noncommissioned Officer)

Location: Armor School, Fort Knox, Ky.
Length: 9–16 weeks.
Objectives: To train enlisted personnel in the duties of the crew, squad, and section noncommissioned officers of a tank company or an armored cavalry troop.
Instruction: Maintenance procedures and inspection; artillery, infantry, and engineer operations; communication equipment and procedure; observed-fire procedure; fire control systems; tank armament controls and equipment.
Credit recommendation, collegiate level: No credit as courses are military in nature.

1. Armor Officer Basic
(Armor Officer Orientation)
2. Regular Army Armor Officer Basic
(Armor Officer Basic (RA))

Location: Armor School, Fort Knox, Ky.
Length: 6–16 weeks.
Objectives: To provide basic branch training and orientation for newly commissioned armor officers.
Instruction: Automotive maintenance system; employment of armored vehicles; nuclear weapons; artillery and infantry operations; engineer operations; communication equipment and procedures; tactical and field communications; weapon familiarization.
Credit recommendation, collegiate level: Credit for each course in advanced military at institutions which regularly offer such credit.

Armor Officer Candidate

Location: Armor School, Fort Knox, Ky.
Length: 23 weeks.
Objectives: To train selected personnel to be second lieutenants in the reserve component of the U.S. Army and capable of performing duties appropriate to their grade in active Army armor units.
Instruction: Automotive department; combined arms; armored cavalry operations; communication equipment and procedure; field and tactical communications; military leadership; map and airphoto reading; methods of instruction; special warfare, military history; arms and gunnery division; drill and command.
Credit recommendation, collegiate level: Credit in advanced military at institutions which regularly offer such credit.

1. Armor Officer Career
2. Armor Officer Advanced

Location: Armor School, Fort Knox, Ky.
Length: 35–37 weeks.
Objectives: To train armor, infantry, or artillery officers in the duties required at battalion headquarters and for positions at combat command level.
Instruction: Procedures for establishing, maintaining, and evaluating a maintenance program for vehicles of armor battalions/squadrons; organization and employment of armored and air cavalry, artillery, and infantry troops; Air Force and amphibious operations; chemical, biological, and nuclear weapons employment; logistical staff duties and command responsibilities; communication requirements and responsibilities; organization and function of engineer units and of field medical units; military leadership; intelligence procedures; personnel management; training responsibilities of the battalion commander; small arms, materiel, and gunnery.

After June 1967, an electives program was added to the Armor Officer Advanced course. The electives program complements the regular curriculum of the school by providing for individual differences in education and experience and enabling students to engage in educational experiences that make a maximum contribution to their ability. The program includes 200–225 hours of study in courses in military arts, history and geography, communicative arts, international relations, and management.

Credit recommendation, collegiate level: 6 semester hours for each course in business organization and management. Additional credit for courses completed in the electives program on the basis of institutional examination.

1. Armor Radio Maintenance
2. Armor Radio Maintenance

Location: Armor School, Fort Knox, Ky.

Length: *Course 1,* 17 weeks; *Course 2,* 12–13 weeks.

Objectives: To train enlisted personnel to operate and to perform organizational maintenance on communication equipment used in armor communication systems or in units employing similar equipment.

Instruction: *Course 1:* Ohm's law, series, parallel, and combination DC circuits, meter theory, capacitance, diode, triode, and pentode tubes, inductance, transformers, AC circuits, and series tuned circuits; radio fundamentals, including electronic power supplies, AM detectors, vacuum tube amplifiers, L/C oscillators, superheterodyne receiver principles, receiver, audio output stages, and loudspeakers, IF amplifier, detector and AVC circuits, and frequency conversion; AM and FM radio sets; radio components, UHF radio sets; tactical communications; communication equipment. *Course 2:* Electrical and radio fundamentals; organizational maintenance and repair of FM and AM radio sets; principles of electronic circuits; characteristics, capabilities, and operation of communication equipment; tactical and field communications; signal supply procedures.

Credit recommendation, collegiate level: CAUTION: *These courses vary in length and recommendation. Require exact identification of course by length. Course 1:* 2 semester hours at the freshman or sophomore level as an elective in electricity, and credit in electrical laboratory on the basis of demonstrated skills and/or institutional examinations. *Course 2:* Credit in electricity and electrical laboratory on the basis of demonstrated skills and/or institutional examinations.

Armor Vehicle Maintenance Supervision
(Armor Automotive Supervision)

Location: Armor School, Fort Knox, Ky.

Length: 8 weeks.

Objectives: To train enlisted men in the supervision of the organizational maintenance and motor activities in armor units.

Instruction: Engine electricity; live tracked vehicle engines; tracked vehicle chassis units; administrative operation of organizational maintenance; wheeled vehicle maintenance; light tank and armored infantry vehicle maintenance; medium tank maintenance; vehicle recovery.

Credit recommendation, collegiate level: This course is technical and vocational in nature. Credit in automotive repair on the basis of demonstrated skills and/or institutional examinations.

Army Air Defense Battery Officer
(AAA and SAM Battery Officer)

Location: Air Defense School, Fort Bliss, Tex.

Length: 23–30 weeks.

Objectives: To provide branch training in the duties and responsibilities of air defense artillery battery-grade officers.

Instruction: Characteristics, capabilities and operation of light, medium, and heavy antiaircraft artillery; surface gunnery techniques; fundamentals of guided missile systems; air defense tactics.

Credit recommendation, collegiate level: No credit as courses are military in nature.

Army/Air Force Exchange Operations
(Army Exchange Operations)

Location: Quartermaster School, Fort Lee, Va.

Length: 5–6 weeks.

Objectives: To train commissioned officers, warrant officers, and noncommissioned officers in general management and operation of installation exchanges.

Instruction: Management, including principles of exchange management, personnel administration, selection and placement of employees, employee status, benefits, and pay system, performance reviews, public relations, bonds and insurance; exchange operations, including departmentalization and numerical coding, price structure, merchandising, procurement, stock control, inventory procedures, and store layout; financial accounting, and budgetary procedures; fundamentals of business law; management of exchange food operations.

Credit recommendation, collegiate level: 3 semester hours in business management.

Army/Air Force Exchange Service Executive
Development

Location: Quartermaster School, Fort Lee, Va.

Length: 3 weeks.

Objectives: To provide experience in an executive approach to exchange service management.

Instruction: Managerial concepts, basic to planning, decision making, controlling, and evaluating comprehensive executive functions; organization and expression of ideas in verbal and written form; systematic methods for problem solving; personnel management; principles of retail management.

Credit recommendation, collegiate level: 2 semester hours in business administration.

Army Aviation Command and Staff Officer
(Aviation Staff Officer)
(Aviation Officer (Advanced))

Location: Aviation School, Fort Rucker, Ala.

Length: 3–8 weeks.

Objectives: To train aviators in the duties and responsibilities of aviation command and staff positions.

Instruction: Structure, functions, and capabilities of tactical aviation units; organization and function of the Army Aviation Special Staff; principles of employment of aviation in support of a field army.

Credit recommendation, collegiate level: No credit as courses are military in nature.

Army Aviation Primary and Tactical Flight Training

Location: Aviation School, Fort Rucker, Ala.
Length: 24 weeks.
Objectives: To train officers in the tactical employment of Army observation fixed-wing aircraft and the support of combat operations of ground arms.
Instruction: Primary and advanced flight training; flight instrument familiarization; navigation; tactical subjects; weather interpretation.
Credit recommendation, collegiate level: 3 semester hours in weather interpretation and elementary navigation.

Army Aviation Tactics

Location: Aviation School, Fort Rucker, Ala.
Length: 19 weeks.
Objectives: To train officers in the tactical employment of Army observation and utility fixed-wing aircraft, in the support of combat operations of ground arms, and as instrument pilots.
Instruction: Advanced flight training; weather interpretation; instrument navigation and techniques.
Credit recommendation, collegiate level: 3 semester hours in weather interpretation and elementary navigation.

Army Aviation Tactics Refresher

Location: Aviation School, Fort Rucker, Ala.
Length: 4 weeks.
Objectives: To train previously rated aviators in current techniques of the employment of aircraft and allied equipment in support of combat operations of the ground arms.
Instruction: Short field and road strip technique; advanced night checkout; familiarization of instrument flying techniques; gunnery; principles and employment of Army aviation.
Credit recommendation, collegiate level: No credit as course is military in nature.

Army Aviator Helicopter

Location: Aviation School, Fort Rucker, Ala.
Length: 10 weeks.
Objectives: To train officers in the operational flying of observation-type helicopters and familiarization with the tactical employment of rotary-wing aircraft.
Instruction: Rotary-wing, pre-solo flight training; traffic patterns; hovering; intermediate flight training; takeoff and approach techniques; autorotations; advanced flight maneuvers; precautionary measures and critical conditions; night operations flight; basic maintenance; tactics.
Credit recommendation, collegiate level: Credit in helicopter flight training on the basis of demonstrated skills and/or institutional examinations.

Army (Aviator) Transport Pilot (RW)

Locations: *Phases I and II:* Camp Walters, Tex.; *Phase III:* Fort Rucker, Ala.
Length: *Phase I,* 4 weeks; *Phase II,* 16 weeks; *Phase III,* 14 weeks.
Objectives: *Phase I:* To train enlisted personnel for entry into *Phases II and III. Phase II:* To give officers, warrant officers, and enlisted personnel primary and basic helicopter flight training. *Phase III:* To train enlisted personnel as warrant officers for assignment to pilot positions in helicopter equipped Army Transport aviation units.
Instruction: *Phase I:* Basic officer orientation; military leadership; supply and food service; map and aerial photo reading. *Phase II:* Primary rotary-wing flight; traffic pattern; night flight operations; cross-country flight training; preliminary and advanced aerodynamics; air navigation; aeronautical charts; computer slide rule; aircraft radio and voice procedure; weather and circulation; weather flight planning; administrative airfield operations. *Phase III:* Light transport helicopter transition training; basic instrument and radio navigation; day and night cross-country training; engine installation and controls; radio navigational aids; weather; advanced aerodynamics.
Credit recommendation, collegiate level: For completion of all three phases, 3 semester hours in primary meteorology and navigation, and credit in helicopter flight training on the basis of demonstrated skills and/or institutional examinations.

1. Army Basic Procurement Operations (Army Station Procurement)
2. Army Procurement

Location: Quartermaster School, Fort Lee, Va.
Length: *Course 1,* 3–4 weeks; *Course 2,* 8 weeks.
Objectives: To train officers and warrant officers in basic procurement principles, techniques, and procedures.
Instruction: *Course 1:* Principles of procurement; basic procurement policies and management; bonds and sureties; purchasing by formal advertising and negotiations; contract procedures; types of contracts; contract administration; comptroller and financial management; in addition to the preceding instruction *Course 2* includes more extensive instruction in the legal aspects of contracts and procurement.
Credit recommendation, collegiate level: CAUTION: *These courses vary in title, length, and recommendation. Require exact identification of course by title and length: Course 1:* 3 semester hours in purchasing or procurement. *Course 2:* 5 semester hours in purchasing or procurement, and credit in public administration on the basis of institutional examination.

Army Career Counselor (Army Career Counseling)

Location: Adjutant General's School, Fort Benjamin Harrison, Ind.
Length: 3 weeks.
Objectives: To train personnel in reenlistment counseling techniques and procedures.
Instruction: Eligibility, opportunities, and benefits;

principles of human relations; oral communication; interviewing and counseling.

Credit recommendation, collegiate level: No credit because of the brevity of the course.

Army Helicopter Transport Tactical

Location: Aviation School, Fort Rucker, Ala.

Length: 7 weeks.

Objectives: To train aviator personnel for command and pilot positions in helicopter equipped Army transport aviation units.

Instruction: Transition flight training to include preflight; cockpit procedures; operation instructions; traffic patterns; hovering flight; emergency procedures; night operations; tactical flight training; cross-country navigation flights; instrument flight training; advanced instrument flight training; synthetic flight training; organizational maintenance on light cargo helicopters; administrative planning of heliborne operations; organization and employment of transport helicopter units.

Credit recommendation, collegiate level: Credit in helicopter flight training on the basis of demonstrated skills and/or institutional examinations.

Army Helicopter Transport Tactical (H-21), (H-34)
(Army Helicopter Transport Tactical (H-34))
(Army Helicopter Transport Tactical (H-21))
(Army Helicopter Transport Tactical (H-19))

Location: Aviation School, Fort Rucker, Ala.

Length: 8 weeks.

Objectives: To train rotary-wing aviators in the operation of light transport-type helicopters.

Instruction: Advanced flight training; cross-country and night operations flight; instrument and transition flight training; radio navigation; basic maintenance; tactics.

Credit recommendation, collegiate level: Credit in helicopter flight training on the basis of demonstrated skills and/or institutional examinations.

Army Installation Management

Location: Army Management School, Fort Belvoir, Va.

Length: 3 weeks.

Objectives: To train commissioned officers in the techniques, practices, and fundamentals of Army installation management.

Instruction: Principles, concepts, and functions of management; personnel and manpower; logistics; comptrollership; effective utilization of resources and the maintenance of readiness at installation level; tools, techniques, and methods available to improve personnel competence and performance in management of Army resources.

Credit recommendation, collegiate level: 2 semester hours in business organization and management.

Army Logistics Management
(Army Supply Management)

Location: Army Logistics Management Center, Fort Lee, Va.

Length: 12 weeks.

Objectives: To train officers in the organization, operations, and problems of the Army supply system.

Instruction: General management considerations; management controls; principles of accounting; analysis of financial data; requirements management; procurement; contract procedures; distribution; function of stock control points; organization for supply; inventory management; property disposal management; transportation and traffic management; maintenance organization; personnel management.

Credit recommendation, collegiate level: 6 semester hours in supply management.

Army Management
(Command Management)
(Management)

Locations: Army Management School, Command Management School, Fort Belvoir, Va.

Length: 3 weeks.

Objectives: To develop the managerial ability of installation commanders and senior staff officers.

Instruction: Army management systems; skills and tools of management including line and staff relationships, military-civilian team, organization, decentralization, and use of consultants; program management; manpower control and management; financial management; problems in the field of congressional, public, and labor relations; development of decision making.

Credit recommendation, collegiate level: 2 semester hours in business organization and management.

Army Medical Service Noncommissioned Officer

Location: Medical Field Service School, Fort Sam Houston, Tex.

Length: 12 weeks.

Objectives: To train enlisted personnel in the duties and responsibilities of Medical Field Service noncommissioned officers.

Instruction: Medical administration; principles of organization, delegation of responsibility, and methods of assuming responsibility; organization of hospitals; personnel management; management techniques in control and supervision of groups of people; supply procedures; operation and function of dental services and field medical services, including emergency medical care of casualty victims; military sciences; preventive medicine.

Credit recommendation, collegiate level: 3 semester hours in hospital administration procedures and 2 semester hours in hygiene and first aid.

Army Nurse Corps Officer Orientation
(Army Nurse Corps Officer Basic)

Location: Medical Field Service School, Fort Sam Houston, Tex.

Length: *AMSC Officers,* 4 weeks; *ANC Officers,* 8–9 weeks.

Objectives: To provide basic branch training and orientation for newly commissioned officers of the Army Medical Service Corps and Army Nurse Corps in the duties and responsibilities appropriate to their grade and expected service.

Instruction: *AMSC Officers:* Basic medical records; familiarization with personnel management and general administration principles; medical supply procedures; chemical and biological warfare, management of mass casualties, and emergency medical treatment procedures; orientation to field medical service; battle indoctrination; fundamentals of staff organization and logistical agencies; duties and responsibilities of nursing service personnel; preventive medicine. *ANC Officers:* In addition to the preceding instruction, Army Nurse Corps officers receive more intensive instruction in nursing responsibilities, including principles of nursing administration, staffing requirements, categorization of patients according to nursing care needs, and supervised nursing practice.

Credit recommendation, collegiate level: These courses are at the preprofessional or professional level. Credit in nursing procedures on the basis of institutional examination.

Army Project Manager

Location: Logistics Management Center, Fort Lee, Va.

Length: 3 weeks.

Objectives: To provide executive training in Army project management for branch-level personnel in project manager offices or for personnel in direct contact with these offices.

Instruction: Authority, responsibility, and functions of the project manager; problem identification and problem solving; control techniques; management techniques; technical management; project definition; project planning; familiarization with procurement management, materiel management, and financial management.

Credit recommendation, collegiate level: 2 semester hours in business administration.

Army Recruiting and Career Counseling

Location: Adjutant General's School, Fort Benjamin Harrison, Ind.

Length: 3–5 weeks.

Objectives: To train enlisted personnel in the techniques and procedures of recruiting and re-enlistment and in the management of a recruiting station and re-enlistment office.

Instruction: Fundamentals of personnel procurement, including eligibility prerequisites, testing procedures, service benefits, and assignment and classification actions; techniques and procedures of interviewing and counseling prospective and in-service personnel; principles and techniques of recruiting; public speaking.

Credit recommendation, collegiate level: No credit because of the specialized nature of the course.

Army Safety Program Organization and Administration

Location: Adjutant General School, Fort Benjamin Harrison, Ind.

Length: 4 weeks.

Objectives: To train commissioned officers in the principles and procedures of the organization and administration of the Army safety program at installation level.

Instruction: Military safety program organization; organizations for accident prevention; staff communication and coordination; effective writing; motor vehicle and traffic safety; management and functions of the accident prevention mission; military safety problems; specialized safety areas.

Credit recommendation, collegiate level: Credit in organization of safety education on the basis of institutional examinations.

Army Supply Officer

Location: Quartermaster School, Fort Lee, Va.

Length: 7 weeks.

Objectives: To train commissioned officers and warrant officers in the policies and procedures applicable to all classes of supply and to assignments in the continental United States installations, the division, direct support, general support and overseas depot units.

Instruction: Unit and organization supply; supply publications; field supply procedures; types of property; property records; financial management; stock accounting; field storage procedures; application of management principles; maintenance; procurement; automated supply systems; supply operations in the theater of operations.

Credit recommendation, collegiate level: 3 semester hours in supply management.

1. Army Transport Helicopter Pilot—Phase III
2. Army Aviator Basic Flight Training (Helicopter)

Location: Aviation School, Fort Rucker, Ala.

Length: *Course 1,* 14 weeks; *Course 2,* 12 weeks.

Objectives: To train officers, warrant officers, and enlisted personnel for pilot assignments in helicopter equipped transport aviation units and medical service ambulance detachments.

Instruction: *Course 1:* Basic rotary-wing flight maneuvers; advanced and field operational use of the helicopter; instrument training; organizational maintenance, mission, organization, and employment of Army transport aviation. *Course 2:* Intermediate and advanced flight training; instrument interpretation and aircraft control; training for heliborne operations including cargo transport, reconnaissance, aero-medical evacuation, and infantry support missions; emergency and medical treatment for the wounded; organizational maintenance.

Credit recommendation, collegiate level: CAUTION: *These courses vary only slightly in title, length, and recommendation. Require exact identification of course by title and length. Course 1:* Credit in helicopter flight training on the basis of demonstrated skills and/or institutional examinations. *Course 2:* 2 semester hours in first aid and hygiene, and credit in helicopter flight training on the basis of demonstrated skills and/or institutional examinations.

Artillery Ballistic Meteorology

Location: Artillery and Missile School, Fort Sill, Okla.

Length: 9–11 weeks.

Objectives: To train commissioned officers, warrant officers, and enlisted personnel in the installation and operation of an artillery meteorological station.

Instruction: Elementary meteorology; organization of artillery meteorological sections and the requirements of the artillery for ballistic metro data; surface instruments and equipment; pilot balloon and surface observation method; operation and maintenance of radiosondes and associated equipment; determination of ballistic temperatures, densities, and wind speed from the rawinsonde system.

Credit recommendation, collegiate level: 2 semester hours in elementary meteorology.

Artillery Calibration

Location: Ordnance School, Aberdeen Proving Ground, Md.

Length: 8 weeks.

Objectives: To train enlisted personnel to perform all phases of artillery calibration.

Instruction: Orientation to ballistic teams; fundamentals of exterior, interior, and terminal ballistics; familiarization with artillery ammunition.

Credit recommendation, collegiate level: No credit as course is military in nature.

Artillery Fire Control System Maintenance SCR-584 and Director M9 or M10

Location: Antiaircraft Artillery and Guided Missile School, Fort Bliss, Tex.

Length: 16 weeks.

Objectives: To train warrant officers and enlisted personnel of the National Guard to employ, operate, adjust, and maintain artillery fire control systems and associated IFF equipment.

Instruction: Basic electronics, including AC and DC series and parallel circuits, diodes and power supplies, triodes and biasing, multi-element vacuum tubes; use of test equipment; radar principles, systems, and components; operational employment of the AAA gun battery.

Credit recommendation, collegiate level: Credit in electronics and electrical laboratory on the basis of demonstrated skills and/or institutional examinations.

Artillery Flash Ranging Advanced

Location: Artillery and Missile School, Fort Sill, Okla.

Length: 6 weeks.

Objectives: To train enlisted personnel in the installation, operation, and organizational maintenance of a field artillery flash ranging unit.

Instruction: Care, maintenance, and operation of equipment; flash ranging techniques, operations, and field exercises; survey computations; basic survey planning and operations.

Credit recommendation, collegiate level: Credit in surveying on the basis of institutional examination.

Artillery Motor Transport

Location: Artillery and Missile School, Fort Sill, Okla.

Length: 8–14 weeks.

Objectives: To train commissioned officers and warrant officers in the supervision of organizational maintenance of wheeled and tracked vehicles and turrets, in maintenance management, and in the operation and recovery of vehicles used in artillery units.

Instruction: Basic and advanced engine maintenance; disassembly and reassembly; basic and advanced chassis maintenance; systems and units of M4, M5, and M6 tractors; systems and units of self-propelled carriages; maintenance and maintenance supervision; driver training.

Credit recommendation, collegiate level: This course is technical and vocational in nature. Credit in automotive repair on the basis of demonstrated skills and/or institutional examinations.

Artillery Officer Advanced
(Artillery Officer Career)

Locations: Air Defense School, Fort Bliss, Tex.; Artillery and Guided Missile School, Fort Sill, Okla.

Length: 32–42 weeks.

Objectives: To provide branch training in the duties and responsibilities of artillery officers and to provide a general knowledge of artillery weapons systems.

Instruction: Characteristics, organization, and maintenance management of artillery and communication equipment; cannon fire direction operations, techniques, and procedures; operational procedures for weapon employment; duties and responsibilities of artillery commanders and staff officers; air defense operations and tactics, including functions and principles of missile systems.

After May 1967, an elective program was added to the Artillery Officer Advanced course. Students must select one subject from each of three phases totaling 197 hours of instruction. The elective subjects are: *Phase I*—management, psychological operations, effective writing, and oral presentation. *Phase II*—stability operations, military history, field artillery target acquisition and survey, meteorology, field artillery guided missile systems, and advanced gunnery. *Phase III*—operations research and systems analysis, and automatic data processing.

Credit recommendation, collegiate level: 6 semester hours in business organization and management. Additional credit for courses completed in the electives program on the basis of institutional examination.

Artillery Officer Basic

Locations: Artillery and Missile School, Fort Sill, Okla.; Air Defense School, Fort Bliss, Tex.

Length: 20 weeks.

Objectives: To train newly commissioned artillery officers in the entire spectrum of artillery weapons and to familiarize them with the particular weapons manned by the units to which they will be assigned.

Instruction: Communication procedures and equipment; fundamentals of field artillery fire, and operation of the firing battery; introduction to missile gunnery; principles of the LaCrosse system and the Honest John rocket; capabilities and limitations of the Redstone and Corporal field artillery missile systems, orientation to the Hawk and Nike systems; air defense tactics.

Credit recommendation, collegiate level: Credit in advanced military at institutions which regularly offer such credit.

Artillery Radio Maintenance

Location: Artillery and Missile School, Fort Sill, Okla.

Length: 12–14 weeks.

Objectives: To train enlisted personnel to install, operate, and perform organizational maintenance on radio communication systems or units employing similar equipment.

Instruction: AC and DC series and parallel circuits, DC motors and generators, AC principles, inductance, transformers, oscilloscopes, capacitance, and series and parallel resonance; fundamentals of radio, including vacuum tubes, diodes, power supplies, filters, triode, tetrode, pentode, and beam power tubes, voltage regulators, amplifiers, oscillators, transmitters, superheterodyne introduction, detectors and AVC, frequency modulation, limiter circuits, antenna fundamentals, and transistors; operation, troubleshooting, and maintenance of radio sets, receiver-transmitter sets, and radio teletypewriter sets.

Credit recommendation, collegiate level: 2 semester hours at the freshman or sophomore level as an elective in electricity and radio, and credit in electrical laboratory on the basis of demonstrated skills and/or institutional examinations.

Artillery Sound Ranging
(Artillery Sound Ranging (Advanced))

Location: Artillery and Missile School, Fort Sill, Okla.

Length: 7–8 weeks.

Objectives: To train enlisted personnel in the installation, operation, and organizational maintenance of a field artillery sound ranging unit.

Instruction: Map reading; logarithms; computation of coordinates, azimuth and distance; sound ranging weather data; sound record reading; plotting fan; plot interpretation; plotting charts; calculator; electrical fundamentals; functions and maintenance of sound ranging sets; communications; sound ranging techniques, procedures, and application.

Credit recommendation, collegiate level: Credit in surveying or plotting on the basis of demonstrated skills and/or institutional examinations.

Artillery Survey Noncommissioned Officer

Location: Artillery and Missile School, Fort Sill, Okla.

Length: 4 weeks.

Objectives: To train enlisted personnel to supervise, coordinate, and participate in the operations of an artillery survey party, battery detail, or survey information center.

Instruction: Artillery survey; mathematics; logarithms; survey computations; maps; care and use of survey equipment; traverse; triangulation; astronomy; artillery battalion survey; division artillery survey; corps artillery survey.

Credit recommendation, collegiate level: CAUTION: *Courses in artillery survey vary slightly in title, length, and recommendation. Require exact identification of course by title and length.* 2 semester hours in general surveying.

Artillery Survey Officer

Location: Artillery and Missile School, Fort Sill, Okla.

Length: 7–8 weeks.

Objectives: To train commissioned officers in reconnaissance and survey procedures.

Instruction: Observation survey; survey records and survey equipment; traverse; triangulation; resection; field artillery battalion survey; observation battalion and division artillery surveys; astronomic observation for artillery; mathematics; maps and photos.

Credit recommendation, collegiate level: CAUTION: *Courses in artillery survey vary slightly in title, length, and recommendation. Require exact identification of course by title and length.* 5 semester hours in general surveying.

1. Artillery Survey Specialist
(Artillery Survey Advanced)
2. Artillery Survey Specialist

Location: Artillery and Missile School, Fort Sill, Okla.

Length: *Course 1,* 8–9 weeks; *Course 2,* 5 weeks.

Objectives: To train enlisted personnel in artillery survey procedures.

Instruction: *Courses 1 and 2:* Mathematics; care, use, and adjustments of survey equipment; traverse methods and computations; triangulation; resection; corps and division artillery survey; artillery battalion survey; astronomic observations; maps; fire direction; communication procedures and security; communication equipment and systems.

Credit recommendation, collegiate level: CAUTION: *These courses vary in title, length, and recommendation. Require exact identification of course by title and length. Course 1:* 5 semester hours in surveying. *Course 2:* 3 semester hours in general surveying.

Artillery Target Acquisition Officer
(Artillery Observation)

Location: Artillery and Missile School, Fort Sill, Okla.

Length: 9–12 weeks.
Objectives: To train officers in sound ranging, flash ranging, and observation battalion survey techniques and to familiarize them with field artillery radar and ballistic meteorology.
Instruction: Survey equipment; traverse; triangulation; observation battalion survey; astronomic orientation; mathematics and maps; flash ranging equipment, techniques, and operations; sound ranging equipment, techniques, and operations.
Credit recommendation, collegiate level: Credit in surveying on the basis of demonstrated skills and/or institutional examinations.

Artillery Vehicle Maintenance Supervisors
(Artillery Vehicle Maintenance Supervision)
Location: Artillery and Missile School, Fort Sill, Okla.
Length: 4–12 weeks.
Objectives: To train enlisted personnel in the supervision of organizational maintenance of wheeled and tracked vehicles and turrets, in maintenance management, and in recovery and field expedients of vehicles used in the artillery.
Instruction: Air cooled engines; turret maintenance; chassis and power train; preventive maintenance; liquid cooled engines; chassis and power train components; wheeled and tracked vehicles; maintenance of wheeled and tracked vehicles.
Credit recommendation, collegiate level: This course is technical and vocational in nature. Credit in automotive repair on the basis of demonstrated skills and/or institutional examinations.

Assistant Systems Analyst
Location: Adjutant General School, Fort Benjamin Harrison, Ind.
Length: 4–5 weeks.
Objectives: To train enlisted personnel in the principles and techniques employed in the performance of systems analysis and design studies for Army automatic data processing applications with emphasis on integration of proposed and operating automatic data processing systems into systems which meet the essential needs for information and data at all levels of command and in all functional areas.
Instruction: Automatic data processing fundamentals and programming; systems analysis and design; Army applications.
Credit recommendation, collegiate level: 2 semester hours in systems analysis in the field of computing science.

Associate Adjutant General Company Officer
Location: Adjutant General School, Fort Benjamin Harrison, Ind.
Length: 12–14 weeks.
Objectives: To provide officers with branch training in the duties and responsibilities of company-grade Adjutant General Corps officers.
Instruction: Principles of effective communication;

organization, functions, and capabilities of combat units; preparation and administration of staff records and reports; knowledge of general staff functions, procedures, and techniques necessary to operate with all levels of command; principles and methods of the organization and administration of Adjutant General sections; office management and techniques; personnel requirements and staffing; organization and operation of postal units; personnel management operations.
Credit recommendation, collegiate level: 3 semester hours in business organization and management.

Associate Adjutant General Officer Career
(Associate Adjutant General Officer Advanced)
Location: Adjutant General's School, Fort Benjamin Harrison, Ind.
Length: 12–16 weeks.
Objectives: To provide branch training in the duties and responsibilities of Adjutant General's Corps officers.
Instruction: Military leadership; oral and written communications; records and publications management; principles, objectives, and procedural techniques of personnel actions, including pay, absences, separations, and personal affairs; personnel management, including testing, interviewing and counseling, classification and distribution, assignments, promotions, records, qualifications, and evaluation; familiarization with data processing operations; postal service operation; supervision of special services; command and staff operations; responsibilities of the combined arms; combat support operations.
Credit recommendation, collegiate level: 3 semester hours in personnel management.

Associate Air Defense Artillery Battery Officer
(Associate AAA Battery Officer)
Location: Air Defense School, Fort Bliss, Tex.
Length: 14–17 weeks.
Objectives: To provide training in the duties and responsibilities of battery-grade air defense artillery officers assigned to other than missile units.
Instruction: Familiarization with staff procedures and principles of communication; description, operation, and employment of light, medium, and skysweeper AAA gunnery; surface gunnery; organization, employment, and tactics of the combined arms.
Credit recommendation, collegiate level: No credit as courses are military in nature.

1. Associate Air Defense Officer Career
(Associate Air Defense Officer Advanced)
2. Associate AAA and SAM Officer Advanced
3. Associate SAM Officer Advanced
4. Associate AAA Officer Advanced
Location: Air Defense School, Fort Bliss, Tex.
Length: 14–21 weeks.
Objectives: To train officers in the duties and responsibilities of air defense weapon systems.
Instruction: Principles of leadership and management organization; communication systems; review of

artillery weapons and gunnery techniques; maintenance procedures and inspection; organization and tactics of the combined arms; employment, techniques and operations of missile systems.

Credit recommendation, collegiate level: 3 semester hours in business organization and management, for each course.

Associate Armor Company Officer

Location: Armor School, Fort Knox, Ky.

Length: 15–16 weeks.

Objectives: To provide branch training to officers in the duties and responsibilities of company-grade armor officers.

Instruction: Maintenance operation; employment of tank and armored infantry platoons; artillery, infantry, and engineer operations; tactical and field communications.

Credit recommendation, collegiate level: No credit as course is military in nature.

Associate Armor Officer Career
(Associate Armor Officer Advanced)

Location: Armor School, Fort Knox, Ky.

Length: 15–19 weeks.

Objectives: To provide advanced branch training to officers in the duties and responsibilities appropriate to field-grade armor officers.

Instruction: Automotive maintenance management; organization and employment of the tank and armored rifle and infantry battalions; nuclear weapons; intelligence; armor administration and logistics; artillery and infantry operations; engineer operations; communication procedures and equipment; tactical and field communications; military leadership and management; principles and techniques of small arms and allied armored equipment.

Credit recommendation, collegiate level: 3 semester hours in business organization and management.

Associate Army Logistics Management

Location: Logistics Management Center, Fort Lee, Va.

Length: 8 weeks.

Objectives: To train Reserve component officers in the management and operation of maintenance, depot distribution, procurement, and requirements aspects of the Army logistics system.

Instruction: Application of management skills and practices, communicative skills, problem solving, and decision making; interrelationship of logistical functions; financial management and budget systems; inventory management, including cataloging, requirements computation, distribution management, rebuild, and disposal; fundamentals of procurement; planning and awarding of contracts; contract administration; distribution systems and organization of the wholesale logistics elements; materiel management; packing, packaging and preservation; warehouse operations; controls for the maintenance function; maintenance management, including production management, reporting, customer relations, repair parts management, contract maintenance, and the economics of maintenance.

Credit recommendation, collegiate level: 6 semester hours in supply management.

Associate Army Medical Service Company Officer

Location: Medical Field Service School, Fort Sam Houston, Tex.

Length: 15 weeks.

Objectives: To train officers as commanders of detachments, platoons, and companies, as staff officers of Army Medical Service battalions and groups, and as special staff officers of battalions and appropriate higher echelons.

Instruction: Hospital organization; medical supply procedures; hospital plant planning and maintenance; records and reports; basic principles of personnel management; organization and employment of units of the combined arms; military leadership; weapons familiarization; fundamentals of staff responsibility, intelligence procedures, and logistical procedures at regimental level; organization, function, and employment of field medical service through division level; preventive medicine; professional management of wounded patients in combat.

Credit recommendation, collegiate level: 3 semester hours in business organization and management.

Associate Chemical Officer Career
(Associate Chemical Officer Advanced)

Location: Chemical Center and School, Fort McClellan, Ala.

Length: 16–20 weeks.

Objectives: To train officers in the duties and responsibilities of Chemical Corps Officers.

Instruction: Personnel and administrative procedures; logistics; management; CBR plans, training and operations; combat arms; nuclear warfare and radiological defense.

Credit recommendation, collegiate level: 4 semester hours in business organization and management, and credit in chemistry on the basis of institutional examination.

Associate Command and General Staff Officer

Location: Command and General Staff College, Fort Leavenworth, Kan.

Length: 16–18 weeks.

Objectives: To prepare officers for duty as commanders and as general staff officers of divisions and combat or logistical commands.

Instruction: Basic staff organization and procedures; principles of war; fundamentals of combat; organization capabilities and limitations of all types of combat divisions and logistical commands.

Credit recommendation, collegiate level: 3 semester hours in business organization and management.

Associate Engineer Officer Advanced

Location: Engineer School, Fort Belvoir, Va.

Length: 15–16 weeks.

Objectives: To provide branch training in the major responsibilities of Corps of Engineer officers.

Instruction: Staff organization, functions, and procedures; organization and employment of combat and combined arms operations; engineer logistical support; bridge design and classification; engineer planning of field fortifications; soils engineering and geology; planning and construction of roads, airfields, and drainage systems; types, composition, and characteristics of bituminous paving materials and concrete; characteristics and requirements of military installations and facilities; utilization of engineer equipment.

Credit recommendation, collegiate level: 3 semester hours in engineering construction and 2 semester hours in business organization and management.

Associate Field Artillery Battery Officer
(Associate Field Artillery Missile Battery Officer)

Location: Artillery and Missile School, Fort Sill, Okla.

Length: 16–18 weeks.

Objectives: To provide a working knowledge of the duties and responsibilities appropriate to battery-grade field artillery officers.

Instruction: Application of the principles of field artillery tactics and techniques; familiarization with field artillery weapons, materiel, and associated arms; communication procedures and equipment; operation and procedures of the firing battery; orientation to field artillery rockets and missiles.

Credit recommendation, collegiate level: No credit as courses are military in nature.

Associate Field Artillery Officer Career
(Associate Field Artillery Officer Advanced)

Location: Artillery and Missile School, Fort Sill, Okla.

Length: 18–19 weeks.

Objectives: To provide training in the duties and responsibilities appropriate to field artillery officers.

Instruction: Organization, characteristics, capabilities and factors affecting the employment of the infantry and armored divisions; fundamentals and organization for fire support coordination; organization of air defense units; tactical employment of all artillery weapons; organization and employment of the combined arms team; command and staff procedures; nuclear weapons employment; characteristics and functions of missile systems.

Credit recommendation, collegiate level: 3 semester hours in business organization and management.

Associate Finance Officer Career

Location: Finance School, Fort Benjamin Harrison, Ind.

Length: 19 weeks.

Objectives: To provide branch training in the duties and responsibilities of Finance Corps officers.

Instruction: Principles, procedures, and techniques of military and financial accounting and financial management; employment of computers in accounting systems; program and budget formulation and execution; management engineering; techniques and procedures of progress and statistical reporting and analysis; staff organization; government purchasing and contracting.

Credit recommendation, collegiate level: CAUTION: *These courses are similar in content but varied in the intensity of instruction in the specific academic areas each year. Therefore credit will be recommended according to the year the course was given. Require exact identification of course by year of attendance. Academic year 1962–1963:* 2 semester hours in business administration, 3 semester hours in government accounting, 3 semester hours in finance and disbursing, and 3 semester hours in computer principles in the field of data processing. *Academic year 1963–1964:* 3 semester hours in business administration, 4 semester hours in government accounting, 3 semester hours in finance and disbursing, and 1 semester hour in computer principles in the field of data processing. *Academic year 1964–1965:* 2 semester hours in business administration, 3 semester hours in government accounting, 3 semester hours in finance and disbursing, and 1 semester hour in computer principles in the field of data processing.

Associate Infantry Officer Career
(Associate Infantry Officer Advanced)

Location: Infantry School, Fort Benning, Ga.

Length: 19 weeks.

Objectives: To provide branch training in the duties and responsibilities of infantry officers.

Instruction: Command and staff functions; principles of personnel management; principles and techniques of combat intelligence; duties of the brigade and battalion operations staff officer; logistics; tactical doctrine; employment of the infantry in offensive and defense operations; organizational structure and employment of aviation, amphibious, and artillery operations; employment of the rifle company; military leadership; communications responsibilities, requirements, and concepts; organization of a battalion maintenance program.

Credit recommendation, collegiate level: 3 semester hours in business organization and management.

Associate Medical Service Officer Advanced

Location: Medical Field Service School, Fort Sam Houston, Tex.

Length: 15 weeks.

Objectives: To train officers as commanders and staff officers of Medical Service detachments, companies, battalions, and groups; as special staff officers of regiments, combat commands, and divisions; and to perform other commensurate field-grade duties.

Instruction: Organization of hospitals; principles and methods of problem solving; familiarization with financial management; principles and standards for hospital plant planning; fundamentals of medical and military law; medical records and reports; principles of personnel management; professional management of battle casualties; organization and operation of field medical service; organization of the combined arms;

principles of staff organization and functions; logistics; military leadership; familiarization with neuropsychiatry, veterinary service, and preventive medicine.

Credit recommendation, collegiate level: 4 semester hours in business organization and management.

Associate Military Intelligence Officer Advanced

Location: Intelligence School, Fort Holabird, Md.
Length: 14 weeks.
Objectives: To train officers in the duties and responsibilities appropriate to intelligence field-grade officers.
Instruction: Command and staff responsibilities; organization and tactics of foreign armies; command considerations in the employment of atomic weapons; organization and function of the intelligence sections of infantry, airborne, and armored divisions; collection and processing of information; reconnaissance responsibilities; intelligence reports and documents; intelligence planning; mission, organization, functions, and responsibilities of censorship, counterintelligence corps, interrogation of prisoners of war, order of battle, and technical intelligence personnel; theory and principles of democracy and communism; military intelligence support in a theater of operations.
Credit recommendation, collegiate level: 3 semester hours in business organization and management, 3 semester hours in intelligence methods, and credit in political science on the basis of institutional examinations.

Associate Military Police Company Officer

Location: The Provost Marshal General's School, Fort Gordon, Ga.
Length: 13 weeks.
Objectives: To provide branch training to officers in the duties and responsibilities appropriate to company-grade Military Police Corps officers.
Instruction: Tactical employment of the combined arms; fundamental command and staff procedures; marksmanship; introduction to chemical, biological, and radiological warfare; military transportation; military justice; nuclear warfare; civil disturbances; confinement facilities; criminal investigative activities; organization and operations of military police units; prisoners of war; traffic control.
Credit recommendation, collegiate level: 3 semester hours in police methods.

Associate Military Police Officer Career
(Associate Military Police Officer Advanced)

Locations: The Provost Marshal General's School, Fort Gordon, Ga.; Military Police School, Fort Gordon, Ga.
Length: 14 weeks.
Objectives: To provide branch training in the duties and responsibilities of Military Police Corps officers.
Instruction: Tactical employment of the combined arms; staff organization and procedures; mine warfare; supply economy; fundamentals of the Army Command Management System, including programming, bud-

geting, scheduling, and review and analysis; chemical, biological, and radiological warfare; civil affairs organization, operation, and functions; military leadership; motor vehicle maintenance inspection; military justice; nuclear weapons employment; duties and responsibilities of military police in civil disturbances; operation and supervision of confinement facilities; criminal investigation facilities; methods, procedures, and policies related to military police organizations and operations; prisoners of war; communications; traffic control; civil defense, industrial defense, and natural disaster relief; principles of physical security.
Credit recommendation, collegiate level: 9 semester hours in police methods and administration.

Associate Ordnance Company Officer

Location: Ordnance School, Aberdeen Proving Ground, Md.
Length: 14 weeks.
Objectives: To provide officers with a working knowledge of the duties and responsibilities appropriate to company-grade Ordnance Corps officers.
Instruction: Ordnance service; military leadership; field and depot supply and maintenance management; problems in ordnance service management; ordnance materiel; tactics and staff procedure.
Credit recommendation, collegiate level: 3 semester hours in supply management.

Associate Quartermaster Company Officer

Location: Quartermaster School, Fort Lee, Va.
Length: 15 weeks.
Objectives: To provide branch training in the duties and responsibilities appropriate to company-grade Quartermaster officers.
Instruction: Supply economy; property accounting and responsibility; unit and organization supply; installation organization for supply; stock records; storage principles and procedures; commissary operations; financial inventory accounting; finance and reporting techniques; company administration; procurement; food service; organization and operation of unit motor pools and field maintenance shops; command and staff operations; intelligence; tactical employment of the combat arms; logistical support required by combat units and organizations; missions and function of division Quartermaster within a theater of operations; familiarization with primary commodity items procured, stored, and distributed by the Quartermaster Corps.
Credit recommendation, collegiate level: 3 semester hours in supply management and 3 semester hours in business organization and management.

Associate Quartermaster Officer Career
(Associate Quartermaster Officer Advanced)

Location: Quartermaster School, Fort Lee, Va.
Length: 15–16 weeks.
Objectives: To provide branch training in the duties and responsibilities of Quartermaster Corps officers.
Instruction: Military justice and basic military administrative law; weapons; oral and written communica-

tion; command and staff organization and procedures; organization, missions, and tactical employment of division units; functions within a theater of operations, including combat support, employment of supply installations, principles and procedures for determining requirements for and affecting receipt, storage, and issue of supplies, administrative and logistical service support, requirements computations for logistical support of division type units, and transportation movement; personnel management principles; financial management; procedures for supplies in division, direct support, installation, general support, and oversea depot supply operations; installation service activities; procurement; supply control, storage, and distribution; maintenance management.

Credit recommendation, collegiate level: 4 semester hours in supply management and 2 semester hours in business organization and management.

1. Associate SAM Battery Officer
2. Associate Air Defense Missile Battery Officer
   (Associate AAA Missile Battery Officer)

Location: Air Defense School, Fort Bliss, Tex.
Length: 16–17 weeks.
Objectives: To train officers in the duties and responsibilities of battery-grade air defense officers assigned to SAM units.
Instruction: *Course 1:* Basic electricity, including electron theory, electrical components, AC and DC series and parallel circuits, and analyses of schematic diagrams; familiarization with communication and radar systems; introduction to the Nike system; characteristics, purpose, and functioning of the missile guidance unit; SAM tactics. *Course 2:* Characteristics and capabilities of artillery radio and missile radar systems; principles of the Nike-Ajax system; integrated battery operations; air defense tactics; organization and employment of the combined arms.
Credit recommendation, collegiate level: CAUTION: *These courses vary only slightly in title and recommendation. Require exact identification of course by title. Course 1:* 2 semester hours as an elective in electricity, and credit in electrical laboratory on the basis of demonstrated skills and/or institutional examinations. *Course 2:* No credit as courses are military in nature.

Associate SSM Battery Officer

Location: Antiaircraft Artillery and Guided Missile School, Fort Bliss, Tex.
Length: 15 weeks.
Objectives: To provide minimum essential training to officers in the duties and responsibilities appropriate to battery-grade artillery officers in surface-to-surface guided missile units.
Instruction: Motors and generators; map reading and survey; basic electronics; communications; Corporal external guidance; internal guidance, checkout and firing procedures; propulsion system, uncrating and assembly, and service area checkout; ground-handling equipment; SSM gunnery and Corporal firing; staff procedures; combined arms; SSM tactics.
Credit recommendation, collegiate level: 2 semester hours in basic electricity.

Associate SSM Officer Advanced

Location: Artillery and Guided Missile School, Fort Bliss, Tex.
Length: 15 weeks.
Objectives: To train officers in the duties and responsibilities necessary for field-grade artillery officers in surface-to-surface guided missile units.
Instruction: General supply and training management; leadership; communications; Corporal external guidance and fire control; internal guidance and preparation for firing; Corporal mechanical system, mechanics, and handling; nuclear weapons; combined arms; SSM tactics; logistics; intelligence, military transportation; new developments.
Credit recommendation, collegiate level: 2 semester hours in business organization and management.

Associate Signal Officer Career
(Associate Signal Officer Advanced)

Location: Signal School, Fort Monmouth, N.J.
Length: 12–18 weeks.
Objectives: To train officers in the duties and responsibilities of Signal Corps officers.
Instruction: Managing communications systems at brigade, division, corps and army, and theater level; military security; communications security; low-level cryptosystems; teletypewriter operations and procedures; tactical security equipment; communications center operations and procedures, planning, installation, and operation of security equipments; organization, weapons and tactical employment of basic combined arms units; command and staff relationships; responsibilities and functions of operations and intelligence staff officers; division organization and tactics; telephone communications; nuclear warfare and CBR operations; automatic data processing systems; methods of instruction; administrative operations; personnel management; logistics.
Credit recommendation, collegiate level: 4 semester hours in business organization and management.

Associate Transportation Officer Advanced

Location: Transportation School, Fort Eustis, Va.
Length: 12 and 16 weeks.
Objectives: To train commissioned officers in the duties and responsibilities appropriate to field-grade Transportation Corps officers.
Instruction: Personnel and administration; map reading and intelligence organization, operations, and training; logistics; highway transportation; rail, terminal, and water transport; aviation; traffic management; general transportation.
Credit recommendation, collegiate level: 3 semester hours in transportation management.

Associate Transportation Officer Career

Location: Transportation School, Fort Eustis, Va.
Length: 12 and 17 weeks.
Objectives: To train commissioned officers in the duties and responsibilities of Transportation Corps officers.
Instruction: Logistics; supply requirements theater of

operations; operations and intelligence; air mobile operations; nuclear weapons employment; transportation organization, plans, and employment; aviation; transportation movements; rail transport; motor transport; terminal and water transport; transportation technical training.

Credit recommendation, collegiate level: 3 semester hours in transportation management.

Auditing

Location: Finance School, Fort Benjamin Harrison, Ind.

Length: 8 weeks.

Objectives: To train officers, warrant officers, and enlisted personnel to establish control operations or audit systems of accounts and related financial activities.

Instruction: Integrated accounting; property accounting; fiscal code regulations; nature, sources and uses of nonappropriated funds; principles and procedures of auditing and preparation of audit reports.

Credit recommendation, collegiate level: 3 semester hours in general accounting and 3 semester hours in auditing.

1. Automatic Data Processing Systems Analysis
2. Automatic Data Processing Systems Analysis Officer

Location: Adjutant General's School, Fort Benjamin Harrison, Ind.

Length: *Course 1,* 3 weeks; *Course 2,* 4 weeks.

Objectives: To train commissioned officers and warrant officers in the principles and procedures of analyzing and designing applications of automatic data processing systems (ADPS).

Instruction: *Course 1:* Characteristics, capabilities, and operating principles of the equipment components of ADPS; fundamentals of block diagramming and programming; principles and techniques of systems analysis; acquisition and installation of ADPS. *Course 2:* Principles of punched card data processing; number systems and binary codes; characteristics of ADP equipment; computer programming, including flow charting and block diagramming, programming techniques, computer languages, and file description entry formats and functions of optional entries; principles and techniques applied in the process of problem definition, systems analysis, and systems design of ADPS; ADP management.

Credit recommendation, collegiate level: CAUTION: *These courses vary only slightly in title, length, and recommendation. Require exact identification of course by title and length. Course 1:* Credit in computer programming and analysis in the field of data processing on the basis of institutional examination. *Course 2:* 2 semester hours in computer programming and analysis in the field of data processing.

Automatic Data Processing Systems for Staff Officers

Location: Signal School, Fort Monmouth, N.J.

Length: 3–5 weeks.

Objectives: To train commissioned officers in the basic fundamentals, applications, and systems engineering techniques of automatic data processing systems.

Instruction: Fundamentals and principles of operation of an automatic data processing system; familiarization with the principles and techniques of programming in a digital computer; systems analysis and the development of systems specifications; current and future military command systems.

Credit recommendation, collegiate level: No credit because of the brevity and limited technical nature of the course.

Automatic Data Processing Systems Programming

Location: Adjutant General's School, Fort Benjamin Harrison, Ind.

Length: 4 weeks.

Objectives: To train warrant officers and enlisted personnel in techniques for devising coded programs of operating instructions for automatic data processing equipment.

Instruction: Numbering systems and basic operations; input-output media; basic programming, including operation codes and input-output format control; loop and address modification; flow charting; scaling; program testing; input checking; program switch; advanced programming; usage techniques of the computer console and program debugging.

Credit recommendation, collegiate level: 2 semester hours in computer programming in the field of computing science.

Automatic Weapons Maintenance
(Light Antiaircraft Artillery Maintenance)

Location: Antiaircraft Artillery and Guided Missile School, Fort Bliss, Tex.

Length: 4–7 weeks.

Objectives: To train enlisted personnel to perform organizational maintenance on unit small arms and light antiaircraft artillery weapons.

Instruction: Characteristics, functions, assembly, disassembly, maintenance, and repair of weapons.

Credit recommendation, collegiate level: These courses are technical and vocational in nature. Credit in mechanical shop on the basis of demonstrated skills and/or institutional examinations.

Automotive Maintenance and Repair Officer

Location: Ordnance School, Aberdeen Proving Ground, Md.

Length: 7–8 weeks.

Objectives: To train commissioned officers and warrant officers to maintain automotive vehicles and to direct and supervise personnel engaged in repair maintenance.

Instruction: Automotive maintenance management; automotive shop tools and equipment; shop safety, sections, and supply; inspections and production control; automotive maintenance problems; shop layout; forms, records, and reports; vehicle storage; shop operation and management; automotive engines; carburetors; batteries; generators; engine disassembly and reassembly; power trains; transmission; coupling; gears; chassis components; vehicle driving; engine tuneup procedure; recovery equipment and problems.

Credit recommendation, collegiate level: 2 semester hours in maintenance management. At the technical level, credit in automotive repair on the basis of demonstrated skills and/or institutional examinations.

Automotive Rebuild

Location: Ordnance School, Aberdeen Proving Ground, Md.

Length: 12 weeks.

Objectives: To train enlisted personnel to rebuild engines, power train units, and chassis components of wheel and track vehicles.

Instruction: Lifting and handling equipment; types of shops; wheel and track vehicle, power train, and wheel vehicle chassis rebuild procedure.

Credit recommendation, collegiate level: This course is technical and vocational in nature. Credit in automotive repair on the basis of demonstrated skills and/or institutional examinations.

Automotive Repair
(Track Vehicle Repair)

Location: Ordnance School, Aberdeen Proving Ground, Md.

Length: 14 weeks.

Objectives: To train enlisted personnel to maintain and repair wheeled and tracked vehicle engines and accessories, power train units, and chassis components.

Instruction: Hand tools; shop safety; operation, construction, disassembly, assembly, inspection, and trouble diagnosis of wheeled vehicle engines; power train components; torque transmitters and converters; axle assemblies; brakes; steering; planetary gearing; hydromatic transmission; wheeled vehicle suspension; tracked vehicle engines; tracked vehicle transmission.

Credit recommendation, collegiate level: This course is technical and vocational in nature. Credit in automotive repair on the basis of demonstrated skills and/or institutional examinations.

1. Automotive Repair Parts Specialist
2. Aircraft Repair Parts Specialist
3. Communications-Electronics Repair Parts Specialist
4. Special Purpose Equipment Repair Parts Specialist

Location: Quartermaster School, Fort Lee, Va.

Length: 4–5 weeks.

Objectives: To train enlisted personnel in the receipt, storage, inspection, identification, preservation and shipment of repair parts.

Instruction: Army maintenance system equipment records; supply bulletins; item identification; repair parts records; storage operations; shipping procedures.

Credit recommendation, collegiate level: These courses are technical and vocational in nature. Credit in stock accounting procedures on the basis of institutional examination.

1. Aviation Electronic Equipment Repair
2. Aviation Electronic Equipment Maintenance

Location: Southeastern Signal School, Fort Gordon, Ga.

Length: 19–28 weeks.

Objectives: To train enlisted personnel in the organizational maintenance of aircraft electronic equipment.

Instruction: Principles of electricity; aircraft wiring and diagrams; fundamentals of electronics including principles of power and inductance, capacitance, tuned circuits and transformers, diodes, triodes, and multi-element tubes, power supply, bridge and metallic rectifiers, voltage regulators, transistors and transistor circuits, amplifiers, and oscillators; organizational maintenance of aircraft electronic equipment.

Credit recommendation, collegiate level: 2 semester hours, for each course, at the freshman or sophomore level as an elective in electricity and electronics, and credit in electrical laboratory on the basis of demonstrated skills and/or institutional examinations.

Avionic Communications Equipment Repair

Location: Southeastern Signal School, Fort Gordon, Ga.

Length: 19 weeks.

Objectives: To train enlisted personnel to perform support maintenance of airborne electronic communication, identification, and associated ground equipment.

Instruction: Voltage and resistance measurements; Ohm's law; DC circuits; receiver input power circuits; receiver power supply; receiver audio section; radio transmitters; techniques, procedures, and test equipment necessary for maintenance of airborne VHF communications equipment, airborne UHF transistorized communications equipment, airborne FM transistorized communications equipment, airborne SSB transistorized communications equipment, FM and UHF airborne equipment, and VHF and UHF ground equipment.

Credit recommendation, collegiate level: Credit in electricity and electrical laboratory on the basis of demonstrated skills and/or institutional examinations.

1. Avionic Equipment Maintenance Supervisor
2. Avionic Equipment Maintenance Supervisor

Location: Southeastern Signal School, Fort Gordon, Ga.

Length: *Course 1,* 22 weeks; *Course 2,* 19 weeks.

Objectives: To train enlisted personnel to apply advanced maintenance techniques and to supervise activities involved in the maintenance of avionic equipment.

Instruction: *Course 1:* Basic and advanced electronic principles, including AC and DC circuits, magnetism, capacitance, inductance, transformers, series and parallel circuits, vacuum tubes, power supplies, amplifiers, oscillators, amplitude modulation, transistors, computer circuits, and synchros and servos; test equipment; maintenance on avionic systems; supply procedures; supervisory controls; leadership and management principles. *Note*—depending on previous training, students will also receive instruction in either two or three of the following areas—avionics communications equipment, avionic navigation equipment, and/or automatic flight control equipment. *Course 2:* This course is very similar in content to the preceding course, but contains less instruction in electronics theory.

Credit recommendation, collegiate level: CAUTION: *These courses vary slightly in length and recommendation. Require exact identification of course by length. Course 1:* 2 semester hours in electronics, and credit in electrical laboratory on the basis of demonstrated skills and/or institutional examinations. *Course 2:* Credit in electronics and electrical laboratory on the basis of demonstrated skills and/or institutional examinations.

Avionic Flight Control Equipment Repair

Location: Southeastern Signal School, Fort Gordon, Ga.

Length: 14 weeks.

Objectives: To train enlisted personnel to perform direct and general support maintenance on automatic flight control equipment.

Instruction: Fundamental mathematics and the metric system of linear measurement; automatic flight control system AN/ASW-12 (V); alternating and direct current; Ohm's law; series and parallel circuits; semiconductors; power supply; transistors; block diagram analysis of AN/ASW-12 (V), roll channel, pitch channel, and yaw channel; function of instrument landing systems; maintenance of avionic stability augmentation and speed trim systems and automatic stabilization equipment.

Credit recommendation, collegiate level: Credit in electricity and electrical laboratory on the basis of demonstrated skills and/or institutional examinations.

Avionic Navigation Equipment Repair

Location: Southeastern Signal School, Fort Gordon, Ga.

Length: 17 weeks.

Objectives: To train enlisted personnel to perform direct and general support maintenance on electronic navigation equipment.

Instruction: Radio terms; principles, circuitry, and radio repair procedures applicable to radio receivers and transmitters; use of test equipment and hand tools; maintenance and repair of Marker Beacon equipment, including audio circuits, power and control circuits, semiconductors, and transistors; maintenance and repair of radio direction finding equipment; VOR and glidescope equipment, gyromagnetic compass and navigational computer equipment, and airborne and ground navigation equipment.

Credit recommendation, collegiate level: Credit in electricity and electrical laboratory on the basis of demonstrated skills and/or institutional examinations.

Ballistic Missile Digital Computer Repair (Pershing)

Location: Missile and Munitions School, Redstone Arsenal, Ala.

Length: 27–29 weeks.

Objectives: To train enlisted personnel to inspect, test, and repair the Pershing Fire Data Computer systems and associated equipment.

Instruction: Ohm's law and series-parallel circuits; motors and generators; resonance circuits; RC and LR circuits; vacuum tube circuits; voltage regulators; transistor theory and principles; missile digital control; arithmetic, storage, input/output and control units; number systems and positional notation; commands and programming; system analysis; Pershing Fire Data Computer operation, distribution, wiring, programming, and operation of monitor panel; computer logic and memory drum; maintenance procedures.

Credit recommendation, collegiate level: 4 semester hours at the freshman or sophomore level as an elective in electricity and electronics, and credit in electrical laboratory on the basis of demonstrated skills and/or institutional examinations.

Ballistic Missile General Support Shop Set Repair (Sergeant)

Location: Missile and Munitions School, Redstone Arsenal, Ala.

Length: 18 weeks.

Objectives: To train enlisted personnel to inspect, test, and repair the general support shop set and Sergeant missile electronic systems and associated equipment through field maintenance level.

Instruction: Missile electronics, including heterodyne receivers, AM and FM transmitters, radio waves, RF amplifiers, filters, oscillators, mixers and pulse circuits, missile digital controllers; precision soldering; operational procedures; organizational and field maintenance of the Sergeant general support shop set; piece-part repair of Sergeant ground support electronic subassemblies.

Credit recommendation, collegiate level: This course is technical and vocational in nature. Credit in electrical shop on the basis of demonstrated skills and/or institutional examinations.

Ballistic Missile Guidance and Control Repair

Location: Ordnance Guided Missile School, Redstone Arsenal, Ala.

Length: 13–20 weeks.

Objectives: To train enlisted personnel to operate, inspect, test, and perform field maintenance and repair on ballistic missile guidance and control systems, components and associated test equipment.

Instruction: Series-parallel circuits; motors and generators; transformers; resonance circuits; RC and LR circuits; power supplies; vacuum tube circuits; magnetic amplifiers; transistors; ground and missile power supplies; circuit analysis and repair of the program system; gyroscopes and accelerometers; components, operation, and maintenance of the stabilized platform; operation and repair of the central computer, relay box and actuators, guidance computers, and propulsion system; Redstone trainer component configuration, circuitry and systems operations and repair.

Credit recommendation, collegiate level: 2 semester hours at the freshman or sophomore level as an elective in electricity and electronics, and credit in electrical laboratory on the basis of demonstrated skills and/or institutional examinations.

Ballistic Missile Helper
(Ballistic Missile Repair (Entry))

Location: Ordnance Guided Missile School, Redstone Arsenal, Ala.

Length: 8–9 weeks.

Objectives: To train enlisted personnel in missile electronics, electromechanics, and repair of ballistic missile systems and associated equipment.

Instruction: Ballistic missile systems; shop procedures; ballistic missile maintenance and repair; soldering; direct and alternating current principles, circuits, and applications; power supplies, vacuum tubes; voltage regulators; basic transistors and circuits.

Credit recommendation, collegiate level: 2 semester hours at the freshman and sophomore level as an elective in electricity, and at the technical level, credit in electrical shop on the basis of demonstrated skills and/or institutional examinations.

Ballistic Missile Inertial Guidance and Control Repair (Sergeant)
(Ballistic Missile Inertial Guidance and Control Repair (Pershing))

Location: Missile and Munitions School, Redstone Arsenal, Ala.

Length: 23–29 weeks.

Objectives: To train enlisted personnel to inspect, test, and maintain electronic guidance and control assemblies of missiles and related equipment.

Instruction: Series and parallel circuits; resistors; magnetism and induction; inductance, capacitance, and impedance; RC and LR circuits; vacuum tube circuits; voltage regulators; oscillators and multivibrators; inertial guidance systems networks; drive circuits; servo systems; repair equipment; motors and generators maintenance; transformers; diodes; power supplies; magnetic amplifiers; synchro devices; gating circuits; missile power supplies and cable systems; inertial guidance systems and test equipment; voltage and current regulators; bi-stable circuits; function and operation of the missile system, operational procedures and organizational and field maintenance of the missile system.

Credit recommendation, collegiate level: 3 semester hours at the freshman or sophomore level as an elective in electricity and electronics, and credit in electrical laboratory on the basis of demonstrated skills and/or institutional examinations.

Ballistic Missile Maintenance Technician (Pershing)

Location: Missile and Munitions School, Redstone Arsenal, Ala.

Length: 31 and 34 weeks.

Objectives: To train warrant officers and noncommissioned officers in the inspection, testing, and performing of support maintenance procedures on major items of equipment of the Pershing missile system.

Instruction: Pershing mechanical, hydraulic, and electrical components; missile digital control; Pershing fire data computer; Pershing guidance and control; Pershing test equipment, warhead, and system analysis; ordnance service in the field.

Credit recommendation, collegiate level: Credit in electrical laboratory on the basis of demonstrated skills and/or institutional examinations.

Ballistic Missile Maintenance Technician (Sergeant)

Location: Missile and Munitions School, Redstone Arsenal, Ala.

Length: 23–46 weeks.

Objectives: To train warrant officers and enlisted personnel to inspect, test, and repair the Sergeant missile system and associated equipment through support maintenance level.

Instruction: Sergeant mechanical, hydraulic, and electrical components; Sergeant missile, firing set, organization, and field maintenance test stations; missile systems analysis; Sergeant test equipment ordnance service; Sergeant missile warheads.

Credit recommendation, collegiate level: Credit in electricity and electronics on the basis of institutional examinations, and credit in electrical laboratory on the basis of demonstrated skills and/or institutional examinations.

Ballistic Missile Propulsion and Structures Repair

Location: Ordnance Guided Missile School, Redstone Arsenal, Ala.

Length: 10–15 weeks.

Objectives: To train enlisted personnel to operate, inspect, test, and perform field maintenance and repair on ballistic missile propulsion and structures systems and associated test equipment.

Instruction: Operation, test, and repair of Redstone pneumatic and propellant systems and components; checkout procedures and systems analysis; Redstone missile handling and fueling equipment and ordnance procedures; firing site operation.

Credit recommendation, collegiate level: This course is technical and vocational in nature. Credit in electrical and mechanical shop on the basis of demonstrated skills and/or institutional examinations.

Ballistic Missile Propulsion and Structures Repair (Pershing)

Location: Missile and Munitions School, Redstone Arsenal, Ala.

Length: 12–14 weeks.

Objectives: To train enlisted personnel to inspect, test, and repair the Pershing missile electro-mechanical systems and associated equipment.

Instruction: Series and parallel circuits; multimeters; resistors; DC and AC power; magnetism and inductance; motors and generators; electrical circuits; transformers; capacitance and impedance; missile mechanics; hydraulic system; system components and pumps; steering and servo systems; pneumatic system; compressors, check and vent valves; motor-driven ground power equipment; Pershing ground support equipment; tools and test equipment; storage and handling equipment; erector launcher; system analysis.

Credit recommendation, collegiate level: 2 semester hours at the freshman or sophomore level as an elective in electricity and electronics, and credit in electrical laboratory on the basis of demonstrated skills and/or institutional examinations.

1. Ballistic Missile Test Instrument Repair
2. Ballistic Missile Test Instrument Repair
(Redstone)

Location: Ordnance Guided Missile School, Redstone Arsenal, Ala.

Length: *Course 1,* 14 weeks; *Course 2,* 13 weeks.

Objectives: To train enlisted personnel in the operation, trouble diagnosis, and maintenance of ballistic missile guidance and control test instruments.

Instruction: *Courses 1 and 2:* Actuator; control computer and inverter test fixture; relay box; program device and ST-80 test fixture; guidance computer test fixture. In addition to the preceding instruction, *Course 1* includes vacuum tubes; rectifiers and voltage multipliers; triodes and multi-element tubes; RC coupled, audio power, RF and DC amplifiers; LC and RC oscillators; multivibrators; circuit synthesis.

Credit recommendation, collegiate level: *Course 1:* 2 semester hours at the freshman or sophomore level as an elective in electricity and electronics, and credit in electrical laboratory on the basis of demonstrated skills and/or institutional examinations. *Course 2:* Credit in electricity and electrical laboratory on the basis of demonstrated skills and/or institutional examinations.

Ballistic Missile Test Station Repair (Pershing)

Location: Missile and Munitions School, Redstone Arsenal, Ala.

Length: 29–34 weeks.

Objectives: To train enlisted personnel to inspect, test, and repair the Pershing test stations and associated equipment through support maintenance level.

Instruction: Series-parallel circuits; resistors; magnetism and induction; transformers, capacitance and impedance; test equipment; resonance circuits; RC and LR circuits; vacuum tube circuits; voltage regulators; semiconductors; converters, oscillators and multivibrators; control unit; frequency regulators; modulators and demodulators; drive circuits; servo systems; Pershing test equipment; programmer test station; supplemental countdown chassis; pneumatic test set; troubleshooting; logic rack; measurement rack; digital multimeter and counter; system analysis.

Credit recommendation, collegiate level: 4 semester hours at the freshman or sophomore level as an elective in electricity and electronics, and credit in electrical laboratory on the basis of demonstrated skills and/or institutional examinations.

Ballistic Missile Test Station Repair (Sergeant)

Location: Missile and Munitions School, Redstone Arsenal, Ala.

Length: 23–27 weeks.

Objectives: To train enlisted personnel to inspect, test, and repair the Sergeant missile electronic systems and associated equipment through support maintenance level.

Instruction: Series-parallel circuits; motors and generators; transformers; inductance, capacitance, and impedance; resonance circuits; RC and LR circuits; vacuum tube circuits; voltage regulators; transistor circuits; square wave generator, oscillators, and multivibrators; voltage, current, and frequency regulators; Sergeant test equipment; power distribution and control

panel assemblies; programming and comparison systems; power control and test control assemblies; synchronizer; programmer; system analysis; tape control and tape reader; stepping switches and relays.

Credit recommendation, collegiate level: 3 semester hours at the freshman or sophomore level as an elective in electricity and electronics, and credit in electrical laboratory on the basis of demonstrated skills and/or institutional examinations.

Basic Army Administration (Clerical Procedures and Typing)

Location: U. S. Army Training Centers.

Length: 8 weeks.

Objectives: To train enlisted personnel in the duties of clerk and clerk-typist.

Instruction: Familiarization of office procedures with emphasis on typing and the keeping of military records.

Credit recommendation, collegiate level: Credit in typing on the basis of institutional examination.

1. Basic Avionics Maintenance Officer
2. Avionics Mechanic

Location: Southeastern Signal School, Fort Gordon, Ga.

Length: *Course 1,* 4 weeks; *Course 2,* 18 weeks.

Objectives: To train commissioned and warrant officers and enlisted personnel in maintenance procedures on aircraft electronic communication, navigation, stabilization, identification, and associated ground technical equipment.

Instruction: *Course 1:* Preventive maintenance and operational check on the avionics configuration installed in light transport and observation aircraft, and in command, transport, and surveillance aircraft; operational and maintenance tests on ground communication, navigation, and radar equipment; supply procedures. *Course 2:* This course contains intensive instruction in the organizational maintenance on the systems and equipment included in *Course 1.*

Credit recommendation, collegiate level: Credit, for each course, in electrical laboratory on the basis of demonstrated skills and/or institutional examinations.

Basic Field Radio Repair

Location: Southeastern Signal School, Fort Gordon, Ga.

Length: 17–18 weeks.

Objectives: To train enlisted personnel to perform basic organizational and field maintenance on field radio equipment.

Instruction: Radio terms, principles, circuitry, and radio repair procedures; troubleshooting of radio receivers; basic CW and AM transmitters; superheterodyne radio receiving sets; field radio-teletypewriter equipment; transistorized FM radio sets; radio relay equipment; standardized series of FM radio sets; radio repair shop practices; preventive maintenance procedures.

Credit recommendation, collegiate level: This course is technical and vocational in nature. Credit in radio maintenance on the basis of demonstrated skills and/or institutional examinations.

Basic Fixed Plant Carrier Equipment Repair

Location: Signal School, Fort Monmouth, N.J.
Length: 15 weeks.
Objectives: To train enlisted personnel in the techniques required to operate and maintain fixed-plant carrier equipment.
Instruction: Electrical and electronic fundamentals; telephone and telegraph carrier fundamentals; telegraph carrier and telegraph terminal sets; semi-conductor fundamentals; fixed station integrated communication system.
Credit recommendation, collegiate level: Credit in electricity on the basis of institutional examinations. At the technical level, credit in fixed plant carrier equipment repair on the basis of demonstrated skills.

1. Basic Infantry Officer
2. Infantry Officer Basic
(Infantry Officer Orientation)

Location: Infantry School, Fort Benning, Ga.
Length: 15 weeks.
Objectives: To train officers in the duties and responsibilities of infantry platoon leaders of rifle and weapons platoons of the rifle company.
Instruction: Familiarization with rifles; techniques of rifle and machine gun fire; familiarization with mine warfare equipment; fundamentals, principles, and techniques involved in individual, squad, and platoon-level offensive, defensive and retrograde tactics; tactical employment of the tank and armored infantry platoons; combined arms operations; operation and control of infantry vehicles; bayonet training; intelligence responsibilities; logistics; infantry organization and equipment.
Credit recommendation, collegiate level: Credit in advanced military at institutions which regularly offer such credit.

Basic Microwave Radio Equipment Repair

Location: Signal School, Fort Monmouth, N.J.
Length: 15–19 weeks.
Objectives: To provide enlisted personnel with a limited knowledge of the installation, operation, and repair of microwave fixed-station and transportable radio equipment.
Instruction: Electrical and electronic fundamentals, including cells and batteries, resistors, series, parallel and series-parallel circuits; induction, alternating current, power, inductance, capacitance, transformers, motors and generators, diodes and triodes, power supply rectifiers, filters, and amplifiers; basic radio transmitters and receivers; wave circuitry; microwave radio communications; transportable microwave radio systems; fundamentals of solid state devices.
Credit recommendation, collegiate level: 2 semester hours at the freshman or sophomore level as an elective in electricity and electronics, and credit in electrical laboratory on the basis of demonstrated skills and/or institutional examinations.

Basic Military Journalist

Locations: Defense Information School, Fort Slocum, N.Y.; Fort Benjamin Harrison, Ind.
Length: 9–10 weeks.
Objectives: To train enlisted men of the Armed Forces in printed, oral, and radio and television communication.
Instruction: Information policies and programs; community relations practices; theories and techniques of editorial and pictorial writing, including the researching, writing and distributing of news and feature stories; oral communications; preparation of material for radio and television broadcast; international relations and government.
Credit recommendation, collegiate level: 3 semester hours in journalism, and credit in the area of social studies and oral communications on the basis of institutional examination.

Basic Radar Repair

Location: Signal School, Fort Monmouth, N.J.
Length: 19 weeks.
Objectives: To train enlisted personnel in the techniques required to maintain common radar equipment.
Instruction: Electrical fundamentals, including conduction and resistance, batteries, use of the voltmeter, resistors, Ohm's law, series, parallel, and series-parallel circuits, DC power, magnetism, inductance, alternating current, oscilloscope operation, and transformers; basic electronics, including semiconductor and vacuum tube diodes, rectification, capacitance, power supplies, reactive circuits, AC power, resonant circuits, fundamentals of radio receivers and transistors, triode vacuum tube and amplifier, multi-element vacuum tubes, oscillators, principles of heterodyning, receiver analysis and alignment, signal substitution and tracing, amplitude modulation, and voltage regulators; analyzing, testing, and locating troubles in nonsinusoidal circuits and typical radar circuits; adjustment, troubleshooting and repair of radar sets AN/PPS-4, AN/TPS-1 and AN/MPQ-4A.
Credit recommendation, collegiate level: 3 semester hours at the freshman or sophomore level as an elective in electricity and electronics, and credit in electrical laboratory on the basis of demonstrated skills and/or institutional examinations.

Basic Radio Relay and Carrier Repair

Location: Southeastern Signal School, Fort Gordon, Ga.
Length: 19 weeks.
Objectives: To train enlisted personnel in the installation, lineup, operation, and performance of organizational support and depot maintenance on radio relay and carrier equipment.
Instruction: Direct current, basic circuitry, magnetism and electromagnetism, generation of AC, inductance, motors and generators, transformers, capacitance, reactance, AC circuits, resonance, special wave forms, and time constants; principles of electronic circuits, special circuits, and high-frequency techniques including diodes, filter bleeders, and metallic rectifiers; DC amplifiers; triode amplifiers; theory of oscillation; tetrode and pentode amplifiers; automatic frequency control and automatic gain control; audio amplifiers; FM

modulation methods; RF tuners; troubleshooting and repair of radio sets, telephone terminal system, telephone repeater, telegraph-telephone terminal sets, and telegraph terminal sets.

Credit recommendation, collegiate level: 3 semester hours at the freshman or sophomore level as an elective in electricity and electronics, and credit in electrical laboratory on the basis of demonstrated skills and/or institutional examinations.

Basic Stevedore
(Stevedore)

Location: Transportation School, Fort Eustis, Va.

Length: 5–6 weeks.

Objectives: To train enlisted personnel in the basic stevedore activities involved in loading and unloading cargo at ports, beaches, and docks.

Instruction: Water terminals and associated activities; construction and use of wire rope splices; blocks and tackle; ship's gear; cargo handling gear; rigging and stowing of heavy lifts; wench operations; deck loads; basic stevedoring; general stevedoring (loading); advanced stevedoring (discharging); cargo transfer operations.

Credit recommendation, collegiate level: This course is technical and vocational in nature. Credit in stevedore operations on the basis of demonstrated skills and/or institutional examinations.

Battalion Surgeon Assistant

Location: Medical Field Service School, Fort Sam Houston, Tex.

Length: 4 weeks.

Objectives: To train company-grade Medical Service Corps officers to recognize and treat emergency and routine medical conditions which commonly occur and to assist the Medical Corps officer in patient care.

Instruction: Diagnosis and care of common diseases; nursing care procedures; uses of emergency medical apparatus; administration, description, uses, and doses of basic drugs; principles of emergency treatment of combat casualties; familiarization with psychiatric and neurologic problems; communicable disease control measures and environmental sanitation methods.

Credit recommendation, collegiate level: 2 semester hours in first aid and hygiene.

Boilermaker

Location: Transportation School, Fort Eustis, Va.

Length: 10 weeks.

Objectives: To train enlisted personnel to dismantle, repair, and overhaul steam boilers, fireboxes, tenders, tank cars, and other heavy steel plate containers and to maintain railway boilers and allied equipment.

Instruction: Hand, measuring, and pneumatic tools; oxyacetylene cutting and welding; electric arc welding; tubes and flues; smokebox and appliances; riveting; locomotive tenders; stay bolts and firebox; boiler inspection.

Credit recommendation, collegiate level: This course is technical and vocational in nature. Credit in boiler

repair on the basis of demonstrated skills and/or institutional examination.

Bread Baking

Location: Quartermaster School, Fort Lee, Va.

Length: 8 weeks.

Objectives: To train enlisted personnel as bread bakers in field baking units and garrison bakeries.

Instruction: Introduction to baking; bread ingredients; operation of bread bakeries; small quantity bread baking; maintenance of baking equipment.

Credit recommendation, collegiate level: This course is technical and vocational in nature. Credit in bread baking on the basis of demonstrated skills and/or institutional examinations.

CBR Enlisted
(CBR Course (Enlisted))

Location: Chemical Center and School, Fort McClellan, Ala.

Length: 4 weeks.

Objectives: To train enlisted personnel in chemical, biological, and radiological operations.

Instruction: CBR plans, training, and operations; technical aspects of biological operations; technical aspects of chemical operations; nuclear warfare and radiological defense, CBR defense and materiel.

Credit recommendation, collegiate level: No credit because of the limited technical nature of the course.

CBR Officer
(CBR Course (Officer))

Location: Chemical Center and School, Fort McClellan, Ala.

Length: 4 weeks.

Objectives: To train officers in chemical, biological, and radiological operations.

Instruction: CBR plans, training, and operations; technical aspects of biological operations; technical aspects of chemical operations; nuclear warfare and radiological defense, CBR defense, and materiel.

Credit recommendation, collegiate level: No credit because of the limited technical nature of the course.

CFR Test Engine

Location: Quartermaster School, Fort Lee, Va.

Length: 8 weeks.

Objectives: To train enlisted personnel in the principles and procedures used in the installation, operation, inspection, and maintenance of Cooperative Field Research (CFR) test engines.

Instruction: Principles of internal combustion engines and combustion knock; installation of CFR test engines; engine maintenance and overhaul procedures; maintenance of CFR electrical apparatus; reference fuels; determination of humidity; Motor and Research methods for rating fuels; Aviation method for rating aviation fuels.

Credit recommendation, collegiate level: This course is technical and vocational in nature. Credit in operation and maintenance of cooperative fuels research test engines on the basis of institutional examination.

CH-21 (Shawnee) Pilot Transition

Location: Aviation School, Fort Rucker, Ala.

Length: 4 weeks.

Objectives: To qualify selected officers and warrant officers in the CH-21 (Shawnee) helicopter.

Instruction: Night flight operations; transition flight training; traffic patterns; hovering; normal and steep approaches; running landings; CH-21 power plant; fuel and oil systems; transmission; rotor systems; electrical and hydraulic systems.

Credit recommendation, collegiate level: Credit in helicopter flight training on the basis of demonstrated skills and/or institutional examinations.

CH-37 (Mojave) Aviator Transition

Location: Army Aviation School, Fort Rucker, Ala.

Length: 6 weeks.

Objectives: To provide commissioned and warrant officers with transition flight training in the CH-37 helicopter.

Instruction: Flight maneuvers; load operations; night flight operations; preflight inspection; takeoff and landing procedures; description and function of the mechanical and electrical systems; organization and employment of Army transport aviation; tactical instrument procedures; flight planning.

Credit recommendation, collegiate level: Credit in helicopter flight training on the basis of demonstrated skills and/or institutional examinations.

CH-37 (Mojave) National Guard Transition and Instructor Pilot

Location: Army Aviation School, Fort Rucker, Ala.

Length: 7–10 weeks.

Objectives: To qualify National Guard commissioned and warrant officers in the CH-37 helicopter.

Instruction: This course is divided into two parts, *Transition Training* and *Instructor Pilot Training*, each of 7–10 weeks duration. Students will be given training in one or the other area, depending on previous experience. *Transition Training:* Transition flight maneuvers; load operations; tactical instrument flight; aircraft maintenance; theory of lashing cargo in the CH-37. *Instructor Pilot Training:* Transition flight training; instructor pilot flight training; methods of instruction and standardization training; aircraft maintenance; theory of lashing cargo in the CH-37.

Credit recommendation, collegiate level: CAUTION: *Credit is recommended according to the specific part of this course completed. Require exact identification of area of instruction. Transition Flight Training:* Credit in helicopter flight training on the basis of demonstrated skills and/or institutional examinations. *Instructor Pilot Training:* Credit in instructional methods on the basis of institutional examinations, and credit in helicopter flight training on the basis of demonstrated skills and/or institutional examinations.

CH-47 (Chinook) Instructor Pilot Qualification

Location: Army Aviation School, Fort Rucker, Ala.

Length: 3–6 weeks.

Objectives: To qualify commissioned and warrant officer Army aviators as instructor pilots for the conduct of CH-47 standardization training and transition training of CH-37 qualified aviators in the CH-47 helicopter.

Instruction: Techniques and principles of basic flight training; advanced flight training; principles of instruction of flight maneuvers; familiarization with CH-47 maintenance.

Credit recommendation, collegiate level: Credit in instructional methods on the basis of institutional examinations.

CH-47 (Chinook) Pilot Transition

Location: Aviation School, Fort Rucker, Ala.

Length: 6–8 weeks.

Objectives: To provide officers and warrant officers with transition flight training in the CH-47 (Chinook) helicopter.

Instruction: Transition flight training; night operations flight; advanced flight training; cross-country flight training; basic instruments; advanced instrument training; CH-47 power plants and related systems; fuel, oil, and transmission systems; flight controls; electrical systems; emergency operations.

Credit recommendation, collegiate level: Credit in helicopter flight training on the basis of demonstrated skills and/or institutional examinations.

CH-54 Pilot Transition

Location: Aviation School, Fort Rucker, Ala.

Length: 6–7 weeks.

Objectives: To qualify officers and warrant officers in the operation of the CH-54 helicopter.

Instruction: Transition flight training, including cockpit procedures and operating instructions; taxiing, hovering, climbs and descents, approach and landing, and emergency procedures; maintenance of power plant and related systems; transmission and power train; flight control; hydraulic systems; recovery operations.

Credit recommendation, collegiate level: Credit in helicopter flight training on the basis of demonstrated skills and/or institutional examinations.

1. CV-2 (Caribou) Pilot Transition
2. AC-1 (Caribou) Aviator Transition

Location: Aviation School, Fort Rucker, Ala.

Length: 6 weeks.

Objectives: To train fixed-wing aviators in the operation of multi-engine STOL aircraft.

Instruction: Ground procedures; normal take-offs and landings; night operations; formation flying; instrument familiarization; strip operations; familiarization with multi-engine aircraft mechanics for inspection purposes; transport operations; aerial delivery equipment; low-level mission planning.

Credit recommendation, collegiate level: No credit as courses are military in nature.

Cable Splicing

Location: Southeastern Signal Corps, Fort Gordon, Ga.

Length: 14–15 weeks.

Objectives: To provide enlisted personnel with a working knowledge of splicing, installing, and maintaining the various types of communications cables.

Instruction: Basic cable splicing; exchange and toll cable installation; locating and clearing cable faults.

Credit recommendation, collegiate level: This course is technical and vocational in nature. Credit in telephone cable installation on the basis of demonstrated skills and/or institutional examinations.

Calibration Technician and Specialist
(Calibration Specialist)
(Calibration Technician)

Location: Ordnance School, Aberdeen Proving Ground, Md.

Length: 15–19 weeks.

Objectives: To train warrant officers and enlisted personnel to perform calibration of standards and all test and measuring equipment and to perform maintenance and repair on secondary reference and secondary transfer calibration standards.

Instruction: Mathematics; purpose, operation, and detailed circuit analysis of DC and low-frequency standards; microwave measurement techniques, to include power, frequency, voltage standing wave ratio, and attenuation; calibration of high-frequency test equipment and standards; physical standards; radiac equipment; calibration of test and measuring equipment.

Credit recommendation, collegiate level: 4 semester hours at the freshman or sophomore level as an elective in electricity and electronics, and credit in electrical laboratory on the basis of demonstrated skills and/or institutional examinations.

Camera Equipment Repair

Location: Signal School, Fort Monmouth, N.J.

Length: 12–13 weeks.

Objectives: To train enlisted personnel to maintain and repair still and motion picture cameras and related equipment.

Instruction: Principles of camera equipment repair; between-the-lens type cameras; press type cameras; aerial, focal plane type, and motion picture cameras.

Credit recommendation, collegiate level: This course is technical and vocational in nature. Credit in camera equipment repair on the basis of demonstrated skills and/or institutional examinations.

Camouflage

Location: Engineer School, Fort Belvoir, Va.

Length: 5 weeks.

Objectives: To train enlisted personnel in camouflage techniques and construction and to supervise and instruct in camouflage methods.

Instruction: Camouflage materials; concealment of individuals, weapons, vehicles, and bivouacs; deceptive measures; methods of instruction.

Credit recommendation, collegiate level: No credit because of the limited technical nature of the course.

Canvas and Webbed Equipage Repair
(Canvas and Leather Repair)

Location: Quartermaster School, Fort Lee, Va.

Length: 7–8 weeks.

Objectives: To train enlisted personnel to repair canvas and webbed equipage.

Instruction: Care and storage of canvas; hand repair methods; maintenance, care, and operation of sewing machines; production work— canvas and webbed items.

Credit recommendation, collegiate level: This course is technical and vocational in nature. Credit in canvas and leather repair shop on the basis of demonstrated skills and/or institutional examinations.

Cartographic Drafting

Location: Engineer School, Fort Belvoir, Va.

Length: 10–11 weeks.

Objectives: To train enlisted personnel to draw cultural, topographic, hydrographic, and other features for final reproduction as a military map.

Instruction: Map and aerial photograph reading; basic and advanced cartographic drafting; map projections and grids; mapping control; basic photogrammetry; map compilation and revision.

Credit recommendation, collegiate level: 4 semester hours in mapping and drafting.

Central Office Supervision

Location: Southeastern Signal School, Fort Gordon, Ga.

Length: 19 weeks.

Objectives: To train experienced communications personnel in the capabilities, use, characteristics, operational procedures, and control of communications equipment and facilities in a central office.

Instruction: Principles of telephony; substation equipment; tactical switchboards; PBX switchboards; automatic exchanges; telegraph systems; carrier and repeater; outside plant; outside plant testing; radio sets; technical administration; instructor training and development; central office operations.

Credit recommendation, collegiate level: Credit in instructional methods and central office telephone, telegraph, and radio repair on the basis of demonstrated skills and/or institutional examinations.

Chemical Company Grade Officer Refresher

Location: Chemical Corps School, Fort McClellan, Ala.

Length: 4 weeks.

Objectives: To provide officers with refresher training in the duties and responsibilities appropriate to company-grade Chemical Corps officers.

Instruction: Command and staff procedures; employment of atomic weapons; employment of smoke; airground operations; mine warfare; combined arms; logistics; atomic, biological, and chemical warfare; protection.

Credit recommendation, collegiate level: No credit because of the refresher nature of the course.

Chemical Company Officer

Location: Chemical Corps School, Fort McClellan, Ala.

Length: 13–25 weeks.

Objectives: To train commissioned officers in the duties and responsibilities of Chemical Corps officers.

Instruction: Personnel and administration; supply and logistics; management; map and air photograph reading; intelligence; field engineering and mine warfare; weapons; methods of instruction; combat arms; chemical, biological, and radiological plans, training, and operations; chemical, biological, atomic, and radiological warfare; protection and materiel.

Credit recommendation, collegiate level: Credit in advanced military at institutions which regularly offer such credit.

Chemical Corps Orientation

Location: Chemical Corps School, Fort McClellan, Ala.

Length: 6 weeks.

Objectives: To train officers in the organization, operation, and management techniques of the Chemical Corps.

Instruction: Logistical planning and management; personnel management; executive development; management techniques; CBR warfare.

Credit recommendation, collegiate level: 2 semester hours in business organization and management.

Chemical (Entry)
(Chemical Operations Apprentice)

Location: Chemical Corps School, Fort McClellan, Ala.

Length: 8–9 weeks.

Objectives: To train enlisted personnel in technical and tactical operations of Chemical Corps units.

Instruction: Mine warfare; map reading; biological, chemical, and radiological operations; flame operations; smoke operations, smoke generator maintenance; decontamination.

Credit recommendation, collegiate level: This course is technical and vocational in nature. Credit in protective service operations on the basis of demonstrated skills and/or institutional examinations.

---

1. Chemical Equipment Repair
2. Chemical Equipment Repair Supervision

Location: Chemical Center and School, Fort McClellan, Ala.

Length: *Course 1*, 11 weeks; *Course 2*, 3 weeks.

Objectives: To train enlisted personnel in inspection, maintenance, and repair of chemical equipment, such as protective masks, smoke generators, portable flame throwers, and decontaminating equipment.

Instruction: Logistics; CBR protection and materiel; shop procedures; maintenance and repair of chemical equipment.

Credit recommendation, collegiate level: *Course 1* is technical and vocational in nature. Credit in mechanical shop on the basis of demonstrated skills and/or institutional examinations. *Course 2:* No credit because of the limited technical nature of the course.

Chemical Field Grade Officer Refresher

Location: Chemical Corps School, Fort McClellan, Ala.

Length: 4 weeks.

Objectives: To provide refresher training to officers in the duties and responsibilities of Chemical Corps officers.

Instruction: CBR operations, plans, and training; chemical supply and maintenance; CBR warfare; new developments in weapons, organization, and tactics.

Credit recommendation, collegiate level: No credit because of the limited technical nature of the course.

Chemical Laboratory Procedures
(Chemical Laboratory)

Location: Chemical Corps School, Fort McClellan, Ala.

Length: 8–10 weeks.

Objectives: To train enlisted personnel to perform standardized laboratory tests using chemicals and special equipment to analyze, identify, or develop a variety of organic and inorganic substances.

Instruction: Biological warfare, chemical warfare, nuclear warfare and radiological defense, including instruction in general chemistry, organic chemistry, and semi-micro and microanalytical techniques.

Credit recommendation, collegiate level: 5 semester hours in general chemistry.

Chemical Officer Basic
(Chemical Officer Orientation)

Location: Chemical Center and School, Fort McClellan, Ala.

Length: 8–12 weeks.

Objectives: To provide basic training and orientation for newly commissioned Chemical Corps officers.

Instruction: Personnel and administration; organization, operations, plans, and training; logistics; CBR warfare; protection and materiel; combined arms operations.

Credit recommendation, collegiate level: No credit because of the limited technical nature of the course.

Chemical Officer Career
(Chemical Officer Advanced)

Location: Chemical Center and School, Fort McClellan, Ala.

Length: 28–38 weeks.

Objectives: To train officers in the duties and responsibilities of Chemical Corps officers.

Instruction: Personnel and administrative procedures; supply management; procurement and industrial mobilization planning; supply policies and procedures; theater supply and service operations; management engineering and financial management; chemical and biological weapons systems; nuclear warfare and radiological defense.

Credit recommendation, collegiate level: 6 semester hours in business organization and management, and credit in chemistry on the basis of institutional examinations.

Chemical Officer Familiarization

Location: Chemical Corps School, Fort McClellan, Ala.

Length: 6 weeks.

Objectives: To provide familiarization training to officers in the organization, operational functions, duties and responsibilities of the Chemical Corps.

Instruction: CBR plans, training, and operations; technical aspects of CBR warfare; CBR protection and materiel.

Credit recommendation, collegiate level: No credit because of the limited technical nature of the course.

Chemical Staff Specialist

Location: Chemical School, Fort McClellan, Ala.

Length: 7–12 weeks.

Objectives: To give advanced training to enlisted personnel in the technical aspects of CBR operations, supply, maintenance, and intelligence.

Instruction: CBR tactics, techniques, supply and administrative procedures, intelligence, plans, and operations.

Credit recommendation, collegiate level: This course is technical and vocational in nature. Credit in protective service occupation on the basis of demonstrated skills and/or institutional examination.

Chemical Supply

Location: Chemical Corps School, Fort McClellan, Ala.

Length: 8 weeks.

Objectives: To train enlisted personnel to receive, store, issue, ship, and salvage chemical supplies and equipment including chemical munitions.

Instruction: Chemical, biological, and radiological technical training; CBR protection; map reading; logistics; principles of supply; disposition of property; station and depot supply forms; supply publications; packaging, packing, and marking; storage shipment; warehouse and depot operations; disposal of chemical agents and munitions; mixing and transfer of fuels; toxic gas handling.

Credit recommendation, collegiate level: This course is technical and vocational in nature. Credit in stockroom procedures on the basis of institutional examination.

Chemical Supply Supervision

Location: Chemical Corps School, Fort McClellan, Ala.

Length: 3 weeks.

Objectives: To train enlisted personnel to supervise chemical supply operations.

Instruction: Chemical supply procurement, transportation, supply policies, and procedures; chemical weapons systems; protection and materiel; maintenance.

Credit recommendation, collegiate level: No credit because of the limited technical nature of the course.

Civic Action

Location: Civil Affairs School, Fort Gordon, Ga.

Length: 5–6 weeks.

Objectives: To train commissioned and warrant officers in planning, programming, administering and expanding military civic action programs and activities.

Instruction: Concept, background, and bases of civic action; organization and activities of military and nonmilitary agencies in civic action; cultural influences; development of civic action programs and projects; demonstration of military capabilities for civic action.

Credit recommendation, collegiate level: 3 semester hours as an elective in the area of social science.

Civil Affairs Advisor, Vietnam

Location: Civil Affairs School, Fort Gordon, Ga.

Length: 6 weeks.

Objectives: To train commissioned officers in those Civil Affairs—Civic Action theories, functions, and operations applicable to the role of the Civil Affairs advisor in Vietnam.

Instruction: Sociological, economical, and political considerations in working with or advising native personnel in creating social and economic change; insurgency and counterinsurgency measures; application of the civil affairs functions to nation-building activities and civic action program and counterinsurgency activities in Vietnam; military organizations involved in civic action programs; governmental structure; organization and operation of civilian agencies; sociological, political, and economic conditions in Vietnam; development of Civil Affairs-Civic Action programs applicable to a stability operation.

Credit recommendation, collegiate level: 3 semester hours as an elective in social science.

Civil Affairs and Military Government Officer

Location: Civil Affairs School, Fort Gordon, Ga.

Length: 4 weeks.

Objectives: To provide officers with basic training in the fundamentals of the organization, policies, and operational procedures of the Civil Affairs and Military Government (CAMG) activity at the platoon and company levels.

Instruction: Military organization and command and staff functions as needed to integrate CAMG operations into overall military operations; United States CAMG policies; command and staff techniques; supervision of local government; field operations; specialized military operations, including civil emergencies.

Credit recommendation, collegiate level: 2 semester hours in military government.

1. Civil Affairs and Military Government Officer Advanced
2. Military Government Advanced

Locations: Civil Affairs and Military Government School, Fort Gordon, Ga; The Provost Marshall General's School, Fort Gordon, Ga.

Length: 4 weeks.

Objectives: To train officers in the conduct of Civil Affairs and Military Government (CAMG) operations with emphasis on the support of combat operations.

Instruction: *Course 1: Note*—this course changed in its emphasis after April 1958. The instruction and credit recommendation will reflect this change. *Prior to May 1958:* Organization, general policies, and planning processes of CAMG for an occupied country; procedures and command techniques required to coordinate the staff work of a CAMG national headquarters in a theater of operations; sociological aspects of policy planning; basic principles of civil government; economic problems of occupation administration; the role of CAMG in the implementation of United States foreign policy; rear area defense and area damage control; the Army's role in civil emergencies; martial law. *After April 1958:* Organization and staff procedures of CAMG area headquarters; development of overall plans, logistic plans, theater Army CAMG directives, field Army CAMG operation plans, and standing operating procedures; tactical units and operations; CAMG operations in support of combat; problems in controlling the production and distribution of civilian goods in areas of military operation; civil emergencies. *Course 2:* This course contains the same academic material as *Course 1* as given prior to May 1958.

Credit recommendation, collegiate level: CAUTION: *These courses vary slightly in title and recommendation. Require exact identification of course by title. Course 1: Prior to May 1958:* 2 semester hours in military government. *After April 1958:* 2 semester hours in business organization and management, and credit in military government on the basis of institutional examination. *Course 2:* 2 semester hours in military government.

Civil Affairs in the Cold War

Location: Civil Affairs School, Fort Gordon, Ga.

Length: 4 weeks.

Objectives: To train commissioned officers in the civil affairs aspects of the Cold War.

Instruction: Communist ideology and strategy; Sino-Soviet Cold War activities; United States policy, its conduct, organization, and implementation; history of civil-military affairs; organization for civil affairs; civic action and community programming; capitalism in the United States military assistance program; economic systems in social structures; effects of culture and mores in Cold War operations; language of politics; institutions in developed and undeveloped societies; Cold War planning and programming.

Credit recommendation, collegiate level: 4 semester hours in political science, including international relations.

Civil Affairs Officer

Location: Civil Affairs School, Fort Gordon, Ga.

Length: 8 weeks.

Objectives: To train commissioned officers in the organization, policies, and operational procedures of civil affairs at all levels of command and to instruct officers in the application of current civil affairs doctrine in planning the support for peace, cold war, and combat.

Instruction: Problems at municipal government level in civilian communities and the operations of a civil affairs platoon in handling such problems; problems at provincial government level in civilian populations and of the Civil Affairs Group and Civil Affairs Company assigned to either a tactical organization or a Civil Affairs Command; supervision of, or assistance in, the administration of a national government and the operations of theater-level headquarters and civil affairs organizations, which perform such supervision in situations of limited or general war; current civil affairs operations.

Credit recommendation, collegiate level: 3 semester hours in military government.

Clinical Psychology Procedures
(Clinical Psychology Enlisted)

Location: Medical Field Service School, Fort Sam Houston, Tex.

Length: 7–8 weeks.

Objectives: To train enlisted personnel to assist in the administration of standard psychodiagnostic instruments and to obtain observational and historical psychiatric information.

Instruction: Responsibilities of and procedures for neuropsychiatric nursing; neuropsychiatric disorders, including their etiology and treatment; cultural aspects of human behavior; interviewing techniques; psychological theory; test administration, scoring, and interpretation.

Credit recommendation, collegiate level: 3 semester hours in abnormal psychology.

Clinical Technician

Location: Medical Field Service School, Fort Sam Houston, Tex.

Length: 48 weeks.

Objectives: To train enlisted personnel in advanced nursing procedures and ward management functions.

Instruction: Principles and procedures of patient care; common diseases; personal and community health; body structure and function; first aid; care of neuropsychiatric patients; child care; clinical application in care of medical, surgical, neurosurgical, outpatient, and orthopedic patients; clinical application in mother and child care.

Credit recommendation, collegiate level: This course is at the preprofessional or professional level. 2 semester hours in first aid and hygiene, and credit in physiology on the basis of institutional examinations.

Combat Engineering, Bridging, and Construction Supervision

Location: Engineer School, Fort Belvoir, Va.
Length: 15 weeks.
Objectives: To train enlisted personnel to plan, control, and supervise the tactical and technical training and employment of an engineer squad or platoon.
Instruction: Assembly, use, handling, maintenance, and operation of floating bridges; fundamentals of fixed bridges; principles of location, construction, and maintenance of roads, airfields, and railroads; construction of military buildings and utilities; soils engineering fundamentals; procedures for bituminous and concrete construction; demolition operations; mine warfare; rigging operations; familiarization with electrical construction; operation and maintenance of engineer equipment.
Credit recommendation, collegiate level: Credit in engineering construction on the basis of demonstrated skills and/or institutional examinations.

Combat Missile System Repair (Redeye-Shillelagh-Tow)

Location: Missile and Munitions School, Redstone Arsenal, Ala.
Length: 14 weeks.
Objectives: To train enlisted personnel to inspect, test, and perform direct and general support maintenance on the Redeye weapon system with orientation on Shillelagh and Tow weapons systems.
Instruction: Basic electricity and electronics; transistors; regulated power supplies; oscillators; synchro devices; advanced missile circuits troubleshooting; servo systems; drive circuits; missile digital controllers; logic circuits; programming; Redeye weapon system; guided missile test set; XM42 trainer; introduction to Shillelagh and Tow weapon systems.
Credit recommendation, collegiate level: 3 semester hours at the freshman or sophomore level as an elective in electricity and electronics, and credit in electrical laboratory on the basis of demonstrated skills and/or institutional examinations.

Combat Surveillance Photographic Equipment Repair

Location: Signal School, Fort Monmouth, N.J.
Length: 23–24 weeks.
Objectives: To train enlisted personnel in the installation, operation, and field and depot repair of combat surveillance photographic equipment.
Instruction: Principles of photographic equipment

repair; day aerial cameras; electrical and electronic fundamentals; day-night aerial cameras; automatic surveillance camera; magnetic amplifiers; transistor fundamentals; automatic camera control system; system analysis and repair.
Credit recommendation, collegiate level: 2 semester hours at the freshman or sophomore level as an elective in electronics. At the technical level, credit in surveillance photographic equipment repair on the basis of demonstrated skills and/or institutional examinations.

Command and General Staff Officer (Command and General Staff Officer Regular)

Location: Command and General Staff College, Fort Leavenworth, Kan.
Length: 38–42 weeks.
Objectives: To prepare officers for duty as commanders and general staff officers at division, corps, and field army levels.
Instruction: International relations; foreign military systems; management; leadership; strategic studies; joint, combined, and special operations; command; administrative and logistical support of forces; special weapons employment.
Credit recommendation, collegiate level: CAUTION: *This course varies slightly in title, length, and recommendation. Require exact identification of course by title and dates of attendance. For course completed in 1955 and through 1962:* 9 semester hours in business organization and management. *For course completed in 1963:* 9 semester hours in business organization and management, and credit in political science and international relations on the basis of institutional examination. *For course completed in 1964 and through 1967:* 9 semester hours in business organization and management, and 3 semester hours in political science, including international relations.

Command Stock Fund Accounting

Location: Finance School, Fort Benjamin Harrison, Ind.
Length: 3 weeks.
Objectives: To train commissioned officers, warrant officers, and noncommissioned officers in stock fund accounting.
Instruction: Review of the double entry system; item accounting and its effect on Army stock fund accounting; military supply accounting; chart of accounts; stock fund journals and ledgers; principles of capitalization, cash control, and budget preparation; stock fund transactions between installations; month-end procedures; financial reports; familiarization with machine accounting operations.
Credit recommendation, collegiate level: 2 semester hours in stock fund accounting.

Commissary Management

Location: Quartermaster School, Fort Lee, Va.
Length: 7 weeks.
Objectives: To train commissioned officers and senior

enlisted personnel in the principles, procedures, and responsibilities for obtaining, storing, issuing, selling, and accounting for authorized subsistence supplies at installation level.

Instruction: Commissary organization, commissary account, and procedures utilized in transactions pertaining to obtaining, receipt, issue, sale, transfer, and inventory of all subsistence supplies and the receipt and deposit of funds; methods and techniques of operating the grocery department and procedures used in display planning, tray stocking, vertical stocking, display supervision, and store layout; personnel management; commissary equipment; fiscal procedures; produce and meat market processing and merchandising; food inspection techniques.

Credit recommendation, collegiate level: 3 semester hours in store management.

1. Commissary Officer
2. Commissary Operations
3. Commissary Operations

Location: Quartermaster School, Fort Lee, Va.

Length: *Course 1,* 4 weeks; *Course 2,* 5 weeks; *Course 3,* 6–7 weeks.

Objectives: To train commissioned officers in the operation of an installation commissary or commissary store.

Instruction: *Courses 1 and 2:* Organization, operation, and personnel requirements; familiarization with accounting procedures; price lists; sources of supply; receipt and storage of subsistence; the garrison ration; issue of the field ration; cash and charge sales; meat and produce market operations; account closing and reports; inventories and inventory adjustments; management principles; fiscal procedures related to the commissary; principle methods of procurement; food service activities. In addition to the preceding instructions, *Course 3* also includes overseas commissary accounting procedures and a longer period of instruction in subsistence processing and merchandising principles.

Credit recommendation, collegiate level: CAUTION: *These courses vary only slightly in title, length, and recommendation. Require exact identification of course by title and length. Courses 1 and 2:* 2 semester hours, for each course, in store management. *Course 3:* 3 semester hours in store management.

Communication Center Specialist
(Communication Center Operation)

Location: Southeastern Signal School, Fort Gordon, Ga.

Length: 8–12 weeks.

Objectives: To train enlisted personnel in communication center operations, cryptographic systems and equipment.

Instruction: Communications, keyboard operations; cryptography; message center operations; comcenter operations; communications security.

Credit recommendation, collegiate level: This course is technical and vocational in nature. Credit in cryptography, message handling, and teletype operation on the basis of demonstrated skills and/or institutional examinations.

Communications Center Operation
(Communications Center Operations Officer)

Location: Signal School, Fort Monmouth, N.J.

Length: 7–8 weeks.

Objectives: To train officers in communications center operations within the division, corps, and field army communication system.

Instruction: Organization and operation of communication centers; cryptography; communications center supervision and planning.

Credit recommendation, collegiate level: 2 semester hours in communications center management.

1. Communications Chief
2. Armor Communication Chief
   (Armor Communication Supervision, Enlisted)
3. Artillery Communication Supervisors
   (Artillery Communication Supervision)
   (Artillery Communications Enlisted)
4. Infantry Communication Supervision
   (Infantry Communications Enlisted)

Locations: *Courses 1 and 3,* Artillery and Missile School, Fort Sill, Okla.; *Course 2,* Armor School, Fort Knox, Ky.; *Course 4,* Infantry School, Fort Benning, Ga.

Length: *Course 1,* 12 weeks; *Course 2,* 5–9 weeks; *Course 3,* 13–16 weeks; *Course 4,* 11–13 weeks.

Objectives: To train enlisted personnel to supervise the installation, operation, and maintenance of communication equipment.

Instruction: Organizational maintenance; equipment and procedure; wire communications; radio; cryptography; applied communications.

Credit recommendation, collegiate level: These courses are technical and vocational in nature. Credit in electricity and radio operation and maintenance on the basis of demonstrated skills and/or institutional examinations.

1. Communications Officer
2. Armor Communication Officer
   (Armor Communication)
3. Artillery Communications Officer
4. Infantry Communications Officer

Locations: *Courses 1 and 3,* Artillery and Missile School, Fort Sill, Okla.; *Course 2,* Armor School, Fort Knox, Ky.; *Course 4,* Infantry School, Fort Benning, Ga.

Length: *Course 1,* 10–11 weeks; *Course 2,* 8–10 weeks; *Course 3,* 11–15 weeks; *Course 4,* 11 weeks.

Objectives: To train officers to supervise and coordinate the installation, operation, and maintenance of communication systems of nonsignal corps units.

Instruction: Organizational maintenance; electricity and radio; wire communications; FM radio equipment; AM radio equipment; message center procedure and cryptography; applied communications.

Credit recommendation, collegiate level: These courses are technical and vocational in nature. Credit in electricity and radio operation and maintenance on the basis of demonstrated skills and/or institutional examinations.

Computer Programming

Location: U.S. Army Management Engineering Training Agency, Rock Island, Ill.

Length: 3 weeks.

Objectives: To provide personnel with an understanding of digital computer programming languages and the relative advantages and disadvantages of each language for specific types of computer applications.

Instruction: Introduction to automatic data processing and numbering systems; program documentation; programming languages.

Credit recommendation, collegiate level: 2 semester hours in computer management.

Construction Drafting

Location: Engineer School, Fort Belvoir, Va.

Length: 10–11 weeks.

Objectives: To train enlisted personnel in the preparation of working drawings for the construction of roads, airfields, bridges, buildings, and other structures.

Instruction: Drafting fundamentals, including use of instruments, applied geometry, scales, orthographic projection, dimensioning, isometric drawings, and mechanical lettering; wood, concrete and masonry, and steel structural drawings; building plans; material estimates; electrical wiring, piping, ductwork and utilities drawings; road and airfield construction drawings.

Credit recommendation, collegiate level: 4 semester hours in engineering drawing.

Construction Planning and Operations
(Construction Planning and Management)

Location: Engineer School, Fort Belvoir, Va.

Length: 3 weeks.

Objectives: To provide newly commissioned Corps of Engineers officers with a working knowledge of construction management.

Instruction: Introduction to construction drawings; T/O building plans and materials; construction of T/O buildings; electrical distribution; California bearing ratio; earthwork estimation; run off and drainage ditches and structures; concrete mix design; maintenance of bituminous surface and bituminous estimates; critical path method; selection and utilization of loading and lifting equipment; rock crushing, asphalt, concrete paving, quarrying, compaction, grading and ditching, and earth moving equipment.

Credit recommendation, collegiate level: No credit because of the brevity and limited technical nature of the course.

Construction Surveying

Location: Engineer School, Fort Belvoir, Va.

Length: 9–10 weeks.

Objectives: To train enlisted personnel in the fundamentals of plane surveying with special emphasis on problems connected with military construction.

Instruction: Basic drafting; map and aerial photograph reading; mathematics; leveling; transit traverse; plane table; construction layout; earthwork plotting and computing.

Credit recommendation, collegiate level: 6 semester hours in general surveying and 3 semester hours in construction surveying.

Cooking

Locations: Quartermaster School, Fort Lee, Va.; Army Area Food Service Schools.

Length: 8 weeks.

Objectives: To train enlisted personnel to prepare and serve food according to standard Army recipes, and to clean and maintain mess equipment in a consolidated or unit mess.

Instruction: Duties and responsibilities of food service personnel; small quantity cooking; cake and pastry baking; meat cutting; care, maintenance, and operation of field mess equipment; preparation and serving of food under field conditions.

Credit recommendation, collegiate level: This course is technical and vocational in nature. Credit in cooking on the basis of demonstrated skills and/or institutional examinations.

Corporal Computer Repair
(SSM Computer Repair)

Location: Ordnance Guided Missile School, Huntsville, Ala.

Length: 11–13 weeks.

Objectives: To train enlisted personnel to inspect, test, maintain, and repair the Corporal computer system.

Instruction: Computer electrical and electronic circuits; test, maintenance, and repair of Corporal computers; ordnance test equipment operation and maintenance; maintenance and repair of power supplies and accessory equipment.

Credit recommendation, collegiate level: Credit in electricity and electrical laboratory on the basis of demonstrated skills and/or institutional examinations.

Corporal Doppler Repair
(SSM Doppler Repair)

Location: Ordnance Guided Missile School, Redstone Arsenal, Ala.

Length: 10–12 weeks.

Objectives: To train enlisted personnel to inspect, test, and perform field repair and maintenance on the Corporal Doppler system and associated test equipment.

Instruction: Function of the Corporal system; operation of test equipment used in repair of the AN/MRQ-7 radio set; operation, maintenance, and repair of the AN/MRQ-7 radio set, including AC and DC power distribution, power and signal wiring layout, voltage regulators, power supply, amplifiers, oscillators, electronic voltmeters, frequency counters, oscilloscopes, signal generators, and control selectors.

Credit recommendation, collegiate level: Credit in electricity and electrical shop on the basis of demonstrated skills and/or institutional examinations.

Corporal Electronic Materiel Maintenance

Location: Artillery and Missile School, Fort Sill, Okla.

Length: 28–29 weeks.

Objectives: To train warrant officers and enlisted personnel to assemble, install, calibrate, adjust and maintain on-missile electronic guidance control components and systems.

Instruction: Fundamentals of electricity, including series and parallel AC and DC circuits, inductance, transformers, capacitance, resonant circuits; radio electronics, including diodes and rectifiers, triodes and biasing, multi-element tubes, voltage bridges and bridge rectifiers, amplifiers and oscillators, transmitters, detectors, diode and triode limiting and clamping, video amplifiers, cathode followers, superheterodyne receivers; radar electronics, including sweep generators, cathode-ray tube and power supplies, synchroscope and oscilloscope, multivibrators, circuit synthesis, automatic frequency control, selsyns, magnetic amplifiers, servomechanisms; maintenance and repair of Corporal system equipment.

Credit recommendation, collegiate level: 3 semester hours at the freshman or sophomore level as an elective in the areas of radio and electronics, and credit in electrical laboratory on the basis of demonstrated skills and/or institutional examinations.

Corporal Fire Control System Maintenance

Location: Artillery and Missile School, Fort Still, Okla.

Length: 32 weeks.

Objectives: To train warrant officers and enlisted personnel to adjust, maintain, and operate the fire control systems for the Corporal missile.

Instruction: Electricity, including magnetism, series and parallel AC and DC circuits, use of the multimeter and vacuum tube voltmeter, voltage, inductance and inductive reactance, transformers, generators, AC and DC motor principles, capacitance, resonant circuits; electronics, including principles of radio waves, frequency classifications, and components of radio communication systems, diodes, rectifiers, filters, voltage dividers, amplifiers, triodes, multi-element and miniature tubes, oscillators, transmitters and receivers, detectors; principles, terminology, and components of radar systems; maintenance and repair of radar equipment; circuitry and operation of the radio set and Corporal computer; operational employment of the fire control system.

Credit recommendation, collegiate level: 4 semester hours at the freshman or sophomore level as an elective in electricity and electronics, and credit in electrical laboratory on the basis of demonstrated skills and/or institutional examinations.

1. Corporal Ground Guidance Repair
2. Corporal Ground Guidance Repair

Location: Ordnance Guided Missile School, Redstone Arsenal, Ala.

Length: *Course 1,* 33 weeks; *Course 2,* 23 weeks.

Objectives: To train enlisted personnel to inspect, test, and perform field maintenance and repair of the Corporal ground guidance system and associated test equipment.

Instruction: *Courses 1 and 2:* Truck mounted electronic shop; power supplies function and analysis; radar, power distribution, and test equipment; radar set AN/MPQ-25; radio set AN/MRQ-7; Corporal computer group; Corporal missile test station; guided missile firing station; communications and flight simulator; ground guidance system analysis. In addition to the preceding instruction, *Course 1* includes Ohm's law; motors and generators; vacuum tubes; resonance circuits; RC and LR circuits; vacuum tube circuits; voltage regulators; synchro and servo devices; heterodyne receiver; transmitter system; transistors; oscillators; voltage regulators, and multivibrators.

Credit recommendation, collegiate level: CAUTION: *These courses vary in title, length, and recommendation. Require exact identification of course by title and length. Course 1:* 4 semester hours at the freshman or sophomore level as an elective in electricity and electronics, and credit in electrical laboratory on the basis of demonstrated skills and/or institutional examinations. *Course 2:* Credit in electrical laboratory on the basis of demonstrated skills and/or institutional examinations.

Corporal Ground Handling Equipment Repair
(Corporal Mechanical Systems Repair)
(SSM Mechanical Systems Repair)
(SSM Mechanical Repair)

Location: Ordnance Guided Missile School, Huntsville, Ala.

Length: 7–14 weeks.

Objectives: To train enlisted personnel to inspect, operate, test, and perform field maintenance and repair of Corporal ground-handling equipment.

Instruction: Corporal missile mechanical system components; Corporal ground-handling equipment; function, operation, maintenance, supply procedures, repair, and testing of the Corporal missile systems and ground-handling equipment.

Credit recommendation, collegiate level: This course is technical and vocational in nature. Credit in electrical shop on the basis of demonstrated skills and/or institutional examinations.

Corporal Handling Equipment Maintenance

Location: Artillery and Missile School, Fort Sill, Okla.

Length: 4 weeks.

Objectives: To train officers and enlisted personnel in the operation and maintenance of Corporal handling equipment.

Instruction: Electricity; electrical theory; electrical circuits; construction, operation and maintenance of the XM2 Erector; operation and organizational maintenance of Corporal handling equipment.

Credit recommendation, collegiate level: This course is technical and vocational in nature. Credit in electrical shop on the basis of demonstrated skills and/or institutional examinations.

Corporal Maintenance Officer

Location: Artillery and Missile School, Fort Sill, Okla.

Length: 32–33 weeks.

Objectives: To train officers in the function, operation, maintenance, and inspection of Corporal fire control systems, handling equipment, and on-missile equipment.

Instruction: AC and DC series and parallel circuits; resonant circuits; diodes, triodes, and rectifiers; oscillators; transmitters; amplitude modulation; electron tubes; servomechanisms; maintenance and repair of electronic equipment.

Credit recommendation, collegiate level: 4 semester hours as an elective in electricity and electronics at the freshman or sophomore level, and credit in electrical laboratory on the basis of demonstrated skills and/or institutional examinations.

Corporal Maintenance Supervision
(Guided Missile Maintenance Supervision (Corporal))
(Guided Missile Systems Maintenance Supervisors, Corporal II)

Location: Ordnance Guided Missile School, Huntsville, Ala.

Length: 43 weeks.

Objectives: To train officers and enlisted personnel to supervise the maintenance of Corporal guided missile systems.

Instruction: Corporal system components; radar, Doppler, and computer systems; propellants and ground-handling equipment; internal guidance and control system; guided missile checkout, maintenance, and analysis.

Credit recommendation, collegiate level: Because of the prerequisite training required for admission to this course, any additional credit in electricity and electronics and electrical laboratory should be granted on the basis of demonstrated skills and/or institutional examinations.

Corporal Mechanical Materiel Maintenance
(Missile Mechanical Materiel Maintenance Corporal)
(Redstone Mechanical Materiel Maintenance)

Location: Artillery and Missile School, Fort Sill, Okla.

Length: 7–10 weeks.

Objectives: To train enlisted personnel to assemble, install, maintain, and adjust mechanical on-missile guidance control systems and test equipment.

Instruction: Basic electricity, including construction and operation of AC and DC motors; operation of missile propulsion systems, guidance and control systems, and mechanical systems; procedures and techniques in handling and fueling of the missile; maintenance of lightweight erection equipment.

Credit recommendation, collegiate level: This course is technical and vocational in nature. Credit in mechanical shop on the basis of demonstrated skills and/or institutional examinations.

1. **Corporal Missile Repair**
2. **Corporal Missile Repair**
   (Corporal Internal Guidance Repair)
   (SSM Internal Guidance System Repair)

Location: Ordnance Guided Missile School, Redstone Arsenal, Ala.

Length: *Course 1,* 27 weeks; *Course 2,* 11–17 weeks.

Objectives: To train enlisted personnel to inspect, test, perform field maintenance and repair on internal electronic and mechanical components of the Corporal missile system and associated test equipment.

Instruction: *Courses 1 and 2:* Corporal missile components and ground-handling equipment; troubleshooting techniques; power supplies; radio beacon test set; signal generator and electronic counter circuit analysis; main air supply system and components; propellant system and component testing, firing station, and electrical circuits; service area checkout procedures. In addition to the preceding instruction, *Course 1* includes series-parallel circuits; motors and generators; resonance circuits; RC and LR circuits; vacuum tube circuits; voltage regulators; synchro and servo devices; heterodyne receiver; transmitter system; transistors; oscillators, voltage regulators and multivibrators; transmitter circuit analysis.

Credit recommendation, collegiate level: CAUTION: *These courses vary only in length and recommendation. Require exact identification of course by length. Course 1:* 4 semester hours at the freshman or sophomore level as an elective in electricity and electronics, and credit in electrical laboratory on the basis of demonstrated skills and/or institutional examinations. *Course 2:* Credit in electrical laboratory on the basis of demonstrated skills and/or institutional examinations.

Corporal Officer

Location: Artillery and Guided Missile School, Fort Sill, Okla.

Length: 9–10 weeks.

Objectives: To train officers in the characteristics, operating principles, capabilities, and limitations of the Corporal missile and associated equipment.

Instruction: Communication and electronics; basic electricity; radio and radar electronics; Corporal internal guidance and propulsion; Corporal ground guidance.

Credit recommendation, collegiate level: Credit in electricity and electrical laboratory on the basis of demonstrated skills and/or institutional examinations.

Corporal Radar Repair
(SSM Radar System Repair)

Location: Ordnance Guided Missile School, Redstone Arsenal, Huntsville, Ala.

Length: 15–18 weeks.

Objectives: To train enlisted personnel to inspect, test, and perform field repair and maintenance on the Corporal radar system and associated test equipment.

Instruction: AC and DC circuits; motors and generators; synchros and servosystems; vacuum tubes and power supplies; solid state devices; amplifiers, oscillators; special circuits; organizational and field maintenance procedures for the AN/MPQ-25 radar test equipment; maintenance of the AN/MPQ-25 radar set.

Credit recommendation, collegiate level: Credit in electrical laboratory on the basis of demonstrated skills and/or institutional examinations.

Correctional Specialist

Location: Military Police School, Fort Gordon, Ga.

Length: 4 weeks.

Objectives: To train enlisted personnel in the basic requirements for the administration, operation, and management of stockades and the correctional treatment of confined personnel.

Instruction: Organizational structure of a post stockade; duties of custodial personnel; physical security; custody and control; disciplinary measures; recreation and welfare activities; emergency procedures; transfer and release procedures; correctional treatment at a disciplinary barracks; legal considerations of confinement.

Credit recommendation, collegiate level: No credit because of the brevity and nature of the course.

1. Corrections and Confinement Officer
2. Confinement Supervision (Enlisted)
(Confinement Supervision)

Location: The Provost Marshal General's School, Fort Gordon, Ga.

Length: 4–6 weeks.

Objectives: To train officers and enlisted personnel in the supervision, administration, and operation of installation confinement facilities, and as custodial personnel in correctional installations.

Instruction: Fundamentals of military law; weapons; principles of personal encounters; mission, organization, management, and operation of military confinement facilities; techniques of searching people; methods of controlling riots and disorders; basic investigative methods.

Credit recommendation, collegiate level: These courses are vocational in nature. Credit in protective service occupations on the basis of institutional examination.

Counterinsurgency and Special Warfare Staff Officer

Location: Special Warfare School, Fort Bragg, N.C.

Length: 4 weeks.

Objectives: To provide officers with information on the latest doctrine and concepts of special warfare.

Instruction: History of special warfare; present state of world politics; special forces operations; counterinsurgency and roles of government agencies; political factors in psychological operations.

Credit recommendation, collegiate level: 3 semester hours in political science.

Counterinsurgent Operations
(Counterinsurgency Operations)

Location: Special Warfare School, Fort Bragg, N.C.

Length: 7–10 weeks.

Objective: To train officers in the nature and conduct of counterinsurgency operations and in the various aspects of military and non-military participation in the counterinsurgency program.

Instruction: World politics; American foreign policy; the developing nations; Communist insurgency methodology; objectives, strategy, and tactics of Communism; Communist propaganda and agitation; doctrine, concepts, and techniques of U.S. counterinsurgency effort; principles governing the development of effective counterinsurgency programs.

Credit recommendation, collegiate level: 3 semester hours in political science.

Court Reporting (Electronic)

Locations: The Judge Advocate General's School, Charlottesville, Va.; U.S. Naval School, Newport, R.I.

Length: 6 weeks.

Objectives: To train enlisted personnel in reporting general court-martial and similar proceedings and in the use of the face-mask recording device.

Instruction: Operation and use of the recorder-reproducer set AN/TNH3; duties and responsibilities of a court reporter; procedural and substantive law of court-martial; requirements of a verbatim record.

Credit recommendation, collegiate level: No credit because of the limited technical nature of the course.

Crewman

Location: Transportation School, Fort Eustis, Va.

Length: 4 weeks.

Objectives: To train enlisted personnel in the duties and responsibilities of a crewman on watercraft.

Instructions: Shipboard communications; marlinspike seamanship; ship's gear; deck maintenance; nautical charts; towing and line handling; operation of landing craft.

Credit recommendation, collegiate level: This course is technical and vocational in nature. Credit in seamanship on the basis of demonstrated skills and/or institutional examinations.

1. Criminal Investigation
2. Criminal Investigation Supervisor
3. Criminal Investigation Supervision

Location: The Provost Marshal General's School, Military Police School, Fort Gordon, Ga.

Length: *Course 1, 8–9 weeks; Course 2, 7 weeks; Course 3, 4–5 weeks.*

Objectives: To train enlisted personnel, warrant officers, and officers of the Military Police Corps to conduct and supervise investigations of crimes committed by or against individuals subject to military jurisdiction.

Instruction: *Course 1:* Military justice and its application to criminal investigation; operation and administration of criminal investigation units; methods and techniques of investigation; report writing; capabilities and limitations of scientific analysis of evidence; investigative photography; finger printing and lie detection; organization and functions of military police units. *Courses 2 and 3:* These courses include similar instrution to *Course 1* but cover the material somewhat less intensively.

Credit recommendation, collegiate level: CAUTION: *These courses vary slightly in title, length, and recommendation. Require exact identification of course by title and length. Course 1: 5 semester hours in protective service occupations. Course 2: 4 semester hours in protective service occupations. Course 3: 3 semester hours in protective service occupations.*

Cryptography

Location: Southeastern Signal School, Fort Gordon, Ga.

Length: 9 weeks.

Objectives: To train personnel to use cryptographic systems and equipment to encrypt and decrypt classified messages.

Instruction: Communications; basic comcenter procedure; keyboard operation; tape relay and teletypewriter procedure; advanced military cryptography.

Credit recommendation, collegiate level: This course is technical and vocational in nature. Credit in cryptography and message handling on the basis of demonstrated skills and/or institutional examinations.

DECCA Charting and Reproduction

Location: Engineer School, Fort Belvoir, Va.

Length: 6 weeks.

Objectives: To train enlisted personnel in the theory of the DECCA navigation system and flight log chart production.

Instruction: Graphic method of constructing a DECCA hyperbolic plotting chart; determination of the flight pattern; determination of the X and Y scales; construction of the flight log pattern; plotting of topographic detail; plotting of UTM grid; determination of computer key data; color preparation of the flight log manuscript; reproduction and montaging of the flight log chart; loading of the flight log cassette using drafting, shop, and reproduction equipment.

Credit recommendation, collegiate level: This course is technical and vocational in nature. Credit in flight log charting and drafting on the basis of demonstrated skills and/or institutional examinations.

DECCA Transmitting Equipment Repair

Location: Southeastern Signal School, Fort Gordon, Ga.

Length: 9 weeks.

Objectives: To train enlisted personnel to operate and maintain DECCA Mark 5 transmitting equipment and DECCA Mark 10 equipment circuits.

Instruction: Introduction to aircraft hyperbolic navigational system; operation, maintenance, repair and signal analysis of Mark 5 and Mark 10 master and slave transmitters; station layout; lane identification receiver circuits; circuit analysis of the automatic monitoring equipment; master drive, junction rack, transmitter and antenna coupling system.

Credit recommendation, collegiate level: This course is technical and vocational in nature. Credit in elec-

trical shop on the basis of demonstrated skills and/or institutional examinations.

DSU/GSU Mechanized Stock Control

Location: Quartermaster School, Fort Lee, Va.

Length: 3 weeks.

Objectives: To train enlisted personnel in mechanized supply record keeping and stock management at DSU/GSU levels.

Instruction: Series 500 system operation procedures; conversion from manual to mechanized accounting; supply management codes and processing procedures; DSU/GSU operations.

Credit recommendation, collegiate level: No credit because of the limited technical nature of the course.

Data Processing Equipment Operator

Location: Adjutant General School, Fort Benjamin Harrison, Ind.

Length: 7-8 weeks.

Objectives: To train enlisted personnel to operate and wire control panels for electrical accounting machines and auxiliary electronic computer equipment.

Instruction: Techniques and principles of operation of the IBM punch card, sorter, interpreter, reproducing punch, collator, accounting machine, and calculator.

Credit recommendation, collegiate level: This course is technical and vocational in nature. Credit in data processing machine operation on the basis of demonstrated skills and/or institutional examinations.

Davy Crockett Training Program

Location: Armor School, Fort Knox, Ky.

Length: 3 weeks.

Objectives: To train noncommissioned officers as cadre for Davy Crockett sections.

Instruction: Driving and maintenance of tracked vehicles; basic concepts of nuclear war employment; communication equipment and procedures; Davy Crockett weapons system.

Credit recommendation, collegiate level: No credit as the course is military in nature.

Defense Acquisition Radar Maintenance

Location: Army Air Defense School, Fort Bliss, Tex.

Length: 17-18 weeks.

Objectives: To train enlisted personnel in the operation, adjustment, and maintenance of air defense acquisition and alternate battery acquisition radars, and associated IFF equipment.

Instruction: AC and DC circuits; magnetism; inductance; capacitance; resonant circuits; three-phase power; transformers; diodes and rectifiers; triodes; filters, voltage dividers, and potentiometers; multielement tubes; amplifiers; oscillators; cathode followers; superheterodyne receiver; sweep generators; vacuum tubes; test equipment; radar, modulator, transmitter, power supply, and RF systems; receiver and moving-target indication systems; indicator and antenna positioning systems; AN/TPS-1G and AN/FPS-36 radars; IFF Mark X system; electronic warfare.

Credit recommendation, collegiate level: 3 semester hours at the freshman or sophomore level as an elective in electricity and electronics, and credit in electrical laboratory on the basis of demonstrated skills and/or institutional examinations.

Defense Advanced Disposal Management

Location: Logistics Management Center, Fort Lee, Va.

Length: 4 weeks.

Objectives: To provide officers with training in the technical and management skills of disposal management.

Instruction: Management techniques, tools, and systems; administration of holding activities; property control; methods of marketing surplus property; processing property at holding activities; scrapyard operations; warehouse operations; contract law; sales terms and conditions; contract administration; legal aspects of disposal; collection and distribution proceeds of sales.

Credit recommendation, collegiate level: 3 semester hours in surplus property disposal management.

1. Defense Advanced Traffic Management (Advanced Traffic Management)
2. Advanced Traffic Management

Location: Transportation School, Fort Eustis, Va.

Length: *Course 1,* 4 weeks; *Course 2,* 6 weeks.

Objectives: To provide officers with advanced managerial training in commercial traffic and military transportation.

Instruction: Military traffic management; economics of transportation; military traffic management agency organization; transportation as a function of logistics; Navy, Army, and Air Force transportation; transportation regulations; military sea and air transportation service; the rail and motor carrier; transportation and supply movements, Department of Defense; industrial traffic manager; case studies; household goods; industrial general traffic office; claim prevention; rate negotiation and classification adjustments.

Credit recommendation, collegiate level: CAUTION: *These courses vary in title, length, and recommendation. Require exact identification of course by title and length. Course 1:* 2 semester hours in transportation management. *Course 2:* 3 semester hours in transportation management.

Defense Against Sound Equipment

Locations: *Phase I,* Ordnance Guided Missile School, Redstone Arsenal, Ala.; *Phase II,* Intelligence School, Fort Holabird, Md.

Length: *Phase I,* 8–11 weeks; *Phase II,* 8–9 weeks.

Objectives: To provide officers, warrant officers, and enlisted personnel with a working knowledge of specialized electronic equipment and techniques used in the detection and location of listening devices, and a working knowledge of electricity, electronics, solid state devices and transistor circuits.

Instruction: *Phase I:* Soldering; Ohm's law; multimeter; series circuits; parallel circuits; series-parallel circuits; DC power; induction and inductance; alternating current; capacitance and impedance; series and parallel resonance; transients in LR and RC circuits; power supplies; AM and FM transmission and reception; switching and gating circuits; multistage circuits; multivibrator. *Phase II:* Audiofrequency devices; radio frequency devices; defense-against-sound equipment aspect of telephones; intrusion detection; wiring analysis; intelligence field applications and communications; X-ray countermeasures techniques; counterintelligence technical surveys.

Credit recommendation, collegiate level: *Phase I:* 3 semester hours at the freshman or sophomore level as an elective in electricity and electronics. *Phase II:* Credit in electrical laboratory on the basis of demonstrated skills and/or institutional examinations.

Defense Depot Operations Management

Location: Logistics Management Center, Fort Lee, Va.

Length: 6 weeks.

Objectives: To provide depot directorate-level management instruction to commissioned officers assigned to Department of Defense distribution systems.

Instruction: Problem solving and decision making; manpower management; scientific management and controls; financial management; familiarization with the functions and capabilities of automatic data processing in depot operations; fundamentals of procurement; procedure for disposing of excess and surplus property; depot maintenance; inventory management; distribution systems; receipt and storage; physical inventory; care and preservation of material in storage; material handling; packing and packaging; quality assurance and control; issue and shipping; installation management.

Credit recommendation, collegiate level: 4 semester hours in supply management.

1. Defense Inventory Management
2. Defense Advanced Inventory Management

Location: Logistics Management Center, Fort Lee, Va.

Length: 5–6 weeks.

Objectives: To train commissioned officers in the management of the materiel inventories of the defense supply system.

Instruction: *Course 1:* Management skills and practices; financial management and controls; management tools; cataloging, requirements computation, procurement, distribution management, major item management, and minor item and repair parts management. *Course 2:* Executive skills; interrelationship of logistical functions; financial management and budget systems; management control techniques; the computer as a management tool; inventory control techniques; relationship of inventory management to maintenance and procurement functions; international logistics project.

Credit recommendation, collegiate level: CAUTION

These courses vary only slightly in title and recommendation. Require exact indentification of course by title. Course 1: 3 semester hours in principles of inventory management. Course 2: 3 semester hours in inventory management.

1. **Defense Procurement Management**
   (Defense Basic Procurement)
   (Armed Services Procurement Management)
2. **Defense Advanced Procurement Management**
   Location: Logistics Management Center, Fort Lee, Va.
   Length: *Course 1, 5–6 weeks; Course 2, 3 weeks.*
   Objectives: To provide basic and avanced procurement training to officers from Department of Defense procurement activities.
   Instruction: *Course 1:* Familiarization with the source, historical background, and current interpretation of statutory laws, administrative laws, and procedures and policies in the procurement field; elements of a contract and the law of agency; laws and regulations pertaining to the management and administration of contracts; purchasing by formal advertising; multi-year procurement; purchasing by negotiation method; cost and price analysis; contract types and purposes; contract clauses and provisions; contractor financing; bonds, surety, and insurance; labor; transportation factors; value engineering. *Course 2:* Procurement planning; funding procurement actions; contractor selection; methods of procurement; selection of the type of contract, with emphasis on incentive contracting, contract clauses, government provided property, and financing of contractors; administration of contractor progress, contract modification, post award authorization and approvals, claims and disputes, and contract terminations; procurement management problem areas.
   Credit recommendation, collegiate level: CAUTION: *These courses vary only slightly in title, length, and recommendation. Require exact identification of course by the title and length. Course 1: 3 semester hours in principles of procurement. Course 2: 2 semester hours in procurement management.*

Dental Assistant (Advanced)

Location: Medical Field Service School, Fort Sam Houston, Tex.
Length: 16–20 weeks.
Objectives: To train enlisted personnel to assist the dental officer in dental procedures.
Instruction: Oral and dental anatomy, histopathology, pharmacology, and bacteriology; maintenance of dental equipment; dental reports, and records; clinical application, composition, properties, and manipulation of impression compound, impression paste, and agar and alginate hydrocolloids; familiarization with oral surgery and prosthesis procedures; principles of oral hygiene, X-ray techniques.
Credit recommendation, collegiate level: Credit in dental technology on the basis of institutional examination.

---

1. **Dental Laboratory Procedures (Basic)**
   (Dental Laboratory)
2. **Dental Laboratory Procedures (Advanced)**
   (Dental Laboratory Advanced)
   Location: Medical Field Service School, Fort Sam Houston, Tex.
   Length: 16–20 weeks.
   Objectives: To train enlisted personnel in basic and advanced dental laboratory techniques.
   Instruction: *Course 1:* Dental anatomy; care and use of equipment; dental materials; construction of inlays, crowns, and bridges; planning, surveying, and construction of partial and complete dentures; dental laboratory operations and administration. *Course 2:* This course covers the same academic material as *Course 1* but at a more advanced level.
   Credit recommendation, collegiate level: Credit for each course in dental laboratory technology on the basis of institutional examination.

Dental Specialist (Basic)
(Dental Assistant (Basic))
(Dental Specialist)

Location: Fort Sam Houston, Tex.
Length: 8 weeks.
Objectives: To train enlisted personnel to assist in the examination, care, and treatment of teeth and in the operation and maintenance of dental equipment.
Instruction: Clinical reports and records; organization and operation of field dental units; care and maintenance of dental equipment; familiarization with dental materials and their use; introduction to dental anatomy and related dental sciences; oral hygiene; instrument set-ups, clinical procedures, sterilization techniques, and medicaments; dental X rays.
Credit recommendation, collegiate level: Credit in dental technology on the basis of institutional examination.

Design and Analysis of Experiments

Location: Army Management Engineering Training Agency, Rock Island, Ill.
Length: 3 weeks.
Objectives: To train officers in the statistical concepts and techniques which are essential to industrial or research experimentation.
Instruction: Calculation and uses of statistical measures; concepts and laws of probability; probabilistic mathematical models and concepts of sampling distribution; statistical estimation; concept, format, and analysis aspects in testing statistical hypotheses; linear regression; design selection and analysis of derived experimental data.
Credit recommendation, collegiate level: 2 semester hours in statistics or operations research in the field of computing science.

Dial Central Office Repair
(Dial Central Office Maintenance)

Location: Signal School, Fort Monmouth, N.J.
Length: 19–25 weeks.

Objectives: To train enlisted personnel to perform field maintenance and depot repair and to assist in the installation of dial central office telephone exchange equipment.

Instruction: Telephony; principles of electricity as applied to telephony; basic manual telephone circuitry; fundamentals of automatic telephony; telephone dials; Strowger two motion switch; central office installation practices; dial central office circuits, power, trunking, and testing; attendant's cabinet; XY dial systems.

Credit recommendation, collegiate level: Credit in electrical laboratory on the basis of demonstrated skills and/or institutional examinations.

Diesel-Electric Locomotive Repair

Location: Transportation School, Fort Eustis, Va.

Length: 10 weeks.

Objectives: To train enlisted personnel in inspecting, maintaining, overhauling, and repairing non-electric sections, their component parts and assemblies, of diesel-electric locomotives.

Instruction: Basic blueprint reading and machine sketching; diesel engines and diesel engine assemblies; compression ignition and ratio; principles of combustion; location and general purpose of equipment to the locomotive; operation, maintenance, and overhauling of Cummins, General Motors, Alco, and Caterpillar diesel engines; diesel engine governors.

Credit recommendation, collegiate level: This course is technical and vocational in nature. Credit in diesel engine repair shop on the basis of demonstrated skills and/or institutional examinations.

Diesel Engine Repair

Location: Engineer School, Fort Belvoir, Va.

Length: 11 weeks.

Objectives: To train enlisted personnel to repair diesel engines used as power units on heavy engineer equipment.

Instruction: Principles of operation, maintenance, assembly, disassembly, and repair of the Caterpillar, Cummins, General Motors, and International Harvester diesel engines.

Credit recommendation, collegiate level: This course is technical and vocational in nature. Credit in diesel engine repair on the basis of demonstrated skills and/or institutional examinations.

Disbursing Specialist

Location: Finance School, Fort Benjamin Harrison, Ind.

Length: 4–6 weeks.

Objectives: To train enlisted personnel in the methods and procedures used in the examination and computation of vouchers pertaining to entitlements and in accounting for receipts and payments.

Instruction: Procedures for military and civilian personnel pay; computation and payment of travel allowances; regulations for payment for supplies and non-personnel services; finance office operations and organization and functions of the disbursing branch.

Credit recommendation, collegiate level: 3 semester hours in fiscal procedures.

Distribution Management
(Storage and Distribution Management)

Location: Logistics Management Center, Fort Lee, Va.

Length: 8 weeks.

Objectives: To train officers in storage and distribution management.

Instruction: Concepts of military materiel distribution and inventory control; centralized and decentralized control of stocks; patterns and methods of physical distribution; tools and principles of depot management; management of receipt, storage, and issue operations; traffic management; financial management of distribution.

Credit recommendation, collegiate level: 3 semester hours in supply management.

Diving

Location: Transportation School, Fort Eustis, Va.

Length: 17 weeks.

Objectives: To train commissioned officers and enlisted personnel to direct and perform underwater searching, repair, salvage, and demolition work, using deep-sea and shallow water equipment.

Instruction: Diving equipment and techniques; diver tending principles; rigging, surface burning and welding, including electric arc welding, and oxyacetylene welding and cutting; methods of electric arc cutting and welding steel underwater; underwater inspection, repairs, and construction; explosives and demolition materiel.

Credit recommendation, collegiate level: This course is technical and vocational in nature. Credit in welding shop on the basis of demonstrated skills and/or institutional examination.

1. Electric Motor and Generator Repairman
2. Electric Motor and Generator Repair

Location: Engineer School, Fort Belvoir, Va.

Length: 10 weeks.

Objectives: To train enlisted personnel to perform depot maintenance and repair on alternating and direct current electric motors, dynamotors, motor generators, generators, and allied control and starting equipment.

Instruction: Fundamentals of AC and DC theory; familiarization with hand and power tools, lathe operation, and welding and brazing; internal combustion engines; AC and DC portable generators; AC and DC motors; rewinding single-phase and three-phase motors; maintenance of electric machinery.

Credit recommendation, collegiate level: Credit for each course in electricity and electrical shop on the basis of demonstrated skills and/or institutional examinations.

Electrical Accounting Machine Repair

Location: Signal School, Fort Monmouth, N.J.

Length: 28–32 weeks.

Objectives: To train enlisted personnel to inspect, test, adjust, and repair electrical accounting machine equipment.

Instruction: Electrical fundamentals; functional units of electrical accounting machines; keypunching and verifying equipment; data transceiver; collating equipment; interpreting equipment; reproducing equipment; accounting machine 407; punchcard machine sorting equipment; card processor.

Credit recommendation, collegiate level: Credit in electricity and electrical laboratory on the basis of demonstrated skills and/or institutional examinations. At the technical level, credit in electrical accounting machine repair on the basis of demonstrated skills and/or institutional examinations.

Electrical Instrument Repair

Location: Southwestern Signal School, Fort Gordon, Ga.

Length: 12 weeks.

Objectives: To train enlised personnel to inspect, test, adjust, calibrate, and repair electrical indicating instruments.

Instruction: Principles of electricity; direct current and alternating current meters; multipurpose meters; meteorological instruments; electrical instrument repair procedures.

Credit recommendation, collegiate level: This course is technical and vocational in nature. Credit in electrical instrument repair on the basis of demonstrated skills and/or institutional examinations.

Electroencephalographic Procedures
(Electroencephalographic Specialist)

Location: Medical Service School, Fort Sam Houston, Tex.

Length: 8 weeks.

Objectives: To train enlisted personnel in the operation of electroencephalographic apparatus and in the proper conduct of the electrocardiographic laboratory.

Instruction: Familiarization with basic neuroanatomy; introduction to clinical neurology; operation and maintenance of electroencephalographic machines; interpretation of records; electronics utilized in the electroencephalograph.

Credit recommendation, collegiate level: This course is technical and vocational in nature. Credit in electroencephalographic apparatus operation and maintenance on the basis of demonstrated skills and/or institutional examinations.

1. Electronic Devices Repair
2. Electronic Devices Repair
(Electronic Instrument Repair)
3. Electronic Instrument Repair

Location: Southeastern Signal School, Fort Gordon, Ga.

Length: *Course 1*, 16 weeks; *Course 2*, 18–26 weeks; *Course 3*, 27 weeks.

Objectives: *Courses 1 and 2:* To train enlisted personnel to inspect, test, adjust, calibrate, and repair electronic test equipment. *Course 3:* To train enlisted personnel to perform direct and general support maintenance on general purpose electronic test equipment.

Instruction: *Course 1:* Electron fundamentals, principles of electricity, alternating current, power and diode rectifiers, resistors, capacitors, and half-wave rectification, amplification, electron tubes, voltage and power amplifiers, transformers, operation, use, and repair of electronic instruments. *Course 2:* Principles of electricity and electronics, current, voltage, and resistance, primary and secondary cells, circuit analysis, electromagnetism, AC circuits with inductance, capacitance, and resistance, tuned circuits and resonance, transformers, AC and DC machines; diode, triode, multi-electrode, and special purpose tubes; principles and repair of test instruments. *Course 3:* AC and DC meters; multimeters; multipurpose meters; audio oscillators; AM and FM signal generators; oscilloscopes; microwave pulse signal generators; RF power meters; electronic voltmeters; radiac devices; frequency meters; frequency counters; polygraphs; repair of electronic test equipment.

Credit recommendation, collegiate level: CAUTION: *These courses vary only slightly in length and recommendation. Require exact identification of course by length. Course 1:* 2 semester hours at the freshman or sophomore level as an elective in electricity and electronics, and credit in electrical laboratory on the basis of demonstrated skills and/or institutional examinations. *Course 2:* 3 semester hours at the freshman or sophomore level as an elective in electricity and electronics, and credit in electrical laboratory on the basis of demonstrated skills and/or institutional examinations. *Course 3:* Credit in electricity and electronics and electrical laboratory on the basis of demonstrated skills and/or institutional examinations.

1. Electronic Navigation Equipment Repair
2. Electronic Navigation Equipment Repair

Location: Southwestern Signal School, Fort Gordon, Ga..

Length: *Course 1*, 23 weeks; *Course 2*, 31 weeks.

Objectives: To train enlisted personnel to inspect, test, and perform field maintenance on avionics equipment.

Instruction: *Course 1:* Principles of electricity, including alternating current, direct current, voltage and resistance, series and parallel circuits, resistive bridge circuits, electromagnetism, inductance and inductive reactance, capacitance, impedance; electron tubes; amplifiers and oscillators; power supplies and transmitters; detectors and receivers; operation and corrective maintenance of aircraft communication and navigation equipment. *Course 2:* Radio fundamentals, including series and parallel circuits, amplifier and oscillator circuits, resistors and capacitors, rectifier circuits, transistor circuit theory, and its application to practical circuits; application of radio fundamentals to maintenance of navigation equipment.

Credit recommendation, collegiate level: CAUTION: *These courses vary only slightly in length and recommendation. Require exact identification of course by length. Course 1:* 3 semester hours at the freshman or sophomore level as an elective in electricity and electronics, and credit in electrical laboratory on the basis of demonstrated skills and/or institutional examinations. *Course 2:* 2 semester hours at the freshman or sophomore level as an elective in electricity, and credit in electrical laboratory on the basis of demonstrated skills and/or institutional examinations.

Electronic Warfare Equipment Repair

Location: Signal School, Fort Monmouth, N.J.
Length: 33 weeks.
Objectives: To train enlisted personnel to inspect, test, and repair electronic warfare equipment.
Instruction: Electrical fundamentals; electronics applied to basic receivers and transmitters; oscillator-amplifier circuitry; timer indicator components; microwave transmitters and modulators; servo and data circuitry; repair of communications equipment.
Credit recommendation, collegiate level: 3 semester hours at the freshman or sophomore level as an elective in the areas of radio and electronics, and credit in electrical laboratory on the basis of demonstrated skills and/or institutional examinations.

Electronic Warfare Officer

Location: Signal School, Fort Monmouth, N.J.
Length: 7 weeks.
Objectives: To train officers to plan and supervise electronic warfare combat operations and to direct and supervise location, installation, and technical employment of electronic countermeasures and electronic countermeasure equipment.
Instruction: Introduction to electronic warfare activities; wave propagation; oscilloscopes, modulation, transmission lines, and antennas; fundamentals of radar; missile guidance systems, multipurpose and fuze jammers.
Credit recommendation, collegiate level: Credit in electronics on the basis of institutional examination.

1. **Engineer Equipment Maintenance**
2. **Engineer Equipment Repair**
3. **Engineer Equipment Repair, Enlisted**
   Location: Engineer School, Fort Belvoir, Va.
   Length: 8–12 weeks.
   Objectives: To train enlisted personnel to perform organizational maintenance on engineer construction equipment.
   Instruction: Functioning, repair, adjustment, and maintenance of crane-shovels, air compressors, tractors, motorized graders, internal combustion engines, diesel engines, and related equipment; care and use of hand and power tools.
   Credit recommendation, collegiate level: These courses are technical and vocational in nature. Credit in heavy equipment repair shop on the basis of demonstrated skills and/or institutional examinations.

---

1. **Engineer Equipment Officer**
2. **Engineer Equipment Maintenance Officer**
   Location: Engineer School, Fort Belvoir, Va.
   Length: 8–10 weeks.
   Objectives: To train officers in the supervision, inspection, maintenance and repair of engineer equipment.
   Instruction: Function, operation, and maintenance of engineer track and wheel equipment.
   Credit recommendation, collegiate level: These courses are technical and vocational in nature. Credit in heavy equipment maintenance shop on the basis of demonstrated skills and/or institutional examinations.

Engineer Equipment Repair Technician

Location: Engineer School, Fort Belvoir, Va.
Length: 11 weeks.
Objectives: To train warrant officers and noncommissioned officers in engineer equipment and repair activities at organizational, direct support, general support and depot levels.
Instruction: Familiarization with maintenance management procedures; repair parts supply; internal combustion engine principles and gasoline engine maintenance; operation and maintenance of diesel engine fuel system; function, adjustments, and repair of major components of engineer construction equipment; principles and application of oxyacetylene, electric arc and tungsten gas welding; troubleshooting, testing, and repair of conventional and precise power generators and associated electrical equipment; gas turbine generator repair; principles of operation, component systems, and maintenance points of air conditioners, heaters and refrigeration equipment; maintenance points of high-pressure air compressors and Nike elevators; maintenance of power packs.
Credit recommendation, collegiate level: This course is technical and vocational in nature. Credit in engineer equipment repair on the basis of demonstrated skills and/or institutional examinations.

Engineer Missile Equipment Maintenance

Location: Engineer School, Fort Belvoir, Va.
Length: 9 weeks.
Objectives: To train enlisted personnel in the installation, operation, and organizational maintenance of engineer equipment used in missile systems.
Instruction: Internal combustion engine systems maintenance; electrical fundamentals; high-pressure air compressors; air conditioning; elevator assembly.
Credit recommendation, collegiate level: This course is technical and vocational in nature. Credit in air conditioning equipment repair shop on the basis of demonstrated skills and/or institutional examinations.

Engineer Missile Equipment Repair

Location: Engineer School, Fort Belvoir, Va.
Length: 5 weeks.
Objectives: To train enlisted personnel in the repair of representative-type air conditioning units and high-pressure air compressors used in missile systems.

Instruction: Introduction to air conditioning; air conditioning equipment; reciprocating compressor; refrigerants; thermostatic expansion valve; troubleshooting; mechanical and electrical systems; repair and troubleshooting of the air cycle conditioning system; high-pressure air compressors; hygrometer operation and maintenance.

Credit recommendation, collegiate level: This course is technical and vocational in nature. Credit in air conditioning equipment repair on the basis of demonstrated skills and/or institutional examinations.

Credit recommendation, collegiate level: CAUTION: *These courses vary only slightly in title, length, and recommendation. Require exact identification of course by title and length. Note*—credit for training in any one of the above mentioned elective areas should be based upon institutional examination. *Course 1:* 6 semester hours in business organization and management and 3 semester hours in engineering construction. *Courses 2 and 3:* 3 semester hours in business organization and management and 3 semester hours in engineering construction, for each course.

Engineer Noncommissioned Officer

Location: Engineer School, Fort Belvoir, Va.
Length: 14 weeks.
Objectives: To train enlisted personnel in Corps of Engineer tactics and duties appropriate to engineer noncommissioned officers.
Instruction: Construction surveys, sketching, and drawings; supply systems; combat operations; camouflage materials and construction methods; basic rigging; engineer reconnaissance; explosives and demolitions; mine warfare; floating equipment; soils and geology; construction principles and theories of roads and airfields; construction materials; fixed bridges and bridge classification; theater of operations buildings and construction; utilization and maintenance of engineer equipment.
Credit recommendation, collegiate level: 3 semester hours in engineering construction.

1. Engineer Officer Advanced
2. Engineer Officer Advanced
3. Engineer Officer Career

Location: Engineer School, Fort Belvoir, Va.
Length: *Course 1,* 39 weeks; *Course 2,* 32 weeks; *Course 3,* 23–29 weeks.
Objectives: To provide branch training in the duties and responsibilities of Corps of Engineer officers.
Instruction: *Course 1:* Staff organization and procedures; task analysis and organization; allocation of engineer troops in support of the engineer mission; logistical support and administration; training management of an engineer combat battalion; operational methods and missions of the combined arms team; signal communications; organization, planning, and execution of amphibious operations; principles of atomic weapons; military leadership; planning and supervision of field fortifications; design criteria and methods of port construction; construction of roads and airfields; use of concrete and bituminous material; terrain evaluation; engineering and construction of railroads, pipelines, and bridges; utilization of engineering equipment. *Courses 2 and 3:* These courses include similar instruction in engineering construction but devote less training to the organization and management phases. During 1962 they were changed to include additional instruction in nuclear, biological, or chemical warfare; materiel management; contract construction and procurement management; geodesy, mapping, and terrain intelligence; maintenance and repair parts; supply; Post Engineer; construction management and civil works; psychological operations; civil affairs; Army aviation.

Engineer Officer Basic

Location: Engineer School, Fort Belvoir, Va.
Length: 9–14 weeks.
Objectives: To provide newly commissioned officers with basic training appropriate to their rank and expected service.
Instruction: Introduction to staff functions and procedures; fundamentals of combat and combined arms operations; characteristics of military high explosives; fundamentals of rigging; engineer reconnaissance; familiarization with engineering and construction of field fortifications, military roads, airfields, and bridges; characteristics of paving material; basic principles of soils engineering; mine warfare.
Credit recommendation, collegiate level: Credit in advanced military at institutions which regularly offer such credit.

Engineer Supply

Location: Engineer School, Fort Belvoir, Va.
Length: 10 weeks.
Objectives: To train enlisted personnel in the performance of supply duties at company, organizational, station, and depot level.
Instruction: Army administrative procedures; military publications; company and organization supply; engineer supply procedures at station level; depot supply operations; storage of engineer supplies; engineer repair parts supply; air movement operations; map supply.
Credit recommendation, collegiate level: This course is technical and vocational in nature. Credit in stockroom procedures on the basis of institutional examination.

Engineer Supply and Spare Parts Officer

Location: Engineer School, Fort Belvoir, Va.
Length: 8 weeks.
Objectives: To train commissioned officers and warrant officers to direct and supervise procurement, receipt, storage, issue of, and accounting for engineer supplies, equipment, and spare parts.
Instruction: Organization for supply; depot organization; depot services; supply manuals and engineer material; stock control; storage; engineer supply control office; engineer repair parts supply; maintenance; special problems in theater of operations; case studies of supply problems.

Credit recommendation, collegiate level: 4 semester hours in supply management.

Essential Medical Training for AMEDS Aviators

Location: Medical Field Service School, Fort Sam Houston, Tex.

Length: 3 weeks.

Objectives: To train Medical Service Corps aviators in the problems encountered in aeromedical evacuation of the sick and wounded.

Instruction: Familiarization with medical field records and medical supply procedures; review of basic anatomy and physiology; basic pharmacology; general treatment of common medical conditions; emergency treatment of patients; nursing care procedures, including administration of injections, use of oxygen, blood pressure and pulse, preoperative and postoperative care, and aseptic techniques; familiarization with employment of USAF aeromedical evacuation operations; principles of transporting casualties; basic combat psychiatry; medical aspects of nuclear and chemical weapons; environmental sanitation methods.

Credit recommendation, collegiate level: 2 semester hours in first aid.

Explosive Ordnance Disposal Supervisor

Location: Ordnance School, Aberdeen Proving Ground, Md.

Length: 6 weeks.

Objectives: To train officers and enlisted personnel in the supervisory and management functions of explosive ordnance disposal operations.

Instruction: Fundamentals of ordnance service in the field; area clearance procedures; administration and operation of explosive ordnance disposal units; technical ammunition service; disposal of ammunition, chemical filters, and guided missile fuels; instructional methods and practices.

Credit recommendation, collegiate level: No credit as the course is military in nature.

Field Artillery Battery Officer
(Field Artillery and SSM Battery Officer)

Location: Artillery and Missile School, Fort Sill, Okla.

Length: 33–36 weeks.

Objectives: To provide branch training in the duties and responsibilities of field artillery battery-grade officers.

Instruction: Fundamentals of communication equipment and systems; field artillery operation, techniques, and tactics; employment of field artillery radar.

Credit recommendation, collegiate level: No credit as course is military in nature.

Field Artillery Field Grade Officer Refresher

Location: Artillery and Missile School, Fort Sill, Okla.

Length: 4 weeks.

Objectives: To provide refresher training in the duties and responsibilities of field-grade field artillery officers.

Instruction: Familiarization with new developments in artillery organization, tactics, techniques, and associated arms; review of observed fire and fire direction operations; refresher training in field artillery weapons and ammunition.

Credit recommendation, collegiate level: No credit as course is military in nature.

Field Artillery Missile Officer Basic

Location: Artillery and Missile School, Fort Sill, Okla.

Length: 15 weeks.

Objectives: To train newly commissioned officers in field artillery operations and to provide them with a working knowledge of the duties of the guidance platoon leader, the firing platoon leader, and the ammunition train commander of a Corporal missile unit.

Instruction: Field artillery organization and tactics; fundamentals of communication systems and equipment; procedures for fire battery operations; principles of fire direction; characteristics of artillery weapons; introduction to the Corporal missile system.

Credit recommendation, collegiate level: Credit in advanced military at institutions which regularly offer such credit.

Field Artillery Officer Basic
(Field Artillery Officer Orientation)

Location: Artillery and Missile School, Fort Sill, Okla.

Length: 8–17 weeks.

Objectives: To provide basic branch training and orientation in field artillery for newly commissioned artillery officers.

Instruction: Principles of field artillery organization and tactics; characteristics and operation of artillery weapons; techniques and procedures for operation of the firing battery; familiarization with communication equipment and systems; introduction to, and tactical employment of, field artillery missiles.

Credit recommendation, collegiate level: Credit in advanced military at institutions which regularly offer such credit.

Field Artillery Officer Candidate

Location: Artillery and Missile School. Fort Sill Okla.

Length: 23 weeks.

Objectives: To train selected personnel to be second lieutenants capable of performing duties appropriate to their grade in field artillery units and who, with the minimum of additional training, will be prepared to serve as platoon leaders of other designated branches

Instruction: Artillery transport; communication equipment and procedures; gunnery; materiel; tactics and combined arms; target acquisition; OCS command

Credit recommendation, collegiate level: Credit in

advanced military at institutions which regularly offer such credit.

Field Artillery Officer Candidate (Reserve Component)
(Field Artillery National Guard Officer Candidate)

Location: Artillery and Missile School, Fort Sill, Okla.

Length: 11 weeks.

Objectives: To train personnel to be second lieutenants capable of performing duties appropriate to their grade in field artillery units of the U.S. Army Reserve or National Guard.

Instruction: Tactics and combined arms; communications; gunnery; materiel; motors; observation; OCS commander.

Credit recommendation, collegiate level: 3 semester hours in military science.

Field Artillery Officer Familiarization

Location: Artillery and Missile School, Fort Sill, Okla.

Length: 6–8 weeks.

Objectives: To provide commissioned officers with branch familiarization training in the organization, operational functions, duties, and responsibilities of field artillery.

Instruction: Basic cannon and rocket battery fire direction procedures; characteristics and operation of cannon artillery; tactical subjects.

Credit recommendation, collegiate level: No credit as course is military in nature.

Field Artillery Operations and Intelligence Assistant
(Field Artillery Operations and Intelligence Noncommissioned Officer)

Location: Artillery and Missile School, Fort Sill, Okla.

Length: 11 weeks.

Objectives: To provide enlisted personnel with a working knowledge of all phases of fire direction, intelligence, and liaison in cannon units and a general knowledge of these activities in rocket and guided missile units.

Instruction: Field artillery and guided missile tactics; fire direction organization and techniques; duties and responsibilities of field artillery operations and intelligence assistance.

Credit recommendation, collegiate level: No credit as course is military in nature.

Field Artillery Radar

Location: Artillery and Missile School, Fort Sill, Okla.

Length: 3–7 weeks.

Objectives: To train commissioned officers and warrant officers in the tactical employment of field artillery radar.

Instruction: Procedures for locating weapons and moving targets; organization and mission of FA radar sections; electronic countermeasures; position fixing and vectoring of light aircraft; radar gunnery; principles of fire direction necessary for radar gunnery.

Credit recommendation, collegiate level: No credit as the course is military in nature.

1. Field Artillery Radar Maintenance
(Field Artillery Radar Maintenance (Advanced))
2. Field Artillery Radar Maintenance
3. Weapons Support Radar Maintenance

Location: Artillery and Missile School, Fort Sill, Okla.

Length: *Course 1*, 24 and 30 weeks; *Course 2*, 26–27 weeks and 32–33 weeks; *Course 3*, 26–27 weeks.

Objectives: To train commissioned officers, warrant officers, and enlisted personnel to employ, operate, adjust, and maintain field artillery radar equipment.

Instruction: *Course 1:* Ohm's law; direct and alternating current circuits; inductance, capacitance, transformers; fundamentals of vacuum tubes and vacuum tube circuits; amplifiers, rectifiers, filters, oscillators, and clampers; multivibrators and sweep generators; cathode-ray tubes; servos and servosystems; high-frequency generators; three-phase power; circuit analysis. *Courses 2 and 3:* In addition to the previous instruction, these courses contain more intensive instruction in electronics theory and in the operation and maintenance of countermortar radar AN/MPQ-4A and radar set AN/TPS-25.

Credit recommendation, collegiate level: CAUTION: *These courses vary slightly in title, length, and recommendation. Require exact identification of course by title and length. Course 1:* 3 semester hours at the freshman or sophomore level as an elective in electricity and electronics, and credit in electrical laboratory on the basis of demonstrated skills and/or institutional examinations. *Courses 2 and 3:* For each course, 4 semester hours at the freshman or sophomore level as an elective in electricity and electronics, and credit in electrical laboratory on the basis of demonstrated skills and/or institutional examinations.

Field Artillery Radar Operation

Location: Artillery and Missile School, Fort Sill, Okla.

Length: 8–10 weeks.

Objectives: To train personnel in the tactical employment and utilization of field artillery radar.

Instruction: Plotting, map reading, and radar fundamentals; operation, care, and maintenance of radar equipment; procedures for location of weapons; organization and missions of field artillery radar; radar gunnery.

Credit recommendation, collegiate level: No credit as the course is military in nature.

1. Field Artillery Repair
2. Antiaircraft Artillery Repair

Location: Ordnance School, Aberdeen Proving Grounds, Md.

Length: 7–9 weeks.

Objectives: To train enlisted personnel to repair and rebuild light, medium, and heavy artillery, related materiel, and mounts.

Instruction: Assembly, disassembly, and maintenance of various artillery equipment.

Credit recommendation, collegiate level: These courses are technical and vocational in nature. Credit in mechanical shop on the basis of demonstrated skills and/or institutional examinations.

Field Artillery Transition Officer

Location: Artillery and Missile School, Fort Sill, Okla.

Length: 11 weeks.

Objectives: To familiarize officers with field artillery gunnery, materiel, communications, and combined arms.

Instruction: Principles of battery-level artillery tactics; orientation to the artillery's role in combined arms operations; fundamentals of communication systems and procedures; characteristics of artillery weapons; techniques and procedures of the firing battery.

Credit recommendation, collegiate level: No credit as course is military in nature.

Field Radio Repair

Locations: Signal School, Fort Monmouth, N.J.; Southeastern Signal School, Fort Gordon, Ga.

Length: 21–25 weeks.

Objectives: To train enlisted personnel to perform field and depot maintenance on field radio equipment.

Instruction: *Note*—This course varies in content from March 1954 to August 1964. *From March 1954 to November 1959:* Principles of electricity, including electron theory, principles of current, voltage, resistance, and electric circuits; principles of alternating current, motors and generators, inductance, impedance, transformers, and capacitance; principles of series and parallel tuned circuits; principles of operation of vacuum tubes used in communication systems; amplifier circuits; audiofrequency amplifiers; oscillator, CW and AM transmitter, and antenna circuits; test instruments; portable AM field radio sets; low-power AM transmitters; field radio teletypewriter equipment; principles of frequency modulation; portable FM transceivers; radio relay equipment; standardized series of FM sets; mobile air-ground communication equipment; radio repair shop procedures. *From December 1959:* Radio terms, principles, circuitry and radio repair procedures applicable to radio receivers; sectionalizing, localizing, and isolating troubles in radio receivers; test instruments; basic CW and AM transmitters; field radio teletypewriter equipment; standardized series of FM sets; radio relay equipment; field radio equipment; radio shop repair practices.

Credit recommendation, collegiate level: CAUTION: *Require identification of course by year of attendance. March 1954–November 1959:* 3 semester hours at the freshman or sophomore level as an elective in electricity and electronics, and credit in electrical laboratory on the basis of demonstrated skills and/or institutional examinations. *From December 1959:* Credit in electrical laboratory on the basis of demonstrated skills and/or institutional examinations.

1. **Finance Officer Advanced (Finance Officer Career)**
2. **Finance Officer Career**

Location: Finance School, Fort Benjamin Harrison, Ind.

Length: *Course 1,* 33–36 weeks; *Course 2,* 23 weeks.

Objectives: To provide branch training in the duties and responsibilities of Finance Corps officers.

Instruction: *Course 1:* Management, engineering activities, performance analysis, survey techniques, production planning and control; principles of economics, functions and types of business organization, supply and demand, principles of money and banking, price determination, business cycle, management and labor problems; law of contracts, negotiable instruments, and agency; accounting principles and procedures, analysis and interpretation of financial and cost data, cost accounting techniques, organization of the finance and accounting offices; fiscal code, budget management techniques, budget formulation and execution, purchasing and contracting, administrative control of funds, disbursements; principles, practices, and problems of personnel management; international finance; utilization of automatic data processing equipment in accounting; consumer, stock, and industrial funds. *Course 2:* Accounting principles and procedures; utilization of automatic data processing equipment systems; concepts, processes, and procedures of financial operations, including resources, management, Army financing, cost effectiveness, budgeting, and principles of review and analysis; fundamentals, application, tools, and techniques of management; government purchasing and contracting; responsibilities and functions of a staff finance officer; economic aspects of geopolitics; administrative practices.

Credit recommendation, collegiate level: CAUTION: *These courses are similar in content but vary in the intensity of instruction in the specific academic areas each year. Therefore, credit will be recommended according to the year the course was given. Require exact identification of course by title, length, and year of attendance. Academic year 1955–56:* 6 semester hours in business administration, 4 semester hours in economics, 3 semester hours in business law, and 6 semester hours in general accounting. *Academic years 1956–58:* 6 semester hours in basic accounting, 6 semester hours in intermediate accounting, 3 semester hours in cost accounting, and 6 semester hours in business administration. *Academic years 1958–60:* 3 semester hours in general accounting, 3 semester hours in cost accounting, 3 semester hours in finance and disbursing, 3 semester hours in personnel management, and 2 semester hours in business administration. *Academic year 1960–1961:* 3 semester hours in general accounting, 3 semester hours in cost accounting, 3 semester hours in finance and disbursing, 2 semester hours in business administration, and 2 semester hours in personnel management. *Academic years 1961–63:* 3 semester hours in general accounting, 3 semester hours in cost accounting, 3 semester hours in finance and disbursing, 2 semester hours in business administration, and 3 semester hours in computer principles in the field of data processing. *Academic year 1963–64:* 3 semester hours in general accounting, 3 semester hours in cost accounting, 3 semester hours in finance and disbursing, and 2 semester hours in busines administration. *Academic years 1964–65 and 1967–68:* 3 semester hours in general accounting, 3 semester hours in cost accounting, 3 semester hours in finance and disbursing, 2 semester hours in business administration, and 3 semester hours in computer principles in the field of data processing.

Course 2: Academic years 1965–67: 3 semester hours in general accounting, 2 semester hours in finance and fiscal procedures, 2 semester hours in business administration, and 2 semester hours in computer principles in the field of data processing. *Note—additional credit in money and banking, statistics, business law and auditing may be granted for all courses on the basis of institutional examinations.*

1. Finance Officer Basic
2. Finance Officer Orientation
3. Finance Officer Orientation—MBA
   (Finance Officer Orientation)

Location: Finance School, Fort Benjamin Harrison, Ind.

Length: *Courses 1 and 2,* 8–14 weeks; *Course 3,* 5–6 weeks.

Objectives: *Courses 1 and 2:* To provide newly commissioned officers with basic branch training and orientation in the duties and responsibilities of Finance Corps officers. *Course 3:* To orient Army Reserve officers procured through the Finance Corps MBA procurement program in basic military subjects.

Instruction: *Courses 1 and 2:* Accounting procedures; entitlements; organization and functions of the finance and accounting office; fiscal code; disbursing operations. *Course 3:* Orientation to military activities.

Credit recommendation, collegiate level: CAUTION: *Courses 1 and 2 are similar in content but vary in the intensity of instruction in the specific academic areas each year. Therefore credit will be recommended according to the year the course was given. Require exact identification of course by date of attendance. Course 3 must be identified by length. Courses 1 and 2: August 1955—June 1960,* 3 semester hours in accounting procedures and 3 semester hours in finance and disbursing; *July 1960—June 1964,* 2 semester hours in accounting procedures and 3 semester hours in finance and disbursing; *July 1964—June 1966,* 1 semester hour in accounting procedures and 3 semester hours in finance and disbursing. *Course 3: From July 1966,* 3 semester hours in financing and disbursing, and credit in accounting procedures on the bases of institutional examination.

Finance Operations Noncommissioned Officer

Location: Finance School, Fort Benjamin Harrison, Ind.

Length: 8–9 weeks.

Objectives: To train enlisted personnel in the organization, functions, and employment of the Army, with emphasis on financial functions, and to provide a broad background in the field of financial management.

Instruction: *Phase I:* All students complete *Phase I* training—application of automatic data processing equipment in business operations; techniques of management, including functions and responsibilities of military comptrollers, basic statistics, internal review and control, manpower management, logistical management, cost reduction, reports control systems, and systems and procedures analysis; programming and budgeting, including resource management, program

systems, Army budget formulation cycle, installation procurement budgeting, budget adjustments, and review and analysis; government purchasing and contracting; staff finance and accounting operations; administrative practices.

Phase II is divided into two parts: *Accounting Specialists* receive instruction in pay of military personnel, travel allowances, civilian pay, commercial accounts, and disbursing operations; *Disbursing Specialists* receive instruction in procedures for accounting from installation-level through higher command. *Note—*Fiscal year 1968 students received instruction in all of the above with no division into phases.

Credit recommendation, collegiate level: 3 semester hours in general accounting procedures.

Finance Procedures

Location: Finance School, Fort Benjamin Harrison, Ind.

Length: 5–8 weeks.

Objectives: To train enlisted personnel in finance procedures relating to the acquisition, disbursing, and accounting for public funds.

Instruction: Entitlements; disbursing operations; fiscal code; organization, function, and operation of a finance and accounting office; basic accounting procedures.

Credit recommendation, collegiate level: 3 semester hours in government accounting.

Financial Management—Inventory Accounting and Army Stock Fund Operations

Location: Finance School, Fort Benjamin Harrison, Ind.

Length: 3 weeks.

Objectives: To train commissioned officers and warrant officers in the financial management aspects of financial inventory accounting and stock fund operations.

Instruction: Inventory accounting; stock control procedures; principles and concepts of integrated accounting employed in financial inventory accounting; stock fund accounting procedures; management and analysis of financial inventory accounting statements.

Credit recommendation, collegiate level: 3 semester hours in financial management.

Financial Management Systems-Automated Application

Location: Finance School, Fort Benjamin Harrison, Ind.

Length: 4 weeks.

Objectives: To train commissioned officers, warrant officers, and enlisted personnel in the methods and techniques utilized in the development of financial and supply accounting automated applications.

Instruction: Automatic data processing equipment; procedure development; processing codes; consumer fund procedure development; magnetic tape and random access, processing, flow charting, and programming; introduction to the supply system; development of computerized stock fund system; COBOL; automatic data processing controls.

Credit recommendation, collegiate level: 2 semester hours in computer programming and analysis in the field of data processing.

1. **Financial Management Systems-Automatic Data Processing**
2. **Financial Management-Machine Accounting Systems**
3. **Financial Management-Machine Accounting**

Location: Finance School, Fort Benjamin Harrison, Ind.

Length: 3–5 weeks.

Objectives: To train commissioned officers, warrant officers, and enlisted personnel in the application of automatic data processing equipment in business-type operations.

Instruction: *Course 1:* Introduction to automatic data processing; machine language; automatic data processing equipment; block diagraming and programming techniques; systems and procedures for maintenance of accounts and report preparation for financial and supply accounting and customer billing. *Course 2:* In addition to the preceding instruction, this course contains application of punched card machines to process data, update accounts, and produce reports for financial and supply accounting systems; mechanized pay procedures. *Course 3:* Machine accounting networks; methods of mechanizing operations; accounting systems employing machines; preparation of financial data for computer processing and internal accounting control.

Credit recommendation, collegiate level: CAUTION: *These courses vary only slightly in title and recommendation. Require exact identification of course by title. Courses 1 and 2:* For each course, 2 semester hours in data processing (financial operations). *Course 3:* No credit because of the limited technical nature of the course.

Fire Control Computer Repair

Locations: Ordnance School, Aberdeen Proving Ground, Md.; Missile and Munitions School, Redstone Arsenal, Ala.

Length: 25 weeks.

Objectives: To train enlisted personnel in the operation, maintenance, and repair of the field artillery digital automatic computer system.

Instruction: Series and parallel circuits, resistor application, DC power, induction and inductance, AC, motors and generators, capacitance, impedance, and transformers; power supplies, vacuum tubes, voltage regulators, amplifiers, oscillators, synchro devices, servosystems, and gyros; basic solid state theory and circuits; testing, identifying, and analyzing malfunctions within a digital controller; principles of the components and functioning of the electronic circuits utilized in the computer, gun, and direction computer, M18; electronic circuits for signal data reproducer (SDR) M36; electronic circuits in the use of logic equations; operation and maintenance of the AR-85 viewer computer portion of the AN/TSQ-43 system.

Credit recommendation, collegiate level: 2 semester hours at the freshman or sophomore level as an elective in electricity and electronics, and credit in electrical laboratory on the basis of demonstrated skills and/or institutional examinations.

1. **Fire Control Instrument Repair**
2. **Fire Control Instrument Repair (Basic)**

Location: Ordnance School, Aberdeen Proving Ground, Md.

Length: 8–12 weeks.

Objectives: To train enlisted personnel to inspect, adjust, and repair optical and non-optical precision instruments and related equipment.

Instruction: Fundamentals of optics, optical systems and repair of telescopes, aiming circles, and binoculars; description, operation, and maintenance of the range finder, computer, ballistic drive, and periscope in fire control systems; adjustment and maintenance of the quadrant, mount, and instrument accessories.

Credit recommendation, collegiate level: These courses are technical and vocational in nature. Credit in precision instrument repair on the basis of demonstrated skills and/or institutional examinations.

Fire Distribution Integration Systems Repair (AN/GSG-5)
(Fire Distribution Integration Systems Repair (AN/GSG-5 and 6))

Location: Air Defense School, Army Signal Fire Distribution Systems Training Activity, Fort Bliss, Tex.

Length: 22–27 weeks.

Objectives: To train warrant officers and enlisted personnel to perform organizational and direct support maintenance on the fire distribution integration systems AN/GSG-5 and 6.

Instruction: Digital fundamentals and power supplies used in the AN/GSG-5 system; theory and operation of the display subsystem; purpose and operation of the AN/GSG-5 computer; theory and operation of the BDL and SAGE subsystem; operation and troubleshooting procedures of the AN/GSG-6 system.

Credit recommendation, collegiate level: Credit in electrical laboratory on the basis of demonstrated skills and/or institutional examinations.

1. **Fire Distribution Systems Electronics**
2. **Fire Distribution System Maintenance (Fire Distribution Systems Electronics Fundamentals)**

Locations: Army Air Defense School, Fort Bliss, Tex.; Signal School, Fort Monmouth, N.J.

Length: *Course 1,* 9 weeks; *Course 2,* 18 weeks.

Objectives: *Course 1:* To train enlisted personnel in basic electronics and in the use and maintenance of test equipment. *Course 2:* To train enlisted personnel in electrical and electronic fundamentals and in the function, test, and repair of representative vacuum tube and solid state digital, analogue, display, and other pulse and logic circuits utilized in air defense fire distribution systems.

Instruction: *Course 1:* Electrical units; DC circuits; AC fundamentals; inductance; capacitance; reactive circuits; diodes, rectifiers, and power supplies, triodes and triode circuits and biasing; untuned and tuned amplifiers; oscillators; modulation, demodulation, and superheterodyne receivers; special purpose oscillators and amplifiers, multivibrators, and wave-shaping circuits; presentation system and oscilloscope; basic radars and RF components; motors, generators, three-phase power, relays, and control devices, servosystems and synchros; gating and coincidence tubes; transistors, transistor amplifiers, oscillators, and semiconductors; use of test equipment. *Course 2:* In addition to the preceding instruction this course contains further training in pulse and indicator circuitry, semiconductors, and analogue and digital computer circuitry.

Credit recommendation, collegiate level: CAUTION: *These courses vary only slightly in title, length, and recommendation. Require exact identification of course by title and length. Course 1:* 3 semester hours at the freshman or sophomore level as an elective in electricity and electronics, and credit in electrical laboratory on the basis of demonstrated skills and/or institutional examinations. *Course 2:* 4 semester hours at the freshman or sophomore level as an elective in electricity and electronics, and credit in electrical laboratory on the basis of demonstrated skills and/or institutional examinations.

Fixed Plant Carrier Equipment Operation

Location: Signal School, Fort Monmouth, N.J.
Length: 14 weeks.
Objectives: To train enlisted personnel in the operation and operators maintenance of fixed-plant carrier telephone, telegraph, and radio.
Instruction: Fundamentals of telephony; long and short haul telephone carrier equipment; fundamentals of carrier telegraphy; installation, operation, and maintenance of telegraph terminal equipment; "C" carrier and "O" carrier systems operation; field telephone and telegraph carrier equipment; fixed-station radio layout; single-side-band carrier terminal and telegraph terminal equipment; multiplex terminal equipment.
Credit recommendation, collegiate level: This course is technical and vocational in nature. Credit in telegraph, telephone, and radio operation, and credit in electrical shop on the basis of demonstrated skills and/or institutional examinations. *See* page 364 for repair course.

Fixed Station Radio Equipment Operation and Maintenance

Location: Signal School, Fort Monmouth, N.J.
Length: 14–15 weeks.
Objectives: To train enlisted personnel to perform operating adjustments on fixed-station radio equipment, to maintain operating efficiency of circuits, and to assist in installation and repair of fixed-station electronic equipment.
Instruction: Electrical fundamentals, including Ohm's law, series, parallel and series-parallel circuits, power, AC fundamentals, capacitance, impedance, and resonance; fundamentals of electronics and their application to communications circuits; fixed-station layouts; fundamentals of telegraph systems; carrier fundamentals and propagation theory; radio transmitters and receivers; carrier equipment; single-side-band

transmitters and receivers; control and coordination of activities in a fixed-station integrated communication system.
Credit recommendation, collegiate level: Credit in electricity and electronics and electrical laboratory on the basis of demonstrated skills and/or institutional examinations.

Fixed Station Receiver Repair

Location: Signal School, Fort Monmouth, N.J.
Length: 20–22 weeks.
Objectives: To train enlisted personnel to install, operate, and repair fixed-station radio receiving and associated equipment.
Instruction: Fundamentals of electricity, including current, voltage, and resistance, use of the multimeter, series, parallel, and series-parallel circuits, electrical measurements, filament circuits, alternating current, inductors, transformer fundamentals, capacitors, capacitive and inductive reactance, and series and parallel tuned circuits; electronic fundamentals, including electron emission, diode vacuum tubes and rectifiers, voltage dividers, oscilloscopes, power supplies, triodes, tetrode and pentode tubes, amplifier characteristics and coupling, voltage amplifier, IF amplifier, detector and AVC circuits, oscillator circuits, radio reception, superheterodyne receiver, and voltage and resistance measurements; antenna fundamentals; diversity receiving equipment; fixed-station fundamentals; radio teletypewriter terminal equipment; single-side-band fundamentals and receiving equipment; fixed-station integrated communication system; sectionalization, localization, and isolation of troubles in fixed-station receiver and associated equipment.
Credit recommendation, collegiate level: 3 semester hours at the freshman or sophomore level as an elective in electricity and electronics, and credit in electrical laboratory on the basis of demonstrated skills and/or institutional examinations.

Fixed Station Terminal Repair

Location: Signal School, Fort Monmouth, N.J.
Length: 24 weeks.
Objectives: To train enlisted personnel to install, operate, and repair fixed-station terminal radio communications equipment, and to rebuild and overhaul fixed-station radio transmitter, receiver, and terminal equipment.
Instruction: Basic electricity, including magnetism, current and voltage, AC voltage measurements, AC theory, capacitor theory, capacitive reactance and impedance, rectification, inductance, inductive reactance and impedance, magnetic coupling and transformers, and tuned circuits and resonance; basic electronic circuits, including audio and radio frequencies, principles of radio transmission, theory and analysis of audio amplifier, detector, IF amplifier, oscillator, and first detector circuits of a superheterodyne radio receiver, triode, tetrode, and pentode vacuum tube theory, and audio frequency amplifiers and coupling; fixed-station fundamentals; telephone and telegraph fundamentals; antenna system; fixed-station carrier terminal equipment; twelve-channel carrier terminal equipment; single-side-band carrier terminal equipment; single-chan-

nel radio teletype equipment; single-side-band radio equipment; multiplex terminal equipment; fixed-station integrated communication system.

Credit recommendation, collegiate level: 3 semester hours at the freshman or sophomore level as an elective in electricity and electronics, and credit in electrical laboratory on the basis of demonstrated skills and/or institutional examinations.

Fixed Station Transmitter Repair
(Fixed Station Radio Transmitter Repair)

Location: Signal School, Fort Monmouth, N.J.
Length: 21–24 weeks.
Objectives: To train enlisted personnel to install, operate, and repair fixed-station radio transmitting and associated equipment.

Instruction: Current, resistance, and voltage; series, parallel, and series-parallel circuits; power; alternating current; inductors; capacitors; electron theory; diode and triode vacuum tube; filter circuits; tetrodes and pentodes; amplifier coupling; tuned circuits; oscillators; fundamental transmitter circuits; antenna systems; frequency measuring and keying equipment; single-channel radio teletype transmitters; servo tuned transmitting sets; single-side-band fundamentals; fixed-station integrated communication equipment.

Credit recommendation, collegiate level: 3 semester hours at the freshman or sophomore level as an elective in electricity and electronics, and credit in electrical laboratory on the basis of demonstrated skills and/or institutional examinations.

1. Fixed-Wing Instrument Flight Examiner
2. Rotary-Wing Instrument Flight Examiner
(Helicopter Instrument Flight Examiner)
3. Instrument Flight Examiner

Location: Army Aviation School, Fort Rucker, Ala.
Length: 4–7 weeks.
Objectives: To train Army aviators as fixed-wing and rotary-wing instrument flight examiners.

Instruction: Advanced instrument flight training; examiner techniques, including flight and oral testing, grading standards, flight test maneuvers, and issuance of certificates.

Credit recommendation, collegiate level: No credit because of the limited technical nature of these courses.

1. Fixed-Wing Instrument Qualification (National Guard/Foreign Military Training)
(Fixed-Wing Instrument Qualification)
2. Rotary-Wing Instrument Qualification

Location: Army Aviation School, Fort Rucker, Ala.
Length: 5–9 weeks.
Objectives: To train Army aviators in instrument flying.

Instruction: Basic and advanced instrument flight training; flight regulations; air traffic control; radio communications and navigation; flight planning.

Credit recommendation, collegiate level: For each course, credit in instrument flying on the basis of institutional examination.

Fixed-Wing Qualification

Location: Army Aviation School, Fort Rucker, Ala.
Length: 6–16 weeks.
Objectives: To train commissioned and warrant officers in fixed-wing aircraft flying techniques and to familiarize them with the tactical employment of observation airplanes.

Instruction: Flight training; short field and road strip techniques, flight planning and navigation; fundamentals of meteorology; organizational maintenance; tactical employment of aircraft.

Credit recommendation, collegiate level: Credit in elementary navigation and meteorology on the basis of institutional examination.

1. Fixed-Wing Technical Inspector
2. Rotary-Wing Technical Inspector

Location: Transportation School, Fort Eustis, Va.
Length: 5–12 weeks.
Objectives: To train enlisted personnel in the techniques and procedures of technical inspection of fixed-wing and rotary-wing aircraft.

Instruction: Interpretation of engineering drawing; weight and balance classification of aircraft; shop safety; maintenance; maintenance forms and records; determination of repair requirements; inspection of aircraft structures, parts, and systems.

Credit recommendation, collegiate level: These courses are technical and vocational in nature. Credit in aircraft maintenance inspection on the basis of demonstrated skills and/or institutional examinations.

Flight Operations Specialist

Location: Army Aviation School, Fort Rucker, Ala.
Length: 4–5 weeks.
Objectives: To train enlisted personnel to schedule and coordinate aircraft flights and to perform other administrative and related support functions pertaining to airfield operations.

Instruction: Theory of aircraft flight; aircraft characteristics; basic principles of weather; rules, regulations and procedures applicable to Army aviation; familiarization with techniques in navigation flight planning and scheduling.

Credit recommendation, collegiate level: No credit because of the limited technical nature of this course.

Flight Simulator Operations and Maintenance

Location: Army Aviation School, Fort Rucker, Ala.
Length: 8–15 weeks.
Objectives: To train enlisted personnel to operate and maintain flight simulators in order to provide instruction in instrument flight techniques to rated Army aviators.

Instruction: Operation of the synthetic trainer; basic instrument flying procedures; techniques and procedures in navigation; adjustments and inspection of equipment.

Credit recommendation, collegiate level: No credit because of the limited technical nature of this course.

Food Inspection

Locations: Medical Service School, Fort Sam Houston, Tex.; Medical Service Meat and Dairy Hygiene School, Chicago, Ill.

Length: 10 weeks.

Objectives: To train enlisted personnel in the fundamentals of food sanitation, inspection, and the essential aspects of food technology.

Instruction: Fundamentals and procedures of food and sanitary inspection; public health aspects of food inspection; food preservation; statistical sampling inspection procedures; selection and inspection of meats, fish, poultry, dairy products, and fruits and vegetables; principles and standard procedures for preparation, processing, storage, and inspection of canned foods.

Credit recommendation, collegiate level: 3 semester hours in meat and dairy hygiene.

1. Food Inspection Procedures (Advanced)
2. Food Inspection Advanced

Location: Medical Service School, Fort Sam Houston, Tex.

Length: *Course 1,* 16 weeks; *Course 2,* 24 weeks.

Objectives: To train enlisted personnel in advanced techniques of food inspection.

Instruction: *Course 1:* Bacteriology, food contamination, and food poisoning; food inspection regulations; sampling plans and procedures; principles of food chemistry and laboratory procedures; effects of nuclear, biological, and chemical agents on food; techniques of antemortem and postmortem inspection; food preservation; organization, mission, authority, and procedures for procurement and inspection of food; food inspection reports and records; surveillance inspection; sanitary standards for food processing plants; advanced methods in food processing and inspection. *Course 2:* This course contains the same academic material as *Course 1* but the instruction is more intense.

Credit recommendation, collegiate level: CAUTION: *These courses vary only slightly in title, length, and recommendation. Require exact identification of course by title and length. Course 1:* 3 semester hours in meat and dairy hygiene and 3 semester hours in veterinary laboratory procedures. *Course 2:* 3 semester hours in meat and dairy hygiene and 6 semester hours in veterinary laboratory procedures.

1. Food Service Supervision
2. Food Service Supervision
(Food Service Supervision, Officer)

Location: Quartermaster School, Fort Lee, Va.

Length: *Course 1,* 12 weeks; *Course 2,* 16 weeks.

Objectives: To train commissioned officers and warrant officers to function as staff advisers on the food program within a command.

Note—Naval officers attended these courses between 1958 and 1965 and were trained in the functions of commissary officers of general messes with the Navy.

Instruction: *Course 1:* Duties and responsibilities of a food adviser; organization and functions for food service in Army areas and installations; mess management, including requisition and supply of mess equipment, mess accounting, mess sanitation and inspection; principles of nutrition; menu planning and nutritional analysis; supervision of meat processing facilities; supervisory techniques of food preparation; baking principles; types, purposes, and functions of field messes; open mess management; supervision of garrison messes; relationship of the commissary officer with the food adviser. *Course 2:* These courses contain the same academic subjects but include a longer period of instruction in the areas of food preparation and nutrition.

Credit recommendation, collegiate level: CAUTION: *These courses vary only slightly in title, length, and recommendation. Require exact identification of course by title and length. Course 1:* 3 semester hours in food preparation and nutrition and 3 semester hours in food service management. *Course 2:* 3 semester hours in nutrition, 3 semester hours in food preparation, and 3 semester hours in food service management.

1. Food Service Supervision, Enlisted
2. Food Service Supervision, Enlisted
3. Food Service Supervision, Enlisted

Location: Quartermaster School, Fort Lee, Va.

Length: *Course 1,* 8–9 weeks; *Course 2,* 11 weeks; *Course 3,* 16 weeks.

Objectives: To train enlisted personnel to assist food advisers in the supervision of messes and the coordination of food service activities within a command.

Instruction: *Course 1:* Functions and operation of the commissary; duties and responsibilities of the food adviser and supervisor; mess management, including procedures for requisitioning supplies and equipment, regulations governing mess accounting, and types of rations; administration of open messes and post restaurants, prevention of food spoilage, and mess inspection and supervision; nutrition and menu planning; supervision of meat cutting and baking facilities; analysis of food preparation; organization and operation of field messes; supervision of garrison mess facilities. *Courses 2 and 3:* These courses include the same academic subjects as *Course 1* but the instruction is somewhat more intense.

Credit recommendation, collegiate level: CAUTION: *These courses vary only slightly in length and recommendation. Require exact identification of course by length. Course 1:* 3 semester hours in food service management. *Course 2:* 4 semester hours in food service management. *Course 3:* 5 semester hours in food service management.

Fuel and Electrical Systems Repair

Location: Ordnance School, Aberdeen Proving Ground, Md.

Length: 10–12 weeks.

Objectives: To train enlisted personnel to inspect,

test, and diagnose malfunctions, and to perform adjustments and repairs on fuel and electrical system components.

Instruction: Vehicle driving; maintenance and installation procedures; vehicle characteristics; construction, operation, inspection, and repair of wheeled and track-wheeled vehicle fuel systems and components; principles of automotive electricity, including operation of electrical measuring instruments and automotive accessories, function and operation of wheeled and track-wheeled vehicle electrical system components, and use of test equipment for mechanical and electrical adjustments; disassembly, repair, test, and reassembly of alternating electrical system components.

Credit recommendation, collegiate level: This course is technical and vocational in nature. Credit in automotive shop and electrical shop on the basis of demonstrated skills and/or institutional examinations.

Gas Turbine and Generator Repair
(Gas Turbine Generator Repair)

Location: Engineer School, Fort Belvoir, Va.
Length: 11–12 weeks.
Objectives: To train enlisted personnel in the maintenance and repair of electronic control circuitry, electric motors and generators, gas turbine engines, and gasoline and diesel engines.

Instruction: Internal combustion engine repair; gas turbine engines; repair of fuel systems; repair of engine control systems; troubleshooting of shaft loaded gas turbine engines; engine removal and replacement; troubleshooting of combination loaded gas turbine engines; conventional generator and motor repair; precise power generator repair; gas turbine generator.

Credit recommendation, collegiate level: This course is technical and vocational in nature. Credit in gas turbine and generator repair on the basis of demonstrated skills and/or institutional examinations.

1. General Drafting (Entry)
2. General Drafting

Locations: Engineer School, Fort Belvoir, Va.; Engineer Training Center, Fort Leonard Wood, Mo.
Length: 9 weeks.
Objectives: To train enlisted personnel in general drafting details, cartographic, model making, and related drafting activities.

Instruction: Principles and techniques of drafting; projection theory; preparation of plans, elevations, and views; construction of buildings, bridges, and roads; methods of construction, computations, and materials used in construction work by blue print reading.

Credit recommendation, collegiate level: 4 semester hours in engineering drafting for each course.

1. General Officer Fixed-Wing Flight Training
2. General Officer Rotary-Wing Flight Training

Location: Aviation School, Fort Rucker, Ala.
Length: 15–17 weeks.
Objectives: To train general officers to pilot fixed-wing and rotary-wing aircraft and to familiarize them with aviation problems.

Instruction: Basic and advanced flight training; instrument flight familiarization; basic navigation; tactical employment of aircraft; flight planning; aviation weather.

Credit recommendation, collegiate level: Credit for each course in elementary navigation and meteorology on the basis of institutional examination.

General Officer Rotary Wing Qualification

Location: Army Aviation School, Fort Rucker, Ala.
Length: 5 weeks.
Objectives: To qualify general officers as rotary-wing aviators and provide a working knowledge of maintenance and general flight subjects.

Instruction: Operation of observation helicopters; transition flight training in the UH-1-type helicopter; instrument flying; general aircraft maintenance; principles of rotary-wing aerodynamics; tactical aviation operations; familiarization with navigation and aviation weather.

Credit recommendation, collegiate level: Credit in helicopter flight training on the basis of demonstrated skills and/or institutional examinations.

General Supply Specialist
(Unit Supply)

Location: Quartermaster School, Fort Lee, Va.
Length: 6 weeks.
Objectives: To train enlisted personnel to perform general unit supply duties, to assist in general supply and logistical operations, and to perform organizational maintenance of small arms.

Instruction: Unit and organization supply; installation supply; packing and crating; organizational maintenance of small arms.

Credit recommendation, collegiate level: This course is technical and vocational in nature. Credit in office procedures and small arms repair on the basis of demonstrated skills and/or institutional examinations.

General Supply Supervision
(Unit and Organization Supply NCO)

Location: Quartermaster School, Fort Lee, Va.
Length: 5–6 weeks.
Objectives: To train enlisted personnel to supervise and perform general unit supply duties and to assist in general supply operations and logistics.

Instruction: Army supply system; unit and organization supply; military packaging; installation supply; storage operations; logistical support in a theater of operations; quartermaster operations in the combat zone; maintenance and inspection of small arms.

Credit recommendation, collegiate level: This course is technical and vocational in nature. Credit in general supply procedures on the basis of institutional examination.

General Warehousing

Location: Quartermaster School, Fort Lee, Va.

Length: 8 weeks.

Objectives: To train enlisted personnel to receive, store, issue, and ship supplies.

Instruction: Familiarization with the Army supply system; packaging and packing; inventory procedures; storage operations, including planning and storage layout, handling and storage procedures, protection and inspection of stored supplies, and shipping and receiving; materials handling equipment.

Credit recommendation, collegiate level: This course is technical and vocational in nature. Credit in stockroom procedures on the basis of demonstrated skills and/or institutional examinations.

Graves Registration, Officer

Location: Quartermaster School, Fort Lee, Va.

Length: 4 weeks.

Objectives: To train commissioned officers in the duties and responsibilities of graves registration officers.

Instruction: Graves registration service; science of identification; introduction to topographical sketching and analysis; battlefield search and recovery operations; cemetery operations; return program and current death operations.

Credit recommendation, collegiate level: No credit because of the specialized nature of the course.

Ground Control Radar Repair
(Ground Control Approach Equipment Repair)

Location: Signal School, Fort Monmouth, N.J.

Length: 20–30 weeks.

Objectives: To train enlisted personnel to inspect, test, and perform repair and depot maintenance on ground control approach equipment.

Instruction: Electrical fundamentals; electronics applied to basic audio amplifiers; semiconductor fundamentals; electronics applied to basic receivers; generation of RF energy; nonsinusoidal circuitry; time indicator components; microwave transmitters and modulators; radar sets; air traffic control radar beacon systems; interrogator set.

Credit recommendation, collegiate level: 4 semester hours at the freshman or sophomore level as an elective in electricity and electronics, and credit in electrical laboratory on the basis of demonstrated skills and/or institutional examinations.

Ground Surveillance and Tracking and Plotting Radar Repair

Location: Army Combat Surveillance and Target Acquisition Training Command, Fort Huachuca, Ariz.

Length: 14 weeks.

Objectives: To train enlisted personnel to perform organizational and field maintenance on ground surveillance radar sets AN/PPS-4, AN/TPS-33, and AN/TPS-25, and tracking and plotting radar AN/MPQ-29.

Instruction: Use of test equipment; interpretation of schematics; diagnosis of equipment malfunction and methods of repair; operation and utilization of associated power units.

Credit recommendation, collegiate level: Credit in electrical laboratory on the basis of demonstrated skills and/or institutional examinations.

Ground Surveillance Radar Mechanic
(AN/TPS-33 and AN/PPS-4)

Location: Combat Surveillance School, Fort Huachuca, Ariz.

Length: 6 weeks.

Objectives: To train enlisted personnel to emplace, adjust, and perform organizational maintenance on ground surveillance radars AN/TPS-33 and AN/PPS-4.

Instruction: Operational characteristics, capabilities, and limitations of the AN/TPS-33 and AN/PPS-4 radar sets; radar maintenance procedures; field operations.

Credit recommendations, collegiate level: Credit in electrical laboratory on the basis of demonstrated skills and/or institutional examinations.

Ground Surveillance Radar Repair

Location: Signal School, Fort Monmouth, N.J.

Length: 24–29 weeks.

Objectives: To train enlisted personnel to inspect, test, and perform repairs on ground surveillance radar equipment.

Instruction: Electrical fundamentals, including batteries, resistors, DC power, Ohm's law, alternating current, inductance, capacitance, impedance, filters, and transformers; filament circuits; diodes; half-wave rectifications; triode tubes; voltage amplification; tetrode tubes; use of the multimeter and oscilloscope; fundamentals of semiconductors; RF signal generators; superheterodyne reception; amplification of intermediate and radio frequencies; oscillators; mixers and converters; receiver alignment; generation of RF energy; nonsinusoidal circuitry; timer-indicator component circuits; microwave transmitters and modulators; microwave receiver; servo and data circuitry; transformer-receiver performance measurements; adjustments and repair of radar sets AN/PPS-4, AN/TPS-33, AN/TPS-25, and AN/MPQ-29.

Credit recommendation, collegiate level: 6 semester hours at the freshman or sophomore level as an elective in electricity and electronics, and credit in electrical laboratory on the basis of demonstrated skills and/or institutional examinations.

Guided Missile Electronic Materiel Maintenance, SSM

Location: Artillery School, Fort Bliss, Tex.

Length: 28 weeks.

Objectives: To train warrant officers and enlisted personnel to assemble, install, calibrate, and adjust on-missile electronic guidance control components and systems and associated test equipment for surface-to-surface missiles.

Instruction: Mathematics; Ohm's law; direct and alternating current; inductance; capacitance; meters;

time constants; RC circuits; oscilloscope; transformers; actions of simple circuits and effects of various components; radar electronics; resonant circuits; vacuum tubes; vacuum tube circuits; filters; amplifiers; potentiometers; voltage regulator tubes; oscillators; CW transmitters; AM and FM; assembly and operation of radio circuits; operation and application of radar circuits; Corporal system and test equipment; missile components and test equipment; Corporal missile checkout and firing.

Credit recommendation, collegiate level: 4 semester hours at the freshman or sophomore level as an elective in electricity and electronics, and credit in electrical laboratory on the basis of demonstrated skills and/or institutional examinations.

Guided Missile Fire Control System Maintenance, SSM

Location: Artillery School, Fort Bliss, Tex.

Length: 32 weeks.

Objectives: To train warrant officers and enlisted personnel to adjust, maintain, employ, and operate a surface-to-surface guided missile fire control system.

Instruction: Mathematics; Ohm's law, direct and alternating current circuits; inductance; capacitance; meters; time constants; RC circuits; oscilloscope; transformers; actions of simple circuits and effects of various components; resonant circuits; vacuum tubes and vacuum tube circuits; assembly and operation of radio circuits; radar electronics; Radar AN/MPQ-25; Computer AN/MSA-6; Doppler AN/MRQ-7; Corporal fire control system.

Credit recommendation, collegiate level: 4 semester hours at freshman or sophomore level as an elective in electricity and electronics, and credit in electrical laboratory on the basis of demonstrated skills and/or institutional examinations.

Guided Missile Installation Electrical Equipment Repair

Location: Engineer School, Fort Belvoir, Va.

Length: 12 weeks.

Objectives: To train enlisted personnel to install, operate, and perform organizational and limited field maintenance on high output generators, motors, frequency changers, power distribution systems, elevator control systems, and other engineer equipment employed by guided missile units.

Instruction: Principles, operation, maintenance, and repair of gasoline engines, diesel engines; high PSI air compressor electrical motors, alternators, and frequency converters; installation, operation and maintenance of air conditioning equipment; elevator assembly and allied equipment.

Credit recommendation, collegiate level: This course is technical and vocational in nature. Credit in electrical and mechanical shop on the basis of demonstrated skills and/or institutional examinations.

Guided Missile, Nuclear Weapons, and ARADCOM Safety

Location: Guided Missile School, Redstone Arsenal, Ala.

Length: 3 weeks.

Objectives: To train commissioned officers, warrant officers, and enlisted personnel in guided missile and nuclear weapon safety practices, hazards, and precautions peculiar to ARADCOM Nike tactical sites.

Instruction: Guided and ballistic missiles; propellant safety; nuclear weapons storage and transportation safety; electrical, mechanical, radiological, and missile safety; ARADCOM Nike tactical site safety; assembly and disassembly of Hercules missile; Ajax missile, handling, assembly and tests, fueling and defueling operations; launching area safety hazards.

Credit recommendation, collegiate level: No credit because of the brevity and nature of the course.

Guided Missile Propellants and Explosives (Guided Missile Propellants-Explosive Specialist)

Locations: Missile and Munitions School, Redstone Arsenal, Ala.; Ordnance School, Aberdeen Proving Ground, Md.

Length: 6–8 weeks.

Objectives: To train enlisted personnel in the field surveillance, storage, and issuing of guided missile propellants and explosives; maintenance of propellant and explosives handling and storage equipment.

Instruction: Classification of explosives; principles of storing and handling ammunition; propellant identification; preparation of solutions; solid propellants; storage and handling of GM propellants and components; SAM and SSM servicing; propellant storage site operations.

Credit recommendation, collegiate level: No credit as course is military in nature.

Guided Missile Repair Helper (Ordnance Electronics (Entry))

Locations: Ordnance Guided Missile School, Redstone Arsenal, Ala.; Signal School, Fort Monmouth, N.J.

Length: 10–11 weeks.

Objectives: To train enlisted personnel in missile electronics and repair of missile equipment.

Instruction: Electron flow, voltage, current, and resistance; primary and secondary cells; series and parallel circuits; motors and generators; transformers; inductance and capacitance; RC and LR circuits; diodes and voltage dividers; power supplies; vacuum tube circuits; oscillators; voltage regulators; magnetic amplifiers; synchro and servo devices; radio waves, RF filters, and sine wave oscillators; signal generators, mixers, and AM detectors; receivers and transmitters.

Credit recommendation, collegiate level: 3 semester hours at the freshman or sophomore level as an elective in the areas of radio and electronics, and credit in electrical laboratory on the basis of demonstrated skills and/or institutional examinations.

1. Guided Missile Systems Officer
2. Guided Missile Systems Officer
3. Guided Missile Staff Officer
4. Guided Missile Staff Officer

Location: Air Defense School, Fort Bliss, Tex.

Length: *Course 1,* 39 weeks; *Course 2,* 38 weeks; *Course 3,* 35 weeks; *Course 4,* 26 weeks.

Objectives: To train commissioned officers in essential material pertaining to research and development, testing analysis, and military application of guided missile systems.

Instruction: Mathematics; engineering electronics including vacuum tubes, solid state devices; transistors, amplitude and frequency modulation, wave-shaping circuits, microwaves, radar systems; physics including statics, dynamics, thermodynamics and aerospace dynamics; analogue and digital computers; aerodynamics; propulsion; guidance and control; system analysis; nuclear physics and reactors; tactics; guided missile systems.

Credit recommendation, collegiate level: CAUTION: *These courses vary in title, length, and recommendation. Require exact identification of course by title and length. Course 1:* 15 semester hours as an elective in the areas of engineering electronics, mechanics, aeropropulsion, and aerodynamics; 3 semester hours in systems analysis, and additional credit in mathematics and physics on the basis of institutional examination. *Course 2:* 15 semester hours as an elective in the areas of engineering electronics, mechanics, aeropropulsion, and aerodynamics, and additional credit in mathematics and physics on the basis of institutional examination. *Course 3:* 12 semester hours as an elective in the areas of engineering electronics, mechanics, aeropropulsion, and aerodynamics, and additional credit in mathematics and physics on the basis of institutional examination. *Course 4:* 10 semester hours as an elective in the areas of engineering electronics, mechanics, aeropropulsion, and aerodynamics, and additional credit in mathematics and physics on the basis of institutional examination.

1. H-13/H-19 Transition Flight Training
2. H-13/H-34 Transition Flight Training

Location: Aviation School, Fort Rucker, Ala.

Length: 13 weeks.

Objectives: To train previously rated Army aviators in the operational flying of H-13, H-19, and H-34 type helicopters.

Instruction: Flight maneuvers; familiarization with aviation maintenance; mission, organization, and employment of transport aviation.

Credit recommendation, collegiate level: Credit in helicopter flight training on the basis of demonstrated skills and/or institutional examinations.

H-37 Helicopter Crew Training

Location: Aviation School, Fort Rucker, Ala.

Length: 6 weeks.

Objectives: To provide transition flight training and maintenance training in the H-37 helicopter for selected crews of officers, warrant officers, and enlisted men from transport helicopter units which are being converted to H-37 helicopter units.

Instruction: Preflight inspection; power plants; transmission; rotor head actuating mechanisms hydraulic systems; utility systems; periodic inspections; aviators receive flight training; members of the crew receive maintenance training.

Credit recommendation, collegiate level: *For aviators,* credit in helicopter flight training on the basis of demonstrated skills and/or institutional examinations. *For members of the crew—*flight engineer, crew chief, and mechanic—credit in helicopter repair on the basis of demonstrated skills and/or institutional examinations.

H-37 Helicopter Mechanic Training
(H-37 Helicopter Organizational Maintenance)

Location: Aviation School, Fort Rucker, Ala.

Length: 5–8 weeks.

Objectives: To train enlisted men in organizational maintenance of H-37 helicopters.

Instruction: Maintenance of airframe group; power plants; transmission; rotor head actuating systems; hydraulic system; electrical systems; utility systems; periodic inspections.

Credit recommendation, collegiate level: This course is technical and vocational in nature. Credit in helicopter repair shop on the basis of demonstrated skills and/or institutional examinations.

H-37 Helicopter Pilot Transition Training
(Army H-37 Helicopter Pilot Transition Flight Training)

Location: Aviation School, Fort Rucker, Ala.

Length: 4–6 weeks.

Objectives: To train aviators, officers, and warrant officers with transition flight training and maintenance training in the H-37 helicopter.

Instruction: Flight training, including familiarization of radio and flight instruments, engine, flight controls, fuel, oil, and hydraulic systems operation in flight; maneuvers; tactical operations; load operations; night operations.

Credit recommendation, collegiate level: Credit in helicopter flight training on the basis of demonstrated skills and/or institutional examinations.

HU-1A Helicopter Repair

Location: Transportation School, Fort Eustis, Va.

Length: 3 weeks.

Objectives: To train enlisted personnel to repair the HU-1A helicopter.

Instruction: Repair of the HU-1A main rotor and stabilizer bar assemblies; tail rotor assemblies; fuselage; utility systems; power plant; instrument and electrical system; transmission; hydraulics; flight control systems; inspections and maintenance procedures.

Credit recommendation, collegiate level: This course is technical and vocational in nature. Credit in helicopter repair shop on the basis of demonstrated skills and/or institutional examinations.

Harbor Craft Deck Operations
(Harbor Craft Deck Officer)

Location: Transportation School, Fort Eustis, Va.

Length: 18–19 weeks.

Objectives: To train officers and enlisted personnel to plan, direct, and supervise deck operations on military harbor craft.

Instruction: Trigonometric functions; navigational equipment; courses and bearings; nautical rules-of-the-road; weather, tides, and currents; celestial sphere; lines of position, time, and azimuths; navigation by the sun, stars, planets, and moon; cargo storage and handling; communications and ship handling.

Credit recommendation, collegiate level: 4 semester hours in navigation and credit in trigonometry on the basis of institutional examination.

Harbor Craft Engine Operation (Advanced)

Location: Transportation School, Fort Eustis, Va.

Length: 17–19 weeks.

Objectives: To train officers, warrant officers, and enlisted personnel in the operation and maintenance of engines on military harbor craft.

Instruction: Shipboard procedures; organizational administration; marine engineering, including mechanical drawing; diesel and gasoline engine operation, maintenance and repair; shipfitting; pipe fitting; marine electricity; fuel injection equipment; refrigeration.

Credit recommendation, collegiate level: This course is technical and vocational in nature. Credit in diesel engine repair on the basis of demonstrated skills and/or institutional examinations.

Harbor Craft Operator
(Harbor Craft Boatswain)

Location: Transportation School, Fort Eustis, Va.

Length: 5–11 weeks.

Objectives: To train enlisted personnel in the operation and deck maintenance of floating craft.

Instruction: Administration; care and maintenance of vessel; signaling; safety at sea; cargo handling and stowage; ship handling; piloting and navigation.

Credit recommendation, collegiate level: No credit because of the limited technical nature of the course.

1. Hawk Continuous Wave (CW) Radar Repair
2. Hawk Continuous Wave (CW) Radar Repair

Location: Ordnance Guided Missile School, Missile and Munitions School, Redstone Arsenal, Ala.

Length: *Course 1,* 19–24 weeks; *Course 2,* 31–34 weeks.

Objectives: To train enlisted personnel to inspect, test, and repair the Hawk Illuminator and CW acquisition radar missile electronic systems and associate test equipment.

Instruction: *Course 1:* Function, description, and operation of the Hawk Illuminator and CW acquisition radars, including illuminator transmitter and receiver assembly, Doppler tracking and ranging unit, antenna positioning system, power supplies, azimuth and speed indicator, control amplifier and control indicator

panel, and maintenance of CW acquisition radar, transmitter, receiver, Doppler spectrum analyzer and velocity gate scanner; field maintenance test equipment. *Course 2:* In addition to the preceding instruction this course contains training in missile electricity, missile electronics, pulse circuits, principles of heterodyne receivers, to include function of RF amplifiers, filters, oscillators, RF mixers, AM detectors, and automatic gain control.

Credit recommendation, collegiate level: CAUTION: *These courses vary only in length and recommendation. Require exact identification of course by length. Course 1:* Credit in electrical laboratory on the basis of demonstrated skills and/or institutional examinations. *Course 2:* 3 semester hours at the freshman or sophomore level as an elective in electricity and electronics, and credit in electrical laboratory on the basis of demonstrated skills and/or institutional examinations.

Hawk Continuous Wave Radar Maintenance
(Hawk CW Radar Maintenance)

Location: Army Air Defense School, Fort Bliss, Tex.

Length: 22–28 weeks.

Objectives: To train warrant officers and enlisted personnel to install, test, adjust, and perform organizational maintenance on Hawk system continuous-wave radars and the assault fire command console.

Instruction: AC and DC circuits, vacuum tubes and basic electronics and radio circuits, amplifier and oscillator theory and circuits, transmission techniques and indicators, servosystems; assembling, analyzing and troubleshooting circuits; Hawk system operation, continuous-wave radars, and consolidated continuous-wave radar component functioning; illuminator radar; continuous-wave acquisition radar; assault phase fire command console; range-only radar functioning.

Credit recommendation, collegiate level: 3 semester hours at the freshman or sophomore level as an elective in electricity and electronics, and credit in electrical laboratory on the basis of demonstrated skills and/or institutional examinations.

Hawk Fire Control Repair

Location: Missile and Munitions Center and School, Redstone Arsenal, Ala.

Length: 33 weeks.

Objectives: To train enlisted personnel to inspect, test, and repair, through support maintenance level, the Hawk Battery Control Central, Assault Fire Command Console, and Radar Signal Simulator electronic systems and associated test equipment.

Instruction: Care and use of soldering tools and materials; electricity and electronics, including Ohm's law, series and parallel circuits, AC and DC circuits, magnetism, batteries, induction, motors and generators, capacitance, impedance, transformers, use of multimeter, oscilloscope, and vacuum tube voltmeter, series and parallel resonance, sinusoidal circuits, transients in RC circuits, RC differentiation and integration, diodes, triodes, power supply, amplifiers, synchro devices, microwave principles and techniques, transmission lines, frequency measurement, microwave receivers, missile semiconductors, transistor circuits, and cathode-ray tubes; function, description, operation, and maintenance of Battery Control Central and Assault Fire Command Console equipment and Hawk Guided Missile System Radar Signal Simulator.

Credit recommendation, collegiate level: 3 semester hours in electricity and electronics, and credit in electrical laboratory on the basis of demonstrated skills and/or institutional examinations.

1. **Hawk Internal Guidance and Launcher Electronics Repair**
2. **Hawk Internal Guidance and Launcher Electronics Repair**

Location: Ordnance Guided Missile School, Redstone Arsenal, Ala.

Length: *Course 1,* 25 weeks; *Course 2,* 15 weeks.

Objectives: To train enlisted personnel to inspect, test, perform field maintenance, and repair the Hawk internal guidance and launcher electronics systems and associated equipment.

Instruction: *Course 1:* Series and parallel circuits; motors and generators; DC power; control devices; transformers; inductance and capacitance; resonance circuits; RC and LR circuits; diodes and voltage dividers; vacuum tube circuits; sine-wave oscillators; synchro and servo devices; amplifier circuits and oscillators; multivibrators and gating circuits. *Course 2:* Principles of Hawk guidance; electronic circuits; operation, organizational and field maintenance of test equipment; missile handling and organizational maintenance; receiver; speedgate; antenna control and autopilot; missile organizational test shop; launcher; abbreviated missile test station.

Credit recommendation, collegiate level: CAUTION: *These courses vary in length and credit recommendation. Require exact identification of course by title and length. Course 1:* 4 semester hours in electricity and electronics, and credit in electrical laboratory on the basis of demonstrated skills and/or institutional examinations. *Course 2:* Credit in electrical laboratory on the basis of demonstrated skills and/or institutional examinations.

Hawk Mechanical Repair

Location: Ordnance Guided Missile School, Redstone Arsenal, Ala.

Length: 8 weeks.

Objectives: To train enlisted personnel in the function, operation, and maintenance of the Hawk mechanical system and associated equipment.

Instruction: Components, organizational and field maintenance of surface-to-air missile systems; Hawk mechanic and hydraulic systems, launcher, loader, missile, and associated test equipment.

Credit recommendation, collegiate level: This course is technical and vocational in nature. Credit in mechanical shop on the basis of demonstrated skills and/or institutional examinations.

Hawk Missile and Launcher Maintenance

Location: Air Defense School, Fort Bliss, Tex.

Length: 19–24 weeks.

Objectives: To train officers and enlisted personnel in the operation, adjustments, maintenance, and troubleshooting of the loader, launcher, missile, and associated test equipment of the Hawk system.

Instruction: Electronics, including AC and DC circuits, vacuum tubes, electronic and radio circuits, amplifiers, oscillators, servosystems, modulation techniques, assembly and analyzing circuits, pulse acquisition radar, battery control center, AC generators, diesel engines, hydraulics, launcher mechanical systems, synchros, transformers, transmitters, integrators, special circuits, Hawk missile and guidance system, speedgate, antenna control, mixers, discriminators, Doppler, diodes, detonation; cabling, energizing, and assembly procedures of missile test sets.

Credit recommendation, collegiate level: 3 semester hours at the freshman or sophomore level as an elective in electricity and electronics, and credit in electrical laboratory on the basis of demonstrated skills and/or institutional examinations.

Hawk Missile and Launcher Repair (Transition Instruction)

Location: Missile and Munitions Center and School, Redstone Arsenal, Ala.

Length: 21 weeks.

Objectives: To train mechanical repairmen to inspect, test, perform support maintenance and repair of the Hawk missile and launcher electronic systems and associated equipment.

Instruction: Introduction to electricity; Ohm's law; series circuits; parallel circuits; series-parallel circuits; DC power; alternating current; capacitance and impedance; transformers; oscilloscope; series and parallel resonance; transients in LR and RC circuits; diodes; power supplies; amplifiers; advanced soldering; synchro devices; microwave measurement; frequency converters; AM detectors; receiver testing; pulse modulated transmitter; FM transmitter; system troubleshooting; power supplies; multistage circuits; pulse circuits; multivibrator; phantastron circuits; video amplifiers; Hawk missile launcher and associated test equipment.

Credit recommendation, collegiate level: 4 semester hours in electronics, and credit in electrical laboratory on the basis of demonstrated skills and/or institutional examinations. *See* page 365 for 32-week course.

Hawk Officer (Hawk Officer Qualification)

Location: Air Defense School, Fort Bliss, Tex.

Length: 5–7 weeks.

Objectives: To provide artillery officers with a working knowledge of essential materiel and tactics pertaining to the Hawk system.

Instruction: The Hawk system and equipment; Hawk fire control platoon; Hawk firing platoon; Hawk firing battery and air defense tactics.

Credit recommendation, collegiate level: No credit because of the military nature of the course.

Hawk Organizational Maintenance Supervisor

Location: Air Defense School, Fort Bliss, Tex.

Length: 32–40 weeks.

Objectives: To train warrant officers and enlisted personnel in the operation and organizational maintenance of the Hawk missile system and associated equipment.

Instruction: Pulse acquisition radar; AC–DC circuits; distribution and power supplies; transmitters; receivers; range-only radar; antenna control; system analysis and maintenance; continuous wave acquisition radar; test set; special circuits; Doppler; high-powered illuminator; loader, launcher, and missile; speedgate; battery control central; IFF Mark X system.

Credit recommendation, collegiate level: 2 semester hours in maintenance management, and credit in electrical laboratory on the basis of demonstrated skills and/or institutional examinations.

Hawk Pulse Acquisition Radar and Battery Control Central Maintenance
(Hawk Pulse Acquisition Radar and Battery Control Center Maintenance)

Location: Army Air Defense School, Fort Bliss, Tex.

Length: 29–34 weeks.

Objectives: To train warrant officers and enlisted personnel to install, test, adjust, and perform organizational maintenance on the pulse acquisition radar, range-only radar, and battery control central of the Hawk missile system.

Instruction: Electricity and electronics, including AC and DC circuits, inductance, capacitance, transformers, three-phase power, resonant circuits, diodes and rectifiers, filters, voltage dividers and potentiometers, triodes, multi-element tubes, amplifiers, cathode followers, oscillators, modulation techniques, detectors-mixers, superheterodyne receiver, multivibrators, sweep generators, synchros, and servosystems; operation, adjustment, maintenance, and troubleshooting of the pulse acquisition radar; characteristics, capabilities, circuits, and operational adjustments for the basic system for identification, friend or foe; maintenance, adjustments, and operation of range-only radar and battery control central.

Credit recommendation, collegiate level: 3 semester hours at the freshman or sophomore level as an elective in electricity and electronics and credit in electrical laboratory on the basis of demonstrated skills and/or institutional examinations.

1. **Hawk Pulse Acquisition Radar and Battery Control Repair**
2. **Hawk Pulse Acquisition Radar and Battery Control Repair**
3. **Hawk Pulse Radar Repair**

Location: Ordnance Guided Missile School, Missile and Munitions School, Redstone Arsenal, Ala.

Length: *Course 1,* 21–25 weeks; *Courses 2 and 3,* 31–46 weeks.

Objectives: To train enlisted personnel to inspect, test, and repair the Hawk pulse acquisition radar and associated electronic equipment.

Instruction: *Course 1:* Function, operation, organizational and support maintenance of the Hawk pulse acquisition radar, range-only radar, battery control central, and assault fire command console. *Courses 2 and 3:* In addition to the previous instruction these courses contain electricity and electronics, including Ohm's law, AC and DC circuits, inductance, capacitance and impedance, motors, and generators, transformers, diodes, power supplies, triode tubes, multielement tubes, oscillators, synchro devices, amplifiers, transmitters, heterodyne receivers, indicators, multivibrator, transister circuits, cathode and emitter followers, phantastron circuits, filters, RF mixers, AM detectors, and automatic gain control.

Credit recommendation, collegiate level: CAUTION: *These courses vary in title, length, and recommendation. Require exact identification of course by title and length. Course 1:* Credit in electrical laboratory on the basis of demonstrated skills and/or institutional examinations. *Courses 2 and 3:* For each course, 4 semester hours at the freshman or sophomore level as an elective in electricity and electronics, and credit in electrical laboratory on the basis of demonstrated skills and/or institutional examinations.

Heating and Ventilating

Location: Engineer School, Fort Belvoir, Va.

Length: 8 weeks.

Objectives: To train enlisted personnel to install, maintain, and repair heating and ventilating units and associated control devices.

Instruction: Blueprint reading; heat transfer; insulation; combustion; thermostats, humidistats, pneumatic controls; pipe fitting; fuel burners; warm air heating systems; steam heating; hot water heating; ventilation.

Credit recommendation, collegiate level: This course is vocational in nature. Credit in boiler repair on the basis of demonstrated skills and/or institutional examinations.

Heavy Fire Control Equipment Repair

Location: Ordnance School, Aberdeen Proving Ground, Md.

Length: 19 weeks.

Objectives: To train enlisted personnel to inspect, test, and perform field and depot maintenance on heavy integrated electronic fire control equipment.

Instruction: Principles of fire control systems; M33 radar components; acquisition and track radar with computer; test equipment and procedures; radar transmitters and receivers; transmission lines and wave components; synchros and resolvers; theory and maintenance of power supplies, regulators, and AC and DC distribution in the M33 radar system; circuitry and adjustment of the track radar presentation and servo systems; adjustment and troubleshooting of the computer fire control system; operation of plotting boards.

Credit recommendation, collegiate level: Credit in electronics and electrical laboratory on the basis of demonstrated skills and/or institutional examinations.

1. Heavy Mortar and Davy Crockett Officer
   (Battalion Mortar and Davy Crockett Platoon
       Officer)
   (Infantry Heavy Mortar)
2. Heavy Mortar and Davy Crockett NCO
   (Battalion Mortar and Davy Crockett NCO)

Location: Infantry School, Fort Benning, Ga.

Length: 6 weeks.

Objectives: To train officers and noncommissioned officers to command, supervise, and direct the fire of heavy mortar units and/or a Davy Crockett section in support of infantry combat units.

Instruction: Offensive, defensive, retrograde, and counterguerrilla operations; effects of nuclear weapons; communications equipment and procedures; mechanical training, crew drill, forward observation, and fire direction procedures; Davy Crockett gunnery; techniques for controlling the fires of a mortar section and a Davy Crockett section.

Credit recommendation, collegiate level: No credit as these courses are military in nature.

Helicopter Instrument Flying

Location: Aviation School, Fort Rucker, Ala.

Length: 10–11 weeks.

Objectives: To train aviators to operate helicopters during actual or simulated instrument conditions.

Instruction: Basic and advanced instrument flight; air traffic control; IFR flight planning and navigation; weather flight planning; meteorology; frontal weather; air masses; pressure and winds; enroute and approach charts; maintenance of fuel and oil systems, transmission, rotor systems, and auxiliary equipment.

Credit recommendation, collegiate level: 2 semester hours in elementary meteorology and navigation.

High Speed Radio Operation

Location: Southeastern Signal School, Fort Gordon, Ga.

Length: 23 weeks.

Objectives: To train enlisted personnel to operate radio communication equipment, to receive international Morse code at a minimum speed of 25 five-letter random code groups per minute, and to transmit at a minimum speed of 20 five-letter random code groups per minute.

Instruction: Army method of printing; phonetic alphabet; principles of communication security; transmitting and receiving international Morse code at the required speeds; familiarization with signal supply procedures; Mill typing; radiotelegraph and radiotelephone procedures; teletypewriter procedure and operation; radio net operation, including traffic handling and use of prescribed radiotelegraph procedure; field radio equipment and operation.

Credit recommendation, collegiate level: This course is technical and vocational in nature. Credit in radio operation on the basis of demonstrated skills and/or institutional examinations.

Hospital Administration

Location: Medical Field Service School, Fort Sam Houston, Tex.

Length: 39 weeks.

Objectives: To train commissioned officers to direct and supervise the administrative activities in the Army Medical Service, with particular emphasis on the military hospital.

Instruction: Principles of administration as applied to medical facilities; organization and administration of hospitals; financial management and accounting; administration of medical facilities in theaters of operation; organization of medical food services; planning, design, conversion, operation, and maintenance of medical facilities; policy formulation, decisions, and administrative responsibility; familiarization with medical law; medical records and patient administration; supply procedures; personnel management; training in the ability to think logically and creatively in administrative problems; research methods; statistical analysis of hospital administrative problems; orientation to medical science.

Credit recommendation, collegiate level: 9 semester hours in hospital administration, 6 semester hours in personnel management, and 3 semester hours in statistical analysis.

Image Interpretation (Enlisted)

Location: Intelligence School, Fort Holabird, Md.

Length: 13 weeks.

Objectives: To train enlisted personnel in the techniques of tactical image interpretation and reporting, aerial surveillance organization, planning, and operation.

Instruction: Map reading; general military and intelligence; aerial surveillance organization, operation, and planning; radar imagery interpretation; metrics; terrain; stereovision.

Credit recommendation, collegiate level: 3 semester hours in imagery interpretation.

Image Interpretation Officer
(Photo Interpretation Officer)

Location: Intelligence School, Fort Holabird, Md.

Length: 19–24 weeks.

Objectives: To train commissioned officers in the techniques and principles of image interpretation and in the performance of tactical imagery interpretation duties.

Instruction: Doctrine, principles, and techniques of combat intelligence and counterintelligence; techniques and procedures of photo interpretation; photogrammetry; preparation of terrain studies from aerial photography; methods of reporting and disseminating information derived from photographs.

Credit recommendation, collegiate level: 5 semester hours in photographic interpretation.

Impregnation Equipment Operation

Location: Chemical Corps School, Fort McClellan, Ala.

Length: 8 weeks.

Objectives: To train enlisted personnel in the operation, installation, inspection, and maintenance of impregnation equipment.

Instruction: Chemical munitions and materiel; methods and procedures used for impregnation of clothing; decontaminating materials and procedures; processing plant operations, including site preparation, pipe fitting, rigging, plant disassembly and assembly, laboratory analysis, calculation and preparation of a base suspension, and preparation of clothing for impregnation; maintenance of processing plant equipment.

Credit recommendation, collegiate level: This course is technical and vocational in nature. Credit in impregnation equipment operation and maintenance on the basis of demonstrated skills and/or institutional examinations.

Improved Alternate Battery Acquisition Radar Maintenance Transition
(Defense Acquisition Radar/Alternate Battery Acquisition Radar Maintenance (National Guard))

Location: Army Air Defense School, Fort Bliss, Tex.
Length: 3–7 weeks.
Objectives: To train warrant officers and enlisted personnel in the operation, adjustment, and organizational maintenance of improved alternate battery acquisition radars and associated ECCM consoles.

Instruction: Function and maintenance of the improved alternate battery acquisition radar with electronic counter-countermeasure consoles; operation and tie-in of associated equipment.

Credit recommendation, collegiate level: Credit in electrical laboratory on the basis of demonstrated skills and/or institutional examinations.

1. Improved Nike-Hercules Fire Control System Maintenance
2. (Nike-Hercules Fire Control System Maintenance)
3. (Nike-Universal Fire Control System Maintenance)

Location: Air Defense School, Fort Bliss, Tex.
Length: *Course 1,* 40 and 48 weeks; *Course 2,* 44 weeks; *Course 3,* 41, 44, and 46 weeks.
Objectives: To train warrant officers and enlisted personnel to operate, adjust, and maintain the Nike-Universal fire control system and associated equipment.

Instruction: AC and DC circuits; vacuum tubes; electronic and radio circuits; amplifiers; oscillators; radio; CW and AM transmitters; radar circuits; interlocks; timers; regulators; acquisition radar track synchronizer, transmitting system magnetron, and antenna control; target-tracking radar transmitting system components; radar test set; target-tracking radar receiving and presentation systems; range and antenna positioning systems; computer basic circuits, prelaunch configuration, and steering configuration; multichannel data recorder and associated circuits; missile track radar command, transmitting, receiving, range, and elevation systems; troubleshooting; overall checkout.

Credit recommendation, collegiate level: CAUTION:

These courses vary in title, length, and recommendation. Require exact identification of course by title and length. Course 1, 48 weeks; *Course 3,* 46 weeks: 6 semester hours at the freshman or sophomore level as an elective in electricity and electronics, and credit in electrical laboratory on the basis of demonstrated skills and/or institutional examinations, for each course. *Course 1,* 40 weeks; *Course 3,* 41 and 44 weeks; *Course 2:* 4 semester hours at the freshman or sophomore level as an elective in electricity and electronics, and credit in electrical laboratory on the basis of demonstrated skills and/or institutional examinations, for each course.

1. Improved Nike-Hercules Fire Control System Maintenance Transition
2. Improved Nike-Hercules Fire Control System Maintenance Transition

Location: Air Defense School, Fort Bliss, Tex.
Length: *Course 1,* 5–6 weeks; *Course 2,* 11 weeks.
Objectives: To provide commissioned officers, warrant officers, and enlisted personnel—qualified in the employment, operation, and maintenance of the Nike–Hercules fire control system—with training in the Improved Nike-Hercules fire control system.

Instruction: *Course 1:* Target-range and target-track radars, including systems analysis and functions of all major items of equipment. In addition, *Course 2* includes instruction in the Improved Nike-Hercules high-powered and low-powered acquisition radars.

Credit recommendation, collegiate level: Credit in electronics and electrical laboratory for each course on the basis of demonstrated skills and/or institutional examinations.

Improved Nike-Hercules High Power Acquisition Radar Maintenance

Location: Army Air Defense School, Fort Bliss, Tex.
Length: 5 weeks.
Objectives: To train commissioned officers, warrant officers, and enlisted personnel, who are qualified in the employment, operation, adjustment, and maintenance of the Improved Nike-Hercules fire control system, in the Improved Nike-Hercules high power acquisition radar.

Instruction: Acquisition, transmitting, stagger, receiving, and MTI systems; system checkout.

Credit recommendation, collegiate level: Credit in electrical laboratory on the basis of demonstrated skills and/or institutional examinations.

Infantry Advanced Noncommissioned Officer

Location: Infantry School, Fort Benning, Ga.
Length: 16 weeks.
Objectives: To train enlisted personnel to control and supervise the training and tactical employment of a platoon of an infantry rifle or heavy weapons company.

Instruction: Infantry weapons; basic tactics techniques; characteristics, operation, and employment of communication equipment; automotive maintenance;

drill and command; bayonet fighting; familiarization with aircraft and aerial delivery; air-ground operations.

Credit recommendation, collegiate level: No credit as this course is military in nature.

Infantry Automotive Supervision

Location: Infantry School, Fort Benning, Ga.
Length: 10 weeks.
Objectives: To train enlisted personnel to supervise motor pool operation, organizational maintenance, and recovery of wheel vehicles in infantry units.
Instruction: Tactical driver training methods; motor pool operation; construction, functioning, care and abuse of general purpose vehicle engines and electrical systems; functioning, adjustments, lubrication, and trouble diagnosis of chassis components; operation and maintenance familiarization with full track vehicles; preventive maintenance services on wheeled vehicles and trailers; vehicle recovery maintenance and evacuation.
Credit recommendation, collegiate level: This course is technical and vocational in nature. Credit in automotive repair on the basis of demonstrated skills and/or institutional examinations.

Infantry Counterfire Supervision

Location: Infantry School, Fort Benning, Ga.
Length: 5 weeks.
Objective: To train personnel to supervise the training and tactical employment of an infantry counterfire platoon, squad, or team.
Instruction: Forward observation procedures; target-grid method of fire control; artillery organization, function and application in countermortar/counterbattery fire.
Credit recommendation, collegiate level: No credit as the course is military in nature.

Infantry Motor Transportation

Location: Infantry School, Fort Benning, Ga.
Length: 10 weeks.
Objectives: To train commissioned officers and warrant officers in motor transport and motor maintenance duties in infantry units.
Instruction: Tactical driver training methods; organization for maintenance; care and use of tools; maintenance forms and records; vehicle inspections; motor pool operation; trains area selection and occupation; map and route reconnaissance; construction, functioning, care and abuses of general purpose vehicles engines and electrical systems; functioning, adjustments, lubrication, and trouble diagnosis of chassis components; operation and maintenance familiarization with full track vehicles; preventive maintenance services on wheeled vehicles; map and aerial photograph reading.
Credit recommendation, collegiate level: This course is technical and vocational in nature. Credit in automotive repair on the basis of demonstrated skills and/or institutional examinations.

Infantry Officer Candidate

Location: Infantry School, Fort Benning, Ga.
Length: 22–23 weeks.
Objectives: To train selected personnel to be second lieutenants capable of performing duties appropriate to their grade in active Army Infantry units or, with a minimum of additional training, capable of serving as second lieutenants in other designated branches.
Instruction: Combined arms tactics; staff department; military leadership; effective speaking; map and aerial photograph reading; legal and medical subjects; communications electronics; Army maintenance system and unit-materiel readiness; weapons.
Credit recommendation, collegiate level: Credit in advanced military at institutions which regularly offer such credit.

Infantry Officer Candidate (Reserve Component) (Infantry Army Reserve Officer Candidate) (National Guard Infantry Officer Candidate)

Location: Infantry School, Fort Benning, Ga.
Length: 8–9 weeks.
Objectives: To train National Guard and Army Reserve personnel in the duties and responsibilities appropriate to platoon leaders of infantry rifle and weapon platoons.
Instruction: Weapons; leadership; map and aerial photograph reading; signal communication; mobility department; command and staff department.
Credit recommendation, collegiate level: 3 semester hours in military science.

Infantry Officer Career (Infantry Officer Advanced)

Location: Infantry School, Fort Benning, Ga.
Length: 34–36 weeks.
Objectives: To provide branch training in the duties and responsibilities of infantry officers.
Instruction: Command and staff procedures; personnel functions and staff responsibilities; familiarization with basic administrative law; principles and techniques of combat intelligence; duties of the battalion and brigade staff officer; training management responsibilities; logistical system; tactical methods and techniques at the battalion, brigade, and division level; planning and execution of offensive and defensive operations; armor, artillery, and amphibious operations; organizational structure, missions, and techniques of employment of Army aviation units; combined arms operations; field engineering techniques; nuclear weapons employment; communications; organization of a battalion maintenance program and vehicle inspection; characteristics and techniques of fire of infantry weapons; military leadership.
Credit recommendation, collegiate level: 6 semester hours in business organization and management.

Infantry Radio Maintenance

Location: Infantry School, Fort Benning, Ga.
Length: 12–15 weeks.
Objectives: To train enlisted personnel to perform

organizational maintenance on field-type radio and associated electronic equipment of infantry units.

Instruction: Basic electricity, including magnetism and the electron, Ohm's law, series and parallel DC circuits, alternating current, inductance and inductive reactance, transformer characteristics, capacitance, series and parallel L-C-R circuits, power supplies, triode and multi-element tubes, and AC circuits; radio receivers and transmitters; antenna systems; troubleshooting procedures; maintenance and repair of radio sets and miscellaneous electronic equipment.

Credit recommendation, collegiate level: 2 semester hours at the freshman or sophomore level as an elective in electricity. At the technical level, credit in radio repair on the basis of demonstrated skills and/or institutional examinations.

1. **Information Officer**
2. **Information Officer**
3. **Public Information Officer**
4. **Troop Information and Education Officer**

Location: Information School, Fort Slocum, N.Y.

Length: *Course 1,* 10 weeks; *Courses 2, 3, and 4,* 8 weeks.

Objectives: To train officers to plan, program, coordinate, supervise, and participate in the preparation and dissemination of troop and/or public information.

Instruction: *Course 1:* Policy and operational procedures; methods and techniques of oral communication; pictorial journalism; collection, preparation, and editing of news releases; evaluation and preparation of information for radio and television broadcast; United States, military and world affairs. *Courses 2, 3, and 4:* These courses contain the same academic material as *Course 1* but include somewhat less instruction in oral communications.

Credit recommendation, collegiate level: CAUTION: *These courses vary only slightly in title, length, and recommendation. Require exact identification of course by title and length. Course 1:* 2 semester hours in the area of social studies, 2 semester hours in oral communications, and credit in journalism on the basis of institutional examinations. *Courses 2, 3, and 4:* 2 semester hours in the area of social studies, 1 semester hour in oral communications, and credit in journalism on the basis of institutional examinations, for each course.

1. **Information Officer Basic (USN, USMC)**
   (Abbreviated)
2. **Information Officer Basic**

Locations: Defense Information School, Fort Slocum, N.Y.; Fort Benjamin Harrison, Ind.

Length: *Course 1,* 4 weeks; *Course 2,* 8 weeks.

Objectives: *Course 1:* To train Army, Air Force, Navy, Marine, and Coast Guard officers in the preparation and dissemination of information through the various communications media. *Course 2:* To provide Army and Air Force officers with additional training in this area. *Note—*Beginning July 1966, officers of all the services received the entire 8 weeks of instruction.

Instruction: *Course 1:* Information policies, objectives, plans, and programs; theories and techniques of editorial and pictorial journalism; methods and tech-

niques of oral communication; principles, policies, and procedures for preparing tape recorded interviews, and program and background material for radio and television broadcast. *Course 2:* In addition to the preceding instruction, this course includes international relations and government and more intensive instruction in policy and plans, oral communications, and radio and television news and broadcast writing techniques.

Credit recommendation, collegiate level: CAUTION: *These courses vary only in length and recommendation. Require exact identification of course by title and length. Course 1:* Credit in oral communications and journalism on the basis of institutional examinations. *Course 2:* 2 semester hours in the area of social studies, 1 semester hour in oral communications, and credit in journalism on the basis of institutional examination.

1. **Information Specialist**
2. **Public Information Enlisted**
3. **Troop Information and Education Enlisted**

Location: Information School, Fort Slocum, N.Y.

Length: 8 weeks.

Objectives: To train enlisted personnel in the selection, evaluation, preparation, and dissemination of public and troop information.

Instruction: Organization, objectives, and communications media for internal, external, and community relations programs; techniques of public speaking; applied journalism; preparation of information for release to the radio and television media; military, United States, and world affairs.

Credit recommendation, collegiate level: For each course, 2 semester hours in the area of social studies, 1 semester hour in oral communications, and credit in journalism on the basis of institutional examinations.

Installation/Direct Support Supply Officer

Location: Quartermaster School, Fort Lee, Va.

Length: 6 weeks.

Objectives: To train commissioned officers and warrant officers in the procedures involved in supplying equipment and repair parts to using organizations.

Instruction: Unit and organization supply; installation direct support–general support supply procedures; installation and field storage procedures; procurement; financial management; management skills; maintenance and supply relationship; organization for supply operations in the theater of operations.

Credit recommendation, collegiate level: 3 semester hours in supply management.

Installation Intelligence

Location: Intelligence School, Fort Holabird, Md.

Length: 3 weeks.

Objectives: To train commissioned officers and enlisted personnel in installation intelligence, counterintelligence, and physical security functions and responsibilities.

Instruction: Counterintelligence; installation intelligence; investigative legal principles; security; personnel security investigation; countersabotage; counterespion age; defense against methods of entry; investigative potential of photography; physical evidence; extremist groups; interviewing and incidental informants; questioning techniques.

Credit recommendation, collegiate level: 2 semester hours in intelligence methods.

1. Installation Stock Control
(Quartermaster Stock Control)
2. Quartermaster Stock Control

Location: Quartermaster School, Fort Lee, Va.
Length: *Course 1, 3–4 weeks; Course 2, 6 weeks.*
Objectives: To train officers and warrant officers in quartermaster stock control and accounting procedures at post, camp, and station level.
Instruction: Supply economy; unit and organization supply; station supply; classification and disposal; depot operations; stock management; comptroller and financial management.
Credit recommendation, collegiate level: *Course 1:* 3 semester hours in supply management. *Course 2:* 4 semester hours in supply management.

Installation Supply Procedures

Location: Quartermaster School, Fort Lee, Va.
Length: 3 weeks.
Objectives: To train enlisted personnel in supply procedures and operations at continental United States consolidated supply activities.
Instruction: Basic supply procedures; installation supply procedures; property disposal activities; stock accounting; procurement; storage procedures; financial management.
Credit recommendation, collegiate level: This course is technical and vocational in nature. Credit in stock accounting procedure on the basis of institutional examination.

1. Installation Traffic Management
2. Installation Transportation

Location: Transportation School, Fort Eustis, Va.
Length: *Course 1,* 4 weeks; *Course 2,* 8 weeks.
Objectives: To train commissioned officers in the economical and efficient performance of commercial and military traffic functions and in the military transportation functions of an installation transportation officer.
Instruction: Organization and field installations; movement of baggage and household goods in the continental United States; freight and passenger transportation in the continental United States; movement problems; Transportation Corps field services in the continental United States; administration and supply.
Credit recommendation, collegiate level: CAUTION: *These courses vary only slightly in title, length, and recommendation. Require exact identification of courses by title and length. Course 1:* 2 semester hours in transportation management. *Course 2:* 4 semester hours in transportation management.

Integrated Data Link Repair

Location: Army Air Defense School, Fort Bliss, Tex.
Length: 29 weeks.
Objectives: To train warrant officers and enlisted personnel to perform organizational and field maintenance on AN/FSG-1 missile master equipment within the Army air defense system.
Instruction: Mission, functions, and operation of the air defense system AN/FSG-1; operation and schematic analysis of the power supplies and control circuitry; troubleshooting and preventive maintenance procedures; SAGE receiving subsystem, including the digital data converter; purpose and analysis of the TDDL timing and data flow, designation switchboard, designation function, and broadcast function; battery data link function; SAGE transmission subsystem.
Credit recommendation, collegiate level: Credit in electrical laboratory on the basis of demonstrated skills and/or institutional examinations.

Intelligence Enlisted

Location: Intelligence School, Fort Holabird, Md.
Length: 13 weeks.
Objectives: To train enlisted personnel to assist intelligence staff officers in the collection, processing, and dissemination of military information and intelligence, in the preparation of intelligence reports, and in the preparation and supervision of intelligence training programs.
Instruction: Intelligence clerical and editing duties; familiarization with the organization, tactics, and operations of the Armed Forces and selected foreign nations; doctrine, principles, and techniques of combat intelligence and counterintelligence; principles, functions, and operations of intelligence specialists, including such areas as censorship, editing, field operations intelligence, photo interpretation, and interrogation of prisoners of war.
Credit recommendation, collegiate level: 3 semester hours in intelligence methods.

1. Intelligence Research Officer
2. Military Intelligence (Analysis), Enlisted

Location: Intelligence School, Fort Holabird, Md.
Length: 14 weeks.
Objectives: To train commissioned officers and enlisted personnel to collect, evaluate, and disseminate information pertaining to espionage, sabotage, treason, sedition, disaffection, and/or subversive activities, and to conduct investigations of personnel within the jurisdiction of the Army.
Instruction: Mission of intelligence units; intelligence procedures; administration in intelligence units; investigative reports; security; observation and description; investigations; countersabotage and counterespionage; surveillance; raids and searches; physical evidence; combat operations; investigative legal principles.
Credit recommendation, collegiate level: For each course, 3 semester hours in intelligence methods.

1. Intelligence Research Officer/Technician
2. Military Intelligence Specialist

Location: Intelligence School, Fort Holabird, Md.
Length: 13–15 weeks.
Objectives: To train commissioned officers, warrant officers, and enlisted personnel in signal communications, friendly and hostile intelligence agencies, and counterintelligence and in the planning, execution, and direction of general counterintelligence activities, security services, security investigations, and counterintelligence special operations.
Instruction: Combat intelligence; sources of information; observation and description; investigative legal principles; surveillance, internal attack, internal defense; foreign intelligence; interrogations and report writing; counterintelligence surveys and inspections; raids and searches; sabotage, subversion, and espionage; informants.
Credit recommendation, collegiate level: 5 semester hours in intelligence methods or police methods.

Intelligence Staff Officer

Location: Intelligence School, Fort Holabird, Md.
Length: 10 weeks.
Objectives: To train commissioned officers in the duties of intelligence staff officers.
Instruction: Familiarization with Army organization, United States tactics and operations, reconnaissance, atomic warfare, and organization and tactics of foreign armies; doctrine, principles, and techniques of combat intelligence; censorship; interrogation of prisoners of war; order of battle intelligence.
Credit recommendation, collegiate level: 3 semester hours in intelligence methods.

Internal Review
(Internal Review and Systems Improvements)

Location: Finance School, Fort Benjamin Harrison, Ind.
Length: 3–4 weeks.
Objectives: To train commissioned officers, warrant officers, and senior noncommissioned officers in procedures and techniques of internal review and systems improvements.
Instruction: Concepts and principles of internal review; key procedures and problem areas prevalent in installation activities; internal review of the finance and accounting offices and operating activities; current problems and new developments in automatic data processing systems; systems analysis and improvement; application of audit principles.
Credit recommendation, collegiate level: 2 semester hours in analysis of business procedures.

Interrogation (Enlisted)

Location: Intelligence School, Fort Holabird, Md.
Length: 7 weeks.
Objectives: To train enlisted personnel in the conduct of intelligence interrogations, screening operations, and foreign document exploitation.
Instruction: Map and photo reading; combat intelligence; evaluation, interpretation and dissemination of information; counterintelligence; area intelligence; order of battle; organization and tactics of selected foreign armies; methods of interrogation, and document exploitation.
Credit recommendation, collegiate level: 2 semester hours in intelligence methods.

Interrogation (Enlisted Non-Linguist)

Location: Intelligence School, Fort Holabird, Md.
Length: 4 weeks.
Objectives: To train enlisted non-linguist personnel in the techniques required for the collection of tactical intelligence information through interrogation employing interpreters.
Instruction: Handling of prisoners of war; enemy documents for intelligence; screening operations; interrogation techniques and application of methods.
Credit recommendation, collegiate level: Credit in intelligence methods on the basis of institutional examination.

Interrogation Officer

Location: Intelligence School, Fort Holabird, Md.
Length: 6 weeks.
Objectives: To train commissioned officers to direct and participate in the collection of tactical and strategic intelligence through the interrogation of human sources and the exploitation of documents.
Instruction: Familiarization with counterintelligence activities, area intelligence, aerial surveillance and reconnaissance, and photo reading and interpretation; order of battle and organization and tactics of selected foreign armies; methods of interrogation and document exploitation.
Credit recommendation, collegiate level: 2 semester hours in intelligence methods.

LOH Transition/Gunnery IP Qualification
(OH-6 Transition/Gunnery IP Qualification)

Location: Aviation School, Fort Rucker, Ala.
Length: 5–7 weeks.
Objectives: *Phase I:* To train officers and warrant officer aviators in the conduct of transition training in the LOH. *Phase II:* To train LOH instructor pilots in the gunnery systems associated with the LOH helicopters.
Instruction: *Phase I:* Transition flight training; methods of instruction flight training, including preflight and cockpit procedures; hovering; maneuvers and traffic patterns; approach, takeoff, and landing procedures; principles of instruction at night; learning fundamentals; effective teaching methods; OH-6 maintenance; inspections; *Phase II:* XM27 components and sighting system; 40 mm grenade launcher; principles of air-to-ground gun fire.
Credit recommendation, collegiate level: Credit in instructional methods on the basis of institutional examinations.

LaCrosse Electromechanical System Maintenance

Location: Ordnance Guided Missile School, Redstone Arsenal, Ala.

Length: 7 weeks.

Objectives: To train enlisted personnel to inspect, test, and perform field maintenance on the LaCrosse electromechanical system.

Instruction: Operation, test, and repair of the LaCrosse weapon system; handling equipment and missile structures; electrical systems; motors and generators; soldering and solderless connections; relays; batteries; circuits; hydraulic systems; launcher and systems; system analysis.

Credit recommendation, collegiate level: This course is technical and vocational in nature. Credit in electrical shop on the basis of demonstrated skills and/or institutional examinations.

1. LaCrosse External Guidance Repair
(LaCrosse External Guidance System Repair)
2. LaCrosse External Guidance Repair

Location: Ordnance Guided Missile School, Redstone Arsenal, Ala.

Length: *Course 1, 17–19 weeks; Course 2, 29 weeks.*

Objectives: To train enlisted personnel to inspect, test, and perform field maintenance on the LaCrosse external guidance system and its associated test equipment.

Instruction: *Courses 1 and 2:* Operations and checkout procedures of missile guidance central; function, operation and maintenance of missile radar, missile radar circuits, generators, power distribution, oscillators, modulators, transmitters, mixers, amplifiers, antennas, interrogators, indicator panels, associated test equipment; troubleshooting; ordnance shop practices. In addition to the preceding training, *Course 2* includes instruction in series parallel circuits; DC power; transformers; inductance and capacitance; resonance circuits; RC and LR circuits; vacuum tube circuits; voltage regulators; synchro and servo devices; transistors.

Credit recommendation, collegiate level: CAUTION: *These courses vary in title, length, and recommendation. Require exact identification of course by title and length. Course 1:* Credit in electrical laboratory on the basis of demonstrated skills and/or institutional examinations. *Course 2:* 4 semester hours at the freshman or sophomore level as an elective in electricity and electronics, and credit in electrical laboratory on the basis of demonstrated skills and/or institutional examinations.

LaCrosse Fire Control Operation

Location: Artillery and Missile School, Fort Sill, Okla.

Length: 3–5 weeks.

Objectives: To train enlisted personnel to adjust, maintain, and operate the LaCrosse missile guidance station and auxiliary equipment.

Instruction: Functioning and operation of the missile guidance control; operations in the firing position and assembly area; use of computed firing data; familiarization with the LaCrosse missile system; procedures and equipment used in the assembly and firing areas;

organization and employment of the LaCrosse battalion.

Credit recommendation, collegiate level: No credit because of the brevity and limited technical nature of the course.

1. LaCrosse Fire Control System Maintenance
2. LaCrosse Fire Control System Maintenance

Location: Artillery and Missile School, Fort Sill, Okla.

Length: *Course 1,* 6 weeks; *Course 2,* 24 weeks.

Objectives: To train warrant officers and enlisted personnel in the maintenance operations of the LaCrosse fire control and associated equipment.

Instruction: *Course 1:* Principles and capabilities of the LaCrosse system and the procedures and equipment used in the assembly and firing areas; operation and maintenance of power supplies, angular tracker and test set calibration unit, missile tracking antenna, range indicator, guidance computer, target ranging and measuring equipment, guidance central system, and missile trajectory simulator; in addition *Course 2* contains instruction in electron theory, series and parallel AC and DC circuits, use of the oscilloscope, inductance and reactance, resonant circuits, transformers, AC and DC motors and generators; electronics, including diodes and rectifiers, filters, voltage dividers, and potentiometers, multi-element and miniature tubes, voltage regulators, gas tubes and thyratrons, amplifiers, wave forms, cathode followers, oscillators, transistors, transmitters, amplitude and frequency modulation, superheterodyne receiver, sweep circuits, multivibrators, phantastron delay circuit, servomechanisms, microwave components, high-frequency generators, and photoelectric devices.

Credit recommendation, collegiate level: CAUTION: *These courses vary only in length and recommendation. Require exact identification of course by length. Course 1:* Credit in electronics and electrical laboratory on the basis of demonstrated skills and/or institutional examinations. *Course 2:* 4 semester hours at the freshman or sophomore level as an elective in electricity and electronics, and credit in electrical laboratory on the basis of demonstrated skills and/or institutional examinations.

LaCrosse Firing Battery

Location: Artillery and Missile School, Fort Sill, Okla.

Length: 4–5 weeks.

Objectives: To train enlisted personnel to supervise and instruct subordinates to assemble, test, adjust, operate, and maintain the LaCrosse field artillery missile, launcher and associated equipment.

Instruction: Maintenance of the LaCrosse missile and launcher; missile assembly and checkout procedures; LaCrosse warheads; artillery transport; target acquisition.

Credit recommendation, collegiate level: This course is technical and vocational in nature. Credit in electrical shop on the basis of demonstrated skills and/or institutional examinations.

1. LaCrosse Internal Guidance Repair
2. LaCrosse Internal Guidance Repair
   (LaCrosse Internal Guidance System Repair)

Location: Ordnance Guided Missile School, Redstone Arsenal, Ala.

Length: *Course 1,* 25 weeks; *Course 2,* 11–15 weeks.

Objectives: To train enlisted personnel to inspect, test, and perform field maintenance on the LaCrosse internal guidance system and its associated test equipment.

Instruction: LaCrosse systems operation; tracking system; ranging loop block diagram; computer system; operation, application and block diagram analysis of the general test equipment; flight controller system; missile power supply; missile electrical components; transistors; missile automatic checker. In addition *Course 1* includes series parallel circuits; motors and generators; resonance circuits; RC and LR circuits; vacuum tube circuits; oscillators; voltage regulators; heterodyne receiver; transmitter system.

Credit recommendation, collegiate level: *Course 1:* 3 semester hours at the freshman or sophomore level as an elective in electricity and electronics, and credit in electrical laboratory on the basis of demonstrated skills and/or institutional examinations. *Course 2:* Credit in electrical laboratory on the basis of demonstrated skills and/or institutional examinations.

LaCrosse Officer

Location: Artillery and Missile School, Fort Sill, Okla.

Length: 4–5 weeks.

Objectives: To train officers in the characteristics, operating principles, and capabilities of the LaCrosse missile system.

Instruction: Gunnery; principles of LaCrosse and new field artillery developments; LaCrosse missile and launcher; missile assembly and checkout; motors; LaCrosse guidance systems; tactics and combined arms.

Credit recommendation, collegiate level: No credit because of the brevity and military nature of the course.

LaCrosse Ordnance Maintenance Supervision

Location: Ordnance Guided Missile School, Redstone Arsenal, Ala.

Length: 29 weeks.

Objectives: To train warrant officers and enlisted personnel to supervise the maintenance of the LaCrosse guided missile system and associated test equipment.

Instruction: Ordnance support, maintenance and supply structure; supply accounting; management control, inspections, and preventive maintenance; electrical fundamentals, motors and generators; electrical systems, circuits, relays; missile hydraulics; mounting, checkout and firing procedures; LaCrosse guidance systems; tracker, computer, and target survey unit; LaCrosse test equipment maintenance and repair; LaCrosse system analysis; field maintenance.

Credit recommendation, collegiate level: 2 semester hours in shop management, and credit in electrical laboratory on the basis of demonstrated skills and/or institutional examinations.

Laundry and Drycleaning Operations (Navy)

Location: Quartermaster School, Fort Lee, Va.

Length: 6 weeks.

Objectives: To train Navy enlisted personnel in laundry processing and dry cleaning.

Instruction: Receiving, marking, cleaning, finishing, and issuing of clothing; use of various supplies and chemicals required in laundry and dry-cleaning processes; identification of various fibers and fabrics used in Navy clothing and the chemicals that will damage or decompose them; operation of various pieces of laundry and dry-cleaning equipment; operator preventive maintenance on all laundry and dry-cleaning equipment; safety precautions.

Credit recommendation, collegiate level: No credit as the course is vocational in nature.

Laundry and Fumigation Officer

Location: Quartermaster School, Fort Lee, Va.

Length: 6 weeks.

Objectives: To train Quartermaster officers to supervise and direct the operation of mobile, semimobile, or fixed laundries, dry-cleaning plants, shower-bath units, or fumigation and delousing facilities.

Instruction: Laundry and dry-cleaning procedures; fiber origin and classification; fabric identification and damage; laundry supplies; washing formulas; decontamination; organization and function of a fixed-laundry plant; operation of static laundry equipment; dry-cleaning equipment; working properties of soaps and chemicals, characteristics of petroleum, solvents and soaps; operation of dry-cleaning equipment; mobile laundry equipment; mobile field bath unit; fumigation equipment.

Credit recommendation, collegiate level: This course is vocational in nature. Credit in laundry and dry-cleaning plant operation and maintenance on the basis of demonstrated skills.

Laundry and Impregnation

Location: Quartermaster School, Fort Lee, Va.

Length: 8 weeks.

Objectives: To train enlisted personnel in the operation and maintenance of laundry, impregnating, dry-cleaning, bath and fumigation equipment; preparation of formulas used in washing, impregnating, and dry-cleaning solutions.

Instruction: Laundry, dry-cleaning and impregnating procedures; sorting and marking of clothing; field laundry supplies; field laundry washing formulas; decontamination; operation and maintenance of static laundry equipment; dry-cleaning equipment, semimobile two-trailer laundry units, delousing equipment, and field bath unit.

Credit recommendation, collegiate level: This course is vocational in nature. Credit in laundry and dry-cleaning operations on the basis of demonstrated skills.

Light and Heavy Weapons Infantryman

Location: Army Special Warfare Center, Fort Bragg N.C.

Length: 8 weeks.

Objectives: To train enlisted personnel in light and heavy weapons of the Army and selected foreign armies and their application to Special Forces operations.

Instruction: Characteristics, capabilities, assembly, disassembly, functioning, and firing of handguns, rifles, carbines and shotguns, submachine guns, machine guns, antitank weapons, and mortars.

Credit recommendation, collegiate level: No credit as the course is military in nature.

1. Light Fire Control Equipment Repair
   (Integrated Fire Control Electronics Repair, T-38)
2. Integrated Fire Control Electronics Repair, M-33

Location: Ordnance School, Aberdeen Proving Ground, Md.

Length: 13–16 weeks.

Objectives: To train enlisted personnel to inspect, test, and perform field maintenance on light and heavy integrated electronic fire control systems.

Instruction: Principles of operation of fire control systems; function of the servo system components; radar tracker operation; transmitting and receiving circuits and related control circuits; power supplies; maintenance and repair of the computer unit; systems analysis.

Credit recommendation, collegiate level: Credit in electronics and electrical laboratory on the basis of demonstrated skills and/or institutional examinations.

Light Target Missile Controller

Location: Combat Surveillance School, Fort Huachuca, Ariz.

Length: 8 weeks.

Objectives: To provide commissioned officers and enlisted personnel with the working knowledge required of radio controlled light target missile operations in visual flight.

Instruction: Familiarization with light target missile systems; primary, secondary, and advanced and integrated field operations.

Credit recommendation, collegiate level: No credit as this course is military in nature.

Light Target Missile Flight Control System Maintenance

Location: Combat Surveillance School, Fort Huachuca, Ariz.

Length: 13 weeks.

Objectives: To train enlisted personnel to operate and perform organizational and field maintenance on the light target missile flight control system.

Instruction: Basic electricity and electronics, including series and parallel circuits, DC power, alternating current, inductance, capacitance, impedance, series and parallel resonance, filters, transformers, electron emission, diodes, triode tubes, voltage amplification, tetrode tubes, pentode and beam power tubes, voltage regulators, semiconductors, transistor configurations, transistor amplifiers and multivibrator, RF signal generators, RF power amplifiers, basic transmitters, funda-

mentals of superheterodyne reception, amplification of intermediate and radio frequencies, mixers and converters, automatic gain control, and receiver alignment; operation and field maintenance of the MQM-33 Light target missile control system.

Credit recommendation, collegiate level: 2 semester hours at the freshman or sophomore level as an elective in electricity and electronics, and credit in electrical laboratory on the basis of demonstrated skills and/or institutional examinations.

Light Target Missile Launcher Operation and Airframe and Engine Maintenance
(Surveillance Drone and Radio Controlled Airplane Target Launcher Operation and Airframe and Engine Maintenance)

Location: Combat Surveillance School, Fort Huachuca, Ariz.

Length: 7–11 weeks.

Objectives: To train enlisted personnel to launch and recover the unmanned aircraft, to operate the equipment and perform organizational maintenance on the launchers and associated ground support equipment, and to perform organizational and direct support maintenance on aircraft airframe and engines.

Instruction: Engine theory, fuel system, and ignition system; engine disassembly, assembly, and troubleshooting; adjustment and replacement of parts of the airframe and wing; ground-handling equipment; launch and recovery of the target aircraft; parachute packing and fabrication of tow targets; light target missile field operations.

Credit recommendation, collegiate level: This course is technical and vocational in nature. Credit in airframe maintenance and mechanical shop on the basis of demonstrated skills and/or institutional examinations.

Lineman

Location: Signal Training Center, Fort Gordon, Ga.

Length: 7–8 weeks.

Objectives: To train enlisted personnel to construct, maintain, and repair open wire, cable, and field wire communication systems.

Instruction: Line route maps and symbols; pole climbing; field wire splices, ties, and tagging; theory of sound transmission by wire; field telephones and switchboards; testing and maintenance of telephone circuits; cables; construction and recovery of a field wire system; open wire construction and maintenance; lead covered cable construction and maintenance.

Credit recommendation, collegiate level: This course is technical and vocational in nature. Credit in telephone cable installation on the basis of demonstrated skills and/or institutional examinations.

Liquid Oxygen-Nitrogen Plant Operation
(Liquid Oxygen Plant Operation)

Location: Engineer School, Fort Belvoir, Va.

Length: 10–11 weeks.

Objectives: To train enlisted personnel to operate

and perform preventive and organizational maintenance of equipment used in production, storage, and handling of liquid oxygen and liquid nitrogen.

Instruction: Fire fighting and safety; theory and operation of liquid oxygen-nitrogen processing equipment; operation and operator maintenance of refrigeration equipment; storage, transfer, and handling of liquid oxygen, and maintenance of equipment utilized.

Credit recommendation, collegiate level: This course is technical and vocational in nature. Credit in liquid oxygen and nitrogen plant operation on the basis of demonstrated skills and/or institutional examinations.

Lithographic Platemaking

Location: Engineer School, Fort Belvoir, Va.
Length: 6–8 weeks.
Objectives: To train enlisted personnel in the preparation and processing of materials for offset plate production to be used in the lithographic printing process.
Instruction: Layout and stripping procedures; offset platemaking, albumin plate processing; blueline and scribe-sheet process; presensitized plate; diazo-wipe-on plate; proofs.
Credit recommendation, collegiate level: This course is technical and vocational in nature. Credit in lithographic platemaking on the basis of demonstrated skills and/or institutional examinations.

Locomotive Electrician
(Diesel-Electric Locomotive Electrician)

Location: Transportation School, Fort Eustis, Va.
Length: 10 weeks.
Objectives: To train enlisted personnel in the inspection, repair, and maintenance of electrical equipment and accessories of diesel-electric locomotives.
Instruction: Electricity and magnetism; insulators and conductors; electrical power measurements; generators and traction motors; contactors; shunts; interlocks and interlock data; voltage regulator; alternating current; tracing of electrical wiring; diagrams and blueprints; batteries; troubleshooting.
Credit recommendation, collegiate level: This course is technical and vocational in nature. Credit in diesel locomotive electrical repair shop on the basis of demonstrated skills and/or institutional examinations.

Locomotive Operation
(Railway Locomotive Operation)

Location: Transportation School, Fort Eustis, Va.
Length: 8–10 weeks.
Objectives: To train enlisted personnel to operate or to assist in the operation of steam and diesel-electric locomotives used in yard and road service.
Instruction: Train movement by timetable and train orders; general signal rules; steam and diesel engine locomotive operation; lubrication; firing; coupling; switching; road operation; practical exercise on the B&O Railroad, including yard switching, operation on double track, operation on single track.
Credit recommendation, collegiate level: This course

is technical and vocational in nature. Credit in railway locomotive operation and maintenance on the basis of demonstrated skills and/or institutional examinations.

M-22 Gunnery Qualification

Location: Aviation School, Fort Rucker, Ala.
Length: 3 weeks.
Objectives: To train aviators in aerial gunnery, including advanced tactical employment of UH-1 helicopter with the M-22 aerial gunnery subsystem.
Instruction: Major components of the M-22 antitank guided missile system; M-22 control and guidance equipment, sighting system, test equipment, launching equipment; principles of target attack; simulators; range firing; low-level navigation.
Credit recommendation, collegiate level: No credit as the course is military in nature.

1. **M33 Fire Control System Maintenance**
2. **M38 Fire Control System Maintenance**
3. **M38 Fire Control System Maintenance**
   (Artillery Fire Control System Maintenance, T38)
4. **M33, SCR-584 Fire Control System Maintenance**
   (Artillery Fire Control System Maintenance, M33)

Location: Air Defense School, Fort Bliss, Tex.
Length: *Courses 1 and 2,* 24–27 weeks; *Courses 3 and 4,* 30–39 weeks.
Objectives: To train warrant officers and enlisted personnel to operate, adjust, and maintain artillery fire control systems, remote control systems, and associated IFF equipment.
Instruction: *Courses 1 and 2:* Basic electricity, including AC and DC circuits, inductance and capacitance, resonant circuits, generator principles, voltage, current, and power relationships in generators, AC and DC motors; radio electronics, including diodes and triodes, voltage doublers, metallic rectifiers, and bridge rectifiers, filters, voltage dividers, and potentiometers, triode circuits, multi-element tubes, amplifiers, cathode followers, oscillators, modulation techniques, superheterodyne receivers, gas-filled tubes, and circuit and operation of hard tube sweep generators; maintenance and repair of acquisition and track radar systems; function of major computer components; operational control of fire control systems. *Courses 3 and 4:* These courses contain generally the same academic material as *Courses 1 and 2,* but the instruction includes more theory.
Credit recommendation, collegiate level: CAUTION: *These courses vary only slightly in title, length, and recommendation. Require exact identification of course by title and length. Courses 1 and 2:* 3 semester hours at the freshman or sophomore level as an elective in electricity and electronics, and credit in electrical laboratory on the basis of demonstrated skills and/or institutional examinations. *Courses 3 and 4:* 4 semester hours at the freshman or sophomore level as an elective in electricity and electronics, and credit in electrical laboratory on the basis of demonstrated skills and/or institutional examinations.

Machine Accounting

Location: Adjutant General School, Fort Benjamin Harrison, Ind.

Length: 7–8 weeks.

Objectives: To train enlisted personnel to wire and operate electrical accounting machines and to perform related entry-level duties in machine accounting activities.

Instruction: Functions capabilities, and operation of the card punch, sorter, reproducing punch, collator, accounting machine, and calculating punch.

Credit recommendation, collegiate level: This course is technical and vocational in nature. Credit in electrical accounting machine operation on the basis of demonstrated skills and/or institutional examinations.

Machinist

Location: Ordnance School, Aberdeen Proving Ground, Md.

Length: 10–15 weeks.

Objectives: To train enlisted personnel to fabricate metal parts and to modify machine parts, metal castings, and forgings for armament, automotive, and other military equipment and tools by use of various sizes and types of metalworking machinery, measuring devices, and related shop equipment.

Instruction: Hand and power tools; measuring instruments; vertical bandsaw and shaper; lathe operations; surface and universal grinders; milling machine operations.

Credit recommendation, collegiate level: This course is technical and vocational in nature. Credit in machine shop on the basis of demonstrated skills and/or institutional examinations.

Maintenance Management

Location: Logistics Management Center, Fort Lee, Va.

Length: 6–8 weeks.

Objectives: To train officers from the Office of the Deputy Chief of Staff for Logistics, offices of the heads of technical services, depots and arsenals, national maintenance points, inventory control points, and major commands in the management of maintenance activities.

Instruction: Interrelationship of logistical elements, including activities of personnel management, requirements, procurement, distribution, and maintenance; planning, programming, and budgeting; maintenance policies and organization; production management; parts management; maintenance scheduling; cost estimates; field maintenance operations; manufacture, stockage, and issue of new items; contract maintenance.

Credit recommendation, collegiate level: 3 semester hours in maintenance management.

Maintenance Officer

Location: Ordnance School, Aberdeen Proving Ground, Md.

Length: 8 weeks.

Objectives: To train commissioned officers to direct, supervise, and coordinate operations of composite maintenance activities.

Instruction: Elements of the maintenance system and the Army equipment records system and procedures; organization, capabilities, responsibilities, and operation of organizational maintenance; support maintenance operations and management.

Credit recommendation, collegiate level: 3 semester hours in maintenance management.

1. Manpower Control Officer
2. Manpower Control Officer

Location: Adjutant General School, Fort Benjamin Harrison, Ind.

Length: *Course 1, 3–4 weeks; Course 2, 5–6 weeks.*

Objectives: To train officers in the principles and procedures employed in control, distribution, and utilization of manpower at all levels of command and in the methods and techniques used in the determination of manpower requirements at major command and installation levels.

Instruction: *Course 1:* Manpower management policies; organization for manpower control; management methods; tables of distribution; manpower vouchers; staffing guides; manpower reports; personnel management; manpower survey techniques. *Course 2:* In addition to the preceding instruction this course includes more intensive study in the areas of management and control techniques.

Credit recommendation, collegiate level: CAUTION: *These courses vary only slightly in length and recommendation. Require exact identification of course by length. Course 1:* 2 semester hours in manpower management. *Course 2:* 3 semester hours in manpower management.

Manual Central Office Repair
(Manual Central Office Maintenance)

Location: Southeastern Signal School, Fort Gordon, Ga.

Length: 14–15 weeks.

Objectives: To train enlisted personnel to install and perform organizational, direct support, and general support maintenance on telephones and manual central office exchange equipment.

Instruction: Principles of electricity; basic telephony; common battery telephone circuits; central office power equipment; switchboard maintenance; transportable and permanent telephone central office installation; outside plant testing.

Credit recommendation, collegiate level: Credit in electricity on the basis of institutional examination. At the technical level, credit in manual central office telephone equipment repair on the basis of demonstrated skills and/or institutional examinations.

1. Map Compiling
2. Multiplex Map Compiling

Location: Engineer School, Fort Belvoir, Va.

Length: *Course 1,* 10 weeks and 13 weeks; *Course 2,* 10 weeks.

Objectives: *Course 1:* To train enlisted personnel in photogrammetry. *Course 2:* To train enlisted personnel in the theory and techniques of map compiling by the multiplex method.

Instruction: *Course 1:* Map reading; basic drafting; projection and grids; interpretation of aerial photographs; principles of topographic surveying and plotting control; selection and marking of photo control points; map compilation and revision; stereocomparagraph principles and operations; mosaics. *Note*—Beginning December 1967, Air Force enlisted personnel receive an additional 3 weeks' instruction which includes Air Force procedures in charting and revision of air target materials. *Course 2:* Theory and techniques in the use of multiplex equipment; compilation operations; method of extending photo control.

Credit recommendation, collegiate level: For each course, 4 semester hours in mapping and drafting.

Marine Engine Operation and Maintenance

Location: Transportation School, Fort Eustis, Va.
Length: 5–8 weeks.
Objectives: To train enlisted personnel to operate and maintain gasoline and diesel marine engines.
Instruction: Maintenance procedures for fuel injection units; disassembly, technical inspection, reassembly, operation, and troubleshooting on four-stroke cycle gasoline engines, two-stroke cycle propulsion engines, and four-stroke cycle propulsion engines; fundamental electrical principles relating to shipboard electrical equipment.
Credit recommendation, collegiate level: This course is technical and vocational in nature. Credit in marine engine maintenance and electrical shop on the basis of demonstrated skills and/or institutional examinations.

Marine Engineering and Repair Supervision

Location: Transportation School, Fort Eustis, Va.
Length: 12 weeks.
Objectives: To train enlisted personnel in the supervision of engine room activities on harbor craft and in the organizational maintenance and repair of marine engines and auxiliary equipment.
Instruction: Review of diesel engine theory; use and care of hand and precision tools; fundamentals of marine electricity; pipe design and theory; lathe operation; theory and principles of refrigeration; function, operation and maintenance of fuel injectors; repair and operation of diesel engines.
Credit recommendation, collegiate level: This course is technical and vocational in nature. Credit in diesel engine repair and electrical shop on the basis of demonstrated skills and/or institutional examinations.

1. Marine Hull Repair
2. Marine Hull Repair Supervision

Location: Transportation School, Fort Eustis, Va.
Length: 9–12 weeks.
Objectives: To train enlisted personnel to repair and to supervise the repair of wood and/or steel hulls and related structures of floating and landing craft.

Instruction: Marine welding; pipe fitting; shipfitting and sheet-metal working; ship carpentry.
Credit recommendation, collegiate level: These courses are technical and vocational in nature. Credit in carpentry and/or welding shop on the basis of demonstrated skills and/or institutional examinations.

Martin-Baker J-5 Ejection Seat Specialist

Location: Transportation School, Fort Eustis, Va.
Length: 3–4 weeks.
Objectives: To train enlisted personnel to inspect, adjust, repair, and maintain the Martin-Baker J-5 ejection seat, aircraft survival seat kit, and the 9E2A ejection seat simulator, from organizational through general support categories of maintenance.
Instruction: Ejection seat removal; disassembly, inspection, and reassembly procedures; forms, records, and field area problems; periodic inspection procedures; OV-1 aircraft survival equipment; ejection seat trainer 9E2A device.
Credit recommendation, collegiate level: No credit because of the brevity and limited technical nature of the course.

Materiel Command Comptrollership

Location: Finance School, Fort Benjamin Harrison, Ind.
Length: 6 weeks.
Objectives: To train commissioned officers in the principles and practices of comptrollership.
Instruction: Operations, concepts, processes, and procedures of financial programming and budgeting functions; revolving funds, management accounts, and managerial uses of the financial information obtained from the system; military accounting; concepts and principles of internal review; concepts, principles, general procedures, and techniques of progress and statistical reporting and analysis; techniques of management utilized in military comptrollership; the comptrollership role in support of materiel resources management; familiarization with data systems and processing.
Credit recommendation, collegiate level: 3 semester hours in finance and fiscal procedures.

Mathematical Programming

Location: U.S. Army Management Engineering Training Agency, Rock Island, Ill.
Length: 3 weeks.
Objectives: To provide personnel with a thorough understanding of, and facility with, the methods and techniques of mathematical programming, the application of which permits the simultaneous consideration of a large number of variables or alternate courses of action, and the development of a solution representing the optimum balancing of these elements.
Instruction: Operations research and mathematical programming; matrix algebra; the general linear programming problem; the simplex algorithm; special algorithms of mathematical programming; computer techniques; nonlinear programming; game theory.

Credit recommendation, collegiate level: 2 semester hours in operations research in the field of computing science.

Meat Cutting

Location: Quartermaster School, Fort Lee, Va.
Length: 8 weeks.
Objectives: To train enlisted personnel to cut meat in a central meat processing facility and to prepare processed meat, poultry and fish for delivery to mess kitchens and other using agencies.
Instruction: Meat cutting, including meat cutting terms and types and grades of meat; meat processing.
Credit recommendation, collegiate level: This course is technical and vocational in nature. Credit in meat processing on the basis of demonstrated skills and/or institutional examinations.

Meat Plant Management

Location: Quartermaster School, Fort Lee, Va.
Length: 8 weeks.
Objectives: To train enlisted personnel to supervise the operation of a central meat plant or field butchery unit.
Instruction: Types, classes, and grades of fresh meat and poultry; meat plant administration and organization; meat plant operations, including methods of production and the establishment of effective work schedules; meat processing; practical management and supervision.
Credit recommendation, collegiate level: 3 semester hours in meat plant management.

Mechanical Maintenance Officer
(Field Maintenance Officer)

Location: Ordnance School, Aberdeen Proving Ground, Md.
Length: 8 weeks.
Objectives: To train commissioned officers in materiel maintenance and in the supervision of personnel engaged in the repair of conventional materiel.
Instruction: Supervision and administration of a field maintenance operation; repair parts supply procedures; characteristics, construction, operation, maintenance and repair procedures for tactical vehicles, heavy equipment, special equipment, electronics and communication equipment; armament materiel; operation of service section equipment; use and limitation of recovery equipment.
Credit recommendation, collegiate level: 3 semester hours in maintenance management.

Mechanized Flame Thrower Surveillance

Location: Chemical Corps School, Fort McClellan, Ala.
Length: 4 weeks.
Objectives: To train Chemical Corps officers and enlisted personnel to perform and direct the maintenance, repair, and surveillance of mechanized flame-throwers.
Instruction: Flame fuels; mechanized flame thrower functioning, sponson group, transmission group, gun group, and electrical system; visual and manual surveillance; auxiliary servicing equipment; operation and procedure for firing; troubleshooting and maintenance; fuel and air systems; service equipment.
Credit recommendation, collegiate level: No credit because of the brevity and limited technical nature of the course.

1. Medical Aidman (Basic)
2. Medical Aidman (Advanced)

Locations: Medical Service School, Fort Sam Houston, Tex.; Army Hospitals.
Length: *Course 1,* 12 weeks; *Course 2,* 20 weeks.
Objectives: To train enlisted personnel in the basic and advanced techniques and procedures of field medicine and surgery, in the principles of preventive medicine and field sanitation, and in dispensary and sick call procedures.
Instruction: Medical reports and supplies; anatomy and physiology; principles of pharmacology; familiarization with neuropsychiatry; bandaging and splinting; introduction to field surgery; symptoms, causes, and treatment of various diseases; diagnostic and emergency nursing procedures; preventive medicine; practical hospital experience. *Course 2:* This course contains the same academic material as *Course 1* but the instruction is more intense, especially in the area of anatomy and physiology.
Credit recommendation, collegiate level: CAUTION: *These courses vary only slightly in title, length, and recommendation. Require exact identification of course by title and length. Course 1:* Credit in first aid and hygiene on the basis of institutional examination. *Course 2:* 3 semester hours in physiology and hygiene.

Medical Laboratory Procedures (Advanced)
(Medical Laboratory Specialist Advanced)

Locations: Armed Forces Institute of Pathology, Washington, D.C.; Fitzsimons General Hospital, Denver, Colo.; Medical Field Service School, Fort Sam Houston, Tex.; Walter Reed General Hospital, Washington, D.C.
Length: 50 weeks.
Objectives: To train enlisted personnel in medical technology and to provide an opportunity to gain proficiency in clinical, epidemiological, investigative, and control procedures used in medical laboratories.
Instruction: Fundamentals of anatomy and physiology; laboratory mathematics; medical physics; bacteriology; mycology; virology; parasitology; serology; histological and pathological techniques; principles of inorganic and organic chemistry; food chemistry; biochemistry; toxicology; urinalysis; hematology; immunohematology and blood bank procedures.
Credit recommendation, collegiate level: CAUTION: *The courses given after 1955 contain more intensive instruction in the areas of bacteriology, chemistry, biochemistry, and hematology. Therefore credit recommendations will be according to year of attendance. Courses prior to 1956:* 10 semester hours in basic

science if a student is preparing for a nonscientific degree. In preparation for a scientific degree, 5 semester hours is recommended in biology or chemistry if applied to a science minor. *Courses after 1955:* 30 semester hours in medical technology (internship) if applied to a major in medical technology. If a student is not majoring in medical technology, 10 semester hours is recommended in biology or chemistry if applied to a science minor.

Medical Laboratory Procedures (Basic)
(Medical Laboratory Procedure)
(Medical Laboratory Specialist)

Location: Medical Field Service School, Fort Sam Houston, Tex.

Length: 14–16 weeks.

Objectives: To train enlisted personnel in basic techniques and principles of medical laboratory procedures.

Instruction: Basic clinical chemistry methodology, including analytical techniques and blood chemical constituents; elementary urinalysis, hematology, immunohematology, serology, and parasitology; basic procedures in bacteriology; elementary physiology related to clinical pathology.

Credit recommendation, collegiate level: 6 semester hours in bacteriology and blood chemistry.

1. Medical Records and Reports (Basic)
2. Medical Records Clerk Advanced
(Medical Records)

Location: Medical Field Service School, Fort Sam Houston, Tex.

Length: 6–15 weeks.

Objectives: To train enlisted personnel in basic and advanced medical records administrative procedures.

Instruction: Preparation, processing, and review of medical records and reports; familiarization with medical terminology; general administrative principles applicable to medical units.

Credit recommendation, collegiate level: These courses are technical and vocational in nature. Credit in office procedures on the basis of demonstrated skills and/or institutional examinations.

Medical Service Company Officer

Location: Medical Field Service School, Fort Sam Houston, Tex.

Length: 22–26 weeks.

Objectives: To provide branch training in the duties and responsibilities of company-grade Medical Service officers.

Instruction: Medical administration; personnel management; hospital plant planning, construction, and maintenance; financial management; medical and military law, hospital organization; scientific problem solving; medical supply principles and procedures; human relations; organization function, and employment of field medical service through division level; medical estimates, plans, and orders; organization and employment of the combined arms; staff responsibilities, intelligence procedures, and logistical procedures; military leadership; orientation to neuropsychiatry; concepts, methods, and practices in control of communicable diseases and preventable injuries; military sanitation, and insect and rodent control.

In the professional science area students received training in dental science, field medicine and surgery, and veterinary science. Degree of instruction in these special areas is dependent upon the medical branch to which the student was attached.

Credit recommendation, collegiate level: 5 semester hours in business organization and administration and 2 semester hours in hygiene and first aid.

1. Medical Service Corps Officer Orientation
(Medical Service Corps Officer Basic)
2. Medical Service Officer Orientation
(Medical Service Officer Basic)

Location: Medical Field Service School, Fort Sam Houston, Tex.

Length: *Course 1,* 8–16 weeks; *Course 2,* 4–6 weeks.

Objectives: To provide basic branch training and orientation for newly commissioned Medical Service officers or Medical, Dental, and Veterinary Corps officers.

Instruction: *Course 1:* Organization within the Medical Service; administrative functions and personnel management; medical records and reports; supply procedures; emergency medical care; organization, mission, and employment of the combined arms; means and methods of handling casualties and techniques of planning for evacuation of casualties; military leadership; weapons familiarization; fundamentals of staff organization and functions; preventive medicine; familiarization with the Nurse Corps, veterinary service, and neuropsychiatry. *Course 2:* This is an orientation course in the duties and reponsibilities of Medical Service Corps officers.

Credit recommendation, collegiate level: CAUTION: *These courses vary in title, length, and recommendation. Require exact identification of course by title and length. Course 1:* 2 semester hours in business organization, and credit in advanced military at institutions which regularly offer such credit. *Course 2:* No credit because of the brevity and limited technical nature of the course.

1. Medical Service Officer Career
2. Medical Service Officer Career
3. Medical Service Officer Advanced
4. Medical Service Officer Advanced

Location: Medical Field Service School, Fort Sam Houston, Tex.

Length: *Course 1,* 21 weeks; *Course 2,* 33 weeks; *Course 3,* 22 weeks; *Course 4,* 34 weeks.

Objectives: To provide branch training in the duties and responsibilities of Medical Service officers.

Instruction: *Courses 1 and 3:* Principles of administration and their relationship to the command, the staff, and the organization; fundamentals of effective communication; personnel management; financial management; medical supply procedures; medical records and reports; familiarization with medical and military law; capabilities, functions, and utilization of various medical units; organization and tactical employment of Army forces; organization and operation of field medical service; military leadership; staff organization; group behavior; nuclear science; duties and responsibilities in preventive medicine; policies and procedures in dental command and staff positions; mission and function of the Army Nurse Corps. *Courses 2 and 4:* These courses contain the same academic material as *Courses 1 and 3,* but include more intensive instruction in managerial functions.

Credit recommendation, collegiate level: CAUTION: *These courses vary slightly in title, length, and recommendation. Require exact identification of course by title and length. Courses 1 and 3:* For each course, 6 semester hours in business organization and management. *Courses 2 and 4:* For each course, 9 semester hours in business organization and management.

Medical Specialist
(Medical Technician)

Location: Medical Service School, Fort Sam Houston, Tex.

Length: 12–14 weeks.

Objectives: To train enlisted personnel to assist in the care and treatment of patients in hospitals, clinics, and other medical treatment facilities.

Instruction: Anatomy and physiology; introduction to pharmacology; procedures and techniques of patient care; assistance with diagnostic procedures and treatment; familiarization with neuropsychiatry; field sanitation and prevention of disease; practical nursing application.

Credit recommendation, collegiate level: 2 semester hours in physiology and hygiene.

Medical Specialist (Advanced)

Locations: Brook General Hospital, Fort Sam Houston, Tex.; DeWitt Army Hospital, Fort Belvoir, Va.; Fitzsimons General Hospital, Denver, Colo.; Letterman General Hospital, San Francisco, Calif.; Madigan General Hospital, Tacoma, Wash.; Womack Army Hospital, Fort Bragg, N.C.

Length: 40 weeks.

Objectives: To train enlisted personnel to supervise and perform patient-care duties appropriate to hospital and field medical assistants.

Instruction: Emergency medical and dental care; mass disaster casualties; preventive medicine; medical terminology; familiarization with pharmacology; advanced principles and procedures of patient care; procedures for care of patients with medical and surgical illnesses; familiarization with mental illness; prenatal, postnatal, and pediatric care; dispensary procedures; medical records and reports; clinical experience.

Credit recommendation, collegiate level: This course is at the preprofessional or professional level. 2 semester hours in first aid and hygiene, 2 semester hours in principles of administration and management of nursing service, and credit in physiology on the basis of institutional examination.

Medical Supply Officer

Location: Medical Field Service School, Fort Sam Houston, Tex.

Length: 10 weeks.

Objectives: To train officers to apply the principles of item and financial accounting for medical supplies and equipment and to direct and supervise the requisitioning, receipt, storage, and issue of those supplies and equipment.

Instruction: Medical supply procedures, including classification of supplies, stock management and control, supply control, and warehousing; personnel management; management methods and work simplification techniques; principles of human relations; organization, function and employment of the medical units in a theater of operation; organization and function of supply and logistical agencies.

Credit recommendation, collegiate level: 6 semester hours in supply management.

Medical Supply Procedures

Location: Medical Field Service School, Fort Sam Houston, Tex.

Length: 4 weeks.

Objectives: To train enlisted personnel in the procedures of medical supply.

Instruction: Medical supply procedures; medical codes and symbols; medical supply directives; bookkeeping and accounting procedures; procedures for medical libraries and hospital linen controls; special procedures for handling medical supplies and pharmaceuticals; management methods; stock management; stock control; supply control; warehousing.

Credit recommendation, collegiate level: This course is technical and vocational in nature. Credit in stock accounting procedures on the basis of institutional examination.

Medium Antiaircraft Artillery Maintenance
(Medium and Heavy Antiaircraft Artillery
Maintenance)

Location: Air Defense School, Fort Bliss, Tex.

Length: 4–6 weeks.

Objectives: To train enlisted personnel to perform organizational maintenance on small arms and medium antiaircraft artillery weapons.

Instruction: Characteristics, assembly, disassembly, and maintenance.

Credit recommendation, collegiate level: This course is technical and vocational in nature. Credit in mechanical shop on the basis of demonstrated skills and/or institutional examinations.

Memorial Activities
(Recovery and Disposition, Enlisted)
(Graves Registration Specialist)
(Graves Registration)

Location: Quartermaster School, Fort Lee, Va.

Length: 8 weeks.

Objectives: To train enlisted personnel to collect,

evacuate, identify, and bury deceased personnel subject to military jurisdiction, to collect and dispose of personal effects found on the deceased, and to supervise such tasks.

Instruction: Organization and operating procedures of the graves registration service; identification of the dead; map and aerial photograph reading; battlefield collection and evacuation.

Credit recommendation, collegiate level: No credit because of the specialized nature of the course.

Mess Stewards
(Mess Management)

Location: Quartermaster School, Fort Lee, Va.
Length: 6 weeks.
Objectives: To train enlisted personnel for mess management duties in a unit or consolidated mess.

Instruction: Organizational and personnel management in food service operations; management of pastry baking and meat cutting operations; techniques and procedures for the preparation and service of food; mess management in field operations; nutrition and menu planning.

Credit recommendation, collegiate level: 2 semester hours in institutional (culinary) management.

Metal Body Repair

Location: Ordnance School, Aberdeen Proving Ground, Md.
Length: 6–9 weeks.
Objectives: To train enlisted personnel to repair, repaint, and install metal body components, radiators, fuel tanks and to modify other related items.

Instruction: Tools and equipment used to install glass, trim, and hardware; oxyacetylene welding; repair of radiator and fuel tanks; metal body repair procedures and equipment; major body repairs.

Credit recommendation, collegiate level: This course is technical and vocational in nature. Credit in metal shop on the basis of demonstrated skills and/or institutional examinations.

Metal Working (Entry)

Location: Ordnance School, Aberdeen Proving Ground, Md.
Length: 8 weeks.
Objectives: To train enlisted personnel to assist in setting up, operating, and maintaining all types of tools and equipment used in metal body repair.

Instruction: Care and use of hand and power tools; function and use of metal body repair tools and equipment, welding tools and equipment, machinist tools and equipment, and forging equipment.

Credit recommendation, collegiate level: This course is technical and vocational in nature. Credit in metal shop on the basis of demonstrated skills and/or institutional examinations.

Meteorological Equipment Mechanic
(Weather Equipment Maintenance)

Location: Artillery and Missile School, Fort Sill, Okla.
Length: 13–15 weeks.
Objectives: To train warrant officers and enlisted personnel in the organizational maintenance of electrical and electronic meteorological equipment used in artillery ballistic meteorology sections.

Instruction: Series and parallel DC circuits; AC; inductance; capacitance; transformers; diodes and triodes; multi-element tubes; receivers; power supplies; amplifiers; oscillators; frequency converters; transmitters; principles of AM modulation; transmitter modulation; cathode followers; DC motors and generators; servo mechanisms; synchros; rawin set; radiosonde recorders and auxiliary equipment.

Credit recommendation, collegiate level: 2 semester hours at the freshman or sophomore level as an elective in electricity and electronics, and credit in electrical laboratory on the basis of demonstrated skills and/or institutional examinations.

Meteorological Equipment Repairman

Location: Artillery and Missile School, Fort Sill, Okla.
Length: 20 weeks.
Objectives: To train enlisted personnel in the organization, direct support, general support, and depot maintenance of electrical and electronic meteorological equipment used in artillery ballistic meteorology sections and research and development activities.

Instruction: Series and parallel DC circuits, AC, inductance, capacitance, transformers, resonance; types of electron tubes, power supplies, audio amplifiers, oscillators, and radio frequency amplifiers; transmitters and receivers; cathode followers, multivibrators, AC and DC motors, servomechanisms and synchros; troubleshooting, maintenance and repair of the rawin set, radiosonde recorder, and surface observing and recording equipment.

Credit recommendation, collegiate level: 2 semester hours at the freshman or sophomore level as an elective in electricity and electronics, and credit in electrical laboratory on the basis of demonstrated skills and/or institutional examinations.

Meteorological Observation

Location: Signal School, Fort Monmouth, N.J.
Length: 13–19 weeks.
Objectives: To train enlisted personnel in the observation, interpretation, and compilation of meteorological phenomena at locations away from weather installations.

Instruction: Meteorological theory, including atmospheric physics, cloud principles, fog and atmospheric phenomena, constant-level charts, meteorological geography, and climatology; techniques of operation of various weather instruments; surface observations; surface and upper air plotting charts; winds-aloft observations; upper air soundings; surface and upper air observation practices; micrometeorological instrumentation.

Credit recommendation, collegiate level: 3 semester hours in meteorology.

Microwave Radio Equipment Repair

Location: Signal School, Fort Monmouth, N.J.

Length: 26–30 weeks.

Objectives: To train enlisted personnel to supervise and participate in the installation, operation, repair, and depot maintenance of microwave fixed-station and transportable radio equipment.

Instruction: Electron theory; series, parallel, and series-parallel circuits; alternating current; inductance; capacitance; transformers; diode and triode vacuum tubes; vacuum tube rectifiers; power supplies; amplification; multi-element tubes; basic transmitter and receiver circuitry; complex-wave circuitry; pulse modulation; fixed-microwave transmitting and receiving equipment; fixed-microwave radio system; transportable microwave radio relay equipment; transportable microwave radio system; tropospheric scatter communications systems.

Credit recommendation, collegiate level: 4 semester hours at the freshman or sophomore level as an elective in electricity and electronics, and credit in electrical laboratory on the basis of demonstrated skills and/or institutional examinations.

Microwave Radio Officer

Location: Signal School, Fort Monmouth, N.J.

Length: 12–14 weeks.

Objectives: To train commissioned officers to direct and supervise the installation, operation, and organizational maintenance of microwave radio and tactical tropospheric scatter equipment.

Instruction: AC and DC principles; series and parallel circuits; AC and DC power supplies; vacuum tubes; transistors; rectifiers; amplifiers; test equipment; CW and AM transmitter circuitry; AM and FM receivers and FM transmitters; antennas; radio-wave propagation, and frequency allocation; fixed and transportable microwave equipment and systems; tropospheric scatter equipment and systems.

Credit recommendation, collegiate level: Credit in electricity, electronics, and electrical laboratory on the basis of demonstrated skills and/or institutional examinations.

Microwave Radio Relay Operation

Location: Signal School, Fort Monmouth, N.J.

Length: 10 weeks.

Objectives: To train enlisted personnel in the operation and operator's maintenance of microwave radio relay and associated equipment.

Instruction: Alignment, operation, and routine maintenance of the radio-telephone terminal set, radio repeater set, fixed-station and transportable microwave radio relay system, multiplexer set, and the radio set AN/TRC-29.

Credit recommendation, collegiate level: This course is technical and vocational in nature. Credit in radio operation on the basis of demonstrated skills and/or institutional examinations.

---

1. **Military Accounting**
   (Financial Management-Integrated Accounting)
2. **Financial Management-Integrated Accounting**

Location: Finance School, Fort Benjamin Harrison, Ind.

Length: *Course 1,* 4–5 weeks; *Course 2,* 3 weeks.

Objectives: To train commissioned officers and enlisted personnel in the procedures, operations, and reports pertinent to military accounting.

Instruction: *Course 1:* Accounting procedures; document and fund flow; basic records; chart of accounts, document processing; closing procedures; fiscal code; disbursing operations. *Course 2:* This course covers the same instruction as *Course 1* but somewhat less intensively.

Credit recommendation, collegiate level: CAUTION: *These courses vary only slightly in title, length, and recommendation. Require exact identification of course by length. Course 1:* 4 semester hours in government accounting. *Course 2:* 3 semester hours in government accounting.

1. **Military Assistance Training Advisor**
2. **Military Assistance Training Advisor Senior Noncommissioned Officers**
3. **Military Assistance Training Advisor Corps/Division**
4. **Military Assistance Training Advisor Sector/Unit**

Location: Special Warfare School, Fort Bragg, N.C.

Length: 4–6 weeks.

Objectives: To train officers and enlisted personnel for advisory duty in the Republic of Vietnam.

Instruction: Familiarization with the general characteristics of the area to include industry, history, religion, customs, and government; counterinsurgency tactics and techniques; weapons, demolitions, and communications; health hazards and first aid measures; intelligence operations; psychological operations; civil affairs and civil action programs; State Department activities in Vietnam; introduction to the Vietnamese language. *Note:* Prior to September 1967, *Course 4* did not contain language instruction.

Credit recommendation, collegiate level: For each course, credit in Vietnamese on the basis of institutional examination.

Military Comptrollership

Location: Finance School, Fort Benjamin Harrison, Ind.

Length: 5–6 weeks.

Objectives: To train commissioned officers in the principles and practices of comptrollership and the utilization of techniques and procedures in the performance of comptroller functions.

Instruction: Techniques of the management function of military comptrollership; concepts, principles, procedures, and techniques of progress and statistical reporting and analysis; managerial uses of financial information; internal review and control; general accounting procedures; functions of supply accounting; familiarization in automatic data processing systems.

Credit recommendation, collegiate level: 3 semester

hours in business organization and management, and credit in general accounting on the basis of institutional examination. *See* page 366 for 10-week course.

Military Intelligence Coordinator

Location: Intelligence School, Fort Holabird, Md.
Length: 8 weeks.
Objectives: To train enlisted personnel in the clerical duties to be performed in military intelligence units, and to develop a general knowledge in the processing of intelligence data associated with counterintelligence and intelligence collection activities.
Instruction: Preparation of military and intelligence correspondence; maintenance of intelligence files; typing at 25 wpm minimum; combat intelligence; investigations; report writing; security; human sources of information; surveillance; counterespionage; counterinsurgency operations; intelligence collection operations; familiarization with the theories of communism.
Credit recommendation, collegiate level: Credit in intelligence methods and typing on the basis of institutional examination.

Military Intelligence (Enlisted)

Location: Intelligence School, Fort Holabird, Md.
Length: 10 weeks.
Objectives: To train enlisted personnel in clerical and operational administrative duties included in the processing of intelligence reports and messages.
Instruction: Military, general intelligence, counterintelligence, and legal clerical administration.
Credit recommendation, collegiate level: This course is technical and vocational in nature. Credit in office practice on the basis of institutional examination.

Military Intelligence Officer Advanced

Location: Intelligence School, Fort Holabird, Md.
Length: 38 weeks.
Objectives: To provide advanced training in the duties and responsibilities of field-grade officers in the area of intelligence.
Instruction: Command and staff responsibilities; management techniques; photo interpretation; communication security; principles of offensive and defensive combat leadership; employment of atomic weapons; air-ground operations; organization and tactics of foreign armies; combat intelligence; collection, evaluation, and interpretation of information; intelligence reports and documents; joint intelligence operations; fundamentals of interrogation; order of battle intelligence; geography, history, economy, and political structure of strategic world areas; intelligence operations in a theater of war.
Credit recommendation, collegiate level: 3 semester hours in business organization and management, 6 semester hours in political science, and 6 semester hours in intelligence methods.

Military Intelligence Officer Orientation

Location: Intelligence School, Fort Holabird, Md.
Length: 4–6 weeks.
Objectives: To provide initial intelligence training for commissioned officers whose actual or anticipated assignment is to intelligence duties.
Instruction: Introduction to intelligence; order of battle; interrogation; imagery interpretation; collection and dissemination of information; counterintelligence and security; hostile threat; Sino-Soviet intelligence agencies.
Credit recommendation, collegiate level: 2 semester hours in intelligence methods.

Military Personnel Officer/Unit Personnel Technician (Military Personnel Officer)

Location: Adjutant General School, Fort Benjamin Harrison, Ind.
Length: 5 weeks.
Objectives: To train officers and warrant officers in the duties of a military personnel officer or unit personnel technician.
Instruction: Personnel operations and management techniques; tests and measurements; interviews; classification and utilization of enlisted personnel; officer and enlisted qualification records; personnel control devices; personnel actions, compensation, records, and reports.
Credit recommendation, collegiate level: 2 semester hours in personnel management.

Military Police Field Grade Officer Refresher

Location: Military Police School, Fort Gordon, Ga.
Length: 4 weeks.
Objectives: To provide refresher training in the duties and responsibilities appropriate to field-grade Military Police Corps officers.
Instruction: Fundamentals and principles of staff organization and procedures; application of military justice within units; employment of military police units in civil disturbances; physical security system; prisoner custody and control methods; traffic control; military police operations in a theater of operations.
Credit recommendation, collegiate level: No credit because of the refresher nature of the course.

Military Police Noncommissioned Officer

Location: The Provost Marshal General's School, Fort Gordon, Ga.
Length: 3 weeks.
Objectives: To provide refresher training for noncommissioned officers in the basic duties and functions of the Military Police Corps.
Instruction: Familiarization with chemical, biological, and radiological agents; fundamentals of military law; weapons; civil disturbances; familiarization with the military police criminal investigation program; organization and functions of military police units; traffic control; military confinement facilities; handling of prisoners of war.

Credit recommendation, collegiate level: No credit because of the brevity and limited technical nature of the course.

Military Police Officer Advanced
(Military Police Officer Career)

Locations: The Provost Marshal General's School, Fort Gordon, Ga.; Military Police School, Fort Gordon, Ga.

Length: 33–35 weeks.

Objectives: To provide branch training in the duties and responsibilities of Military Police Corps officers.

Instruction: Military leadership; logistics; chemical and biological operations; administration at battalion level; oral and written communication; military organization, operations and provost marshal functions; planning and conducting military police operations during domestic emergencies; methods and techniques used to reduce security hazards; military law; criminal investigation activities, records, and procedures; management, operation, and supervision of confinement facilities; traffic planning and control; methods of handling prisoners of war; command and staff procedures; nuclear weapons employment; military police communications; command post and field exercises.

Credit recommendation, collegiate level: 6 semester hours in police methods and administration and 6 semester hours in business organization and management.

1. Military Police Officer Basic
(Military Police Officer Orientation)
2. Military Police Officer Orientation

Location: The Provost Marshal General's School, Military Police School, Fort Gordon, Ga.

Length: *Course 1,* 8–13 weeks; *Course 2,* 4 weeks.

Objectives: *Course 1:* To provide basic branch training for newly commissioned Military Police Corps officers. *Course 2:* To provide initial branch training and orientation for commissioned officers assigned to the Military Police Corps.

Instruction: *Course 1:* Orientation to officer basic administrative duties; military police organizations and operations; domestic emergencies; military justice; criminal investigations; confinement facilities; traffic control; prisoners of war; combined arms operations; command and staff procedures; employment of the infantry division provost marshall section and military police detachment during combat operations. *Course 2:* Orientation to military police functions and operations.

Credit recommendation, collegiate level: CAUTION: *These courses vary only slightly in title, length, and recommendation. Require exact identification of course by title and length.* Course 1: Credit in advanced military at institutions which regularly offer such credit. *Course 2:* No credit because of the brevity and nature of the course.

Military Police Officer Familiarization

Location: The Provost Marshal General's School, Fort Gordon, Ga.

Length: 6 weeks.

Objectives: To provide branch familiarization training in the organization, operational functions, duties, and responsibilities of the Military Police Corps.

Instruction: Military justice; responsibility in the management and operations of confinement facilities; supervision of criminal investigations; fundamentals of military police organizations, operations and provost marshal functions; signal communications; planning, coordination, and supervision of traffic control for administrative, logistical, and combat operations; civil defense and natural disaster relief; physical security.

Credit recommendation, collegiate level: 2 semester hours in police methods.

Military Police Officer Mobilization Advanced
1. Phase II
2. Phase III

Location: Military Police School, Fort Gordon, Ga.

Length: *Phase II,* 4–5 weeks; *Phase III,* 4–5 weeks.

Objectives: To train military police officers, of the Reserve components not on extended active duty during peacetime, and military police officers, of all components during mobilization, for branch command and staff duties at battalion through brigade or comparable levels in both divisional and nondivisional units.

Note—Reserve officers complete *Phase I* through service extension courses provided by the Department of the Army. These courses are not evaluated by the Commission.

Instruction: *Phase II:* United States and foreign police systems; analysis of police statistics; crime prevention; policies, legal aspects, and tactics of civil disturbances; stockade administration; disciplinary measures and correction treatment; criminal investigation; physical security; industrial defense. *Phase III:* Traffic regulations, planning, and control; organization, mission, equipment, and capabilities of various types of police battalions; communication equipment; organization of military police in the field army; command control information systems; prisoners of war; motor movements; employment of the combined arms.

Credit recommendation, collegiate level: *Phases II and III are usually completed in residence. When the phases are completed in residence, the following recommendation applies: Phase II:* 3 semester hours in police methods and administration. *Phase III:* 3 additional hours in police methods and administration.

Military Police Supervision
(Military Police Supervision (Enlisted))

Location: The Provost Marshal General's School, Fort Gordon, Ga.

Length: 6 weeks.

Objectives: To train enlisted personnel in the supervision of enlisted military policemen.

Instruction: Principles of military law; tactical and organizational concepts of military police units; physical security; confinement facilities; investigation methods and activities; military police operations at a post, camp, or station, and in support of combat operations; communication procedures; traffic control; civil emergencies.

Credit recommendation, collegiate level: This course is vocational in nature. Credit in protective service occupations on the basis of institutional examination.

1. Missile Maintenance Officer
2. Ordnance Missile Systems Maintenance Officer
(Ordnance Guided Missile Officer, FAM)
(Ordnance Guided Missile Officer, FAGM)
(Ordnance Guided Missile Officer, ADM)
(Ordnance Guided Missile Officer, AAGM)

Location: Missile and Munitions School, Redstone Arsenal, Ala.

Length: 19–20 weeks.

Objectives: To train commissioned officers in the operation, maintenance, test, and checkout procedures for guided missile systems and associated equipment.

Instruction: *Course 1:* Missile system supply at depot level; funding for missile equipment and repair parts; missile maintenance shop management; missile support maintenance shop; packing, packaging, and storing; maintenance of management personnel. *Course 2:* Direct current laws and circuitry; trigonometry; alternating current laws, circuitry, and test equipment; theory of radio and circuitry; theory of radar systems and methods; transistors; computer propellants; conventional missile warheads and nuclear weapons; missile systems; ordnance missile systems; special ammunition logistics.

Credit recommendation, collegiate level: *Course 1:* 3 semester hours in maintenance management, and credit in electrical laboratory on the basis of demonstrated skills and/or institutional examinations. *Course 2:* 3 semester hours at the freshman or sophomore level as an elective in electronics, and credit in electrical laboratory on the basis of demonstrated skills and/or institutional examinations.

Missile Master Fire Unit Integration Facility Maintenance
(Missile Master Battery Terminal Equipment Maintenance)

Location: Air Defense School, Fort Bliss, Tex.

Length: 8–10 weeks.

Objectives: To train warrant officers and enlisted personnel in the function, operation, organizational maintenance, and inspection of fire unit integration facility equipment.

Instruction: Orientation; basic theory; coordinate data set transmitter and receiver; data conversion circuits.

Credit recommendation, collegiate level: Credit in electrical laboratory on the basis of demonstrated skills and/or institutional examinations.

Missile Master Systems Management Officers

Location: Air Defense School, Fort Bliss, Tex.

Length: 12 weeks.

Objectives: To train commissioned officers and war-

rant officers in general operational and maintenance procedures and administrative requirements necessary for supervision of maintenance personnel within the Army Air Defense System AN/FSG-1.

Instruction: Introduction to AN/FSG-1 system; basic electricity; tracking subsystem; sweep function; video function; track channels and data computer; switching and control; azimuth positioning; TSQ-7 transmitter; broadcast subfunction testing; designation switchboard; designate subfunction testing; data link and power equipment; fire unit integration facility subsystem; SAGE receiver and transmitter; multiplexing and multiplexing controls; analogue to digital computer; functional analysis of the AN/FSG-1 system.

Credit recommendation, collegiate level: Credit in electrical laboratory on the basis of demonstrated skills and/or institutional examinations.

Missile Monitor Operations Central and Terminal Equipment Repair
(Missile Monitor Repair)

Location: Signal Fire Distribution Systems Training Activity, Fort Bliss, Tex.

Length: 18 weeks.

Objectives: To train warrant officers and enlisted personnel to perform organizational and field maintenance on the operations central AN/MSQ-18 and field maintenance on the coder-decoder subsystems of the Missile Monitor.

Instruction: Digital fundamentals; introduction to AN/MSQ-18 system; coordinate data set; power supplies; coder-decoder group; detailed circuit analysis of operations central; ground-to-slant converter; coder-decoder group communications system; troubleshooting and repair techniques.

Credit recommendation, collegiate level: Credit in electrical laboratory on the basis of demonstrated skills and/or institutional examinations.

Missile Repair Parts Specialist

Location: Quartermaster School, Fort Lee, Va.

Length: 5 weeks.

Objectives: To train enlisted personnel in the receipt, storage, inspection, identification, preservation, and shipment of missile repair parts.

Instruction: Army maintenance system and equipment records; supply publications; missile component and missile repair parts identification; repair parts procedures; storage operation; shipping procedures.

Credit recommendation, collegiate level: No credit because of the brevity and nature of the course.

Mobilization Command and General Staff Officer

Location: Command and General Staff College, Fort Leavenworth, Pa.

Length: 8 weeks.

Objectives: To prepare officers for duty as general staff officers of division and logistical commands, corps, and field army, and for participation in joint and combined operations.

Instruction: Joint, combined, and special operations; larger unit operations; division operations.

Credit recommendation, collegiate level: No credit as the course is military in nature.

Motion Picture Photography

Location: Signal School, Fort Monmouth, N.J.

Length: 14 weeks.

Objectives: To train enlisted personnel in the operation and preventive maintenance of motion picture cameras and allied equipment and to take indoor and outdoor motion pictures of ground and aerial subjects for technical, tactical, and informational purposes.

Instruction: Basic photography; motion picture principles and their application; controlled and uncontrolled action; interior lighting; combat, color, aerial, and newsreel photography; production camera techniques; advanced story and continuity problems.

Credit recommendation, collegiate level: 3 semester hours in photography.

Motor Transport Operation and Maintenance
(Highway Transportation Operation and
Maintenance)
(Highway Transport Operations)

Location: Transportation School, Fort Eustis, Va.

Length: 8–9 weeks and 12 weeks.

Objectives: To train commissioned officers and warrant officers in the management and supervision of operation and maintenance activities of motor transport units and motor pools.

Instruction: Personnel and administration; logistics; intelligence and operations; transportation organization, plans, and employment; motor transport organization and operations; transportation technical training; motor transport maintenance operations.

Credit recommendation, collegiate level: CAUTION: *These courses vary in title, length, and recommendation. Require exact identification by title and length. 8–9 week Course:* 4 semester hours in transportation and maintenance management. *12-week Course:* 6 semester hours in transportation and maintenance management.

1. Multi-Engine Airplane Repair
2. Single-Engine Airplane Repair
3. Airplane Repair

Location: Transportation School, Fort Eustis, Va.

Length: 12–19 weeks.

Objectives: To train enlisted personnel in the maintenance of single- and multi-engine fixed-wing aircraft.

Instruction: Maintenance and general repair procedures for various aircraft systems and components, including basic flight control components, fuel systems, sheet metal repair, aircraft plastics, structural repair; basic hydraulics, aircraft instruments, electrical and power supply systems, and aircraft inspection; electrical fundamentals; maintenance and repair procedures associated with single- and multi-engine fixed-wing aircraft engine and propeller systems.

Credit recommendation, collegiate level: These

courses are technical and vocational in nature. Credit in mechanical and electrical shop on the basis of demonstrated skills and/or institutional examinations.

Multi-Engine Medium Transport Helicopter
Maintenance

Location: Aviation School, Fort Rucker, Ala.

Length: 5–6 weeks.

Objectives: To train enlisted personnel in organizational maintenance of multi-engine medium transport helicopters.

Instruction: Maintenance of power plants and accessories; transmission; rotor-head actuating mechanisms; hydraulic systems; landing gear; ignition system; troubleshooting; servicing of gear boxes; power train; inspections.

Credit recommendation, collegiate level: This course is technical and vocational in nature. Credit in helicopter engine repair shop on the basis of demonstrated skills and/or institutional examinations.

Multi-Engine, Single-Rotor Helicopter Repair
(Medium Transport Helicopter Repair)

Location: Transportation School, Fort Eustis, Va.

Length: 10–17 weeks.

Objectives: To train enlisted personnel in the field maintenance of multi-engine medium helicopters.

Instruction: Operation, inspection, maintenance, and troubleshooting of components of the medium cargo helicopter; field maintenance procedures associated with aircraft structures, rotary-wing blades, aircraft instruments, electrical systems, power plants, and hydraulics.

Credit recommendation, collegiate level: This course is technical and vocational in nature. Credit in helicopter engine repair shop on the basis of demonstrated skills and/or institutional examinations.

Multi-Engine Tandem-Rotor Helicopter Repair
(CH-47 Aircraft Repair Transition)
(CH-47A Aircraft Repair Transition)

Location: Transportation School, Fort Eustis, Va.

Length: 6–13 weeks.

Objectives: To provide officers and enlisted personnel with a working knowledge of organizational, support, and field maintenance of helicopters.

Instruction: Principles of operation, function, description and repair procedures; propulsion and related systems.

Credit recommendation, collegiate level: These courses are technical and vocational in nature. Credit in helicopter repair shop on the basis of demonstrated skills and/or institutional examinations.

Multi-Engine Utility Airplane Repair

Location: Transportation School, Fort Eustis, Va.

Length: 4–5 weeks.

Objectives: To train enlisted personnel in user support maintenance of the multi-engine utility airplane.

Instruction: U-21A aircraft maintenance, including description, inspection, flight controls, electrical system, utility system, landing gear, weight, and balance.

Credit recommendation, collegiate level: This course is technical and vocational in nature. Credit in airplane maintenance on the basis of demonstrated skills and/or institutional examinations.

Neuropsychiatric Nursing

Location: Medical Service School, Fort Sam Houston, Tex.

Length: 20 weeks.

Objectives: To train officers to perform nursing duties in wards for patients with psychiatric and neurological diseases.

Instruction: Neuroanatomy and neurology; principles and practices of neuropsychiatric nursing, including observation and reporting, nurse-patient relationships, emergency measures, control of hazards on psychiatric wards, physical care, restraint procedures, therapeutic activities, nursing care needs, care of patients with the various neuropsychiatric diseases, administration and supervision in the neuropsychiatric head nurse unit; recognition, management, and treatment of psychiatric disorders; behavior development and personality theory; familiarization with psychological testing; philosophy of social work, principles of interviewing, and cultural aspect of human behavior.

Credit recommendation, collegiate level: 3 semester hours in abnormal psychology, and credit in psychiatric nursing procedures on the basis of institutional examination.

Neuropsychiatric Procedures (Basic)
(Neuropsychiatric Specialist)

Location: Medical Field Service School, Fort Sam Houston, Tex.

Length: 12 weeks.

Objectives: To train enlisted personnel to assist in the care and treatment of neuropsychiatric patients.

Instruction: Principles and practices of neuropsychiatric patient care; psychiatric nomenclature; description of the psychiatric patient; recognition of abnormal behavior; development, motivation, and learning; anxiety, stress, and frustration; mechanism of defense; social and emotional aspects of illness; functions and responsibilities of the neuropsychiatric specialist; clinical application.

Credit recommendation, collegiate level: This course is at the preprofessional or professional level. Credit in neuropsychiatric nursing procedures on the basis of institutional examination.

Neuropsychiatric Techniques (Advanced)

Location: Medical Service School, Fort Sam Houston, Tex.

Length: 20 weeks.

Objectives: To train enlisted career personnel in a higher level of skill and acceptance of greater responsibility in the care and treatment of neuropsychiatric patients.

Instruction: Principles of neuroanatomy and neurological disorders; specialist-patient relationships; protective and supportive care; role and responsibility of the specialist in somatic therapies and other special procedures; ward management; occupational therapy; psychiatry, including the psychiatric patient, defense mechanisms, character and behavior disorders, psychoneurotic reactions, techniques of psychotherapy, psychological aspects of illness and injury in combat, mental hygiene, psychosomatic conditions, and child psychiatry; psychological theories of personality growth and development; techniques for evaluating personality; social and welfare needs of patients.

Credit recommendation, collegiate level: 3 semester hours in clinical psychology and 3 semester hours in elementary psychiatry.

1. **Nike Acquisition Radar and Computer Repair**
2. **Nike Acquisition Radar and Computer Repair**
   (Nike Acquisition Radar and Computer Systems Repair (Ajax-Hercules))
   (SAM Acquisition Radar and Computer Systems Repair)

Location: Ordnance Guided Missile School, Redstone Arsenal, Ala.

Length: *Course 1*, 34 weeks; *Course 2*, 17–25 weeks.

Objectives: To train enlisted personnel to inspect, test, and perform field maintenance on Nike I acquisition radar system, computer system, and associated field maintenance test equipment.

Instruction: *Courses 1 and 2:* Nike-Ajax acquisition radar system major components and test equipment; circuit analysis; general radar electronics components; MTI system; receiver and presentation systems; Nike-Ajax computer system; Nike-Ajax field maintenance test equipment; Nike-Hercules acquisition radar system analysis and maintenance; Nike-Hercules computer system operation and maintenance. In addition to the preceding instruction, *Course 1* includes series parallel circuits; motors and generators; inductance and capacitance; resonance circuits; RC and LR circuits; vacuum tube circuits; voltage regulators; heterodyne receiver; transmitter system; multivibrators and gating circuits; indicator circuits; receiver.

Credit recommendation, collegiate level: CAUTION: *These courses vary in title, length, and recommendation. Require exact identification of course by title and length. Course 1:* 4 semester hours at the freshman or sophomore level as an elective in electricity and electronics, and credit in electrical laboratory on the basis of demonstrated skills and/or institutional examinations. *Course 2:* Credit in electrical laboratory on the basis of demonstrated skills and/or institutional examinations.

1. **Nike Acquisition Radar and Computer Repair**
   (Improved Hercules Transition)
2. **Nike Acquisition Radar and Computer Repair**
   (Hercules Transition)

Location: Ordnance Guided Missile School, Redstone Arsenal, Ala.

Length: *Course 1,* 11–13 weeks; *Course 2,* 5 weeks.

Objectives: To train enlisted personnel to inspect, test, and perform field maintenance and repair of the Improved Nike-Hercules acquisition radar system.

Instruction: Nike-Hercules acquisition radar systems analysis and maintenance; Nike-Hercules computer fundamentals; steering computer analysis, operation, and maintenance; battery control and fire data computer systems analysis and operation.

Credit recommendation, collegiate level: For each course, credit in electrical laboratory on the basis of demonstrated skills and/or institutional examinations.

1. Nike Air Defense Missile Repair
   (Nike Maintenance Supervision)
   (Nike Maintenance Supervision (Ajax-Hercules))
   (Guided Missile Maintenance Supervision, Nike)
   (Guided Missile Systems Maintenance
       Supervisors, Nike I)
2. Nike Maintenance Supervision (Improved
       Hercules Transition)
   (Nike Maintenance Supervision (Hercules
       Transition))
3. Air Defense Missile Maintenance Technician
   (Nike)

Location: Missile and Munitions School, Redstone Arsenal, Ala.

Length: *Course 1,* 41–52 weeks; *Course 2,* 14–16 weeks; *Course 3,* 54–55 weeks.

Objectives: To train officers, warrant officers, and enlisted personnel in the supervision of maintenance of Nike guided missile systems and associated equipment.

Instruction: *Courses 1 and 3:* Principles of ordnance service; supply accounting; storage operations; management control, inspections, and preventive maintenance; operation and maintenance of Nike-Hercules acquisition radar, computer, track radar, internal guidance, launcher control, mechanical, and all associated equipment. *Course 2:* Nike acquisition radar; Nike tracking radars; field maintenance test equipment.

Credit recommendation, collegiate level: CAUTION: *These courses vary in title, length, and recommendation. Require exact identification of course by title and length. Course 1:* 3 semester hours in shop management, and credit in electrical laboratory on the basis of demonstrated skills and/or institutional examinations. *Course 2:* Credit in electrical laboratory on the basis of demonstrated skills and/or institutional examinations. *Course 3:* 3 semester hours in shop management and credit in electricity and electrical laboratory on the basis of demonstrated skills and/or institutional examinations.

1. Nike-Ajax Fire Control System Maintenance
2. SAM Fire Control System Maintenance, Nike-Ajax

Location: Air Defense School, Fort Bliss, Tex.

Length: *Course 1,* 37–38 weeks; *Course 2,* 42 weeks.

Objectives: To train warrant officers and enlisted personnel to employ, operate, adjust, and maintain the Nike-Ajax fire control system and associated IFF equipment.

Instruction: Basic electronic and radio circuits; amplifier and oscillator theory and circuits; radio transmission techniques and indicators, radar fundamentals,

schematics; AC and DC distribution; interlocks; timers; power supplies; acquisition radar; transmitter and RF systems; acquisition magnetron channel; automatic frequency control channel; moving target indicator; PPI and receiver systems; TTR transmitting systems; RF test set; receiver system; TTR range and antenna positioning system; computer prelaunch and basic circuitry; computer steering and initial turn section; MTR system; tactical control circuitry; checkout; Mark X IFF.

Credit recommendation, collegiate level: *Course 1:* 3 semester hours at the freshman or sophomore level as an elective in electricity and electronics, and credit in electrical laboratory on the basis of demonstrated skills and/or institutional examinations. *Course 2:* 6 semester hours at the freshman or sophomore level as an elective in electricity and electronics, and credit in electrical laboratory on the basis of demonstrated skills and/or institutional examinations.

1. Nike-Ajax Missile Electronic Maintenance
   (Nike-Ajax Missile Electronic Materiel
       Maintenance)
2. (SAM Electronic Materiel Maintenance, Nike)
3. (Guided Missile Electronic Materiel Maintenance,
       SAM)

Location: Air Defense School, Fort Bliss, Tex.

Length: 21–28 weeks.

Objectives: To train warrant officers and enlisted personnel in the technical aspects of the Nike-Ajax missile launching area and associated equipment.

Instruction: Resonant circuits; Ohm's law; direct and alternating current amplifiers; voltage regulator tubes; oscillators; amplitude and frequency modulation; superheterodyne receiver; radio circuits; radar circuits; transmission lines; servo-loop components; Nike computer and radars; theory, circuit analysis, assembly, test, and repair of missile electronic components; RF test set; missile checkout; launching equipment.

Credit recommendation, collegiate level: CAUTION: *These courses vary in title, length, and recommendation. Require exact identification of course by title and length. Course 1:* 2 semester hours at the freshman and sophomore level as an elective in electricity and electronics, and credit in electrical laboratory on the basis of demonstrated skills and/or institutional examinations. *Course 2:* 3 semester hours at the freshman and sophomore level as an elective in electricity and electronics, and credit in electrical laboratory on the basis of demonstrated skills and/or institutional examinations. *Course 3:* 4 semester hours at the freshman or sophomore level as an elective in electricity and electronics, and credit in electrical laboratory on the basis of demonstrated skills and/or institutional examinations.

Nike-Ajax Missile Mechanical Maintenance

Location: Air Defense School, Fort Bliss, Tex.

Length: 5–6 weeks.

Objectives: To train enlisted personnel to assemble, install, maintain, and adjust Nike-Ajax mechanical and hydraulic on-missile guidance control systems and associated test equipment, to assemble missiles, and perform required checks on Nike-Ajax propulsion and mechanical systems.

Instruction: Basic electricity; Nike-Ajax system operation and equipment familiarization; propulsion system; hydraulic system; Ajax launcher; assembly area equipment; missile repair; preparation for fire; depreparation; electrical checkout.

Credit recommendation, collegiate level: Credit in electrical laboratory on the basis of demonstrated skills and/or institutional examinations.

Nike-Hercules Electronic Maintenance
(Nike-Universal Electronic Maintenance)
(Nike-Universal Electronic Materiel Maintenance)

Location: Air Defense School, Fort Bliss, Tex.
Length: 24–27 weeks.
Objectives: To train warrant officers and enlisted personnel in the assembly and maintenance of the Nike-Hercules missile and associated equipment.
Instruction: AC and DC circuits; vacuum tubes; electronic and radio circuits; amplifiers; oscillators; radio transmission techniques; assembly and analyzing of circuits; Nike-Hercules propulsion, hydraulics, and control; missile guidance unit; RF test set; Nike-Universal launching area equipment; AG transmission system; Nike-Hercules warheads.
Credit recommendation, collegiate level: 3 semester hours at the freshman or sophomore level as an elective in electricity and electronics, and credit in electrical laboratory on the basis of demonstrated skills and/or institutional examinations.

Nike-Hercules Fire Control System Maintenance Transition

Location: Air Defense School, Fort Bliss, Tex.
Length: 9–12 weeks.
Objectives: To train warrant officers and enlisted personnel, qualified in the employment, operation, adjustment, and maintenance of the Nike-Ajax fire control system and associated IFF equipment, to be comparably proficient in the Nike-Hercules system.
Instruction: Acquisition radar transmitter and receiver circuits, checks and adjustment, presentation system operation; tracking radar and command systems; computer capabilities, analysis, and adjustments.
Credit recommendation, collegiate level: Credit in electronics and electrical laboratory on the basis of demonstrated skills and/or institutional examinations.

Nike-Hercules Missile Electronic Maintenance Transition
(Nike-Hercules Missile Electronic Materiel Maintenance Transition)

Location: Air Defense School, Fort Bliss, Tex.
Length: 8–11 weeks.
Objectives: To train warrant officers and enlisted personnel, qualified in the maintenance of the Nike-Ajax missile, to be comparably proficient with the Nike-Hercules missile and equipment.
Instruction: Components, operation, and circuitry of the guidance set and RF test set; missile test equipment and missile checkout; basic nuclear principles;

missile preparations and de-preparation; operation and maintenance of equipment in the launcher area.

Credit recommendation, collegiate level: Credit in the areas of radio and electronics on the basis of institutional examination.

Nike-Hercules Missile Mechanical Materiel Maintenance Transition

Location: Air Defense School, Fort Bliss, Tex.
Length: 3–5 weeks.
Objectives: To train enlisted personnel who are qualified in assembling, installing, maintaining, and adjusting mechanical and hydraulic on-missile control systems and related test equipment and in assembling and checking propulsion, hydraulic, and mechanical systems for the Nike-Ajax missile to a comparable level of proficiency on the Nike-Hercules missile.
Instruction: Nike-Hercules missile mechanics; launching area equipment; missile preparation and de-preparation; organizational maintenance.
Credit recommendation, collegiate level: Credit in electrical laboratory on the basis of demonstrated skills and/or institutional examinations.

Nike-Hercules Officer

Location: Air Defense School, Fort Bliss, Tex.
Length: 4–8 weeks.
Objectives: To provide artillery officers with a working knowledge of essential materiel and tactics pertaining to the Nike-Hercules system.
Instruction: Nike-Hercules system; associated warheads; nuclear principles and effects; tactics and techniques of air defense units and the employment of Nike-Hercules in the surface-to-surface role.
Credit recommendation, collegiate level: No credit as the course is military in nature.

Nike-Hercules Officer Transition

Location: Air Defense School, Fort Bliss, Tex.
Length: 3–6 weeks.
Objectives: To provide officers with transition training in the Nike-Hercules battery operations, tests, and inspections.
Instruction: Nike-Hercules system; battery control area; assembly and launching area; acquisition radar; target tracking radar; missile tracking radar; Nike-Hercules computer; warheads.
Credit recommendation, collegiate level: No credit because of the brevity and limited technical nature of the course.

Nike High Power Acquisition Radar and Radar Simulator Repair

Location: Missile and Munitions School, Ordnance Guided Missile School, Redstone Arsenal, Ala.
Length: 40–44 weeks.
Objectives: To train enlisted personnel to inspect, test, and perform support maintenance on the high-power acquisition radar and radar signal simulator station AN/MPQ-T1.

Instruction: Series and parallel circuits, DC power, inductance, alternating current, capacitance and impedance, transformers, use of the multimeter and oscilloscope, series and parallel resonance, sinusoidal circuits, transients in LR and RC circuits, diodes, power supplies, triode tubes, amplifiers, oscillators, synchro devices, microwave principles and techniques, heterodyne reception, RF and IF amplifiers, AM detectors, pulse modulated transmitter, cathode-ray tubes and indicator circuits, semiconductor diodes, transistor circuits, phantastron ciruits, video amplifiers, synchronizer, transmitter, receiver, multistage transistor circuits, and missile power supplies; high-power acquisition radar; radar signal simulator station AN/MPQ-T1.

Credit recommendation, collegiate level: 6 semester hours in electricity and electronics, and credit in electrical laboratory on the basis of demonstrated skills and/or institutional examinations.

Nike Internal Guidance Repair (Hercules Transition)

Location: Ordnance Guided Missile School, Redstone Arsenal, Ala.

Length: 4–5 weeks.

Objectives: To train enlisted personnel who are qualified in inspecting, testing, and performing field maintenance on the Nike-Ajax internal guidance system and associated test equipment to a comparable level of proficiency in the Nike-Hercules internal guidance system.

Instruction: Nike-Hercules internal guidance set and control system; guidance set chassis field maintenance checkout lab; detonation control and transistors; RF test set analysis; guidance set and complete missile checkout.

Credit recommendation, collegiate level: Credit in electrical laboratory on the basis of demonstrated skills and/or institutional examinations.

1. ### Nike Launcher Control Repair
2. ### Nike Launcher Control Repair
3. ### Nike Launcher Control Systems Repair (Ajax-Hercules)
   ### (SAM Launcher Control System Repair)

Location: Missile and Munitions School, Redstone Arsenal, Ala.

Length: *Course 1,* 16 weeks; *Course 2,* 10–14 weeks; *Course 3,* 7–9 weeks.

Objectives: To train enlisted personnel to inspect, test, and perform general support maintenance and repair on the Nike-Hercules launcher control electrical, mechanical and electronic components, and associated test equipment.

Instruction: *Course 1:* DC–AC circuits; Ohm's law; series-parallel circuits; capacitance and impedance; LR and RF circuits; diodes; power supplies; triode tubes; amplifiers; oscillators; synchro devices. *Course 2:* Introduction to electricity; series circuits; Kirchhoff's law; motors and synchros; power supplies and regulators; amplifiers, coupling circuit and oscillators. *Course 3:* Troubleshooting procedures; power distribution; circuits analysis; launcher functional tester; missile firing simulator; launcher hydraulic system; launcher mainte-nance; missile firing sequence analysis; shop operations.

Credit recommendation, collegiate level: CAUTION: *These courses vary slightly in title, length, and recommendation. Require exact indentification by title and length. Course 1:* 2 semester hours at the freshman or sophomore level as an elective in electricity or electronics, and credit in electrical laboratory on the basis of demonstrated skills and/or institutional examinations. *Course 2:* Credit in electricity and electrical laboratory on the basis of demonstrated skills and/or institutional examinations. *Course 3:* This course is technical and vocational in nature. Credit in electrical shop on the basis of demonstrated skills and/or institutional examinations.

Nike Mechanical Repair
(Nike Mechanical Systems Repair (Ajax-Hercules))
(SAM Mechanical Systems Repair)

Location: Ordnance Guided Missile School, Redstone Arsenal, Ala.

Length: 6–9 weeks.

Objectives: To train enlisted personnel to inspect, test, and perform field repair and maintenance on Nike missile mechanical systems, airframes, and ground-handling equipment.

Instruction: Fundamentals of the mechanics of, and complete familiarization with, the operation, function, and field maintenance of the missile.

Credit recommendation, collegiate level: This course is technical and vocational in nature. Credit in mechanical shop on the basis of demonstrated skills and/or institutional examinations.

1. ### Nike Missile Repair
   ### (Nike Missile Repairman)
   ### (Nike Internal Guidance Repair)
2. ### Nike Internal Guidance Repair
   ### (Nike Internal Guidance System Repair (Ajax-Hercules))
   ### (SAM Internal Guidance System Repair)

Location: Missile and Munitions School, Redstone Arsenal, Ala.

Length: *Course 1,* 23–28 weeks; *Course 2,* 7–13 weeks.

Objectives: To train enlisted personnel to inspect, test, and perform maintenance and repair of the Nike-Hercules missile internal guidance system and associated equipment.

Instruction: *Courses 1 and 2:* Basic ordnance shop practice; Nike-Hercules-Ajax internal guidance set circuitry; commercial test equipment; transponder control test set group; guidance section test set group; guidance sets and chassis checkout labs; RF test set and missile electrical test set labs. In addition to the preceding instruction, *Course 1* includes series and parallel circuits; motors and generators; resonance circuits; RC and LR circuits; diodes and voltage dividers; vacuum tube circuits; voltage regulators; signal generators, mixers, AM detectors, and AGC; heterodyne receiver; transmitter system; RC and LR circuits; amplifier circuits and oscillators; multivibrators and gating circuits; presentation system circuits.

Credit recommendation, collegiate level: CAUTION:

These courses vary in title, length, and recommendation. Require exact identification of course by title and length. Course 1: 3 semester hours at the freshman or sophomore level as an elective in electricity and electronics, and credit in electrical laboratory on the basis of demonstrated skills and/or institutional examinations. Course 2: Credit in electrical laboratory on the basis of demonstrated skills and/or institutional examinations.

Nike Radar and Computer Repair

Location: Missile and Munitions School, Redstone Arsenal, Ala.

Length: 44 weeks.

Objectives: To train enlisted personnel to inspect, test, and perform support maintenance on Nike-Hercules-Lopar missile-tracking radar, target-tracking radar, computer, and associated test equipment.

Instruction: Missile electronics, including soldering; Ohm's law and series-parallel circuits; resistors; electrical circuits; inductance and capacitance; resonance circuits; vacuum tube circuits; voltage regulators; oscillators; generators; mixers; amplifiers; receiver; transmitter; indicator circuits; receiver and transmission lines; CRT and presentation systems; multivibrators and gating circuits; RC and LR circuits.

Credit recommendation, collegiate level: 4 semester hours at the freshman or sophomore level as an elective in electricity and electronics, and credit in electrical laboratory on the basis of demonstrated skills and/or institutional examinations.

Nike System Maintenance Officer Transition
(SAM Staff Officer Transition (Hercules))
(Nike Hercules Maintenance Officer Transition)

Location: Air Defense School, Fort Bliss, Tex.

Length: 14–21 weeks.

Objectives: To train officers, qualified in the technical operation, organizational maintenance, and inspection of the Nike-Ajax fire control systems, to a comparable level of proficiency for the Nike-Hercules systems.

Instruction: Acquisition radar; Nike-Hercules computer; tracking radars; missile and guidance set; test equipment and checkout; warhead; launcher area.

Credit recommendation, collegiate level: Credit in electrical laboratory on the basis of demonstrated skills and/or institutional examinations.

Nike Test Equipment Repair

Location: Missile and Munitions School, Redstone Arsenal, Ala.

Length: 33–34 weeks.

Objectives: To train enlisted personnel to inspect, test, and repair Nike test equipment.

Instruction: Series-parallel circuits; inductance and capacitance; RC and LR circuits; vacuum tube circuits; voltage regulators; signal generators, mixers, amplifiers, and detectors; heterodyne receiver; transmitter; semiconductors; multivibrators; gating circuits; power sup-

ply and distribution; range calibrators; pulse generators; servo test equipment; computer units and indicator maintenance.

Credit recommendation, collegiate level: 4 semester hours at the freshman or sophomore level as an elective in electricity and electronics, and credit in electrical laboratory on the basis of demonstrated skills and/or institutional examinations.

1. Nike Track Radar Repair
(Nike Track Radar Systems Repair
(Ajax-Hercules))
(SAM Track Radar Systems Repair)
2. Nike Track Radar Repair

Location: Ordnance Guided Missile School, Redstone Arsenal, Ala.

Length: *Course 1, 20–26 weeks; Course 2, 36 weeks.*

Objectives: To train enlisted personnel to inspect, test, and perform field maintenance and repair on Nike I or Nike-Hercules-Ajax missile-tracking and target-tracking radar systems and associated test equipment.

Instruction: *Courses 1 and 2:* Nike I or Nike-Hercules-Ajax systems, including ground guidance area, launcher area, missile and booster, basic system operation and analysis of all components, use of voice communication facilities, system schematics, and test equipment. *Course 2:* In addition to the preceding instruction this course contains series-parallel circuits, motors and generators, DC power, control devices, transformers, inductance and capacitance, resonance circuits, RC and LR circuits, diodes and voltage dividers, power supplies, vacuum tube circuits, voltage regulators, synchro and servo devices, radio waves, RF filters and sine-wave oscillators, heterodyne receiver, transmitter system, amplifier circuits and oscillators, multivibrators and gating circuits, radar and transmitter circuit analysis, indicator circuits, and antennas.

Credit recommendation, collegiate level: CAUTION: *These courses vary in title, length, and recommendation. Require exact identification of course by title and length. Course 1:* Credit in electrical laboratory on the basis of demonstrated skills and/or institutional examinations. *Course 2:* 4 semester hours at the freshman or sophomore level as an elective in electricity and electronics, and credit in electrical laboratory on the basis of demonstrated skills and/or institutional examinations.

1. Nike Track Radar Repair (Improved Hercules
Transition)
2. Nike Track Radar Repair (Hercules Transition)

Location: Ordnance Guided Missile School, Redstone Arsenal, Ala.

Length: *Course 1, 11–12 weeks; Course 2, 3–4 weeks.*

Objectives: To train qualified enlisted personnel to inspect, test, and perform field maintenance on the Nike-Hercules target and tracking radar system.

Instruction: *Course 1:* Improved tracking and ranging radar; synchronizer and transmitter; receiver system and countermeasures range sweep presentations; panoramic system; parallax correction, control circuits, and maintenance; transmitter and control circuits; receiver, ranging and presentation systems; system analysis; Improved Nike-Hercules field maintenance test equipment. *Course 2:* Introduction to the Nike-Hercules system; power distribution; transmitter system; ranging and presentation systems; antenna positioning system; command system operation and maintenance; system analysis.

Credit recommendation, collegiate level: For each course, credit in electrical laboratory on the basis of demonstrated skills and/or institutional examinations.

Nike Universal Officer
(Nike-Universal Officer Qualification)
(Officer Qualification, Nike-Ajax)
(Nike-Ajax Officer Qualification (Reserve Component))

Location: Air Defense School, Fort Bliss, Tex.
Length: 8–10 weeks.
Objectives: To train artillery officers in essential tactics and materiel pertaining to Nike-Universal system.
Instruction: Orientation of Nike-Ajax system; basic radars; basic electricity; electrical and radar circuits; control devices and servosystems; soldering; Nike-Ajax introduction and launcher area; Nike-Ajax assembly area equipment and operation; Nike-Ajax battery control area equipment and operation; Nike-Ajax battery operation and inspection; AAA missile tactics.
Credit recommendation, collegiate level: Credit in electrical laboratory on the basis of demonstrated skills and/or institutional examinations.

Noncommissioned Officer Logistics Program

Location: Quartermaster School, Fort Lee, Va.
Length: 8 weeks.
Objectives: To train NCO's whose assignments are to NCO Logistic Program positions in wholesale and field logistics operations.
Instruction: Organization for logistics; supply management procedures; automated supply system; installation logistics management; maintenance management; management practices; inventory management; depot operations; supply operations; procurement management; installation transportation management; financial management.
Credit recommendation, collegiate level: 4 semester hours in supply management.

1. Nuclear, Biological and Chemical (NBC) Weapons Employment
2. Nuclear Weapons Employment

Locations: Armor School, Fort Knox, Ky.; Army Command and General Staff College, Fort Leavenworth, Kan.; Artillery and Missile School, Fort Sill, Okla.; Chemical Center and School, Fort McClellan, Ala.; Infantry School, Fort Benning, Ga.
Length: 3–5 weeks.
Objectives: To train commissioned officers as nuclear weapons employment officers.
Instruction: Weapons systems; effects of nuclear weapons; fundamentals of nuclear, biological, and chemical employment; tactical application of nuclear, biological and chemical weapons employment.
Credit recommendation, collegiate level: No credit because of the brevity and nature of these courses.

Nuclear Weapons Effects Officer

Location: Chemical Corps School, Fort McClellan, Ala.
Length: 12 weeks.
Objectives: To train Chemical Corps officers to perform staff functions associated with the offensive employment of, and defensive measures against, nuclear weapons.
Instruction: Operational aspects of fallout; linear equations, law of exponents, slide rule, quadratic equations, trigometric functions, vectors, logarithms, curve plotting, graphs, and analysis; table of nuclides, radiation units, fission, fusion, and radioactivity; units and dimensions of constants, theory of heat, and wave motion; kinetic molecular theory, electrons and ions, elementary quantum theory, electronic structure of the atom, X-rays, and periodic table of the elements; electrostatics, current electricity, electromagnetism, electron tubes, and transistors; atomic nucleus, natural radioactivity, binding energy and nuclear forces, neutrons, alpha and beta emission, and decay of radioactive fallout; radiac instruments; radiological surveys; weapons effects.
Credit recommendation, collegiate level: 6 semester hours in general physics and 2 semester hours in general mathematics.

Nuclear Weapons Employment and Radiological Defense
(Nuclear Weapons Employment and Radiological Warfare)
(Atomic Defense)

Location: Chemical Corps School, Fort McClellan, Ala.
Length: 6–7 weeks.
Objectives: To train commissioned officers and warrant officers in nuclear and radiological warfare and defense measures.
Instruction: Technical aspects of atomic weapons, their effects, and employment; use of radiac instruments; principles of radiological survey; characteristics, capabilities, and limitations of atomic weapons and the associated delivery means; target analysis techniques; problems of atomic warfare.
Credit recommendation, collegiate level: No credit because of the limited technical nature of the course.

Nuclear Weapons Maintenance (Entry)
(Atomic Weapons Electronics (Entry))

Location: Signal School, Fort Monmouth, N.J.
Length: 12 weeks.
Objectives: To train enlisted personnel in electronics and to assist in the repair of nuclear weapons systems and equipment.
Instruction: Electrical fundamentals; electronics ap-

plied to basic receivers, including radio frequency energy, diodes, half-wave rectification, power supply filters, triode tubes, voltage amplification, transformer and resistance-capacitance coupling, pentode and beam power tubes, series and parallel resonance, amplification of radio frequencies, and mixer circuits; basic electronics applied to reactive components, filters, oscillators, amplifiers, and voltage regulated power supplies; testing of nonsinusoidal electronic circuitry; operation, adjustment, and maintenance of the AN/VRC-19 radio set.

Credit recommendation, collegiate level: 3 semester hours at the freshman or sophomore level as an elective in the areas of radio and electronics, and credit in electrical laboratory on the basis of demonstrated skills and/or institutional examinations.

OH-6A Helicopter Repair

Location: Transportation School, Fort Eustis, Va.
Length: 3 weeks.
Objectives: To train enlisted personnel in user and support maintenance of the OH-6A aircraft.
Instruction: OH-6A utility and instrument systems; armament systems; airframe and airframe maintenance; power train maintenance; rotor systems; flight control; electrical systems; gas turbine engine maintenance; troubleshooting.
Credit recommendation, collegiate level: This course is technical and vocational in nature. Credit in helicopter repair shop on the basis of demonstrated skills and/or institutional examinations.

OV-1 (Mohawk) Aviator Combat Surveillance Qualification

Location: Combat Surveillance School, Fort Huachuca, Ariz.
Length: 4 weeks.
Objectives: To train OV-1 aviators in the employment of aerial radar, infrared, camera, and Doppler navigation systems and to provide them with a general knowledge of the organization and operation of the aerial surveillance unit.
Instruction: Aerial surveillance unit organization and operation; OV-1B/OV-1C Mohawk airplane checkout and low-level navigation; AN/UPD-2 side-looking aerial radar system; AN-VAS-4 surveillance infrared system operation; AN/ASN-64 Doppler navigation system; KS-61 photographic surveillance system; intelligence and aerial surveillance plan.
Credit recommendation, collegiate level: This course is technical and vocational in nature. Credit in operation of cameras and camera equipment on the basis of demonstrated skills and/or institutional examinations.

OV-1 (Mohawk) Aviator Transition
(OV-1 (Mohawk) Pilot Transition)
(AO-1 (Mohawk) Aviator Transition)

Location: Aviation School, Fort Rucker, Ala.
Length: 6–8 weeks.
Objectives: To train Army aviators in the operation of combat surveillance multi-engine STOL aircraft.

Instruction: General flight orientation; takeoffs and landings; night operations; short field operations; aerobatics; instrument flying; low-level operation; cruise control and flight planning; familiarization with aircraft maintenance; tactical employment.
Credit recommendation, collegiate level: No credit as course is military in nature.

1. OV-1 (Mohawk) Instructor Pilot Qualification
2. CV-2 (Caribou) Instructor Pilot Qualification

Location: Army Aviation School, Fort Rucker, Ala.
Length: 6 weeks.
Objectives: To qualify commissioned and warrant officer Army aviators as instructor pilots in the OV-1 or CV-2 airplanes.
Instruction: Methods of flight instruction for standardized maneuvers and procedures; duties of an instructor pilot; familiarization with aircraft maintenance; techniques of tactical flying.
Credit recommendation, collegiate level: Credit in instructional methods on the basis of institutional examination.

OV-1 Suppressive Fire

Location: Aviation School, Fort Rucker, Ala.
Length: 3–4 weeks.
Objectives: To provide OV-1 aviators with a working knowledge of the techniques of fixed-wing air-to-ground machine gun and rocket firing.
Instruction: Gunnery safety; sight and armament equipment; formation flying and flight team tactics, glide rocketry and strafing.
Credit recommendation, collegiate level: No credit as this course is military in nature.

Occupational Therapy Enlisted

Location: Medical Field Service School, Fort Sam Houston, Tex.
Length: 12 weeks.
Objectives: To train enlisted personnel to assist occupational therapists in the treatment of patients through instruction in workshop activities and arts and crafts.
Instruction: Anatomy and physiology; introduction to physical medicine; occupational therapy for general medicine and surgery patients, neuropsychiatric patients, physically disabled patients, and tuberculosis patients; familiarization with medical terms, diseases, and surgical conditions; introduction to psychiatry; principles and techniques of general craft activities, including instruction of patients in these crafts; techniques of leatherwork, plastics, and woodworking.
Credit recommendation, collegiate level: Credit in occupational therapy on the basis of institutional examination.

Office Machine Repair

Location: Quartermaster School, Fort Lee, Va.

Length: 26 weeks.

Objectives: To train enlisted personnel to repair and adjust typewriters, adding machines, calculators, and duplicating machines.

Instruction: Maintenance and repair of typewriters, adding machines, calculators, and duplicating machines.

Credit recommendation, collegiate level: This course is technical and vocational in nature. Credit in office machine repair on the basis of demonstrated skills and/or institutional examinations.

Officer Fixed-Wing Aviator
Phase A, Primary
Phase B, Advanced Contact and Tactics
Phase C, Instruments

Location: Aviation School, Fort Rucker, Ala.

Length: *Phase A,* 16–18 weeks; *Phase B,* 12 weeks; *Phase C,* 9–10 weeks.

Objectives: *Phases A and B:* To train officers in the basic flying techniques and tactical employment of Army observation and utility fixed-wing aircraft and in the duties of officer aviators in support of combat operations of ground arms. *Phase C:* To train officers in instrument aviation.

Instruction: *Phase A:* Primary flight training; primary instrument flight; fundamentals of aircraft maintenance; principles of meteorology; radio communication; navigation. *Phase B:* Advanced flight training; advanced meteorology; principles and organization of aircraft maintenance; tactical subjects. *Phase C:* Advanced instrument navigation; procedures and techniques of instrument flying.

Credit recommendation, collegiate level: *Phase A:* 2 semester hours in primary meteorology and navigation. *Phase B:* 1 semester hour in primary meteorology. *Phase C:* No credit. *Completion of Phases A, B, and C:* 3 semester hours in primary meteorology and navigation.

1. Officer Rotary-Wing Aviator
2. Officer/Warrant Officer Rotary-Wing Aviator
3. Warrant Officer Rotary-Wing Aviator
4. Warrant Officer Candidate Rotary-Wing Aviator

Locations: Army Aviation School, Fort Rucker, Ala.; Army Primary Helicopter School, Fort Wolters, Tex.

Length: 28–50 weeks.

Objectives: To train commissioned officers, warrant officers, and warrant officer candidates in the flying techniques of rotary-wing aircraft.

These courses are divided into various phases. All students receive instruction in at least the primary phase. The additional phases include transition flight training, tactics and aerial gunnery, advanced contact, and instruments. Because of the military nature of the latter phases, credit will be based upon mainly the primary phase.

Instruction: Primary training, including rotary-wing training, helicopter maintenance, aerodynamics, methods of navigation, aeronautical charts, determination of headings, flight planning, introduction to weather and circulation, temperature and dew point, pressure and wind, air masses, frontal weather, thunderstorms, icing and fog, and weather maps; advanced and field operational use of the helicopter; instrument flying; low-level, cross-country, and night flight training; employment techniques of the armed helicopter; aerial suppressive firing; employment of utility-cargo-type helicopters.

Credit recommendation, collegiate level: For each course, 3 semester hours in primary meteorology and navigation and credit in helicopter flight training on the basis of demonstrated skills and/or institutional examinations.

Officer/Warrant Officer Fixed-Wing Aviator

Locations: Aviation School, Fort Rucker, Ala.; Aviation School, Fort Stewart, Ga.

Length: 33–35 weeks.

Objectives: To train commissioned officers, warrant officers, and warrant officer candidates in the flying techniques of fixed-wing aircraft.

This course is divided into 4 phases; only 2 include subject matter of academic content—the Primary phase and the Advanced Contact phase. The course given in 1962 and 1963 included 18 weeks of training in *Phase A,* Primary. For this course the credit recommendation is based only on the Primary phase. After 1963, the academic content of the Primary phase was given in the 8- to 10-week *Phase A,* Primary and in the 8- to 10-week *Phase B,* Advanced Contact. For those completing the course after 1963 the credit recommendation applies only if the Primary and Advanced Contact phases have been completed.

Instruction: Primary and advanced flight training; organizational aircraft maintenance; meteorology, including heat processes and moisture in the atmosphere, pressure and winds, fog and cloud formation, air masses, fronts, thunderstorms, icing, and flight forecast; radio and flight planning; instrument flight navigation, including aeronautical charts, distance and direction, effects of wing and vector analysis, dead reckoning computer, cross-country charts and logs, determination of headings, selection and use of check points, and night navigation; tactical subjects.

Credit recommendation, collegiate level: CAUTION: *Require verification of completion of either the 18-week Primary phase or a combination of the Primary and Advanced Contact phases.* 3 semester hours in primary meteorology and navigation for the 18-week Primary or for a combination of the 8- to 10-week Primary and the 8- to 10-week Advanced Contact phases.

1. Officer/Warrant Officer Rotary Wing Qualification (Reserve Component/Allied) (Officer/Warrant Officer Rotary Wing Qualification)
2. Officer/Warrant Officer Rotary Wing Qualification (Active Army)

Location: Army Aviation School, Fort Rucker, Ala.

Length: 8–12 weeks.

Objectives: To qualify commissioned officer and warrant officer aviators in rotary-wing flying techniques.

Instruction: *Course 1:* Presolo, primary, and advanced flight maneuvers of observation helicopters;

rotor aircraft aerodynamics; aircraft maintenance; tactical employment of rotary-wing aircraft. *Course 2:* In addition to the preceding instruction this course includes transition flight training in the UH-1 helicopter, and tactical instrument flight training.

Credit recommendation, collegiate level: For each course, credit in helicopter flight training on the basis of demonstrated skills and/or institutional examinations.

Offset Press Operation

Location: Engineer School, Fort Belvoir, Va.
Length: 7–8 weeks.
Objectives: To train enlisted personnel in the operation of lithographic offset presses; reproduction of maps, charts, and other printed line work; fundamentals of printing and binding.
Instruction: Introduction to photolithography; offset press operation; bindery equipment fundamentals.
Credit recommendation, collegiate level: This course is technical and vocational in nature. Credit in lithographic press operation on the basis of demonstrated skills and/or institutional examinations.

1005 Card Processor Programer

Location: Adjutant General School, Fort Benjamin Harrison, Ind.
Length: 3 weeks.
Objectives: To train enlisted personnel in the principles and techniques of programming and operating the 1005 card processor.
Instruction: Computer programming; characteristics of the 1005 card processor; 1005 single address assembly language; software packages.
Credit recommendation, collegiate level: Credit in computer programming in the area of data processing on the basis of institutional examination.

1. Open Mess Management
2. Consolidated and Open Mess Management

Location: Quartermaster School, Fort Lee, Va.
Length: 7 weeks.
Objectives: *Course 1:* To train Army and Air Force officers and enlisted personnel as officers-in-charge and as club stewards, in an officers' open mess and as a club secretary in a noncommissioned officers' open mess, respectively. *Course 2:* To train Army officers in the functions of a field ration consolidated mess or an officers' open mess.
Instruction: Requisition, purchase, operation, and maintenance of open mess facilities and equipment; principles of food storage and mess sanitation; management of open mess facilities, including guest housing, recreation activities, beverage dispensing activities, dining facilities, and entertainment programs; menu planning and food preparation; food purchase and cost determination; familiarization with basic accounting principles.
Credit recommendation, collegiate level: For each course, 3 semester hours in institutional (culinary) management and 2 semester hours in introduction to food and nutrition.

Operating Room Procedures (Basic)
(Operating Room Procedures)
(Operating Room Technician)

Location: Medical Field Service School, Fort Sam Houston, Tex.
Length: 12–14 weeks.
Objectives: To train enlisted personnel in basic operating room and central materiel procedures.
Instruction: Anatomy and physiology; introduction to pharmacology; nursing procedures, including isolation procedures, respiratory treatments, administration of medication, injections, and diagnostic tests; sterilization of instruments; care and preparation of all operating room materiel; operating room equipment and procedures; introduction to anesthesia and suturing; surgical preparation of the patient; practical training.
Credit recommendation, collegiate level: 2 semester hours in physiology and hygiene.

1. Operations and Intelligence Specialist
(Special Forces Operations and Intelligence Specialists)
2. Infantry Intelligence and Operations Specialist

Location: John F. Kennedy Center for Special Warfare, Fort Bragg, N.C.
Length: 8 weeks.
Objectives: To train enlisted personnel in the duties, skills, and knowledge required of operations and intelligence specialists to include specific application to Special Forces organization and operation concepts.
Instruction: Map and aerial photograph reading; photography techniques applicable to Special Forces operations; techniques of fingerprinting; guerrilla communications; intelligence procedures and techniques, including safeguarding defense information, order of battle, weather and terrain intelligence, collection and processing of information, pre-infiltration intelligence, area assessment, informants, interrogation, and target analysis; operations associated with unconventional warfare.
Credit recommendation, collegiate level: 3 semester hours in intelligence methods for each course.

Operations Central and Coder-Decoder Group Repair

Location: Air Defense School, Fort Bliss, Tex.
Length: 20 weeks.
Objectives: To train warrant officers and enlisted personnel in the performance of organizational and direct-general support maintenance of the operations central, AN/TSQ-38, and coder-decoder, OA-2789/TSQ-38, subsystem of the missile monitor.
Instruction: Introduction to the AN/TSQ-38; coordinate data set, AN/TSQ-36; coder-decoder group; operations central; ground-to-slant converter; troubleshooting and repair techniques; system procedures.
Credit recommendation, collegiate level: Credit in electrical laboratory on the basis of demonstrated skills and/or institutional examinations.

Optical Laboratory Specialist
(Optical Technician)

Locations: Fitzsimons General Hospital, Denver, Colo.; St. Louis Medical Depot, St. Louis, Mo.

Length: 20–24 weeks.

Objectives: To train enlisted personnel in the grinding, polishing, and edging of lenses in accordance with prescriptions, spectacle assembly, and the use and maintenance of optical equipment and precision instruments.

Instruction: Basic optical theory; interpretation of prescriptions and fabrication of spectacles, including cutting, edging, assembly, inspection, packing, and mailing; repair, maintenance, and use of tools, equipment, and machinery; blocking, grinding, fining, and polishing lens blanks; computation of lens curves; supply procedures.

Credit recommendation, collegiate level: This course is technical and vocational in nature. Credit in precision instrument maintenance on the basis of demonstrated skills and/or institutional examinations.

Ordnance Ammunition Officer

Location: Ordnance School, Aberdeen Proving Ground, Md.

Length: 7 weeks.

Objectives: To train commissioned officers and warrant officers in the organization and management of ammunition supply and renovation installations.

Instruction: Ammunition supply procedures; management of storage operations; management of ammunition stock control procedures; ammunition transportation management; management of maintenance and renovation activities.

Credit recommendation, collegiate level: 3 semester hours in supply management.

Ordnance Field Grade Officer Refresher

Location: Ordnance School, Aberdeen Proving Ground, Md.

Length: 4 weeks.

Objectives: To provide refresher training in the duties and responsibilities appropriate to field-grade ordnance officers.

Instruction: Military tactics and staff; ordnance service fundamentals; military leadership; management of field and depot supply and maintenance logistics; ordnance general supply; guided missile and special weapons logistics; ordnance materiel.

Credit recommendation, collegiate level: No credit because of the brevity and limited technical nature of the course.

Ordnance Fire Control Materiel Maintenance

Location: Ordnance School, Aberdeen Proving Ground, Md.

Length: 19 weeks.

Objectives: To train commissioned officers and warrant officers to supervise the maintenance and repair of fire control equipment.

Instruction: Fundamentals of alternating and direct current, including electrical measuring devices, series and parallel circuits, inductance and capacitance, transformers, generators, AC and DC motors, and multiphase power; fundamentals of radio components with emphasis on superheterodyne receivers and circuitry; theory and components implicated in basic radar; familiarization with shop organization and management; operation, function, and adjustment of remote control systems; fuze setter-rammers and power control systems; principles of operation, characteristics, and adjustments of the M33 and M38 fire control system.

Credit recommendation, collegiate level: 3 semester hours at the freshman or sophomore level as an elective in basic electronics, and credit in electrical laboratory on the basis of demonstrated skills and/or institutional examinations.

Ordnance General Supply Officer

Location: Ordnance School, Aberdeen Proving Ground, Md.

Length: 5–6 weeks.

Objectives: To train commissioned officers and warrant officers in the organization and management of ordnance general supply and to direct and supervise personnel engaged in ordnance general supply activities.

Instruction: Supply publications and supply accounting procedures; warehousing and storage; supply operations in the zone of interior; financial management; supply operations in a theater of operations; special weapons and guided missile supply operations.

Credit recommendation, collegiate level: 3 semester hours in supply management.

Ordnance Guided Missile Company Grade Officer

Location: Ordnance Guided Missile School, Huntsville, Ala.

Length: 10 weeks.

Objectives: To train officers in the general supervision and direction of the logistical support required for ordnance guided missile systems.

Instruction: Introduction to electronics; DC and electron theory; series, parallel, and voltage divider circuits; magnetism; alternating current; frequency spectrum; capacitance; inductance; power supply; voltage regulators; oscillators; transmitters; receivers; cathode-ray tubes; radar systems and methods; radar receivers and indicators; Nike I missile; propulsion system; launching equipment; assembly site; field maintenance shop; receiver and transmitter; acquisition radar; tracking radars; ground guidance system; Nike computer; Corporal missile; propulsion system; propellant system; erector; guidance and attitude systems; flight control system; test station; Corporal radar command and transmitter systems; antenna positioning; computers; Doppler; logistical support.

Credit recommendation, collegiate level: Credit in electricity and electrical laboratory on the basis of demonstrated skills and/or institutional examinations.

Ordnance Officer Advanced
(Ordnance Officer Career)

Location: Ordnance School, Aberdeen Proving Ground, Md.

Length: 22–36 weeks.

Objectives: To train officers in the duties and responsibilities appropriate to field-grade Ordnance Corps officers.

Instruction: Organization for logistics; administration and operations; tactics and staff procedures; logistics management; management functions and techniques; supply and maintenance operations; problems in ordnance service management; ordnance materiel; guided missiles and nuclear weapons.

Credit recommendation, collegiate level: 6 semester hours in business organization and management.

Ordnance Officer Basic

Location: Ordnance School, Aberdeen Proving Ground, Md.

Length: 9 weeks.

Objectives: To train newly commissioned officers in the duties and responsibilities of ordnance officers.

Instruction: Administration and operations; military leadership; tactics and staff procedures; ordnance service organization; supply; ordnance field service; ordnance materiel.

Credit recommendation, collegiate level: 2 semester hours in supply management, and credit in advanced military at institutions which regularly offer such credit.

Ordnance Parts Supply

Location: Ordnance School, Aberdeen Proving Ground, Md.

Length: 6 weeks.

Objectives: To train enlisted personnel in the use, interchangeability, identification, and storage of ordnance repair parts.

Instruction: Ordnance supply publications and manuals; supply accounting; stock record account; fire control, armament, and automotive materiel; parts identification; storage functions and procedures.

Credit recommendation, collegiate level: This course is technical and vocational in nature. Credit in supply accounting procedures on the basis of institutional examination.

Ordnance Service Section Officer

Location: Ordnance School, Aberdeen Proving Ground, Md.

Length: 6 weeks.

Objectives: To train officers and warrant officers in the organization and management of a service section shop and in the direction and supervision of personnel engaged in service section activities.

Instruction: Welding-blacksmith procedures; machine shop procedures; metal body repair; allied trades; shop organization vehicle recovery operations.

Credit recommendation, collegiate level: This course is technical and vocational in nature. Credit in machine shop on the basis of demonstrated skills and/or institutional examinations.

Ordnance Staff Officer Guided Missile and Special Weapons Logistics

Location: Ordnance School, Aberdeen Proving Ground, Md.

Length: 3 weeks.

Objectives: To train commissioned officers in guided missiles and special weapons logistics.

Instruction: Guided missiles and rockets; special weapons materiel; stock control and distribution maintenance; storage and transportation of atomic weapons; guided missile supply and maintenance procedures.

Credit recommendation, collegiate level: No credit because of the brevity of the course.

Ordnance Supply

Location: Ordnance School, Aberdeen Proving Ground, Md.

Length: 5–8 weeks.

Objectives: To train enlisted personnel to maintain stock records and to perform stock accounting and storage functions pertaining to requisition, receipt, storage, identification, and issue of ordnance equipment and supplies.

Instruction: Cataloging; supply accounting procedures; stock record account; parts identification; supply functions and procedures; storage functions and procedures.

Credit recommendation, collegiate level: This course is technical and vocational in nature. Credit in stock accounting procedures on the basis of institutional examination.

Ordnance Technical Intelligence

Location: Ordnance School, Aberdeen Proving Ground, Md.

Length: 13 weeks.

Objectives: To train commissioned officers, warrant officers, and enlisted personnel to collect, identify, and evaluate foreign ordnance materiel or relevant technical documents, and to disseminate pertinent information.

Instruction: Organization and mission of a technical intelligence system; sources of information; familiarization with Russian ammunition terms; fundamentals of foreign small arms, artillery weapons, service vehicles, armored vehicles, rockets, missiles, and ammunition; demolition explosives and equipment; familiarization with foreign fire control instruments and equipment.

Credit recommendation, collegiate level: No credit as the course is military in nature.

Organizational Maintenance Officer

Location: Aviation School, Fort Rucker, Ala.

Length: 10 weeks.

Objectives: To train officers to supervise and instruct mechanic personnel of Aviation Company, or Helicopter Company, in aircraft maintenance.

Instruction: Aircraft forms and reports; technical orders; aircraft engines; H-13, H-34, and H-21 rotor heads and blades, flight controls, and power transmission; propellers; fixed-wing and rotary-wing aircraft rigging and inspections; test flights; supply and maintenance.

Credit recommendation, collegiate level: This course is technical and vocational in nature. Credit in helicopter repair on the basis of demonstrated skills and/or institutional examinations.

Orthopedic Laboratory Procedures (Orthopedic Specialist)

Location: Medical Service School, Fort Sam Houston, Tex.

Length: 4 weeks.

Objectives: To train enlisted personnel to assist in fabricating, repairing, and adjusting casts and orthopedic devices.

Instruction: Introduction to general anatomy, including skeletal, muscular, organ, and systematic anatomy; familiarization with the various orthopedic conditions; types of orthopedic appliances and their use; materials and tools for constructing orthopedic appliances; practical training with orthopedic patients.

Credit recommendation, collegiate level: No credit because of the brevity and limited technical nature of this course.

1. **Parachute Packing, Maintenance, and Airdrop**
   (Parachute Packing, Maintenance, and Air
     Delivery)
   (Parachute Packing, Maintenance, and Aerial
     Delivery)
2. **Parachute Maintenance and Aerial Supply Officer**
   (Parachute Maintenance and Airdrop Officer)
3. **Airdrop Loadmaster**

Location: Quartermaster School, Fort Lee, Va.

Length: *Course 1*, 11–14 weeks; *Course 2*, 6 weeks; *Course 3*, 3 weeks.

Objectives: *Course 1:* To train officers, warrant officers, and enlisted personnel in the inspection, packing, repairing, and maintenance of personal and cargo parachutes and airdrop equipment; rigging, loading, and securing cargo in aircraft; inflight preparation of cargo for ejection; recovery of parachutes and airdrop equipment. *Course 2:* To prepare officers as supervisors in the objectives listed for *Course 1. Course 3:* To qualify in the packing procedures of cargo parachutes used in airdrop and in technical procedures involving airdrop containers and Army aircraft operations.

Instruction: Parachute and cargo parachute packing; aerial delivery; sewing machine operation and maintenance; airborne operations and procedures.

Credit recommendation, collegiate level: *Courses 1 and 2.* These courses are technical and vocational in nature. Credit in sewing and parachute maintenance on the basis of demonstrated skills and/or institutional examinations. *Course 3:* No credit because of the brevity and limited technical nature of the course.

Pathfinder

Location: Infantry School, Fort Benning, Ga.

Length: 4–5 weeks.

Objectives: To qualify officers and enlisted parachutists as pathfinders.

Instruction: Pathfinder orientation, helicopter landing zone techniques; drop zone techniques; airplane landing zone techniques; pathfinder field exercises; communications electronics; map and airphoto reading.

Credit recommendation, collegiate level: No credit because of the military nature of the course.

Patient Administration

Location: Medical Field Service School, Fort Sam Houston, Tex.

Length: 8 weeks.

Objectives: To train commissioned officers in the principles and procedures required for administration of medical treatment facilities.

Instruction: Principles and procedures related to medical records and reports; functions of the registrar of an Army hospital; data processing functions as applied to the registrar field; oral and written communications; analysis of statistical data; familiarization with personnel management; principles of medical and military law; introduction to medical and dental science.

Credit recommendation, collegiate level: This course is technical and vocational in nature. Credit in office procedures on the basis of institutional examination.

Pay/Disbursing Specialist

Location: Finance School, Fort Benjamin Harrison, Ind.

Length: 7–8 weeks.

Objectives: To train enlisted personnel in the methods and procedures used in the maintenance of financial data records folders, in the preparation, examination, and computation of vouchers pertaining to entitlements, and in accounting for receipts and payments by finance disbursing officers.

Instruction: Pay of military personnel; travel allowances; disbursing operations, including cashiers' duties, preparation of deposits, insurance and reporting for treasury checks, vouchers, and cash book; finance office practice; fiscal code.

Credit recommendation, collegiate level: 3 semester hours in finance and disbursing.

Pershing Missile Battery

Location: Artillery and Missile School, Fort Sill, Okla.

Length: 6–9 weeks.

Objectives: To train enlisted personnel in the assembly, checkout, organizational maintenance, and operation of the Pershing missile and associated equipment.

Instruction: Communication electronics; Pershing missile system; guidance computer; programmer test station; fire data computer equipment; azimuth laying; power station; ground-handling equipment; erector launcher; firing platoon operations.

Credit recommendation, collegiate level: Credit in electrical laboratory on the basis of demonstrated skills and/or institutional examinations.

Pershing Officer

Location: Artillery and Missile School, Fort Sill, Okla.

Length: 7–8 weeks.

Objectives: To train commissioned officers in the characteristics, tactical employment, system maintenance, and general operating procedures of the Pershing missile system.

Instruction: Communication systems and equipment; basic electronics and electrical safety; digital computer fundamentals; theory and functioning of the Pershing missile; Pershing fire data computer; automatic laying and guidance sequencing equipment; test and checkout; power station and ground-handling equipment; erector-launcher; missile handling, battery area, firing position procedures, and azimuth laying; Pershing warhead; tactics-combined arms.

Credit recommendation, collegiate level: No credit because of the limited technical nature of the course.

Pershing Specialist
(Pershing System Maintenance)

Location: Artillery and Missile School, Fort Sill, Okla.

Length: 17–20 weeks.

Objectives: To train warrant officers and enlisted personnel in the assembly, checkout, organizational maintenance, and operation of the Pershing missile and associated equipment.

Instruction: Communication electronics; mathematics; multimeter; Ohm's law and series DC circuits; parallel DC circuits; magnetism; vectors; alternating current and voltage; oscilloscope; inductance and capacitance; series and parallel AC circuits; motors, generators, and inverters; servomechanisms; digital computer fundamentals; Pershing theory and functioning; Pershing fire data computer; automatic laying and guidance sequencing equipment; power station and ground-handling equipment; erector-launcher; missile handling, battery area firing position procedures, and azimuth laying; Pershing warhead.

Credit recommendation, collegiate level: Credit in electricity, electronics, and electrical laboratory on the basis of demonstrated skills and/or institutional examinations.

1. **Personnel Administration Specialist**
2. **Personnel Administration Specialist**
3. **Pay Specialist**

Locations: Adjutant General School, Fort Benjamin Harrison, Ind.; U.S. Army Training Centers.

Length: *Course 1,* 8 weeks; *Course 2,* 3–4 weeks; *Course 3,* 3–4 weeks.

Objectives: To train enlisted personnel in personnel administrative functions, records, and compensations.

Instruction: *Course 1:* Typing, administrative fundamentals, including reports, records, and correspondence; familiarization with office machines. *Course 2:* Procedures for orders and directives; regulations and policies governing personnel actions; personnel compensation procedures. *Course 3:* Pay administration, records, and operations.

Credit recommendation, collegiate level: CAUTION: *These courses vary only slightly in title, length, and recommendation. Require exact identification of course by title and length. Course 1:* Credit in typing on the basis of institutional examinations. *Courses 1, 2, and 3:* At the vocational level, for each course, credit in general office practice on the basis of institutional examinations.

Personnel and Administration (Reserve Component)

Location: Adjutant General School, Fort Benjamin Harrison, Ind.

Length: 3 weeks.

Objectives: To train enlisted personnel in personnel and administration policies, procedures, and techniques.

Instruction: Administrative functions; officer and enlisted qualification record and classification; pay and allowances; tests and measurements.

Credit recommendation, collegiate level: No credit because of the brevity and nature of the course.

Personnel Management for Executives

Location: Civilian Training Center, The Pentagon, Washington, D.C.

Length: 3 weeks.

Objectives: To provide senior officers with the current developments in personnel management.

Instruction: Relationship of personnel management to total management function; principles of organization; delegation of authority; human behavior, motivations, and productivity; interpersonal relationships; communication media and channels; management techniques and approaches.

Credit recommendation, collegiate level: 2 semester hours in personnel management.

Personnel Management Specialist

Location: Adjutant General School, Fort Benjamin Harrison, Ind.

Length: 4–6 weeks.

Objectives: To provide enlisted personnel with a working knowledge of the principles, functions, and procedures involved in personnel management duties as a personnel management specialist or classification interviewer.

Instruction: Administrative functions; Army statistical and accounting system; principles and functions of personnel management; interviews; tests and measurements; utilization of enlisted personnel; personnel control devices; enlisted and officer qualification records; command and staff organization and procedures.

Credit recommendation, collegiate level: 2 semester hours in personnel management.

Personnel Resources Management
(Personnel Management Officer)

Location: Adjutant General School, Fort Benjamin Harrison, Ind.

Length: 4–5 weeks.

Objectives: To train officers and warrant officers in the principles, functions, and procedures of the Army personnel management system and in the duties and responsibilities of a personnel management officer or classification and assignment officer.

Instruction: Principles of management; office management techniques; manpower management system; personnel management; psychology and human behavior; utilization of enlisted and officer personnel; command and staff organization procedures.

Credit recommendation, collegiate level: 3 semester hours in personnel management.

Petroleum Distribution Supervision

Location: Quartermaster School, Fort Lee, Va.

Length: 6 weeks.

Objectives: To train enlisted personnel to supervise the receipt, storage, and issue of petroleum products and the operation of cross-country pipelines.

Instruction: Petroleum organization and supply procedures; petroleum mathematics; procurement and distribution; laboratory tests; petroleum supply in the combat zone; equipment operation and operations; terminal operations; pipeline operations and maintenance.

Credit recommendation, collegiate level: This course is technical and vocational in nature. Credit in petroleum products handling on the basis of demonstrated skills and/or institutional examinations.

Petroleum Products Analysis
(Petroleum Products Analysis Enlisted)

Location: Quartermaster School, Fort Lee, Va.

Length: 11–14 weeks.

Objectives: To train officers and enlisted personnel in the principles and procedures used in laboratory testing and analysis of petroleum products.

Instruction: Basic laboratory tests and techniques; petroleum tests of light distillate fuels, lube oils, and greases; chemical solutions; physical and chemical tests of petroleum products; inspection, maintenance, and operation of coordinated fuel research test engines; laboratory rotation; calibration and maintenance of laboratory equipment.

Credit recommendation, collegiate level: 4 semester hours in laboratory testing of petroleum products.

Petroleum Products Analysis, Officer

Location: Quartermaster School, Fort Lee, Va.

Length: 8 weeks.

Objectives: To train officers in the principles and procedures used in laboratory testing and analysis of petroleum products.

Instruction: Distribution, storage, and handling of petroleum products; physical and chemical tests of petroleum products; laboratory rotation; coordinated fuel research engine tests; petroleum products laboratory operations.

Credit recommendation, collegiate level: 3 semester hours in laboratory testing of petroleum products.

1. Petroleum Products Supply
2. Petroleum Officer
(Petroleum Products Supply Officer)
(Petroleum Products Analysis and Supply)
(Petroleum Products Analysis and Control Officer)

Location: Quartermaster School, Fort Lee, Va.

Length: *Course 1,* 8 and 14 weeks; *Course 2,* 13–16 weeks.

Objectives: To train officers in the laboratory analysis and testing of military petroleum products and in principles of petroleum management.

Instruction: *Course 1:* Petroleum operations, supply, and distribution; refining and processing; mathematics; petroleum testing laboratories; significance of petroleum tests; supply point and depot operations. In addition to the preceding instruction, *Course 2* includes physical and chemical laboratory tests; identification of unknown petroleum products; CFR test engines; terminal operations and supply.

Credit recommendation, collegiate level: CAUTION: *These courses vary in title, length, and recommendation. Require exact identification of course by title and length. Course 1:* 8 weeks—2 semester hours in petroleum products supply management; 14 weeks—3 semester hours in petroleum products supply management. *Course 2:* 2 semester hours in petroleum products supply management and 2 semester hours in laboratory analysis of petroleum products.

Petroleum Storage Specialist
(Petroleum Storage)

Location: Quartermaster School, Fort Lee, Va.

Length: 8 weeks.

Objectives: To train enlisted personnel to receive, store, issue, dispense, and ship petroleum products.

Instruction: Petroleum storage operations; petroleum supply system; safety measures; methods of transportation; military pipelines; tank farm operations; gauging and sampling; basic mathematics; processing, packaging, crating, and marking; materials handling equipment.

Credit recommendation, collegiate level: This course is technical and vocational in nature. Credit in petroleum products storage on the basis of demonstrated skills and/or institutional examinations.

Pharmacy Specialist

Location: Medical Field Service School, Fort Sam Houston, Tex.

Length: 18 weeks.

Objectives: To train enlisted personnel in the sources, preparation, uses, symbols, terms, and storage procedures of drugs and in filling prescriptions under the supervision of a pharmacist or Medical Corp officer.

Instruction: Supply procedures for pharmacy operations; pharmaceutical mathematical calculations; principles of general chemistry; familiarization with anatomy and physiology; nature, principles of action, uses, and potential hazards of drugs; pharmaceutical preparations, procedures for preparation, and doses; laboratory practice.

Credit recommendation, collegiate level: 3 semester hours in pharmaceutical laboratory procedures and 2 semester hours in pharmaceutical mathematics.

Photo Interpretation Enlisted

Location: Intelligence School, Fort Holabird, Md.

Length: 17 weeks.

Objectives: To train enlisted personnel to perform photo interpretation duties in military intelligence units.

Instruction: Organization, tactics, and operations; general intelligence; photo reading; photo interpretation; photogrammetry; terrain; photo interpretation reports.

Credit recommendation, collegiate level: 5 semester hours in photographic interpretation.

Photogrammetric Compilation

Location: Engineer School, Fort Belvoir, Va.

Length: 9–10 weeks.

Objectives: To train enlisted personnel in the principles and techniques of map compiling.

Instruction: Multiplex equipment; relative orientation; regular and irregular terrain; horizontilization and scaling; drawing planimetry; compiling topography; printing and processing.

Credit recommendation, collegiate level: 3 semester hours in photogrammetry.

Photographic Laboratory Operation

Location: Signal School, Fort Monmouth, N.J.

Length: 10–15 weeks.

Objectives: To train enlisted personnel in the principles and techniques of photographic processing as required to produce negatives and prints for technical, tactical, and public relation purposes.

Instruction: Basic laboratory practices; developing materials and techniques; printing processes and techniques; special photographic processes; reproduction techniques; color processing; reconnaissance photostrips; laboratory darkroom; motion picture film processing.

Credit recommendation, collegiate level: 3 semester hours in photographic laboratory.

Physical Reconditioning Specialist

Location: Medical Service School, Fort Sam Houston, Tex.

Length: 12 weeks.

Objectives: To train enlisted personnel in the application of techniques used in the treatment and rehabilitation of patients through exercise, physical therapy, or working activities.

Instruction: Administration of activities for psychiatric patients; anatomy and physiology; conditioning aquatics and conditioning exercises; body mechanics and muscle analysis; objectives and administrative procedures for physical reconditioning; familiarization with various medical and surgical conditions; introduction to psychiatry; direction of gymnasium exercise; clinical observation and practice.

Credit recommendation, collegiate level: 3 semester hours in physical education instruction.

Physical Security Supervision

Location: The Provost Marshal General's School, Fort Gordon, Ga.

Length: 3 weeks.

Objectives: To train commissioned and warrant officers in physical security principles, methods, and techniques and to indoctrinate officers in the physical security planning, training, and personnel management responsibilities.

Instruction: Legal jurisdiction; handling and protection of evidence; civil defense and disaster relief responsibilities; methods of handling personnel problems; principles of physical security, including techniques used to reduce or eliminate security hazards, recognition, and methods; security planning.

Credit recommendation, collegiate level: 2 semester hours in intelligence or police methods.

1. Physical Therapy Procedures
2. Physical Therapy Specialist (Physical Therapy Enlisted)

Location: Medical Field Service School, Fort Sam Houston, Tex.

Length: *Course 1,* 4 weeks; *Course 2,* 12 weeks.

Objectives: To train enlisted personnel to assist the physical therapist in treating patients.

Instruction: *Course 1:* Physical therapy applied to medical, surgical, orthopedic, and neurological conditions; physiological effects, uses, and techniques of massage; electrotherapy, hydrotherapy, and phototherapy. *Course 2:* In addition to the preceding instruction this course contains the skeletal, muscular, nervous, and vascular systems; bandaging and sterile technique; therapeutic exercise and equipment.

Credit recommendation, collegiate level: CAUTION: *These courses vary in title, length, and recommendation. Require exact identification of course by title and length. Course 1:* Credit in physical therapy techniques on the basis of institutional examination. *Course 2:* Credit in anatomy and physiology and physical therapy techniques on the basis of institutional examination.

Polar Navigation

Location: Transportation School, Fort Eustis, Va.
Length: 9 weeks.
Objectives: To train officers and warrant officers in the fundamentals of terrestrial and celestial polar navigation.
Instruction: Geography and meteorology of the polar regions; navigational instruments; celestial navigation; mathematics; charts, projections, and maps; communication and signals; courses and bearings; weather principles; surveying.
Credit recommendation, collegiate level: 6 semester hours in navigation.

1. Polygraph Examiner Training
2. Polygraph
(Lie Detector Operator)

Locations: Military Police School, Fort Gordon, Ga.; The Provost Marshal General's School, Fort Gordon, Ga.
Length: *Course 1,* 12 weeks; *Course 2,* 7–8 weeks.
Objectives: To train commissioned officers, warrant officers, and enlisted personnel in the utilization of the lie detector as a scientific aid in the investigation of criminal violations.
Instruction: *Course 1:* Major areas of military law; nomenclature, assembly, disassembly, and functions of lie detection equipment; relationship between physiology and psychology and the field of instrumental detection of deception; deception detecting techniques, including pre-test interviews, post-test interrogations, methods of test construction, marking and numbering test charts, interpretation of polygrams, procedures and requirements of personnel screening, and intelligence-type testing; polygraph examination techniques. *Course 2:* This course includes the same academic material as *Course 1* but contains less instruction in the areas of deception detecting techniques and polygraph examination techniques.
Credit recommendation, collegiate level: CAUTION: *These courses vary slightly in title, length, and recommendation. Require exact identification of course by title and length. Course 1:* 5 semester hours in intelligence or police methods. *Course 2:* 3 semester hours in intelligence or police methods.

Position-Fixing Navigation Equipment Repair

Location: Southeastern Signal School, Fort Gordon, Ga.
Length: 3 weeks.
Objectives: To train enlisted men to perform direct and general support maintenance on airborne position-fixing navigation equipment.
Instruction: Hyperbolic area coverage navigation; position-fixing navigation set; installation and system analysis; black box troubleshooting; receiver master and slave channels; signaling channel and relay sequence; receiver circuit analysis; support maintenance procedures; flight log equipment and system support maintenance.
Credit recommendation, collegiate level: Credit in electrical laboratory on the basis of demonstrated skills and/or institutional examinations.

Post Engineer Management
(Post Engineer)

Location: Engineer School, Fort Belvoir, Va.
Length: 3–4 weeks.
Objectives: To train officers in the supervision and administration of construction, operation, and maintenance of installation facilities.
Instruction: Post engineer organization; civilian personnel procedures; responsibilities and functions of a post planning board; principles of effective management; cost engineering, budgets, and funds; methods and procedures for purchasing and contracting; property accounting; management concepts of building and structures responsibilities; responsibilities for custodial services, water and sewage facilities, and refuse collection and disposal; management procedures for maintenance of roads, utility railroads, and grounds; operation and safety measures of electrical distribution systems; functioning of heating and air-conditioning systems; fire protection and prevention.
Credit recommendation, collegiate level: 3 semester hours in business organization and management.

Postal Operations

Location: Adjutant General School, Fort Benjamin Harrison, Ind.
Length: 4–5 weeks.
Objectives: To train enlisted personnel in the techniques and procedures involved in the operation of the Army and Air Force postal service.
Instruction: Postal organizations and facilities; classifications of mail and rates of postage; postal financial operations; duties and responsibilities of postal clerks; mail handling, distribution, and dispatch; administrative postal procedures; directory service; international and customs mail.
Credit recommendation, collegiate level: This course is vocational in nature. Credit in post office clerical procedures on the basis of demonstrated skills and/or institutional examinations.

Power Equipment Maintenance

Location: Southeastern Signal School, Fort Gordon, Ga.
Length: 10 weeks.
Objectives: To train enlisted personnel to install, operate, and perform organizational maintenance on portable electrical power generating equipment.
Instruction: Electrical fundamentals; organizational maintenance of motors; generators and alternators; principles, operation, and maintenance of fuel, ignition, cooling, and lubricating systems; engine valves; portable gasoline power units; diesel engines; generating components; power unit installation.
Credit recommendation, collegiate level: This course is technical and vocational in nature. Credit in maintenance of portable gasoline and diesel power generating equipment on the basis of demonstrated skills and/or institutional examinations.

Power Pack Specialist

Location: Engineer School, Fort Belvoir, Va.

Length: 4 weeks.

Objectives: To train enlisted personnel in the operation, maintenance, and troubleshooting procedures for the power station and associated ground support equipment used in the Pershing missile system.

Instruction: Power station; gas turbine engine control circuits; power generation control circuits; high-pressure air compressor; air cycle conditioning system; removal and replacement of power station components; troubleshooting the power station; power station equivalent set; associated support equipment.

Credit recommendation, collegiate level: This course is technical and vocational in nature. Credit in power station equipment repair on the basis of demonstrated skills and/or institutional examinations.

Powerman

Location: Engineer School, Fort Belvoir, Va.

Length: 6–7 weeks.

Objectives: To train enlisted personnel in the installation, operation, and organizational maintenance of gasoline and diesel engine driven portable generating equipment.

Instruction: Internal combustion engine systems maintenance; diesel engine maintenance; electrical fundamentals; conventional generator sets.

Credit recommendation, collegiate level: This course is technical and vocational in nature. Credit in maintenance of gasoline and diesel engine driven portable generating equipment on the basis of demonstrated skills and/or institutional examinations.

Precise Power Generation

Location: Engineer School, Fort Belvoir, Va.

Length: 4 weeks.

Objectives: To train enlisted personnel in the installation, operation, and organizational maintenance of precise power generating equipment.

Instruction: Review of electrical fundamentals; precise power generators; motor generators; gas turbine driven generators; paralleling and emergency power transfer; precise power performance evaluation; gas turbine engines.

Credit recommendation, collegiate level: This course is technical and vocational in nature. Credit in precise power generator repair on the basis of demonstrated skills and/or institutional examinations.

1. **Preventive Medicine Procedures (Basic)**
   (Preventive Medicine Specialist)
   (Preventive Medicine Enlisted)
2. **Preventive Medicine Procedures (Advanced)**
3. **Preventive Medicine Procedures (Advanced)**
   (Preventive Medicine Advanced)

Location: Medical Field Service School, Fort Sam Houston, Tex.

Length: *Course 1*, 9–12 weeks; *Course 2*, 9–10 weeks; *Course 3*, 16–20 weeks.

Objectives: To train enlisted personnel in the basic and advanced principles of preventive medicine.

Instruction: *Course 1:* Methods of disease control; laboratory testing techniques; control of respiratory diseases; characteristics of insect and rodent diseases and methods employed against these diseases; pest control; epidemiology and control of intestinal diseases; food sanitation; water supply and purification; waste disposal; evaluation of housing standards; inspection procedures in civilian and military facilities. *Courses 2 and 3:* These courses contain the same material as *Course 1* but at a more advanced level.

Credit recommendation, collegiate level: CAUTION: *These courses vary only slightly in title, length, and recommendation. Require exact identification of course by title and length. Course 1 is a prerequisite for Courses 2 and 3. Course 1:* 4 semester hours in sanitation and disease control. *Course 2:* 2 additional semester hours in sanitation and disease control. *Course 3:* 3 additional semester hours in sanitation and disease control.

1. **Prisoner of War Interrogation Enlisted**
2. **Prisoner of War Interrogation Enlisted**
3. **Order of Battle Intelligence Enlisted**

Location: Intelligence School, Fort Holabird, Md.

Length: *Course 1*, 8 weeks; *Courses 2 and 3*, 13 weeks.

Objectives: To train enlisted personnel to perform clerical duties in intelligence sections and to assist in interrogation, censorship, photo interpretation, and order of battle intelligence.

Instruction: *Course 1:* Organization, tactics, and operations of the Armed Forces and of selected foreign armies; familiarization with atomic warfare; signal communications; doctrine, principles, and techniques of combat intelligence, counterintelligence, order of battle intelligence, and interrogation of prisoners of war. *Courses 2 and 3:* These courses contain the same academic material as *Course 1* but they involve a longer period of instruction.

Credit recommendation, collegiate level: CAUTION: *These courses vary only slightly in title, length, and recommendation. Require exact identification of course by title and length. Course 1:* 2 semester hours in intelligence methods. *Courses 2 and 3:* For each course, 3 semester hours in intelligence methods.

1. **Prisoner of War Interrogation Officer**
2. **Prisoner of War Interrogation Officer**
3. **Order of Battle Intelligence Officer**

Location: Intelligence School, Fort Holabird, Md.

Length: *Course 1*, 8 weeks; *Courses 2 and 3*, 10 weeks.

Objectives: To train officers in military intelligence, counterintelligence, special operations, and techniques of interrogation and evaluation of enemy tactical and strategic order of battle intelligence.

Instruction: *Course 1:* Army organization, tactics, and operations; doctrine, principles, and techniques of combat intelligence, including evaluation of information, reports, reconnaissance, and security; techniques of interrogation and order of battle intelligence. *Courses 2 and 3:* These courses contain the same academic material as *Course 1* but they involve a longer period of instruction.

Credit recommendation, collegiate level: CAUTION: *These courses vary only slightly in title, length, and recommendation. Require exact identification of course by title and length. Course 1: 2 semester hours in intelligence methods. Courses 2 and 3: For each course, 3 semester hours in intelligence methods.*

Probabilistic Methods in Operations Research

Location: U.S. Army Management Engineering Training Agency, Rock Island, Ill.

Length: 3 weeks.

Objectives: To train personnel in the theory of probability and random variables and the development of mathematical models which have important application in the field of operations research.

Instruction: Calculus and ordinary differential equations; partial fractions; calculus of finite differences; difference equations; generating functions; vectors and matrices; introduction to probability; distribution theory; random variables; stochastic processes; finite Markov chains; statistical inference; queuing models; simulation; inventory models; decision theory.

Credit recommendation, collegiate level: 2 semester hours in operations research in the field of computing science.

Process Photography

Location: Engineer School, Fort Belvoir, Va.

Length: 6–8 weeks.

Objectives: To train enlisted personnel in the operation of the process camera, development of film and production of material for use in photolithography.

Instruction: Process photography; photolithography; film processing; operation and care of process cameras; photographic chemicals; line copying; contact prints; continuous tone copying; magenta contact screen; photographic printing.

Credit recommendation, collegiate level: This course is technical and vocational in nature. Credit in process photography on the basis of demonstrated skills and/or institutional examinations.

Procurement Management

Location: Logistics Management Center, Fort Lee, Va.

Length: 8 weeks.

Objectives: To train officers of the management group of the Army supply system in procurement management.

Instruction: Statutes, regulations, and policies governing procurement; determination of potential contractors; nature, importance, and shortcomings of specifications; advertising; negotiation; cost and price analysis; small purchase methods; types and purposes of contracts; contract administration and financing; familiarization with contract law; relationship of procurement to other logistical functions.

Credit recommendation, collegiate level: 6 semester hours in purchasing or procurement.

Procurement Sergeant

Location: Quartermaster School, Fort Lee, Va.

Length: 4 weeks.

Objectives: To train enlisted personnel in the fundamentals of procurement, procurement function, award functions, and procurement administration.

Instruction: Procurement regulations general policies and authorization; small business and labor surplus program; purchasing by formal advertisement and negotiation; contract clauses and provisions; patents and data, taxes, bonds, surety, insurance, and labor; small purchases; contract performances; government furnished property inspection and acceptance; disputes and appeals.

Credit recommendations, collegiate level: 2 semester hours in procurement policies.

Programming and Budgeting
(Financial Management-Budget)

Location: Finance School, Fort Benjamin Harrison, Ind.

Length: 3–5 weeks.

Objectives: To train commissioned officers, warrant officers, and senior enlisted personnel at field installation level in the principles and procedures of programming and budget formulation and execution.

Instruction: Principles of the Army appropriations structure; program systems; budget formulation and budgeting techniques; statistical analysis in budgeting; integrated accounting and its use in the budget process.

Credit recommendation, collegiate level: 3 semester hours in budgeting.

Projector Equipment Repair
(Sound Projector Repair)

Location: Signal School, Fort Monmouth, N.J.

Length: 10–11 weeks.

Objectives: To train enlisted personnel to maintain and repair motion picture projectors and related equipment.

Instruction: Principles of electricity; electron tubes and associated circuits; principles of amplification; advanced audio amplifier circuits; repair of still and sound motion picture projectors.

Credit recommendation, collegiate level: This course is technical and vocational in nature. Credit in photographic equipment repair on the basis of demonstrated skills and/or institutional examinations.

Property Disposal Management
(Property Disposal)

Locations: Army Logistics Management Center, Fort Lee, Va.; Quartermaster School, Fort Lee, Va.

Length: 4–5 weeks.

Objectives: To train officers in the functions, duties, and responsibilities of property disposal management.

Instruction: Organization for property disposal; receipt and processing; preparation for disposal; merchandising and advertising; disposition; commercial law; financial management; records and reports; personnel management.

Credit recommendation, collegiate level: 2 semester hours in property disposal management.

Property Disposal Operations
(Army Basic Property Disposal Operations)

Location: Quartermaster School, Fort Lee, Va.

Length: 4 weeks.

Objectives: To train disposal personnel in all functions involved in the operation of offices or activities related to property disposal.

Instruction: General supply procedures; receipt, processing, and storage of property for disposal; records and accounting procedures; disposition of property by sale and other methods; commercial law and legal aspects of disposal operations; disposal in oversea commands.

Credit recommendation, collegiate level: 2 semester hours in property disposal management.

Psychological Operations Enlisted

Location: Special Warfare School, Fort Bragg, N.C.

Length: 3–4 weeks.

Objectives: To train enlisted personnel in psychological operations necessary for assignment to command and control intelligence and propaganda teams of Special Warfare units.

Instruction: Psychological operations organization; Communism and Communist propaganda; factors of human behavior and social organization; propaganda theory; psychological operations intelligence; propaganda media; American history and government; psychological operations seminars.

Credit recommendation, collegiate level: Credit in social psychology on the basis of institutional examination.

Quarry Machine Operation

Location: Engineer School, Fort Belvoir, Va.

Length: 3 and 5 weeks.

Objectives: To train enlisted personnel to operate and perform operator maintenance on self-powered machines used in crushing, grading, and cleaning rock and gravel.

Instruction: Principles of internal combustion engines and air compressors; operation, maintenance, and adjustment of rock crushers, screens, and washers. *Note*—personnel having completed the 5-week course will have additional instruction in the operation of 235 TPH equipment.

Credit recommendation, collegiate level: This course is technical and vocational in nature. Credit in operation and maintenance of construction equipment on the basis of demonstrated skills and/or institutional examinations.

Quartermaster Commodity

Location: Quartermaster School, Fort Lee, Va.

Length: 10 weeks.

Objectives: To train officers in the nature and characteristics of the primary commodities procured, stored, and distributed.

Instruction: Food, petroleum, chemical, textile, metal, leather, and forest products and industries; procurement, storage, and supply.

Credit recommendation, collegiate level: 3 semester hours in supply management.

1. Quartermaster Company Officer
2. Quartermaster Company Officer
3. Quartermaster Company Officer

Location: Quartermaster School, Fort Lee, Va.

Length: *Course 1*, 20 weeks; *Course 2*, 24 weeks; *Course 3*, 35–36 weeks.

Objectives: To provide branch training in the duties and responsibilities appropriate to company-grade Quartermaster Corps officers.

Instruction: *Course 1:* Command and staff organization; company administration; intelligence; military leadership; budgeting, financial inventory accounting, performance analysis, and personnel management; organization and tactics of the combat arms; supply and distribution procedures, including unit and organization supply, installation storage operations, maintenance and inspection, and procurement; mission and function of the Quartermaster Corps in a theater of operations. *Course 2:* In addition to the preceding instruction this course contains further training in supply management and procedures. *Course 3:* This course contains the same academic material as *Courses 1 and 2* and in addition, instruction in commodities, their source, production, and processing.

Credit recommendation, collegiate level: CAUTION: *These courses vary slightly in length and recommendation. Require exact identification of course by length. Course 1:* 2 semester hours in business organization and management and 4 semester hours in supply management. *Course 2:* 2 semester hours in business organization and management and 5 semester hours in supply management. *Course 3:* 3 semester hours in business organization and management and 6 semester hours in supply management.

1. Quartermaster Equipment Repair
2. Quartermaster Heavy Equipment Repair
3. Quartermaster Light Equipment Repair
4. Quartermaster Equipment Repair Supervision

Location: Quartermaster School, Fort Lee, Va.

Length: 6–14 weeks.

Objectives: *Courses 1, 2, and 3:* To train enlisted personnel to repair, install, and adjust quartermaster machinery and equipment. *Course 4:* To train enlisted personnel to supervise the repair of quartermaster equipment.

Instruction: Carpentry; pipe fitting; oxyacetylene welding; adjustment and repair of electrical components; internal combustion engines; repair of mobile laundry equipment, bakery equipment, mobile shoe equipment, clothing and textile equipment; maintenance of burner equipment and metal items.

Credit recommendation, collegiate level: These courses are technical and vocational in nature. Credit in mechanical and electrical shop on the basis of demonstrated skills and/or institutional examinations.

1. Quartermaster Maintenance Supervision
2. Quartermaster Maintenance Supervision

Location: Quartermaster School, Fort Lee, Va.

Length: *Course 1,* 3 weeks; *Course 2,* 6 weeks.

Objectives: To train commissioned officers in the principles, methods, and techniques of supervising quartermaster maintenance operations.

Instruction: *Course 1:* Administrative and supervisory procedures related to maintenance activities, including personnel management, work-load scheduling, and performance analysis; establishment, layout, and operation of a depot maintenance shop; technical inspection of equipment. *Course 2:* In addition to the preceding instruction this course includes further training in personnel and shop supervision and supply procedures.

Credit recommendation, collegiate level: CAUTION: *These courses vary only slightly in length and recommendation. Require exact identification of course by length. Course 1:* 2 semester hours in shop management. *Course 2:* 3 semester hours in shop management.

1. Quartermaster Officer Advanced
2. Quartermaster Officer Advanced
3. Quartermaster Officer Career

Location: Quartermaster School, Fort Lee, Va.

Length: *Course 1,* 33–35 weeks; *Course 2,* 32 weeks; *Course 3,* 24–30 weeks.

Objectives: To provide branch training in the duties and responsibilities of Quartermaster Corps officers.

Instruction: *Course 1:* General military training, including weapons, civil emergencies, and signal communications; command and staff organization; maintenance management; Army Command Management System; communicative skills; staff organization and planning; management techniques; installation programming and operating budgets; performance analysis; administrative orders; transportation movements; procurement; inventory accounting; storage procedures; installation exchange operations; organizations, missions, and employment of the combat arms operations at battle group, combat command, and division artillery level; administration of supply and service support for the combat arms; supply and distribution procedures; responsibilities and organization of the Quartermaster Corps in airborne activities, the combat zone, and the communication zone. *Courses 2 and 3:* These courses include generally the same subject matter as *Course 1* but contain less instruction in the organizational and administrative phases of supply and operations in a theater of operations.

Credit recommendation, collegiate level: CAUTION: *These courses vary only slightly in title, length, and recommendation. Require exact identification of course by title and length. Course 1:* 4 semester hours in supply management and 6 semester hours in business organization and management. *Courses 2 and 3:* For each course 4 semester hours in supply management and 4 semester hours in business organization and management.

1. Quartermaster Officer Basic
   (Quartermaster Officer Orientation)
2. Quartermaster Officer Orientation

Location: Quartermaster School, Fort Lee, Va.

Length: *Course 1,* 8–14 weeks; *Course 2,* 4 weeks.

Objectives: To provide basic branch training and orientation for newly commissioned Quartermaster officers.

Instruction: *Course 1:* Organization and missions of the Quartermaster Corps; nuclear warfare; signal communications; managerial and supervisory aspects of company administration; logistics, use of training programs, and schedules and procedures; military leadership; principles of unit and organization supply; installation supply; mess administration; maintenance requirements; organization and procedure for supply in a theater of operations; organization and tactics of the combat arms; weapons. *Course 2:* This course contains only the supply management subjects included in the preceding instruction.

Credit recommendation, collegiate level: CAUTION: *These courses vary only slightly in title, length, and recommendation. Require exact identification of course by title and length. Course 1:* 2 semester hours in supply management, 2 semester hours in business organization and management, and credit in advanced military at institutions which regularly offer such credit. *Course 2:* 2 semester hours in supply management.

Quartermaster Officer Candidate

Location: Quartermaster School, Fort Lee, Va.

Length: 23 weeks.

Objectives: To train selected personnel to be second lieutenants in the Reserve component of the U.S. Army capable of performing duties appropriate to their grade in quartermaster-type assignments.

Instruction: Maintenance and inspection; combined arms; unit staff and administration; artillery operations; engineer operations; CBR and nuclear operations; field and tactical communications; military leadership; map and air photograph reading; methods of instruction; weapons training; unit and organizational supply; field supply procedures; financial management; automated supply systems; field storage procedures; supply operations in the theater of operations.

Credit recommendation, collegiate level: 6 semester hours in business organization and management, and credit in advanced military at institutions which regularly offer such credit.

Quartermaster Officer Familiarization

Location: Quartermaster School, Fort Lee, Va.

Length: 5 weeks.

Objectives: To provide branch familiarization training in the organization, operational functions, and duties of the Quartermaster Corps.

Instruction: Installation supply and stock control procedures; procurement operations; depot and storage operations; military management; maintenance and inspection of equipment; petroleum distribution; supply of quartermaster commodities in a theater of operations.

Credit recommendation, collegiate level: 2 semester hours in supply management.

Quartermaster Parts Supply

Location: Quartermaster School, Fort Lee, Va.
Length: 4 weeks.
Objectives: To train enlisted personnel in the use, interchangeability, identification, receipt, storage, and issue of repair parts for quartermaster equipment.
Instruction: Basic mathematics; supply and accounting procedures; identification, inspection, and interchangeability of quartermaster parts; depot operations; storage operations; processing, packing, crating, and marking of spare parts.
Credit recommendation, collegiate level: This course is technical and vocational in nature. Credit in supply accounting procedures on the basis of institutional examination.

Quartermaster Storage

Location: Quartermaster School, Fort Lee, Va.
Length: 8 weeks.
Objectives: To train enlisted personnel to receive, store, issue and ship Class II and IV quartermaster supplies, and to perform salvage duties for all types of supplies and equipment.
Instruction: Basic mathematics; unit and organization supply; identification and interchangeability of parts; depot operations; storage operations; processing, packing, crating, and marking; materials-handling equipment; classification and disposal.
Credit recommendation, collegiate level: This course is technical and vocational in nature. Credit in stockroom procedures on the basis of demonstrated skills and/or institutional examinations.

Quartermaster Supply

Location: Quartermaster School, Fort Lee, Va.
Length: 4 weeks.
Objectives: To train enlisted personnel in the receipt, storage, issue, and stock control procedures of quartermaster supplies and material.
Instruction: Unit and organization supply; station supply; stock record accounts; commissary operations; packing and crating; classification and disposal storage operations; stock control, depot level.
Credit recommendation, collegiate level: This course is technical and vocational in nature. Credit in supply accounting procedures on the basis of institutional examination.

Quartermaster Supply Procedures

Location: Quartermaster School, Fort Lee, Va.
Length: 4 weeks.
Objectives: To train commissioned officers in quartermaster supply and stock control.
Instruction: Installation supply procedures; supply control and stock management; organization for property disposal; supply and distribution procedures; Army command management system; supply support of direct support–general support concept.
Credit recommendation, collegiate level: 2 semester hours in supply management.

Quartermaster Supply Supervision

Location: Quartermaster School, Fort Lee, Va.
Length: 8 weeks.
Objectives: To train enlisted personnel in the supervision of quartermaster supply activities excluding petroleum and subsistence stores.
Instruction: Supply management; administrative procedures; basic mathematics; financial management; supply and accounting procedures; station supply mission and organization; stock record accounts; depot operations; storage operations; procurement; classification and disposal; staff organization and logistics; supply procedures in a theater of operations; processing, packaging, crating, and marking.
Credit recommendation, collegiate level: 3 semester hours in supply management.

RCAT Airframe and Engine Maintenance

Location: Air Defense School, Fort Bliss, Tex.
Length: 8–9 weeks.
Objectives: To train enlisted personnel to maintain and repair Army target airplane engines, airframes, and associated equipment.
Instruction: Engine and airframe disassembly, repair, and troubleshooting; sheet metal and wing repair; familiarization with searchlight control stations, tow targets, parachutes, and ground launching equipment.
Credit recommendation, collegiate level: This course is technical and vocational in nature. Credit in airframe maintenance and mechanical shop on the basis of demonstrated skills and/or institutional examinations.

RCAT Operation

Locations: Air Defense School, Fort Bliss, Tex.
Length: 11–12 weeks.
Objectives: To train officers and enlisted personnel in the techniques of launching, flying, and recovery of radio-controlled airplane targets and the performance of combined functions required in support of these operations.
Instruction: Assembly, disassembly, repairing, and general maintenance of airframes; installation of radar reflectors; assembly, timing, carburetion, and troubleshooting of RCAT engines; basic principles, functioning, and physical layout of radio-controlled systems; principles of flight control; practical exercise in

launching and recovery techniques; remote control operations.

Credit recommendation, collegiate level: This course is technical and vocational in nature. Credit in airframe maintenance on the basis of demonstrated skills and/or institutional examinations.

RCAT Radio Maintenance
(Radio-Controlled Airplane Target Radio Maintenance)

Location: Army Air Defense School, Fort Bliss, Tex.
Length: 7–9 weeks.
Objectives: To train enlisted personnel to test, adjust, and maintain radio-controlled airplane target radios, gyros, and autopilot equipment.
Instruction: RCAT transmitter and receiver; RPS-1 control system; C2 flight control system; control systems preflight procedures; fundamentals of electricity.
Credit recommendation, collegiate level: Credit in electricity on the basis of institutional examinations. At the technical level, credit in radio maintenance on the basis of demonstrated skills and/or institutional examinations.

Radar and Countermeasures Equipment Repair Officer

Location: Signal School, Fort Monmouth, N.J.
Length: 18 weeks.
Objectives: To train officers to direct and supervise maintenance and repair of radar and electronic countermeasures equipment.
Instruction: Resonant circuits; transformers; transients; complex wave forms; diodes and rectifiers; triode principles; multi-element and special purpose tubes; vacuum tube amplifiers; cathode followers; voltage regulators; transistors; oscillators; sweep generators; multivibrators; transmission lines; modulation; special power supplies; radar synchronizer and transmitters; RF systems; synchros; AC and DC motors and generators; radar antenna drives; coincidence tubes; adjustment, troubleshooting, and repair of radar sets AN/TPS-1D, AN/MPO-4 (AN/MPQ-10), rawin set AN/GMD-1A, and IFF equipment; equipment employed in electronic countermeasures.
Credit recommendation, collegiate level: 3 semester hours at the freshman or sophomore level as an elective in electricity and electronics, and credit in electrical laboratory on the basis of demonstrated skills and/or institutional examinations.

Radar Data Processing Center Repair

Location: Army Air Defense School, Fort Bliss, Tex.
Length: 28–31 weeks.
Objectives: To train warrant officers and enlisted personnel in the function, testing, troubleshooting, and repair of the radar data processing center.
Instruction: Basic digital circuit theory; test equipment; power supplies, communications, and memory read-write components; radar data converter, signal modifiers, control indicator, target simulator, and central display controls; detector-tracker console, detector-

tracker console controls, range-height indicator consoles, and range-height indicator programmer; tracking equipment and circuitry; extrapolator circuitry and the data exchange system, including input and output buffers, digital transmitter and receiver, and frequency shift transmitter and receiver.
Credit recommendation, collegiate level: Credit in electrical laboratory on the basis of demonstrated skills and/or institutional examinations.

Radar Display Equipment Repair

Location: Army Air Defense School, Fort Bliss, Tex.
Length: 30 weeks.
Objectives: To train warrant officers and enlisted personnel to perform organizational and field maintenance on missile master equipment within the Army Air Defense system AN/FSG-1.
Instruction: Maintenance procedures on the AN/FSG-1 missile master, including the sweep generation, video presentation, and special circuits used in the target-tracking subsystem; tag presentation circuits; auxiliary target-tracking circuits; status storage, electrical switching, height finder radar positioning and range height indicator console circuits; tactical display equipment.
Credit recommendation, collegiate level: Credit in electrical laboratory on the basis of demonstrated skills and/or institutional examinations.

Radar Repair

Location: Signal School, Fort Monmouth, N.J.
Length: 33 weeks.
Objectives: To train enlisted personnel to inspect, test, and perform repairs and depot maintenance on ground radar equipment.
Instruction: AC and DC circuits, magnetism and electromagnetism, inductance, use of oscilloscope, capacitance, impedance, series and parallel resonance, filters, AF signal generators, transformers, and DC power; filament circuits; diodes; triode tubes; tetrode tubes; pentode and beam power tubes; semiconductor fundamentals; RF signal generators; fundamentals of superheterodyne reception; amplification of intermediate and radio frequencies; method of coupling IF and RF stages; generation of RF energy; nonsinusoidal circuitry; microwave transmitters and modulation; microwave receivers; servo and data circuitry; transmitter-receiver performance measurements; repair of all components of radar sets, rawinsonde system, radar chronograph set, and identification equipment.
Credit recommendation, collegiate level: 6 semester hours at the freshman or sophomore level as an elective in electricity and electronics, and credit in electrical laboratory on the basis of demonstrated skills and/or institutional examinations.

1. Radar Tracking Station Equipment Repair
2. Radar Tracking Station Repair

Locations: Army Air Defense School and Signal Fire Distribution Systems Training Activity, Fort Bliss, Tex.
Length: 18–27 weeks.

Objectives: To train warrant officers and enlisted personnel to perform organizational and field maintenance on the radar tracking station.

Instruction: Radar netting system and radar tracking station, including basic circuits, standard cards, memory drum, power supplies, and energizing and de-energizing procedures; purpose, functions, circuit theory and troubleshooting techniques of the master timer; radar tracking station sweep area; display area circuitry, adjustment, and maintenance practices; tracking control and data entry circuitry, alignment, and maintenance practices; computer, extrapolator, and the automatic data link input and output areas; memory area and universal tester circuitry.

Credit recommendation, collegiate level: *Courses 1 and 2:* For each course, credit in electrical laboratory on the basis of demonstrated skills and/or institutional examinations.

ry; radio propagation; test equipment; advanced circuitry; radio frequency hazard measurement; radio frequency interference; propagation phenomena and frequency predictions; oblique incidence sounding systems. *Course 2:* In addition to the preceding instruction this course contains more intensive instruction in the area of electronics.

Credit recommendation, collegiate level: CAUTION: *These courses vary only slightly in title and recommendation. Require exact identification of course by title. Course 1:* 4 semester hours at the freshman or sophomore level as an elective in electricity and electronics, and credit in electrical laboratory on the basis of demonstrated skills and/or institutional examinations. *Course 2:* 6 semester hours at the freshman or sophomore level as an elective in electricity and electronics, and credit in electrical laboratory on the basis of demonstrated skills and/or institutional examinations.

1. Radio Officer
2. Field and Fixed Station Radio Officer

Location: Signal School, Fort Monmouth, N.J.
Length: 11–13 weeks.
Objectives: To train officers in the planning and supervision required for installation, operation, and maintenance of tactical and fixed-station radio equipment and of signal center operations within the division, corps, and field army communication system.

Instruction: Electrical fundamentals; vacuum tubes and amplifiers; CW and AM transmitters; AM and FM receivers; FM transmitters; fundamentals of transistors, radar, and television; tactical and fixed antenna systems; radio wave propagation; frequency control procedures; technical characteristics, capabilities, limitations, and operation of tactical AM and FM radio equipment; tactical radio-teletypewriter equipment; tactical radio relay equipment; fixed-station radio single channel transmitting and receiving systems, fixed-station multichannel systems, and radio operations; radio-telegraph operations; specialized radio equipment; telephone, teletypewriter equipment and systems; maintenance procedures; familiarization with automatic data processing systems, communications center operations, and tactical signal communications.

Credit recommendation, collegiate level: For each course, credit in electricity and electrical laboratory on the basis of demonstrated skills and/or institutional examinations.

1. Radio Propagation
2. Radio Wave Propagation

Location: Signal School, Fort Monmouth, N.J.
Length: 29 weeks.
Objectives: To train enlisted personnel to install, operate, and perform field maintenance on radio frequency hazards and interference measuring equipment and oblique incidence sounding equipment.

Instruction: *Course 1:* Series and parallel circuits, induction, principles of AC, inductance, capacitance, impedance, transformers, and DC power; vacuum tubes and vacuum tube low-frequency amplifiers; semiconductor fundamentals; electronics applied to basic receivers; generation of RF energy; nonsinusoidal circuit-

1. Radio Relay and Carrier Attendant
2. Radio Relay and Carrier Operation

Location: Southeastern Signal School, Fort Gordon, Ga.
Length: 8–12 weeks.
Objectives: To train enlisted personnel to install, operate, and perform organizational maintenance on field radio, carrier, and associated equipment.

Instruction: Basic carrier telephone and telegraph systems; advanced carrier and radio relay systems; radio relay antennas and power units; installation and operation of field radio relay systems; radio relay and carrier area communication systems.

Credit recommendation, collegiate level: These courses are technical and vocational in nature. Credit in radio operation and maintenance on the basis of demonstrated skills and/or institutional examinations.

1. Radio Relay and Carrier Repair
2. Radio Relay and Carrier Repair
3. Carrier Equipment Repair
4. Field Carrier Equipment Repair
(Fixed Plant Carrier Equipment Repair)
(Repeater and Carrier Equipment Installation
and Maintenance)

Locations: Signal School, Fort Monmouth, N.J.; Southeastern Signal School, Fort Gordon, Ga.
Length: *Course 1,* 14 weeks; *Course 2,* 28 weeks; *Course 3,* 25 weeks; *Course 4,* 20–33 weeks.
Objectives: To train enlisted personnel to install, line up, operate and perform organizational, field, and depot maintenance on specific equipment mentioned in title.

Instruction: *Course 1:* Radio sets troubleshooting and analysis; telegraph terminal and telegraph carrier equipment; troubleshooting and repair of circuits; telephone repeaters. *Courses 2 and 3:* Electrical and electronic fundamentals; AC and DC circuits; vacuum tubes; oscilloscopes; amplifiers; carrier equipment circuits; repair of basic carrier systems; development of troubleshooting techniques; system analysis, test, and repair of telephone terminal sets and associated equipment; telephone repeaters; test and repair of telegraph-telephone terminal sets; system analysis, test, and repair of telegraph terminal sets. *Course 4:* Fundamentals of electricity and electronics; parallel and series circuits; vacuum tube circuits; rectifiers; system analysis and telephone terminal and associated equipment; overall carrier and VHF system operation and repair.

Credit recommendation, collegiate level: CAUTION: *These courses vary in title, length, and recommendation. Require exact identification of course by title and length. Course 1:* Credit in electrical laboratory on the basis of demonstrated skills and/or institutional examinations. *Courses 2 and 3:* 3 semester hours at the freshman or sophomore level as an elective in electronics and radio, and credit in electrical laboratory on the basis of demonstrated skills and/or institutional examinations. *Course 4:* 2 semester hours at the freshman or sophomore level as an elective in electricity and radio, and credit in electrical laboratory on the basis of demonstrated skills and/or institutional examinations.

Radio Set LRC-3 Repair

Location: Signal School, Fort Monmouth, N.J.

Length: 8 weeks.

Objectives: To train enlisted personnel to install and perform all levels of maintenance on radio set LRC-3.

Instruction: Fundamentals of solid state devices; transmit and receive sections of the LRC-3; auxiliary equipment; multiplex equipment; system operation and maintenance.

Credit recommendation, collegiate level: Credit in electrical laboratory on the basis of demonstrated skills and/or institutional examinations.

Radio-Teletypewriter Operator
(Radio-Teletype Operation)

Location: Southeastern Signal School, Fort Gordon, Ga.

Length: 11 and 15 weeks.

Objectives: To train enlisted personnel to install, operate, and perform operator's maintenance on field radio-teletypewriter sets and associated equipment.

Instruction: International Morse code receiving and transmitting; teletypewriter keyboard operation; radiotelegraph and radio-teletypewriter procedures; installation, operation and maintenance of field radio-teletypewriter equipment; cryptographic devices; operator's maintenance on radio sets and related power equipment; operation through simulated enemy jamming.

Credit recommendation, collegiate level: This course is technical and vocational in nature. Credit in radioteletypewriter operation on the basis of demonstrated skills and/or institutional examinations.

Radio-Teletypewriter Repair

Location: Southeastern Signal School, Fort Gordon, Ga.

Length: 22 weeks.

Objectives: To train enlisted personnel to install and perform repair and depot maintenance on mobile or fixed radio-teletypewriter transmitting and receiving equipment used in single channel radio-teletypewriter systems.

Instruction: Series and parallel circuits, magnetism. alternating current, motors and generators, inductance, transformers, and capacitance; diode and triode vacuum tubes; multi-element and multi-unit tubes; AC power supplies; amplifiers; oscillators; transmitters; antennas; detectors; receivers; amplitude modulation; fixed-station fundamentals; diversity receiving equipment; field radio-teletypewriter equipment.

Credit recommendation, collegiate level: 3 semester hours at the freshman or sophomore level as an elective in electricity and electronics, and credit in electrical laboratory on the basis of demonstrated skills and/or institutional examinations. At the technical level, credit in radio repair on the basis of demonstrated skills and/or institutional examinations.

Radio Terminal Set AN/TRC-90 (RF Portion)

Location: Signal School, Fort Monmouth, N.J.

Length: 5 weeks.

Objectives: To train enlisted personnel to install and perform field and depot maintenance on the AN/TRC-90 radio terminal set.

Instruction: Operation and repair of tropospheric communication systems, including operation and adjustment of teletypewriters; analysis of service channel amplifiers; analysis of voice monitor unit; level sitting procedures; frequency division multiplexing system; signal patching; HF radio order wire system; power distribution and blower panels; engine-generator and air-conditioner-heater units.

Credit recommendation, collegiate level: Credit in electricity and electrical laboratory on the basis of demonstrated skills and/or institutional examinations.

1. Radiographic Procedures (Basic)
(X-ray Procedures (Basic))
(X-ray Specialist)
2. X-ray Techniques Advanced

Location: Medical Field Service School, Fort Sam Houston, Tex.

Length: *Course 1,* 16–19 weeks; *Course 2,* 20 weeks.

Objectives: To train enlisted personnel in the various radiographic positioning techniques and in operating fixed and portable X-ray equipment.

Instruction: *Course 1:* Appendicular skeleton; axial skeleton; familiarization with internal anatomy and physiology; biological effects of radiation; elementary principles of X-ray machines; applied physics of radiology; darkroom principles and techniques; radiographic positioning of the extremities, trunk, and skull; electrical and radiational protection; applied laboratory exercises; foreign body localization; special equipment and procedures for field radiography; clinical application. *Course 2:* Advanced anatomy and physiology; practical laboratory exercises; technical personnel management and radiographic administration; X-ray technical teaching; electronics and X-ray; calibration of X-ray apparatus; principles of radiographic exposure; advanced concepts of X-ray darkrooms; film evaluation and assembly; variations of standard positions; complex X-ray procedures.

Credit recommendation, collegiate level: CAUTION: *These courses vary only slightly in title, length, and recommendation. Require exact identification of course* *by title and length. Course 1:* 3 semester hours in anatomy. At the technical level, credit in X-ray technology on the basis of institutional examination. *Course 2:* 3 semester hours in physiology. At the technical level, credit in X-ray technology on the basis of institutional examination.

Railway Car Repair

Location: Transportation School, Fort Eustis, Va.
Length: 10 weeks.
Objectives: To train enlisted personnel to repair and overhaul passenger and freight cars and to maintain rolling stock in safe and efficient operating condition.
Instruction: Care and use of hand tools; blueprint reading; welding and cutting; types of railway cars and their construction; riveting and metalworking; car carpentry; brake equipment for rolling stock; repair to trucks, draft gears, and couplers; car and train inspection; spray and brush painting and stenciling.
Credit recommendation, collegiate level: This course is technical and vocational in nature. Credit in railway car repair shop on the basis of demonstrated skills and/or institutional examinations.

Railway Dispatching

Location: Transportation School, Fort Eustis, Va.
Length: 10 weeks.
Objectives: To train enlisted personnel in the control and coordination of train movements and in the operation of a railway station.
Instruction: Transportation rules; general signal rules; introduction to timetables and standard time; movement of trains; block signal rules and indications; manual and automatic block rules; yard operations; principles of loading, blocking, and bracing; hand brake theory and application; ICC and AAR rules.
Credit recommendation, collegiate level: No credit because of the limited technical nature of the course.

1. Railway Maintenance and Operations Officer
2. Railway Maintenance and Operations Officer

Location: Transportation School, Fort Eustis, Va.
Length: *Course 1,* 12 weeks; *Course 2,* 20 weeks.
Objectives: To train commissioned officers in the maintenance of way and structures, maintenance and repair of equipment, and main line and terminal operations.
Instruction: *Course 1:* Organization and functions of the Transportation Railway Service, basic safety and operating rules, and signals with their relationship to train operation; principles of maintenance of way and structures, including railway surveys and constructions, track structure, turnout construction, subgrade, ballast and tie maintenance, surfacing and lining track, construction and maintenance of railroad bridges and tunnels; principles of maintenance and repair of steam and diesel-electric locomotives and railway rolling stock; main line and terminal operations and the duties and responsibilities of the operating personnel; principles and techniques involved to determine capacities and capabilities of rail lines in logistical support

in a theater of operations. *Course 2:* This course includes the same academic material as the preceding course but involves more intensive instruction in all areas.
Credit recommendation, collegiate level: CAUTION: *These courses vary only in length and recommendation. Require exact identification of course by length. Course 1:* 3 semester hours in railway maintenance and operation. *Course 2:* 6 semester hours in railway maintenance and operation.

Railway Operations

Location: Transportation School, Fort Eustis, Va.
Length: 10 weeks.
Objectives: To train enlisted personnel in the coordination and control of railway rolling stock through proper car distribution and car accounting.
Instruction: Railway operations in a theater of operations; familiarization with the construction and capacities of railway rolling stock; safety rules; military railway terms, signal rules, timetables, documentation, and operations in a railway yard; car accounting and car distribution; ICC and AAR rules and regulations.
Credit recommendation, collegiate level: No credit because of the limited technical nature of the course.

Railway Section Foreman

Location: Transportation School, Fort Eustis, Va.
Length: 10 weeks.
Objectives: To train enlisted personnel to supervise maintenance of way section gangs or track maintenance platoons in maintaining railway tracks, roadbeds, switches, and appurtenant structures.
Instruction: Function of the transportation railway operating battalion; safety rules; railway signals; railway roadbed; track structure; ballast, cross and switch tie maintenance; rail maintenance; track and turnout construction and maintenance; types of curves; miscellaneous maintenance.
Credit recommendation, collegiate level: This course is technical and vocational in nature. Credit in railway maintenance on the basis of demonstrated skills and/or institutional examinations.

Railway Shop Foreman

Location: Transportation School, Fort Eustis, Va.
Length: 10 weeks.
Objectives: To train enlisted personnel to supervise the operation of a shop engaged in the repair, disassembly, inspection, and overhaul of railway equipment.
Instruction: Shop materiel and special equipment; repair of locomotive running gear and appurtenances, and locomotive boilers; assembly, storage, and methods of handling motive power and rolling stock at ports of embarkation and debarkation; operation and maintenance of locomotive air brake equipment; equipment and material of railway wreck trains; types of rolling stock; general construction of freight cars; couplers and draft gear; passenger and ambulance car construction;

operation and maintenance of various diesel-electric locomotives.

Credit recommendation, collegiate level: This course is technical and vocational in nature. Credit in railway repair shop on the basis of demonstrated skills and/or institutional examinations.

Ranger

Location: Infantry School, Fort Benning, Ga.

Length: 7–9 weeks; for recent graduates of Basic Infantry Officer—5 weeks.

Objectives: To develop, by practical training, the military command and leadership potential of officers and enlisted personnel in order to improve the leadership and training capabilities of all units.

Instruction: Physical conditioning exercises; review of bayonet training; hand-to-hand combat; demolitions; principles and techniques of tactical training; jungle and mountain training.

Credit recommendation, collegiate level: No credit as the course is military in nature.

Reconnaissance Helicopter Maintenance

Location: Aviation School, Fort Rucker, Ala.

Length: 5–6 weeks.

Objectives: To train enlisted personnel in organizational maintenance of reconnaissance-type helicopters.

Instruction: Reconnaissance helicopter maintenance, including engine installation and controls; main rotor head and blades; flight controls and rigging; postflight and periodic inspections; troubleshooting.

Credit recommendation, collegiate level: This course is technical and vocational in nature. Credit in helicopter repair shop on the basis of demonstrated skills and/or institutional examinations.

Reconnaissance Helicopter Repair

Location: Transportation School, Fort Eustis, Va.

Length: 13–17 weeks.

Objectives: To train enlisted personnel to repair rotary-wing reconnaissance-type aircraft.

Instruction: Aircraft engines; powertrain; structural rigging; rotor blade repair; aircraft hydraulics; flightline service and maintenance.

Credit recommendation, collegiate level: This course is technical and vocational in nature. Credit in helicopter repair shop on the basis of demonstrated skills and/or institutional examinations.

1. Recovery and Evacuation
2. Recovery and Evacuation

Location: Ordnance School, Aberdeen Proving Ground, Md.

Length: *Course 1,* 7–9 weeks; *Course 2,* 11 weeks.

Objectives: To train enlisted personnel to perform recovery and evacuation operations for abandoned, damaged, disabled, or mired vehicles.

Instruction: *Course 1:* Familiarization with the operation and use of the medium wrecker, medium and heavy recovery vehicles, and the tank transporter; purpose, types, use, and care of blocks and tackles, knots, bends, and hitches; oxyacetylene cutting; emergency repairs and adjustments on disabled vehicles; problems encountered in recovery; driving track vehicles. *Course 2:* In addition to the preceding instruction this course includes principles of automotive maintenance; care and use of hand tools; basic electrical systems, fuel systems, automotive engines, power trains, and chassis components.

Credit recommendation, collegiate level: CAUTION: *These courses vary only in length and recommendation. Require exact identification of course by length. Course 1:* No credit because of the limited technical nature of the course. *Course 2:* This course is technical and vocational in nature. Credit in automotive maintenance on the basis of demonstrated skills and/or institutional examinations.

1. Recruiting Indoctrination, WAC Officer
2. Recruiting, WAC Enlisted

Location: The Adjutant General's School, Fort Benjamin Harrison, Ind.

Length: 3 weeks.

Objectives: To train WAC officers and enlisted personnel in the principles and techniques of recruiting for Women's Army Corps members.

Instruction: Eligibility, opportunity, and benefits; fundamentals of recruiting; effective speaking; interviewing and selection; recruiting management.

Credit recommendation, collegiate level: No credit because of the brevity and specialized nature of these courses.

1. Recruiting, Reenlistment, and Induction Officer (Recruiting and Reenlistment Officer)
2. Recruiting Management Officer
3. Recruiting (Recruiting, Enlisted)

Location: Adjutant General's School, Fort Benjamin Harrison, Ind.

Length: 3–4 weeks.

Objectives: To train officers and enlisted personnel in recruiting, reenlistment, and induction techniques and in the management of a recruiting activity.

Instruction: Fundamentals of recruiting and reenlistment procedures; recruiting techniques; public speaking; management of a recruiting and reenlistment sales force.

Credit recommendation, collegiate level: No credit because of the brevity and specialized nature of these courses.

Redstone Electronic Materiel Maintenance

Locations: Artillery and Missile School, Fort Sill, Okla.; Redstone Arsenal, Ala.

Length: 20–22 weeks.

Objectives: To train warrant officers and enlisted personnel to assemble, install, calibrate, adjust and maintain on-missile electronic guidance control components and systems and associated electronic test equipment for the Redstone missile.

Instruction: Electron theory; use of the multimeter; Ohm's law; series, parallel, and series-parallel AC and DC circuits; magnetism; vectors; alternating current and voltage; use of the oscilloscope; inductance; capacitance; transformers; AC and DC motors and generators; three-phase power; diodes and rectifiers; voltage doublers and bridge rectifiers; filters, voltage dividers, and potentiometers; triodes; multi-element and miniature tubes; electronic voltage regulators; amplifiers; methods of coupling; cathode followers; transistors; superheterodyne receivers; servomechanisms; synchros; selsyns; troubleshooting techniques; checkout, presetting operation, and organizational maintenance of the Redstone guidance and control system.

Credit recommendation, collegiate level: 4 semester hours at the freshman or sophomore level as an elective in electricity and electronics, and credit in electrical laboratory on the basis of demonstrated skills and/or institutional examinations.

Redstone Officer

Locations: Artillery and Missile School, Fort Sill, Okla.; Redstone Arsenal, Ala.

Length: 7–9 weeks.

Objectives: To train commissioned officers in the characteristics, operating principles, capabilities, and limitations of the Redstone missile and associated equipment.

Instruction: Basic electrical theory; principles of operation of electrical devices on the Redstone missile system; gunnery and fire direction center operations; familiarization with the Redstone missile system, missile guidance systems, missile propulsion systems, and erection and handling equipment; prefiring procedures and organizational maintenance on the Redstone Warhead section; organization, employment, characteristics, and capabilities of the Redstone Battalion, the Field Artillery Missile Group, and the Army Missile Command.

Credit recommendation, collegiate level: Credit in electricity and electrical laboratory on the basis of demonstrated skills and/or institutional examinations.

Refrigeration Equipment Repair

Location: Engineer School, Fort Belvoir, Va.

Length: 11–13 weeks.

Objectives: To train enlisted personnel in the assembly, installation, operation, maintenance, and repair of Army refrigeration and air-conditioning units.

Instruction: Theory of refrigeration; basic components of a refrigeration cycle; fundamental skills of refrigeration repair work; electricity as applied to refrigeration; testing, servicing, and troubleshooting small open-type and hermetically sealed refrigeration units; operating principles of gasoline engine driven systems; operation and servicing of ice plants; operation, maintenance, and troubleshooting of cold storage warehouses; air-conditioning and heating units.

Credit recommendation, collegiate level: This course is technical and vocational in nature. Credit in refrig-

eration and air-conditioning equipment repair on the basis of demonstrated skills and/or institutional examinations.

Regular Army Air Defense Artillery Officer Basic

Location: Air Defense School, Fort Bliss, Tex.

Length: 6 weeks.

Objectives: To train newly commissioned Air Defense Artillery officers for their first duty assignment.

Instruction: Army aviation; familiarization with command and staff procedures; nuclear weapons fundamentals; tactics and techniques of the combined arms team; air defense communication procedures and equipment; maintenance and supply procedures; air defense tactics; Nike-Hercules, Hawk-Missile, or forward area weapons systems.

Credit recommendation, collegiate level: Credit in advanced military at institutions which regularly offer such credit.

Regular Army Engineer Officer Basic

Location: Engineer School, Fort Belvoir, Va.

Length: 6 weeks.

Objectives: To train newly commissioned Regular Army engineer officers for their first duty assignment in the Corps of Engineers.

Instruction: Familiarization with the organization and function of engineer combat units; demolition and mine warfare; river crossing equipment and amphibious bridges; principles of rigging; camouflage, reconnaissance, and field fortifications; fundamentals of quarrying, soils properties, classification, concrete construction, and roads and airfields construction; fixed bridges; employment of nuclear weapons; engineer construction equipment.

Credit recommendation, collegiate level: Credit in advanced military at institutions which regularly offer such credit.

Regular Army Field Artillery Officer Basic

Location: Artillery and Missile School, Fort Sill, Okla.

Length: 6 weeks.

Objectives: To train newly commissioned Regular Army artillery officers for their first duty assignment in Field Artillery.

Instruction: Maintenance management; communications equipment; observed fire procedures and techniques; cannon firing battery techniques; fire direction operations; cannon materiel; organization and employment of field artillery; artillery survey.

Credit recommendation, collegiate level: Credit in advanced military at institutions which regularly offer such credit.

Regular Army Signal Officer Basic

Location: Southeastern Signal School, Fort Gordon, Ga.

Length: 6 weeks.

Objectives: To prepare newly commissioned Regular Army Signal Corps officers for their first duty assignment in the Signal Corps.

Instruction: Weapons and combined arms; communications center operations; wire communications; radio communications; applied communications.

Credit recommendation, collegiate level: 3 semester hours in military science.

Reproduction Equipment Repair

Location: Engineer School, Fort Belvoir, Va.

Length: 13–14 weeks.

Objectives: To train enlisted personnel in the methods and techniques of repairing major items of reproduction equipment.

Instruction: Use of hand tools and precision measuring instruments; basic electricity; operation, repair, and maintenance of copy cameras, contact printers, print dryers, arc lamps, photocopying machines and ammonia process machines; care and maintenance of layout and platemaking equipment; operation, repair and maintenance of offset press and bindery equipment.

Credit recommendation, collegiate level: This course is technical and vocational in nature. Credit in reproduction equipment repair on the basis of demonstrated skills and/or institutional examinations.

Requirements Management

Location: Logistics Management Center, Fort Lee, Va.

Length: 8 weeks.

Objectives: To train officers in the general management skills and the specific procedures of worldwide inventory control.

Instruction: Methods of computing requirements; asset determination; collection, interpretation, and projection of demand data; supply control methods; policies on retention and ultimate disposal of materiel; techniques of inventory management, including financial management, standardization, modernization, economic inventory, and order quantity concepts.

Credit recommendation, collegiate level: 6 semester hours in business management.

SSM Maintenance

Location: Antiaircraft Artillery and Guided Missile School, Fort Bliss, Tex.

Length: 31 weeks.

Objectives: To train officers in the function, technical operation, characteristics, maintenance, and inspection of guided missile fire control systems, launching and handling equipment, and on-missile materiel.

Instruction: Direct and alternating current circuits; inductance, capacitance, meters, and resonant circuits; vacuum tubes and vacuum tube circuits; amplifiers, filters, potentiometers, voltage regulator tubes, oscillators; continuous-wave transmitters, cathode followers, phase inverters, detectors, cathode-ray tubes, and power supplies; operation and assembly of radio circuits; radar

circuits; principles of radar, sweep circuits, multivibrators, oscillators, synchroscope, ring modulators and demodulators, oscilloscope; RF components, wave-guides cavity resonators; servo-loop components; assembly and operation of basic radar circuits; Corporal propulsion, electronic, and fire control systems; computer; Doppler; Corporal missile components and test equipment.

Credit recommendation, collegiate level: 4 semester hours at the freshman or sophomore level as an elective in electricity and electronics, and credit in electrical laboratory on the basis of demonstrated skills and/or institutional examinations.

SSM Mechanical Materiel Maintenance

Location: Antiaircraft Artillery and Guided Missile School, Fort Bliss, Tex.

Length: 8 weeks.

Objectives: To train enlisted personnel to assemble, install, maintain, and adjust SSM mechanical on-missile guidance control systems and associated test equipment and to assemble missiles and perform required checks on SSM propulsion and mechanical systems.

Instruction: Basic electricity; basic tools and test equipment; Corporal missile orientation; propulsion system, missile uncrating and assembly, and service area checkout; Corporal missile ground-handling equipment.

Credit recommendation, collegiate level: This course is technical and vocational in nature. Credit in electrical shop on the basis of demonstrated skills and/or institutional examinations.

SSM Officer Basic

Location: Antiaircraft Artillery and Guided Missile School, Fort Bliss, Tex.

Length: 14–16 weeks.

Objectives: To provide minimum essential training for officers in the duties and responsibilities appropriate to their grade and expected service.

Instruction: Motors and generators; mathematics, map reading, and survey; basic electronics; communications; Corporal external guidance, internal guidance, checkout, and firing procedures; missile propulsion system, missile uncrating and assembly, and service area checkout; ground-handling equipment and firing-area operation; SSM gunnery and firing; command and staff; SSM tactics.

Credit recommendation, collegiate level: 2 semester hours in basic electricity, and credit in advanced military at institutions which regularly offer such credit.

Seaman

Location: Transportation School, Fort Eustis, Va.

Length: 6–10 weeks.

Objectives: To train enlisted personnel to assist in the operation, maintenance, and repair of all types of harbor craft, landing craft, and floating equipment.

Instruction: Basic seamanship which includes nautical terms; nomenclature of ships and ships' gear; care and use of tools; deck maintenance; emergency stations and drills; watches; small boat operations and landing craft; training cruise; operational maintenance and repair of marine engines; engine principles, systems, and related auxiliaries; vessel repair; cargo operations.

Credit recommendation, collegiate level: This course is technical and vocational in nature. Credit in seamanship on the basis of demonstrated skills and/or institutional examinations.

Senior Army Officer Flight Training

Location: Aviation School, Fort Rucker, Ala.

Length: 35 weeks.

Objectives: To train senior army officers in the tactical employment of aircraft and to qualify them as Army aviators for assignment to aviation command and staff positions.

Instruction: Primary, tactical, and operational flight training in fixed- and rotary-wing aircraft; instrument flying; navigation; weather interpretation; organizational maintenance.

Credit recommendation, collegiate level: 2 semester hours in elementary navigation and meteorology.

Senior Field Artillery Officer

Location: Artillery and Missile School, Fort Sill, Okla.

Length: 3–5 weeks.

Objectives: To familiarize senior artillery officers with field artillery organization, tactics, techniques, and equipment.

Instruction: Gunnery techniques, procedures, and tactics applicable to artillery weapons with atomic capability; operating principles of missile systems and warheads; familiarization with the employment of nuclear weapons.

Credit recommendation, collegiate level: No credit as course is military in nature.

Sergeant Electrical-Mechanical Repair
(Ballistic Missile Rocket Motor and Structures Repair (Sergeant))

Location: Missile and Munitions School, Redstone Arsenal, Ala.

Length: 13 weeks.

Objectives: To train enlisted personnel to inspect, test, and repair the Sergeant missile electromechanical systems and associated equipment.

Instruction: Basic ordnance shop practices; Ohm's law and series-parallel circuits; motors and generators; inductance and capacitance; missile structures, performance, and mechanical advantages; hydraulic system fundamentals, components, and pumps; pneumatic system; Sergeant missile system; tool sets, special tools, and hydraulic test set; erector-launcher and GTGS; Sergeant guidance section, propulsion system and control surface assemblies; emplacement operations.

Credit recommendation, collegiate level: This course is technical and vocational in nature. Credit in electrical and mechanical shop on the basis of demonstrated skills and/or institutional examinations.

Sergeant Firing Set Repairman

Location: Missile and Munitions School, Redstone Arsenal, Ala.

Length: 22 weeks.

Objectives: To train enlisted personnel to inspect, test, repair, and perform support maintenance on the Sergeant firing set.

Instruction: Soldering; Ohm's law, series and parallel circuits; multimeter; capacitance, impedance, transformers; transients in RC and LR circuits; amplifier tubes and circuits; voltage regulator; missile switching, amplifying and regulating circuits; multivibrators and gating circuits; drive circuits; servo system; introduction to Sergeant system; maintenance forms, records and procedures; power distribution and control subsystem; power supply; assemblies testing; automatic firing and monitoring system; Sergeant missile and missile trainer; computer subsystems; parameter converter subsystem; sensing and control subsystem.

Credit recommendation, collegiate level: 3 semester hours at the freshman or sophomore level as an elective in electricity and electronics, and credit in electrical laboratory on the basis of demonstrated skills and/or institutional examinations.

Sergeant Missile Battery

Location: Artillery and Missile School, Fort Sill, Okla.

Length: 5–6 weeks.

Objectives: To train warrant officers and enlisted personnel in the assembly, checkout, maintenance, and operation of the Sergeant missile and associated ground-handling equipment.

Instruction: Communication equipment and systems; launching station; missile components; azimuth orientation system; firing set; organizational maintenance test set; Sergeant system operation; warhead section.

Credit recommendation, collegiate level: This course is technical and vocational in nature. Credit in electrical shop on the basis of demonstrated skills and/or institutional examinations.

Sergeant Missile Guidance Repairman

Location: Missile and Munitions School, Redstone Arsenal, Ala.

Length: 19 weeks.

Objectives: To train enlisted personnel in the function and operations of the Sergeant missile system, in the operational procedures, organizational and support maintenance of the Sergeant missile guidance section and organizational maintenance test station, and in the Sergeant missile trainer systems.

Instruction: Ohm's law, series, parallel, and series-parallel circuits; capacitance, impedance and transformers; RC and LR circuits; power supplies; amplifier tubes and circuits; semi-conductors; missile transistor amplifiers; missile gating circuits test equipment; Sergeant system and maintenance procedures; functional and circuit analysis of organizational maintenance test station; Sergeant missile; missile trainer; shop operations.

Credit recommendation, collegiate level: 3 semester hours at the freshman or sophomore level as an elective in electricity and electronics, and credit in electrical laboratory on the basis of demonstrated skills and/or institutional examinations.

Sergeant Officer

Location: Artillery and Missile School, Fort Sill, Okla.

Length: 4–6 weeks.

Objectives: To train officers in the characteristics, tactical employment, system maintenance, and general operating procedures of the Sergeant missile system.

Instruction: Communication equipment and systems used by a Sergeant missile unit; launching station; Sergeant missile; azimuth orientation; firing set; organizational maintenance test station; Sergeant warhead section; tactics and combined arms.

Credit recommendation, collegiate level: No credit because of the brevity and limited technical nature of the course.

Sergeant Test Equipment Repairman

Location: Missile and Munitions Center, Redstone Arsenal, Ala.

Length: 32 weeks.

Objectives: To train enlisted personnel to inspect, test, and repair the Sergeant field maintenance test station, field maintenance shop equipment, and Sergeant missile electronic systems and associated equipment.

Instruction: Series and parallel circuits; DC and AC; magnetism, induction, and inductance; electrical circuits; capacitance, impedance and transformers; RC and LR circuits; amplifiers and coupling circuits; voltage regulators; multivibrators; transistors; integrating and differentiating networks; modulators and demodulators; bistable and drive circuits; servo systems; Sergeant test equipment; Sergeant system and maintenance procedures; programming system; computer testing; FMTS system analysis; SCART system and system analysis; M-321 and M-767 oscilloscopes; digital measuring systems; SMTS matrix control and programming.

Credit recommendation, collegiate level: 3 semester hours at the freshman or sophmore level as an elective in electricity and electronics, and credit in electrical laboratory on the basis of demonstrated skills and/or institutional examinations.

Shoe Repair

Location: Quartermaster School, Fort Lee, Va.

Length: 6 weeks.

Objectives: To train enlisted personnel to repair leather and rubber footwear and to modify standard issue by affixing prescribed orthopedic devices.

Instruction: Hand shoe repair methods; operation and maintenance of mobile shoe repair equipment; orthopedic work and repair of rubber footwear.

Credit recommendation, collegiate level: This course is vocational in nature. Credit in shoe repair on the basis of demonstrated skill.

1. Signal Company Grade Officer Refresher
2. Signal Field Grade Officer Refresher

Location: Signal School, Fort Monmouth, N.J.

Length: 4 weeks.

Objectives: To provide refresher training in the duties and responsibilities appropriate to field-grade and company-grade Signal Corps officers.

Instruction: Signal supply and maintenance; wire communications equipment and engineering; radio communications equipment and engineering; communications center operations; Signal Corps organization and functions.

Credit recommendation, collegiate level: No credit because of the military nature of these courses.

Signal Company Officer

Location: Signal School, Fort Monmouth, N.J.

Length: 27 weeks.

Objectives: To train officers in the duties and responsibilities appropriate to company-grade Signal Corps officers.

Instruction: Map and aerial photograph reading; administration and management; command and staff procedures; methods of instruction and training; unit and team tactics; organization and tactics; modern warfare; weapons; division signal communications; theater of operations signal units; signal supply and maintenance; electrical and radio fundamentals; radio communications equipment; radar and electronics; wire communications; communications center operations.

Credit recommendation, collegiate level: 6 semester hours in radio communications and electricity.

1. Signal Equipment Maintenance and Repair Officer
2. Signal Equipment Maintenance and Repair Officer
(Signal Material Maintenance Officer)

Location: Signal School, Fort Monmouth, N.J.

Length: *Course 1*, 10 weeks; *Course 2*, 8 weeks.

Objectives: To train officers to direct or supervise the receipt, storage, testing, maintenance, repair, overhaul, and reissue of equipment.

Instruction: *Course 1:* Principles of maintenance operations; repair parts supply; direct and general support maintenance; depot and theater maintenance operations; tactical communications equipment; electrical fundamentals; basic audio amplifiers and basic receivers electronics; semiconductor fundamentals; generation of RF energy. *Course 2:* Principles of signal maintenance; organizational supply and maintenance; organization and supervision of a field and depot maintenance shop; signal supply and maintenance in the theater of operations; communications equipment.

Credit recommendation, collegiate level: CAUTION: *These courses vary only slightly in length and recommendation. Require exact identification of course by length. Course 1:* 3 semester hours in maintenance management, and credit in electricity and electrical laboratory on the basis of demonstrated skills and/or institutional examinations. *Course 2:* 4 semester hours in maintenance management.

1. Signal Officer Basic
   (Signal Corps Officers Basic)
   (Signal Officer Orientation)
2. Signal Corps Officers Basic

Locations: Signal School, Fort Monmouth, N.J.; Southeastern Signal School, Fort Gordon, Ga.

Length: *Course 1,* 8–10 weeks; *Course 2,* 19 weeks.

Objectives: To train newly commissioned officers in the duties and responsibilities appropriate to their grade and expected service.

Instruction: *Course 1:* Administration and personnel management; battle indoctrination; CBR warfare; intelligence; map and aerial photo reading; methods of instruction; military leadership; military transportation and motor vehicle maintenance; supply economy and management; combined arms; field engineering; unit and team tactics; weapons; communications center procedures and operations; radio and wire communications; duties and functions of Signal Corps officers; signal supply and maintenance. *Course 2* has more extensive instruction in these same areas.

Credit recommendation, collegiate level: CAUTION: *These courses vary in title, length, and recommendation. Require exact identification of course by title and length. Course 1:* Credit in radio and wire communications on basis of institutional examination. *Course 2:* 2 semester hours in business organization and management and 3 semester hours in radio and electricity.

Signal Officer Candidate

Location: Southeastern Signal School, Fort Gordon, Ga.

Length: 23 weeks.

Objectives: To train second lieutenants to perform duties appropriate to their grade in active Army Signal Corps units.

Instruction: Leadership; medical service; methods of instruction; military justice; personnel administration; logistics; map and air photograph reading; combined arms; weapons and mobility; communications center operations; wire communications; radio communications; applied communications.

Credit recommendation, collegiate level: Credit in advanced military at institutions which regularly offer such credit.

Signal Officer Career
(Signal Officer Advanced)

Location: Signal School, Fort Monmouth, N.J.

Length: 29–36 weeks.

Objectives: To train officers in the duties and responsibilities of Signal Corps officers.

Instruction: Map and aerial photo reading; combined arms; command and staff procedures; communication center procedures and principles; tactical wire equipment; field radio communications; division signal communications; planning for large communication center; military cryptography; modern warfare; radio wave propagation and frequency allocation; Corps signal communications; fixed-plant wire equipment; systems engineering-wire; fixed-station radio systems engineering; signal supply and maintenance; large communications center theater of operations; amphibious and naval operations; theater signal planning; military leadership; methods of instruction; management improvement; program system; budgeting; radar electronics; research.

Credit recommendation, collegiate level: 6 semester hours in business organization and management, and credit in electronics and communications engineering on the basis of demonstrated skills and/or institutional examinations.

Signal Officer Familiarization

Location: Signal School, Fort Monmouth, N.J.

Length: 6 weeks.

Objectives: To provide branch familiarization training in the organization, operational functions, and duties and responsibilities of the Signal Corps.

Instruction: Logistics; automatic data processing systems; organization and tactics; radio communications; telephone communications; communications center operations; signal plans and operations.

Credit recommendation, collegiate level: Credit in radio and wire communications on the basis of institutional examination.

Signal Officer Mobilization Basic

Location: Southeastern Signal School, Fort Gordon, Ga.

Length: *Phase II,* 6 weeks.

Objectives: To provide basic branch training for Signal Corps Reserve and/or National Guard officers not on active duty so that they will have a working knowledge of the duties and responsibilities appropriate to their grade and branch of service.

Instruction: *Note—Phase I is provided by the Department of the Army through service extension courses. These courses are not evaluated by the Commission. Phase II:* Combined arms; CBR operations; weapons and mobility; communications center operations; wire communications; radio communications; mobile signal equipment; organization and employment of tactical signal units.

Credit recommendation, collegiate level: *Phase II:* Credit in radio and wire communications on the basis of demonstrated skills and/or institutional examinations.

Signal Parts Supply

Location: Southeastern Signal School, Fort Gordon, Ga.

Length: 5 weeks.

Objectives: To train enlisted personnel to provide technical advice and assistance on the use, availability, interchangeability, and identification of signal parts and to maintain stock records pertaining to receipt, storage, and issue of parts for signal equipment.

Instruction: Introduction to communications; Signal Corps stock numbering system; signal portion of the federal cataloging system; lists of components; signal parts identification; stock control and parts storage; signal maintenance and salvage; receiving, storing, accounting for, identifying, classifying, and substituting parts for signal equipment.

Credit recommendation, collegiate level: This course is vocational in nature. Credit in stock accounting procedures on the basis of institutional examination.

Signal Supply and Parts Specialist
(Signal Supply)

Location: Southeastern Signal School, Fort Gordon, Ga.

Length: 5–7 weeks.

Objectives: To train enlisted personnel to receive, store, issue, ship, identify, and salvage signal supplies and equipment.

Instruction: Introduction to communications; signal supply catalogs; federal cataloging system and stock list of all items; item identification; stock control procedures and records; signal storage; supply operations; station and depot positions.

Credit recommendation, collegiate level: This course is technical and vocational in nature. Credit in stock accounting procedures on the basis of institutional examination.

Signal Supply Officer
(Signal Supply Basic)

Location: Signal School, Fort Monmouth, N.J.

Length: 8 weeks.

Objectives: To train commissioned officers and warrant officers to direct and supervise the receipt, storage, and issue of Signal Corps supplies and equipment.

Instruction: Fundamentals of supply operation; organizational supply procedures; property responsibility, accountability, requisitioning and turn-in; maintenance and inspection; Army field stock control system; signal field maintenance; storage and material handling; military installation problem; Army command management system; financial management; manpower management; theater signal supply; continental United States signal supply system; observation and study of supply operations.

Credit recommendation, collegiate level: 2 semester hours in business organization and management.

Signal Supply Officer Advanced
(Signal Supply Advanced)

Location: Signal School, Fort Monmouth, N.J.

Length: 12–13 weeks.

Objectives: To train commissioned officers in the broad aspects of signal supply activities including requirements, national stock control, and supply control.

Instruction: Depot and station supply procedures; oral and written techniques; command and staff procedures; industrial management; personnel management; general management; depot command management system; supply and national stock control; financial inventory management; production management; theater signal supply and maintenance; Signal Corps procurement; defense of supply installations.

Credit recommendation, collegiate level: 3 semester hours in business organization and management.

1. Single-Engine Observation and Utility Airplane Maintenance
2. Single-Engine Light Transport Airplane Maintenance
3. Multi-Engine Observation Airplane Maintenance
4. Multi-Engine Medium Transport Airplane Maintenance
5. Multi-Engine Command Airplane Maintenance

Location: Aviation School, Fort Rucker, Ala.

Length: 3–6 weeks.

Objectives: To train enlisted personnel in the maintenance of single- and multi-engine fixed-wing airplanes.

Instruction: Preflight inspection; ground-handling and servicing procedures; landing gear and brake system; fuel and induction system; propeller system; instrument and related systems; electrical systems; utility systems; flight controls; aircraft tools.

Credit recommendation, collegiate level: These courses are technical and vocational in nature. Credit in airplane repair shop on the basis of demonstrated skills and/or institutional examinations.

Single-Engine, Single-Rotor Helicopter Repair
(Observation, Utility and Transport Helicopter Repair)

Location: Transportation School, Fort Eustis, Va.

Length: 13–22 weeks.

Objectives: To train enlisted personnel in the maintenance of single-engine, single-rotor helicopters.

Instruction: Army aviation maintenance; aircraft engines; types and components of cargo and utility-type, single-rotor helicopter blades; electrical circuits; aircraft ignition and power supply systems; hydraulic systems; gas turbine engines; main rotor and tail rotor assemblies; field maintenance procedures; observation helicopter flight control systems; landing gear; transmission and quick change assemblies; engine clutch and tail change.

Credit recommendation, collegiate level: This course is technical and vocational in nature. Credit in helicopter engine repair shop on the basis of demonstrated skills and/or institutional examinations.

Single-Engine, Tandem-Rotor Helicopter Repair
(Tandem-Rotor Helicopter Repair)
(Utility and Cargo Tandem-Rotor Helicopter Repair)

Location: Transportation School, Fort Eustis, Va.

Length: 13–15 weeks.

Objectives: To train enlisted personnel in the field maintenance of single-engine, tandem-rotor helicopters.

Instruction: Aircraft engine maintenance tools and equipment; carburetors; spark plugs; cylinders; pistons; valves; engine handling; fuel systems and components; transmission; rotor head; lubrication system; structural and rigging shop; weights and balance; aircraft hydraulics; component parts of rotor blades; shop management and aircraft inspection.

Credit recommendation, collegiate level: This course is technical and vocational in nature. Credit in helicopter engine repair shop on the basis of demonstrated skills and/or institutional examinations.

Single-Rotor Helicopter Maintenance
(Utility and Cargo, Single-Rotor Helicopter Maintenance)

Location: Aviation School, Fort Rucker, Ala.

Length: 5–6 weeks.

Objective: To train enlisted personnel in organizational maintenance of utility and transport helicopters of single-rotor configuration.

Instruction: Maintenance of the H-19 aircraft fuel and oil systems; transmission; electrical system; rotor systems; landing gear and brakes; hydraulic system; engine and engine controls; inspections; troubleshooting.

Credit recommendation, collegiate level: This course is technical and vocational in nature. Credit in helicopter repair shop on the basis of demonstrated skills and/or institutional examinations.

Single-Rotor Light Transport Helicopter Maintenance
(Single-Rotor Utility and Light Transport Helicopter Maintenance)

Location: Aviation School, Fort Rucker, Ala.

Length: 4–5 weeks.

Objectives: To train enlisted personnel in the organizational maintenance of single-rotor, single-engine, utility and light transport helicopters.

Instruction: Maintenance of the single-rotor utility and light transport helicopter, including landing gear and brakes; electrical and hydraulic systems; power transmission; rotor systems; engine installation and controls; inspections.

Credit recommendation, collegiate level: This course is technical and vocational in nature. Credit in helicopter engine repair shop on the basis of demonstrated skills and/or institutional examinations.

Single-Rotor Observation Helicopter Maintenance

Location: Aviation School, Fort Rucker, Ala.

Length: 5 weeks.

Objectives: To train enlisted personnel in the organizational maintenance of the single-engine, single-rotor observation helicopters.

Instruction: Maintenance of reconnaissance helicopters; engine installation and controls; fuel and oil system; transmission; flight controls rigging; inspections and troubleshooting.

Credit recommendation, collegiate level: This course is technical and vocational in nature. Credit in helicopter engine repair shop on the basis of demonstrated skills and/or institutional examinations.

Single-Rotor Turbine Util.ty Helicopter Maintenance

Location: Aviation School, Fort Rucker, Ala.

Length: 3 weeks.

Objectives: To provide single-rotor helicopter mechanics with a working knowledge in the organizational maintenance of single-rotor, single-engine turbine utility helicopters.

Instruction: Maintenance of the power plant and related systems; rotor system; electrical system; transmission; utility system; inspections; troubleshooting.

Credit recommendation, collegiate level: No credit because of the brevity and limited technical nature of the course.

Single-Rotor Turbine Utility Helicopter Repair

Locations: Transportation School, Fort Eustis, Va.; Aviation School, Fort Rucker, Ala.

Length: 11 weeks.

Objectives: To train enlisted personnel in organizational and direct-general support maintenance of the single-rotor utility helicopter.

Instruction: Aircraft maintenance; electricity; power supply systems; hydraulics; flight control components; auxiliary ground-handling equipment; ignition power plant and related systems; tail boom and rotor systems; inspections.

Credit recommendation, collegiate level: This course is technical and vocational in nature. Credit in helicopter repair shop on the basis of demonstrated skills and/or institutional examinations.

Skysweeper Gun Section Fire Control Maintenance
(T38 Gun Section Fire Control Maintenance)
(Gun Section Fire Control Maintenance, T38)

Location: Air Defense School, Fort Bliss, Tex.

Length: 15–18 weeks.

Objectives: To train enlisted personnel to operate, employ, adjust, and maintain the M38 and T38 artillery fire control system.

Instruction: Introduction to electronics; test instruments; analysis and repair of radar, computer, and power systems; familiarization with the skysweeper and the components of the integrated fire control system.

Credit recommendation, collegiate level: Credit in electronics and electrical laboratory on the basis of demonstrated skills and/or institutional examinations.

Skysweeper Maintenance

Location: Antiaircraft Artillery and Guided Missile School, Fort Bliss, Tex.

Length: 4 weeks.

Objectives: To train enlisted personnel to perform organizational maintenance on unit small arms and the skysweeper gun.

Instruction: Assembly, disassembly, maintenance, and repair of small arms and the caliber .50 machine gun; antiaircraft artillery generator sets; 75-mm gun mount, M84; 75-mm gun M34 and recoil system M29; loader-rammer, M17; inspection and maintenance procedures; skysweeper fire control system.

Credit recommendation, collegiate level: No credit as course is military in nature.

Small Arms Repair

Location: Ordnance School, Aberdeen Proving Ground, Md.

Length: 6–8 weeks.

Objectives: To train enlisted personnel to repair and

rebuild hand-and-shoulder-type weapons and crew-served weapons.

Instruction: Disassembly, assembly, maintenance and inspection of rifles, mortars, rocket launchers, submachine gun, pistols, carbines, pyrotechnic projector and shotguns; use, care, and maintenance of small arms repair truck; machine guns and automatic rifles; preservation, storage, decontamination, and destruction of small-arms materiel.

Credit recommendation, collegiate level: This course is technical and vocational in nature. Credit in small arms repair on the basis of demonstrated skills and/or institutional examinations.

Small Missile Systems Repair

Location: Ordnance School, Aberdeen Proving Ground, Md.

Length: 10–13 weeks.

Objectives: To train enlisted personnel to inspect, test, and perform field maintenance on small missile systems, simulators, and test equipment.

Instruction: Basic electricity and electronics; AC and DC circuits; solid state electronics; Entac antitank guided missile system; Entac Type-IV test equipment; simulator components and controls.

Credit recommendation, collegiate level: Credit in electricity on the basis of institutional examination. At the technical level, credit in electrical shop on the basis of demonstrated skills and/or institutional examinations.

Smoke Generation Supervision

Location: Chemical Corps School, Fort McClellan, Ala.

Length: 4 weeks.

Objectives: To train enlisted personnel in supervision of operations and maintenance of chemical smoke generators.

Instruction: Fundamentals of leadership; instruction and training aids; map and aerial photograph reading; communications; combined arms; smoke operations; supply and maintenance; chemical warfare; materiel.

Credit recommendation, collegiate level: No credit because of the brevity and limited technical nature of the course.

Social Work Procedures
(Social Work Enlisted)

Location: Medical Service School, Fort Sam Houston, Tex.

Length: 8 and 16 weeks.

Objectives: To train enlisted personnel to assist the social worker in obtaining information for social histories of individuals and in carrying out treatment plans formulated by the professional staff.

Instruction: Familiarization with anatomy, physiology, and various diseases; introduction to psychiatric nursing; symptoms, causes, and treatment of neuropsychiatric disorders; behavior development and personality theory; duties and responsibilities of the social

work specialist; clinical training. The 16-week course differs from the 8-week course in that it includes 8 weeks of applicatory training.

Credit recommendation, collegiate level: 3 semester hours in abnormal psychology.

Social Work/Psychology Procedures

Location: Medical Field Service School, Fort Sam Houston, Tex.

Length: 10 weeks.

Objectives: To train enlisted personnel in the social work and psychology fields and in the skills necessary to function as an assistant to the social work and psychology officers.

Instruction: Sociology and psychiatry as related to the social, cultural, and psychological determinants of behavior, including basic concepts of human behavior, social groups, stages of psychological development, adaption to stress, mental illness, social problems of the emotionally ill, and personality; neurotic and psychotic disorders; basic skills and techniques in interviewing and recording of social and psychological data; administration and scoring of psychological tests.

Credit recommendation, collegiate level: 3 semester hours in abnormal psychology.

Soils Analysis
(Soils Technician)

Location: Engineer School, Fort Belvoir, Va.

Length: 7–9 weeks.

Objectives: To train enlisted personnel in the testing of soils, concrete, bituminous and allied construction materials for use in the design, control, and evaluation of roads and airfields.

Instruction: Geology; soil analysis; California bearing ratio lab tests; soil exploration, trafficability, examination and testing; bituminous testing; Marshall stability method of mix design; concrete testing; construction procedures; military roads and airfields.

Credit recommendation, collegiate level: 4 semester hours as an elective in the general science field, or in an engineering program, credit equivalent to the laboratory testing portion of a soil mechanics course.

Special Amphibian Transition

Location: Transportation School, Fort Eustis, Va.

Length: 5 weeks.

Objectives: To train enlisted personnel in the operation and maintenance of amphibious lighters.

Instruction: Disassembly, inspection, reassembly, operation, and troubleshooting of the lighter amphibious vehicles.

Credit recommendation, collegiate level: This course is technical and vocational in nature. Credit in automotive maintenance on the basis of demonstrated skills and/or institutional examinations.

Special Electrical Device Repair

Location: Engineer School, Fort Belvoir, Va.

Length: 10–14 weeks.

Objectives: To train enlisted personnel to repair searchlights, sniperscopes, and related infrared devices.

Instruction: Use and care of hand and power tools; electrical fundamentals, including current resistance and voltage, circuit diagrams and symbols, series and parallel circuits, multimeters, wire measurements, primary and secondary cells, magnetism, relays, inductance and inductive reactance, transformer AC and DC generators and motors, dynamotors, and amplidyne generators; electronic fundamentals, including vacuum tubes, photo tubes, cathode-ray tubes, electronic rectifiers, voltage multipliers and regulators, audio and power amplifiers, amplitude modulation, and electronic motor controls; principles and characteristics of infrared light; maintenance and repair of equipment.

Credit recommendation, collegiate level: 2 semester hours at the freshman or sophomore level as an elective in electricity, and credit in electrical laboratory on the basis of demonstrated skills and/or institutional examinations.

1. Special Electrical/Electronic Device Repair
2. Senior Special Electrical/Electronic Device Repair

Location: Engineer School, Fort Belvoir, Va.

Length: *Course 1,* 11 weeks; *Course 2,* 9 weeks.

Objectives: *Course 1:* To train enlisted personnel in organizational and direct support maintenance of electronic night vision and detection equipment. *Course 2:* To train enlisted personnel in organizational and general support maintenance on electronic distance measuring and orientation equipment and in general support maintenance on night vision equipment.

Instruction: *Course 1:* Basic electrical theory; electrical terms and symbols; Ohm's law; tools and instruments; series and parallel DC circuits; analyzation of AC circuits; infrared and searchlight equipment; mine detection equipment. *Course 2:* Operation, maintenance, and adjustment of night vision equipment; advanced electronic instrumentation; electronic distance measuring equipment; electronic azimuth orientation equipment.

Credit recommendation, collegiate level: CAUTION: *These courses vary only slightly in title, length, and recommendation. Require exact identification by title and length. Course 1:* Credit in electricity on the basis of institutional examinations. At the technical level, credit in electrical shop on the basis of demonstrated skills and/or institutional examinations. *Course 2:* This course is technical and vocational in nature. Credit in electrical shop on the basis of demonstrated skills and/or institutional examinations.

Special Forces Aidman (Airborne)

Location: Medical Field Service School, Fort Sam Houston, Tex.

Length: 17 weeks.

Objectives: To train enlisted personnel in the specialized procedures and techniques necessary to assume the duties and responsibilities of a Special Forces aidman.

Instruction: Emergency dental conditions and treatment; anatomical and physiological functions of the human body; familiarization with pharmacology; etiology, symptomatology, and general treatment of common medical and surgical conditions; nursing care procedures; basic combat psychiatry; fundamentals of preventive medicine; familiarization with laboratory procedures, including urinalysis, hematology, microbiology, and parasitology; veterinary preventive medicine and animal care; clinical application.

Credit recommendation, collegiate level: 3 semester hours in physiology and hygiene and 2 semester hours in medical laboratory procedures.

Special Forces Engineer Training

Location: Engineer School, Fort Belvoir, Va.

Length: 6–7 weeks.

Objectives: To train Special Forces engineer enlisted personnel in engineer tactics and techniques.

Instruction: Fundamentals of combat operations; equipment used in river crossing operations; basic soil properties and soil classification; construction surveys, alignments for roads and airfields, masonry construction, utilities, and bridges; bituminous materials and estimation of quantities for bituminous surfaces; principles of construction sketching and drawing; engineer equipment.

Credit recommendation, collegiate level: 2 semester hours in engineering construction.

Special Forces Officer

Location: Special Warfare School, Fort Bragg, N.C.

Length: 11–12 weeks.

Objectives: To train officers in the latest doctrine and techniques of guerrilla warfare and special forces operations.

Instruction: Combat developments in special warfare; intelligence requirements; organization and buildup of resistance forces; operational base; political aspects of subversion; interdiction systems; target analysis and selection; nontechnical communications; evasion and escape; strategic village defense; air and amphibious operations; field engineering and demolitions; chemical, biological, and radiological techniques; medical aspects of Special Forces operations; psychological operations; propaganda process; counterinsurgency operations; population and resources control.

Credit recommendation, collegiate level: No credit as course is military in nature.

Special Forces Officer Intelligence

Location: Intelligence School, Fort Holabird, Md.

Length: 6 weeks.

Objectives: To train Special Forces officers in general intelligence subjects, combat intelligence specialties, basic area intelligence and counterintelligence.

Instruction: Interrogation; aerial surveillance and reconnaissance; order of battle; production of combat intelligence; area intelligence; utilization of human sources; counterintelligence interrogations; foreign intelligence, and security agencies.

Credit recommendation, collegiate level: 2 semester hours in intelligence methods.

Special Forces Officer (Modified)

Location: Special Warfare School, Fort Bragg, N.C.
Length: 8 weeks.
Objectives: To train officers in the latest doctrine and techniques of unconventional warfare and Special Forces operations.
Instruction: Special warfare and resistance operations; air and amphibious operations; communications; weapons familiarization; field engineering and demolition; psychological operations; counterinsurgency doctrine and techniques.
Credit recommendation, collegiate level: No credit as the course is military in nature.

Special Services Officer

Location: Adjutant General's School, Fort Benjamin Harrison, Ind.
Length: 3 weeks.
Objectives: To train officers in administration and operation of Special Services activities.
Instruction: Personnel requirements, staffing, and administration; facilities, supplies, and procurement activities; appropriated funds, nonappropriated funds, and budgets; Army crafts, entertainment, library, motion picture service, service club, and sports programs.
Credit recommendation, collegiate level: 2 semester hours in recreational programming.

Specialized Teletypewriter Equipment Repair

Location: Southeastern Signal School, Fort Gordon, Ga.
Length: 6–7 weeks.
Objectives: To train Army Security Agency enlisted personnel to install and perform organizational and field maintenance on special teletypewriter equipment.
Instruction: Troubleshooting and repairing special teletypewriter equipment; uses and applications of test equipment; installation, operation, and repair of special teletypewriter sets functions, adjustments, and installation of modified teletypewriter and associated equipment.
Credit recommendation, collegiate level: This course is technical and vocational in nature. Credit in teletypewriter equipment repair on the basis of demonstrated skills and/or institutional examinations.

Specification Management

Location: Logistics Management Center, Fort Lee, Va.
Length: 3 weeks.
Objectives: To provide commissioned officers with training in the development, preparation, or use of specifications.

Instruction: Economic, structural, and standardization principles underlying specifications; requirements of specifications, including methods of stating requirements, value engineering, tolerancing and dimensioning, metrology, reliability and maintainability provisions, and performance specifications; specifications as procurement instruments; quality assurance provisions of a specification; packaging and packing requirements; administrative skills; familiarization with automatic data processing systems.
Credit recommendation, collegiate level: 2 semester hours in procurement management.

Steam Locomotive Repairman

Location: Transportation School, Fort Eustis, Va.
Length: 10 weeks.
Objectives: To train enlisted personnel to inspect, test, repair, lubricate, and overhaul steam operated locomotives and to maintain railway motive power equipment.
Instruction: Machine shop practices; welding; steam locomotive frames, shoes, and wedges; running gear; valves and valve gear; air brakes; boiler feeding and safety appliances; lubrication; locomotive management.
Credit recommendation, collegiate level: This course is technical and vocational in nature. Credit in steam locomotive repair shop on the basis of demonstrated skills and/or institutional examinations.

Stenography

Location: Adjutant General's School, Fort Benjamin Harrison, Ind.
Length: 16 weeks.
Objectives: To train enlisted personnel to take dictation in shorthand at a minimum rate of 90 words per minute, to transcribe and to type at a minimum rate of 45 words per minute, and to perform basic duties of a stenographer in a military office.
Instruction: Shorthand (Gregg simplified) basic and advanced theory; speed building; transcription; typing; machine mastery and timed writings; typing usages and procedures; use and care of duplicating and office machines; English usage and grammar; correspondence; orders and media; publications; awards and decorations; office procedures; military court and board reporting.
Credit recommendation, collegiate level: This course is technical and vocational in nature. Credit in shorthand, typing, and office practice on the basis of demonstrated skills and/or institutional examinations.

Stenography—WAC

Location: Women's Army Corps School, Fort McClellan, Ala.
Length: 4–12 weeks.
Objectives: To train WAC enlisted personnel as stenographers for office duties.
Instruction: Review of Gregg shorthand theory and practice; development of typing skills; English composition; military correspondence; filing; office proce-

dures; use of telephone; orders; publications; supply system; defense information; records and reports; military court and board reports.

Credit recommendation, collegiate level: This course is technical and vocational in nature. Credit in shorthand, typing, and office practice on the basis of institutional examination.

Stevedore Officer

Location: Transportation School, Fort Eustis, Va.
Length: 7–9 weeks.
Objectives: To train officers in the duties and responsibilities of a stevedore officer in transportation terminal units.
Instruction: Use of native labor in oversea terminal commands; defense of rear areas; technical service cargo; signal equipment in terminal units; code marking; military packaging and packing for transportation; rigging of ship's gear; proper stowage; cargo planning and advanced cargo planning; documenting; winch operations and signals; basic stevedoring; advanced stevedoring; general stevedoring; terminal operations; terminal organization and management; stevedore contracting; amphibious operations.
Credit recommendation, collegiate level: This course is technical and vocational in nature. Credit in stevedore management operations on the basis of demonstrated skills and/or institutional examinations.

Stevedore Supervisor
(Stevedore Supervision)

Location: Transportation School, Fort Eustis, Va.
Length: 6–9 weeks.
Objectives: To train enlisted personnel in the supervision of stevedore activities involved in loading and unloading cargo at ports, beaches, and docks.
Instruction: Terminal operations and units; marlinespike seamanship; instructional methods; rigging and cargo-handling gear; cargo operations; stevedore operations; cargo documentation; ocean shipping procedures and related facilities; cargo-planning procedures and requirements; amphibious operations.
Credit recommendation, collegiate level: This course is technical and vocational in nature. Credit in stevedore operations on the basis of demonstrated skills and/or institutional examinations.

Still Photography

Location: Signal School, Fort Monmouth, N.J.
Length: 12–13 weeks.
Objectives: To train enlisted personnel in the techniques required to take indoor and outdoor, black and white, and color photographs of ground and aerial subjects for technical, tactical and informational purposes.
Instruction: Basic, flash, military news and information, tactical air and ground, intelligence operational record, miniature, and color photography.
Credit recommendation, collegiate level: 3 semester hours in photography.

1. Subsistence Officer
2. Subsistence Technology

Location: Quartermaster School, Fort Lee, Va.
Length: *Course 1,* 18 weeks; *Course 2,* 24 weeks.
Objectives: To train commissioned officers in the policies, principles, standards, techniques, and management of the subsistence commodity.
Instruction: *Course 1:* Fundamentals of chemistry and bacteriology; food packaging and packing techniques; production, processing, storage, and utilization of cereals and cereal products; technology and management involved in the production of dairy and poultry products; marketing, grading, and processing of meat and fish products; processing and storage of beverages, sugar, syrups, candy, and condiments; services and functions of marketing; principles and operational aspects of subsistence procurement; subsistence supply and financial management, including requirements determination, subsistence finding and reporting, inventory control, requisition processing, storage, and distribution.
Course 2: This course contains the same academic material as *Course 1* but includes more intense instruction in the areas of nutrition and financial management.
Credit recommendation, collegiate level: CAUTION: *These courses vary only slightly in title, length, and recommendation. Require exact identification of course by title and length. Course 1:* 2 semester hours in applied science, 3 semester hours in food marketing, 4 semester hours in business management, 3 semester hours in food preparation, and 6 semester hours in institutional food management.
Course 2: 2 semester hours in applied science, 2 semester hours in nutrition, 3 semester hours in food marketing, 6 semester hours in business management, 3 semester hours in food preparation, and 6 semester hours in institutional food management.

Subsistence Storage Specialist

Location: Quartermaster School, Fort Lee, Va.
Length: 5–8 weeks.
Objectives: To train enlisted personnel to receive, store, and issue subsistence supplies.
Instruction: Subsistence supply operations; ration procedures at organization and station levels; storage operations; packing and crating; stock control; materials handling equipment.
Credit recommendation, collegiate level: This course is vocational in nature. Credit in food storage and handling on the basis of institutional examination.

1. Subsistence Storage Supervision
2. Subsistence Supply Supervision

Location: Quartermaster School, Fort Lee, Va.
Length: *Course 1,* 5 weeks; *Course 2,* 8 weeks.
Objectives: To train enlisted personnel to supervise the receipt, storage, issue and sale of subsistence supplies.
Instruction: *Course 1:* Supervision and management of personnel; mission, functions, and organization of installation commissaries; depot supply and storage operations; familiarization with the Army financial management plan; logistical procedures. *Course 2:* Commis-

sary operations, including price lists, sources of supply, determination of subsistence requirements, garrison and field rations, meat and produce market operations, inventory preparation and adjustment, and monthly records; familiarization with administrative procedures and financial management; supply and accounting procedures; depot operations; procurement; staff organization; principles of logistics.

Credit recommendation, collegiate level: CAUTION: *These courses vary only slightly in title, length, and recommendation. Require exact identification of course by title and length. Course 1: 2 semester hours in supply management. Course 2: 3 semester hours in business organization.*

Supervisory Field Communications Equipment Maintenance

Location: Signal School, Fort Gordon, Ga.
Length: 20–26 weeks.
Objectives: To train enlisted personnel to apply advanced maintenance techniques and to supervise activities involved in the maintenance of field communications equipment.
Instruction: Advanced electronics; basic and advanced teletypewriter maintenance techniques; basic and advanced radio relay and carrier maintenance techniques; basic and advanced radio maintenance techniques; system trouble location; supervisory and training techniques; maintenance management; maintenance and supply procedures.
Credit recommendation, collegiate level: 2 semester hours in shop management, 2 semester hours at the freshman and sophomore level as an elective in electricity and electronics, and credit in electrical laboratory on the basis of demonstrated skills and/or institutional examinations.

Supervisory Fixed-Station Communication Maintenance

Location: Signal School, Fort Monmouth, N.J.
Length: 25 weeks.
Objectives: To train enlisted personnel to supervise, coordinate, and participate in the operation and maintenance of a fixed-station communication facility.
Instruction: Supervisory responsibilities; maintenance operations; repair parts supply and management; direct and general support maintenance; depot maintenance; theater maintenance operations; instruction techniques; electronic fundamentals; advanced electronic circuitry; radio wave propagation and antenna systems; fixed-station communication systems; installation practices; system repair procedures; maintenance management and practices.
Credit recommendation, collegiate level: 3 semester hours in shop management, 3 semester hours in supply management, 2 semester hours at the freshman and sophomore level as an elective in electricity and electronics, and credit in electrical laboratory and instructional methods on the basis of demonstrated skills and/or institutional examinations.

Supervisory Radar Repair

Location: Signal School, Fort Monmouth, N.J.
Length: 25 weeks.
Objectives: To train enlisted personnel to supervise, coordinate, and participate in the maintenance of all types of nonintegrated radars.
Instruction: Requisitioning and accounting for maintenance shop property; repair parts supply management; personnel management; supervision of a direct and general support maintenance shop; depot maintenance operations; organization and operation of the division support command and maintenance operations; familiarization with instructional techniques; basic electronic concepts; advanced electronic circuitry; new fundamentals concepts and developments within radar; alignment and performance check of weapons support radar; maintenance of ground surveillance radar equipment, and ground control radar equipment; repair, adjustment, and troubleshooting of airborne radar equipment, and air defense radar equipment.
Credit recommendation, collegiate level: 3 semester hours in maintenance management, 2 semester hours at the freshman or sophomore level as an elective in electricity and electronics, and credit in electrical laboratory on the basis of demonstrated skills and/or institutional examinations.

Supply Handling

Location: Quartermaster School, Fort Lee, Va.
Length: 8 weeks.
Objectives: To train enlisted personnel to load and unload supplies and equipment, operate material handling equipment, and assist in receipt, storage, issue, sale, and salvage of technical or general material.
Instruction: Army supply system; supply manual system classification and disposal; processing, packaging, crating and marking; storage operations; commissary operations; basic mathematics; material handling equipment; ropes and rope tying; petroleum products handling.
Credit recommendation, collegiate level: No credit because of the nature of the course.

Supply Specialist Refresher

Location: Quartermaster School, Fort Lee, Va.
Length: 4 weeks.
Objectives: To provide refresher training in supply operations of field supply procedures, in inventory control procedures, and in storage and supply operations in a theater of operations.
Instruction: Field supply procedures; supply authorization media; mechanized stock control; inventory control procedures; fundamentals of automatic data processing and introduction to punched card machines; computer systems; storage and handling procedures; supply operations in a theater of operations.
Credit recommendation, collegiate level: No credit because of the brevity and refresher nature of this course.

Surface-to-Air Missile Mechanical Materiel Maintenance (Nike-Ajax)

Location: Air Defense School, Fort Bliss, Tex.

Length: 8 weeks.

Objectives: To train enlisted personnel to assemble, install, maintain, and adjust Nike-Ajax mechanical and hydraulic on-missile guidance control systems and associated equipment and to assemble missiles and perform required checks on Nike-Ajax propulsion and mechanical systems.

Instruction: Basic electricity; Nike-Ajax missile mechanics; mechanical materiel of assembly and launching areas; missile preparation and depreparation.

Credit recommendation, collegiate level: Credit in electrical laboratory on the basis of demonstrated skills and/or institutional examinations.

1. Surface-to-Air Missile Staff Officer
2. Surface-to-Air Missile Staff Officer (Nike) (SAM Maintenance)
3. SAM Maintenance Officer
4. Nike System Maintenance Officer

Location: Air Defense School, Fort Bliss, Tex.

Length: *Course 1,* 19 weeks; *Courses 2 and 4,* 42–44 weeks; *Course 3,* 49 weeks.

Objectives: To provide officers with a working knowledge of the function, operation, characteristics, organizational maintenance, and inspection of the Nike-Hercules system and associated equipment.

Instruction: *Courses 1 and 2:* DC and AC circuits; electronic and advanced radar vacuum tube circuits; acquisition radar system; target-tracking radars; computers; missile-tracking radar; missile and launching area; warheads and preparation for fire; system analysis and inspection; AN/TSQ-38 system; guided missile radar signal simulator system. In addition to the preceding instruction, *Courses 2, 3 and 4* include basic electricity and radio electronics and radar electronics.

Credit recommendation, collegiate level: CAUTION: *These courses vary in title, length, and recommendation. Require exact identification of course by title and length. Course 1:* Credit in electricity and electrical laboratory on the basis of demonstrated skills and/or institutional examinations. *Course 2:* 2 semester hours at the freshman or sophomore level as an elective in electricity and electronics, and credit in electrical laboratory on the basis of demonstrated skills and/or institutional examinations. *Course 3:* 3 semester hours at the freshman or sophomore level as an elective in electricity and electronics, and credit in electrical laboratory on the basis of demonstrated skills and/or institutional examinations. *Course 4:* 4 semester hours at the freshman or sophomore level as an elective in electricity and electronics, and credit in electrical laboratory on the basis of demonstrated skills and/or institutional examinations.

1. Surface-to-Air Missile Staff Officer (Hawk)
2. Surface-to-Air Missile Staff Officer (Hawk)
3. SAM Staff Officer (Hawk)

Location: Air Defense School, Fort Bliss, Tex.

Length: *Course 1,* 18–19 weeks; *Course 2,* 35 weeks; *Course 3,* 35–37 weeks.

Objectives: To provide officers with a working knowledge of the characteristics, function, operation, organizational maintenance, inspection, and technical employment of the Hawk missile system and associated equipment.

Instruction: DC and AC circuits; vacuum tubes; electronic and radio circuits; amplifier and oscillator theory and circuits; transmission techniques and indicators; circuit analysis; troubleshooting; defense acquisition radar; IFF Mark X and transistor application; Hawk fire control platoon and Hawk firing platoon; pulse acquisition radar; battery control center operation; CW radars; missile assembly and handling; launcher mechanical and hydraulic system; launcher electronics; missile and missile guidance; missile and launcher performance tests; Hawk firing battery; coder-decoder group; air defense tactics.

Credit recommendation, collegiate level: CAUTION: *These courses vary in title, length, and recommendation. Require exact identification of course by title and length. Course 1:* Credit in electrical laboratory on the basis of demonstrated skills and/or institutional examinations. *Course 2:* 2 semester hours at the freshman and sophomore level as an elective in electricity and electronics, and credit in electrical laboratory on the basis of demonstrated skills and/or institutional examinations. *Course 3:* 3 semester hours at the freshman or sophomore level as an elective in electricity and electronics, and credit in electrical laboratory on the basis of demonstrated skills and/or institutional examinations.

Surfacing Machine Operation (Surfacing Machine Operator)

Location: Engineer School, Fort Belvoir, Va.

Length: 10 weeks.

Objectives: To train enlisted personnel to operate and perform operator's maintenance of various types of asphalt, concrete mixing, and surfacing equipment.

Instruction: Surfacing machine fundamentals; asphalt plant and allied equipment; bituminous surfaces; asphalt plant calibration; asphalt plant operation; principles of concrete construction; steel forms, tampers, and batching plants; concrete mixer; concrete paver, spreader, and finisher; concrete construction.

Credit recommendation, collegiate level: This course is vocational in nature. Credit in surfacing machine operation on the basis of demonstrated skill.

Surveillance Radar Maintenance (Artillery Surveillance Radar Maintenance)

Locations: Army Air Defense School, Artillery School, Fort Bliss, Tex.

Length: 22–24 weeks.

Objectives: To train enlisted personnel to employ, operate, adjust, and maintain the antiaircraft artillery surveillance radar AN/TPS-1D and associated IFF equipment.

Instruction: Ohm's law, and DC circuits; AC theory and circuits; multiphase power, motors, and generators; vacuum tubes, and radio circuits; amplifiers and oscilators; theory of radio and analysis of CW and AM transmitters; radar circuits, including detectors, receivers, nonsinusoidal generators, and shock-excited oscillators; high-frequency components and circuits; servomechanisms and circuits; modulator, transmitter, and RF systems; receiver system; moving-target indication system; indicator system of the AN/TPS-1D and PPI repeaters; antenna positioning, power distribution, and DC control systems; circuitry and adjustment of the IFF Mark X system; use of test equipment.

Credit recommendation, collegiate level: 4 semester hours at the freshman or sophomore level as an elective in electricity and electronics, and credit in electrical laboratory on the basis of demonstrated skills and/or institutional examinations.

Switchboard Operator
(Central Office Telephone Swtichboard Operation)

Location: Southeastern Signal School, Fort Gordon, Ga.

Length: 8 weeks.

Objectives: To train enlisted personnel to install, operate, and perform operator's maintenance on local and common battery switchboards.

Instruction: Local battery installation and maintenance; local battery switchboard operation; common battery switchboard installation and maintenance; common battery switchboard operation.

Credit recommendation, collegiate level: This course is technical and vocational in nature. Credit in switchboard operation and switchboard repair shop on the basis of demonstrated skills and/or institutional examinations.

Tactical Circuit Controller

Location: Southeastern Signal School, Fort Gordon, Ga.

Length: 5 weeks.

Objectives: To train enlisted personnel in operating communication patching panels, with associated equipment, in tactical communication systems.

Instruction: Tactical telephone communication systems; installation and operation of switchboards; teletypewriter communications; installation and operation of teletypewriter sets; interconnections of mobile teletypewriter and telephone shelters; communication patching panels; system operations.

Credit recommendation, collegiate level: This course is technical and vocational in nature. Credit in installation and operation of teletypewriter communications on the basis of demonstrated skills and/or institutional examinations.

Tactics and Techniques Course, Phase I

Location: John F. Kennedy Center for Special Warfare, Fort Bragg, N.C.

Length: 4 weeks.

Objectives: To train and orient selected students on general military subjects related to Special Forces.

Instruction: Methods of instruction; map reading and land navigation; patrolling.

Credit recommendation, collegiate level: No credit because of the military nature of the course.

Tandem-Rotor Helicopter Maintenance
(Utility and Cargo, Tandem-Rotor Helicopter Maintenance)

Location: Aviation School, Fort Rucker, Ala.

Length: 4–6 weeks.

Objectives: To train enlisted personnel in organizational maintenance of light transport helicopters of tandem-rotor configuration.

Instruction: Maintenance of the H-21 electrical system; flight controls; alighting gear; power plant; transmission; rotor group; rigging; tracking and vibrations; inspections; troubleshooting.

Credit recommendation, collegiate level: This course is technical and vocational in nature. Credit in helicopter engine repair shop on the basis of demonstrated skills and/or institutional examinations.

Tandem-Rotor Light Transport Helicopter Maintenance

Location: Aviation School, Fort Rucker, Ala.

Length: 4–5 weeks.

Objectives: To train enlisted personnel in the organizational maintenance of single-engine, tandem-rotor, light transport helicopters.

Instruction: Maintenance of the tandem-rotor helicopters; electrical system; flight controls; landing gear and brakes; rigging; power plants; transmission; troubleshooting.

Credit recommendation, collegiate level: This course is technical and vocational in nature. Credit in helicopter repair shop on the basis of demonstrated skills and/or institutional examinations.

Technical Escort

Location: Army Chemical Center and School, Fort McClellan, Ala.

Length: 4 weeks.

Objectives: To train officers and enlisted personnel of all services in the techniques and procedures involved in the escort of shipping chemical, biological or etiological materiel, and radioactive waste.

Instruction: Shipment and storage of biological and etiological agents; shipment containers; munitions and functioning of munitions; safety and precautionary measures in handling material; characteristics, properties, effects on the body, and first aid measures; transportation and disposal of radioactive material.

Credit recommendation, collegiate level: No credit because of the limited technical nature of the course.

Technical Intelligence

Location: Intelligence School, Fort Holabird, Md.

Length: 3 weeks.

Objectives: To provide commissioned officers and enlisted personnel with a general knowledge of the current mission, organization, function, and production of combat intelligence.

Instruction: Basic intelligence principles; responsibilities and functions of intelligence personnel; intelligence organizations in Vietnam; collection, evaluation, interpretation and dissemination of information; interrogation of prisoners of war; order of battle; technical intelligence; Intelligence Corps mission and operation.

Credit recommendation, collegiate level: Credit in intelligence methods on the basis of institutional examination.

Techniques of Review and Analysis

Location: Finance School, Fort Benjamin Harrison, Ind.

Length: 3 weeks.

Objectives: To train commissioned officers and senior enlisted personnel in review and analysis as related to Army activities and programs.

Instruction: Operations, concepts, processes, and procedures of financial management with emphasis at the installation level; procedures in the development of cost and performance data; progress and statistical reporting and analysis; management control systems.

Credit recommendation, collegiate level: 2 semester hours in business management.

Telephone and Teletypewriter Equipment Repair

Location: Signal School, Fort Monmouth, N.J.

Length: 14–15 weeks.

Objectives: To train enlisted personnel in the depot repair of telephone and teletypewriter equipment.

Instruction: Inspection, testing, troubleshooting, and repairing of power equipment, main frames, telephone subsets, local battery switchboards, PBX switchboards, nonmultiple common battery switchboard, multiple common battery central office equipment; telephone and teletypewriter shop procedures.

Credit recommendation, collegiate level: This course is technical and vocational in nature. Credit in telephone and teletypewriter equipment repair on the basis of demonstrated skills and/or institutional examinations.

Telephone and Teletypewriter Officer

Location: Signal School, Fort Monmouth, N.J.

Length: 14 weeks.

Objectives: To train commissioned officers in the supervision, management, planning, installation, operation and maintenance of telephone, teletypewriter, and carrier facilities, equipment and systems; and in the signal center operations within the division, corps, and field area communications system.

Instruction: Electrical fundamentals; telephone transmission principles; outside and inside plant principles and practices; employment, installation, and operation of tactical telephone, switchboard, and auxiliary central office equipment; tactical carrier and fixed teletypewriter and telegraph equipment; tactical voice-frequency telephone repeaters and ringing equipment; installation, employment, and operation of ground mobile communications equipment; transmission and circuit layout engineering; engineering power distribution systems for military signal communications installations; use of radioteletypewriter and radio relay equipment; communications center operations; automatic data processing systems.

Credit recommendation, collegiate level: This course is technical and vocational in nature. Credit in telephone and teletypewriter operation and repair on the basis of demonstrated skills and/or institutional examinations.

Telephone Installation and Repair

Location: Signal School, Fort Gordon, Ga.

Length: 8 weeks.

Objectives: To train enlisted personnel to install, replace, and perform organizational maintenance on both local battery and common battery telephones.

Instruction: Pole climbing; basic electricity; basic telephone theory; installation of field wire, field cable, local battery telephones, and switchboards; complete substation and station wiring plans; installation and test of a substation; telephone equipment maintenance.

Credit recommendation, collegiate level: This course is technical and vocational in nature. Credit in telephone repair on the basis of demonstrated skills and/or institutional examinations.

Teletype Operation
(Teletypewriter Operation)

Location: Southeastern Signal School, Fort Gordon, Ga.

Length: 8 weeks.

Objectives: To train enlisted personnel in the operation of teletypewriter equipment for transmission and reception of messages.

Instruction: Basic signal communications; teletypewriter equipment; keyboard operation; teletypewriter; comcenter operation.

Credit recommendation, collegiate level: This course is technical and vocational in nature. Credit in teletypewriter operation on the basis of demonstrated skills and/or institutional examinations.

Teletypewriter Equipment Repair
(Teletypewriter Equipment Maintenance)

Location: Signal School, Fort Monmouth, N.J.; Southeastern Signal School, Fort Gordon, Ga.

Length: 18–25 weeks.

Objectives: To train enlisted personnel to install and perform organizational through depot maintenance of mechanical and electronic teletypewriter equipment and facsimile equipment.

Instruction: Principles of electricity; use and care of tools; teletypewriter fundamentals, principles of operation, and maintenance; maintenance of fixed-station teletypewriter sets with perforator transmitter and transmitter distributor; maintenance of typing perforator; installation and circuits of teletypewriter equipment; teletypewriter shop operation and maintenance procedures.

Credit recommendation, collegiate level: This course is technical and vocational in nature. Credit in teletypewriter equipment repair on the basis of demonstrated skills and/or institutional examinations.

Television Equipment Repair

Location: Signal School, Fort Monmouth, N.J.
Length: 25–27 weeks.
Objectives: To train enlisted personnel in the installation, operation, maintenance and repair of television receivers, camera chains, studio equipment television microwave links, video tape recorders, and closed circuit systems.
Instruction: Scanning systems; cathode-ray tube theory; clippers and limiters; transients; multivibrators; time base circuits; clamping circuits; cathode followers; television receivers; television electro-optical conversion equipment and associated equipment; television transmitters, associated equipment, and specialized television systems; image orthicon cameras and associated equipment; industrial camera equipment; film projecting and recording; closed circuit systems; television remote and relay systems; studio vidicon cameras; and color television.
Credit recommendation, collegiate level: 4 semester hours at the freshman or sophomore level as an elective in electricity and electronics, and credit in electrical laboratory on the basis of demonstrated skills and/or institutional examinations.

Television Equipment Repair Transition

Location: Signal School, Fort Monmouth, N.J.
Length: 3 weeks.
Objectives: To give enlisted men a working knowledge of solid state devices and of techniques required for maintenance and repair of video tape recorders.
Instruction: Transistors; troubleshooting and repair of transistorized equipment; video tape recording principles; video tape recorder operation, circuitry, and maintenance; color and auxiliary racks; operation of the complete TV system.
Credit recommendation, collegiate level: No credit because of the brevity and nature of the course.

1. Terminal Data Link Fire Unit Integration Facilities (FUIF) Repair
2. Fire Unit Integration Facilities (FUIF) Repair

Location: Army Air Defense School, Army Signal Fire Distribution Systems Training Activity, Fort Bliss, Tex.
Length: 11–14 weeks.
Objectives: To train warrant officers and enlisted personnel to perform field maintenance on the fire unit integration facilities (FUIF) subsystem of the AN/FSG-1 missile master.
Instruction: Repair of FUIF power supplies; AN/TSQ-8 receiver and ground slant computer; AN/TSQ-8 transmitter and the TYA-13 modification data conversion circuits; system analysis; battery presentation system; operation of the target designation data link; familiarization with fire distribution systems AN/MSG-4 and AN/GSG-5 and 6.
Credit recommendation, collegiate level: Credit in electrical laboratory on the basis of demonstrated skills and/or institutional examinations.

Textile Repair
(Clothing and Textile Repair)

Location: Quartermaster School, Fort Lee, Va.
Length: 7–8 weeks.
Objectives: To train enlisted men in the skills required to alter and repair individual clothing, textile items, and raincoats.
Instruction: Inspection and marking of clothing defects; hand sewing; fitting of clothing; operator maintenance, adjustments and operation of clothing and textile repair sewing machines; machine sewing; mobile trailer operations.
Credit recommendation, collegiate level: This course is technical and vocational in nature. Credit in clothing and textile repair on the basis of demonstrated skills and/or institutional examinations.

Tire Repair

Locations: Ordnance School, Aberdeen Proving Ground, Md.; Ordnance Automotive School, Atlanta, Ga.
Length: 7–8 weeks.
Objectives: To train enlisted personnel to repair pneumatic tires, including tires used on earthmoving equipment, and to recondition inner tubes in a fixed or mobile tire repair shop.
Instruction: Fundamentals of tires and tubes; tube repair; preparation and buildup for spot and section repairs; operation of steam and electric section molds and spot presses; preparation and buildup for recap methods; operation of recap mold; open steam chamber vulcanizing (Vitacap); earthmover equipment detreader and tread builder; earthmover equipment mold operation and curing.
Credit recommendation, collegiate level: This course is technical and vocational in nature. Credit in tire repair shop on the basis of demonstrated skills and/or institutional examinations.

Topographic Computing

Location: Engineer School, Fort Belvoir, Va.
Length: 15–16 weeks.
Objective: To train enlisted personnel to perform computations and adjustments of geometric figures, directions of lines, length of lines, and differences of elevations from field surveyors' notes.
Instruction: Algebraic and trigonometric principles; map and aerial photograph reading; traverse computations; projection and grid computations; field astronomy; geodetic computations.
Credit recommendation, collegiate level: 6 semester hours in geodetic computation, and credit in mathematics and field astronomy on the basis of institutional examination.

Topographic Instrument Repair

Location: Engineer School, Fort Belvoir, Va.
Length: 12 weeks.
Objectives: To train enlisted personnel in the maintenance and repair of engineer surveying and mapping instruments and allied equipment.

Instruction: Introduction to principles, functions, and utilization of surveying, mapping, and photogrammetric equipment; use of tools and shop equipment; methods for disassembly, inspecting, cleaning, repair, maintenance assembly, and adjustments of levels, transits, theodolites, astrolabes, plane tables, alidades and related items; inspection, evaluation, repair, reconditioning, packing and crating of photogrammetric instruments.

Credit recommendation, collegiate level: This course is technical and vocational in nature. Credit in topographic instrument repair on the basis of demonstrated skills and/or institutional examinations.

Topographic Surveying

Location: Engineer School, Fort Belvoir, Va.
Length: 9–10 weeks.
Objectives: To train enlisted personnel in the establishment of ground survey control for mapping and support of weapons systems.
Instruction: Map and aerial photograph reading; mathematics; triangulation; traverse procedure; astronomic azimuth determination; plane table; traversing with plane table.
Credit recommendation, collegiate level: 6 semester hours in general surveying and 3 semester hours in topographic surveying.

1. Tracked Vehicle Mechanic
2. Armor Track Vehicle Mechanic
(Armor Tracked Vehicle Mechanic)
(Armor Track Vehicle Maintenance)
3. Artillery Track Vehicle Maintenance

Locations: Armor School, Fort Knox, Ky.; Artillery and Missile School, Fort Sill, Okla.; Infantry School, Fort Benning, Ga.
Length: *Course 1,* 7 weeks; *Course 2,* 15 weeks; *Course 3,* 10–14 weeks.
Objectives: To train enlisted personnel to perform organizational maintenance on wheeled and tracked vehicles and associated equipment.
Instruction: Engine principles; valve adjustment; cooling and lubrication systems; diesel fuel system; magneto ignition; starting systems; engine and accessory troubleshooting; power trains and chassis; transmissions; track and suspension; periodic services; recovery vehicles and equipment; vehicle recovery.
Credit recommendation, collegiate level: These courses are technical and vocational in nature. Credit in automotive repair on the basis of demonstrated skills and/or institutional examinations.

Trainman
(Railway Trainman)

Location: Transportation School, Fort Eustis, Va.
Length: 8–10 weeks.
Objectives: To train enlisted personnel to perform duties as a member of a train crew engaged in operating trains and handling railway cars in railway yards and over the road.
Instruction: Familiarization with safety rules, nomenclature of rolling stock, and security regulations; train movement by timetable and by train orders; general signal rules; ICC and AAR rules; duties of station, train, and engine personnel; functions of hand brakes, air brakes, documentation, train and yard service, switching, and road operation; running repairs to rolling stock; road, yard, and terminal operations.

Credit recommendation, collegiate level: No credit because of the limited technical nature of the course.

1. Transportation Company Officer
2. Transportation Company Officer

Location: Transportation School, Fort Eustis, Va.
Length: *Course 1,* 21 and 30 weeks; *Course 2,* 34–36 weeks.
Objectives: To train commissioned officers in the duties and responsibilities appropriate to company-grade Transportation Corps officers.
Instruction: Personnel and administration; intelligence; organization, operations, and training; logistics; highway transportation; rail, terminal, and water transport; aviation; traffic management; general transportation; instructional methods.
Credit recommendation, collegiate level: CAUTION: *These courses vary in length and recommendation. Require exact identification by length. Course 1:* 3 semester hours in business organization and 3 semester hours in traffic management. *Course 2:* 3 semester hours in business organization and 6 semester hours in traffic management.

1. Transportation Movements Control
2. Transportation Movements Control
(Transportation Movements (Transportation Movement Control))

Location: Transportation School, Fort Eustis, Va.
Length: *Course 1,* 5 weeks; *Course 2,* 7 weeks.
Objectives: To train enlisted personnel in the techniques and procedures necessary to effect and control movements of military supplies and personnel by rail, water, motor, and air transport.
Instruction: *Courses 1 and 2:* Motor transport; rail transport; terminal and water transport; transportation movements to include movement of individuals and groups; freight service and shipment procedures; traffic management; transportation organization and procedures; office records and reports of transportation movements; freight and passenger documentation.
Credit recommendation, collegiate level: CAUTION: *These courses vary in title, length, and recommendation. Require exact identification of course by title and length. Course 1:* 2 semester hours in traffic operations. *Course 2:* 3 semester hours in traffic operations.

Transportation Movements Control Supervision

Location: Transportation School, Fort Eustis, Va.
Length: 5 weeks.
Objectives: To train enlisted personnel in the operating procedures, organization, and supervision of transportation movements in the military service.

Instruction: Transportation movements and regulations; movements planning and procedures; routing of freight shipments; movements of individuals and groups; basic principles of movements; aircraft movement exercise; organized military motor movements; railway operating principles; terminal organization and operations.

Credit recommendation, collegiate level: 2 semester hours in traffic management.

1. **Transportation Officer Advanced**
2. **Transportation Officer Advanced**
   (Transportation Officer Career)
3. **Transportation Officer Career**
   (Transportation Officer Advanced)

Location: Transportation School, Fort Eustis, Va.

Length: *Course 1,* 35–36 weeks; *Course 2,* 23–24 weeks; *Course 3,* 30–34 weeks.

Objectives: To train commissioned officers in the duties and responsibilities appropriate to field-grade Transportation Corps officers.

Instruction: Personnel and administration; intelligence and map reading; organization, operations, and training; logistics; methods of instruction; highway transportation; rail, terminal, and water transport; aviation; traffic management; economics of transportation; general transportation.

Credit recommendation, collegiate level: CAUTION: *These courses vary in title, length, and recommendation. Require exact identification of course by title and length. Course 1:* 3 semester hours in personnel management, 3 semester hours in business organization, and 6 semester hours in traffic management. *Courses 2 and 3:* 3 semester hours in business organization and 6 semester hours in traffic management.

1. **Transportation Officer Basic**
   (Transportation Officer Orientation)
2. **Transportation Officer Orientation**

Location: Transportation School, Fort Eustis, Va.

Length: *Course 1,* 8–11 weeks; *Course 2,* 4–5 weeks.

Objectives: To provide basic branch training and orientation for newly commissioned Transportation Corps officers.

Instruction: Personnel and administration; intelligence; map and photo reading; organization, operation, and training; logistics; highway transportation; rail, terminal, and water transport; aviation; traffic management; methods of instruction.

Credit recommendation, collegiate level: CAUTION: *These courses vary in title, length, and recommendation. Require exact identification of course by title and length. Course 1:* 3 semester hours in transportation organization and management, and credit in advanced military at institutions which regularly offer such credit. *Course 2:* 2 semester hours in transportation organization and management.

Transportation Officer Candidate

Location: Transportation School, Fort Eustis, Va.

Length: 23 weeks.

Objectives: To train selected personnel to be second lieutenants in the Reserve component of the U.S. Army capable of performing duties appropriate to their grade in transportation units.

Instruction: Military science and tactics; military leadership; military operations; map and air photograph reading; logistics; air, motor, rail, terminal, and water transport.

Credit recommendation, collegiate level: 6 semester hours in transportation organization and management, and credit in advanced military at institutions which regularly offer such credit.

Transportation Officer Familiarization

Location: Transportation School, Fort Eustis, Va.

Length: 7 weeks.

Objectives: To train commissioned officers in the organization, operational functions, duties, and responsibilities of the Transportation Corps.

Instruction: Logistics; organization, operations, and intelligence; transportation organization, plans, and employment; aviation; transportation movements; rail and motor transportation; terminal and water transport; transportation technical training.

Credit recommendation, collegiate level: 3 semester hours in transportation organization and management.

Transportation Officer Mobilization Advanced

Location: Transportation School, Fort Eustis, Va.

Length: *Phase II,* 5 weeks; *Phase III,* 4–5 weeks.

Objectives: To prepare Transportation Corps officers of the Reserve components (not on active duty during peacetime and of all components during mobilization) for branch command and staff duties at battalion through brigade or comparable levels in divisional and nondivisional units.

Note—Reserve officers complete *Phase I* through service extension courses provided by the Department of the Army. These courses are not evaluated by the Commission.

Instruction: *Phase II:* Logistics; air transport; rail transport; motor transport. *Phase III:* Logistics; terminal and water transport; transportation movements.

Credit recommendation, collegiate level: *Phase II:* 3 semester hours in business organization and management. *Phase III:* 2 semester hours in transportation management.

Transportation Officer Mobilization Basic

Location: Transportation School, Fort Eustis, Va.

Length: *Phase II:* 7 weeks.

Objectives: To prepare Transportation Corps officers of the Reserve components not on active duty for duty assignments at the company level. *Note*—Reserve officers complete *Phase I* through service extension courses provided by the Department of the Army. These courses are not evaluated by the Commission.

Instruction: Logistics; unit and organization supply procedures; air and rail transport; terminal and water transport; motor transport; transportation movements; movements planning; company administration.

Credit recommendation, collegiate level: *Phase II:* 3 semester hours in traffic management, and credit in advanced military at institutions which regularly offer such credit.

Transportation Parts Supply
(Transportation Parts Specialist)

Location: Transportation School, Fort Eustis, Va.

Length: 4 weeks.

Objectives: To train enlisted personnel to provide technical advice and assistance on the use, interchangeability, and identification of transportation spare parts and to receive, store, and issue parts for transportation equipment.

Instruction: General supply procedures; Army catalog system; identification of Army aviation parts supply; marine parts supply; railway parts supply; classification, and interchangeability of Transportation Corps spare parts; receiving, storage, and issue procedures.

Credit recommendation, collegiate level: This course is technical and vocational in nature. Credit in stockroom procedures on the basis of institutional examination.

Transportation Supply and Parts Specialist
(Transportation Supply)
(Transportation Supply Specialist)

Location: Transportation School, Fort Eustis, Va.

Length: 4–7 weeks.

Objectives: To train enlisted personnel to maintain stock records pertaining to receipt, storage, and issue of transportation supplies.

Instruction: Introduction to Transportation Corps supply; supply manual system and publications; stock record accounts; procedures, publications, forms, and records peculiar to Army aviation supply; nomenclature, methods, and procedures pertaining to marine supply operations; classification and types of Transportation Corps vessels and deck equipment; railway supply.

Credit recommendation, collegiate level: This course is technical and vocational in nature. Credit in stock accounting procedures on the basis of institutional examination.

Transportation Supply Officer

Location: Transportation School, Fort Eustis, Va.

Length: 5 weeks.

Objectives: To train commissioned officers to direct and supervise receipt, storage, and issue of Transportation Corps supplies and equipment.

Instruction: Organization for supply; supply manual systems; storage and warehousing; supply procedures; stock control system; Army program budget system; financial inventory accounting; aircraft reports and maintenance records; Army aviation program; railway

equipment parts; storage of vessels; vessel supply procedure; classification and identification of marine parts.

Credit recommendation, collegiate level: 3 semester hours in supply management.

Tropospheric Scatter Communication Equipment Repair

Location: Signal School, Fort Monmouth, N.J.

Length: 5 weeks.

Objectives: To train enlisted personnel in the techniques required to install and perform field and depot maintenance on tropospheric scatter communications equipment.

Instruction: Introduction to tropospheric scatter communications; tropospheric scatter transmitters; frequency synthesizer; UHF converter amplifier and traveling wave amplifier; power supply unit; power control circuit sequencing and auxiliary circuits; test, adjustment, and repair of transmit section; operation and repair of tropospheric communications system.

Credit recommendation, collegiate level: This course is technical and vocational in nature. Credit in operation and repair of tropospheric scatter communications equipment on the basis of demonstrated skills and/or institutional examinations.

Truckmaster

Location: Transportation School, Fort Eustis, Va.

Length: 9 weeks.

Objectives: To train enlisted personnel to supervise the operation and preventive maintenance of wheeled vehicles (excluding amphibious wheeled vehicles) and to control motor transport movements of personnel, supplies, and equipment.

Instruction: Map reading; maintenance of internal combustion engine, lubrication system, automotive electrical circuits and units; fuels and fuel system units; brakes; transmission; wheels, tires, and mountings; supervision and inspections; motor transport and planning operations; transportation motor pools; dispatching procedures, records, and reports; highway transport service and highway reconnaissance.

Credit recommendation, collegiate level: This course is technical and vocational in nature. Credit in automotive repair on the basis of demonstrated skills and/or institutional examinations.

Turret Artillery Repair

Location: Ordnance School, Aberdeen Proving Ground, Md.

Length: 10–12 weeks.

Objectives: To train enlisted personnel to repair and rebuild turret mechanisms and turret weapons of tanks and other combat vehicles.

Instruction: Inspection, repair, maintenance, and correction of malfunctions of turret hydraulic and electrical systems on tanks and other combat vehicle weapons.

Credit recommendation, collegiate level: This course

is technical and vocational in nature. Credit in mechanical shop on the basis of demonstrated skills and/or institutional examinations.

Turret Maintenance
(Armor Turret Maintenance)
Location: Armor School, Fort Knox, Ky.
Length: 9–10 weeks.
Objectives: To train enlisted personnel in the organizational maintenance of unit tank turret mechanisms and turret-mounted weapons.
Instruction: Troubleshooting, tools, adjustments, repairs, removal, replacement, and organizational maintenance of small arms; tank guns, fire control systems, auxiliary fire control instruments, manual and power control systems, firing circuits, cupolas, searchlights, and turret-mounted machine guns; self-propelled artillery; organizational maintenance of howitzers and elevating and traversing systems.
Credit recommendation, collegiate level: This course is technical and vocational in nature. Credit in mechanical and electrical shop on the basis of demonstrated skill.

Twin-Engine Helicopter Repair
Location: Transportation School, Fort Eustis, Va.
Length: 12 weeks.
Objectives: To train enlisted personnel to repair twin-engine helicopters.
Instruction: Inspection, troubleshooting, and maintenance, of the R-2800-54 power plant and related systems, and the H-37 power train system; aircraft rigging; electrical components, inspection, and troubleshooting of the H-37 electrical system; rotor blade repair; hydraulics; flight-line service and maintenance.
Credit recommendation, collegiate level: This course is technical and vocational in nature. Credit in helicopter engine repair shop on the basis of demonstrated skills and/or institutional examinations.

Typing and Clerical Procedures—WAC
(Clerical Procedures and Typing—WAC)
Location: Women's Army Corps School, Fort McClellan, Ala.
Length: 4–8 weeks.
Objectives: To train WAC enlisted personnel in office duties, including touch-typing at a minimum of 30 words per minute.
Instruction: Publications; correspondence; filing; office procedures; military records; English composition; typing.
Credit recommendation, collegiate level: Credit in typing and clerical procedures on the basis of demonstrated skills and/or institutional examinations.

U-8D (Seminole) Aviator Qualification
Location: Army Aviation School, Fort Rucker, Ala.
Length: 3–4 weeks.
Objectives: To train Army aviators in the operation of multi-engine aircraft.
Instruction: Transition flight briefing; preflight inspection and ground procedures; takeoff and landing procedures; short field operation; instrument operation; familiarization with maintenance of U-8D and T-42A aircraft.
Credit recommendation, collegiate level: No credit because of the limited technical nature of the course.

U-21 Aviator Qualification
Location: Army Aviation School, Fort Rucker, Ala.
Length: 4 weeks.
Objectives: To qualify Army aviators in the operation of the U-21 airplane.
Instruction: Visual flight and instrument flight transition training; flight readiness inspection; U-21A systems.
Credit recommendation, collegiate level: No credit because of the brevity and nature of the course.

1. UH-1 Instructor Pilot Transition Training
2. HU-1 Instructor Pilot Transition Training
3. HU-1A Instructor Pilot Transition Training
Location: Army Aviation School, Fort Rucker, Ala.
Length: 4–5 weeks.
Objectives: To train commissioned and warrant officer aviators as unit instructor pilots in helicopter operation.
Instruction: Helicopter flight training; principles of instruction; familiarization with helicopter maintenance; preflight procedures.
Credit recommendation, collegiate level: Credit in instructional methods on the basis of institutional examination.

1. UH-1 (Iroquois) Instructor Pilot (Transition/Gunnery) Qualification
2. AH-1G (Hueycobra) Instructor Pilot (Transition/Gunnery) Qualification
Location: Army Aviation School, Fort Rucker, Ala.
Length: 6–7 weeks.
Objectives: To train commissioned and warrant officer aviators as instructor pilots for the UH-1 or AH-1G helicopters and to qualify UH-1 or AH-1G instructor pilots to conduct training in the use of helicopter weapons systems.
Instruction: Transition flight training; methods and principles of flight instruction; familiarization with UH-1 or AH-1G maintenance; helicopter gunnery.
Credit recommendation, collegiate level: For each course, credit in instructional methods on the basis of institutional examinations.

UI-A Transition Flight Training
Location: Aviation School, Fort Rucker, Ala.
Length: 3 weeks.
Objectives: To train Army aviation in the operation of the UI-A aircraft.

Instruction: Operation of aircraft under emergency and tactical situations; familiarization with transport-type flying; special operations and safety; organizational maintenance.

Credit recommendation, collegiate level: No credit because of the limited technical nature of the course.

USARADCOM CBR NCO

Location: Chemical Center and School, Fort McClellan, Ala.

Length: 3–4 weeks.

Objectives: To train enlisted personnel in the defensive aspects of chemical, biological and radiological operations to maintain maximum USARADCOM operational effectiveness in a CBR environment.

Instruction: CBR operations and training; technical aspects of biological operations; technical aspects of chemical operations; nuclear warfare and radiological defense.

Credit recommendation, collegiate level: No credit because of the limited technical nature of the course.

Underwater Operations

Location: Special Forces Training Group (Airborne), Eglin Air Force Base, Fla.

Length: 6 weeks.

Objectives: To train selected personnel in the skills and techniques necessary to perform underwater operations as may be required in the accomplishment of a Special Forces operational mission.

Instruction: Surface swim without diving equipment; underwater swim with diving equipment; diving physics; medical aspects of diving; diving equipment; underwater demolition; special techniques and advanced tactics; chamber and resuscitator; free and buoyant ascents; submarine training; small boat training; qualification dive; survival swim; underwater operations; swimmer proficiency training.

Credit recommendation, collegiate level: No credit as the course is military in nature.

Unit Mess Officer
(Mess Administration)

Location: Quartermaster School, Fort Lee, Va.

Length: 3–4 weeks.

Objectives: To train officers in the administration and operation of unit messes.

Instruction: Mess management, including organization of the food program, operational rations, mess accounting, mess equipment, food contamination, food conservation, subsistence inspection and storage, organization and operation of meat cutting plants, and mess inspection; nutrition and menu planning; applied cookery; field mess operations; garrison mess operations.

Credit recommendation, collegiate level: 3 semester hours in institutional (culinary) management.

U.S. Military Academy Preparatory School

Location: Fort Belvoir, Va.

Length: 36 weeks.

Objectives: To prepare enlisted personnel on active duty in the Armed Forces as cadet candidates for the United States Military Academy.

Instruction: English language; literature of England; theme writing; public speaking; American poetry and prose; plane geometry; solid geometry; analytical geometry; intermediate algebra; advanced algebra; introduction to matrix algebra; use of slide rule; plane trigonometry.

Credit recommendation, collegiate level: No credit as this course is college preparatory in nature.

Utilities Foreman

Location: Engineer School, Fort Belvoir, Va.

Length: 11 weeks.

Objectives: To train enlisted personnel to supervise the installation or repair of utilities systems.

Instruction: Practical arithmetic; construction planning; rigging; engineer hand tools; maintenance and repair of building and structures, water supply systems, sewage disposal systems, heating facilities, and electrical systems; waste collection and disposal; insect and rodent control; fuels; sheet metal; plumbing; fire prevention; safety; maintenance of electric motors and generators.

Credit recommendation, collegiate level: This course is technical and vocational in nature. Credit in general shop practices on the basis of demonstrated skills and/or institutional examinations.

Utility and Cargo Single-Rotor Helicopter Repair

Location: Transportation School, Fort Eustis, Va.

Length: 14–18 weeks.

Objectives: To train enlisted personnel to repair rotary-wing aircraft of the single-rotor configuration, utility- and cargo-type.

Instruction: Aircraft engines; power train; structural and rigging; aircraft hydraulics; rotor blade repair, flight-line service and repair.

Credit recommendation, collegiate level: This course is technical and vocational in nature. Credit in helicopter engine repair shop on the basis of demonstrated skills and/or institutional examinations.

1. WAC Officer Basic/WAC Officer Candidate
2. WAC Officer Basic

Location: Women's Army Corps School, Fort McClellan, Ala.

Length: 18–20 weeks.

Objectives: To train newly commissioned WAC officers, Reserve officers on initial call to active duty, and officer candidate graduates in the staff responsibilities appropriate to their grade and branch.

Instruction: Familiarization with combat operations, company-unit administration, principles of personnel management, methods of instruction, military justice and administrative boards, military leadership, officer obligations and responsibilities, physical training, special warfare operations, WAC branch duties, military intelligence, effective communication, supply operations, drill inspections and ceremonies, and fundamentals of automatic data-processing systems.

Credit recommendation, collegiate level: For each course, 2 semester hours in business organization and management.

WAC Officer Career
(WAC Officer Advanced)

Location: Women's Army Corps School, Fort McClellan, Ala.

Length: 20–22 weeks.

Objectives: To provide training in the duties and responsibilities appropriate to field-grade WAC officers.

Instruction: Command and staff responsibilities, organization, functions, and techniques; personnel management and administration; principles of logistics; familiarization with civil affairs and domestic emergencies; international relations and strategic studies; concepts and tools of financial management, the officer as an Army manager, and the responsibilities of the comptroller; principles of the military justice system; military leadership; effective oral and written communication; nuclear weapons; chemical and biological operations; organization, mission, and capabilities of an Army division, of Air Force support to divisions, and of foreign armies; combat service support in a theater of operations.

Credit recommendation, collegiate level: 4 semester hours in business organization and management and 2 semester hours in oral and written communication.

Ward Administration and Supervision

Location: Medical Field Service School, Fort Sam Houston, Tex.

Length: 22 weeks.

Objectives: To train Army Nurse Corps officers in the duties and responsibilities of head nurses and nursing service supervisors in military hospitals.

Instruction: Personnel management; management methods; familiarization with medical and military law; medical records; human and social elements in the operation of hospitals; medical supply system organization and function of hospital elements; military surgery and medicine; psychology of personality; familiarization with neuropsychiatry; introduction to social work; preventive medicine; techniques of nursing instruction; methods of evaluating nursing procedures; advanced medical and surgical nursing; clinical nursing methods; ward administration and supervision; statistical analysis.

Credit recommendation, collegiate level: CAUTION: *The academic content of this course varied in the intensity of instruction between the years 1954 and 1955. Therefore credit will be recommended according to the year the course was given. Require exact identification of course by year of attendance. April 1954 through November 1955:* 2 semester hours in institutional management, 2 semester hours in nursing administration, 2 semester hours in personnel management, 3 semester hours in oral and written communication, and 2 semester hours in abnormal psychology. *After November*

1955: 2 semester hours in institutional management, 3 semester hours in nursing administration, 3 semester hours in personnel management, 3 semester hours in oral and written communication, 2 semester hours in abnormal psychology, and credit in instructional methods on the basis of institutional examinations. *Note— for courses given after August 1954:* 2 semester hours in statistical analysis is also recommended.

Warrant Officer Candidate Preflight Indoctrination-
Fixed Wing
(Warrant Officer Indoctrination Training-Preflight
(Fixed Wing))

Locations: Primary Helicopter School, Fort Walters, Tex.; Aviation School, Fort Rucker, Ala.

Length: 4 weeks.

Objectives: To train enlisted personnel in essential preflight subjects to prepare them for the Warrant Officer Fixed Wing Aviator course.

Instruction: Problems in small unit leadership; national defense organization; map reading; aerial photographs; land navigation; flight maneuvers; physiology; cockpit procedures for the flight trainer; pre-solo maneuvers.

Credit recommendation, collegiate level: No credit because of the brevity and limited technical nature of the course.

Warrant Officer Fixed-Wing Aviator
Phase A, Primary
Phase B, Advanced Contact and Tactics
Phase C, Instruments

Location: Aviation School, Fort Rucker, Ala.

Length: *Phase A,* 16 weeks; *Phase B,* 12 weeks; *Phase C,* 10 weeks.

Objectives: *Phases A and B:* To qualify enlisted warrant officer candidates in the basic flying techniques and tactical employment of Army observation and utility fixed-wing aircraft, and in the duties of Army aviators in support of combat operations of the ground arms. *Phase C:* To qualify enlisted warrant officer candidates in instrument navigation.

Instruction: *Phase A:* Primary flight training; primary instrument flight training; organizational aircraft maintenance; principles of meteorology; radio systems; navigation. *Phase B:* Advanced flight training; advanced meteorology; aircraft maintenance; tactical subjects. *Phase C:* Advanced instrument navigation; procedures and techniques of instrument flying.

Credit recommendation, collegiate level: *Phase A:* 2 semester hours in primary meteorology and navigation. *Phase B:* 1 semester hour in primary meteorology. *Phase C:* No credit. Completion of *Phases A, B, and C:* 3 semester hours in primary meteorology and navigation.

Warrant Officer Orientation

Location: Artillery and Missile School, Fort Sill, Okla.

Length: 3 weeks.

Objectives: To provide newly appointed warrant

officers with an orientation in the basic military arts to facilitate their adjustment to officer status.

Instruction: Familiarization with maintenance management, communications systems, tactical subjects, command and staff, and chemical, biological, and radiological operations.

Credit recommendation, collegiate level: No credit as the course is military in nature.

Water Supply

Location: Engineer School, Fort Belvoir, Va.

Length: 8 weeks.

Objectives: To train enlisted personnel in the analysis, treatment, and distribution of water and in the operation and operator maintenance of portable water purification or water supply equipment.

Instruction: Characteristics of water, types of water sources, hydraulics, measurement and treatment of water, and fundamental chemical principles; control tests, salinity tests, and disinfection tests; decontamination of water and equipment; principles and techniques of operation, and maintenance of pumps and engines and distillation equipment; principles, servicing, operation, and maintenance of field water purification equipment.

Credit recommendation, collegiate level: 2 semester hours in theory of water purification.

Weapons Monitoring Center Repair

Location: Army Air Defense School, Fort Bliss, Tex.

Length: 32 weeks.

Objectives: To train warrant officers and enlisted personnel in the performance of organizational and field maintenance of the weapons monitoring center, AN/MSQ-30.

Instruction: Purpose, composition, and characteristics of the AN/MSG-4 air defense system; auxiliary units of the weapons monitoring center equipment, including power supplies and communications section; function and operation of the local-remote data handling section; functional operation and circuitry of the battalion-battery data handling section; theory and operation of the weapons monitoring center display section; frequency shift unit, frequency shift keying unit, and the 412-L buffer unit; test equipment.

Credit recommendation, collegiate level: Credit in electrical laboratory on the basis of demonstrated skills and/or institutional examinations.

Weapons Support Radar Repair

Location: Signal School, Fort Monmouth, N.J.

Length: 30 weeks.

Objectives: To train enlisted personnel to inspect, test, and perform repairs on weapons support radar equipment.

Instruction: Series and parallel circuits, AC principles, inductance, capacitance, impedance, series and parallel resonance, filters, AF signal generators, transformers, and DC power; vacuum tubes and vacuum tube low-frequency amplifiers; fundamentals of semiconductors; RF signal generators, superheterodyne reception, amplification of intermediate radio frequencies, methods of coupling IF and RF stages, oscillation, mixers and converters, automatic gain control, and receiver alignment; generation of RF energy; nonsinusoidal circuitry; timer-indicator components; microwave transmitter and modulators; microwave receiver; servo and data circuitry; transmitter-receiver performance measurements; adjustments, troubleshooting, and repair of radar sets.

Credit recommendation, collegiate level: 6 semester hours at the freshman or sophomore level as an elective in electricity and electronics, and credit in electrical laboratory on the basis of demonstrated skills and/or institutional examinations.

Welding
(Welder-Blacksmith)

Location: Ordnance School, Aberdeen Proving Ground, Md.

Length: 8–11 weeks.

Objectives: To train enlisted personnel to fuse ferrous and nonferrous metal parts using oxyacetylene or arc welding to repair, maintain, or modify automotive, armorplate, or other metal material.

Instruction: Metal forging; oxyacetylene welding; electric arc welding; inert gas welding; care and use of hand and power tools.

Credit recommendation, collegiate level: This course is technical and vocational in nature. Credit in welding on the basis of demonstrated skills and/or institutional examinations.

Wire Communications Officer

Location: Signal School, Fort Monmouth, N.J.

Length: 11 weeks.

Objectives: To train officers in the installation, employment, operation, and maintenance of telephone and telegraph facilities and equipment in tactical and fixed-plant military communication systems.

Instruction: Electrical fundamentals; principles of telephone transmission lines, special circuits, and grounds; planning and employment of tactical outside plant facilities and equipment, testing and maintenance of field line construction, and principles of fixed-plant open wire and cable construction; employment, installation, and operation of tactical telephone, switchboard, and auxiliary equipment; teletypewriter systems and equipment; voice-frequency and carrier telephony; tactical and fixed communication systems and layouts.

Credit recommendation, collegiate level: This course is technical and vocational in nature. Credit in telephone-telegraph central office maintenance on the basis of demonstrated skills and/or institutional examinations.

Women's Army Corps NCO Leadership

Location: Women's Army Corps School, Fort McClellan, Ala.

Length: 4 weeks.

Objectives: To prepare enlisted women for duties of

increased leadership responsibilities and to train administrative personnel for supervisory positions.

Instruction: Familiarization with unit administration, chemical, biological, and radiological operations, civil defense, drill and command, intelligence and security, land navigation, maintenance and supply economy, methods of instruction, military justice, military leadership, personnel management, and WAC basic branch duty.

Credit recommendation, collegiate level: No credit because of the brevity and limited nature of the course.

1. Work Methods and Standards
2. Methods-Time Measurement (MTM)
3. Manpower Validation

Location: U.S. Army Management Engineering Training Agency, Rock Island, Ill.

Length: *Course 1:* 5 and 8 weeks; *Course 2:* 3 weeks; *Course 3:* 4 weeks.

Objectives: *Course 1:* To provide personnel with the skills necessary to perform the duties of a technician in a sound methods and standards program and to relate this effort to the overall management process. *Course 2:* To provide personnel with the skill and technical knowledge necessary for the design and effective use of work planning and control systems. *Course 3:* To provide personnel with skills necessary to perform the duties of a technician in the manpower validation program and to relate this effort to the overall management of the Air Force.

Instruction: *Courses 1 and 3:* Management process; basic mathematics and statistics; work sampling for management information; methods improvement-analysis techniques; non-engineered standards; time study; work sampling to set standards; methods-time measurement; standard data; uses of work measurement data; Work Methods and Standard Program. In addition to the preceding instruction, *Course 1* (8 weeks) and *Course 3* include methods time measurement. *Course 2:* Developing and improving methods; establishing production time standards; developing standard data; using methods-time measurement data for estimating and scheduling and for operators; general purpose data familiarization.

Credit recommendation, collegiate level: *Course 1* (8 weeks): 4 semester hours in industrial engineering. *Courses 1* (5 weeks), *2, and 3:* For each course 2 semester hours in industrial engineering.

Work Planning and Control

Location: U.S. Army Management Engineering Training Agency, Rock Island, Ill.

Length: 3 weeks.

Objectives: To provide personnel with the skill and technical knowledge necessary for the design and effective use of work planning and control systems.

Instruction: Introduction; functions and analysis of work planning and control; types of work planning and control systems; statistical control of forecasting; product and process planning; material control and management; scheduling and loading; techniques and application of PERT; progress reporting; group case studies.

Credit recommendation, collegiate level: 2 semester hours in industrial engineering.

COAST GUARD

COAST GUARD

Coast Guard Personnel in Courses Operated by Other Services

IN ADDITION to training in the programs listed in this section, schools operated by other armed services frequently enroll Coast Guard personnel. In cases where Coast Guard personnel list training offered by another armed service, the course description will often be found under the heading of that service. If the service operating the school is not clearly indicated and a check of the courses listed in the GUIDE for the various services does not yield a description of the training, the applicant should be requested to give additional information.

---

1. AN/FPN-38 Timer Synchronizer
2. AN/FPN-41 Timer
3. AN/FPN-46 Timer

Locations: Coast Guard Training Station, Groton, Conn.; Coast Guard Electronics Engineering Station, Wildewood, N.J.

Length: 6–7 weeks.

Objectives: To train personnel in the operation, alignment, and maintenance of the equipment indicated in the title.

Instruction: Timing and signal handling; basic servo loops including envelope and phase timing; signal handling portion; receiving antenna; receiving antenna coupler; switched attenuator.

Credit recommendation, collegiate level: Credit in electricity and electrical laboratory on the basis of demonstrated skills and/or institutional examinations.

---

1. AN/SPN-30 Receiver
2. AN/SPN-29 Receiver

Location: Coast Guard Training Center, Groton, Conn.

Length: 7–8 weeks.

Objectives: To train personnel as watch standers, senior technicians, or electronics maintenance officers where the AN/SPN-30 or the AN/SPN-29 receiver is used.

Instruction: Power supplies; master phase servo loop; slow phase servo loop; master derived envelope servo loop; slave derived envelope servo loop; overall servo loop; automatic gain control loop; signal handling section; servo packages; alarm indication circuits; pulse rate generators; code group generator; loran indicator.

Credit recommendation, collegiate level: Credit in electricity and electrical laboratory on the basis of demonstrated skills and/or institutional examinations.

Aviation Electronics Technician (AT) Communications, Class A

Location: Coast Guard Training Center, Groton, Conn.

Length: 3 weeks.

Objectives: To train personnel in basic communications procedure and international Morse code.

Instruction: Receiving Morse code; communications procedures; message format; radiotelephone procedures; handsending.

Credit recommendation, collegiate level: No credit because of the limited technical nature of the course.

Aviation Electronics Technician, Class A

Location: Coast Guard Aircraft Repair and Supply Center, Elizabeth City, N.C.

Length: 16 weeks.

Objectives: To train electronics technicians in the operation, repair, and maintenance of electronic equipment installed in Coast Guard aircraft.

Instruction: Receivers and transmitters; single-sideband; UHF/VHF; aircraft navigation; synchros and servo systems; frequency modulation; radar altimeter; Mark X and SIF identification systems; loran; airborne radar system; aircraft electrical system.

Credit recommendation, collegiate level: Credit in electrical laboratory on the basis of demonstrated skills and/or institutional examinations.

Aviation Machinist's Mate

Location: Coast Guard Aircraft Repair and Supply Center, Elizabeth City, N.C.

Length: 24 weeks.

Objectives: To train personnel as aviation machinist's mates, third class.

Instruction: Mathematics; physics; aircraft electrical systems; publications; introduction to aircraft; aircraft control systems; aerodynamics; aircraft construction materials; aircraft power plants; aircraft lubrication systems; ignition; fuel; propellers; hydraulics; instruments; maintenance, inspection, and troubleshooting.

Credit recommendation, collegiate level: This course is technical and vocational in nature. Credit in aviation machine shop on the basis of demonstrated skills and/or institutional examinations.

Basic Electronics School, Class A
(Telephone Technician, Class A)
(Electronics Technician Communications, Class A)
(Electronics Technician, Class A)

Locations: Coast Guard Training Centers, Groton, Conn., and Governors Island, N.Y.

Length: 17–24 weeks.

Objectives: To provide training in basic electronics and associated skills.

Instruction: *Note*—After completion of a basic Electronics Phase, students are then trained in one of three areas: Telephone Technician, Electronics Technician Communications, and Electronics Technician. The basic Electronics Phase includes DC and AC; transformers; vacuum tubes and power supplies; special circuits; transmitters and receivers. In addition, the *Telephone Technician* receives basic telephone theory and laboratory study; the *Communications Technician* receives communication maintenance procedures and theory; the *Electronics Technician* receives additional electronics training including sonar, loran, and radar.

Credit recommendation, collegiate level: *Electronics Phase:* 3 semester hours at the freshman or sophomore level as an elective in electricity and electronics, and credit in electrical laboratory on the basis of demonstrated skills and/or institutional examinations. *For each specialty, additional credit at the technical level: Telephone Technician* receives credit in telephone line construction on the basis of demonstrated skills and/or institutional examinations; *Communications Technician* receives credit in communications equipment maintenance on the basis of demonstrated skills and/or institutional examinations; *Electronics Technician* receives credit in electronic equipment maintenance on the basis of demonstrated skills and/or institutional examinations.

Basic Gunner's Mate, Class A

Location: Coast Guard Training Center, Groton, Conn.

Length: 18 weeks.

Objectives: To train personnel to maintain and repair guns, gun mounts, launchers, projections, and ammunition handling equipment.

Instruction: Mathematics; handtools; basic machines; electricity; demolition; ammunition; basic hydraulics; practical maintenance.

Credit recommendation, collegiate level: This course is technical and vocational in nature. Credit in metal shop and small arms repair on the basis of demonstrated skills and/or institutional examinations.

Boatswains Mate

Location: Coast Guard Reserve Training Center, Yorktown, Va.

Length: 8 weeks.

Objectives: To train personnel in the duties and responsibilities of shipboard procedures.

Instruction: Marlinespike seamanship; pulling boats; gunnery; cargo-handling; piloting; nuclear, biological, and chemical defense; hoisting equipment; cuyahoga trips; radiotelephone; search and rescue; surface preparation and painting; seamanship; communications; law enforcement; fire fighting.

Credit recommendation, collegiate level: This course is technical and vocational in nature. Credit in seamanship and fire fighting on the basis of demonstrated skills and/or institutional examinations.

Commissaryman, Class A

Location: Coast Guard Training Station, Groton, Conn.

Length: 16 weeks.

Objectives: To train personnel to perform the duties of a petty officer in the commissary branch of the Coast Guard.

Instruction: Cooking and baking for general mess on ships and shore stations; menu preparing; cost accounting; ordering provisions; inspecting food quality.

Credit recommendation, collegiate level: This course is technical and vocational in nature. Credit in cooking and baking on the basis of demonstrated skills and/or institutional examinations.

Damage Controlman

Location: Coast Guard Training Station, Groton, Conn.

Length: 16 weeks.

Objectives: To train personnel in the functions and principles of damage control, including fire fighting, welding, wood joints, basic construction, and repair.

Instruction: Basic carpentry; power machinery; woodworking joints; boat repairs; building techniques; masonry; piping systems; fire fighting; sheet metal; welding.

Credit recommendation, collegiate level: This course is technical and vocational in nature. Credit in woodworking and metal shop on the basis of demonstrated skills and/or institutional examinations.

Electrician's Mate

Location: Coast Guard Training Station, Groton, Conn.

Length: 16 weeks.

Objectives: To provide personnel with a technical background in electricity.

Instruction: Basic electricity; DC and AC; DC rotating equipment; AC rotating equipment and controllers; switchboards; searchlights; gyro compass; I.C. equipment; shop work.

Credit recommendation, collegiate level: Credit in electricity on the basis of institutional examinations. At the technical level, credit in electrical shop on the basis of demonstrated skills and/or institutional examinations.

Engineman, Class A

Location: Coast Guard Training Center, Groton, Conn.

Length: 16 weeks.

Objectives: To train personnel as enginemen strikers.

Instruction: Gas welding and cutting; hydraulics; basic engines; engine fuel systems; engine overhaul; diesel engine troubleshooting; electricity; outboard motors; refrigeration.

Credit recommendation, collegiate level: This course is technical and vocational in nature. Credit in engine repair shop on the basis of demonstrated skills and/or institutional examinations.

General Service Indoctrination

Locations: Coast Guard Academy, New London, Conn.; Coast Guard Reserve Training Center, Yorktown, Va.

Length: 12 weeks.

Objectives: To train officers commissioned from the U.S. Merchant Marine in the fundamentals necessary for performance of duty as commissioned officers in the U.S. Coast Guard.

Instruction: Coast Guard orientation; communications; rules of the road; navigation; combat information center; gunnery; antisubmarine warfare; damage control, including atomic, chemical, and biological warfare; Coast Guard engineering.

Credit recommendation, collegiate level: 6 semester hours in advanced naval science.

Hospital Corpsman (HM)

Location: Coast Guard Training Station, Groton, Conn.

Length: 24 weeks.

Objectives: To train personnel in the fundamental principles of health and nursing.

Instruction: Nursing; anatomy and physiology; first aid; preventive medicine; materia medica and therapeutics; medical administration; medicine; pharmacy; chemistry; laboratory; dental; X ray; clinical experience.

Credit recommendation, collegiate level: 4 semester hours in hygiene, sanitation, and first aid and 2 semester hours in anatomy and physiology.

Instructor Training, Class C

Location: Coast Guard Training Center, Groton, Conn.

Length: 4 weeks.

Objectives: To train personnel as instructors at major training centers, ship training detachments, district training teams, military missions or other instructional duties.

Instruction: Factors affecting learning; subject matter organization; methods of instruction; lesson planning; training aids; oral questioning techniques; use of tests.

Credit recommendation, collegiate level: 2 semester hours in instructional methods.

Loran "A" Enlisted

Location: Coast Guard Training Center, Groton, Conn.

Length: 4 weeks.

Objectives: To train personnel in the function and principles of the operation of a loran "A" transmitting station.

Instruction: Introduction to loran; power supplies; oscillator; receiver and transmitter; amplifier frequency divider.

Credit recommendation, collegiate level: Credit in electrical laboratory on the basis of demonstrated skills and/or institutional examinations.

Loran Officers Indoctrination

Location: Coast Guard Training Center, Groton, Conn.

Length: 3 weeks.

Objectives: To train officers to perform supervisory duties in connection with the operation and maintenance of loran stations overseas.

Instruction: Loran system; loran equipment familiarization and layout; safety precautions; sanitation; law subjects pertaining to an isolated duty station; first aid.

Credit recommendation, collegiate level: No credit because of the specialized nature of the course.

1. Major Aids to Navigation
2. Minor Aids to Navigation
3. Aids to Navigation Course
4. Aids to Navigation School

Location: Coast Guard Training Station, Groton, Conn.

Length: *Courses 1, 2, and 3,* 6 weeks; *Course 4,* 3 weeks.

Objectives: To train personnel in the installation, maintenance, repair, and shop overhaul of aids to navigation equipment.

Instruction: *Courses 1, 2, and 3:* Electricity; batteries; major and/or minor light equipment; fog signals; boat operation. *Course 4:* Battery operated lights; acetylene operated lights; light station management.

Credit recommendation, collegiate level: *Courses 1, 2, and 3:* These courses are technical and vocational in nature. Credit in maintenance of navigational aids on the basis of demonstrated skills and/or institutional examinations. *Course 4:* No credit because of the brevity of the course.

Merchant Marine Safety

Location: Coast Guard Reserve Training Center, Yorktown, Va.

Length: 12 weeks.

Objectives: To train personnel in safety precautions and practices at sea.

Instruction: Engineering materials; welding and nondestructive testing; ship construction; fire protection equipment; lifesaving equipment; deck inspection; hull repair; boilers and pressure vessels; piping systems; load line; electrical inspection; engineering inspection; small passenger vessels; casualty investigations; administrative hearings.

Credit recommendation, collegiate level: This course is technical and vocational in nature. Credit in electrical and mechanical shop on the basis of demonstrated skills and/or institutional examinations.

Merchant Marine Safety Indoctrination School

Locations: Coast Guard Academy, New London, Conn.; Coast Guard Reserve Training Center, Yorktown, Va.

Length: 12 weeks.

Objectives: To prepare officers for assignment to duty in a marine inspection office.

Instruction: Introduction to marine inspection; merchant marine investigation and revocation proceedings; licensing and certificating of merchant marine personnel; naval architecture and ship construction; regulations for passenger, cargo, tank, and uninspected vessels; dangerous cargo, load line, and marine and electrical engineering regulations; equipment specifications; welding; hull and boiler vessel inspection; drydock and vessel repair.

Credit recommendation, collegiate level: 5 semester hours in transportation operations.

Oceanographic Technician, Class C

Location: Coast Guard Training Center, Groton, Conn.

Length: 8–9 weeks.

Objectives: To train personnel in basic oceanographic theory and basic oceanographic field techniques.

Instruction: Mathematics; physical oceanography; geological oceanography; chemical oceanography; biological oceanography; meteorological oceanography; marine geophysics; oceanographic agencies; field procedures; shipboard field oceanography.

Credit recommendation, collegiate level: 3 semester hours in oceanography.

Officer Candidate School

Location: Coast Guard Reserve Training Center, Yorktown, Va.

Length: 17 weeks.

Objectives: To provide candidates with the training prerequisite to active duty as commissioned officers in the Coast Guard.

Instruction: Combat information center; Coast Guard orientation; communications; damage control—atomic, biological, and chemical warfare; gunnery; navigation; seamanship; training vessel; drill; physical education; military law; safety and first aid.

Credit recommendation, collegiate level: 6 semester hours in advanced naval science.

Officers Basic Aids to Navigation, Class O

Location: Coast Guard Training Center, Groton, Conn.

Length: 4 weeks.

Objectives: To train officers in the evaluation, operation, maintenance, and administration of the system of aids to navigation to insure continued reliable and efficient operation.

Instruction: Sound signaling; major and minor aids hardware; electronic aids to navigation; fog signal hardware; buoy positioning; boat operations.

Credit recommendation, collegiate level: This course is technical and vocational in nature. Credit in maintenance of navigational aids on the basis of demonstrated skills and/or institutional examinations.

Ordnance Equipment, Class C

Location: Coast Guard Training Center, Groton, Conn.

Length: 8 weeks.

Objectives: To train personnel to operate and maintain all ordnance equipment on a vessel.

Instruction: Amplidyne power drive; hydraulics; electricity; synchros; radar; power drive; director systems; battery alignment; demolition.

Credit recommendation, collegiate level: This course is technical and vocational in nature. Credit in electrical shop on the basis of demonstrated skills and/or institutional examinations.

1. Port Security/Law Enforcement Officer
2. Port Security/Law Enforcement Enlisted

Location: Coast Guard Reserve Training Center, Yorktown, Va.

Length: 5–6 weeks.

Objectives: To train personnel in the regulations and enforcement of port security.

Instruction: Regulations; incendiaries; small arms; fire fighting and prevention; seamanship; cargo control; first aid. The courses for officers and enlisted personnel are similiar in subject matter but different in emphasis. *Course 1:* Administrative duties. *Course 2:* Operational duties.

Credit recommendation, collegiate level: No credit because of the specialized nature of these courses.

Radioman, Class A

Location: Coast Guard Training Center, Groton, Conn.

Length: 24 weeks.

Objectives: To train personnel as radiomen in the Coast Guard communications system.

Instruction: Procedure; code; communications net; typing; teletype; electronics; handsending.

Credit recommendation, collegiate level: This course is technical and vocational in nature. Credit in radio operation and typing on the basis of demonstrated skills and/or institutional examinations.

Search and Rescue

Location: Search and Rescue School, Governors Island, N.Y.

Length: 4 weeks.

Objectives: To train personnel in the operations, procedures, techniques, and equipment used in saving life and property.

Instruction: Search planning; rescue equipment and techniques; survival factors; special missions; wartime search and rescue.

Credit recommendation, collegiate level: No credit because of the limited technical nature of the course.

Storekeeper, Class A

Location: Coast Guard Training Center, Groton, Conn.

Length: 12 weeks.

Objectives: To train personnel to operate effectively in supply offices on ships or stations.

Instruction: Typewriting; accounting; inventory; requisitions; publications and filing; small purchases; property; travel; transportation; disbursing; military pay and allowances; correspondence.

Credit recommendation, collegiate level: Credit in typing on the basis of demonstrated skills.

Telephone Technician, Class B

Location: Coast Guard Training Center, Groton, Conn.

Length: 25 weeks.

Objectives: To train personnel as telephone technicians.

Instruction: Basic concepts of DC circuits; fundamentals of AC and DC circuit analysis; vacuum tubes and power supplies; amplifiers and oscillators; electronics; wiring; switchboards; repeaters; telegraph; microwave radio fundamentals; public address system; carrier telephone systems; teletype.

Credit recommendation, collegiate level: 2 semester hours at the freshman or sophomore level as an elective in electricity. At the technical level, credit in telephone systems operations on the basis of demonstrated skills and/or institutional examinations.

Yeoman, Class A

Location: Coast Guard Training Center, Groton, Conn.

Length: 12 weeks.

Objectives: To provide personnel with a knowledge of the administrative and/or clerical duties required of a yeoman, third class.

Instruction: Typewriting; Coast Guard organization; files; correspondence; pay and allowance; service records; travel and transfer orders; personnel accounting; discharges and transfers.

Credit recommendation, collegiate level: Credit in typing on the basis of institutional examination.

MARINE CORPS

MARINE CORPS

Marine Corps Personnel in Courses Operated by Other Services

In ADDITION to the training programs listed in this section, schools operated by the other armed services frequently enroll Marine Corps personnel. In cases where Marine Corps personnel list training offered by another armed service, the course will often be found under the heading for that service. If the service operating the school is not clearly indicated, and a check of the courses listed in the GUIDE for the various services does not yield a description of the training, the applicant should be requested to give additional information.

Accountable Officers

Location: Camp Lejeune, N.C.
Length: 12 weeks.
Objectives: To train officers in the supply procedures of the Marine Corps.
Instruction: Budgets, appropriations, funds, and allotment; organic accounting; fiscal accounting; supply operations; storage and materials handling; subsistence; stock accounting.
Credit recommendation, collegiate level: 4 semester hours in supply management.

1. Administrative Chief
2. Administrative Chiefs Personnel Administration

Location: Parris Island, S.C.
Length: *Course 1,* 8 weeks; *Course 2,* 10 weeks.
Objectives: To train selected noncommissioned officers for qualification in the technical requirements as administrative chiefs.
Instruction: Office management; publications; records; personnel accounting system; classification; enlisted records; pay and allowances; naval justice; casualty and combat reporting.
Credit recommendation, collegiate level: *Course 1:* 2 semester hours in personnel records administration. *Course 2:* 3 semester hours in personnel records administration.

Advanced Cook

Location: Camp Lejeune, N.C.
Length: 14 weeks.
Objectives: To train staff noncommissioned officers in advanced methods and supervisory duties of cooking.
Instruction: Mess fundamentals and administration; meat cutting; baking; field equipment and field mess cookery; garrison mess operations; menu planning; storage and processing of subsistence stores.
Credit recommendation, collegiate level: This course is technical and vocational in nature. Credit in food preparation on the basis of demonstrated skills and/or institutional examinations.

Advanced Food Service

Location: Camp Lejeune, N.C.
Length: 8 weeks.
Objectives: To train commissioned and noncommissioned officers in the latest techniques of food preparation and service and in mess administration and mess management.
Instruction: Garrison mess operation and administration; meat cutting; nutrition and menu planning; techniques of cookery; field mess operations.
Credit recommendation, collegiate level: 4 semeser hours in institutional (culinary) management.

Advanced Motor Transport

Location: Camp Lejeune, N.C.
Length: 16–18 weeks.
Objectives: To train staff noncommissioned officers in the automotive field in the supervision, maintenance, and operation of Marine Corps motor transport equipment.
Instruction: Internal combustion engine; carburetion and ignition; power train; hydromatic transmission; brakes and suspension; preventive maintenance; unit removal and replacement; special equipment; body repair; motor pool administration; vehicle inspections.
Credit recommendation, collegiate level: This course is technical and vocational in nature. Credit in automotive repair on the basis of demonstrated skills and/or institutional examinations.

Advanced Special Mess Training
(Special Mess Training)

Location: Camp Lejeune, N.C.
Length: 8 weeks.
Objectives: To provide formal advanced training in the duties and responsibilities of cooks specialists for duty in General Officers quarters.
Instruction: Seating protocol; table arrangement for both formal and informal occasions; social activities; desserts preparation and finishing; nutrition and menu planning; gourmet cooking; baking; beverage preparation.
Credit recommendation, collegiate level: This course is technical and vocational in nature. Credit in special food preparation on the basis of demonstrated skills and/or institutional examinations.

Advanced Steward

Location: Camp Lejeune, N.C.

Length: 11–12 weeks.

Objectives: To train noncommissioned officers in the techniques and management of Marine Corps steward personnel and to provide refresher training in cooking and baking.

Instruction: Mess fundamentals and administration; meat cutting; baking; menu planning; field equipment and field mess cookery; food preparation and proper methods of serving; commissioned officers' mess operation; methods of instruction.

Credit recommendation, collegiate level: 3 semester hours in institutional (culinary) management.

1. Advanced Warehousing
2. Officer Warehousing

Location: Camp Lejeune, N.C.

Length: 4–6 weeks.

Objectives: To train commissioned officers and noncommissioned officers in warehousing operations.

Instruction: Standard methods and procedures of receiving, storing, and issuing supplies; capabilities, limitations, and utilization of all warehousing equipment; stock location; space utilization; care of material in storage; preservation, packaging, and packing; inventory procedures; warehouse automation; field warehousing; freight transportation; Fleet Marine Force combat service support; relationship of Marine aviation to supply; functioning of a supply center.

Credit recommendation, collegiate level: For each course, 3 semester hours in supply management.

Aerial Navigator
(Aerial Navigation)

Location: Cherry Point, N.C.

Length: 16–19 weeks.

Objectives: To train enlisted personnel in aerial navigation.

Instruction: Dead reckoning, including maps and charts, plotting of positions, wind effect, flight instruments, basic ground and air plot, flight planning and range control, and wind determination in flight; celestial and grid navigation; loran; aerology; pressure-pattern flying; radio and radar.

Credit recommendation, collegiate level: 6 semester hours in navigation.

Air Control/Anti-Air Warfare Operators
(Air Control/Anti-Aircraft Warfare Electronics Operator)

Location: San Diego, Calif.

Length: 7 weeks.

Objectives: To train enlisted personnel in the basic operational procedures and techniques employed in tactical air control and anti-air warfare control systems.

Instruction: Marking radar plotting boards; indicating presence, type, number, altitude, speed, course, and identification of aircraft in specified areas; composition and maintenance of status boards; operation and employment of radio and radar equipment; radio-telephone message procedures and phraseology; familiarization with various types of radio and radar jamming; operation and reporting of readings from plan position indicators, and range height indicators; use and interpretation of identification friend or foe responses; use of ultrahigh-frequency radio direction finders.

Credit recommendation, collegiate level: This course is technical and vocational in nature. Credit in air control radar operation on the basis of demonstrated skills and/or institutional examinations.

Air Observation
(8th Class, Air Observation School)
(Air Observation)

Location: Quantico, Va.

Length: 13–17 weeks.

Objectives: To qualify selected Marine Corps personnel as air observers.

Instruction: Observation methods and techniques; tactical aerial observation; communications; staff principles and techniques.

Credit recommendation, collegiate level: No credit because of the limited technical nature of the course.

Air Observers
(Tactical Aerial Observer)

Locations: New River and Camp Lejeune, N.C.

Length: 7–8 weeks.

Objectives: To train company-grade officers to perform duties as air observers in the Fleet Marine Force.

Instruction: Aircraft and survival indoctrination; airborne map reading; communications; principles of combat intelligence; artillery and fire support coordination; naval gunfire; close air support; tactical aerial observation.

Credit recommendation, collegiate level: No credit as the course is military in nature.

Ammunition Handlers
(Ammunition Handling)

Location: Quantico, Va.

Length: 6 weeks.

Objectives: To train enlisted personnel in methods of safe handling, storing and transporting ammunition, with emphasis on Fleet Marine Force procedure, preparatory to assignment in an ammunition handling capacity.

Instruction: Introduction to ammunition; small arms; hand and rifle grenades; artillery and mortar ammunition; pyrotechnics; demolitions; aircraft munitions; storage and safe handling; mines and firing devices; flamethrower fuels; ammunition disposal; ammunition ashore and field storage; supply administration forms and publications; new developments.

Credit recommendation, collegiate level: No credit because of military nature of the course.

Ammunition Officer
Location: Quantico, Va.
Length: 10–12 weeks.
Objectives: To train officers and enlisted personnel to serve as Ammunition Unit officers or to fill staff assignments which require a specialized ammunition background.
Instruction: Ammunition material; supply procedures; ammunition management; inspection and disposal; ammunition support of the Fleet Marine Force; special weapons logistics.
Credit recommendation, collegiate level: This course is technical and vocational in nature. Credit in ammunition handling procedures on the basis of institutional examination.

Ammunition Technician (Advanced)
Location: Quantico, Va.
Length: 7–8 weeks.
Objectives: To train staff noncommissioned officers in the management of ammunition handling, storage and transportation, Class V logistics and administrative procedures, and in the coordination with related ordnance activities.
Instruction: Ammunition materiel; storage, disposal, and supply; ammunition support of the Fleet Marine Force; artillery orientation; infantry weapons orientation.
Credit recommendation, collegiate level: This course is technical and vocational in nature. Credit in ammunition handling procedures on the basis of institutional examination.

Ammunition Technician (Basic)
(Ammunition Technician)
(Ammunition Technician (Basic) (Special))
Location: Quantico, Va.
Length: 4–14 weeks.
Objectives: To train noncommissioned officers and enlisted personnel to identify, receive, inspect, store, ship, and issue ammunition components, military explosives, guided missile warheads and propellants, and to dispose of unserviceable ammunition.
Instruction: Military explosives; ammunition materiel; demolition materiel and destruction of ammunition; foreign ammunition and new developments; storage and surveillance of ammunition; ammunition supply procedures; transportation of ammunition, Class V logistics; rockets and guided missiles.
Credit recommendation, collegiate level: This course is technical and vocational in nature. Credit in ammunition handling procedures on the basis of institutional examination.

Amphibian Tractor Crewman Training, LVT3C, LVTP5
(Armored Amphibian Crewman Training, LVTA5, LVTP5)
Location: Camp Pendleton, Calif.
Length: 6 weeks.
Objectives: To train Marine personnel in the operations, gunnery, communications, and maintenance of amphibian tractors.
Instruction: Operation of the LVT; gunnery; communications; preventive maintenance; maintenance; tactics; map reading.
Credit recommendation, collegiate level: This course is technical and vocational in nature. Credit in tractor operation and maintenance on the basis of demonstrated skills and/or institutional examinations.

Amphibious Vehicle Company Officers
Location: Camp Pendleton, Calif.
Length: 10 weeks.
Objectives: To train company-grade officers in the tactical employment of LVT P-5's and LVT H-6's; in the firing of the 30 caliber and 50 caliber machine guns and the 105-mm howitzer.
Instruction: LVT preventive maintenance; communications; LVT operation; map and aerial photograph reading; direct fire gunnery; tactics; field and night operations; field firing.
Credit recommendation, collegiate level: No credit as course is military in nature.

Amphibious Vehicle Officers Orientation
Location: Camp Pendleton, Calif.
Length: 4 weeks.
Objectives: To familiarize Basic School graduates with the duties of the Amphibious Vehicle officer and with the weapons and equipment of appropriate units.
Instruction: LVT preventive maintenance; communications; LVT operations; tactics; direct fire gunnery; indirect fire; field firing.
Credit recommendation, collegiate level: No credit as course is military in nature.

Amphibious Warfare
(Junior Course)
(Junior School)
Location: Quantico, Va.
Length: 9 months.
Objectives: To provide professional education to Marine Corps officers to prepare them for duty as field-grade officers in the Fleet Marine Force, including command at the battalion/squadron level and staff duty at the regiment/group level.
Instruction: Planning and executing amphibious operations, including tactics, techniques, and command functions; counterinsurgency tactics and techniques; national security; oral and written expression; 100 hours instruction in French or Spanish (began with 1962–63 course).
Credit recommendation, collegiate level: 3 semester hours in business organization and management, 3 semester hours in French or Spanish, if official records show completion, and credit in oral and written communication on the basis of institutional examination.

Armored Amphibian and Amphibious Tractor Unit Leader
(Amphibious Vehicle Unit Leader (Enlisted))
(Amphibious Tractor Unit Leader)

Location: Camp Pendleton, Calif.

Length: 8–12 weeks.

Objectives: To train noncommissioned officers to supervise the crew and assume platoon sergeant responsibilities in an amphibian (armored amphibian) tractor company; to emphasize the techniques of leadership and tactical employment of the platoon in action.

Instruction: LVT maintenance; communications; LVT operation; map and aerial photograph reading; land mine warfare; direct fire gunnery; indirect fire; tactics; field operations; night operations; field firing.

Credit recommendation, collegiate level: No credit as course is military in nature.

Artillery Officer Orientation
(Artillery Basic Orientation)

Location: Quantico, Va.

Length: 4–5 weeks.

Objectives: To familiarize assigned personnel with the duties of the officers of a field artillery firing battery.

Instruction: Artillery officer orientation; observed fire; ammunition and fire control equipment; firing battery; duties of platoon commander; artillery weapons.

Credit recommendation, collegiate level: No credit as this course is military in nature.

1. Artillery Weapons Repair
2. Artillery Weapons Repairman (Basic)
3. Artillery Weapons Repairman
4. Artillery Weapons Repairman (Advanced)

Location: Quantico, Va.

Length: 7–14 weeks.

Objectives: *Courses 1, 2, and 3:* To train enlisted personnel in the maintenance and repair of artillery weapons and related materiel and mounts. *Course 4:* To train noncommissioned officers in the supervision of artillery repair facilities.

Instruction: *Courses 1, 2, and 3:* Hand tools and instruments; basic components of artillery weapons; 105mm howitzer; 155mm howitzer; self-propelled artillery; tracked vehicle guns and mounts; rocket launchers. *Course 4:* Publications and supply; hand tools and repair skills; field artillery materiel; rocket launchers; familiarization with shop management procedures; infantry weapons orientation; ammunition orientation.

Credit recommendation, collegiate level: These courses are technical and vocational in nature. Credit in mechanical shop on the basis of demonstrated skills and/or institutional examinations.

Automotive Maintenance Officers

Location: Camp Lejeune, N.C.

Length: 12–14 weeks.

Objectives: To train recently appointed warrant officers for duty as maintenance officers of automotive equipment.

Instruction: Internal combustion engine; electrical and fuel systems; power train; chassis; forms and reports; preparation of wheeled vehicles for deep water fording and cold weather operations; preventive maintenance; unit removal and replacement; body; radiator and fuel tank repair; supply procedures; accident investigation; operation and management of motor transport.

Credit recommendation, collegiate level: This course is technical and vocational in nature. Credit in automotive repair on the basis of demonstrated skills and/or institutional examinations.

Automotive Mechanic

Location: Camp Lejeune, N.C.

Length: 10–14 weeks.

Objectives: To train enlisted personnel as automotive mechanics.

Instruction: Internal combustion engine; carburetion and ignition; power train; electrical and fuel systems; brakes and suspension; preventive maintenance; unit removal and replacement; preparation for deep water and cold weather; body, radiator, and fuel tank repair.

Credit recommendation, collegiate level: This course is technical and vocational in nature. Credit in automotive repair on the basis of demonstrated skills and/or institutional examinations.

Automotive Organizational Maintenance

Location: Camp Pendleton, Calif.

Length: 6 weeks.

Objectives: To train enlisted personnel as automotive mechanics.

Instruction: Shop and safety procedures; power plants; fuel systems; electrical systems; trouble diagnosis and tune up; power trains; chassis, brakes, and suspension systems; forms and parts manual; preventive maintenance; diesel and multifuel engines; motor vehicle operation.

Credit recommendation, collegiate level: This course is technical and vocational in nature. Credit in automotive repair on the basis of demonstrated skills and/or institutional examinations.

Automotive Preventive Maintenance

Location: Camp Lejeune, N.C.

Length: 5–6 weeks.

Objectives: To train enlisted men as preventive maintenance mechanics for Marine Corps motor transport equipment.

Instruction: Driver training; internal combustion engine; carburetion and ignition; power train; brakes and suspension; preventive maintenance.

Credit recommendation, collegiate level: This course is technical and vocational in nature. Credit in automotive repair on the basis of demonstrated skills and/or institutional examinations.

Aviation Electronics Operator

Location: San Diego, Calif.

Length: 5–6 weeks.

Objectives: To train enlisted personnel in the basic operational procedures and techniques employed in tactical air control agencies.

Instruction: Operational characteristics and operation and adjustment of radar systems, radio direction finding sets, and associated electronic equipment; interpretation of aircraft speed, course, altitude, and identification from radar indications and plots; reverse printing techniques; status and plotting board presentation of all elements of information pertinent to aircraft control; radio-telephone procedure.

Credit recommendation, collegiate level: This course is technical and vocational in nature. Credit in air control radar operation on the basis of demonstrated skills and/or institutional examinations.

Aviation Fire Control Repair

Locations: San Diego, Calif.; Twentynine Palms, Calif.

Length: 7–9 weeks.

Objectives: To train enlisted personnel to perform the duties of aviation fire control repairmen.

Instruction: Erection, operation, adjustment, inspection, and maintenance of radar course directing central set including circuit theory and testing; corrective and preventive maintenance; alignment and troubleshooting; use of associated and related test equipment.

Credit recommendation, collegiate level: Credit in electrical laboratory on the basis of demonstrated skills and/or institutional examinations.

Aviation Radar Repair (A)
(Aviation Radar Repair (B))
(Aviation Radar Repair (C))
(Aviation Radar Repair (D))
(Aviation Radar Repair)

Locations: San Diego, Calif., Twentynine Palms, Calif.

Length: 10–15 weeks.

Objectives: To train enlisted personnel in the duties of the aviation radar repairman.

Instruction: Circuit theory and testing; installation, operation, and maintenance of computer-indicator groups, interrogator sets, video decoders, and radar signal distribution switchboard; radar sets and radar data relay set.

Credit recommendation, collegiate level: Credit in electrical laboratory on the basis of demonstrated skills and/or institutional examinations.

Aviation Radar Technician

Location: San Diego, Calif.

Length: 24–33 weeks.

Objectives: To provide enlisted personnel with technical instruction on the search and height finding radar sets and associated indicators, identification, and data relay equipment organic to ground elements of Fleet Marine Force aviation units.

Instruction: Review of mathematics; shop management; electricity and magnetism, including electron physics, DC power, network theorems, magnetism and electromagnetism, capacitance, alternating voltages and currents, resistance, inductance, series and parallel circuits, AC and DC motors and generators; biasing, load lines, and static and dynamic characteristics of diodes, triodes, multigrid, gas-filled and cathode-ray tubes; physics, construction operation and analysis of semiconductor supplies; transistor and electron tube amplifiers and sinusoidal oscillators; wave-shaping circuits; microwave theory; synchros and servomechanisms; modulation theory; test instruments and measurements; fundamental concepts of logic and circuitry employed in digital computers; installation, operation, adjustment, inspection, and maintenance of radar sets.

Credit recommendation, collegiate level: 3 semester hours at the freshman or sophomore level as an elective in electricity and electronics, and credit in electrical laboratory on the basis of demonstrated skills and/or institutional examinations.

Aviation Radio Repair

Location: San Diego, Calif.

Length: 8–14 weeks.

Objectives: To qualify enlisted personnel to perform duties in aviation radio repair.

Instruction: Ground radio communication and radio direction finding equipment; operating characteristics; circuitry; calibration; installation; ultrahigh frequency principles; single-side-band theory; corrective and preventive maintenance procedures; test equipment; operation and maintenance of associated power sources.

Credit recommendation, collegiate level: Credit in electrical laboratory on the basis of demonstrated skills and/or institutional examinations.

Aviation Radio Technician

Location: San Diego, Calif.

Length: 24 weeks.

Objectives: To train enlisted personnel in the duties of aviation radio technicians.

Instruction: Mathematics; fundamentals of electricity; vacuum tubes; power supplies; AM and FM theory; antennas; test instruments; electronics supply; transistors; servicing methods; high-frequency techniques; shop practices; radiac sets; radio sets; radio transmitter; combat information central; direction finder set.

Credit recommendation, collegiate level: 3 semester hours at the freshman or sophomore level as an elective in radio and electronics, and credit in electrical laboratory on the basis of demonstrated skills and/or institutional examinations.

Aviation Supply Enlisted

Location: Camp Lejeune, N.C.

Length: 5 weeks.

Objectives: To provide enlisted personnel with intermediate-level training in aviation supply.

Instruction: Supply management; office machines; office procedures; procurement; storage operations; supply in marine aviation.

Credit recommendation, collegiate level: This course is technical and vocational in nature. Credit in stock accounting procedures on the basis of demonstrated skills and/or institutional examinations.

Aviation Supply Officer

Location: Camp Lejeune, N.C.

Length: 8–10 weeks.

Objectives: To train officers with limited or no previous supply experience for performance of duty as supply officers with specific emphasis on the duties of aviation supply officer and aviation materiel officer.

Instruction: Introduction to supply management; problem solving techniques; financial management; stock lists, technical publications, and allowance directives; requirements determination; Marine Corps stores system; storage operations; transportation; disposal of surplus personal property; individual clothing; subsistence; organic property control; procurement; office management and personnel supervision; supply in marine aviation; systems study and computer management.

Credit recommendation, collegiate level. 5 semester hours in supply management.

1. Baker
2. Basic Bakers
3. Advanced Baker

Location: Camp Lejeune, N.C.

Length: *Courses 1 and 2,* 10–13 weeks; *Course 3,* 8 weeks.

Objectives: *Courses 1 and 2:* To train enlisted personnel in the fundamentals and principles of baking operations in garrison and in the field. *Course 3:* To train enlisted personnel, who have had previous baking experience, in the techniques and methods used in the manufacture of breads and pastries at post or field installations.

Instruction: *Courses 1 and 2:* Bakery sanitation; garrison bakery operations; baking ingredients; bread and pastry baking; operation and maintenance of equipment. *Course 3:* This course contains the same material as *Courses 1 and 2* but the instruction is at a more advanced level.

Credit recommendation, collegiate level: These courses are technical and vocational in nature. Credit in baking on the basis of demonstrated skills and/or institutional examinations.

Bakery Management

Location: Camp Lejeune, N.C.

Length: 4 weeks.

Objectives: To train noncommissioned officers in the supervision and management of a post or field bakery.

Instruction: Organization and personnel of a garrison bakery; bakery machinery; bakery sanitation; cost accounting and bookkeeping; supervision of the ordering, issuing and use of ingredients.

Credit recommendation, collegiate level: 2 semester hours in bakery management.

Basic Communication Officers
(Communication Officers Orientation)

Location: Quantico, Va.

Length: 4–8 weeks.

Objectives: To familiarize Basic School graduates with the communication systems of units of the Marine division and the Marine aircraft wing with particular emphasis on the battalion landing team.

Instruction: Organization, functions and procedures for communications center operation; organization, installation, operation, and maintenance of the communication systems and equipment; duties and responsibilities of a communication officer; supply and maintenance procedures; message center and cryptocenter operations; ground aviation, and/or amphibious communications, plans, and requirements.

Credit recommendation, collegiate level: 2 semester hours in communications center management.

1. Basic Construction Man
2. Construction Foreman

Location: Camp Lejeune, N.C.

Length: 10–21 weeks.

Objectives: To train enlisted personnel in the construction, repair, and camouflage of military structures and facilities.

Instruction: *Course 1:* Logging methods; manufacture of lumber; construction drawing; hand and power tools; culverts; bridging; rigging; paints, stains and varnishes, preparation of surfaces, tools and equipment, and application of paint; building construction, including building layout, foundations, and framing. *Course 2:* This course contains a review of the basic skills attained in *Course 1,* and in addition, instruction in the advanced skills involved in construction, demolition, and rigging, and in the supervision of construction and repair of military structures and facilities.

Credit recommendation, collegiate level: These courses are technical and vocational in nature. Credit in building construction on the basis of demonstrated skills and/or institutional examinations.

Basic Course, Postgraduate

Location: Quantico, Va.

Length: 4 weeks.

Objectives: To train commissioned officers, and those personnel selected for regular commissions who are recent graduates of the Basic School, in basic administrative policies and procedures of the Marine Corps.

Instruction: Familiarization with disciplinary procedures, personnel systems, career management, record keeping, organization, missions, and functions of the supply system; fiscal accounting procedures, stock recording accounting, audit and accountability, rules of evidence and use of legal documents, handling of classified matter, military pay system, functions of the disbursing officer, and travel regulations.

Credit recommendation, collegiate level: 2 semester hours in business organization and management.

Basic Electrician
(Electrician)

Location: Camp Lejeune, N.C.

Length: 8–18 weeks.

Objectives: To train enlisted personnel to install, operate, maintain, and repair electrical equipment, systems, and accessory material applicable to the Fleet Marine Force.

Instruction: Basic electricity, including electron theory, magnetism, batteries, Ohm's law, AC and DC meters, electrical measurements, electrical power, and induced current; principles of internal combustion engines; principles of operation, types, and characteristics of AC and DC motors and generators; electrical distribution and construction; interior wiring.

Credit recommendation, collegiate level: This course is technical and vocational in nature. Credit in electrical wiring and/or electrical shop on the basis of demonstrated skills and/or institutional examinations.

Basic Electronics

Location: San Diego, Calif.

Length: 15 weeks.

Objectives: To train enlisted personnel in the basic concepts of electricity and electronics in preparation for further training in electronics.

Instruction: Mathematics for electronics; direct current electricity; alternating current; vacuum tubes; vacuum tube circuits; radio frequency systems; oscillators; general receiver theory; amplitude modulation; antennas; transmission lines; basic troubleshooting; semiconductors; transistors; shop practices.

Credit recommendation, collegiate level: 4 semester hours at the freshman or sophomore level as an elective in electricity and electronics, and credit in electrical laboratory on the basis of demonstrated skills and/or institutional examinations.

Basic Food Service

Location: Camp Lejeune, N.C.

Length: 9 weeks.

Objectives: To train enlisted personnel in the basic fundamentals of food preparation and serving and in the duties and responsibilities required in the operation of an organizational mess at post or field installations.

Instruction: Garrison mess fundamentals; meat cutting; baking; techniques of cookery; field mess operations.

Credit recommendation, collegiate level: This course is technical and vocational in nature. Credit in food preparation on the basis of demonstrated skills and/or institutional examinations.

Basic Metalworker

Location: Camp Lejeune, N.C.

Length: 5 weeks.

Objectives: To train enlisted personnel in the nature of metals and the theory of welding; in oxyacetylene, electric arc, and inert gas welding; in sheet metal work as applicable to making repairs to engineer and motor transport equipment.

Instruction: Sheet metal working; oxygen-acetylene welding; electric arc welding; inert gas welding.

Credit recommendation, collegiate level: This course is technical and vocational in nature. Credit in metal shop on the basis of demonstrated skills and/or institutional examinations.

Basic Personnel Administration

Location: Parris Island, S.C.

Length: 4–5 weeks.

Objectives: To train selected personnel in the fundamental aspects of personnel administration.

Instruction: Correspondence; publications; typing; military justice; personnel records; Marine Corps pay; personnel accounting; office procedures and management.

Credit recommendation, collegiate level: This course is technical and vocational in nature. Credit in office practice on the basis of demonstrated skills and/or institutional examinations.

Basic Specialist Training Cooks

Location: Camp Lejeune, N.C.

Length: 4–6 weeks.

Objectives: To train enlisted personnel in the basic fundamentals of food preparation and serving, and in the duties and responsibilities required in the operation of an organizational mess at post and field installations.

Instruction: Use of recipes to prepare pastries; preparation of meats, vegetables, salads, gravies, and beverages; proper use of seasonings; preventive methods of food poisoning; garrison mess and field mess equipment.

Credit recommendation, collegiate level. This course is technical and vocational in nature. Credit in food preparation on the basis of demonstrated skills and/or institutional examinations.

1. Basic Supply Administration
2. Basic Supply Administration (Mechanized)

Location: Camp Lejeune, N.C.

Length: *Course 1,* 6 weeks; *Course 2,* 7–9 weeks.

Objectives: To train enlisted personnel for duty as supply administrative clerks in organic supply billets.

Instruction: Office machines; directives and correspondence; organic property control procedures; mechanized supply operations; stock accounting.

Credit recommendation, collegiate level: These courses are technical and vocational in nature. Credit in stock accounting procedures on the basis of demonstrated skills and/or institutional examinations.

Basic Tank Crewman

Location: Camp Pendleton, Calif.

Length: 4 weeks.

Objectives: To train enlisted personnel to be qualified tank crewmen.

Instruction: Communications; driving and preventive maintenance; gunnery; field firing; night operations.

Credit recommendation, collegiate level: No credit as the course is military in nature.

Cold Weather Field Indoctrination
(Cold Weather Field Indoctrination Training for FMF Cadets and Reservists (Ground))
(Cold Weather Training)

Location: Bridgeport, Calif.

Length: 3 weeks.

Objectives: To conduct rigorous and realistic training to impress the individual Marine with his ability to survive, maintain his mobility, and perform a combat mission in a deep snow and in an extremely cold environment.

Instruction: Cold weather operations; cold weather clothing, equipment, and medical problems; bivouacs; over-snow movement.

Credit recommendation, collegiate level: No credit as the course is military in nature.

1. Combat Engineer Advanced
2. Combat Engineer Advanced (Combat Engineer Foreman)

Location: Camp Lejeune, N.C.

Length: *Course 1,* 13 weeks; *Course 2,* 22–30 weeks.

Objectives: To train noncommissioned officers to plan and supervise engineer missions applicable to the Fleet Marine Force.

Instruction: *Course 1:* Shop mathematics; supply and job planning management; engineer equipment; properties of soils; fundamentals of surveying and surveying equipment; site selection, and road and airfield design; hand and power tools; blueprint reading; building construction of wood frame and prefabricated metal buildings; concrete construction of building foundations, slabs, and walks; material estimation; rigging materials and devices; bridge construction; camouflage and field fortifications; demolitions; mine warfare. *Course 2:* This course includes the same material as *Course 1* but contains more intensive instruction in all areas.

Credit recommendation, collegiate level: *Course 1:* 3 semester hours in engineering construction. *Course 2:* 6 semester hours in engineering construction.

1. Combat Engineer Basic Specialist
2. Combat Engineer Basic

Location: Camp Lejeune, N.C.

Length: *Course 1,* 4 weeks; *Course 2,* 13 weeks.

Objectives: To train enlisted personnel in demolition and mine warfare skills and in the fundamentals of military construction.

Instruction: *Course 1:* Field fortifications; demolitions; camouflage; land mine warfare; rigging; military bridges; building and concrete construction; military road maintenance; engineer equipment. *Course 2:* This course includes the same general material as *Course 1* but contains more intensive instruction in all areas.

Credit recommendation, collegiate level: These courses are technical and vocational in nature. Credit in building construction on the basis of demonstrated skills and/or institutional examinations.

1. Combat Engineer Officer
2. Combat Engineer Officer Orientation

Location: Camp Lejeune, N.C.

Length: 4–6 weeks.

Objectives: To train basic engineer officers for duty as platoon commanders in Fleet Marine Force engineer battalions.

Instruction: Familiarization with engineer equipment, building and concrete construction techniques, rigging materials and devices, camouflage principles, field fortification construction, bridge, road, and airfield construction, principles of soils engineering, job planning and management techniques, demolitions, and land mine warfare.

Credit recommendation, collegiate level: For each course, credit in engineering construction on the basis of institutional examination.

1. Communication Center Man
2. Teletype Operator

Location: San Diego, Calif.

Length: 8–10 weeks.

Objectives: To qualify enlisted personnel to perform duties as a teletype operator throughout the first enlistment.

Instruction: Teletypewriter and typing; message center procedure; communication security; teletype procedure; teletype operation and operator maintenance.

Credit recommendation, collegiate level: These courses are technical and vocational in nature. Credit in teletypewriter operation on the basis of demonstrated skills and/or institutional examinations.

Communication Officer

Location: Quantico, Va.

Length: 22–36 weeks.

Objectives: To train officers in communication command and staff duties for qualification for assignment to appropriate communication billets in the Fleet Marine Force.

Instruction: Principles of staff organization and functioning; supply system and fiscal management procedures; preparation of communication plans and orders; principles, fundamentals, and techniques of ground combat, and the employment of supporting arms and engineer units; radiotelephone and radiotelegraph operating procedures; cryptography; communication center operations; keyboard techniques and teletypewriter operation; familiarization with electricity; fundamentals of radio communication and basic functioning of radio transmitters and receivers; planning, installation, operation, and maintenance of field wire systems; multiplex equipment; capabilities, tactical employment, and operation of visual, sound, and miscellaneous communication-electronics equipment; communication requirements for ground, aviation, and amphibious units.

Credit recommendation, collegiate level: 6 semester hours in communications center organization and management. *Note*—Courses beginning August 1962 may include instruction in French or Spanish. If official transcripts indicate completion of language instruction, 3 semester hours is recommended in French or Spanish.

Cryptographer

Location: San Diego, Calif.
Length: 10 weeks.
Objectives: To train enlisted personnel in the operation and employment of Fleet Marine Force cryptographic aids.
Instruction: Touch-typing on the communications typewriter; communication security; characteristics, installation, and operation of field teletypewriter equipment and associated procedures used in teletype operations; introduction to cryptocenters and cryptosystems; techniques employed in cryptography; handling of classified messages; cryptosystems and code systems.
Credit recommendation, collegiate level: This course is technical and vocational in nature. Credit in cryptography and message handling on the basis of demonstrated skills and/or institutional examinations.

Cryptographic Equipment Maintenance Preparatory

Location: San Diego, Calif.
Length: 6 weeks.
Objectives: To train enlisted personnel in the operation and maintenance techniques of the AN/TGC-14 teletypewriter.
Instruction: Operation, circuitry and electromechanical system of equipment, and the adjustment required for proper functioning; principles of solid state devices; pulse modulation; theory and use of test equipment.
Credit recommendation, collegiate level: This course is technical and vocational in nature. Credit in cryptographic equipment maintenance on the basis of demonstrated skills and/or institutional examinations.

1. Disbursing Clerk
2. Basic Disbursing Clerks
3. Advanced Disbursing Clerks

Location: Camp LeJeune, N.C.
Length: 6–9 weeks.
Objectives: To train enlisted personnel in the duties and functions of an operational disbursing activity.
Instruction: *Course 1:* Preparation and maintenance of military pay records and payments; preparation, computation, and payment of vouchers for reimbursement for official travel. *Course 2:* In addition to the previous instruction, this course contains use of the Marine Corps directives and filing system; laws and publications pertaining to military pay, allowances, and travel; correspondence; familiarization with the typewriter and adding machine. *Course 3:* Military pay and allowances; travel of military personnel; appropriation

accounting involving vouchers; accounting for public funds; maintenance of records; familiarization with techniques of office and personnel supervision.
Credit recommendation, collegiate level: CAUTION: *These courses vary in title and recommendation. Require exact identification by title. Courses 1 and 2:* These courses are technical and vocational in nature. Credit in office practice on the basis of demonstrated skills and/or institutional examinations. *Course 3:* 2 semester hours in disbursing procedures.

Disbursing Officer

Location: Camp Lejeune, N.C.
Length: 8–12 weeks.
Objectives: To train company-grade officers in the major aspects of disbursing.
Instruction: Entitlement to pay and various allowances; substantiation documents for entries on pay records; methods used to effect payments to personnel; disbursing operations applied to travel; appropriation accounting and procedures used in accounting for public funds; maintenance of records.
Credit recommendation, collegiate level: 4 semester hours in finance and disbursement.

Drill Instructor

Locations: San Diego, Calif.; Parris Island, S.C.
Length: 5–8 weeks.
Objectives: To train noncommissioned officers in the knowledge, command presence, and instructional ability required to prepare them for a tour of duty as drill instructors.
Instruction: Techniques and methods of instruction; leadership; troop and command; NCO indoctrination; training, organization, and management.
Credit recommendation, collegiate level. No credit as course is military in nature.

Electronic Teletype Repair

Location: San Diego, Calif.
Length: 16 weeks.
Objectives: To qualify personnel to perform duties in electronic teletype repair.
Instruction: Solid state devices; pulse forming and pulse modulation circuits; time division multiplexing; multivibrators; binary arithmetic; computer logic circuits; test equipment; teletype repair; telephone repair.
Credit recommendation, collegiate level: Credit in electrical laboratory on the basis of demonstrated skills and/or institutional examinations.

1. Engineer Equipment Mechanic (Engineer Equipment Mechanic (Basic))
2. Engineer Equipment Chief (Engineer Equipment Mechanic Foreman)
3. Engineer Equipment Foreman

Location: Camp Lejeune, N.C.
Length: 12–30 weeks.

Objectives: To train enlisted personnel in the supervision, operation, maintenance, and repair of engineer equipment.

Instruction: *Course 1:* Internal combustion engines; engineer equipment components; techniques of employment of equipment; inspection procedures for earthmoving, compaction, material handling, and supporting equipment. *Courses 2 and 3:* In addition to the preceding instruction, these courses contain planning, estimating, and techniques of scheduling; principles of construction surveying; employment of profiles and mass diagrams; soils analysis; drainage; supply procedures.

Credit recommendation, collegiate level: These courses are technical and vocational in nature. Credit in automotive equipment shop on the basis of demonstrated skills and/or institutional examinations.

Engineer Equipment Officer

Location: Camp Lejeune, N.C.

Length: 7–9 weeks.

Objectives: To train officers in the utilization of engineer equipment, engineer equipment maintenance, and metal-working activities.

Instruction: Construction fundamentals; operation, inspection, servicing, maintenance, and repair of gasoline and diesel engines, crawler and pneumatic-tired tractors, and motorized and towed graders; job planning and management; shop supervision; engineer supply.

Credit recommendation, collegiate level: 2 semester hours in maintenance management.

Engineer Equipment Operator

Location: Camp Lejeune, N.C.

Length: 7–11 weeks.

Objectives: To train enlisted personnel in the operation and preventive maintenance of engineer equipment.

Instruction: Stationary equipment; crawler and pneumatic-tired tractors; motorized and towed graders; crawler and mobile cranes; tractor drawn equipment.

Credit recommendation, collegiate level: This course is technical and vocational in nature. Credit in construction equipment operation and maintenance on the basis of demonstrated skills and/or institutional examinations.

Engineer Officer's Orientation

Location: Camp Lejeune, N.C.

Length: 4 weeks.

Objectives: To familiarize commissioned officers with the duties and basic engineer principles used by the engineer platoon commander.

Instruction: Building construction; rigging; military bridging; engineer equipment; roads and airfields; basic soil classification and identification; water supply; field electricity; field plumbing; maintenance; repair records and spare parts; demolitions; mine warefare; barrier planning.

Credit recommendation, collegiate level: Credit in engineering construction on the basis of institutional examination.

Field Medical Service Technic
(Medical Field Service Technic)
(Field Medical Service School)
(Special Medical and Dental Class, Field Medical Service School)
(Dental Technician, Field Service)

Locations: Camp Lejeune, N.C., Camp Pendleton, Calif.

Length: 3–7 weeks.

Objectives: To train officers and enlisted personnel in field medical and dental service.

Instruction: Anatomy and physiology; first aid and evacuation of injured; field sanitation; detection and marking of contaminated areas; survival in the jungle, desert, and Arctic; mass casualty handling; artificial respiration; medical and dental supply and service records.

Credit recommendation, collegiate level: No credit because of the limited nature of the course.

Field Music
(Field Music School)

Locations: Parris Island, S.C.; San Diego, Calif.

Length: 12–16 weeks.

Objectives: To train bandsmen for field music duty.

Instruction: Basic theory; description and position of instruments; bugle instruction and calls; drums and rudiments of drumming; duties and qualifications of field musics; ensemble training.

Credit recommendation, collegiate level: Credit in applied music (bugle and drum) on the basis of demonstrated skills and/or institutional examinations.

First Sergeant Personnel Administration
(First Sergeant)

Location: Parris Island, S.C.

Length: 6 weeks.

Objectives: To train selected first sergeants and sergeants major in personnel administrative duties.

Instruction: Enlisted records; personnel accounting system; classification; Marine Corps pay; naval justice; correspondence.

Credit recommendation, collegiate level: 2 semester hours in personnel records and classification administration.

Food Service

Location: Camp Lejeune, N.C.

Length: 12 weeks.

Objectives: To train enlisted personnel in the fundamentals and principles of Marine Corps garrison and field mess operations.

Instruction: Garrison mess fundamentals and administration; meat cutting; baking; nutrition and menu planning; techniques of cookery; field mess operations.

Credit recommendation, collegiate level: 6 semester hours in institutional (culinary) management.

Food Service Management

Location: Camp Lejeune, N.C.

Length: 7 weeks.

Objectives: To train noncommissioned officers in subsistence management, organization, and administration; individual and consolidated mess system; theory and principles of cooking; management of any food service activity to include commissioned officers' mess and similar activities; field mess operations; disaster feeding.

Credit recommendation, collegiate level: 4 semester hours in food service management.

Food Service Officers

Location: Camp Lejeune, N.C.

Length: 5 weeks.

Objectives: To train officers in the duties and responsibilities of food service officers.

Instruction: Food service and subsistence management; subsistence accounting and food service procedures; supervision of meat processing facilities; field bakery operations; nutrition and menu planning; supervisory techniques in food preparation; field mess operations; disaster feeding.

Credit recommendation, collegiate level: 3 semester hours in food service management.

French Language Refresher

Location: Camp Lejeune, N.C.

Length: 10 weeks.

Objectives: To provide officers and enlisted personnel with refresher training in French.

Instruction: Basic language refresher including grammar, vocabulary, reading, and dictation; military themes and vocabulary; document translation; interpreter exercise; interrogation training.

Credit recommendation, collegiate level: No credit because of the refresher nature of the course.

Fundamentals of Digital Logic

Location: San Diego, Calif.

Length: 3–4 weeks.

Objectives: To train personnel in the fundamental concepts of digital logic preparatory to further training in the maintenance of special devices.

Instruction: Integrating and differentiating networks, transistor theory, configurations, bias and stabilization, clampers, limiters, silicon controlled rectifiers, transistor switching characteristics and circuits, multivibrators and circuit protection devices; introduction to and terminology of number systems and radix conversion and complement arithmetic; introduction to Boolean algebra, axioms, laws and theorems, logic operations, symbolic logic truth tables, simplification of Boolean expressions, and graphic logic symbols; binary counters, storage registers, adder circuits and operations, subtracters, shift operations, logical operations, and control methods.

Credit recommendation, collegiate level: 2 semester hours in digital logic in the field of computing science.

Ground Radar Repair

Locations: San Diego, Calif.; Twentynine Palms, Calif.

Length: 5–10 weeks.

Objectives: To qualify enlisted personnel to perform the duties of radar technician.

Instruction: Technical instruction in the countermortar and battlefield surveillance radar sets organic to the Fleet Marine Force; ground units; operation, maintenance, installation, operating adjustments, interrelation of subunits and circuitry peculiar to each radar set; corrective and preventive maintenance procedures; use of test equipment; schematic diagrams; operation and maintenance of associated power sources.

Credit recommendation, collegiate level: Credit in electrical laboratory on the basis of demonstrated skills and/or institutional examinations.

Ground Radar Technician

Location: San Diego, Calif.; Twentynine Palms, Calif.

Length: 20–28 weeks.

Objectives: To provide enlisted personnel with technical instruction on the countermortar and battlefield surveillance radar systems organic to Fleet Marine Force ground units.

Instruction: Review of algebra and trigonometry; basic and complex analysis of AC and DC circuits; semiconductor physics; vacuum tube principles; power supplies and filters; multi-element tubes; DC and RF amplifiers; cathode followers; vacuum tube oscillators; detectors; clippers; clampers; multivibrators; sawtooth generators; phantastrons; radar circuitry; synchros and servomechanisms; digital computer fundamentals; employment, maintenance, and adjustment of radar sets; test instruments and measurements.

Credit recommendation, collegiate level: 3 semester hours at the freshman or sophomore level as an elective in electronics, and credit in electrical laboratory on the basis of demonstrated skills and/or institutional examinations.

Ground Radio Repair

Location: San Diego, Calif.

Length: 7–12 weeks.

Objectives: To train enlisted personnel to perform the duties of the radio repairman.

Instruction: Radio communication equipment organic to the Fleet Marine Force ground units; theory of operation; circuitry; operating characteristics; adjustments; calibration and installation techniques peculiar to each radio set; corrective and preventive maintenance procedures; use of test equipment; operation and maintenance of associated power sources.

Credit recommendation, collegiate level: Credit in electrical laboratory on the basis of demonstrated skills and/or institutional examinations.

Ground Radio Technician

Location: San Diego, Calif.

Length: 24–25 weeks.

Objectives: To train enlisted personnel in the duties of a ground radio technician.

Instruction: Mathematics; fundamentals of electricity; vacuum tubes; power supplies; AM and FM theory; antennas; test instruments; electronics supply; transistors; servicing methods; high-frequency techniques; shop practices; radiac sets; radio sets; sniperscope; infrared set; mine detector set; troubleshooting.

Credit recommendation, collegiate level: 3 semester hours at the freshman or sophomore level as an elective in radio and electronics, and credit in electrical laboratory on the basis of demonstrated skills and/or institutional examinations.

Guided Missile Fire Control Repair

Location: San Diego, Calif.

Length: 15 weeks.

Objectives: To qualify enlisted personnel as fire control repairmen.

Instruction: Power supplies; acquisition radar; synchronizing and coding equipment; tracking radar system; capture and guidance systems; computer and plotting boards; tactical control, signaling and communications; installation, adjustment, and maintenance procedures.

Credit recommendation, collegiate level: Credit in electrical laboratory on the basis of demonstrated skills and/or institutional examinations.

Infantry Replacement and Individual Combat Training

Location: Camp Pendeleton, Calif.

Length: 6 weeks.

Objectives: To train enlisted personnel for infantry replacement and individual combat training.

Instruction: Camouflage and concealment; field fortifications; combat communications and information; amphibious training; use of compass; map reading; weapons; tactics.

Credit recommendation, collegiate level: No credit as course is military in nature.

Infantry Weapons Armorer (Advanced)

Location: Quantico, Va.

Length: 7 weeks.

Objectives: To train noncommissioned officers in the supervision and management of infantry weapons repair facilities and in the coordination with associated activities.

Instruction: Organization of ordnance units; ordnance supply procedures and service fundamentals; fundamentals of small arms; metal refinishing; inspection, maintenance, and repair of rifles, pistols, machine guns, and mortars; flamethrowers; launchers; rockets.

Credit recommendation, collegiate level: This course is technical and vocational in nature. Credit in small arms repair on the basis of demonstrated skills and/or institutional examinations.

Infantry Weapons Armorer (Basic)
(Infantry Weapons Armorer)

Location: Quantico, Va.

Length: 7–8 weeks.

Objectives: To train officers and enlisted personnel to perform organizational and field maintenance and repair of infantry weapons.

Instruction: Maintenance and repair of small arms, rifles, pistols, machine guns, mortars, recoilless rifles, mounts, flamethrower, and rocket launchers.

Credit recommendation, collegiate level: This course is technical and vocational in nature. Credit in small arms repair on the basis of demonstrated skills and/or institutional examinations.

Instructor Orientation

Location: Quantico, Va.

Length: 3 weeks.

Objectives: To train newly assigned instructors in the principles, methods, and techniques of instruction applicable to the Marine Corps Educational Center and to acquaint them with the mission, organization, and instructional facilities of the Marine Corps schools.

Instruction: Educational psychology; principles of instruction; the teaching process; organization for teaching; methods and techniques of presentation and application; effective military writing.

Credit recommendation, collegiate level: 2 semester hours in instructional methods.

Instrument Repair Officer

Location: Quantico, Va.

Length: 10 weeks.

Objectives: To train lieutenants and warrant officers to supervise and control the maintenance and repair of optical sighting and nonelectronic fire control materiel.

Instruction: Organization, administration, and operation of an optical sighting and nonelectronic fire control repair shop; special test fixtures and equipment used in the inspection, repair, and maintenance of optical telescopes, periscopes, mounts, quadrants, range finders, and related equipment; auxiliary sighting and fire control equipment.

Credit recommendation, collegiate level: This course is technical and vocational in nature. Credit in precision instrument repair on the basis of demonstrated skills and/or institutional examinations.

Interrogation of Prisoners of War (IPW)

Location: Camp Lejeune, N.C.

Length: 3–4 weeks.

Objectives: To train selected personnel in interrogation methods.

Instruction: Combat intelligence orientation; principles of interrogation; documents and reports; foreign language interrogations.

Credit recommendation, collegiate level: No credit because of the brevity and nature of the course.

1. Light AAA Fire Control Repair
   (Fire Control System Maintenance)
2. Medium AAA Fire Control Repair
   Location: San Diego, Calif.
   Length: 16 weeks.
   Objectives: To train enlisted personnel in fire control repair.
   Instruction: Power supplies; acquisition radar system; track radar system; computer and plotting boards; tactical control, signaling and communications; auxiliary equipment; installation and adjustments; maintenance and troubleshooting.
   Credit recommendation, collegiate level: Credit in electrical laboratory on the basis of demonstrated skills and/or institutional examinations.

Marine Corps Command and Staff College

Location: Quantico, Va.
Length: 40–42 weeks.
Objectives: To provide professional education for officers of the ranks of major and lieutenant colonel in order to prepare them for command at the regiment/group level, for staff duty at the division/wing and higher Fleet Marine Force levels, and for duties appropriate to the grade of lieutenant colonel/colonel with departmental, combined, joint and high-level service organizations.
Instruction: Universal functions of leadership, including theory of organization, concept of the leader and leadership, nature of leadership responsibilities, effective oral and written communications, and conference techniques; concepts and operations of automatic data processing machines; personnel management; planning and programming; financial management; supply management; maintenance management; cost reduction; resource management; geopolitics and current world situation, philosophy of Communism, Soviet military strategy, foreign policy and national military strategy, and world social, economic, and industrial implications; organization and functioning for national security; principles involved in the preparation of command and staff estimates, preparation of combat plans and orders, preparation of combat records and reports, and methods of issue; concepts, organization of forces, and command relationships required by sea, land, and air forces in amphibious operations; planning and conduct of counterinsurgency programs, principles of war; basic conversational proficiency in either French, Spanish, or Vietnamese.
Credit recommendation, collegiate level: 3 semester hours in public affairs, 6 semester hours in management administration, 3 semester hours in personnel management, 3 semester hours for independent research thesis. In addition, 3 semester hours in either French, Spanish, or Vietnamese, and credit in English oral and written communications on the basis of institutional examination.

Marine Mechanical Fundamentals Schools

Location: Jacksonville, Fla.
Length: 8 weeks.
Objectives: To train enlisted personnel in marine mechanic fundamentals.

Instruction: Mathematics; fundamentals of electricity; physics; aviation familiarization; aviation mechanics; hand tools; aircraft instruments; aircraft structures; aviation ordnance; technical publications.
Credit recommendation, collegiate level: This course is technical and vocational in nature. Credit in airplane mechanics on the basis of demonstrated skills and/or institutional examinations.

Marine Security Guard School

Locations: Arlington, Va.; Washington, D.C.
Length: 6 weeks.
Objectives: To train enlisted personnel to perform duties as members of a Marine detachment serving under the operational control of the U.S. Department of State for the safeguarding of classified material at Foreign Service missions overseas.
Instruction: Security; protection of lives and property; working relationships; living abroad; detachment training and administration; legal aspects of investigations; security lock work; duties as a noncommissioned officer in charge.
Credit recommendation, collegiate level: This course is vocational in nature. Credit in protective service occupations on the basis of demonstrated skills and/or institutional examinations.

Marine Warrant Officer Basic
(Marine Warrant Basic)
(Marine Warrant Class)

Location: Quantico, Va.
Length: 10–11 weeks.
Objectives: To broaden the general military knowledge of newly selected warrent officers by indoctrinating them in the duties and responsibilities of company-grade officers in order to prepare them for the duties of warrant officer.
Instruction: Concepts, principles, and techniques of leadership; physical training; drill, command, and ceremonies; fundamentals and techniques of military instruction; weapons; combat intelligence; Communist forces; offensive and defensive factors; familiarization with military law; staff organization and functioning; personnel management procedures; logistics and supply; effective camouflage; mine warfare; communications; amphibious operations; nuclear, biological, and chemical defense; U.S. military forces; counterinsurgency/scouting and patrolling.
Credit recommendation, collegiate level: 3 semester hours in advanced military science.

Metalworkers
(Metalworker)
(Metalsmith Foreman)

Location: Camp Lejeune, N.C.
Length: 13–19 weeks.
Objectives: To train noncommissioned officers and enlisted personnel in the skills of welding, blacksmithing and sheet-metal working.
Instruction: Shop sketching and pattern layout;

sheet-metal work; blacksmithing; oxyacetylene welding; electric arc welding; metalsmith application.

Credit recommendation, collegiate level: This course is technical and vocational in nature. Credit in metal shop and welding on the basis of demonstrated skills and/or institutional examinations.

Motor Transport Chief

Location: Camp Lejeune, N.C.
Length: 10–13 weeks.
Objectives: To provide master sergeants through staff sergeants with an understanding of motor transport operations and maintenance to perform the duties of a motor transport chief.
Instruction: Power plant; electrical systems; fuel systems; fuel, electrical tune-up, and trouble diagnosis; power train; chassis; maintenance management; deep water fording and cold weather operations; unit removal and replacement; body, radiator, and fuel tank repair; administration and supply procedures.
Credit recommendation, collegiate level: This course is technical and vocational in nature. Credit in automotive repair on the basis of demonstrated skills and/or institutional examinations.

Motor Transport Officer

Location: Camp Lejeune, N.C.
Length: 12–17 weeks.
Objectives: To train officers for duty in the motor transport field.
Instruction: Internal combustion engine; carburetion and ignition; power train; hydromatic transmission; brakes and suspension; unit removal and replacement; cold weather and fording operations; driver selection and training; motor transport administration; forms, reports, and methods used in operations, maintenance, accident investigation, cost accounting, and supply; preventive maintenance.
Credit recommendation, collegiate level: This course is technical and vocational in nature. Credit in automotive repair on the basis of demonstrated skills and/or institutional examinations.

Motor Transport Officer Orientation

Location: Camp Lejeune, N.C.
Length: 4–6 weeks.
Objectives: To train junior officers who have recently completed the basic officers course, and who have had no prior motor transport experience, for maintenance and operational procedures prescribed for motor transport functions.
Instruction: Internal combustion engine component parts and systems; power plant; power transmission system and chassis; automotive maintenance system; management supply procedures; administration.
Credit recommendation, collegiate level: This course is technical and vocational in nature. Credit in automotive repair on the basis of demonstrated skills and/or institutional examinations.

Motor Vehicle Operator

Location: Camp Lejeune, N.C.
Length: 6 weeks.
Objectives: To train enlisted personnel, who have had little or no previous training or experience as military drivers, for duty as motor vehicle operators.
Instruction: Driving techniques; safe driving practices; traffic regulations; convoy operations; deep water fording; vehicle recovery; first echelon maintenance procedures.
Credit recommendation, collegiate level: This course is technical and vocational in nature. Credit in motor vehicle operation and maintenance on the basis of demonstrated skills and/or institutional examinations.

1. Mountain Operations (Rock Climbing), Summer
2. Mountain Leadership Training, Summer
3. Mountain Operations (Military Skiing), Winter
4. Mountain Leadership Training, Winter

Location: Bridgeport, Calif.
Length: 3–4 weeks.
Objectives: To train commissioned and noncommissioned officers in the specialized techniques involved in operating in mountainous terrain during summer and winter months.
Instruction: *Courses 1 and 2:* Special climbing and mountaineering equipment and its uses; stream crossing; military rope installations; rock climbing; rappelling; mountain tactics; evacuation techniques. *Courses 3 and 4:* Skis and associated equipment; stream crossing; cross-country and downhill skiing; snowshoeing; cold weather clothing and equipment; mountain tactics; evacuation techniques. *Courses 1 and 3:* In addition to the preceding instructions these courses include counterinsurgent operations, and basic principles of evasion, escape, and survival in the field or as a prisoner of war.
Credit recommendation, collegiate level: For each course, 2 semester hours in camping and survival training.

Naval Gunfire Officer

Location: Quantico, Va.
Length: 11 weeks.
Objectives: To train officers in all phases of naval gunfire support, shore bombardment, and shore fire control, with special emphasis on landing forces, in order to fit graduates for duty as naval gunfire officers for division or higher units or as amphibious gunnery staff officers or instructors.
Instruction: Naval gunfire support; fire support ship; materiel; gunnery; conduct of fire; shore bombardment; communications; organization, control, and staff functioning; tactical employment of naval gunfire support; naval gunfire planning; collateral subjects.
Credit recommendation, collegiate level: No credit as this course is military in nature.

1. Noncommissioned Officers Leadership Junior
2. Noncommissioned Officers Leadership Senior
   Location: Parris Island, S.C.
   Length: 3 weeks.
   Objectives: To train noncommissioned officers in the basic military subjects.
   Instruction: Drill, command, inspections, and ceremonies; principles of leadership; weapons; map and aerial photograph reading; tactical employment of the rifle company; techniques of military instruction.
   Credit recommendation, collegiate level: No credit as these courses are military in nature.

Nuclear, Biological and Chemical Warfare Defense

Location: Parris Island, S.C.
Length: 3 weeks.
Objectives: To train personnel in nuclear, biological and chemical warfare defense.
Instruction: Types of radiation; effects of nuclear weapons and biological agents; chemical and physical characteristics, effects and symptoms of casualty, and smoke and incendiary agents; principles of operation of radiac instruments; methods of protection against nuclear, biological and chemical weapons; familiarization with the operation of a radiological control center.
Credit recommendation, collegiate level: No credit because of the brevity and limited technical nature of the course.

Nuclear, Biological, and Chemical Weapons Employment
(Nuclear Weapons Employment)
(Atomic Weapons Employment)

Location: Quantico, Va.
Length: 3–6 weeks.
Objectives: To provide sufficient scope to qualify personnel as atomic or nuclear, biological, and chemical weapons employment officers.
Instruction: Nuclear weapons effects; methods and tools of employment analysis; employment planning; target analysis; weapons description and functioning.
Credit recommendation, collegiate level: No credit because of the brevity and nature of the course.

Officer Candidate

Location: Quantico, Va.
Length: 9–10 weeks.
Objectives: To train and screen candidates for appointment to commissioned rank in the Marine Corps.
Instruction: Characteristics, disassembly, assembly, and care of the M-14 rifle; basic fire team and squad tactics; drill, command, inspections, and ceremonies; physical training and conditioning; concepts, principles, and techniques of leadership.
Credit recommendation, collegiate level: 6 semester hours in advanced military science.

Ontos (M50) Fourth and Fifth Echelon Maintenance

Location: Camp Pendleton, Calif.
Length: 3–4 weeks.
Objectives: To train tracked vehicle repairmen of the rank of PFC and above to specialize in fourth and fifth echelon maintenance of the Ontos (vehicle), excluding turrets, armament, and fire control material.
Instruction: Theory and principles in the maintenance of the hull, track, and suspension system on the Ontos (M50) vehicle; theory and principles of electricity, construction, testing, and maintenance of electrical units; construction, troubleshooting, and maintenance of the GMC 302 engine; power trains.
Credit recommendation, collegiate level: This course is technical and vocational in nature. Credit in heavy automotive repair shop on the basis of demonstrated skills and/or institutional examinations.

Operational Communication Chief

Location: San Diego, Calif.
Length: 21–24 weeks.
Objectives: To train enlisted personnel in the operation, supervision, and employment of Fleet Marine Force communication facilities and agencies.
Instruction: Communication procedures and security; basic electrical theory; radiotelephone and teletype procedures; theory and operation of radio equipment; radio, wire, teletype and radio-relay communication equipment; cryptographic operations; organization and functioning of the communication center; ground, air, and amphibious communication systems.
Credit recommendation, collegiate level: This course is technical and vocational in nature. Credit in radio and cryptographic communications equipment operation on the basis of demonstrated skills and/or institutional examinations.

1. Optical Instrument Repairman
2. Optical Instrument Repairman (Basic)
3. Optical Instrument Repairman (Advanced)
   Location: Quantico, Va.
   Length: 6–14 weeks.
   Objectives: To train enlisted personnel to inspect, adjust, repair, and maintain fire control instruments.
   Instruction: Use and maintenance of tools; elementary optics; methods and materials for cleaning optical components; inspection, disassembly, cleaning, assembly, repair, and adjustment of auxiliary fire control instruments, including the observation telescope, gunners quadrant, binoculars, azimuth indicators, periscope, sight unit, and aiming circle; inspection, troubleshooting, and synchronization of the self-propelled artillery fire control systems and tank fire control systems; timepieces.
   Credit recommendation, collegiate level: These courses are technical and vocational in nature. Credit in precision instrument repair on the basis of demonstrated skills and/or institutional examinations.

Ordnance Chief

Location: Quantico, Va.

Length: 8 weeks.

Objectives: To train noncommissioned officers of the ordnance field in the supervision, management, and administration of ordnance operations.

Instruction: Fundamentals of management; technical inspections, records, and reports; management of garrison and field ordnance maintenance facilities; machine shop organization, capabilities, and functions; tools and equipment; tracked vehicle units, systems, inventory and equipment, and maintenance; artillery and infantry weapons repair shop, maintenance, and inventory; ammunition logistics.

Credit recommendation, collegiate level: 3 semester hours in management principles of supply and maintenance.

1. Ordnance Officer
2. Ordnance Officer

Location: Quantico, Va.

Length: *Course 1,* 10–16 weeks; *Course 2,* 22–26 weeks.

Objectives: To train officers for duty as ordnance staff officers and as commanding officers of division and force maintenance units.

Instruction: *Course 1:* Fundamentals of management; ordnance staff functions; maintenance unit management; weapons repair shop procedures; inspection, maintenance, and repair of artillery and infantry weapons; organization and capabilities of the optical instrument repair section; description, procurement, handling, transporting, and storage of ammunition; operation, care, and maintenance of fire control equipment; inspection, maintenance, and repair of tracked vehicles. *Course 2:* This course contains the same academic material as *Course 1* but includes more intensive instruction in all areas.

Credit recommendation, collegiate level: CAUTION: *These courses vary slightly in length and recommendation. Require exact identification of course by length. Course 1:* 2 semester hours in maintenance management. *Course 2:* 3 semester hours in maintenance management.

1. Platoon Leaders Class (Junior)
2. Platoon Leaders Class (Senior)
3. Platoon Leaders Class (Combined Junior/Senior)
(Platoon Leaders Class (Combined))
4. Platoon Leaders Class (Aviation)

Location: Quantico, Va.

Length: *Courses 1 and 2,* 6 weeks; *Course 3,* 10 weeks; *Course 4,* 12 weeks.

Objectives: To train and screen candidates for appointment to commissioned grade in the Marine Corps Reserve.

Instruction: Drill, command, and inspection; physical training; command and leadership; Marine Corps history; marches and bivouacs; weapons; marksmanship; small unit tactics; chemical warfare; medical subjects.

Explanatory Note: Because the United States Marine Corps does not have a service academy or an on-campus program of its own and nevertheless requires that

officers commissioned from civilian life possess a baccalaureate degree, it must employ other techniques in securing the majority of its newly commissioned officers. In its Platoon Leaders Class, the Marine Corps has devised a method of training future officers while they are still in college. The PLC Program makes no demand of any sort, either as to required subjects or training periods, on the student during the academic year. Those enrolled in the PLC Program are completely free to devote their full attention to their civilian studies. The student must, however, maintain an overall C average to remain in the program.

Students enroll in the PLC Program through the Marine Corps Officer Procurement Team that makes periodic campus visits during the school year or by direct contact with one of the twenty-four Marine Corps Officer Procurement Offices located throughout the nation.

The PLC Program consists of two six-week summer training periods which are designated as the Junior and Senior Courses. Normally, the student attends the first period between his freshman and sophomore years and the second period between his junior and senior years. However, under certain circumstances, both courses may be completed in a single summer.

The Platoon Leaders Class curricula (Junior and Senior Courses) cover extensive classroom instruction and practical field work in leadership, tactics, weapons, history, and other military subjects for a total of 432 instructional hours. Although the military portion of the program is completed prior to the senior year of college, the PLC student must receive his degree before his commission is awarded.

The Platoon Leaders Class (Aviation) consists of six-week indoctrination sessions during two summer vacations from school to be held at the Marine Corps Schools, Quantico, Virginia. Upon completion of the training and coincident with graduation from college, members will be commissioned as second lieutenants in the Marine Corps Reserve. At this time they will be designated student aviators and immediately begin the 15- to 18-month Flight School at the Naval Air Station, Pensacola, Florida.

At the end of each course, the Commandant of the Marine Corps, Headquarters, Marine Corps, Washington, D.C. 20380, furnishes an official service school transcript to the institutions attended by PLC students. These transcripts contain individual grades and class standing, plus a brief of the course. The complete syllabus of each course is also mailed by the Marine Corps when requested by an educational institution.

Credit recommendation, collegiate level: *Courses 1 and 2:* 3 semester hours in advanced military science for each course. *Courses 3 and 4:* 6 semester hours in advanced military science for each course.

Plumbing and Water Supply
(Plumbing and Water Supply Man)
(Plumber and Water Supply Man)

Location: Camp Lejeune, N.C.

Length: 8–12 weeks.

Objectives: To train enlisted personnel in the fundamentals of field plumbing and water supply.

Instruction: Water supply; purification units; distillation units; reconnaissance and development of water points; portable and trailer mounted diatomite units;

field plumbing and sewage installations; heating systems; mine warfare and camouflage.

Credit recommendation, collegiate level: This course is technical and vocational in nature. Credit in water supply and purification on the basis of demonstrated skills and/or institutional examinations.

1. Radar Fundamentals
2. Basic Radar

Location: San Diego, Calif.

Length: *Course 1,* 6–7 weeks; *Course 2,* 13–15 weeks.

Objectives: To train enlisted personnel in electronic theory and servicing principles common to Fleet Marine Force radar and associated electronic equipment.

Instruction: *Course 1:* Radar theory including RC transients, clampers, cathode followers, thyratron control, three-phase power supplies, limiters, electronic supply, transmission lines, wave guides, RF system components, klystrons, mixers, amplifiers, oscilloscopes, magnetrons, generators, multivibrators, pulse oscillators, basic display systems, phantastrons, modulators, synchro systems, servomechanisms, and anti-jam circuits; test equipment; operation of circuitry and components employed in radar equipment; corrective and preventive maintenance procedures. *Course 2:* In addition to the previous instruction this course contains more extensive instruction in the areas of radar theory and equipment.

Credit recommendation, collegiate level: CAUTION: *These courses vary in title, length, and recommendation. Require exact identification of course by title and length. Course 1:* 2 semester hours at the freshman or sophomore level as an elective in electronics, and credit in electrical laboratory on the basis of demonstrated skills and/or institutional examinations. *Course 2:* 4 semester hours at the freshman or sophomore level as an elective in electronics, and credit in electrical laboratory on the basis of demonstrated skills and/or institutional examinations.

Radio Chief

Location: San Diego, Calif.

Length: 20–22 weeks.

Objectives: To train enlisted personnel to perform the duties of a radio chief.

Instruction: Transmission and reception of Morse code; communication security; radiotelegraph procedure; radiotelephone procedure; teletypewriter operation and procedure; communication center functioning; radiotelephone and radiotelegraph radio nets; tactical use of radio relay and wire; installation, use, and preventive maintenance of radio and radio relay equipment; leadership and technique of instruction; map and aerial photograph reading.

Credit recommendation, collegiate level: This course is technical and vocational in nature. Credit in radio operation and repair on the basis of demonstrated skills and/or institutional examinations.

Radio Fundamentals
(Basic Radio)

Location: San Diego, Calif.

Length: 6–10 weeks.

Objectives: To train enlisted personnel in circuits and techniques peculiar to radio equipment and to prepare them for further training in radio repair.

Instruction: Theory and circuitry of amplitude modulation; continuous wave transmitters and receivers; transmitter and receiver circuits; antennas; servicing methods; FM theory and circuits; UHF techniques; SSB theory and circuits; transistor theory and circuits.

Credit recommendation, collegiate level: 2 semester hours at the freshman or sophomore level as an elective in electricity and radio, and credit in electrical laboratory on the basis of demonstrated skills and/or institutional examinations.

Radio Operator School

Location: Cherry Point, N.C.

Length: 18 weeks.

Objectives: To train officers and enlisted personnel as radio operators.

Instruction: Code reception and transmission; radiotelegraph procedure; radio-telephone procedure; primary electronics theory; aviation electronics equipment; communications publications; general communications; pre-flight and flight.

Credit recommendation, collegiate level: This course is technical and vocational in nature. Credit in radio operation on the basis of demonstrated skills and/or institutional examinations.

Radio Relay Repair

Location: San Diego, Calif.

Length: 12–14 weeks.

Objectives: To train enlisted personnel in the duties of radio relay repairmen.

Instruction: Very-high-frequency radio relay techniques; radio sets AN/MRC-62 and AN/MRC-63; installation and use of associated telephone-telegraph loop equipment; principles of microwave; radio sets AN/TRC-27 and AN/MRC-60; installation, operation, and employment of radio relay systems.

Credit recommendation, collegiate level: Credit in electrical laboratory on the basis of demonstrated skills and/or institutional examinations.

1. Radio Technician
2. Radio Technician

Location: San Diego, Calif.

Length: *Course 1,* 15 weeks; *Course 2,* 30–32 weeks.

Objectives: To train enlisted personnel in the duties of radio technician.

Instruction: Radio direction finding theory; radio relay theory; AM and FM radio equipment maintenance; single-side-band theory; servicing methods. In addition to the preceding instruction, *Course 2* includes mathematics; electricity and magnetism; electron tube theory; transistor theory; amplifiers and oscillators; electronic switching; power supplies; antennas; AM and FM theory; test instruments; P band servicing methods.

Credit recommendation, collegiate level: CAUTION: *These courses vary in length and recommendation. Require exact identification of course by length. Course 1:* Credit in electrical laboratory on the basis of demonstrated skills and/or institutional examinations. *Course 2:* 3 semester hours at the freshman or sophomore level as an elective in electricity and electronics, and credit in electrical laboratory on the basis of demonstrated skills and/or institutional examinations.

Radio Telegraph Operator

Location: San Diego, Calif.
Length: 18 weeks.
Objectives: To qualify enlisted personnel to perform duties as a radio telegraph operator.
Instruction: Receiving, sending, and typing of Morse code; operating characteristics, installation, adjustment, and employment of individual radio systems; radiotelephone and radiotelegraph procedures; net operation; air-ground panels; communication vehicle driving.
Credit recommendation, collegiate level: Credit in typing on the basis of institutional examination. At the technical level, credit in radiotelegraph operation on the basis of demonstrated skills and/or institutional examinations.

Recruiters

Location: Parris Island, S.C.
Length: 6 weeks.
Objectives: To train noncommissioned officers to perform duties incident to the procurement of personnel for the Marine Corps.
Instruction: Enlistment forms and requirements; salesmanship; operating of recruiting substations; publicity and public information; public speaking; typing; women's recruiting.
Credit recommendation, collegiate level: Credit in typing and speech on the basis of institutional examinations.

Refrigeration Mechanic
(Basic Refrigeration Man)
(Refrigeration Specialist)
(Refrigeration Man)

Location: Camp Lejeune, N.C.
Length: 9–17 weeks.
Objectives: To train enlisted personnel to install, operate, maintain, and repair refrigeration, air conditioning equipment, and accessory equipment.
Instruction: Engineering mathematics; internal combustion engines; elements of electricity and electrical equipment; refrigeration systems; shop and field application; air conditioning and ventilation; mine warfare and camouflage.
Credit recommendation, collegiate level: This course is technical and vocational in nature. Credit in operation and repair of refrigeration and air conditioning equipment on the basis of demonstrated skills and/or institutional examinations.

Remote Control System Repairman

Location: Quantico, Va.
Length: 12 weeks.
Objectives: To train remote control system repairmen in the maintenance of remote-control fire-control equipment.
Instruction: Mathematics; basic electricity; basic hydraulics; data transmission systems; remote control system operation and maintenance; multiple caliber .50 machine gun mount, M55; local control system operation and maintenance.
Credit recommendation, collegiate level: This course is technical and vocational in nature. Credit in electrical shop on the basis of demonstrated skills and/or institutional examinations.

1. Repair Shop Machinist
2. Weapons Repair Shop Machinist
3. Weapons Repair Shop Machinist

Location: Quantico, Va.
Length: *Courses 1 and 2,* 11–16 weeks; *Course 3,* 4 weeks.
Objectives: To train enlisted personnel in machine shop techniques through field maintenance level preparatory to assignment as repair shop machinists in a mechanical, instructional, or supervisory capacity.
Instruction: Shop operations and hand tools; shop mathematics; blueprints; use of machine tools; machine shop practice; metalizing; heat treatment of metal; welding.
Credit recommendation, collegiate level: These courses are technical and vocational in nature. Credit in machine shop and welding on the basis of demonstrated skills and/or institutional examinations.

Sea Duty Indoctrination

Locations: Portsmouth, Va.; San Diego, Calif.
Length: 3–4 weeks.
Objectives: To prepare enlisted Marines for duty with Marine detachments stationed aboard ships of the United States Navy.
Instruction: Military courtesy and discipline; small arms training; duties of Marines afloat; shipboard orientation; damge control and fire fighting.
Credit recommendation, collegiate level: No credit as the course is military in nature.

Sea School

Locations: San Diego, Calif.; Portsmouth, Va.
Length: 4 weeks.
Objectives: To prepare enlisted Marines for duty with ships' detachments aboard ships of the United States Navy.
Instruction: Drill and ceremonies; physical conditioning; small arms training; naval orientation; shipboard life; duties aboard ship; fire fighting and damage control.
Credit recommendation, collegiate level: No credit as the course is military in nature.

Senior Course
(Senior School)

Location: Quantico, Va.

Length: 39–41 weeks.

Objectives: To provide professional education for Marine Corps officers, of the rank of lieutenant colonel and major, in command and staff duties.

Instruction: Personnel and administration; intelligence; offensive and defensive combat; staff planning; special operations; amphibious operations; base defense; helicopter operations; logistics principles and applications; principles, techniques, and organization of air operations; artillery organization, capabilities, and control; engineer support; mechanized operations; naval gunfire organization, capabilities, and control; atomic, biological, and chemical warfare; organization of naval task forces; principles, techniques, and organization of communications; instructor training; staff-planning problems; base defense; political-military theory and the organization for national security (began with 1960–61 course); 100 hours instruction in French or Spanish (began with 1962–63 course).

Credit recommendation, collegiate level: *For courses completed through June 1960:* 6 semester hours in business organization and management. *For courses completed from June 1961 through June 1962:* 6 semester hours in business organization and management and 2 semester hours in political science. *For courses completed after 1962:* 6 semester hours in business organization and management, 2 semester hours in political science, 3 semester hours in French or Spanish, and credit in oral and written communication on the basis of demonstrated skills and/or institutional examinations.

Senior Enlisted Supply
(Senior Supply Chief)

Location: Camp Lejeune, N.C.

Length: 6–8 weeks.

Objectives: To provide senior staff noncommissioned officers with a broad base of understanding in all elements of supply.

Instruction: Supply management; Marine Corps stock lists; allowances; organic property control; requirements determination; procurements; fleet stock accounts; Marine Corps stores system; financial management; storage and traffic; combat service support units; tactical supply considerations; office and personnel supervision; supply in marine aviation; computerized supply operations.

Credit recommendation, collegiate level: 3 semester hours in supply management.

Sergeants Major Personnel Administration

Location: Parris Island, S.C.

Length: 6 weeks.

Objectives: To train noncommissioned officers in the various phases of personnel administration.

Instruction: Office management; publications; personnel accounting; enlisted records; classification; pay and allowances; naval justice; correspondence; combat and casualty reporting.

Credit recommendation, collegiate level: 2 semester hours in personnel records and classification administration.

Shore Party Basic Specialist

Location: Camp Lejeune, N.C.

Length: 4 weeks.

Objectives: To train enlisted personnel in the techniques and skills required of a shore party man during amphibious and helicopter-borne operations.

Instructions: Shore party battalion organization, equipment, mission, and employment; shore party functions during amphibious operations; shore party functions during helicopter-borne operations; demolitions, land-mine warfare, rigging, and building construction.

Credit recommendation, collegiate level: This course is technical and vocational in nature. Credit in building and concrete construction on the basis of demonstrated skills and/or institutional examinations.

Sound Equipment Repair

Location: San Diego, Calif.

Length: 3–6 weeks.

Objectives: To train for qualification as a sound equipment repairman at the rank of staff sergeant.

Instruction: Audio and magnetic recording theory; tape recorder–reproducer equipment; sound locating equipment; public address systems; mine detecting equipment; lie detecting set; code practice equipment; intercommunication equipment; servicing and troubleshooting.

Credit recommendation, college level: Credit in electrical laboratory on the basis of demonstrated skills and/or institutional examinations.

Spanish Language Refresher

Location: Camp Lejeune, N.C.

Length: 10 weeks.

Objectives: To provide officers and enlisted personnel with refresher training in Spanish.

Instruction: Basic language refresher including grammar, vocabulary, reading, and dictation; military themes and vocabulary; document translation; interpreter exercise; interrogation training.

Credit recommendation, collegiate level: No credit because of the refresher nature of the course.

Special Basic School
(Basic School)

Location: Quantico, Va.

Length: 21–32 weeks.

Objectives: To train newly commissioned officers in the duties and responsibilities of a rifle platoon commander.

Instruction: Amphibious and air support operations; combat intelligence; communication responsibilities; organization, weapons, and employment of field artillery; principles of leadership; field engineering; logistics; infantry weapons; marksmanship; military law; nuclear, biological, and chemical defense; basic administration policies; physical training and conditioning; tactical principles and techniques of employment of infantry units; staff organization and functioning.

Credit recommendation, collegiate level: Credit in advanced military at institutions which regularly offer such credit. *Note:* From May 1962 through March 1964, instruction in French or Spanish was included in this course. For students who completed the course during that time it is recommended that credit in either French or Spanish be granted on the basis of institutional examination.

Special Ground Radio Repair

Location: San Diego, Calif.
Length: 20 weeks.
Objectives: To qualify enlisted personnel as special ground radio repairmen.
Instruction: Radiac instruments; electronic supply and shop management; shop practices; circuit analysis; antenna principles, maintenance, and construction; theory of frequency modulation; test equipment and servicing methods; radio-telephone procedure and security; radio sets; higher frequency techniques.
Credit recommendation, collegiate level: Credit in electrical laboratory on the basis of demonstrated skills and/or institutional examinations.

Special Indoctrination
(Special NAVCAD Indoctrination)

Location: Quantico, Va.
Length: 6 weeks.
Objectives: To provide indoctrination training, for Marine naval aviators who have accepted commissions in the regular Marine Corps, with particular emphasis on the duties and responsibilities of a company-grade ground officer.
Instruction: Leadership; weapons; intelligence; field engineering; supporting arms and services; personnel administration; communications; tactics; military law; amphibious warfare.
Credit recommendation, collegiate level: Credit in advanced military at institutions which regularly offer such credit.

Special Supply Orientation

Location: Camp Lejeune, N.C.
Length: 4 weeks.
Objectives: To familiarize supply duty officers with the functioning of the Marine Corps supply system with particular emphasis on the managerial aspects.
Instruction: Organization for supply management; elements of the cycle of supply; cataloging and allowance system; inventory management; planning and programming; control and appraisal of operations; materiel and service operations; disbursing; supply support programs.
Credit recommendation, collegiate level: 2 semester hours in supply management.

Steward

Location: Camp Lejeune, N.C.
Length: 14–20 weeks.
Objectives: To train enlisted personnel as Marine Corps stewards.
Instruction: Mess fundamentals and administration; meat cutting; baking; menu planning, food preparation, and proper methods of serving; field equipment and field mess cookery.
Credit recommendation, collegiate level: 3 semester hours in institutional (culinary) management.

Supply Administration
(Advanced Supply Administration)

Location: Camp Lejeune, N.C.
Length: 12–17 weeks.
Objectives: To provide formal training in supply to corporals, sergeants, and staff sergeants.
Instruction: Financial management; procurement; transportation; supply operations; identification of supplies; unit accounting; stock accounting; subsistence; warehousing; office and personnel supervision.
Credit recommendation, collegiate level: 6 semester hours in supply management.

1. Survival, Evasion, Resistance to Interrogation and Escape
2. Evasion, Escape, and Survival Training

Location: Bridgeport, Calif.
Length: 3 weeks.
Objectives: To train commissioned and noncommissioned officers in the practical techniques of evasion, escape, and survival.
Instruction: Survival techniques; survival psychology; improvised clothing; shelters and equipment; procurement of food and water; heat and fires; land navigation; interrogation techniques; resistance methods; escape techniques; evasion procedure.
Credit recommendation, collegiate level: For each course, 2 semester hours in woodcraft and survival training.

Tactical Data System Digital Repairman
(Tactical Air Operations Central Digital Repair)
(Digital Repair)

Locations: San Diego, Calif.; Twentynine Palms, Calif.
Length: 14 weeks.
Objectives: To train enlisted personnel in the operation, installation, operational adjustment, and repair of the digital section of the Tactical Air Operations Central (TAOC).
Instruction: Functions, theory of operation, circuit analysis, maintenance and repair procedures on the radar IFF data processor; theory of operation and maintenance procedures for the operation and repair of the polar to Cartesian conversion, height finder programmar and buffer, correlator, and automatic tracking units of the TAOC; intercept computer and information and action units of the TAOC; unit test and maintenance groups and the system operational status

verification procedures; theory, functions, and modes of operation performed by the maintenance and operation unit and the digital tape reader processor; power supplies and methods of power distribution in the various units; identification, localization, and repair of system failures.

Credit recommendation, collegiate level: Credit in electrical laboratory on the basis of demonstrated skills and/or institutional examinations.

Tactical Data System Handling Repairman
(Tactical Air Operations Central Data Handling Repair)
(Data Handling Repair)

Locations: San Diego, Calif.; Twentynine Palms, Calif.

Length: 14 weeks.

Objectives: To train enlisted personnel in the operation, installation, operational adjustments and repair of the data handling section of the Tactical Air Operations Central.

Instruction: Circuitry and functioning of the digital data programmer, digital data buffer, intercenter data terminals, missile battery data terminals, tactical data communication central buffer, teletype programmer, teletype buffer, intercommunications, communication central group, communications group, operation and maintenance unit, and power distribution; corrective and preventive maintenance procedures; use of test equipment; fundamentals of peripheral equipment.

Credit recommendation, collegiate level: Credit in electrical laboratory on the basis of demonstrated skills and/or institutional examinations.

Tactical Data System Technician
(Marine Tactical Data System Technician)
(MTDS Technician)

Locations: San Diego, Calif.; Twentynine Palms, Calif.

Length: 34 weeks.

Objectives: To train personnel in the installation, inspection, testing, maintenance, and repair of the Tactical Air Operations Central at an advanced level.

Instruction: Interrelation of sub-units and circuits, peculiar circuitry and functions of the radar data processing groups, track store data processing units, operator groups, console servicing units, geographic display generation group, weapons control and bookkeeping units, internal and external system digital data links, voice communication units, memory access and monitoring units, power supplies, powere distribution, and maintenance units; maintenance procedures, and use of test equipment.

Credit recommendation, collegiate level: Credit in electrical laboratory on the basis of demonstrated skills and/or institutional examinations.

Tactical Data Systems Analog Repairman
(Analog Repair)
(Tactical Air Operation Central Analog Repair)
(Tactical Data Systems Analog Repair)

Locations: San Diego, Calif.; Twentynine Palms, Calif.

Length: 14 weeks.

Objectives: To train enlisted personnel to perform duties as a tactical data systems analog repairman.

Instruction: Console servicing; memory servicing and module testers; geographic display generation; power supplies and power distribution; analog maintenance complex; analog repair procedures.

Credit recommendation, collegiate level: Credit in electrical laboratory on the basis of demonstrated skills and/or institutional examinations.

Tank/Amphibian Vehicle Officer (Reserve)

Location: Camp Pendleton, Calif.

Length: 3 weeks.

Objectives: To provide refresher occupational training which will increase the mobilization potential of reserve officers in the tank and armored amphibian field.

Instruction: Communications; driving and preventive maintenance; gunnery; tactics; field firing; night operations.

Credit recommendation, collegiate level: No credit because of the refresher nature of the course.

Tank/Amphibious Vehicle Officer

Location: Camp Pendleton, Calif.

Length: 6 weeks.

Objectives: To train basic tracked vehicle officers to supervise duties of the crew and assume responsibility of a platoon commander in a tracked vehicle unit including the techniques of leadership and the tactical employment of the unit in action.

Instruction: Communications; driving and preventive maintenance; gunnery; tactics; field firing; night operations.

Credit recommendation, collegiate level: No credit as the course is military in nature.

Tank Officers' Orientation

Location: Camp Pendleton, Calif.

Length: 4 weeks.

Objectives: To familiarize selected basic school graduates with the duties of the tank officer and with the weapons and equipment of appropriate units.

Instruction: Tank characteristics and limitations; maintenance; driving and preventive maintenance; gunnery; field operations and firing; communications and tactics.

Credit recommendation, collegiate level: This course is technical and vocational in nature. Credit in tracked vehicle operation and repair on the basis of demonstrated skills and/or institutional examinations.

Tank Unit Leaders (Enlisted)

Location: Camp Pendleton, Calif.

Length: 8–12 weeks.

Objectives: To train staff noncommissioned officers in tactics, techniques, and leadership required of a senior noncommissioned officer.

Instruction: Tank maintenance; flame tank and turret familiarization; communications; driving and preventive maintenance; map reading; land mine warfare; gunnery; tactics.

Credit recommendation, collegiate level: This course is technical and vocational in nature. Credit in tracked vehicle operation and repair on the basis of demonstrated skills and/or institutional examinations.

Telephone Repair

Location: San Diego, Calif.

Length: 22 weeks.

Objectives: To train enlisted personnel as telephone repairmen.

Instruction: Mathematics; electrical effects and values; chemical cell; electromagnetism; alternating current; transformers; electrical generators; direct current motors; multimeter test sets; shop practices; power equipment maintenance; cable splicing; operation, maintenance, and repair of telephones, switchboards, and interphone sets; installation, operation, and maintenance of teletypewriter; electronics supply; common battery equipment.

Credit recommendation, collegiate level: This course is technical and vocational in nature. Credit in telephone repair on the basis of demonstrated skills and/or institutional examinations.

Telephone Technician

Location: San Diego, Calif.

Length: 24 weeks.

Objectives: To train enlisted personnel as telephone technicians.

Instruction: Mathematics; electricity; local battery equipment; common battery equipment; cable splicing; power supplies; shop techniques; radio relay and carrier fundamentals; test instruments; teletype maintenance; terminal equipment.

Credit recommendation, collegiate level: Credit in mathematics and electricity on the basis of institutional examination. At the technical level, credit in telephone repair on the basis of demonstrated skills and/or institutional examinations.

1. Telephone-Teletype Repair
2. Telephone-Teletype Repair (Special)

Location: San Diego, Calif.

Length: *Course 1,* 15–18 weeks; *Course 2,* 11–14 weeks.

Objectives: To train enlisted personnel to perform duties in telephone-teletype repair throughout the first enlistment.

Instruction: Teletypewriter equipment and theory; teletypewriter sets; telephone-telegraph terminal set; operation, circuitry, and electromechanical system of equipment; telephone equipment and theory; operation circuitry and adjustments of switchboards and other telephone equipment organic to Fleet Marine Force.

Credit recommendation, collegiate level: These courses are technical and vocational in nature. Credit in telephone and teletype repair on the basis of demonstrated skills and/or institutional examinations.

Terminal Equipment Repair

Location: San Diego, Calif.

Length: 6–7 weeks.

Objectives: To train enlisted personnel in the repair of telephone and telegraph terminal equipment.

Instruction: Fundamentals of telephony and telegraphy; telegraph-telephone terminal; telephone terminal; radio sets; system troubleshooting; field application.

Credit recommendation, collegiate level: Credit in electrical laboratory on the basis of demonstrated skills and/or institutional examinations.

Terrier Missile Launcher System Repair

Location: Quantico, Va.

Length: 14 weeks.

Objectives: To train enlisted personnel in the repair and maintenance, emphasizing field-level maintenance, of the Terrier missile launcher, control system, and associated ordnance equipment, preparatory to assignment as a missile launching system repairman in an instructional, supervisory, or maintenance capacity.

Instruction: Electrical fundamentals and hydraulics; major components and subassemblies of Terrier missile launching system and associated equipment; missile launcher feeder system; principles of operation of mechanical and hydraulic components; electrical components; power drives; main power unit; emplacement and system integration; preventive maintenance; adjustment and trouble analysis; repair and replacement.

Credit recommendation, collegiate level: Credit in electrical laboratory on the basis of demonstrated skills and/or institutional examinations.

Tracked Vehicle Maintenance Officer

Location: Camp Pendleton, Calif.

Length: 9–13 weeks.

Objectives: To train officers to perform duties as maintenance officers of combat tracked vehicles up to and including fifth echelon shop supervision.

Instruction: Tracked vehicle operation; hull track and suspension; electrical systems of tanks, LVT's, Ontos, and track-laying self-propelled guns; ignition systems; generators; hull wiring circuits; internal combustion engines; continental engine; troubleshooting; mechanical and hydraulic operations; transmission; turret operation and maintenance; shop procedures.

Credit recommendation, collegiate level: This course is technical and vocational in nature. Credit in tracked vehicle repair on the basis of demonstrated skills and/or institutional examinations.

Tracked Vehicle Repairman Advanced
(Advanced Tracked Vehicle Repairman)
(Tracked Vehicle Repairman)

Location: Camp Pendleton, Calif.

Length: 8–15 weeks.

Objectives: To train enlisted personnel to perform maintenance of combat vehicles up to and including fifth echelon shop supervision.

Instruction: Theory and principles of vehicle hull, track, and suspension system; electrical systems on tanks, LVT's, Ontos, and track-laying self-propelled guns; ignition systems; generators; wiring circuits; construction, troubleshooting, and maintenance of internal combustion engines; power train.

Credit recommendation, collegiate level: These courses are technical and vocational in nature. Credit in tracked vehicle repair on the basis of demonstrated skills and/or institutional examinations.

Tracked Vehicle Repairman (Amphibian)
(Basic)
(Amphibian Vehicle Repairman)

Location: Camp Pendleton, Calif.

Length: 10 weeks.

Objectives: To train enlisted personnel as amphibian vehicle repairmen.

Instruction: Maintenance procedures and publications; operation, maintenance, and repair of hull and suspension, electrical systems, engines, and power trains; recovery procedures.

Credit recommendation, collegiate level: This course is technical and vocational in nature. Credit in tracked vehicle repair on the basis of demonstrated skills and/or institutional examinations.

Tracked Vehicle Repairman (Ontos) (Basic)
(Ontos Vehicle Repairman)

Location: Camp Pendleton, Calif.

Length: 5 weeks.

Objectives: To train enlisted personnel as tracked vehicle repairmen.

Instruction: Maintenance procedures and publications; operation, maintenance, and repair of hull and suspension systems, electrical systems, engines, and power trains; recovery procedures.

Credit recommendation, collegiate level: This course is technical and vocational in nature. Credit in tracked vehicle repair on the basis of demonstrated skills and/or institutional examinations.

Tracked Vehicle Repairman (Self-Propelled
Artillery) (Basic)
(Self-Propelled Vehicle Repairman)
(Tracked Vehicle Repairman, Tank and
Self-Propelled Artillery)

Location: Camp Pendleton, Calif.

Length: 10 weeks.

Objectives: To train enlisted personnel as self-propelled tracked vehicle repairmen.

Instruction: Maintenance procedures and publications; operation, maintenance, and repair of hull and suspension systems, electrical systems, engines, and power train; recovery procedures.

Credit recommendation, collegiate level: This course is technical and vocational in nature. Credit in tracked vehicle repair on the basis of demonstrated skills and/or institutional examinations.

Tracked Vehicle Repairman (Tank) (Basic)
(Tank Vehicle Repairman)

Location: Camp Pendleton, Calif.

Length: 10 weeks.

Objectives: To train enlisted personnel as tank tracked vehicle repairmen.

Instruction: Maintenance and repair of hull and suspension systems, electrical systems, engines and power trains; recovery procedures.

Credit recommendation, collegiate level: This course is technical and vocational in nature. Credit in tracked vehicle repair on the basis of demonstrated skills and/or institutional examinations.

Turret Repairman

Location: Camp Pendleton, Calif.

Length: 7–14 weeks.

Objectives: To train enlisted personnel as repairmen of turrets and armament of tanks, armored amphibian tractors, and other turreted combat vehicles.

Instruction: Maintenance and repair of weapons used in turreted vehicles; basic hydraulics; electricity, including magnetism, current, voltage and resistance, DC circuits, inductance; gyro stabilizer systems; turret traversing mechanism and commanders cupola; turret electrical and hydraulic systems; maintenance of optical and mechanical devices; flamethrower tank turret; Ontos, self-propelled 106mm, recoilless rifle M-50; practical maintenance and troubleshooting.

Credit recommendation, collegiate level: This course is technical and vocational in nature. Credit in heavy equipment repair shop on the basis of demonstrated skills and/or institutional examinations.

Typing and General Office Procedures (Women)

Location: Parris Island, S.C.

Length: 4 weeks.

Objectives: To train Marine Corps women in typing and general office procedures.

Instruction: Business English; spelling; correspondence; typing; Navy filing system; Marine Corps directives system; general office procedures.

Credit recommendation, collegiate level: Credit in typing on the basis of institutional examinations, and at the technical level, credit in office practice on the basis of demonstrated skills and/or institutional examinations.

Unit Supply Officer

Location: Camp Lejeune, N.C.

Length: 7–10 weeks.

Objectives: To train company-grade officers, with limited or no previous supply experience, for performance of duty as supply officers with specific emphasis on the duties of unit supply officer.

Instruction: Supply management; problem-solving techniques; allowance directives, stock lists and technical publications; organic property control; financial management; service unit accounting; maintenance and disposal of equipment; procurement; storage operations; transportation; Fleet Marine Force combat service support; mock office; computerized supply operations.

Credit recommendation, collegiate level: 4 semester hours in supply management.

Utilities Chief

Location: Camp Lejeune, N.C.
Length: 16–27 weeks.
Objectives: To train enlisted personnel as utilities chief for duty with the Fleet Marine Force.

Instruction: Equipment and procedures used in testing and treating water; operation and maintenance of water purification and distillation units; water points and water sources; plumbing and sewage installation; installation, operation, maintenance, and repair of heating systems; electrical theory, including magnets and electromagnets, induced currents, theory of current generation, AC and DC, series and parallel circuits, and batteries; operation and maintenance of AC motors and generators; power distribution; planning, estimating, code requirements, protection, and division of circuits in interior wiring construction; refrigeration theory; construction, operation, maintenance, and repair of the component parts of a compression refrigeration system; maintenance procedures for refrigeration equipment; air conditioning principles and equipment; blueprint reading; boiler system layouts; principles of gas and diesel engines.

Credit recommendation, collegiate level: Credit in electricity and water supply and purification on the basis of institutional examination. At the technical level, credit in mechanical and electrical shop on the basis of demonstrated skills and/or institutional examinations.

Utilities Officer

Location: Camp Lejeune, N.C.
Length: 8–12 weeks.
Objectives: To train officers in the technical aspects of the utilities field as applicable to the Fleet Marine Force.

Instruction: Methods of supplying potable water; plumbing and sewage disposal procedures; familiarization with the theory of electricity, electrical equipment, materials, power distribution, and electrical wiring; refrigeration and air conditioning; nomenclature, functioning, principles of operations, and troubleshooting of gasoline and diesel engines.

Credit recommendation, collegiate level: This course is technical and vocational in nature. Credit in utilities installation, operation, and maintenance on the basis of demonstrated skills and/or institutional examinations.

Warrant Officer Candidate Screening

Location: Quantico, Va.
Length: 7 weeks.
Objectives: To evaluate and screen candidates for appointment to warrant officer rank.

Instruction: Drill, command, inspections, and ceremonies; physical training and conditioning; leadership; weapons; small unit tactics; review of basic military subjects.

Credit recommendation, collegiate level: No credit as the course is military in nature.

Warrant Officer Personnel Administration

Location: Parris Island, S.C.
Length: 5 weeks.
Objectives: To train newly designated warrant officers in the duties of administrative officers.

Instruction: Preparation and maintenance of enlisted records and forms; supervision of the documents of the personnel accounting system; adjudication of claims; Marine Corps classification system, including enlisted promotion system, testing and interviewing, assignment, and retraining; court-martial orders and investigations; regulations and directives governing entitlement and substantiation for pay allowances; preparation of orders; combat and casualty reporting; administrative procedures relative to separations; retirements and transfers; communications; operation of an organizational postal facility; processing of personnel and dependents for movement overseas; supervision of clerical staff; maintenance of registered publications.

Credit recommendation, collegiate level: 2 semester hours in personnel administration.

Weapons Controller ECCM Operations Officer (Operations Officer Electronic Counter-Countermeasures)

Location: San Diego, Calif.
Length: 3 weeks.
Objectives: To train officers in the basic concepts of electronic countermeasures and electronic counter-countermeasures.

Instruction: Basic principles of ground radars and associated systems; computer introduction; principles of electronic countermeasures; ECCM principles and techniques; characteristics, capabilities, and limitations of displays used in conjunction with ECCM equipment; operation of the Marine Tactical Data System (MTDS) air defense system; radar inputs and countermeasures.

Credit recommendation, collegiate level: No credit because of the brevity and specialized nature of the course.

Weapons Controller/Operator

Location: San Diego, Calif.
Length: 6 weeks.
Objectives: To train officers and enlisted personnel as controllers and operators in the Marine tactical data system.

Instruction: Tactical data systems; radio detection

and ranging; tactical air operations central; IFF data processing groups; height finder programmer and buffer; tactical air operations central system tracking units and communications system; digital data links; digital computers and terminology; numbering systems; grouping methods; complement arithmetic.

Credit recommendation, collegiate level: No credit as the course is military in nature.

Weapons Repair Officer

Location: Quantico, Va.
Length: 12 weeks.
Objectives: To train company-grade officers in the maintenance and repair of infantry and artillery weapons.
Instruction: Repair shop procedures; artillery fundamentals; artillery weapons repair; tank guns and mounts; guided missile launcher systems; inspection, maintenance, and repair of infantry weapons.
Credit recommendation, collegiate level: This course is technical and vocational in nature. Credit in mechanical shop on the basis of demonstrated skills and/or institutional examinations.

Weapons Technician

Location: Quantico, Va.
Length: 6 weeks.
Objectives: To train noncommissioned officers in the supervision and management of weapons repair facilities.
Instruction: Technical and supply publications; supply systems; repair and maintenance of artillery weapons and small arms; tracked vehicle guns and mounts; guns, machine, and submachine guns; ordnance management; machine tool capabilities, welding and heat treatment.
Credit recommendation, collegiate level: This course is technical and vocational in nature. Credit in small arms repair on the basis of demonstrated skills and/or institutional examinations.

1. Welder
2. Basic Welder

Location: Camp Lejeune, N.C.
Length: 5–6 weeks.
Objectives: To train enlisted personnel in welding procedures.
Instruction: Principles, techniques, and theory of electric arc and oxyacetylene welding and cutting; use, care, and adjustments of tools and equipment; welding procedures and positions for various materials.
Credit recommendation, collegiate level: These courses are technical and vocational in nature. Credit in welding on the basis of demonstrated skills and/or institutional examinations.

Woman Marine Noncommissioned Officer Leadership

Location: Quantico, Va.
Length: 4 weeks.
Objectives: To develop and strengthen the leadership ability of women noncommissioned officers.
Instruction: Concepts, principles, and techniques of leadership; drill, inspections, and ceremonies; principles of organization and personnel management; familiarization with military justice; physical fitness and recreational leadership; techniques of instruction.
Credit recommendation, collegiate level: No credit because of the brevity and nature of the course.

Woman Officer Basic
(Woman Officers Indoctrination)

Location: Quantico, Va.
Length: 5–7 weeks.
Objectives: To train newly commissioned women officers in the functions and duties of company and staff officers.
Instruction: Development of leadership abilities; officer responsibilities; personnel administration; military justice; management and administration policies and procedures; oral communication; supply; communications; techniques of instruction.
Credit recommendation, collegiate level: 2 semester hours in business organization and management, and credit in instructional methods on the basis of institutional examination.

Woman Officer Candidate

Location: Quantico, Va.
Length: 9–10 weeks.
Objectives: To screen, train, and prepare women candidates for appointment to commissioned rank in the Marine Corps.
Instruction: Leadership; personnel administration; drill, inspection, and ceremonies; physical training and conditioning; military customs, courtesies, and traditions; organization, mission, and functions of Armed Forces; military operations; military justice; current events.
Credit recommendation, collegiate level: *Prior to March 1963:* 2 semester hours in business organization and management and 2 semester hours in leadership or group organization. *Since March 1963:* 2 semester hours in leadership or group organization.

Woman Recruit Training

Location: Parris Island, S.C.
Length: 9 weeks.
Objectives: To train newly recruited women marines in the duties of women recruits.
Instruction: History; military customs and courtesies; security; discipline and military justice; administration; inspections; guidance; first aid; typing; correspondence; business English; general office procedures.
Credit recommendation, collegiate level: Credit in typing on the basis of institutional examination. At the technical level, credit in office procedures on the basis

of demonstrated skills and/or institutional examinations.

Women Marine Officers' Personnel Administration

Location: Parris Island, S.C.

Length: 6 weeks.

Objectives: To train newly commissioned women Marine officers in the duties of administrative officers.

Instruction: Procedures for processing claims; preparation and maintenance of the service record book, personnel accounting records, and the Officer Qualification Record; Marine Corps classification system; operation of an organizational postal facility; administrative procedures of combat and casualty reporting; supervisory aspects of correspondence practices; retirements; administrative procedures for the retired serviceman's family protection plan; preparation of separation forms; office management; familiarization with the career advisory program and the operation of the Navy Relief and Red Cross; processing of personnel and dependents for movement overseas; maintenance of registered publications; naval justice.

Credit recommendation, collegiate level: 2 semester hours in personnel administration.

1. Women Officers Training (Junior)
2. Women Officers Training (Senior)

Location: Quantico, Va.

Length: 6 weeks.

Objectives: To provide basic theoretical and practical military instruction with emphasis upon indoctrination in Marine Corps concepts.

Instruction: Organization and formation of drills; inspections and ceremonies; military justice; organization, missions, and functions of the Armed Forces; chemical and radiological defense; physical fitness and conditioning; current events; principles of leadership; personnel administration.

Credit recommendation, collegiate level: For each course: 2 semester hours in business organization and management and 2 semester hours in leadership or group organization.

NAVY

NAVY

Navy Schools: Definitions

CLASS A SCHOOLS provide basic technical instruction sufficient to qualify enlisted personnel for their first 6- to 9-months duty on board ship.

CLASS B SCHOOLS provide the advanced technical instruction required to prepare enlisted personnel for the higher petty officer pay grades.

CLASS C SCHOOLS are designed to train enlisted personnel in a particular skill or technique (for example, maintenance of special equipment).

CLASS O SCHOOLS are conducted by the Naval Air Technical Training Command primarily to prepare officer personnel to fill specialized technical aviation billets. In addition to providing instruction in technical fields, the schools train officers to supervise and administer training programs within their technical field for enlisted men.

CLASS P SCHOOLS provide trainees with basic knowledge common to a group of ratings, and serve to direct the individual into the rating for which he is best equipped, based on his interest, experience, background, abilities, and test results.

FUNCTIONAL SCHOOLS provide training for personnel, often in a team situation, in the performance of specialized tasks or functions which are not normal to rating training of enlisted personnel or professional training of officers. The schools also provide training on weapons of new or advanced design which have not yet reached universal fleet usage.

FLEET SCHOOLS ASHORE provide refresher and team training to fleet personnel, officers and enlisted, who are members of a ship's company.

ABC Defense for Shipboard Instructors

Locations: Damage Control Center, Philadelphia, Pa. and Naval Schools Command, Treasure Island, Calif.

Length: 3 weeks.

Objectives: To train personnel to assist ABC Defense Officers, to lead monitoring and decontamination teams, and to organize and conduct training programs for personnel on their ships in ABC defense.

Instruction: Effects of nuclear explosions; radiological shipboard monitoring; self-preservation in a nuclear attack; monitoring and decontamination; biological warfare defense; chemical warfare agents; gas masks; protective clothing; instructor training.

Credit recommendation, collegiate level: No credit because of the brevity and limited technical nature of the course.

ABC Warfare Defense Afloat

Locations: Damage Control Training Center, Philadelphia, Pa., and Naval Schools Command, Treasure Island, Calif.

Length: 5 weeks.

Objectives: To provide training in effective atomic, biological, and chemical warfare defense aboard ship.

Instruction: Nuclear weapons and effects; radiological detection and survey; nuclear weapons accidents; biological and chemical agents and effects; protection and decontamination; disaster recovery; shipboard organization and recovery.

Credit recommendation, collegiate level: No credit because of the specialized nature of the course.

AN/APN-122 Doppler Navigation System Maintenance
(AN/APN-122 Maintenance Training)

Location: Fleet Airborne Electronics Training Unit, Atlantic, Norfolk, Va.

Length: 3 weeks.

Objectives: To train maintenance personnel to conduct preventive and corrective maintenance of the Doppler navigational radar equipment, AN/APN-122(V).

Instruction: Theory of operation; block diagrams; detailed circuit analysis; troubleshooting and maintenance techniques; practical application.

Credit recommendation, collegiate level: Credit in electrical laboratory on the basis of demonstrated skills and/or institutional examinations.

AN/APS-20E Radar System Maintenance
(Maintenance Training AN/APS-20E)

Location: Fleet Airborne Electronics Training Unit, Atlantic, Norfolk, Va.

Length: 6 weeks.

Objectives: To provide electronics maintenance personnel with the necessary knowledge and skill to maintain the AN/APS-20E radar.

Instruction: General description APS-20 radar; low voltage power supply; synchronizer; modulator and transmitter; duplexer and radar receiver; antenna; operators indicator.

Credit recommendation, collegiate level: Credit in electrical laboratory on the basis of demonstrated skills and/or institutional examinations.

AN/APS-38B Radar System Maintenance
(AN/APS-38B Maintenance Training)

Location: Fleet Airborne Electronics Training Unit, Atlantic, Norfolk, Va.

Length: 3 weeks.

Objectives: To provide electronics maintenance personnel with the necessary knowledge and skills to maintain the AN/APS-38B radar.

Instruction: Operating procedures and techniques; detailed circuit analysis; equipment operation, alignment, and component location; associated test equipment; trouble location.

Credit recommendation, collegiate level: Credit in electrical laboratory on the basis of demonstrated skills and/or institutional examination.

AN/ARC-38A SSB Transceiver Maintenance
(AN/ARC-38A Maintenance Training)

Location: Fleet Airborne Electronics Training Unit, Atlantic, Norfolk, Va.

Length: 4 weeks.

Objectives: To provide electronics maintenance personnel with the necessary knowledge and skill to maintain the AN/ARC-38A system.

Instruction: Single-side-band operation; receiver-transmitter; antenna coupler; teletype; signal data converter; practical application.

Credit recommendation, collegiate level: Credit in electrical laboratory on the basis of demonstrated skills and/or institutional examinations.

AN/ARC-94 Single Side Band Transceiver Maintenance
(AN/ARC-94 Maintenance Training)

Location: Fleet Airborne Electronics Training Unit, Atlantic, Norfolk, Va.

Length: 3 weeks.

Objectives: To provide electronics maintenance personnel with the necessary knowledge and skill to maintain the AN/ARC-94 system.

Instruction: SSB operation; receiver-transmitter; antenna coupler; equipment operation and component location; test equipment; trouble location.

Credit recommendation, collegiate level: Credit in electrical laboratory on the basis of demonstrated skills and/or institutional examinations.

AN/ARN-21D TACAN Receiver Maintenance
(AN/ARN-21D TACAN Navigation Set Maintenance)
(AN/ARN-21D Maintenance Training)

Location: Fleet Airborne Electronics Training Unit, Atlantic, Norfolk, Va.

Length: 4 weeks.

Objectives: To provide personnel with the theory of operation, circuit analysis, adjustment and alignment procedures, and practical troubleshooting methods to conduct preventive and corrective maintenance of the Air Navigational Radio Equipment AN/ARN-21D.

Instruction: Theory of operation; alignment; system analysis of common component failures.

Credit recommendation, collegiate level: Credit in electrical laboratory on the basis of demonstrated skills and/or institutional examinations.

AN/ASA-16 Integrated Display System Maintenance
(AN/ASA-16 Data Display Group Maintenance Training)
(AN/ASA-16 Maintenance Training)

Location: Fleet Airborne Electronics Training Unit, Atlantic, Norfolk, Va.

Length: 4 weeks.

Objectives: To train electronics maintenance personnel to maintain the AN/ASA-16 Data Display Group.

Instruction: Introduction; system block diagram; circuit analysis; equipment operation; special test equipment; deductive trouble location.

Credit recommendation, collegiate level: Credit in electrical laboratory on the basis of demonstrated skills and/or institutional examinations.

AN/GRC-27A Radio Equipment Maintenance

Location: Naval School, Treasure Island, Calif.

Length: 3 weeks.

Objectives: To train electronics personnel in the principles, operation, and maintenance of the AN/GRC-27 radio equipment and associated test equipment.

Instruction: Major set functions; transmit functions; receive functions; autotune functions; modulator power supply functions; fault localization; preventive maintenance.

Credit recommendation, collegiate level: Credit in electrical laboratory on the basis of demonstrated skills and/or institutional examinations.

AN/SPN-10 Automatic Carrier Landing System Operator
(AN/SPN-10 Operator Course)

Locations: Fleet Airborne Electronics Training Unit, Atlantic, Norfolk, Va. (Phase I); Naval Air Station, Patuxent River, Md. (Phase II).

Length: 4 weeks.

Objectives: To train prospective CCA officers and AN/SPN-10 operators to utilize all modes of the automatic carrier landing system during the landing phase of carrier operation.

Instruction: Introduction to the AN/SPN-10 system; operational capabilities and limitations; equipment requirements; operator console; emergency procedures; operators maintenance.

Credit recommendation, collegiate level: No credit because of the limited technical nature of the course.

AN/SPS-8 Radar Maintenance, Class C

Location: Naval School, Treasure Island, Calif.

Length: 5 weeks.

Objectives: To train electronics personnel in the maintenance of AN/SPS-8 radar equipment and associated test equipment.

Instruction: Transmitting system and magnetron care and handling; power distribution; receiving system; antenna control system; VL-1 repeater with SN206/SP correlator; CP-458/SPS-8 video integrator

Credit recommendation, collegiate level: Credit in electrical laboratory on the basis of demonstrated skills and/or institutional examinations.

APA-56 Indicator Assembly

Location: Naval Air Station, Patuxent River, Md.
Length: 3 weeks.
Objectives: To train enlisted personnel in the operation and maintenance of the APA-56 indicator and the use of associated test equipment.
Instruction: Introduction of the APA-56 system; power supplies; signal distributor; console indicator; relay priority system; camera; grid map converter.
Credit recommendation, collegiate level: No credit because of the brevity and limited technical nature of the course.

APS-20E Radar Maintenance

Location: Naval Air Station, Patuxent River, Md.
Length: 3 weeks.
Objectives: To train enlisted personnel in the operation and maintenance of the APS-20E radar and the use of associated test equipment.
Instruction: Low-voltage power supply; synchronizer; high-voltage power supply and control circuits; magnetron filament control circuit; radar transmitter; pressurization and cooling system; duplexer; receiver; UPM-44 test set; antenna system and indicator.
Credit recommendation, collegiate level: This course is technical and vocational in nature. Credit in electrical shop on the basis of demonstrated skills and/or institutional examinations.

APS-45 and APS-45A Radar Maintenance

Location: Naval Air Station, Patuxent River, Md.
Length: 3 weeks.
Objectives: To train enlisted personnel in the operation and maintenance of APS-45 and APS-45A and the use of associated test equipment.
Instruction: Power control circuits; low-voltage power supply; air compressor; PRF and rangemark generator; transmitter, mixer, duplexer, local oscillator, and RF plumbing; receivers and video amplifier; azimuth and elevation control systems; synchro power supply; sweep circuits; complete alignment procedure for APS-45 and APS-45A.
Credit recommendation, collegiate level: This course is technical and vocational in nature. Credit in electrical shop on the basis of demonstrated skills and/or institutional examinations.

ASW Tactical Coordinator

Location: Naval Air Station, Glynco, Ga.
Length: 5-6 weeks.
Objectives: To train naval aviation officers in the basic phases of antisubmarine warfare.
Instruction: Fundamental and surface antisubmarine warfare; aerial antisubmarine warfare; procedures and tactics.
Credit recommendation, collegiate level: No credit as the course is military in nature.

Academic Instructor Training

Location: Naval School, Pensacola, Fla.
Length: 4 weeks.
Objectives: To provide teacher training to prospective academic instructors within the Naval Air Basic Training Command.
Instruction: Education, including psychology of learning, techniques of instruction, lesson planning, testing and scoring, student advisement, and classroom management; communication skills; written communications; programmed instruction; leadership and counterinsurgency.
Credit recommendation, collegiate level: 2 semester hours in instructional methods.

Accelerated Basic Hospital Corps School

Locations: Naval Hospital Corps Schools, Great Lakes, Ill. and San Diego, Calif.
Length: 12 weeks.
Objectives: To provide an accelerated course for enlisted personnel on the basic principles and techniques of direct patient care and first aid procedures.
Instruction: Anatomy and physiology; first aid and minor surgery; hygiene and sanitation; principles and techniques of patient care; materia medica and toxicology.
Credit recommendation, collegiate level: 3 semester hours in elementary anatomy and physiology and 2 semester hours in hygiene.

Advanced Nuclear Power
(Advanced Course, Nuclear Power Academic Training Program)

Locations: Bainbridge, Md., Idaho Falls (Arco), Idaho, Mare Island (Vallejo), Calif., New London, Conn.
Length: 22-24 weeks.
Objectives: To provide training for naval personnel in the field of nuclear power plant operation.
Instruction: Advanced mathematics; atomic and nuclear physics; reactor engineering; servomechanisms; reactor and plant control theory; metallurgy and reactor material; chemistry; physics–thermodynamics; nuclear power plant systems and components; reactor control systems and components; health physics.
Credit recommendation, collegiate level: 3 semester hours in reactor engineering.

1. Advanced Sonar, 557
2. Advanced Sonar, 566
3. Advanced Sonar, 567

Location: Fleet Sonar School, Key West, Fla.
Length: *Course 1,* 11 weeks; *Course 2,* 5-6 weeks: *Course 3,* 14-15 weeks.

Objectives: To provide personnel with additional training on sonar equipment.

Instruction: *Course 1:* Mathematics review; synchro units; fire control systems; testing and adjustment of sonar and fire control systems. *Course 2:* New types of sonar equipment; antisubmarine fire control systems; maintenance. *Course 3:* New types of sonar equipment; antisubmarine tactics; sonar circuits; fire control systems; calibration and maintenance.

Credit recommendation, collegiate level: Credit in electrical laboratory on the basis of demonstrated skills and/or institutional examinations.

Advanced Sonar Maintenance
(Sonarman, Class B)

Location: Fleet Sonar School, San Diego, Calif.

Length: 18 weeks.

Objectives: To train personnel in the operation and maintenance of sonar and associated equipment.

Instruction: Fundamentals of DC and AC; series and parallel circuits; magnetism and electromagnetism; inductance; capacitance; vacuum tubes; rectifiers; power supplies; amplifiers; oscillators; servo and synchro systems; circuit analysis.

Credit recommendation, collegiate level: 4 semester hours in electricity and electronics, and credit in electrical laboratory on the basis of demonstrated skills and/or institutional examinations.

Advanced Sonarman

Location: Fleet Sonar School, Key West, Fla.

Length: 37 weeks.

Objectives: To provide advanced training in electrical and electronic theory and in the operation and tactical use of sonar and fire control equipment.

Instruction: DC series and parallel circuits; magnetism and electro magnetism; inductance and capacitance; AC series and parallel circuits; oscilloscope; transformers; power supplies; amplifiers; transistors; computer basics; fire control; sonar equipment.

Credit recommendation, collegiate level: 6 semester hours at the freshman or sophomore level as an elective in electricity and electronics and credit in electrical laboratory on the basis of demonstrated skills and/or institutional examinations.

1. Aerographer's Mate, Class A
2. Aerographer's Mate, Class B

Location: Naval Air Technical Training Unit, Lakehurst, N.J.

Length: *Course 1,* 13–19 weeks; *Course 2,* 20–23 weeks.

Objectives: *Course 1* provides basic training, *Course 2,* advanced training, in meteorology, air observation, and related sciences.

Instruction: *Course 1:* Aviation fundamentals; basic meteorology; upper wind observations; meteorological codes and laboratory work; weather chart entry; basic mathematics and physics; typewriting and teletype procedures. *Course 2:* Meteorology and radar meteorology; mathematics and physics applicable to meteorology; operation and maintenance of standard instruments; wind, wave, and surf forecasting; map analysis, forecasting, and flight observations; land and sea ice; directives and reports; leadership and supervision; satellite meteorology; numerical weather prediction.

Credit recommendation, collegiate level: *Course 1:* 3 semester hours in weather forecasting or meteorology. *Course 2:* 6 semester hours in weather forecasting or meteorology.

Air Conditioning and Refrigeration, Class C

Locations: Naval Schools, Norfolk, Va., and San Diego, Calif.

Length: 8 weeks.

Objectives: To train personnel in the principles of construction and the operation of air conditioning and refrigeration equipment.

Instruction: Introduction to refrigeration; components of refrigerators; electrical controls, switches, valves, and piping in refrigeration systems; compressors, condensers, receivers, and capacity controls for refrigeration systems; air cooled equipment; refrigeration main plant operation; air conditioning; psychrometry; maintenance, repair, and troubleshooting.

Credit recommendation, collegiate level: This course is technical and vocational in nature. Credit in operation and repair of air conditioning and refrigeration equipment on the basis of demonstrated skills and/or institutional examinations.

Air Control, Class O
(Advanced Air Control, Class O)
(Air Control Officer)

Location: Naval Air Station, Glynco, Brunswick, Ga.

Length: 5 weeks.

Objectives: To train officers and chief petty officers in all phases of air control.

Instruction: Air control related information, including types of intercepts, combat information center communications, jets and jet operations, and general air operations; practical application of air control procedures, including synthetic air control and actual air control of jet aircraft.

Credit recommendation, collegiate level: No credit as the course is military in nature.

1. Air Controlman, Class A
2. Air Controlman, Class B

Locations: Naval Air Technical Training Center, Glynco, Ga.; Naval Air Technical Training Unit, Olathe, Kans.

Length: 10–16 weeks.

Objectives: To train Navy and Marine Corps enlisted personnel in basic (*Course 1*) and advanced (*Course 2*) air traffic control procedures.

Instruction: *Course 1:* Aviation fundamentals; regulations and procedures; related military procedures; air traffic control and air traffic rules; air traffic control communications; flight assistance service; air route traffic control; military operations laboratory; military control tower procedures; air traffic control radar

Course 2: Subjects related to air traffic control, including supervision, management, organization, and administration of the operations department, aids to air navigation, ground controlled approach and radar air traffic control center; air traffic control regulations and procedures; aviation weather.

Credit recommendation, collegiate level: These courses are technical and vocational in nature. Credit in air control tower operation on the basis of institutional examination.

1. **Air Controlman R (Radar), Class A**
2. **Air Controlman T (Tower), Class A**
3. **Air Controlman W (Early Warning), Class A**
   (Air Controlman W (Airborne CIC Operator), Class A)

Locations: Naval Air Station, Glynco, Brunswick, Ga.; Naval Air Technical Training Unit, Olathe, Kans.

Length: *Course 1,* 4 and 10 weeks; *Course 2,* 10–14 weeks; *Course 3,* 12–15 weeks.

Objectives: To train Navy and Marine Corps enlisted personnel in the fundamentals of air traffic control procedures.

Instruction: *Course 1* (4-week course, 1956): Communications and voice training; aircraft characteristics; fundamentals of air traffic control; air control radar; basic air navigation. *Course 1* (10-week course) covers the same areas as the 4-week course including also AN/CPN-4 and AN/MPN-5 radar set familiarization and basic operation. *Course 2:* Aircraft characteristics and performance; communications and voice training; air navigation aids; air traffic rules; airport traffic control; basic air navigation; air route traffic control; weather observations; air operations office procedures; advanced air traffic control laboratory; operations office. *Course 3:* Air traffic control; communications; elementary air navigation; electronics; display and plotting; airborne CIC operations; practical application.

Credit recommendation, collegiate level: These courses are technical and vocational in nature. Credit in air control tower operation on the basis of institutional examination.

1. **Air Intelligence Officers Course**
2. **Air Intelligence School**
   (Photographic Interpretation)

Locations: Pacific Fleet, Alameda, Calif.; Atlantic Fleet, Norfolk, Va.; Naval Intelligence School, Washington, D.C.

Length: *Course 1,* 32 weeks; *Course 2,* 6 weeks.

Objectives: To train naval officers in the techniques and basic principles of air intelligence.

Instruction: *Course 1:* General photography; general intelligence; maps and charts; international situations; ground/amphibious operations; weapons; air defense; metrics; target materials; target analysis; radar target analysis; operational and intelligence planning. *Course 2:* Maps and mapping; recognition; briefing and debriefing (public speaking); photographic interpretation; world power—international relations; psychological warfare; aerology and climatology; military science.

Credit recommendation, collegiate level: *Course 1:* 3 semester hours in intelligence methods. *Course 2:* No credit because of the specialized nature of the course.

Air Intercept Control, Class O

Location: Naval Air Technical Training Center, Glynco, Ga.

Length: 6–7 weeks.

Objectives: To train officers, Marine staff noncommissioned officers, and other qualified personnel in all phases of air intercept control.

Instruction: Air intercept control procedures and communications; aircraft operations and weapon systems; general air operations; practical application of air intercept control procedures, including synthetic and actual air intercept control.

Credit recommendation, collegiate level: No credit as the course is military in nature.

Air-Ocean Environment, Class C

Location: Naval Air Technical Training Unit, Lakehurst, N.J.

Length: 7 weeks.

Objectives: To train enlisted personnel for the Antisubmarine Warfare Environmental Prediction System program.

Instruction: Fundamentals of sea water and sound, including the ASWEPS program, physical oceanography, underwater sound, and observational equipment; environmental analyses and prediction, including sea surface temperature charts, layer depth charts, and augmenting oceanic environmental charts; operational analyses and prediction, including sonar range conversion, transmission codes, displays, and briefing aids.

Credit recommendation, collegiate level: Credit in physical oceanography on the basis of institutional examination.

Air Traffic Control Officer, Class O

Locations: Naval Air Technical Training Centers, Glynco, Ga., and Olathe, Kan.

Length: 9–12 weeks.

Objectives: To train officers as ground controlled approach operators and supervisors of GCA units.

Instruction: Air traffic control regulations and procedures; approach control, including emergency descent and unreported aircraft; radar set familiarization and basic operating procedures; synthetic operational training.

Credit recommendation, collegiate level: This course is technical and vocational in nature. Credit in airport control tower operation on the basis of institutional examination.

Airborne CIC Operator, Class C

Location: Naval Air Technical Training Center, Glynco, Ga.

Length: 5–6 weeks.

Objectives: To provide experienced radar operators with formal and in-flight training in airborne combat information center operation.

Instruction: Air navigation; communications; electronics; aircraft characteristics, tactics, and survival; practical application of airborne combat information center tactics.

Credit recommendation, collegiate level: No credit as the course is military in nature.

Airborne Early Warning/Electronics Countermeasures Evaluator Course, Class O

Location: Naval Air Technical Training Center, Glynco, Ga.

Length: 6–7 weeks.

Objectives: To train officers in the operational functions of the equipment specified.

Instruction: Airborne early warning electronics equipment; airborne ECM equipment and operations; airborne navigation; airborne early warning operations; practical applications in synthetic and in-flight training.

Credit recommendation, collegiate level: No credit as the course is military in nature.

Airborne Radar Intercept Operator, Class O

Location: Naval Air Technical Training Center, Glynco, Ga.

Length: 8–10 weeks.

Objectives: To train officers in basic airborne radar controller intercepts and fundamentals of crew duties.

Instruction: Aircraft equipment and armament; flight planning, navigation, operations, safety, and survival; airborne intercept procedures and tactics; practical (trainer) applications of intercept operations.

Credit recommendation, collegiate level: No credit because of the limited technical nature of the course.

Airborne Radio Communication Operator (ARCO)

Locations: Fleet Airborne Electronics Training Unit Detachments, Jacksonville, Fla., and Brunswick, Me.

Length: 12 weeks.

Objectives: To train personnel to receive and send international Morse code.

Instruction: Typing; international Morse code; teletypewriter; communications publications; Naval communications procedure; safety precautions; Navy patrol aircraft power supply system and communications systems.

Credit recommendation, collegiate level: Credit in typing on the basis of institutional examinations.

Airborne Tactical Data System Operations, Class O

Location: Naval Air Technical Training Center, Glynco, Ga.

Length: 18–19 weeks.

Objectives: To train prospective airborne tactical data system officers in basic ATDS operational functions.

Instruction: Airborne tactical data system theory and operation, including systems sensors, computer indicator group, and operator functional task laboratory; fleet anti-air warfare procedures and operations; airborne tactical data system team training; airborne electronic warfare operational flight training (non-ATDS).

Credit recommendation, collegiate level: No credit as the course is military in nature.

Aircraft Maintenance Officer, Class O

Location: Naval Air Technical Training Center, Memphis, Tenn.

Length: 10–19 weeks.

Objectives: To provide prospective squadron maintenance officers with the information necessary to organize, supervise, and administer an aircraft maintenance department.

Instruction: Duties and responsibilities of the airframes division officer; power plant equipment and systems; avionics equipment and systems, including basic electricity and electronics training; personnel management; maintenance department administration.

Credit recommendation, collegiate level: 3 semester hours in maintenance management, and credit in electricity, electronics, and electrical laboratory on the basis of demonstrated skills and/or institutional examinations.

Aircraft Maintenance Radiography School, Class C

Location: Naval Air Technical Training Center, Jacksonville, Fla.

Length: 7–8 weeks.

Objectives: To provide training in aircraft maintenance radiography and develop skills in radiography procedures and interpretation.

Instruction: Radiographic fundamentals, including nondestructive testing, radiation and radioactivity, radiographic equipment, radiation safety, factors governing film exposure, and the arithmetic of exposure; radiographic film and film development; radiography of aircraft and interpretation, including aircraft structures, critical stress areas, and operational defects.

Credit recommendation, collegiate level: This course is technical and vocational in nature. Credit in radiography and film processing on the basis of demonstrated skills and/or institutional examinations.

Alternating Current Power Systems

Location: Fleet Airborne Electronics Training Unit Detachment, Jacksonville, Fla.

Length: 4 weeks.

Objectives: To train aviation electricians to analyze system malfunctions and to isolate malfunctioning components.

Instruction: Review of electron and magnetic principles; review of DC theory; AC principles; inductance and inductive reactance; capacitance and capacitive reactance; RLC circuits and resonance; polyphase AC and AC connections; transformers and saturable core devices.

Credit recommendation, collegiate level: Credit in electrical laboratory on the basis of demonstrated skills and/or institutional examinations.

Antisubmarine Air Control, Class O

Location: Naval Air Technical Training Center, Glynco, Ga.

Length: 3–4 weeks.

Objectives: To train officers and senior petty officers in all phases of antisubmarine air control.

Instruction: Antisubmarine air control procedures, including communications procedures, antisubmarine aircraft characteristics, search planning, control and contact area procedures, antisubmarine warfare aircraft weapons and attack tactics, and search, rescue, and emergency operations; practical application of antisubmarine air control procedures.

Credit recommendation, collegiate level: No credit as the course is military in nature.

Assault Boat Engineer

Location: Naval Amphibious School, Coronado, San Diego, Calif.

Length: 3 weeks.

Objectives: To provide basic training for prospective assault boat engineers.

Instruction: Diesel engine construction and operation; oil systems; water systems; engine disassembly and reassembly; transmission; preventive maintenance and troubleshooting.

Credit recommendation, collegiate level: This course is technical and vocational in nature. Credit in diesel engine maintenance and repair on the basis of demonstrated skills and/or institutional examinations.

Automatic Transmissions, Class C

Location: Naval School, Port Hueneme, Calif.

Length: 5 weeks.

Objectives: To train mechanics to test, adjust, and repair automatic transmissions in automotive and construction equipment.

Instruction: Basic principles of automatic transmissions; Fordomatic transmission; hydromatic transmission; Allison MT series automatic transmission; Caterpillar powershift transmission.

Credit recommendation, collegiate level: This course is technical and vocational in nature. Credit in automatic transmission repair on the basis of demonstrated skills and/or institutional examinations.

Aviation Boatswain's Mate, Class A

Location: Naval Air Material Center, Philadelphia, Pa.

Length: 16 weeks.

Objectives: To provide enlisted personnel with comprehensive aircraft and carrier aircraft equipment training.

Instruction: Airman fundamentals; catapults; arresting gear; aviation seamanship; aircraft carrier fire fighting; aircraft fire fighting; aircraft carrier gasoline and inert gas system.

Credit recommendation, collegiate level: This course is technical and vocational in nature. Credit in seamanship and fire fighting on the basis of demonstrated skills and/or institutional examinations.

Aviation Boatswain's Mate E (Launching and Recovery Equipment), Class A
(Aviation Boatswain's Mate E (Equipments), Class A)

Location: Naval Air Technical Training Unit, Philadelphia, Pa.

Length: 9–10 weeks.

Objectives: To familiarize enlisted personnel with aircraft and the use and maintenance of selected aircraft carrier equipment.

Instruction: Aviation fundamentals; aircraft carrier fire fighting; hydropneumatic catapults; steam catapults; arresting gear, barrier, and optical landing systems.

Credit recommendation, collegiate level: This course is technical and vocational in nature. Credit in fire fighting and operation and maintenance of catapults, arresting gear, and optical landing systems on the basis of demonstrated skills and/or institutional examinations.

Aviation Boatswain's Mate F (Fuels), Class A

Locations: Naval Air Technical Training Units, Lakehurst, N.J., and Philadelphia, Pa.

Length: 8–10 weeks.

Objectives: To train enlisted personnel to operate and maintain aviation fuel and lube oil transfer systems and shore based refuelers and lube oil service units.

Instruction: Airman fundamentals; aircraft carrier fire fighting and rescue of personnel; high capacity aviation fuel system; fundamentals of petroleum and quality control; shore based refueling equipment.

Credit recommendation, collegiate level: This course is technical and vocational in nature. Credit in fire fighting and operation and maintenance of aviation fuel and lube oil transfer systems on the basis of demonstrated skills and/or institutional examinations.

Aviation Boatswain's Mate G (Gasoline Handler), Class A
(Aviation Boatswain's Mate G Gasoline School (Gasoline Handling))

Location: Naval Air Material Center, Philadelphia, Pa.

Length: 7–10 weeks.

Objectives: To train enlisted personnel to handle land and sea planes aboard ship and on land and to operate and maintain associated equipment.

Instruction: Fundamentals of hydraulics, catapults, arresting gear, flight and hangar deck equipment, seamanship, and air-sea rescue; damage control fire fighting; aircraft fire fighting and rescue of personnel; aviation seamanship; aircraft carrier flight and hangar deck operations; aircraft carrier gasoline and inert gas systems; high capacity fuel system.

Credit recommendation, collegiate level: This course is technical and vocational in nature. Credit in seamanship and aircraft fuel systems operation and maintenance on the basis of demonstrated skills and/or institutional examinations.

Aviation Boatswain's Mate H (Aircraft Handling), Class A
(Aviation Boatswain's Mate H (Handling), Class A)

Locations: Naval Air Technical Training Units, Lakehurst, N.J., and Philadelphia, Pa.

Length: 7 weeks.

Objectives: To train enlisted personnel in aircraft handling, including crash handling, procedures ashore and afloat.

Instruction: Airman fundamentals; aircraft carrier fire fighting and rescue of personnel; aircraft fire fighting and rescue ashore; aircraft handling.

Credit recommendation, collegiate level: This course is technical and vocational in nature. Credit in fire fighting on the basis of institutional examination.

Aviation Boatswain's Mate U (Utility), Class A

Location: Naval Air Technical Training Unit, Philadelphia, Pa.

Length: 7–12 weeks.

Objectives: To train aviation boatswain's mates, strikers and third class, in the performance and maintenance of catapults and arresting gear.

Instruction: Aircraft carrier air department organization; marlinespike seamanship; wire rope socketing; principles of hydraulics and fire fighting; arresting gear and catapult operation, preventive maintenance, and safety precautions.

Credit recommendation, collegiate level: This course is technical and vocational in nature. Credit in operation and maintenance of catapult and arresting gear systems on the basis of demonstrated skills and/or institutional examinations.

Aviation Crash Crewman, Class C

Location: Naval Air Technical Training Center, Memphis, Tenn.

Length: 4 weeks.

Objectives: To train Marine Corps personnel in aviation crash, fire-fighting, and rescue procedures.

Instruction: Introduction to fire fighting; aircraft familiarization; mobile equipment–crash fire and rescue truck; crash rescue and fire-fighting drills; crash crew operation; maintenance of mobile equipment.

Credit recommendation, collegiate level: This course is technical and vocational in nature. Credit in fire fighting on the basis of institutional examination.

1. Aviation Electrician's Mate, Class A
2. Aviation Electrician's Mate I (Instrument), Class A
(Aviation Electrician Conversion Course)
3. Aviation Electrician's Mate M (Electricians), (Aviation Electrician Conversion Course) Class A

Location: Naval Air Technical Training Center, Jacksonville, Fla.

Length: 15–22 weeks.

Objectives: To provide basic training in aircraft electrical and/or instrument systems operation, maintenance, and repair.

Instruction: *Course 1:* Mathematics and physics; basic electrical theory and measuring instruments; batteries and electromagnetism; conductors, electrical components, and circuits; DC generators, current motors, systems, and controls; DC systems line maintenance; AC theory, generators, motors, and circuits; AC measuring instruments and bridges; basic electronics applicable to aircraft systems, including power supplies, amplification, discrimination, oscillators, special purpose tubes, and transistors; electronic test equipment and troubleshooting electronic circuits; aircraft systems, including AC power supply systems, inverters, ignition systems, and detection and warning systems; electro-hydraulic control and auxiliary power systems; electrical instruments, aircraft compasses, automatic pilot, and capacitance fuel quantity system. *Courses 2 and 3* cover the same general subject areas with emphasis in the special equipment training phase on either electrical instruments (*Course 2*), or DC and AC machinery (*Course 3*).

Credit recommendation, collegiate level: For each course, 3 semester hours at the freshman or sophomore level as an elective in electricity, and credit in electrical laboratory on the basis of demonstrated skills and/or institutional examinations.

1. Aviation Electrician's Mate, Class B
2. Aviation Electrician's Mate, Class B (Intermediate Course)
3. Aviation Electrician's Mate, Class B (Advanced Course)

Location: Naval Air Technical Training Center, Jacksonville, Fla.

Length: *Course 1,* 33–34 weeks; *Course 2,* 23–24 weeks; *Course 3,* 26 weeks.

Objectives: To provide aviation electricians' mates with advanced technical training in electricity and electronics.

Instruction: *Course 1:* Direct current and related subjects, including arithmetic, algebra, physics, magnets and magnetic circuits, and direct current machinery; alternating current and related subjects, including trigonometry, analysis of networks, transformers, saturating core devices, alternating current machinery, AC machine controls, and synchronous indicating devices; principles of electronics; basic electronic test instruments; fundamental electronic experiments; electron tubes in application; servomechanism practice; gyroscope; magnetic compass; equipment and aircraft system analysis; electrical shop organization. *Courses 2 and 3* cover the same general subject areas in somewhat less depth owing to their shorter lengths.

Credit recommendation, collegiate level: *Course 1:* 9 semester hours at the freshmen or sophomore level as an elective in electricity and electronics, and credit in electrical laboratory on the basis of demonstrated skills and/or institutional examinations. *Courses 2 and 3:* 6 semester hours at the freshman or sophomore level as an elective in electricity and electronics, and credit in electrical laboratory on the basis of demonstrated skills and/or institutional examinations.

Aviation Electronics Fundamentals, Class A

Location: Naval Air Technical Training Center, Memphis, Tenn.

Length: 15 weeks.

Objectives: To train enlisted personnel in basic aviation electronics.

Instruction: Radio electronics fundamentals, including AC electricity, resonant circuit and vacuum tube characteristics, audio amplification, radio receiver theory, and receiver troubleshooting and alignment; transmitter and transistor fundamentals; antenna systems and transmission lines; radar electronics fundamentals, including time constants, pulse-shaping circuits and square-wave generators, pulse circuits and counters, and introduction to radar systems.

Credit recommendation, collegiate level: CAUTION: *Courses in aviation electronics (or avionics) vary in title, length, and recommendation. Require exact identification by full title and length.* 3 semester hours in electronics and 3 semester hours in electronic circuits.

Aviation Electronics Intelligence, Class O/C

Location: Naval Air Technical Training Center, Glynco, Ga.

Length: 7 weeks.

Objectives: To provide selected officers and enlisted personnel with operational training in electronic countermeasures and counter-countermeasures.

Instruction: General electronic warfare information; introduction to ECM (active and passive) equipment; electronic intelligence processing procedures; synthetic and in-flight training.

Credit recommendation, collegiate level: No credit as the course is military in nature.

1. **Aviation Electronics Officers' School, Class O**
2. **Aviation Electronics Officers' School, Class O**

Location: Naval Air Technical Training Center, Memphis, Tenn.

Length: *Course 1,* 40 weeks; *Course 2,* 30–33 weeks.

Objectives: To provide electronics training for officers to qualify them for electrical/electronic maintenance supervision duties.

Instruction: Electrical fundamentals, including DC and AC fundamentals, equipments, and electrical systems; electronic fundamentals, including receivers and amplitude modulated transmitters; communications systems receivers and transmitters; radar fundamentals; typical radar and test equipment; electronic countermeasures; identification and armament control systems; electronic aids to navigation; submarine detection system; radiological defense; recent developments in aviation electronics; aircraft and gyro instruments; automatic flight control; electronics administration and supply. *Course 2* covers the same general subject areas in somewhat less depth owing to its shorter length.

Credit recommendation, collegiate level: CAUTION: *Courses in aviation electronics (or avionics) vary in title, length, and recommendation. Require exact identification by full title and length. Course 1:* 6 semester hours at the freshman or sophomore level as an elective in electricity and electronics and 5 semester hours in engineering electronics. *Course 2:* 6 semester hours at the freshman or sophomore level as an elec-

tive in electricity and electronics and 3 semester hours in engineering electronics.

1. **Aviation Electronics Technician/Advanced, Class B**
2. **Aviation Fire Control Technician/Advanced, Class B**
3. **Intermediate Aviation Fire Control Technician, Class B**
4. **Aviation Electronics Technician, Class B**

Location: Naval Air Technical Training Center, Memphis, Tenn.

Length: *Courses 1 and 2,* 32 weeks; *Course 3,* 34 weeks; *Course 4,* 40 weeks.

Objectives: To provide enlisted personnel with advanced training in the testing and maintenance of avionics systems.

Instruction: *Courses 1 and 2:* Electronics administration and supply; mathematics; physics; electricity and magnetism; alternating current; trigonometry; electronics; transistors and magnetic amplifiers; synchros, servomechanisms, and gyros; television principles and infrared techniques; digital computers; radio theory and systems; communication techniques; advanced techniques in navigation; radar techniques; antisubmarine warfare systems and countermeasures. *Course 3:* Electricity; mathematics; amplifier fundamentals; power supplies and amplifiers; electronic circuits; magnetic amplifiers and RC time; principles of radar, synchros, digital and analog computers; radiation theory and principles of radar; specialized fire control radar; bombing and weapons systems; missile guidance and control test equipment; electronics administration and supply. *Course 4:* DC circuits and physics; series-parallel circuits and magnetism; meters and protective devices; AC circuits and components; resonant and nonresonant circuits; AC circuits, transformers, and coupled circuits; power equipment; electron principles and use of the diode; vacuum tube theory; amplifiers and amplifier circuits; transistors; transmitter and receiver fundamentals; radiation theory; VHF and UHF tubes, circuits, and systems; RC theory, clampers, and limiters; square-wave amplifiers and generators; electrostatic cathode-ray tube and associated circuits; radar transmitters, receivers, indicators, and synchronizers; synchro systems and servomechanisms; advanced and special radar systems; magnetic and sonic airborne submarine detection; electronic countermeasures; radiological safety; supply and publications.

Credit recommendation, collegiate level: CAUTION: *Aviation electronics (or avionics) courses vary in title, length, and recommendation. Require exact identification by full title and length. Courses 1 and 2:* 5 semester hours in mathematics, 5 semester hours in physics, and 5 semester hours in engineering electronics. *Course 3:* 15 semester hours at the freshman or sophomore level in engineering electronics. *Course 4:* 6 semester hours in physics (electricity), and 12 semester hours in engineering electronics.

1. **Aviation Electronics Technician, Class A**
2. **Aviation Electronics Technician, Class A**

Location: Naval Air Technical Training Center, Memphis, Tenn.

Length: *Course 1,* 28 weeks; *Course 2,* 8–9 weeks.

Objectives: To train enlisted personnel in the operation and maintenance of aviation electronics equipment.

Instruction: *Course 1:* International Morse code receiving and sending; electronic fundamentals, including AC and DC electricity, receiver theory and circuits, construction of a superheterodyne receiver, and receiver troubleshooting and alignment; transmitter fundamentals, including vacuum tube operating characteristics and transmitter theory and construction; communication systems; UHF and VHF electronics; radar electronic fundamentals, including pulse timing and counting circuits, altimeter and loran equipment, and operation of a basic radar system; shop maintenance of receivers, transmitters, test sets, analyzers, and aircraft ICS systems; electrical power distribution; antenna and cable construction; flight safety; operation of carrier aircraft and patrol bomber radars; principles of dead reckoning navigation.

Course 2: Airborne radar concepts, including IFF theory and application, search radar, and navigational computer fundamentals; TACAN theory and application; communications transceiver fundamentals; auxiliary system concepts.

Credit recommendation, collegiate level: CAUTION: *Courses in aviation electronics (or avionics) vary in title, length, and recommendation. Require exact identification by full title and length. Course 1:* 6 semester hours at the freshman or sophomore level as an elective in electricity and 12 semester hours in engineering electronics. *Course 2:* Credit in electrical laboratory on the basis of demonstrated skills and/or institutional examinations.

1. Aviation Electronics Technician N (Navigation), Class A
2. Aviation Electronics Technician R (Radar), Class A
3. Aviation Electronics Technician S (Antisubmarine), Class A
4. Aviation Electronics Technician N (Navigation), Class A
5. Aviation Electronics Technician R (Radar), Class A
6. Aviation Antisubmarine Warfare Technician, Class A
   (Aviation Antisubmarine Warfare Technician S (Antisubmarine), Class A)
7. Aviation Electronics Technician W (Airborne CIC Operator), Class A

Locations: Naval Air Technical Training Centers, Memphis, Tenn., and Glynco, Ga.

Length: *Courses 1, 2, and 3,* 21–22 weeks; *Courses 4 through 7,* 6–12 weeks.

Objectives: *Courses 1, 2, and 3:* To train enlisted personnel in aviation electronics. *Courses 4 through 7* provide Aviation Electronics (or Avionics) Fundamentals course graduates with specialized equipment training.

Instruction: *Courses 1, 2, and 3:* Electronics fundamentals, including AC electricity, resonant circuit and vacuum tube characteristics, audio amplification, and radio receiver theory, alignment, and troubleshooting; MHF, VHF, UHF transmitter theory; radar electronics fundamentals, including time constants, pulse-shaping circuits and square-wave generators, pulse circuits and

counters, and introduction to radar equipment; special navigation, radar, or antisubmarine equipment training. *Courses 4 through 7* consist of specialized equipment training for either aviation navigation, radar, antisubmarine, or communications information center purposes.

Credit recommendation, collegiate level: CAUTION: *Courses in aviation electronics (or avionics) vary slightly in title, length, and recommendation. Require exact identification by full title and length. Courses 1, 2, and 3:* For each course, 3 semester hours in electronics, 3 semester hours in electronic circuits, and credit in electrical laboratory on the basis of demonstrated skills and/or institutional examinations. *Courses 4 through 7:* Credit in electrical laboratory on the basis of demonstrated skills and/or institutional examinations.

1. Aviation Fire Control Technician B (Bomb Director), Class A
2. Aviation Fire Control Technician F (Armament Control), Class A
3. Aviation Fire Control Technician F (Fire Control), Class A
   (Aviation Fire Control Technician F (Armament Control), Class A)
4. Aviation Fire Control Technician B (Bomb Director), Class A

Location: Naval Air Technical Training Center, Memphis, Tenn.

Length: *Courses 1 and 2,* 24 weeks; *Courses 3 and 4,* 12 weeks.

Objectives: *Courses 1 and 2:* To provide enlisted personnel with electronics and special equipment training which will enable them to maintain and repair aircraft bomb director or armament control systems. *Courses 3 and 4:* To provide graduates of Aviation Electronics (or Avionics) Fundamentals courses with special equipment maintenance training on either aircraft armament control or bomb director systems.

Instruction: *Courses 1 and 2:* Electronic fundamentals, including AC electricity, resonant circuit and vacuum tube characteristics, audio amplification, radio receiver theory, and receiver troubleshooting and alignment; MHF, VHF, and UHF transmitter theory; gyros, synchros, and servomechanisms; aviation armament control or bomb director systems familiarization, maintenance, repair, and troubleshooting. *Courses 3 and 4* cover only the special equipment phase of the foregoing instruction—gyros, synchros, and servomechanisms, aviation fire control fundamentals, and aircraft fire control or bomb director systems maintenance, repair, and troubleshooting.

Credit recommendation, collegiate level: CAUTION: *Aviation Fire Control Technician courses vary in title, length, and recommendation. Require exact identification of course by full title and length. Courses 1 and 2:* For each course, 6 semester hours at the freshman or sophomore level as an elective in electricity and electronics, and credit in electrical laboratory on the basis of demonstrated skills and/or institutional examinations. *Courses 3 and 4:* Credit in electrical laboratory on the basis of demonstrated skills and/or institutional examinations.

1. Aviation Fire Control Technician (B)
   Conversion Course, Class C
2. Aviation Fire Control Technician (F)
   Conversion Course, Class C

Location: Naval Air Technical Training Center, Jacksonville, Fla.

Length: 27 weeks.

Objectives: To train Navy and Marine Corps enlisted personnel in the maintenance of aircraft bomb director or armament control systems and in the use of associated electronic test equipment.

Instruction: Mathematics; acceleration and position sensing devices; DC theory; fundamentals of optics; AC theory; electron tubes and related devices applied in fire control systems; applications of basic and special circuits to fire control systems; principles of fire control radar; servomechanism principles; aircraft bomb director or armament control systems operation, testing, and maintenance.

Credit recommendation, collegiate level: CAUTION: *Aviation Fire Control Technician courses vary in title, length, and recommendation. Require exact identification by full title and length.* For each course, 4 semester hours in electricity and electronics, and credit in electrical laboratory on the basis of demonstrated skills and/or institutional examinations.

Aviation Fire Control Technician, Class A

Location: Naval Air Technical Training Center, Memphis, Tenn.

Length: 11 weeks.

Objectives: To train enlisted personnel in the maintenance and repair of aircraft weapons systems and in the use of related test equipment.

Instruction: Weapons system radar; basic analog and digital computers; weapons control systems; bomb director systems.

Credit recommendation, collegiate level: CAUTION: *Aviation Fire Control Technician courses vary in title, length, and recommendation. Require exact identification by full title and length.* Credit in electrical laboratory on the basis of demonstrated skills and/or institutional examinations.

Aviation Fuel Systems, Class C

Locations: Naval Air Technical Training Centers, Lakehurst, N.J., and Philadelphia, Pa.

Length: 5 weeks.

Objectives: To provide specialized training in the operation and maintenance of aviation fueling and associated equipment.

Instruction: JP-5/high capacity aviation fuel system; fuel quality control and portable equipment; shore based refueling equipment; low capacity gasoline system and inert gas producer.

Credit recommendation, collegiate level: This course is technical and vocational in nature. Credit in aviation fuel systems operation and repair on the basis of demonstrated skills and/or institutional examinations.

---

1. Aviation Guided Missileman, Class A
2. Aviation Guided Missileman, Class A

Location: Naval Air Technical Training Center, Memphis, Tenn.

Length: *Course 1,* 24 weeks; *Course 2,* 12 weeks.

Objectives: *Course 1:* To provide enlisted personnel with basic electronics training and an operating knowledge of air launched guided missiles and associated test equipment. *Course 2:* To provide graduates of the Aviation Electronics (or Avionics) Fundamentals courses with an operating knowledge of air launched guided missiles and associated test equipment.

Instruction: *Course 1:* Electronics fundamentals, including AC electricity, resonant circuit and vacuum tube characteristics, audio amplification, and radio receiver theory; MHF, VHF, UHF transmitter theory; radar fundamentals, including time constants, pulse-shaping circuits and square-wave generators; pulse circuits and counters, and introduction to radar systems; gyros, synchros, and servomechanisms; aviation guided missile familiarization; guided missile components maintenance and system testing. *Course 2:* Gyros, synchros, and servomechanisms; aviation guided missiles maintenance and testing; missile-handling equipment and handling procedures.

Credit recommendation, collegiate level: CAUTION: *These courses vary in length and recommendation. Require exact identification by title and length. Course 1:* 3 semester hours in electronics, 2 semester hours in electronic circuits, and credit in electrical laboratory on the basis of demonstrated skills and/or institutional examinations. *Course 2:* Credit in electrical laboratory on the basis of demonstrated skills and/or institutional examinations.

---

1. Aviation Machinist's Mate, Class A
2. Aviation Machinist's Mate, Class B

Location: Naval Air Technical Training Center, Memphis, Tenn.

Length: *Course 1,* 14 weeks; *Course 2,* 24 weeks.

Objectives: To provide Navy and Marine Corps enlisted personnel with basic and advanced training in the operation and repair of aircraft reciprocating and jet engines.

Instruction: *Course 1:* Aircraft hardware, handtools, and lubricants; reciprocating power plants and line operations, including disassembly and assembly; reciprocating power plant accessories; reciprocating power plant maintenance; jet power plants assembly and disassembly; axial flow power plant; jet power plant maintenance. *Course 2:* Organization and administration; naval aviation and aircraft maintenance administration; aeronautical publications and records; reciprocating power plants; ignition systems; fuel metering; hydraulically and electrically operated propellers and systems; turbo propellers; jet power plants disassembly and reassembly; engine change, preservation, and storage; helicopter theory, principles of flight, operation, and maintenance.

Credit recommendation, collegiate level: *Course 1* is technical and vocational in nature. Credit in aircraft engine repair shop on the basis of demonstrated skills and/or institutional examinations. *Course 2:* 2 semester hours in maintenance management. At the technical and vocational level, credit in aircraft engine repair shop on the basis of demonstrated skills and/or institutional examinations.

Aviation Machinist's Mate H (Helicopter), Class A

Location: Naval Air Technical Training Center, Memphis, Tenn.

Length: 11–12 weeks.

Objectives: To train Navy and Marine Corps enlisted personnel as helicopter mechanics.

Instruction: Helicopter and power plant principles; fuel metering and carburetion; ignition systems; engine sections and related systems; transmission system; hydraulic system; main rotor and tail rotor drive section and assembly; flight control system; inspection by systems; blade changing and tracking.

Credit recommendation, collegiate level: This course is technical and vocational in nature. Credit in helicopter repair shop on the basis of demonstrated skills and/or institutional examinations.

1. **Aviation Machinist's Mate J (Jet Engine), Class A (Aviation Machinist's Mate J (Turbo Jet), Class A)**
2. **Aviation Machinist's Mate J (Jet Engine), Class B (Aviation Machinist's Mate J (Turbo Jet), Class B)**

Location: Naval Air Technical Training Center, Memphis, Tenn.

Length: *Course 1*, 6–8 weeks; *Course 2*, 12 weeks.

Objectives: To provide basic and advanced training for Navy and Marine Corps enlisted personnel in the inspection and maintenance of aircraft jet engines.

Instruction: *Course 1:* Jet power plant and system familiarization; power plant sections and their components; disassembly and assembly; lubrication, starting, ignition, fuel, and air systems; compressor design; periodic inspections and power plant replacement; jet aircraft line operations. *Course 2:* Aircraft maintenance management; aviation supply system familiarization; aeronautical publications; power plant fundamentals and auxiliary equipment; J-48 and J-57 power plants disassembly, inspection, maintenance, and reassembly; T-56 and J-79 power plants orientation and turbo propeller; leadership and supervision.

Credit recommendation, collegiate level: *Course 1* is technical and vocational in nature. Credit in jet engine repair shop on the basis of demonstrated skills and/or institutional examinations. *Course 2:* 2 semester hours in maintenance management. At the technical and vocational level, credit in jet engine repair shop on the basis of demonstrated skills and/or institutional examinations.

1. **Aviation Machinist's Mate R (Reciprocating), Class A**
2. **Aviation Machinist's Mate R (Reciprocating), Class B**

Location: Naval Air Technical Training Center, Memphis, Tenn.

Length: *Course 1*, 8–9 weeks; *Course 2*, 15 weeks.

Objectives: To provide basic and advanced training for Navy and Marine Corps enlisted personnel in the inspection and maintenance of aircraft reciprocating engines.

Instruction: *Course 1:* Power plant principles; aircraft fuel systems; propellers; power plant sections removal, disassembly, assembly, and installation; line operations; pre- and postflight inspections; power plant accessories; quick engine change assembly; engine buildup, preservation, and depreservation; inspection

systems and preventive maintenance. *Course 2:* Aircraft maintenance management; aviation supply system; aeronautical publications; reciprocating power plants; ignition systems; fuel metering; hydraulically and electrically operated propellers and systems; turbo propellers; leadership and supervision.

Credit recommendation, collegiate level: *Course 1* is technical and vocational in nature. Credit in aircraft reciprocating engine repair shop on the basis of demonstrated skills and/or institutional examinations. *Course 2:* 2 semester hours in maintenance management. At the technical and vocational level, credit in aircraft reciprocating engine repair shop on the basis of demonstrated skills and/or institutional examinations.

Aviation Maintenance Administrationman, Class A (Aviation Maintenance Administration, Class A)

Location: Naval Air Technical Training Center, Memphis, Tenn.

Length: 6 weeks.

Objectives: To provide Navy and Marine Corps aviation personnel with training in aviation clerical and administrative procedures.

Instruction: Basic typing; fundamentals of training; publications; aircraft maintenance system; aircraft accounting; aircraft logs and records; receipt and transfer; weight and balance charts; aircraft engine accounting records and reports; maintenance administration; filing; operation and care of duplicating machines.

Credit recommendation, collegiate level: Credit in typing on the basis of institutional examination. At the technical level, credit in office practices on the basis of demonstrated skills and/or institutional examinations.

1. **Aviation Mechanical Fundamentals, Class A**
2. **Mechanical Fundamentals (Aviation), Class P**

Locations: Class P Aviation Fundamentals Schools, Jacksonville, Fla., and Norman, Okla.; Naval Air Technical Training Center, Memphis, Tenn.

Length: 4–6 weeks.

Objectives: To provide non-rated naval aviation and Marine Corps personnel with basic training preparatory to specialized naval air training.

Instruction: *Course 1:* Technical publications and Federal supply system; hand tools and aircraft hardware; introduction to mathematics, physics, and electricity; mechanics of heat and gases; series and parallel circuits; theory and construction of aircraft batteries; magnetic theory. *Course 2:* Introduction to naval aviation, including aircraft familiarization and handling, safety and survival, first aid, and fire fighting; hand tools and aviation hardware; introduction to mathematics, physics, and electricity.

Credit recommendation, collegiate level: These courses are technical and vocational in nature. Credit in mechanical shop on the basis of demonstrated skills and/or institutional examinations.

Aviation Medicine Technic

Location: Naval School of Aviation Medicine, Pensacola, Fla.

Length: 16 weeks.

Objectives: To train personnel to assist in special examinations and treatment of naval aviators and flight personnel.

Instruction: Advanced anatomy and physiology in the aviation environment; medical aspects of acceleration including ejection seats, survival, psychological testing, night vision, and aviation safety; ophthalmology and optics; adminstration.

Credit recommendation, collegiate level: This course is technical and vocational in nature. Credit in aviation medicine technician training on the basis of demonstrated skills and/or institutional examinations.

Aviation Ordnance Officers, Class O

Location: Naval Air Technical Training Center, Jacksonville, Fla.

Length: 10 weeks.

Objectives: To provide junior line officers with a theoretical and practical background in aircraft ordnance and armament equipment.

Instruction: Basic electricity and administration; generators, motors, and measuring devices; electronics and electrical systems; aviation fire control; aircraft turrets and munitions; aircraft machine guns and boresighting; aerial torpedoes and aircraft releasing equipment.

Credit recommendation, collegiate level: No credit as the course is military in nature.

Aviation Ordnance Officers (Management), Class O

Location: Naval Air Technical Training Center, Jacksonville, Fla.

Length: 4 weeks.

Objectives: To familiarize officers with the management aspects of aviation ordnance ashore and afloat.

Instruction: Aviation ordnance management, including publications, administration, weapons department/division organization, safety, and security; procurement management; control management; standard Navy maintenance and material management system; maintenance data collection and processing.

Credit recommendation, collegiate level: 2 semester hours in supply management.

1. Aviation Ordnanceman, Class A
2. Aviation Ordnanceman (Turrets), Class A
3. Aviation Ordnanceman (Utility), Class A

Location: Naval Air Technical Training Center, Jacksonville, Fla.

Length: 11–18 weeks.

Objectives: To train enlisted personnel for naval aviation ordnance duty.

Instruction: *Course 1:* Basic training in hand tools, hardware, mathematics, physics, and ordnance administration; basic electricity, electronics, and electrical armament circuits; operational equipment, including bomb and torpedo handling equipment; guns; munitions; line operations and operational problems; guided missiles. *Courses 2 and 3* cover most of the same subjects as *Course 1*, with the exception of guided missiles, and emphasize operational and maintenance training in either aircraft hydraulic and electric turrets or guns and munitions.

Credit recommendation, collegiate level: For each course, credit in electricity on the basis of institutional examination. At the technical level, credit in electrical and mechanical shop on the basis of demonstrated skills and/or institutional examinations.

Aviation Ordnanceman, Class B

Location: Naval Air Technical Training Center, Jacksonville, Fla.

Length: 24–25 weeks.

Objectives: To provide enlisted personnel with advanced training in naval aviation ordnance.

Instruction: Administration, including supervision and management, publications, material control, naval aircraft maintenance program, and ammunition stock recording system; mathematics and physics; direct current and direct current devices; alternating current; basic electronics; circuit analysis; small arms and aircraft guns; non-computing sights and boresighting; basic munitions; undersea and nuclear weapons; conventional weapons loading and equipment; semi-active and passive air-to-air missiles; air-to-surface missiles; missile targets.

Credit recommendation, collegiate level: 2 semester hours in maintenance management and 2 semester hours at the freshman or sophomore level as an elective in electricity.

Aviation Physiology Technician
(Aviation Physiology Technic)
(Low Pressure Chamber Technic)

Location: Naval School of Aviation Medicine, Pensacola, Fla.

Length: 6–16 weeks.

Objectives: To train personnel in aviation physiology, cabin pressurization, pressure suits, ejection seat technique, and oxygen use.

Instruction: Personnel equipment; chamber construction, operation, and maintenance; chamber runs; cabin pressurization systems; full pressure suits; ejection seats; physiology; regulators, reducers, and composite disconnects; partial pressure suits; practice lectures; liquid oxygen systems; chamber emergencies; night vision.

Credit recommendation, collegiate level: This course is technical and vocational in nature. Credit in training as aviation physiology technician on the basis of demonstrated skills and/or institutional examinations.

Aviation Storekeeper, Class A

Locations: Naval Air Technical Training Centers, Jacksonville, Fla., and Memphis, Tenn.

Length: 10–12 weeks.

Objectives: To train enlisted personnel in all phases of naval aviation supply procedures.

Instruction: Basic typing; aviation storekeeper fundamentals, including aeronautical supply system ashore, storage of materials, correspondence, material-handling equipment, packing and preservation, and operation of office machines; use of catalogs and publications; fleet aviation supply ashore and afloat.

Credit recommendation, collegiate level: Credit in typing on the basis of institutional examination. At the technical and vocational level, credit in general office practices on the basis of demonstrated skills and/or institutional examinations.

1. **Aviation Structural Mechanic E (Safety Equipment), Class A**
2. **Aviation Structural Mechanic E (Safety Equipment), Class B**

Location: Naval Air Technical Training Center, Memphis, Tenn.

Length: 9–11 weeks.

Objectives: To train Navy and Marine enlisted personnel in aircraft safety equipment operation and maintenance.

Instruction: *Course 1:* Introduction to electricity; circuit troubleshooting; aircraft pressurization, air-conditioning, and engine bleed air systems; oxygen and carbon dioxide systems; egress systems and drogue chutes; operational maintenance. *Course 2* covers the same general areas of instruction at a more advanced level.

Credit recommendation, collegiate level: These courses are technical and vocational in nature. Credit in aircraft systems repair shop on the basis of demonstrated skills and/or institutional examinations.

1. **Aviation Structural Mechanic H (Hydraulic), Class A**
2. **Aviation Structural Mechanic H (Hydraulics), Class B**

Location: Naval Air Technical Training Center, Memphis, Tenn.

Length: *Course 1,* 8–10 weeks; *Course 2,* 12–13 weeks.

Objectives: To provide Navy and Marine enlisted personnel with basic and advanced training in aircraft hydraulic systems maintenance and repair.

Instruction: *Course 1:* Introduction to electricity; troubleshooting circuits; interpretation of maintenance drawings; basic hydraulics and components, including rigid tubing and fittings, flexible hose and fittings, fluids, packings, gaskets, wipers, power system types and servicing, valves and actuating cylinders, maintenance of landing gear units and aircraft brakes; hydraulic system familiarization, troubleshooting, and operational maintenance. *Course 2* covers the same general areas of instruction at a more advanced level.

Credit recommendation, collegiate level: These courses are technical and vocational in nature. Credit in aircraft hydraulic systems repair shop on the basis of demonstrated skills and/or institutional examinations.

1. **Aviation Structural Mechanic S, Class A**
   (Aviation Structural Mechanic S (Structures), Class A)
   (Aviation Structural Mechanic S (Structural), Class A)
2. **Aviation Structural Mechanic S (Structures), Class B**

(Aviation Structural Mechanic S (Structural), Class B)

Location: Naval Air Technical Training Center, Memphis, Tenn.

Length: *Course 1,* 9–12 weeks; *Course 2,* 12–15 weeks.

Objectives: *Course 1* provides basic training, and *Course 2* advanced training, for Navy and Marine enlisted personnel in aircraft construction and airframe maintenance.

Instruction: *Course 1:* Introduction to electricity; circuit troubleshooting; interpretation of maintenance drawings; aircraft sheet metal layout, forming, seaming, riveting, and repair; oxyacetylene welding; nonmetallic materials; airframes and operational maintenance. *Course 2:* Maintenance and material control; blueprint reading and drawing; electricity; heat treatment and metal finishing; metal fabrication and structural repair; oxyacetylene, electric arc, and inert gas arc welding; nonmetallic materials; aircraft operational maintenance; leadership and supervision.

Credit recommendation, collegiate level: These courses are technical and vocational in nature. Credit in aircraft repair shop and metal shop on the basis of demonstrated skills and/or institutional examinations.

1. **Aviation Structural Mechanic School, Class A**
2. **Aviation Structural Mechanic School, Class B**

Location: Naval Air Technical Training Center, Memphis, Tenn.

Length: *Course 1,* 14 weeks; *Course 2,* 24–26 weeks.

Objectives: To provide Navy and Marine Corps enlisted personnel with basic and advanced training in aircraft structural maintenance and repair.

Instruction: *Course 1:* Aircraft sheet metal layout, forming, and seaming; riveting; repair of stressed skin and internal structures; oxyacetylene welding; nonmetallic materials, including rubber, reinforced and transparent plastics, woodworking, fabrics, dopes, and painting; aircraft hydraulics; airframes structural inspection and maintenance. *Course 2:* Review of mathematics and physics; blueprint reading and drawing; aircraft metals heat treating, electroplating, fabrication, and structural repair; oxyacetylene, inert gas, and electric arc welding; nonmetallic materials, including woodworking, transparent and reinforced plastics, fabrics, paints, dopes, self-sealing hose, and fuel cells; aircraft hydraulics; airframes inspection and maintenance; cabin pressurization, air conditioning, and ejection seats; engine starting, ground check, and periodic inspections.

Credit recommendation, collegiate level: These courses are technical and vocational in nature. Credit in metal shop and machine shop on the basis of demonstrated skills and/or institutional examinations.

Aviation Support Equipment Technician, Class A

Location: Naval Air Technical Training Center, Memphis, Tenn.

Length: 11–12 weeks.

Objectives: To train enlisted personnel in one of three types of aviation support equipment maintenance.

Instruction: *Common Phase:* Publications and maintenance organization; applied physics; maintenance materials, inspections and safety. *Electrical Specialty:* Electrical and electronic fundamentals and maintenance; generator and motor fundamentals. *Hydraulics and Structures Specialty:* Chassis maintenance; metal repair; fluidic systems maintenance. *Mechanical Specialty:* Reciprocating engines fundamentals and maintenance; power trains; air conditioning; gas turbine compressors.

Credit recommendation, collegiate level: Credit in electricity by examination for the electrical specialty only. At the technical and vocational level, credit in electrical or mechanical shop by demonstrated skills and/or examination for any specialty.

1. **Avionics, Class B**
2. **Intermediate Avionics, Class B**
   (Avionics Intermediate, Class B)

Location: Naval Air Technical Training Center, Memphis, Tenn.

Length: *Course 1,* 31–32 weeks; *Course 2,* 31–34 weeks.

Objectives: *Course 1:* To train enlisted personnel to maintain and supervise the maintenance of modern complex avionics systems. *Course 2:* To train enlisted personnel in avionics systems maintenance and use of related test equipment.

Instruction: *Course 1:* Administration and supply; mathematics; physics; advanced mathematics; atomic physics; electricity and magnetism; electronics; servomechanisms and analog computers; electronic circuits; transistor physics and circuits; digital computers; radiation theory and systems; communication and radar techniques; antisubmarine warfare systems and countermeasures; advanced techniques in navigation; television and advanced guidance system techniques. *Course 2:* Supervisory training; mathematics; electricity; amplifier fundamentals; amplifier circuits and power supplies; magnetic amplifiers and test equipment; basic transmitter circuits; basic receivers; special circuits; avionics physics; digital and analog computers; principles of antisubmarine warfare; transmission lines and antennas.

Credit recommendation, collegiate level: *Course 1:* 5 semester hours in mathematics, 5 semester hours in physics, and 5 semester hours in engineering electronics. *Course 2:* 6 semester hours at the freshman or sophomore level as an elective in electricity and electronics, and credit in electrical laboratory on the basis of demonstrated skills and/or institutional examinations.

1. **Avionics Fundamentals, Class A**
2. **Avionics Fundamentals, Class A**

Location: Naval Air Technical Training Center, Memphis, Tenn.

Length: *Course 1,* 19 weeks; *Course 2,* 14–16 weeks.

Objectives: To provide enlisted personnel with basic training in aviation electronics.

Instruction: *Course 1:* DC electricity and circuitry; AC fundamentals and electrical apparatus; vacuum tube theory; audio amplification; radio receiver theory; receiver troubleshooting and alignment; transmitter and transistor fundamentals; time constants; pulse-shaping circuits and square-wave generators; pulse circuits, counters, and amplifiers; introduction to radar systems. *Course 2:* DC and AC electrical fundamentals;

vacuum tube theory and transmitters; semi-conductor theory and receivers; wave-shaping circuits; radar circuits and devices; Navy maintenance and material management system; computer fundamentals.

Credit recommendation, collegiate level: CAUTION: *Courses in aviation electronics (or avionics) vary slightly in title, length, and recommendation. Require exact identification by full title and length. Course 1:* 4 semester hours in electronics and 4 semester hours in electronic circuits. *Course 2:* 3 semester hours in electronics and 3 semester hours in electronic circuits.

Basic Civil Engineer Corps
(Basic Civil Engineer Corps Officer's Course)

Location: Naval School, Port Hueneme, Calif.

Length: 8 weeks.

Objectives: To prepare junior officers for duty in one of three areas—public works management, contract administration, or construction operations.

Instruction: All students receive instruction in a *General Course phase* which includes fundamentals of financial management, principles of budgeting, financing for activity public works, control of funds, facilities management, counterinsurgency application and operations, nuclear weapons effects, general protective considerations, organization of the naval facilities engineering command, planning and operations, functional component system, counterinsurgency, engineering management, organizational behavior, network analysis, and production programming. The *Public Works Management specialty* includes introduction to contracts and labor, contract procedures, contract specifications and field administration, engineering management, and industrial relations. The *Contract Administration specialty* includes introduction to contracts and labor, contract procedures and labor law enforcement, contract specifications and field administration, and financial management. *The Construction Battalion specialty* includes construction battalion development and organization, mobile construction battalion administration and personnel, battalion training, mobile construction battalion operations, and mobile construction battalion logistics.

Credit recommendation, collegiate level: For the *General Course phase:* 4 semester hours in business organization and management. Additional credit for the specialty as follows—for the *Public Works Management specialty:* 2 semester hours in public works engineering; for the *Contract Administration specialty:* 2 semester hours in contract administration; for the *Construction Battalion specialty:* 2 semester hours in construction engineering.

Basic Electricity and Electronics for Torpedoman's Mate

Location: Fleet Anti-Submarine Warfare School, San Diego, Calif.

Length: 8 weeks.

Objectives: To provide torpedoman's mates and torpedoman's mate strikers with a background in basic electricity and electronics.

Instruction: Fundamentals of DC and AC; inductance; capacitance; transformers; synchro and servo fundamentals; vacuum tubes; rectifiers; amplifiers; oscillators; transmitters and receivers.

Credit recommendation, collegiate level: 2 semester hours at the freshman or sophomore level as an elective in electricity and electronics.

Basic Electronics Orientation

Locations: Fleet Airborne Electronics Training Unit, Atlantic, Norfolk, Va., and Jacksonville, Fla.

Length: 4 weeks.

Objectives: To provide maintenance personnel with a basic understanding of electronics and to prepare them for training in special fields.

Instruction: Review of mathematics; physics of atomic structure; DC and AC theory; vacuum tube theory; transistor theory; basic electronics circuits; test equipment.

Credit recommendation, collegiate level: 2 semester hours at the freshman or sophomore level as an elective in electricity and electronics.

Basic Helicopter Course, Class C

Location: Naval Air Technical Training Center, Memphis, Tenn.

Length: 7–8 weeks.

Objectives: To train Navy and Marine Corps personnel in helicopter maintenance and repair.

Instruction: Introduction to helicopters; turboshaft power plant; power transmission system and flight controls (single rotor); inspections and line operations; tandem-rotor helicopter familiarization.

Credit recommendation, collegiate level: This course is technical and vocational in nature. Credit in helicopter repair shop on the basis of demonstrated skills and/or institutional examinations.

Basic Jet Navigation, Class O

Location: Naval Air Technical Training Center, Glynco, Ga.

Length: 4 weeks.

Objectives: To provide prospective naval flight officers with basic jet navigation training.

Instruction: Aircraft equipment; flight operations, safety, and survival; flight planning and airways navigation; dead reckoning, low-level, and radar navigation; practical application of navigation operations, including laboratory training, navigation flight planning, and training flights.

Credit recommendation, collegiate level: Credit in navigation on the basis of demonstrated skills and/or institutional examinations.

Basic Nuclear Power
(Basic Course, Nuclear Power Academic Training Program)

Locations: Bainbridge, Md., Idaho Falls (Arco), Idaho, Mare Island (Vallejo), Calif., New London, Conn.

Length: 22–24 weeks.

Objectives: To provide training for naval personnel in the field of nuclear power plant operation.

Instruction: Basic mathematics; modern physics; reactor principles; slide rule; blueprints; AC theory; thermodynamics; water-cooled power plants; liquid-metal-cooled power plants; water technology; health physics; level control systems. In some nuclear power courses the students may also take one of the following specialist phases: reactor control systems, plant control

systems, plant machinery and welding, radiological health and safety, chemistry, or electronics.

Credit recommendation, collegiate level: 3 semester hours in introductory atomic physics or nuclear technology. At the technical level, credit in the field of specialized training on the basis of demonstrated skills and/or institutional examinations.

1. Basic Qualification Course of the Supply Corps
2. Basic Qualification Course of the Supply Corps
3. Basic Qualification Course of the Supply Corps

Location: U.S. Navy Supply Corps School, Athens, Ga.

Length: *Course 1:* 10 weeks; *Course 2:* 14–16 weeks; *Course 3:* 26 weeks.

Objectives: To train officers in shipboard supply and disbursing operations.

Instruction: All courses include the same subjects, but the longer the course the greater the depth of study. Supply management; personnel administration; mess management; retail sales, disbursing afloat; supply review.

Credit recommendation, collegiate level: CAUTION: *These courses vary in length and recommendation. Require exact identification of the course by title and length. Course 1:* 2 semester hours in supply management, and credit in personnel administration on the basis of demonstrated skills and/or institutional examinations. *Course 2:* 3 semester hours in supply management and 2 semester hours in personnel administration. *Course 3:* 4 semester hours in supply management and 3 semester hours in personnel administration.

Basic Quartermaster

Location: Fleet Training Centers, San Diego, Calif. and Pearl Harbor, Hawaii.

Length: 4 weeks.

Objectives: To qualify personnel to stand quartermaster watches under supervision (less visual signaling).

Instruction: Navigational aids; time and timepieces; rules of the road; quartermaster on watch; weather; assisting the navigator.

Credit recommendation, collegiate level: This course is technical and vocational in nature. Credit in navigation and signaling on the basis of demonstrated skills and/or institutional examinations.

Basic Signalman

Location: Fleet Training Group, Pearl Harbor, Hawaii.

Length: 6 weeks.

Objectives: To train personnel in visual communications procedures to qualify them as watchstanders under supervision.

Instruction: Flashing light; flag identification and visual signaling procedures; semaphore; publications and visual signaling procedures.

Credit recommendation, collegiate level: This course is technical and vocational in nature. Credit in signaling on the basis of demonstrated skills and/or institutional examinations.

1. Blood Bank Technique
2. Clinical Laboratory Technique
3. Clinical Laboratory Technique
   (Blood Bank and Clinical Laboratory Technic)

Locations: Naval Medical School, Bethesda, Md., Naval Hospitals, Bremerton, Wash., Chelsea, Mass., Corpus Christi, Tex., Great Lakes, Ill., Oakland, Calif., San Diego, Calif., Philadelphia, Pa., and Portsmouth, Va.

Length: *Course 1,* 8 weeks. *Course 2,* 52 weeks. *Course 3,* 60 weeks.

Objectives: To provide instruction in the basic knowledge and skills required to assist in advanced laboratory procedures and in the operation of all phases of a blood bank.

Instruction: *Course 1:* Blood collecting; blood donor center technique; blood processing technique. *Course 2:* Bacteriology; serology; hematology; pathology; medicine parasitology; blood and clinical chemistry. *Course 3:* Urinalysis, in addition to the subjects of *Courses 1 and 2.*

Credit recommendation, collegiate level: CAUTION: *These courses vary in title, length, and recommendation. Require exact identification of the course by title and length. Course 1:* This course is technical and vocational in nature. Credit in blood bank technology on the basis of demonstrated skills and/or institutional examinations. *Courses 2 and 3:* For each course, 12 semester hours in bacteriology and blood chemistry.

1. Boilermen, Class A
2. Boilermen, Class B

Locations: Naval Training Center, Great Lakes, Ill.; Navy Base, Philadelphia, Pa.

Length: *Course 1,* 6–15 weeks; *Course 2,* 15–18 weeks.

Objectives: *Course 1* provides basic training, *Course 2* advanced training, in the operation, maintenance, and repair of marine boilers, fireroom machinery, pumps, and associated equipment.

Instruction: *Course 1:* Mathematics review and blueprint reading; tools and materials; valves, piping, and fittings; basic principles of steam plants; naval boilers; boiler construction, maintenance, and repair; pumps; forced draft blowers; distilling plants; fuel oil; feed water; fireroom operation; records, reports, and damage control; fireroom casualty control. *Course 2:* Steam plants; boiler blueprints, records, and reports; fuel oil systems and testing; boiler accessories; leadership; fireroom measuring devices; boiler cleaning, inspection, testing, and repair; auxiliary machinery, feed water systems and testing; automatic controls; fireroom operation and casualty control; damage control.

Credit recommendation, collegiate level: These courses are technical and vocational in nature. *Course 1:* Credit in metal shop and operation and maintenance of marine boilers and associated equipment on the basis of demonstrated skills and/or institutional examinations. *Course 2:* Credit in the operation and maintenance of marine boilers and associated equipment on the basis of demonstrated skills and/or institutional examinations.

Builder, Class A

Locations: Naval Schools, Davisville, R.I., and Port Hueneme, Calif.

Length: 12 weeks.

Objectives: To train enlisted personnel in the fundamentals of building and construction work.

Instruction: Carpenter's mathematics; tools and materials; blueprint reading; building layout; field rigging; mixing, placing, and finishing of concrete; concrete form construction; masonry framing of building elements and scaffolds; painting; roofing; erection of advanced base, waterfront, and heavy timber structures.

Credit recommendation, collegiate level: This course is technical and vocational in nature. Credit in mechanical shop and building construction on the basis of demonstrated skills and/or institutional examinations.

Builder, Class B

Locations: Naval Schools, Davisville, R.I., and Port Hueneme, Calif.

Length: 16–17 weeks.

Objectives: To provide selected builders with training in advanced construction techniques.

Instruction: Mathematics; petty officer leadership training; foremanship; light frame structures; advanced base and waterfront structures; shop machinery and safety; masonry; plastering and ceramic tile; concrete and concrete forms.

Credit recommendation, collegiate level: This course is technical and vocational in nature. Credit in carpentry shop and building construction on the basis of demonstrated skills and/or institutional examinations.

C-121 Electrical Systems

Location: Naval Air Station, Patuxent River, Md.

Length: 3 weeks.

Objectives: To provide aviation electricians with specialized training on the C-121 aircraft electrical system.

Instruction: DC and AC power systems; air conditioning and pressurization; fuel and oil systems; Hamilton standard propeller system; Sperry engine analyzer.

Credit recommendation, collegiate level: No credit because of the brevity and specialized nature of the course.

C-121 Electronic Systems

Location: Naval Air Station, Patuxent River, Md.

Length: 3 weeks.

Objectives: To train aviation electronics technicians on the C-121 aircraft electronic components and systems.

Instruction: C-121J (transport) electronic configuration including communication, navigation, and AN/APS-42 radar systems; EC-121K systems including communications, navigation, radar, IFF, and other associated equipment.

Credit recommendation, collegiate level: No credit because of the brevity and specialized nature of the course.

C-121 Structures and Systems Maintenance, Class C

Location: Naval Air Station, Patuxent River, Md.

Length: 3 weeks.

Objectives: To train aviation structural mechanics in the maintenance of structures, airframes, and hydraulic systems on the C-121 aircraft.

Instruction: Introduction to C-121 and hydraulics; flight control and fuel systems; air conditioning and pressurization; refrigeration; air distribution and heaters.

Credit recommendation, collegiate level: This course is technical and vocational in nature. Credit in aircraft systems repair shop on the basis of demonstrated skills and/or institutional examinations.

CIC "Cornerstone"

Location: Naval Air Station, Glynco, Brunswick, Ga.

Length: 7–8 weeks.

Objectives: To provide officers with combat information center basic phases training.

Instruction: Organization and training; electronics; electronic warfare; communications; surface operations fundamentals; air operations.

Credit recommendation, collegiate level: No credit because of the specialized nature of the course.

1. Cardio-Pulmonary Technic
2. Cardio-Pulmonary Technic

Locations: National Naval Medical Center, Bethesda, Md., and Naval Hospital, San Diego, Calif.

Length: *Course 1,* 26 weeks; *Course 2,* 52 weeks.

Objectives: To provide instruction in the basic skills and knowledge necessary to assist in all phases of cardiac catheterizations, angiocardiography, arterial puncture studies, bronchography, and pulmonary function studies.

Instruction: Anatomy and physiology; physics; electrocardiograph monitoring; pulmonary function procedures; cardiac catheterization procedures; surgical technique; X-ray technique; purpose, methods, and tabulation for all other tests; operation and maintenance of machines. *Courses 1 and 2* include the same subjects, but *Course 2* receives instruction at a greater depth with most of the additional time spent in laboratory study.

Credit recommendation, collegiate level: These courses are technical and vocational in nature. Credit in surgical-medical technical procedures on the basis of demonstrated skills and/or institutional examinations.

Carrier Air Traffic Control Center Controller, Class C/O

Location: Naval Air Technical Training Center, Glynco, Ga.

Length: 3–5 weeks.

Objectives: To train air controlmen and officers for carrier air traffic control duties.

Instruction: CATCC air operations; carrier controlled approach; naval tactical data system console training.

Credit recommendation, collegiate level: No credit because of the brevity and specialized nature of the course.

1. Carrier Air Traffic Control Center Equipment Maintenance (AN/SPN-10), Class C
2. Carrier Air Traffic Control Center Equipment Maintenance, AN/SPN-35, Class C
3. Carrier Air Traffic Control Center Equipment Maintenance, AN/SPN-6 and AN/SPN-12 (XN-4), Class C

Location: Naval Air Technical Training Center, Glynco, Ga.

Length: *Course 1,* 15 weeks; *Course 2,* 7–8 weeks; *Course 3,* 3 weeks.

Objectives: To train Navy electronic technicians in the operation and maintenance of the air traffic control center equipment specified.

Instruction: *Course 1:* Computer basics as related to the AN/SPN-10 automatic carrier landing system; radar group and tracking computer; stabilization data generator subsystem and navigational computer; signal data converter; control and monitor equipment; system checkout and trouble analysis. *Course 2:* Radar circuit theory; AN/SPN-35 radar transmitter, receiver, and antenna mount; AN/SPN-35 indicator and system; preventive and corrective maintenance. *Course 3:* AN/SPN-6 radar familiarization and maintenance; AN/SPN-12 (XN-4) air speed radar preventive and corrective maintenance.

Credit recommendation, collegiate level: For each course, credit in electrical laboratory on the basis of demonstrated skills and/or institutional examinations.

Carrier Gasoline and Inert Gas Systems, Class C

Location: Naval Air Material Center, Philadelphia, Pa.

Length: 6 weeks.

Objectives: To provide specialized training in the operation and maintenance of carrier gasoline and inert gas systems.

Instruction: Operation of hydraulic gasoline system and carrier gasoline system; aviation lubricating oil system; carrier inert gas system operation and maintenance; care and operation of analyzers; operation and maintenance of high capacity aviation fuel system.

Credit recommendation, collegiate level: This course is technical and vocational in nature. Credit in fuel systems operation and maintenance on the basis of demonstrated skills and/or institutional examinations.

1. Catapult, Arresting Gear, and Visual Landing Aids CVA (C-13 Catapult), Class C
2. Catapult, Arresting Gear, and Visual Landing Aids CVA (C-7/C-11 Catapults), Class C
3. Catapult, Arresting Gear, and Visual Landing Aids (C-13 Catapult and MK-7 Arresting Gear), Class C
4. Catapult, Arresting Gear, and Visual Landing Aids (C-7/C-11 Catapults and MK-7 Arresting Gear), Class C
5. Catapult, Arresting Gear, and Visual Landing Aids (CVA), Class C
6. Catapult, Arresting Gear, Optical Landing System (CVA Catapult), Class C
7. Catapult, Arresting Gear, and Optical Landing System, Class C
8. CVS Catapult, Arresting Gear, and Visual Landing Aids, Class C
9. Catapult, Arresting Gear, and Visual Landing Aids (CVS), Class C
10. Catapult, Arresting Gear, Optical Landing System (CVS Catapult), Class C

Location: Naval Air Technical Training Unit, Philadelphia, Pa.

Length: *Courses 1 through 7, 8–10 weeks; Courses 8, 9, and 10, 4–5 weeks.*

Objectives: To provide aviation boatswain's mates "E" and other experienced personnel with specialized training in the operation, maintenance, and repair of the equipment specified.

Instruction: *Courses 1 through 10:* Fundamentals, including application of hydraulics, familiarization with handtools, rigging equipment, wire rope and fittings, socket pouring, liquid seals, packings, blueprint reading, and electrical devices; crew organization and standard catapult and arresting gear signals; logs, records, reports, and publications. The remainder of each course deals with the equipment specified—familiarization with its installation; description and function; principles of operation; inspection, lubrication, and mechanical maintenance.

Credit recommendation, collegiate level: These courses are technical and vocational in nature. Credit in mechanical shop and operation and maintenance of catapult and arresting gear equipment on the basis of demonstrated skills and/or institutional examinations.

1. Catapult Course, Class C
2. Arresting Gear Course, Class C
3. Arresting Gear and Optical Landing System, Class C
4. Catapult and Arresting Gear School, Class C

Location: Naval Air Technical Training Unit, Philadelphia, Pa.

Length: *Course 1,* 7 weeks; *Course 2,* 4 weeks; *Course 3,* 3 weeks; *Course 4,* 11 weeks.

Objectives: To provide specialized training in the operation, maintenance, and repair of catapults, and/or arresting gear and optical landing systems.

Instruction: *Course 1:* Introduction to catapults; hydropneumatic and steam catapults operation, inspection, and maintenance. *Course 2:* Introduction to arresting gear; Mark 4, Mark 5–Mod 0, and Mark 7–Mod 1 arresting gear and barriers. *Course 3:* Mark 5 and Mark 7 arresting gear and barriers; operation and maintenance of arresting gear; optical landing system description, operation, and maintenance. *Course 4* is a combination of *Course 1* and *Course 2* or

Course 3. The overall instruction content is the same.

Credit recommendation, collegiate level: These courses are technical and vocational in nature. Credit in mechanical shop and operation and maintenance of catapult and arresting gear equipment on the basis of demonstrated skills and/or institutional examinations.

Central Gyro Reference System (AN/AJA-2), Class C

Location: Naval Air Station, Patuxent River, Md.

Length: 3 weeks.

Objectives: To train aviation electricians in the operation and maintenance of the system specified.

Instruction: Review of basic electricity and electronics pertaining to the central gyro reference system; CGRS three gyro stable platform; timing and functional operations; detailed circuit analysis; preflight checks and maintenance.

Credit recommendation, collegiate level: No credit because of the brevity and limited technical nature of the course.

Chemistry
(Chemistry Technic)

Location: Naval Medical School, Bethesda, Md.

Length: 50–54 weeks.

Objectives: To train enlisted personnel as chemical laboratory assistants.

Instruction: General chemistry; chemical arithmetic; quantitative and qualitative analysis; organic chemistry; toxicology; biochemistry; clinical biochemistry.

Credit recommendation, collegiate level: 4 semester hours in qualitative and quantitative analysis and 4 semester hours in organic chemistry.

Chief Petty Officer Leadership School, Class C
(Chief Petty Officer Academy, Class C)

Location: Naval Air Station, Pensacola, Fla.

Length: 5 weeks.

Objectives: To increase chief petty officers' ability to fulfill their responsibilities in the Navy.

Instruction: Military leadership; management; moral leadership; military justice; drill and command; on-the-job training; conference speaking; world affairs; naval history; naval traditions; physical training.

Credit recommendation, collegiate level: No credit because of the brevity and specialized nature of the course.

Clinical Chemistry Technician, Class C
(Clinical Chemistry Technic)

Location: Naval Medical Center, Bethesda, Md.

Length: 12 weeks.

Objectives: To train personnel to conduct quantitative and qualitative analytical tests.

Instruction: Mathematics of chemistry techniques; quantitative analysis; instrumentation; organic chemistry; enzyme chemistry; steroid chemistry; toxicology; preparation of standards and solutions; techniques and specific analyses of miscellaneous blood and urine.

Credit recommendation, collegiate level: Credit in chemistry on the basis of institutional examination.

Clinical Laboratory Assistant Technic, Class C
(Clinical Laboratory Assistant Technician, Class C)

Locations: Naval Hospitals, San Diego, Calif., St. Albans, N.Y., Portsmouth, Va., Oakland, Calif., and Great Lakes, Ill.

Length: 12 weeks.

Objectives: To train personnel to conduct chemical and bacteriological laboratory tests.

Instruction: Laboratory aparatus and techniques; bacteriology; hematology; blood processing; serology; biochemistry; urinalysis; pathology; parasitology.

Credit recommendation, collegiate level: This course is technical and vocational in nature. Credit in clinical laboratory assistant technician training on the basis of demonstrated skills and/or institutional examinations.

Closed and Semiclosed Scuba

Location: Naval School, Underwater Swimmers, Key West, Fla.

Length: 4 weeks.

Objectives: To provide a refresher course for personnel in scuba.

Instruction: Underwater search and inspection; specific medical problems in closed and semiclosed circuit diving; types of closed and semiclosed circuit scuba; mixed gas theory; repair and maintenance.

Credit recommendation, collegiate level: This course is technical and vocational in nature. Credit in deep sea diving on the basis of demonstrated skills and/or institutional examinations.

Combat Information Center Officer, Class O

Locations: CIC Officer School, Glenview, Ill.; U.S. Naval CIC School, Glynco, Brunswick, Ga.

Length: 7–15 weeks.

Objectives: To train officers in all operational phases of combat information centers.

Instruction: Fundamentals, including organization, training, management, electronics, electronic warfare and communications; surface, air, and advanced operations, including air control, antiair, and antisubmarine warfare.

Credit recommendation, collegiate level: No credit because of the limited technical nature of the course.

Commissaryman, Class B

Locations: Naval Schools, Newport, R.I., and San Diego, Calif.

Length: 15 weeks.

Objectives: To train and qualify personnel for both afloat and ashore commissary billets.

Instruction: Sanitary precautions; nutrition and meal planning; stock control, subsistence, records, and returns; small quantity cooking; small quantity baking; meat cuts; seafood and poultry; galley and mess hall operations.

Credit recommendation, collegiate level: This course is technical and vocational in nature. Credit in cooking and baking on the basis of demonstrated skills and/or institutional examinations.

Communication Officer, Short Course

Location: Naval School, Newport, R.I.

Length: 8 weeks.

Objectives: To provide officers with primary communications training.

Instruction: Communication processes, techniques, equipment, and organizations for supporting command; communications in operational situations; telecommunications security; commercial communications; Navy postal service; censorship.

Credit recommendation, collegiate level: No credit because of the limited technical nature of the course.

Communications Yeoman, Class A

Locations: Naval Schools, Bainbridge, Md., and Norfolk, Va.

Length: 6 weeks.

Objectives: To train communications yeomen in practical clerical skills and certain operator capabilities.

Instruction: Operations and nontechnical maintenance of typewriters and teletype machines; operation and log keeping of voice and teletype circuits; routine administration of communications office; message construction and security precautions.

Credit recommendation, collegiate level: Credit in typing on the basis of institutional examination.

Compressed Gases, Class C

Location: Naval School, Portsmouth, Va.

Length: 14 weeks.

Objectives: To provide petty officers with the specific technical knowledge and skill required in the manufacture, transportation, and storage of compressed gases.

Instruction: Operation and maintenance of gas-generating, storage, and transfer equipment; nature and behavior of gases; storage and handling; safety precautions.

Credit recommendation, collegiate level: This course is technical and vocational in nature. Credit in gas-generating systems operation and maintenance on the basis of demonstrated skills and/or institutional examinations.

1. Computer Basics (Digital Computer Fundamentals)
2. Computer Basics (Digital and Analog Computer Fundamentals)
3. Computer Basics (Computer Basics (Digital, Analog, and Hybrid Computer Fundamentals))

Location: Class C Electronics Technician School, Great Lakes, Ill.

Length: *Course 1,* 8 weeks; *Course 2,* 14 weeks; *Course 3,* 16 weeks.

Objectives: To provide training in the theory and operation of the type, or types, of computer specified.

Instruction: *Course 1:* Number systems; programming; Boolean algebra; arithmetic operations; control; magnetics; semi-conductor logic. *Course 2* is a combination of *Course 1* and analog computer fundamentals which include algebra, analog components and mathematical applications, and analog mechanization. *Course*

3 is a combination of *Courses 1 and 2* and hybrid computer fundamentals which include an introduction to hybrid computing systems, conversion techniques, and the digital differential analyzer.

Credit recommendation, collegiate level: CAUTION: *These courses vary in title, length, and recommendation. Note that Course 1 may be taken separately, or as part of Courses 2 and 3. Course 2 may be taken separately, or as part of Course 3. Require identification of computer basics courses by full title and exact length. Course 1:* 3 semester hours in computing science. *Course 2:* 5 semester hours in computing science. *Course 3:* 6 semester hours in computing science.

Computer Programming Orientation

Location: Fleet Anti-Air Warfare Training Center, San Diego, Calif.

Length: 4 weeks.

Objectives: To provide instruction in the principles of programming the Navy tactical data system digital computer, in the principles of the compiling system used, and in the concepts of modular programming.

Instruction: Introduction to digital computers and programming; number systems; machine computations; Boolean algebra; operation and programming techniques of the NTDS unit computer; programming simple problems; CS-1 compiler language; operators and techniques; data design; modular programming techniques; intercomputer communications; U-PAK and resident control package operation and debugging operations.

Credit recommendation, collegiate level: 2 semester hours in computer management.

Construction Electrician, Class A

Locations: Naval Schools Construction, Port Hueneme, Calif., and Davisville, R.I.

Length: 14 weeks.

Objectives: To train enlisted personnel to install, operate, and repair electrical generating equipment, power and communication lines, and communications equipment.

Instruction: Basic electrical theory; motors and generators; pole line construction; communications; interior welding.

Credit recommendation, collegiate level: Credit in electricity on the basis of institutional examination. At the technical and vocational level, credit in telephone-telegraph equipment installation and maintenance on the basis of demonstrated skills and/or institutional examinations.

Construction Electrician, Class B

Locations: Naval Schools, Port Hueneme, Calif., and Davisville, R.I.

Length: 15–16 weeks.

Objectives: To train personnel as construction electricians with construction battalions.

Instruction: Electrical theory; electrical power generation and distribution; alternating current motors; local and common battery telephone; inter-office communications and public address systems; radiac and gas alarm instruments; cable splicing and fault location; interior wiring.

Credit recommendation, collegiate level: This course is technical and vocational in nature. Credit in electrical shop on the basis of demonstrated skills and/or institutional examinations.

1. Construction Mechanics, Class A
2. Construction Mechanics, Class B

Locations: Davisville, R.I.; Port Hueneme, Calif.

Length: 7–15 weeks.

Objectives: To train enlisted personnel in the basic technical knowledge and practical skills required by the construction mechanic rating, third class.

Instruction: Internal combustion engine principles; electrical system components; gasoline engine diagnosis and adjustment; diesel engines; Caterpillar engines; International engines; General Motors engines; Cummins engines; automotive power trains; construction equipment power trains.

Credit recommendation, collegiate level: These courses are technical and vocational in nature. Credit in engine systems maintenance on the basis of demonstrated skills and/or institutional examinations.

Controllable Pitch Propeller, Class C

Location: Service School Command, Great Lakes, Ill.

Length: 4 weeks.

Objectives: To train petty officers third class, and above, as supervisors of personnel engaged in testing, diagnosing, and repairing controllable pitch propeller systems.

Instruction: Controllable pitch propeller components and functions; servomotor controls; controllable pitch hydraulic systems and components; Kamleva, Liaaen, Baldwin-Lema-Hamilton, and pump and shaft controllable pitch propeller systems.

Credit recommendation, collegiate level: This course is technical and vocational in nature. Credit in controllable pitch propeller systems repair on the basis of demonstrated skills and/or institutional examinations.

Data Analysis, Class C
(Aviation Maintenance Data Analysis, Class C)

Location: Naval Air Technical Training Center, Memphis, Tenn.

Length: 6–7 weeks.

Objectives: To provide officers and enlisted personnel with training applicable to maintenance data reporting, man-hour accounting, and aircraft statistical data reporting.

Instruction: Basic mathematics; algebra; calculating machine familiarization; problem solving; introduction to statistics and correlation; work sampling; exception time accounting and maintenance data collection; electronic accounting machines capabilities; maintenance data collection system capabilities; maintenance summary project.

Credit recommendation, collegiate level: 4 semester hours in managerial statistics.

Data Systems Technician, Class A

Locations: Naval Schools, Treasure Island, Calif., and Great Lakes, Ill.

Length: 38 weeks.

Objectives: To train personnel to assume maintenance responsibilities on equipment and subsystems involved in any data processing system utilized by the Navy.

Instruction: Electronic fundamentals; electronic circuits; transmitters and receivers; oscilloscopes; pulse techniques; microwave techniques; control systems; test methods and practices; digital computer mathematics; digital computer programming; basic logic devices; complex logic devices; data storage; control concepts; digital computer maintenance; input/output concepts.

Credit recommendation, collegiate level: 4 semester hours in computer programming in the field of data processing, 8 semester hours in electricity and electronics, and credit in electrical laboratory on the basis of demonstrated skills and/or institutional examinations.

Dental Technician, Basic, Class A
(General Dental Technician School, Class A)

Locations: Naval Medical Centers, Bethesda, Md. and San Diego, Calif.

Length: 12–16 weeks.

Objectives: To provide basic training for general dental technicians.

Instruction: Dental anatomy; anatomy and physiology; emergency procedures; bacteriology; oral pathology; typing; oral hygiene; operating room assistance; manipulation of dental materials; roentgenology: materia medica; dental charting; dental equipment maintenance; casualty treatment.

Credit recommendation, collegiate level: This course is technical and vocational in nature. Credit in dental technician training on the basis of demonstrated skills and/or institutional examination.

Dental Technician, General, Advanced, Class B
(General Dental Technician School, Class B)
(General Dental Technician, Advanced, Class B)

Location: Naval Medical Center, Bethesda, Md.

Length: 24 weeks.

Objectives: To prepare dental technicians for administrative responsibilities of the senior petty officer.

Instruction: Organization and administration; principles of teaching; clerical procedures; clinical procedures; office management; casualty treatment.

Credit recommendation, collegiate level: Credit in typing and accounting procedures on the basis of institutional examination.

Dental Technician, Maxillofacial Prosthetic, Class C
(Dental Technician, Maxillofacial Prosthetic, Class B)

Location: Naval Dental School, Bethesda, Md.

Length: 24 weeks.

Objectives: To acquaint trainees with the laboratory procedures in fabrication of maxillofacial prosthetic appliances.

Instruction: Ocular prosthesis; auricular, digital, nasal prostheses and materials; protective mouthpiece; cranioplasty; special prostheses and training aids; mammary prosthesis.

Credit recommendation, collegiate level: This course is technical and vocational in nature. Credit in dental laboratory technology on the basis of demonstrated skills and/or institutional examination.

Dental Technician, Prosthetic, Advanced Class B
(Dental Technician, Advanced Prosthetic, Class B)

Location: Naval Medical Center, Bethesda, Md.

Length: 24 weeks.

Objectives: To provide dental technicians with advanced training in the fabrication of prosthetic appliances.

Instruction: Complete denture construction; crown and fixed partial denture construction; ceramics; general administration; property and accounting; clerical procedures; laboratory management; casualty treatment.

Credit recommendation, collegiate level: This course is technical and vocational in nature. Credit in dental laboratory technology on the basis of demonstrated skills and/or institutional examination.

Dental Technician, Prosthetic, Class C
(Dental Prosthetic Technician School, Class C)

Locations: Naval Medical Centers, Bainbridge, Md., Great Lakes, Ill., and San Diego, Calif.

Length: 24–26 weeks.

Objectives: To provide specialized training in prosthetic laboratory procedures and in the maintenance and repair of dental equipment.

Instruction: Constructing a cast; base plate and occlusal rim construction; acrylic tray construction; repairing dentures; laboratory management; complete denture construction; cast partial denture construction; wrought metal technique, fixed partial dentures.

Credit recommendation, collegiate level: This course is technical and vocational in nature. Credit in dental laboratory technology on the basis of demonstrated skills and/or institutional examinations.

Dental Technician, Repair, Class C

Location: Naval Medical Center, Bethesda, Md.

Length: 24–40 weeks.

Objectives: To train dental technicians in the principles of construction, installation, and maintenance of all types of dental equipment used in the naval service.

Instruction: Applied physics; dental operating room equipment; dental prosthetic laboratory equipment; clerical procedures; property and accounting; casualty treatment.

Credit recommendation, collegiate level: These courses are technical and vocational in nature. Credit in dental equipment repair on the basis of demonstrated skills and/or institutional examination.

Dental Technician Research Assistant, Class C

Location: Naval Dental School, Bethesda, Md.

Length: 52 weeks.

Objectives: To train enlisted personnel in the basic knowledge and skills necessary to conduct dental research procedures.

Instruction: Microbiology; experimental animal surgery; experimental animal care; experimental pathology; biochemistry; photography; assisting in research problems; in-service training.

Credit recommendation, collegiate level: Credit in dental laboratory technology on the basis of demonstrated skills and/or institutional examinations.

Dermatology Technic

Location: Naval Hospital, Philadelphia, Pa.

Length: 16–20 weeks.

Objectives: To train personnel to assist medical officers in all phases of the care of patients with skin disorders.

Instruction: Laboratory technique including bacteriology, serology, hematology, pathology, mycology, and medical parasitology; special dermatological treatment procedures; operating room technique; recognition of common dermatoses; reports and records.

Credit recommendation, collegiate level: This course is technical and vocational in nature. Credit in dermatology technician training on the basis of demonstrated skills and/or institutional examinations.

Disaster Recovery Training I and II

Locations: Naval Construction Battalion Centers, Port Hueneme, Calif., Davisville, R.I., and Gulfport, Miss.

Length: 4 weeks.

Objectives: To train personnel to recover a military installation or a civilian community from the effects of any disaster from whatever source.

Instruction: Nuclear, biological, and chemical warfare; natural disaster; protective equipment; communications; decontamination procedures.

Credit recommendation, collegiate level: No credit because of the limited technical nature of the course.

Disbursing Clerks, Class A

Locations: Naval Schools, Newport, R.I., and San Diego, Calif.

Length: 9–11 weeks.

Objectives: To train personnel to compute and prepare payrolls and process transportation requests.

Instruction: Naval accounting; military pay and allowances; savings deposits; allotments of pay; Federal income tax and FICA tax; pay records and accounts; substantiating vouchers; payments; public funds; travel; public vouchers; returns; typing; correspondence.

Credit recommendation, collegiate level: Credit in typing on the basis of institutional examination.

Disease Vector and Pest Control Technology

Locations: Navy Disease Vector Control Centers, Jacksonville, Fla., and Alameda, Calif.

Length: 4 weeks.

Objectives: To train personnel in the identification and control of insects and rodents and the diseases they carry.

Instruction: Introduction to insect and rodent control; biology and identification; pesticides; equipment; weed control; sanitary landfill; insect resistance.

Credit recommendation, collegiate level: 2 semester hours in community sanitation.

1. Diver, First Class
2. Deep-Sea (He & O₂) Diving Officers
3. Medical Deep-Sea Diving Technicians
4. Deep-Sea Divers
5. EOD Diver Candidates
6. Diver, Second Class

1. Diver, First Class
2. Deep-Sea (He & O_2) Diving Officers
3. Medical Deep-Sea Diving Technicians
4. Deep-Sea Divers
5. EOD Diver Candidates
6. Diver, Second Class

Locations: Key West, Fla.; Washington, D.C.

Length: *Courses 1, 2, and 3,* 26 weeks; *Course 4,* 21 weeks; *Course 5,* 10 weeks; *Course 6,* 7 weeks.

Objectives: To train officers and enlisted personnel in diving techniques, use of diving equipment, rescue and salvage operations.

Instruction: Training in dressing and tending divers; working under water; air systems and supply; diving equipment; construction and repair; first aid; hygiene; physiology of diving; rigging boats; burning and welding; electric currents and equipment; communication systems.

Credit recommendation, collegiate level: These courses are technical and vocational in nature. Credit in deep-sea diving on the basis of demonstrated skills and/or institutional examinations.

Electrical/Electronics Fundamentals, Class P

Locations: Class P Aviation Fundamentals Schools, Jacksonville, Fla., and Norman, Okla.

Length: 4–6 weeks.

Objectives: To provide enlisted personnel with instruction basic to the aviation electronics occupational group.

Instruction. Orientation; hand tools; hardware; soldering; mathematics; physics; fundamentals of DC electricity, including basic electrical algebra, slide rule, resistance and resistors, Ohm's law, batteries, series and parallel resistor circuits, Kirchoff's law, combination circuits, magnetic theory, meter movements, DC ammeters, voltmeters, Ohmmeters, and multimeters, and breadboard experiments.

Credit recommendation, collegiate level: 3 semester hours at the freshman or sophomore level as an elective in electricity.

Electrician's Mates, Class A

Locations: Electrician's Mates Class A Schools, Great Lakes, Ill., and San Diego, Calif.

Length: 14 weeks.

Objectives: To train personnel in the principles, operation, maintenance, and repair of electrical equipment.

Instruction: DC and AC circuits and fundamentals; transformers; generators; DC motors; AC motors; test equipment; electrical maintenance; electrical shop work.

Credit recommendation, collegiate level: 3 semester hours in electricity, and credit in electrical laboratory on the basis of demonstrated skills and/or institutional examinations.

Electrician's Mates, Class B

Location: Naval School, Great Lakes, Ill.
Length: 23 weeks.
Objectives: To train electrician's mates to maintain the naval electrical equipment.
Instruction: Electrical mathematics; DC generators; DC lap windings; DC wave windings; DC controllers; AC theory; three-phase motors; alternating current controllers; single-phase motors; meters; shipboard distribution systems; voltage regulators; lighting; electric propulsion; electronics and semiconductors; IC systems; gyro; magnetic amplifiers; basic degaussing; automatic degaussing systems; batteries.

Credit recommendation, collegiate level: 2 semester hours at the freshman or sophomore level as an elective in electricity and electronics, and credit in electrical laboratory on the basis of demonstrated skills and/or institutional examinations.

1. Electricity and Electronics, Class P
   (Common-Core Course)
   (Marine Corps Electronics Technician School, Class A)
2. Basic Electricity Phase of the Class P Electricity and Electronics School

Location: Naval School, Great Lakes, Ill.
Length: *Course 1:* 16 weeks; *Course 2,* 6 weeks.
Objectives: *Course 1:* To train Navy and Marine personnel in the basic technical terminology and principles of electricity and electronics. *Course 2:* To train personnel in the basic technical terminology and principles of electricity.
Instruction: *Courses 1 and 2:* Fundamentals of DC and AC; DC and AC circuits; DC and AC machinery, including generators and motors. In addition, *Course 1* includes power supplies; audio amplifiers; video amplifiers; RF amplifiers; oscillators; transmitters; receivers; semiconductor devices.

Credit recommendation, collegiate level: *Course 1:* 1 semester hour in basic electricity and 3 semester hours at the freshman or sophomore level as an elective in the general areas of radio and electronics. *Course 2:* 1 semester hour in basic electricity.

Electrocardiography and Basal Metabolism Technician, Class C
(Electrocardiography and Basal Metabolism Technic)

Locations: Naval Hospitals, Bethesda, Md., Portsmouth, Va., and San Diego, Calif.
Length: 16 weeks.

Objectives: To train personnel to assist the medical officer in conducting electrocardiograph and basal metabolism examinations.
Instruction: Physiology of circulation; technique of electrocardiography; principles of metabolism and clinical application of tests; basal metabolism machines.

Credit recommendation, collegiate level: Credit in electrocardiograph and basal metabolism technician training on the basis of demonstrated skills and/or institutional examinations.

Electroencephalography Technician, Class C
(Electroencephalography Technic)

Locations: Naval Hospitals, Bethesda, Md., Chelsea, Mass., Oakland, Calif., San Diego, Calif., and St. Albans, N.Y.
Length: 16 weeks.
Objectives: To train personnel to assist medical officers in performing electroencephalography tests.
Instruction: Prepares patients for examinations; assists in operation of electroencephalography equipment; records test results; maintains equipment; anatomy and diseases of the brain.

Credit recommendation, collegiate level: This course is technical and vocational in nature. Credit in electroencephalography technician training on the basis of demonstrated skills and/or institutional examinations.

Electronics Administrative Officer, Class O
(Aviation Electronics Indoctrination, Class O)

Location: Naval Air Technical Training Center, Memphis, Tenn.
Length: 18 weeks.
Objectives: To prepare officers for electronics/electrical maintenance supervisory duties.
Instruction: Basic electricity, including magnetism, AC theory, simple electrical and coupled circuits; and transformers; basic electronics, including vacuum tubes, amplifiers, oscillators, microphones, transmitters, and receivers; advanced electronics, including radar antennas and duplexers, synchro theory, complete synthetic radar system, and electronic aids to navigation; electrical systems; electronics administration and supply.

Credit recommendation, collegiate level: 6 semester hours at the freshman or sophomore level as an elective in electricity and electronics, and credit in electrical laboratory on the basis of demonstrated skills and/or institutional examinations.

Electronics Officers Administrative

Location: Electronics Officers School, Great Lakes, Ill.
Length: 14–16 weeks.
Objectives: To provide junior officers with theoretical and practical training in naval electronic equipment.
Instruction: Electronics fundamentals; electron tubes; power supplies; sound reproduction; equipment nomenclature; amplifiers; oscillators; modulation; transmitters; receivers; principles of radio and radar; electronics administration and supply.

Credit recommendation, collegiate level: 2 semester hours at the freshman or sophomore level as an elective in electricity and electronics, and credit in electrical laboratory on the basis of demonstrated skills and/or institutional examinations.

Electronics Officers (Maintenance)

Location: Naval School, Great Lakes, Ill.

Length: 48–52 weeks.

Objectives: To provide officers, who have a substantial practical electronic background, with academic, management, and advanced technical knowledge in electronics.

Instruction: Algebra and trigonometry; analytic geometry; calculus; number systems and Boolean algebra; physics; circuit element analysis; electromechanical devices; electronic power supplies; vacuum tubes and semiconductor devices; amplifier analysis; oscillators; modulation and detection; special electronic circuits; energy transmission; microwave components and circuits; servomechanisms; electronic administration; electronic systems and test methods.

Credit recommendation, collegiate level: 5 semester hours in mathematics, 3 semester hours in physics, and 10 semester hours in engineering electronics.

Electronics Technical Officer, Class O
(Aviation Electronics Advanced, Class O)

Location: Naval Air Technical Training Center, Memphis, Tenn.

Length: 52 weeks.

Objectives: To provide selected warrant and limited duty officers with advanced, professional-level electronics engineering training.

Instruction: Mathematics, including algebra, trigonometry, calculus, and differential equations; physics, including mechanics, heat, sound, light, and modern physics; technical composition, including English, grammar, technical and general writing, and technical speech; engineering drawing, including drawing principles and techniques, engineering drawing fundamentals, and graphic representation; electrical engineering, including direct current theory, electricity and magnetism, and alternating current circuits; electronics engineering, including electronic circuit design, electronic measurements, antennas and propagation, automatic control systems, electronic digital computers, and avionics systems; naval aviation maintenance and material management; leadership and supervision.

Credit recommendation, collegiate level: 4 semester hours in mathematics, 4 semester hours in physics, 2 semester hours in technical English composition, and 15 semester hours in engineering electronics.

Electronics Technician, Class A,
Guided Missilemen (GS) Conversion

Locations: Naval School, Treasure Island, Calif.

Length: 20 weeks.

Objectives: To provide personnel with the basic electricity and electronics training necessary for guided missilemen.

Instruction: Fundamentals of DC and AC; DC and AC circuits; DC and AC machinery, including genera-

tors and motors; power supplies; audio amplifiers; video amplifiers; RF amplifiers; oscillators; transmitters; receivers; semiconductor devices.

Credit recommendation, collegiate level: 1 semester hour in basic electricity and 3 semester hours at the freshman or sophomore level as a technical elective in the general areas of radio and electronics.

Electronics Technician, Class B

Location: Naval School, Treasure Island, Calif.

Length: 46 weeks.

Objectives: To train electronics technicians to analyze, isolate, and repair malfunctions in electronic equipment and systems.

Instruction: Numbers for analysis; numbers systems; real numbers; vectors and graphs; functions; circular functions; powers and roots; rate of change; exponential and logarithmic function; trigonometry; linear equations and matrices; fundamentals of DC and AC; advanced fundamentals; circuit applications; communications systems; radar systems and basic computers.

Credit recommendation, collegiate level: 4 semester hours in mathematics and 12 semester hours in engineering electronics.

1. Electronics Technician (Communications) Class A
(Communications Technician (M) Class A)
2. Electronics Technician (Communications) Class A

Locations: Naval Schools, Great Lakes, Ill., and Treasure Island, Calif.

Length: *Course 1,* 38 weeks; *Course 2,* 24–28 weeks.

Objectives: To train personnel in the fundamentals of electronics, in the use of electronic test equipment, and in the use of equipment technical manuals for the maintenance of electronic equipment.

Instruction: *Course 1:* Electronics fundamentals; power supplies; vacuum tubes, amplifiers and oscillators; electronic circuits; transmitter application; receiver application; oscilloscope application; pulse techniques; microwave techniques; control systems; test methods and practices; communication receivers; communication transmitters; teletype terminal equipment; single-side-band equipment. *Course 2:* Fundamentals of DC and AC; DC and AC circuits; fundamentals of DC and AC motors and generators; power supplies and vacuum tubes; amplifiers and oscillators; transmitters and receivers; teletype equipment; UHF equipment; communications receivers; communications transmitters.

Credit recommendation, collegiate level: CAUTION: *These courses vary slightly in length and recommendation. Require exact identification by title and length. Course 1:* 6 semester hours in physics (electricity) and 12 semester hours in engineering electronics. *Course 2:* 1 semester hour in basic electricity and 6 semester hours at the freshman or sophomore level as an elective in the general areas of radio and electronics.

Electronics Technician, Senior Conversion

Locations: Naval Schools, Treasure Island, San Francisco, Calif., and Great Lakes, Ill.

Length: 48 weeks.

Objectives: To train personnel as electronics technicians.

Instruction: Fundamentals of DC and AC; DC and AC circuits; power supplies; audio amplifiers; video amplifiers; RF amplifiers; oscillators; transmitters; receivers; radar special circuits; synchro/servo mechanisms; UHF/VHF transmitter-receiver maintenance; loran; air search radar; IFF equipment; radar repeater; sonar equipment; teletypewriter terminal equipment.

Credit recommendation, collegiate level: 6 semester hours in physics (electricity) and 12 semester hours in engineering electronics.

Electronics Technicians, Class A, A1 Course, Electronics Fundamentals

Locations: Naval Schools, Great Lakes, Ill., and Treasure Island, Calif.

Length: 13–14 weeks.

Objectives: To provide personnel with knowledge and skills of the fundamentals of electronics.

Instruction: Basic electronics; basic circuits; transmitters and receivers; solid state receiver circuits; amplifiers and oscillators.

Credit recommendation, collegiate level: 3 semester hours at the freshman or sophomore level as an elective in electricity and electronics.

Electronics Technicians, Class A, A2 Course, Electronic

Locations: Naval Schools, Treasure Island, Calif., and Great Lakes, Ill.

Length: 9–12 weeks.

Objectives: To provide personnel with knowledge and skills applicable to electronic circuits.

Instruction: Pulse circuits; oscilloscope circuits; microwave circuits; control devices; advanced test equipment; electronics administration.

Credit recommendation, collegiate level: 3 semester hours at the freshman or sophomore level as an elective in electricity and electronics, and credit in electrical laboratory on the basis of demonstrated skills and/or institutional examinations.

1. Electronics Technicians (Radar), Class A
2. Electronics Technicians (Radar), Class A

Locations: Naval Schools, Treasure Island, Calif., and Great Lakes, Ill.

Length: *Course 1,* 38 weeks; *Course 2,* 26–28 weeks.

Objectives: To train personnel in the fundamentals of electronics, in the use of electronic test equipment, and in the use of equipment technical manuals for the maintenance of electronic equipment.

Instruction: *Course 1:* Electronics fundamentals; power supplies; amplifiers and oscillators; electronic circuits; transmitter application; receiver application; oscilloscope application; pulse techniques; microwave techniques; control systems; test methods and practices; radar equipment fundamentals; radar equipment; radar repeaters; IFF systems. *Course 2:* Fundamentals

of DC and AC; DC and AC currents; fundamentals of DC and AC motors and generators; power supplies and vacuum tubes; amplifiers and oscillators; transmitters and receivers; radar fundamentals; radar special circuits; synchro and servo fundamentals; radar repeater.

Credit recommendation, collegiate level: CAUTION: *These courses vary slightly in length and recommendation. Require exact identification by title and length. Course 1:* 6 semester hours in physics (electricity) and 12 semester hours in engineering electronics. *Course 2:* 1 semester hour in basic electricity and 9 semester hours at the freshman or sophomore level in the general area of radio and electronics.

Electronics Technicians (Sonar), Class A

Locations: Naval Schools, Great Lakes, Ill., and Treasure Island, Calif.

Length: 24 weeks.

Objectives: To train personnel in the fundamentals of electronics, in the use of electronic test equipment, and in the use of equipment technical manuals for the maintenance of electronic equipment.

Instruction: Fundamentals of DC and AC; DC and AC circuits; DC motors and generators; AC motors and generators; power supplies and vacuum tubes; amplifiers and oscillators; transmitters and receivers; sonar fundamentals; special circuits; search sonar; attack aids.

Credit recommmendation, collegiate level: 1 semester hour in basic electricity and 3 semester hours at the freshman or sophomore level as an elective in the general areas of radio and electronics.

Engineering Aid, Class A School

Location: Port Hueneme, Calif.

Length: 16 weeks.

Objectives: To train petty officers in the basic skills of drafting and surveying.

Instruction: Mathematics; basic drafting; structural drafting; electrical drafting; material estimating; basic survey work; topographic surveying; construction surveying.

Credit recommendation, collegiate level: 3 semester hours in drafting and 3 semester hours in construction surveying.

Engineering Aid, Class B School

Locations: Davisville, R.I.; Port Hueneme, Calif.

Length: 15–16 weeks.

Objectives: To train senior petty officers to estimate materials, labor, and plant requirements, and fundamentals of procurement for construction projects.

Instruction: Construction surveying; route, structural, and utilities layout; construction drafting; architectural, mechanical, and electrical layout of buildings; material, labor, and plant estimates; quality control; soils, asphalt, and concrete testing.

Credit recommendation, collegiate level: 6 semester hours in construction surveying and 3 semester hours in drafting.

Engineman, Class A

Location: Service School Command, Great Lakes, Ill.

Length: 12 weeks.

Objectives: To train personnel in the basic skills of enginemen.

Instruction: Mathematics review and blueprint reading; temperature and pressure measuring instruments; valves, piping, tubing, and fittings; pumps; reciprocating internal combustion engines; lubricating oil and cooling systems; fuel and fuel systems; electrical systems; two-stroke cycle diesel engine; four-stroke cycle diesel engine; gas turbine engines; drive mechanisms and hydraulic steering; purification; air compressors; auxiliary boilers; distilling plants; refrigeration and air conditioning; damage control and firefighting.

Credit recommendation, collegiate level: This course is technical and vocational in nature. Credit in engine systems maintenance and repair on the basis of demonstrated skills and/or institutional examinations.

Engineman, Diesel Engines, Class C

Location: Naval School, Great Lakes, Ill.

Length: 6 weeks.

Objectives: To train personnel in the operation, maintenance, and repair of diesel engines.

Instruction: Fundamentals of diesel engines; diesel engine systems and auxiliaries; logs and records; progressive maintenance, adjustments, operation, and troubleshooting.

Credit recommendation, collegiate level: This course is technical and vocational in nature. Credit in diesel engine systems maintenance on the basis of demonstrated skills and/or institutional examinations.

Engineman, Gas Turbine Engines, Class C

Location: Naval School, Great Lakes, Ill.

Length: 7–8 weeks.

Objectives: To provide the necessary training for maintenance and repair of gas turbine engines.

Instruction: Principles of operation, maintenance, and repair of specific engines; details of construction, disassembly, assembly, functional adjustment, and troubleshooting.

Credit recommendation, collegiate level: This course is technical and vocational in nature. Credit in engine systems maintenance on the basis of demonstrated skills and/or institutional examination.

1. Enlisted Embarkation (Basic) (LFTU-9)
2. Officer Embarkation (Basic) (LFTU-3)

Location: Naval Amphibious Base, Little Creek, Norfolk, Va.

Length: 4 weeks.

Objectives: To train U.S. and Allied enlisted personnel, or officers of any service, to plan the combat load of amphibious vessels for participation in an amphibious assault.

Instruction: Collection and sources of data; techniques for preparation of required documentation; characteristics, capabilities, limitations, and missions of amphibious vessels; planning factors; cargo terminology; stowage diagram drafting techniques; review of mathematics functions.

Credit recommendation, collegiate level: No credit because of the specialized nature of the courses.

Equipment Operators (Blasting and Quarry Operation), Class C
(Blasting and Quarry Operation, Class C)

Location: Naval School, Port Hueneme, Calif.

Length: 4 weeks.

Objectives: To train enlisted personnel in construction and quarry blasting procedures.

Instruction: Drilling and placing charges; detonating procedures; construction blasting; quarry layout, development, and operation; rock crushing plant operation.

Credit recommendation, collegiate level: No credit because of the brevity and nature of the course.

Equipment Operators, Class A

Location: Naval Schools, Construction, Port Hueneme, Calif.

Length: 12 weeks.

Objectives: To train personnel to operate equipment for construction, earth-moving, and road-building operations.

Instruction: Tools and lubrication equipment; engines, power trains, fuels, and lubricants; hauling equipment; loaders, fork lifts, and ditchers; gradework, soils, and compaction equipment; crawler tractors and attachments; scrapers.

Credit recommendation, collegiate level: This course is technical and vocational in nature. Credit in earthmoving equipment operation on the basis of demonstrated skills and/or institutional examinations.

Equipment Operators, Class B

Location: Port Hueneme, Calif.

Length: 16–18 weeks.

Objectives: To train equipment operators (petty officers second and above) as supervisors of personnel in the performance of construction, earthmoving, road-building, rock crushing, and asphalt mixing and paving operations.

Instruction: Advanced instruction in the operation, operator's maintenance, and safety precautions of automotive, weight handling, construction, and heavy earthmoving equipment.

Credit recommendation, collegiate level: This course is technical and vocational in nature. Credit in earthmoving equipment operation on the basis of demonstrated skills and/or institutional examinations.

Eye, Ear, Nose, and Throat Technic

Locations: Naval Hospitals, Bethesda, Md., Oakland, Calif., San Diego, Calif., and Philadelphia, Pa.

Length: 26–38 weeks.

Objectives: To train personnel to assist the medical

officer in the care and treatment of patients for eye, ear, nose, and throat conditions.

Instruction: Medical and surgical conditions of ear, nose, and throat; audiometry; emergencies; medical and surgical conditions of ophthalmology; nursing care; operating room.

Credit recommendation, collegiate level: This course is technical and vocational in nature. Credit in medical technician training on the basis of demonstrated skills and/or institutional examinations.

Fire Control Technician, Class A

Locations: Naval Schools, Great Lakes, Ill., Bainbridge, Md., Mare Island, Calif., and San Diego, Calif.

Length: 24–31 weeks.

Objectives: To provide personnel with the basic technical knowledge and skills necessary for fire control technicians.

Instruction: Fundamentals of DC and AC; DC and AC circuits; DC and AC machinery, including generators and motors; power supplies; audio amplifiers; video amplifiers; oscillators; transmitters; synchro-servo fundamentals; fire control radar special circuits; fire control fundamentals; surface, air, and wind problems.

Credit recommendation, collegiate level: 6 semester hours at the freshman or sophomore level as an elective in the general areas of electricity, radio, and electronics, and credit in electrical laboratory on the basis of demonstrated skills and/or institutional examinations.

Fire Fighter Instructor's Course

Locations: Naval Schools, Philadelphia, Pa., and Treasure Island, Calif.

Length: 4 weeks.

Objectives: To train senior petty officers for duty as fire-fighting instructors aboard ship and at Navy fire-fighting schools.

Instruction: Fire-fighting methods and techniques; operation and care of equipment; first aid; special hazards fires; instructor techniques.

Credit recommendation, collegiate level: This course is technical and vocational in nature. Credit in fire fighting on the basis of demonstrated skills and/or institutional examinations.

Fleet Ballistic Missile (F.B.M.) Navigation Officers' Course
(Special Technology Course)

Location: Naval Guided Missiles School, Dam Neck, Va.

Length: 13 weeks.

Objectives: To train officers as navigators on an F.B.M. submarine.

Instruction: Inertial navigation; transmission systems; electronics and transistors; computers; ships inertial navigation system; marine differential analyzer computer; system calibration techniques; navigation aids.

Credit recommendation, collegiate level: No credit because of the specialized nature of the course.

1. Flight Instructors Training
2. Flight Instructors Indoctrination Group

Location: Naval School, Pensacola, Fla.

Length: 3 weeks.

Objectives: To train naval and marine aviators for flight instructor duty in the Naval Air Base Training Command.

Instruction: Oral communications; instructor orientation; leadership; applied aerodynamics; flight phase.

Credit recommendation, collegiate level: No credit because of the brevity and specialized nature of the course.

GFCS MK 37 (Less Radar) Operation and Maintenance
(GFCS MK 37 Maintenance (Less MK 25 MOD 3 Radar))

Locations: Fleet Training Group, Pearl Harbor, Hawaii; Fleet Training Center, San Diego, Calif.

Length: 3 weeks.

Objectives: To indoctrinate trainees in the operation, function, and maintenance of the MK 37 GFCS (less radar).

Instruction: MK 37 gun fire control system; gun director MK 37; computers MK 1A and MK 1 (Starshell); stable element MK 6; fire control switchboard and logs.

Credit recommendation, collegiate level: No credit as the course is military in nature.

1. Ground Controlled Approach, Class C, Operator
2. Ground Controlled Approach Controller, Class C

Locations: Naval Air Technical Training Center, Glynco, Ga.; Naval Technical Training Unit, Olathe, Kans.

Length: 5–8 weeks.

Objectives: To provide training in the operation of ground controlled approach equipment.

Instruction: *Course 1:* AN/CPN-4 and AN/MPN-5 radar set familiarization and basic operating procedures; operational training. *Course 2:* Ground controlled approach basic operating procedures and air traffic control radar familiarization; precision control procedures and surveillance control training; operational training; ground controlled approach organization; in-flight training.

Credit recommendation, collegiate level: These courses are technical and vocational in nature. Credit in radar and radio ground approach equipment operation on the basis of demonstrated skills and/or institutional examinations.

1. Ground Controlled Approach Electronics
     Maintenance, Radar Set AN/MPN-5, Class C
2. Ground Controlled Approach Electronics
     Maintenance, Radar Set AN/CPN-4A, Class C
3. Ground Controlled Approach, Electronics
     Technician, Radar Set AN/MPN-1B, Class C
4. Ground Controlled Approach, Electronics
     Technician, AN/MPN-5, Class C

Locations: Naval Air Technical Training Center, Glynco, Ga.; Naval Air Technical Training Unit, Olathe, Kans.

Length: 15–18 weeks.

Objectives: To train electronics maintenance officers and technicians in the operation and preventive maintenance of ground controlled approach installations.

Instruction: Radar circuit theory and communications equipment; search and precision radars; search and precision antennas and indicators; radar systems measurements and auxiliary equipment.

Credit recommendation, collegiate level: For each course, 2 semester hours at the freshman or sophomore level as an elective in electricity and electronics, and credit in electrical laboratory on the basis of demonstrated skills and/or institutional examinations.

1. Ground Controlled Approach Maintenance
     (Engineman), Radar Sets AN/CPN-4A
     and AN/MPN-5, Class C
2. Ground Controlled Approach School, Class C,
     Engineman, AN/MPN-5

Locations: Naval Air Technical Training Center, Glynco, Ga.; Naval Air Technical Training Unit, Olathe, Kans.

Length: 8–10 weeks.

Objectives: To provide training in the theory, operation, and maintenance of the power, air conditioning, heater, and air distribution equipment specified.

Instruction: Basic electricity; operations and maintenance of AN/CPN-4A and/or AN/MPN-5 power equipment and air conditioner heating system.

Credit recommendation, collegiate level: Credit in electricity and electrical laboratory on the basis of demonstrated skills and/or institutional examinations.

Ground Controlled Approach/Radar Air Traffic
     Control Center, Electronics Maintenance
     Officer, Class O

Location: Naval Air Technical Training Center, Glynco, Ga.

Length: 3–4 weeks.

Objectives: To train Naval and Marine Corps officers in the maintenance requirements and organizational procedures used in support of ground controlled approach units.

Instruction: Naval air station ground electronics; Marine air traffic control unit organization; supply and maintenance organization, including naval supply system, spare parts system, safety programs, maintenance policies, overhaul and repair; equipment inspections, training programs, publications, and administrative control.

Credit recommendation, collegiate level: 2 semester hours in maintenance management.

Heat Treatment of Metals, Class C

Location: Naval School, San Diego, Calif.

Length: 7 weeks.

Objectives: To train personnel as metal heat treatment specialists with the fleet.

Instruction: Properties of metals applicable to heat treating; identification and classification of metals; heat treatment of metals; surface treatments; corrosion of metals.

Credit recommendation, collegiate level: This course is technical and vocational in nature. Credit in metal shop on the basis of demonstrated skills and/or institutional examinations.

Hospital Corpsman, Advanced General Service
     Technician, Class B
(Advanced Hospital Corps Technician, Class B)
(Advanced Hospital Corps School)

Locations: Naval Medical Centers, San Diego, Calif. and Portsmouth, Va.

Length: 20–26 weeks.

Objectives: To provide instruction in advanced principles and techniques of patient care with emphasis on tentative diagnosis and on acquiring skills necessary for assignment to duty independent of direct medical officer supervision.

Instruction: Advanced medical and surgical conditions; first aid and emergency procedures; materia medica and pharmacology; routine laboratory technique; pharmacy; preventive medicine; nuclear, biological, and chemical warfare; embalming; administration.

Credit recommendation, collegiate level: 4 semester hours in hygiene, sanitation, and first aid and 2 semester hours in anatomy and physiology.

Hospital Corpsman, Class A
(Basic Hospital Corps School (Class A))

Locations: Naval Hospital Corps Schools, Great Lakes, Ill., and San Diego, Calif.

Length: 16–20 weeks.

Objectives: To train enlisted personnel in the basic principles and techniques of direct patient care and first aid procedures.

Instruction: Anatomy and physiology; principles and techniques of patient care; first aid and minor surgery; hygiene and sanitation; materia medica; toxicology; metrology; nuclear, biological, and chemical warfare defense.

Credit recommendation, collegiate level: 3 semester hours in elementary anatomy and physiology and 2 semester hours in hygiene.

Ice Observer, Class C

Location: Naval Air Technical Training Unit, Lakehurst, N.J.

Length: 6 weeks.

Objectives: To train aerographer's mates for ice reconnaissance duties during routine operations of naval forces.

Instruction: Arctic operations; ice terminology and identification; oceanographic data; observational records and reports; physical geography of sea ice, its behavior and general and regional distribution.

Credit recommendation, collegiate level: No credit because of the specialized nature of the course.

Illustrator Draftsman, Class A School

Location: Port Hueneme, Calif.

Length: 15 weeks.

Objectives: To train personnel as illustrator draftsmen.

Instruction: Mathematics; basic drafting; machine drafting; ship and aircraft structural drafting; electrical and electronic drafting; basic illustration; media; visual aids; methods of reproduction; screen process reproduction.

Credit recommendation, collegiate level: 3 semester hours in basic drafting.

Information Officers Course

Location: Naval School, Great Lakes, Ill.

Length: 4–5 weeks.

Objectives: To familiarize officers with the field of public relations so that they may carry out assignments of prime responsibility in the Navy's information program.

Instruction: Public relations and communication; civil and community relations; newswriting; media and media relations; case studies and practical problems; Navy information programs.

Credit recommendation, collegiate level: Credit in newswriting on the basis of demonstrated skills and/or institutional examinations.

Instructor Basic, Course A, Class C
(Instructors, Class C-1)

Locations: Naval Schools, Great Lakes, Ill., San Diego, Calif., and Norfolk, Va.

Length: 4 weeks.

Objectives: To train Navy personnel in the methods and techniques of instruction.

Instruction: Principles of learning; public speaking; planning instruction; methods of instruction; test construction; use of training aids; analysis of instruction; preparation and use of instruction sheets; shop layout; safety precautions; practice instruction.

Credit recommendation, collegiate level: 2 semester hours in instructional methods.

Instructor Training, Class C

Location: Naval Air Technical Training Center, Memphis, Tenn.

Length: 4–5 weeks.

Objectives: To provide Navy and Marine Corps personnel with training in teaching principles to qualify them as instructors.

Instruction: Teaching situations and methods; training aids; instructional management; testing and grad-

ing; instructor and trainee; supervised practice teaching.

Credit recommendation, collegiate level: 2 semester hours in instructional methods.

Interior Communication Electrician, Class A

Locations: Naval Schools, Great Lakes, Ill., and San Diego, Calif.

Length: 11–18 weeks.

Objectives: To teach personnel the principles, operation, maintenance, and repair of interior communications equipment.

Instruction: DC and AC fundamentals; DC and AC circuits and machinery; power supplies; voltage amplification; power amplifiers; semiconductors; magnetic amplifiers; distribution; indicating systems; gyro compasses and associated equipment; motion picture operation; IC circuits; hand tools, wiring, and cables; basic electronics; announcing systems; synchros and IC applications; gyro compasses and associated devices; sound-powered telephone; damage control; storage batteries.

Credit recommendation, collegiate level: 3 semester hours in electricity and electronics, and credit in electrical laboratory on the basis of demonstrated skills and/or institutional examinations.

Interior Communication Electrician, Class B
(I. C. Electrician, Class B)

Location: Naval School, Great Lakes, Ill.

Length: 34 weeks.

Objectives: To train personnel to perform advanced operation, maintenance, and repair of interior communications equipment.

Instruction: Fundamental electricity; circuits; introduction to AC; inductance and capacitance; transformers; electrical meters; electrical drawings; electron tubes; amplifiers and oscillators; audiovisual IC systems; sound recorders and reproducers; salinity indicating system; bearing temperature monitoring equipment; ship control and metering system; constant-frequency equipment; IC switchgear and switchboards; synchro units; propeller revolution indication systems; wind direction and intensity; magnetic amplifier; electromagnetic underwater logs; shipboard administration; regular gyro; special gyro; automatic telephones; maintenance.

Credit recommendation, collegiate level: 3 semester hours at the freshman or sophomore level as an elective in electricity and electronics, and credit in electrical laboratory on the basis of demonstrated skills and/or institutional examinations.

Introduction to Traffic and Terminal Management

Location: Naval Supply Center, Oakland, Calif.

Length: 4 weeks.

Objectives: To train personnel in the fundamental principles of transportation, traffic, and terminal management.

Instruction: Basic concepts of Federal and state transportation regulations; transportation geography; services offered by various modes of transportation; capabilities of transportation equipment; freight classification and classification rules; types of motor freight rates; transit privileges; demurrage; loading rules; loss and damage procedures; documentation and principles of terminal organization and management.

Credit recommendation, collegiate level: 3 semester hours in traffic operation.

Journalists, Class A

Location: Naval School, Great Lakes, Ill.

Length: 12 weeks.

Objectives: To train enlisted personnel in the requirements of the journalist rating.

Instruction: Journalism; newspaper layout and makeup; newswriting; radio and television; photography; Navy public relations; public information.

Credit recommendation, collegiate level: 4 semester hours in journalism.

Journalists, Class B School

Location: Naval Training Center, Great Lakes, Ill.

Length: 8 weeks.

Objectives: To train first class and chief journalists in public information policy and public relations practices.

Instruction: Advanced writing; public relations; radio and television; comprehensive problems; photojournalism.

Credit recommendation, collegiate level: 3 semester hours in journalism.

Leadership Schools, Class C

Locations: Naval Schools, Great Lakes, Ill., Norfolk, Va., and San Diego, Calif.

Length: 4 weeks.

Objectives: To train petty officers as instructors of leadership training.

Instruction: Instructional methods to be employed; foundation of naval leadership; human relations in naval leadership; factors affecting human behavior.

Credit recommendation, collegiate level: No credit because of the brevity and limited technical nature of the course.

1. Legal Clerk and Court Reporting
2. Legal Clerk

Location: U.S. Naval Justice School, Newport, R.I.

Length: 7 weeks.

Objectives: To train personnel for legal clerkship duties.

Instruction: Preparation of records; preparation of charges and specifications; investigations; administrative matters relating to discipline.

Credit recommendation, collegiate level: This course is technical and vocational in nature. Credit in legal clerking on the basis of demonstrated skills and/or institutional examinations.

1. Limited Duty Officer Indoctrination
2. Limited Duty Officer Indoctrination

Location: Naval Station, Newport, R.I.

Length: *Course 1,* 7–10 weeks; *Course 2,* 5 weeks.

Objectives: To orient newly commissioned officers and further develop their naval leadership and administrative skills.

Instruction: *Course 1:* Naval officer orientation; duties of division officers and watch officers; naval leadership and the Uniform Code of Military Justice; naval operations; seamanship; moral basis for leadership. *Course 2:* Orientation; administration and leadership; Uniform Code of Military Justice; communications (correspondence and speech); moral basis for leadership.

Credit recommendation, collegiate level: CAUTION: *These courses vary slightly in length and recommendation. Require exact identification by title and length. Course 1:* 3 semester hours in naval science. *Course 2:* 2 semester hours in naval science.

MK 84 Fire Control System Technician

Location: Naval Guided Missile School, Dam Neck, Va.

Length: 28 weeks.

Objectives: To train personnel in the operation and maintenance of the MK 84 Fire Control System.

Instruction: Fleet ballistic missile weapons system including MK 3 missile, launcher, navigation, MK 84, FCS, digital, testing, MK 113 FCS, and MK 2 missile; polaris MK 84 system including digital geoballistic computer, MTRE MK 6, MTRE MK 7, MOTS MK 412, testing, final system, and MK 3 missile.

Credit recommendation, collegiate level: Credit in electrical laboratory on the basis of demonstrated skills and/or institutional examinations.

Machinery Repairman, Class A

Location: Naval School, San Diego, Calif.

Length: 12 weeks.

Objectives: To train personnel as skilled machinists, machine tool operators, and auxiliary equipment repairmen.

Instruction: Hand tools and measuring instruments; blueprint reading and sketching; basic layout procedures; shop mathematics; classification, physical properties, and identification of metals; materials, lubricants, and coolants; single point cutting tools; drills and drilling machines; bench and pedestal grinders; lathe operation; milling machine operations; shapers; valves and piping; planned maintenance system.

Credit recommendation, collegiate level: This course is technical and vocational in nature. Credit in machine repair on the basis of demonstrated skills and/or institutional examinations.

Machinery Repairman, Class B

Location: Naval School, San Diego, Calif.
Length: 18 weeks.
Objectives: To train personnel as skilled machinists, machine tool operators, and auxiliary equipment repairmen.
Instruction: Precision measuring instruments; shop mathematics; physical metallurgy and plastics; single point tools; toolmakers' lathe; turret lathe; grinding machines; grinding wheels; grinding principles, operations, and techniques; balancing machines; milling machines; spur gears; helical gears; bevel gears; worn gears; stub tooth gears; symmetrical and nonsymmetrical gears; metal spraying.
Credit recommendation, collegiate level: This course is technical and vocational in nature. Credit in machine repair shop on the basis of demonstrated skills and/or institutional examinations.

Machinist's Mates, Class A

Location: Naval Training Center, Great Lakes, Ill.
Length: 12–14 weeks.
Objectives: To train enlisted personnel to operate the main propulsion steam equipment of ships.
Instruction: Mathematics review; blueprint reading; tools, instruments, and materials; basic principles of steam engineering; valves, pipes, tubings, and fittings; auxiliary equipment; pumps; lubricating oil systems; damage control; distilling plants; turbines; main propulsion plant; refrigeration.
Credit recommendation, collegiate level: This course is technical and vocational in nature. Credit in machine shop on the basis of demonstrated skills and/or institutional examinations.

Management Accounting Seminar

Location: Naval School, Washington, D.C.
Length: 10 weeks.
Objectives: To train management at all levels in fundamental accounting concepts, Navy accounting, and management controls.
Instruction: Department of the Navy annual financial report; Navy accounting; master general ledger entries; appropriation accounting; performance budget and budgetary cycle; Navy settlement office and appropriation cash accounts; survey and analysis of registers; administration control of funds; field accounting procedures; integration of supply and accounting; Navy industrial fund–shipyards; management functions and development of controls; organization; production planning and office operations; graphics, charting, and statistics; internal audit; work measurement; budgetary control; fundamental accounting concepts; balance sheet equation; merchandise operations; inventory; additional income and expense accounts; specialized books of original entry; departmental operations; man-

ufacturing accounts; voucher system; cash; fixed assets; inventories; cost controls; financial statements; process and job order cost accounting.
Credit recommendation, collegiate level: 8 semester hours in business management including accounting principles, internal and managerial accounting, and auditing and budgeting.

Marine Air Traffic Control Unit Equipment Maintenance, Class C

Location: Naval Air Technical Training Center, Glynco, Ga.
Length: 18 weeks.
Objectives: To familiarize Marine Corps radar technicians with the operation of major marine air traffic control unit equipments.
Instruction: Basic radar circuits and transistors; power supply circuits; radar transmitters and receivers; AN/TPN-8 radar transmitter, receiver, and antenna mount; AN/TPN-8 indicator and system; AN/TSQ-18 radar surveillance central; Mark X IFF; marine air traffic control unit composition, function, and operation.
Credit recommendation, collegiate level: Credit in electricity and electrical laboratory on the basis of demonstrated skills and/or institutional examinations.

Marine Aviation Operations Clerical Course, Class C

Location: Naval Air Technical Training Center, Memphis, Tenn.
Length: 4–6 weeks.
Objectives: To train Marine Corps personnel in basic clerical aviation operations skills.
Instruction: Basic typing; introduction to aviation operations, flight records and reports, aviation pay records and reports, security, aircraft mishap reporting procedures, organization and standards of an airfield, aviators individual flight log, weather sequence reports, and aircraft clearance; standard directives system; operation and care of office machines.
Credit recommendation, collegiate level: Credit in typing on the basis of institutional examination. At the technical level, credit in office procedures on the basis of demonstrated skills and/or institutional examinations.

Marine Aviation Supply, Class C
(Marine Supply, Class C)

Locations: Naval Air Technical Training Centers, Jacksonville, Fla., and Memphis, Tenn.
Length: 6–10 weeks.
Objectives: To train Marine Corps personnel for aviation supply duty in Fleet Marine Force aviation units.
Instruction: Basic typing; administrative procedures material identification and publications; Bureau of Naval Weapons allowance and initial outfitting lists Marine Aircraft Squadron Material Unit procurement accounting, records, reports, and requisitioning proce

dures; Marine aircraft group supply department procedures; warehousing.

Credit recommendation, collegiate level: Credit in typing and property accounting on the basis of institutional examination.

Marine Corps Short Airfield for Tactical Support, Class C

Locations: Naval Air Technical Training Units, Lakehurst, N.J., and Philadelphia, Pa.

Length: 5 weeks.

Objectives: To train Marine Corps personnel in the installation, operation, and maintenance of recovery, launch, and landing gear.

Instruction: Arresting gear and barricades; catapults and support equipment; runway matting; visual landing aids; expeditionary arresting gear.

Credit recommendation, collegiate level: This course is technical and vocational in nature. Credit in operation and maintenance of catapult and arresting gear equipment on the basis of demonstrated skills and/or institutional examinations.

1. Medical Administrative Technic
2. Medical Administrative Technician, Class C
(Medical Administrative Technic)
3. Medical Administrative Technic, Dental

Locations: Naval Medical Centers, San Diego, Calif. and Portsmouth, Va.

Length: *Course 1,* 41–42 weeks; *Courses 2 and 3,* 30–36 weeks.

Objectives: To train personnel to prepare, maintain, and account for medical supplies, equipment, and staff and patient personnel records.

Instruction: Hospital administration; personnel and office management; food service management; business English; effective speaking; teaching methods and typing. *Course 1* includes the same subject matter as *Courses 2 and 3,* but in greater depth.

Credit recommendation, collegiate level: For each course, 15 semester hours in institutional management and typing on the basis of institutional examination. In addition, *Course 1* receives credit in instructional methods and speech on the basis of demonstrated skills and/or institutional examinations.

Medical Illustration Technic

Location: Naval Medical School, Bethesda, Md.

Length: 26 weeks.

Objectives: To train personnel to prepare medical illustrations of various kinds.

Instruction: Advanced anatomy; use of microscope and laboratory equipment as they pertain to the work of the artist; quick sketches and detailed drawings from slides and tissue.

Credit recommendation, collegiate level: 4 semester hours in anatomy and credit in medical illustration techniques on the basis of demonstrated skills and/or institutional examinations.

Medical Photography Technician, Class C
(Medical Photography Technic)

Location: Naval Medical School, Bethesda, Md.

Length: 24–26 weeks.

Objectives: To train personnel to perform medical photography duties.

Instruction: Operates and maintains various types of photographic, photomicrographic, photofluorographic, lantern, movie projection, and darkroom apparatus and equipment; takes, processes, finishes, and mounts medical photographs; application of photocopying lanternslide technique and color-photograph procedures.

Credit recommendation, collegiate level: 4 semester hours in photography, or, 12 semester hours in medical photography at institutions which regularly offer such credit.

1. Medical Repair Mechanic, Class C
(Medical Equipment Repair Technic)
2. Medical Equipment Repair Technic

Locations: Gunter AFB, Montgomery, Ala., Army Medical Optical and Maintenance Activity, St. Louis, Mo., and Fitzsimons General Hospital, Denver, Colo.

Length: *Course 1,* 40–50 weeks; *Course 2,* 16 weeks.

Objectives: To provide enlisted personnel with basic and advanced technical training in maintaining and repairing all types of medical equipment.

Instruction: *Course 1:* Fundamentals of DC and AC; electrical circuits; inductance and inductive reactance; capacitance reactance; meters and motors; mathematics review; tools; general medical equipment; X-ray equipment; dental equipment; electronic medical equipment; maintenance and repair. *Course 2:* Maintenance mathematics; tools; fundamentals of electricity and electronics; general medical equipment; medical X-ray equipment; electronic medical equipment; maintenance shop procedures.

Credit recommendation, collegiate level; CAUTION: *These courses vary slightly in title, length, and recommendation. Require exact identification by title and length. Course 1:* 3 semester hours at the freshman or sophomore level as an elective in electricity, and credit in electrical laboratory on the basis of demonstrated skills and/or institutional examinations. *Course 2:* Credit in electricity and electrical laboratory on the basis of demonstrated skills and/or institutional examinations.

Meteorological Satellite Course, Class C

Location: Naval Air Technical Training Center, Lakehurst, N.J.

Length: 3–4 weeks.

Objectives: To train enlisted personnel in the operation of automatic picture transmission terminal ground equipment.

Instruction: Operational satellite system; data acquisition and gridding; extraction and use of automatic picture transmission data; synoptic application; operational use of APT data.

Credit recommendation, collegiate level: No credit because of the brevity and specialized nature of the course.

Methods Engineering

Location: Bureau of Supplies and Accounts, Washington, D.C.

Length: 7 weeks.

Objectives: To train personnel to manage the activities of the Bureau of Supplies and Accounts.

Instruction: Process charting; operation analysis; motion study; layout study; developing and installing improved methods; time study; methods-time measurement; standard data; work sampling; standards for materials-handling equipment; engineered time standards.

Credit recommendation, collegiate level: 4 semester hours in applied management analysis.

Metrical Photographic Interpretation

Location: Naval Receiving Station, Washington, D.C.

Length: 14 weeks.

Objectives: To train personnel in metrical photographic interpretation.

Instruction: Elementary optics; camera calibration; film processing; photo and map specifications; position determination; reconnaissance surveying; map and chart projections; photogeometrics; terrestrial photogrammetry; slotted templet control extension; stereocomparagraph; vertical sketchmaster; oblique geometrics; instrumental rectification; trimetrogon mapping.

Credit recommendation, collegiate level: 4 semester hours in photographic interpretation.

Microwave Fundamentals

Location: Treasure Island, Calif.

Length: 4 weeks.

Objectives: To train electronics technicians to maintain electronic equipment and systems utilizing microwave components and devices.

Instruction: Microwave transmission line theory; microwave circuit components; microwave measurements and test equipment; microwave amplifier and oscillators; microwave antennas and antenna systems.

Credit recommendation, collegiate level: Credit in electrical laboratory on the basis of demonstrated skills and/or institutional examinations.

Military Justice Course (Officer)

Location: Naval Justice School, Newport, R. I.

Length: 7 weeks.

Objectives: To provide officers with a thorough grounding in the court-martial system.

Instruction: Procedure, including pretrial, trial, and post-trial; substantive law, including preparation of specifications and punishments; evidence.

Credit recommendation, collegiate level: 3 semester hours in political science.

Mine Detection Sonar Technical Maintenance

Location: Fleet Sonar School, San Diego, Calif.

Length: 4 weeks.

Objectives: To train personnel to operate, test, and repair mine detection sonar.

Instruction: Test equipment; special circuits; theory of operation; calibration and alignment.

Credit recommendation, collegiate level: Credit in electrical laboratory on the basis of demonstrated skills and/or institutional examination.

Missile Technician, Class A
(Guided Missileman, Class A)

Location: Naval Guided Missiles School, Dam Neck, Va.

Length: 24 weeks.

Objectives: To train enlisted personnel in the basic technical knowledge and skills required of guided missilemen.

Instruction: Fundamentals of AC and DC; power supplies; amplifiers and oscillators; transmitters and receivers; special circuits; multivibrators; generators; guided missile fundamentals; factors affecting missile flight; guided missile components; missile propulsion systems; missile control systems; principles of missile guidance; guided missile ships and systems; mathematics.

Credit recommendation, collegiate level: 6 semester hours at the freshman or sophomore level as an elective in electricity and electronics, and credit in electrical laboratory on the basis of demonstrated skills and/or institutional examinations.

Missile Technician, Class B
(Guided Missileman, Class B)

Location: Naval Guided Missiles School, Dam Neck, Va.

Length: 38 weeks.

Objectives: To train personnel in the fundamentals, theory, and practical application of guided missiles.

Instruction: Numbering systems; algebra; equations; special products and factoring; slide rule and powers of ten; fractions and fractional equations; trigonometry; calculus; plane vectors; exponents and radicals; logarithms; mechanics; properties of matter; heat; sound; light; electricity and magnetism; fundamentals of DC and AC; power supplies and amplifiers; synchros and servos; modulation and demodulation; special circuits; transistors.

Credit recommendation, collegiate level: 4 semester hours at the freshman level in physics, 5 semester hours at the freshman level in mathematics, 3 semester hours in electricity and electronics, and credit in electrical laboratory on the basis of demonstrated skills and/or institutional examinations.

Molders, Class B

Location: Naval School, San Diego, Calif.

Length: 12 weeks.

Objections: To train personnel as molders with the fleet.

Instruction: Fundamentals of mold construction; melting equipment; metallurgy of cast metals; identification and testing of metal castings; nonferrous alloy casting technology; ferrous alloy casting technology; foundry management.

Credit recommendation, collegiate level: This course is technical and vocational in nature. Credit in molding on the basis of demonstrated skills and/or institutional examinations.

Motion Picture School, Class C
(Motion Picture Camera School, Class C)

Location: Naval Air Technical Training Unit, Pensacola, Fla.

Length: 10–14 weeks.

Objectives: To provide enlisted men with advanced training in motion picture photography.

Instruction: Basic motion picture photography, including camera familiarization, light sensitive materials, optics, exposure and color temperature meters, laboratory procedures, and projection theory and equipment; techniques of motion picture photography, including composition, coverage, continuity, and camera angles; lighting equipment and techniques; processing and printing; editing, titling, and splicing; specialized motion picture photography, including high-speed, tropical, cold weather, aerial, and underwater photography.

Credit recommendation, collegiate level: 3 semester hours in motion picture photography.

NBC Warfare Defense Ashore

Locations: Naval Unit, Army Chemical Center, Fort McClellan, Ala. and Naval Schools Command, Treasure Island, Calif.

Length: 6 weeks.

Objectives: To train personnel as disaster control officers.

Instruction: Biological and chemical agents and their effects; protection and decontamination; biological and chemical agent munitions accident control; nuclear weapons and effects; radiological detection and survey; protection against nuclear attack; nuclear accident control; disaster control organization and recovery.

Credit recommendation, collegiate level: No credit because of the brevity and limited technical nature of the course.

NTDS Basic Programmer Course (Operational)

Location: Fleet Anti-Air Warfare Training Center, San Diego, Calif.

Length: 7 weeks.

Objectives: To provide personnel with comprehensive instruction in the basic principles of programming digital computers.

Instruction: Basics of digital computers; basic principles of programming; NTDS unit computer principles of operation; NTDS unit computer programming techniques; practical programming; computer utilization.

Credit recommendation, collegiate level: 4 semester hours in computer programming in the field of computer science.

NTDS Intermediate Programmer Course (CS-1)
(CS-1 Compiling System)

Location: Fleet Anti-Air Warfare Training Center, San Diego, Calif.

Length: 3 weeks.

Objectives: To provide comprehensive instruction in the use of the CS-1 compiling system.

Instruction: Principles and concepts; data design; debugging; programming techniques; program preparation; communications; practical application; program overview.

Credit recommendation, collegiate level: 2 semester hours in computer programming in the field of computer science.

Naval Air Reserve Training Command Avionics Fundamentals School, Class A

Location: Naval Air Reserve Electronics Training Unit, Los Alamitos, Calif.

Length: 12 weeks.

Objectives: To provide enlisted personnel with basic aviation electronics training.

Instruction: Electrical/electronic fundamentals, including DC electricity, circuitry, and movements and AC and electrical fundamentals; radio electronics fundamentals, including vacuum tube theory, audio amplification, and radio receiver theory; transmitter fundamentals; antenna systems and transmission lines; basic transistor theory and practice; radar electronics fundamentals, including time constants, pulse-shaping circuits and square-wave generators, pulse circuits, counters, amplifiers, and introduction to radar systems and publications.

Credit recommendation, collegiate level: CAUTION: *Courses in aviation electronics (or avionics) vary in title, length, and recommendation. Require exact identification by full title and length.* 3 semester hours at the freshman or sophomore level as an elective in electricity and electronics and 3 semester hours in electronic circuits.

Naval Air Weapons Systems Orientation, Class O

Location: Naval Air Technical Training Center, Jacksonville, Fla.

Length: 8 weeks.

Objectives: To train junior Navy and Marine Corps officers to supervise the maintenance of naval air weapons systems in operational squadrons.

Instruction: Aircraft armaments control systems, including basic concepts of fire control, fire control sights and systems, typical day and all-weather aero armament control systems, missile guidance system, all-weather navigation and bombing weapon system, and electronic turret familiarization; air launched and command guided missiles; air-to-underwater missile system; passive, semiactive, and active homing missiles; beam-rider missiles.

Credit recommendation, collegiate level: No credit as the course is military in nature.

Naval Aviation Observer (Controller), Class O

Location: Naval Air Station, Glynco, Brunswick, Ga.

Length: 4–5 weeks.

Objectives: To train officers in the functions of a naval aviation observer in airborne combat information center operations.

Instruction: Equipment familiarization and airborne combat information center, including survival, airborne electronics and associated equipment, air navigation, and airborne combat information center operating techniques, tactics, and operations.

Credit recommendation, collegiate level: No credit because of the limited technical nature of the course.

Naval Gunfire Air Spotters

Location: Naval Amphibious School, Coronado, San Diego, Calif.

Length: 3 weeks.

Objectives: To train officers to perform duties as naval gunfire air spotters.

Instructions: Naval ordnance; gunfire support ships; communications; map reading; conduct of fire; naval gunfire planning; tactics; coordination of supporting arms; supporting arms evaluator; air support.

Credit recommendation, collegiate level: No credit as the course is military in nature.

Naval Gunfire Liaison Officer

Location: Naval Amphibious School, Coronado, San Diego, Calif.

Length: 7 weeks.

Objectives: To train naval officers as naval gunfire liaison officers.

Instruction: General amphibious warfare; naval ordnance; gunfire support ships; communications; map reading; conduct of fire; naval gunfire planning; tactics; field artillery; coordination of supporting arms; supporting arms evaluator; intelligence; air support.

Credit recommendation, collegiate level: No credit as the course is military in nature.

Naval Gunfire Spotters (Troop Officers)

Location: Naval Amphibious School, Coronado, San Diego, Calif.

Length: 3 weeks.

Objectives: To train landing force officers in the tactics, techniques, and procedures for the employment and conduct of naval gunfire against land targets during amphibious operations.

Instruction: Naval ordnance; gunfire support ships; communications; conduct of fire; naval gunfire planning; tactics; coordination of supporting arms; supporting arms evaluator; air support.

Credit recommendation, collegiate level: No credit as the course is military in nature.

Naval Gunfire Support Planning

Location: Naval Amphibious School, Coronado, San Diego, Calif.

Length: 5–6 weeks.

Objectives: To train officers in naval gunfire support with special emphasis on landing force aspects.

Instruction: Naval ordnance; gunfire support ships; communications; conduct of fire; naval gunfire planning; tactics; coordination of supporting arms; field artillery; mechanized tactics; air support; supporting arms evaluator; naval gunfire planning.

Credit recommendation, collegiate level: No credit as the course is military in nature.

1. Naval School, Stewards, Class A (Stewards, Class A)
2. Steward Apprentice, Class P

Locations: Naval Training Centers, San Diego, Calif. and Bainbridge, Md.

Length: 6–7 weeks.

Objectives: To train enlisted personnel in stateroom care and maintenance, wardroom care and food service.

Instruction: Stateroom; wardroom; preparation and serving of food; pantry; food refrigeration; hot and cold beverages; safety factors.

Credit recommendation, collegiate level: This course is technical and vocational in nature. Credit in food preparation on the basis of demonstrated skills and/or institutional examinations.

Naval School of Hospital Administration

Location: Naval Medical Center, Bethesda, Md.

Length: 40 weeks.

Objectives: To provide advanced instruction in the modern theory and practice of Hospital Administration for Medical Service Corps officers of Navy and officers of other services.

Instruction: Accounting; business mathematics; English; fundamentals of instruction; office management; speech; financial management; food service management; law; maintenance management; personnel management; principles of organization; records management; security management; special services management; supply management.

Credit recommendation, collegiate level: 15 semester hours in institutional management.

Naval Tactical Data System Data Transmission Group Maintenance, Class C

Location: Naval Tactical Data Systems Maintenance School, Mare Island, Vallejo, Calif.

Length: 20 weeks.

Objectives: To provide training in the operation and maintenance of naval tactical data system data transmission equipment.

Instruction: Data transmission introduction; control and channeling equipment familiarization; transmit sequence control and generator; transmit and receive buffers; channel error indicators; computer control fault locator and remote control panels; phase and frequency multiplexing and demultiplexing; multicou plers, frequency standard, and frequency comparator; radio test set; communications patching switchboard and converter indicator; "A" link checkout and maintenance routines; USC-2 link familiarization.

Credit recommendation, collegiate level: Credit in electrical laboratory on the basis of demonstrated skills and/or institutional examinations.

Naval Tactical Data Systems Maintenance

Location: Naval Tactical Data Systems Maintenance School, Mare Island, Vallejo, Calif.

Length: 19–20 weeks.

Objectives: To provide training in the maintenance of naval tactical data systems.

Instruction: Introduction to NTDS system maintenance; USQ-20 major sequences, input/output timing chain, data flow, and intercomputer operations; keyset complex; data display group; data input/data utilization consoles; height/size console; digital communications group; NTDS system complex.

Credit recommendation, collegiate level: Credit in electrical laboratory on the basis of demonstrated skills and/or institutional examinations.

Naval Tactical Data System Operations, Class O

Location: Naval Air Technical Training Center, Glynco, Ga.

Length: 5–6 weeks.

Objectives: To provide officers with operational training in all phases of the Navy tactical data system.

Instruction: NTDS operations and equipment, including input and user modes of operation and automatic data links and keysets; integrated operations, including anti-air warfare voice communications, systems initiation and control, and associated system functions; computer programming, including introduction to computers and peripheral equipment, computer instructions and basic programming; application of NTDS concepts.

Credit recommendation, collegiate level: 2 semester hours in computer principles in the field of data processing.

Navy Purchase Course

Location: Bureau of Supplies and Accounts, Washington, D.C.

Length: 4 weeks.

Objectives: To train personnel in the purchase methods employed by the Navy.

Instruction: Preliminary purchase procedures; purchase from Government sources of supply; small purchase procedures ($2500 or less); formal advertising procedures and related subjects; negotiated purchase procedures; contract administration; office administration; mobilization planning; future trends in purchasing; case studies.

Credit recommendation, collegiate level: 2 semester hours in principles of procurement.

Neuropsychiatric Clerical Technic

Location: Naval Hospital, Bethesda, Md.

Length: 16 weeks.

Objectives: To train personnel as neuropsychiatric clerical technicians.

Instruction: Terminology and nomenclature; regulations; vital statistics; Boards of medical survey; consultation and clinical management; correspondence; discipline; practical application.

Credit recommendation, collegiate level: This course is technical and vocational in nature. Credit in training for clerical assistants in neuropsychiatry on the basis of demonstrated skills and/or institutional examinations.

Neuropsychiatry Technic

Locations: Naval Hospitals, Bethesda, Md., Oakland, Calif., and Philadelphia, Pa.

Length: 16 weeks.

Objectives: To train personnel to assist in the care and treatment of neuropsychiatric patients.

Instruction: Neuropsychiatric problems and special rules and regulations; practical training in first aid with emphasis upon injuries of mental patients; ward service; attendance at clinics; special therapies; general psychiatric nursing.

Credit recommendation, collegiate level: This course is technical and vocational in nature. Credit in specialized nurse training on the basis of demonstrated skills and/or institutional examinations.

Nondestructive Testing of Metals (Course IV)

Location: Naval School, San Diego, Calif.

Length: 14 weeks.

Objectives: To train personnel in the duties and responsibilities of the nondestructive test operator.

Instruction: Nondestructive related inspections; mathematics; magnetic particle testing; dye penetrant inspection; ultrasonic inspection; radiographic inspecting.

Credit recommendation, collegiate level: Credit in metal testing on the basis of demonstrated skills and/or institutional examinations.

Nuclear Medicine Technician, Class C
(Nuclear Medicine Technic)

Locations: Naval Submarine Medical Centers, New London and Groton, Conn.

Length: 12 weeks.

Objectives: To train personnel to perform duties of radiation monitor, radiation surveys, and gas and liquid analyses.

Instruction: Mathematics; physics; radiation physics; reactor systems; radiobiology; health physics; radiological administration; atmosphere control and toxicology.

Credit recommendation, collegiate level: This course is technical and vocational in nature. Credit in nuclear medicine technician training on the basis of demonstrated skills and/or institutional examinations.

Nuclear Submarine Medicine Technic

Location: Naval Submarine Medical Center, Groton, Conn.

Length: 30 weeks.

Objectives: To train personnel to give medical care aboard nuclear and conventional submarines.

Instruction: Health physics; radiobiology; personnel dosimetry; dental diagnosis and treatment; submarine medicine practices; psychology; minor surgery and first aid; materia medica and therapeutics.

Credit recommendation, collegiate level: Credit in medical technician training on the basis of institutional examination.

Occupational Therapy Technician, Class C
(Occupational Therapy Technic)

Locations: Naval Hospitals, San Diego, Calif., and Bethesda, Md.

Length: 21–24 weeks.

Objectives: To train personnel to apply occupational therapy in the treatment of orthopedic, neuropsychiatric, medical, and surgical patients under supervision of the medical officer.

Instruction: Anatomy; physiology; physics; neurology; psychology and psychiatry; principles of rehabilitation; craft analysis; theory of occupational therapy; minor crafts; textile painting; leatherwork; metalwork; ceramics; weaving; woodwork; clinical practice.

Credit recommendation, collegiate level: This course is technical and vocational in nature. Credit in occupational therapy technician training on the basis of demonstrated skills and/or institutional examinations.

Officer Candidate School
(Naval School, Officer Candidate)

Location: Naval School, Newport, R.I.

Length: 16 weeks.

Objectives: To train officer candidates in the naval subjects essential to qualify them as officers in the U.S. Naval Service.

Instruction: Engineering; navigation; operations; naval orientation and administration; seamanship; naval weapons.

Credit recommendation, collegiate level: 6 semester hours in advanced naval science.

Officers Damage Control Course

Locations: Naval Schools, Philadelphia, Pa., and Treasure Island, Calif.

Length: 4 weeks.

Objectives: To train officers in the operation, maintenance, and application of damage control.

Instruction: Ship nomenclature and compartmentation; shipboard systems; stability of ships; tools and techniques of damage control; publications, records, tests, and reports; organization, education, and training.

Credit recommendation, collegiate level: No credit because of the brevity and limited technical nature of the course.

Operating Room Technic

Locations: Naval Hospitals, Bethesda, Md., Oakland, Va., Portsmouth, Va., Jacksonville, Fla., San Diego, Calif., Camp Pendleton, Calif., Chelsea, Mass., Great Lakes, Ill., Philadelphia, Pa., and St. Albans, N.Y.

Length: 24–26 weeks.

Objectives: To train personnel to prepare and maintain operating rooms for surgery.

Instruction: Sterilization; instruments; sutures, surgical needles; operating room technique; preparation of materials and solutions; plaster and plaster splint technique.

Credit recommendation, collegiate level: This course is technical and vocational in nature. Credit in surgical technician training on the basis of demonstrated skills and/or institutional examinations.

Optical Landing Systems Maintenance, Class C

Location: Naval Air Technical Training Unit, Philadelphia, Pa.

Length: 4–6 weeks.

Objectives: To provide enlisted personnel with specialized training in electrical troubleshooting and maintenance of optical and visual landing aid systems.

Instruction: Specialized electricity; electrical devices; solid state devices applicable to Fresnel lens optical landing system; stabilization circuitry; operation, repair, maintenance, and troubleshooting of Fresnel lens optical landing system; lighting circuitry operation, maintenance, repair, and troubleshooting; manually operated visual landing aid.

Credit recommendation, collegiate level: Credit in electricity on the basis of institutional examination.

Optician (General) Technician, Class C
(Optician (General))
(Optometric Fabrication)

Location: Naval Medical School, Bethesda, Md.

Length: 24 and 40 weeks.

Objectives: To train personnel to adjust, fit, and dispense spectacles.

Instruction: Introduction to optics; ocular anatomy and physiological optics; physical and geometric optics; spectacle fabrication and dispensing; mechanical optics. In addition to the above instruction, the 40-week course includes ophthalmic surfacing.

Credit recommendation, collegiate level: This course is technical and vocational in nature. Credit in optical technology on the basis of demonstrated skills and/or institutional examinations.

Optician Laboratory Technician, Class C
(Optician Technic (Laboratory))

Location: Naval Medical School, Bethesda, Md.

Length: 7 weeks.

Objectives: To train personnel to adjust, fit, and dispense spectacles and to fabricate multifocal spectacles to prescription.

Instruction: Lense fabrication; surface grinding and polishing of special single-vision and multifocal lenses from ophthalmic lens blanks; spectacle repair and replacement service.

Credit recommendation, collegiate level: This course is technical and vocational in nature. Credit in optician laboratory technician training on the basis of demonstrated skills and/or institutional examinations.

Orthopedic Appliance Technician, Class C
(Orthopedic Appliance Technic)
(Orthopedic Appliance Mechanics)

Location: Naval Hospital, Oakland, Calif.

Length: 52 weeks.

Objectives: To train personnel to make and fit various types of braces, splints, supports, artificial limbs, and other orthopedic appliances.

Instruction: Anatomy and physiology; prosthetic training and fitting; plastic and plastic construction; above-knee construction; below-knee construction; arm construction; leather and foot construction; orthopedic brace construction; painting and finishing.

Credit recommendation, collegiate level: This course is technical and vocational in nature. Credit in orthopedic appliance technician training on the basis of demonstrated skills and/or institutional examinations.

1. Oxygen Equipment, Class C
2. Oxygen Equipment, Class C

Location: Naval Air Technical Training Unit, Lakehurst, N.J.

Length: *Course 1,* 14 weeks; *Course 2,* 8 weeks.

Objectives: To train enlisted personnel in the maintenance, testing, and repair of aircraft oxygen regulators and full pressure suits.

Instruction: *Course 1:* Oxygen characteristics, cylinders, instruments, masks and tubing, plumbing, and various oxygen systems; carbon dioxide properties; oxygen and carbon dioxide transfer; oxygen regulator repair and test; liquid oxygen characteristics, transfer, storage, and recharging; pilots' full pressure suit maintenance and operation. *Course 2* covers the same general areas of instruction with the omission of pressure suit training.

Credit recommendation, collegiate level: These courses are technical and vocational in nature. Credit in oxygen equipment maintenance on the basis of demonstrated skills and/or institutional examinations.

1. Parachute Rigger, Class A
2. Parachute Rigger (Survival), Class A
(Parachute Rigger S (Survivalman), Class A)
3. Parachute Rigger (Maintenance), Class A
(Parachute Rigger M (Maintenance), Class A)
4. Parachute Rigger, Class B

Location: Naval Air Technical Training Unit, Lakehurst, N.J.

Length: *Course 1,* 13–16 weeks; *Course 2,* 10 weeks; *Course 3,* 7 weeks; *Course 4,* 12–19 weeks.

Objectives: To train Navy and Marine Corps enlisted personnel in the care and packaging of parachutes and the operation, inspection, and repair of other aviation survival equipment.

Instruction: *Course 1:* Military and naval aviation orientation; aviation personnel survival; aircraft familiarization; parachute rigging and packing; parachute descent training; drogue chutes; oxygen masks and carbon dioxide; survival techniques and equipment; pilots' survival equipment; sewing machines and fabric work; sewing projects. *Course 2:* Parachute rigging and packing; parachute descent; sewing machines and fabric shop work; survival equipment. *Course 3:* Oxygen and carbon dioxide systems operation; ground crew line maintenance; oxygen regulator test stands; liquid oxygen properties, controls, transfer and storage equipment and procedures; full pressure suit description and construction; ready room and flight line procedures. *Course 4:* Aviators' Equipment Division administration, including supervision and management, naval aircraft maintenance program, blueprint reading and sketching, teaching methods; sewing machine use and repair; liquid oxygen equipment; oxygen regulators; pressure suits and components.

Credit recommendation, collegiate level: *Courses 1, 2, and 3* are technical and vocational in nature. *Courses 1 and 2:* For each course, credit in sewing and parachute rigging on the basis of demonstrated skills and/or institutional examinations. *Course 3:* Credit in oxygen equipment maintenance on the basis of demonstrated skills and/or institutional examinations. *Course 4:* 2 semester hours in maintenance management. At the technical and vocational level, credit in oxygen equipment maintenance on the basis of demonstrated skills and/or institutional examinations.

Patternmaker, Class A

Location: Naval School, San Diego, Calif.

Length: 20 weeks.

Objectives: To train personnel in simple and complex wood and plaster patternmaking.

Instruction: Shop math; blueprint reading and pattern layout; patternmaker's hand and portable power tools; pattern materials; pattern machinery operation, maintenance, and safety precautions; patternmaking fundamentals; pattern joinery; types of patterns and pattern construction; layout and construction; pattern finishing.

Credit recommendation, collegiate level: This course is technical and vocational in nature. Credit in patternmaking on the basis of demonstrated skills and/or institutional examinations.

Personnelman, Class A

Location: Naval School, Bainbridge, Md.

Length: 10 weeks.

Objectives: To train personnel to perform clerical office duties in a personnel office.

Instruction: Typewriting; personnel accounting; personnel administration; correspondence; classification of enlisted personnel; welfare.

Credit recommendation, collegiate level: 3 semester hours in personnel classification, and credit in typing on the basis of institutional examination.

Personnelman, Class C, Career Information and Counseling

Location: Navy Schools, Norfolk, Va., and San Diego, Calif.

Length: 3 weeks.

Objectives: To train officers to present career information to groups and to counsel individuals in the selection of careers.

Instruction: Navy career opportunities and benefits; civilian career opportunities; speaking to groups; individual differences and motivation; interviewing and counseling; principles of human relations.

Credit recommendation, collegiate level: 2 semester hours in personnel classification.

Personnelman, Class C, Enlisted Classification

Location: Naval School, San Diego, Calif.

Length: 4 weeks.

Objectives: To train officers in the techniques of interviewing and counseling.

Instruction: Enlisted classification in the Navy; principles of interviewing; classification testing and interpretation; identifying and evaluating civilian work experience in counseling; occupational analysis.

Credit recommendation, collegiate level: 3 semester hours in personnel classification.

Personnelman, Class C, Interviewing and Classification

Location: Naval Training Center, San Diego, Calif.

Length: 8–10 weeks.

Objectives: To train personnel as skillful classification interviewers.

Instruction: Enlisted classification in the Navy; principles of interviewing; classification testing and interpretation; naval occupational analysis; Navy enlisted classification codes; identifying and evaluating civilian work experience in counseling; organizational planning and work simplification for naval units.

Credit recommendation, collegiate level: 3 semester hours in personnel classification.

Personnelman, Class C, Naval Management Analysis

Location: Naval Training Center, San Diego, Calif.

Length: 4 weeks.

Objectives: To train personnel in the technical elements of recruiting, classification and interviewing, management analysis, and career information and counseling.

Instruction: Manpower utilization; naval occupational analysis; work simplification and improvement; management/manpower survey methods; reports and written communication.

Credit recommendation, collegiate level: 2 semester hours in methods of management/manpower analysis.

Personnelman, Class C, Recruit Procurement

Locations: Naval Schools, Bainbridge, Md., and San Diego, Calif.

Length: 6 weeks.

Objectives: To train chief petty officers and petty officers, first class, for general recruiting duty.

Instruction: Administrative procedures; recruiting service; practical interview exercises; recruiting aids; officer program; re-enlistment program; correspondence; public speaking; recruit training.

Credit recommendation, collegiate level: Credit in oral and written communication on the basis of demonstrated skills and/or institutional examinations.

Pharmacy Technic

Locations: Naval Medical Centers, Bethesda, Md., San Diego, Calif., and Portsmouth, Va.

Length: 32–38 weeks.

Objectives: To train personnel to assist medical and pharmacy officers in the compounding and dispensing of pharmaceutical preparations.

Instruction: Principles of pharmacy; operative and dispensing pharmacy; compounding pharmacy; pharmaceutical mathematics; inorganic and organic chemistry; basic pharmacology and toxicology; pharmacy administration.

Credit recommendation, collegiate level: 5 semester hours in pharmaceutical mathematics and 2 semester hours in pharmaceutical laboratory techniques.

1. **Photographer's Mate School, Class A**
2. **Photographer's Mate, Class A**
3. **Photographer's Mate (Aerial Photography), Class A**
4. **Photographer's Mate A (Aerial Cameraman), Class A**
5. **Photographer's Mate G (Cameraman), Class A**

Location: Naval Air Technical Training Unit, Pensacola, Fla.

Length: *Courses 1 and 3,* 15–18 weeks; *Course 2,* 14 weeks; *Courses 4 and 5,* 8–9 weeks.

Objectives: To train enlisted personnel in the operation of various types of photographic equipment and the techniques of photography.

Instruction: *Course 1:* Aviation fundamentals; fundamentals of still camera photography; motion picture, small camera, and aerial photography; laboratory procedures and equipment. *Course 2:* Elementary photography, including light and exposure factors, photographic chemicals, and laboratory procedures; controlling light; spectral distribution; lamps and lenses; projection printing and equipment; elementary motion pictures, including operation of Navy cameras and accessories, editing, splicing, and projecting; photography administration procedures; basic aviation photography. *Course 3* covers the same instruction as *Course 2* including familiarization with aerial photographic flights mosaics, high and low oblique, flight and safety equipment, and intercommunication equipment. *Course 4* Principles of photography; camera operation; photographic techniques; laboratory procedures; aerial photography, including laboratory techniques and equipment, oblique and vertical photography, and photographic flights; administrative authority; fixed installation photography. *Course 5:* Still photography, includ ing principles of photography, camera operation, photographic techniques, laboratory equipment.

Credit recommendation, collegiate level: CAUTION: *These courses vary in title, length, and recommendation. Require exact identification by full title and length. Courses 1, 2, and 3: 6 semester hours in photography. Courses 4 and 5: 3 semester hours in photography.*

1. Photographer's Mate School, Class B
   (Advanced Photographer's Mate School, Class B)
2. Photographic Officers' Course, Class O
3. Photographic Reconnaissance Officers' Course, Class O
   (Photographic Reconnaissance Course, Class O)
4. Photographic Reconnaissance Officers' Course, Class O
5. Photographic Reconnaissance Officers' Course, Class O

Location: Naval Air Technical Training Unit, Pensacola, Fla.

Length: *Courses 1, 2, and 3, 20–24 weeks; Course 4, 8 weeks; Course 5, 4–6 weeks.*

Objectives: *Course 1* trains photographers' mates, *Courses 2 and 3* train officers, in the operation and routine maintenance of naval cameras and equipment and in the production of photographs for tactical, documentary, intelligence, and educational use by the Navy and for public information. *Courses 4 and 5:* To familiarize naval aviators/naval aviation observers with aerial photographic reconnaissance.

Instruction: *Courses 1, 2, and 3:* General photography, including light characteristics and exposure meters, filters, optics, exposure, processing, printing, corrective photography, portraiture, composition, records, and photographic supply; color photography and printing; motion picture photography, including uncontrolled action and documentary coverage, editing, sound and high speed cameras, processing, printing, and television shorts; aerial photography, including radarscope, vertical, oblique, and night aerial photography, mosaic maps, processing, and printing; leadership and supervision. *Course 4:* General photography, including light characteristics, photographic optics, exposure, chemistry, processing, and printing; administration, supply, reports, and records; aerial photography, including Navy camera control systems, aerial equipment and laboratory techniques, air intelligence and photo interpretation; radarscope photography. *Course 5:* Administration; photographic intelligence; aerial photography; laboratory procedures; camera control systems; aerial photographic techniques.

Credit recommendation, collegiate level: CAUTION: *These courses vary in length and recommendation. Require identification by full title and exact length. Courses 1, 2, and 3: 6 semester hours in photography. Courses 4 and 5: 3 semester hours in photography.*

1. Photographic Equipment Repair, Class C
   (Camera Repair School—Mechanical Repair Course, Class C)
2. Photographic Electronics Systems, Class C
   (Camera Repair School—Photographic Electronics Systems Repair Course, Class C)
3. Camera Repair School, Class C
4. Camera Repair School, Class C
5. Camera Repair School, Class C
   (Camera Repair, Class C)

Location: Naval Air Technical Training Unit, Pensacola, Fla.

Length: *Courses 1 and 2, 15 weeks; Course 3, 30 weeks; Course 4, 19 weeks; Course 5, 12 weeks.*

Objectives: To train photographers' mates and other enlisted personnel in the maintenance and repair of standard naval photographic equipment.

Instruction: *Course 1:* Basic electricity; hand tools, abrasives, and lubricants; aerial camera body drives and shutters; aerial camera magazines; aerial still and gun cameras; laboratory equipment maintenance; aerial processing equipment; continuous strip printer; advanced aerial equipment, including night cameras and electrical Rapidyne shutter theory, inspection, repair, and reassembly. *Course 2:* DC and AC circuit theory; vacuum tubes; gas and cathode-ray tubes; cathode-ray oscilloscope; radio receivers; electronic laboratory equipment; Navy camera control systems troubleshooting and repair. *Course 3* is a combination of *Courses 1 and 2* and should be distinguished by length from courses of the same name. *Course 4:* Hand tools; electricity; aerial camera shutters, body drives, and magazines; motion picture and still (ground) cameras; laboratory processing equipment; AC electricity; vacuum tubes; rectifiers, power supplies, and amplifiers; test instruments; signal generator; oscilloscope; Navy camera control systems troubleshooting and repair. *Course 5:* Hand tools; electricity; accessory motors and circuits; aerial, motion picture, and still (ground) camera repair and reassembly.

Credit recommendation, collegiate level: CAUTION: *These courses vary in length and recommendation. Require exact identification by full title and length. Courses 1 and 5:* Credit in electricity on the basis of institutional examination. At the technical and vocational level, credit in camera and photographic equipment repair on the basis of demonstrated skills and/or institutional examinations. *Courses 2 and 4:* 3 semester hours at the freshman or sophomore level as an elective in electricity and electronics. At the technical and vocational level, credit in camera and photographic equipment repair on the basis of demonstrated skills and/or institutional examinations. *Course 3:* 4 semester hours at the freshman or sophomore level as an elective in electricity and electronics. At the technical and vocational level, credit in camera and photographic equipment repair on the basis of demonstrated skills and/or institutional examinations.

Photographic Intelligenceman (PT)
(Photographic Interpretation/Radar Target Analysis)

Location: Naval Receiving Station, Washington, D.C.

Length: 14–16 weeks.

Objectives: To train personnel for duty in the areas of air intelligence, photographic interpretation, and radar target analysis.

Instruction: General photography; general intelligence; maps and charts; ground/amphibious; weapons; air; metrics; target materials; target analysis; operational and intelligence planning.

Credit recommendation, collegiate level: 4 semester hours in photographic interpretation.

Physical Therapy Technic

Locations: Naval Medical School, Bethesda, Md., and Naval Hospital, San Diego, Calif.

Length: 21–26 weeks.

Objectives: To train personnel to assist the medical officer in administering all types of physical therapy.

Instruction: Anatomy; physiology; physics; psychology and psychiatry; principles of rehabilitation; massage; electrotherapy; radiation therapy; neurology; hydrotherapy; therapeutic exercise; clinical practice.

Credit recommendation, collegiate level: This course is technical and vocational in nature. Credit in physical therapy techniques on the basis of demonstrated skills and/or institutional examinations.

Pilots' C-121 Simulator and Advanced Flight

Location: Naval Air Station, Patuxent River, Md.

Length: 6 weeks.

Objectives: To train prospective C-121 second pilots and plane commanders in C-121 ground and flight techniques.

Instruction: C-121 operational flight simulator familiarization, check lists, and drills; normal and emergency flight procedures; instructional flights with emphasis on emergencies and in-flight and ground-handling characteristics of the aircraft; landing, takeoff, and taxi techniques.

Credit recommendation, collegiate level: No credit because of the specialized nature of the course.

Pilots' C-121 Simulator and Basic Flight

Location: Naval Air Station, Patuxent River, Md.

Length: 3 weeks.

Objectives: To train prospective C-121 third pilots in basic C-121 ground and flight procedures.

Instruction: C-121 operational flight simulator cockpit familiarization, drills, and use of check lists; complete C-121 flight, including emergency procedures and ground-controlled and instrument landings.

Credit recommendation, collegiate level: No credit because of the brevity and specialized nature of the course.

Planning and Estimating Construction Group Ratings, Class C

Location: Port Hueneme, Calif.

Length: 8 weeks.

Objectives: To train petty officers in the fundamentals of procurement, and in planning and estimating materials, labor, time, tools, equipment, and facilities.

Instruction: Blueprints and specifications; drafting fundamentals and aids; material estimating; material procurement; labor and equipment estimating and scheduling.

Credit recommendation, collegiate level: This course is technical and vocational in nature. Credit in procurement planning and estimating for construction on the basis of demonstrated skills and/or institutional examinations.

Polaris Electronics, Class A

Location: Naval Guided Missiles School, Dam Neck, Va.

Length: 22 weeks.

Objectives: To provide personnel with basic training in electricity and electronics.

Instruction: Basic mathematics; basic electricity; fundamentals of DC and AC; basic electronics; transistors; vacuum tubes; magnetic amplifiers; computers; missile system fundamentals; mechanics of motion; inertial components; analog components; guidance methods; records; data transmission circuits; general maintenance; programming techniques; motors and generators; solderless connections; countermeasures; control systems; ordnance; electronic equipment; optics; missiles; navigation.

Credit recommendation, collegiate level: 3 semester hours at the freshman or sophomore level as an elective in electricity and electronics, and credit in electrical laboratory on the basis of demonstrated skills and/or institutional examinations.

Postal Clerk, Class A

Locations: Naval Schools, Bainbridge, Md., and San Diego, Calif.

Length: 5 weeks.

Objectives: To train personnel in the organization and regulations of the Navy postal service and in the handling of mail.

Instruction: Administrative and clerical training; typewriting; organization of the Navy postal service; operation of Navy post offices; international mail; handling and treatment of mail; audits; inspections, and report; disestablishment of Navy post offices; inquiries, complaints, and claims.

Credit recommendation, collegiate level: No credit because of the limited technical nature of the course.

Preventive Medicine Technic
(Environmental Sanitation Technic)

Location: Naval Hospital, Oakland, Calif.

Length: 20–22 weeks.

Objectives: To train enlisted personnel to assist medical officers in epidemiological and sanitation work.

Instruction: Bacteriology; immunology; mathematics; vital statistics; epidemiology; parasitology; entomology; military sanitation.

Credit recommendation, collegiate level: 3 semester hours in community sanitation and 8 semester hours in pathogenic bacteriology and epidemiology.

1. Programmed Instruction Techniques
2. Instructional Programmer, Class C

Location: Naval Schools, Great Lakes, Ill., and Memphis, Tenn.

Length: 3 weeks.

Objectives: To train instructor personnel to teach and supervise Navy programmers.

Instruction: Basic principles of instruction and learning theory; task analysis; training objectives; program outlines; linear programs; intrinsic programs; writing and editing linear and intrinsic programs.

Credit recommendation, collegiate level: 3 semester hours in construction of programmed instruction courses for each course.

Prospective Engineer Officer

Location: Fleet Training Center, San Diego, Calif.

Length: 8 weeks.

Objectives: To prepare officers for Engineering Department work and for primary duty in steam and diesel drive ships.

Instruction: Administration: boiler construction and inspection; auxiliaries; steam propulsion machinery; diesel propulsion machinery; electrical systems and equipment; firefighting; damage control; NBC warfare defense.

Credit recommendation, collegiate level: No credit because of the specialized nature of the course.

Prospective Officer of the Deck

Location: Naval School, San Diego, Calif.

Length: 3 weeks.

Objectives: To provide basic instruction for officers in the duties of the Officer of the Deck underway and in port.

Instruction: General duties; seamanship; navigation; rules of the road; communications; tactics; maneuvering board.

Credit recommendation, collegiate level: No credit because of the brevity and limited technical nature of the course.

R3350-42 Engine Maintenance

Location: Naval Air Station, Patuxent River, Md.

Length: 3 weeks.

Objectives: To train aviation machinist mates on the R3350–42 engine and accessories as applicable to C-121 aircraft.

Instruction: Introduction to C-121 aircraft; basic engine theory; lubrication; two-speed supercharger; carburetion; fuel injection system; propeller systems; torquemeter; QEC units; power recovery turbines; ignition systems.

Credit recommendation, collegiate level: This course is technical and vocational in nature. Credit in aircraft engine repair shop on the basis of demonstrated skills and/or institutional examinations.

RADIAC Instrument Maintenance

Location: Treasure Island, Calif.

Length: 4 weeks.

Objectives: To provide personnel with a comprehensive knowledge of nuclear radiation detection, radiological safety, and radio instrument operation, maintenance, and calibration.

Instruction: Operation, calibration, maintenance, and circuit analysis; leakage tests; calibration and maintenance of radiac instruments; monitoring procedures; decontamination procedures.

Credit recommendation, collegiate level: Credit in electrical laboratory on the basis of demonstrated skills and/or institutional examinations.

Radar Target Intelligence

Location: Naval Receiving Station, Washington, D.C.

Length: 11 weeks.

Objectives: To provide training in the interpretation of radar scope photography for intelligence purposes.

Instruction: Target area analysis; building density, structure, and height determination; preparing rail and intelligence overlay; principles of radar; radarscope photo interpretation and plotting; composite overlay; prediction and simulation; mission planning; field trips; new developments in radar.

Credit recommendation, collegiate level: 4 semester hours in photographic interpretation.

1. Radarman, Class A
2. Radarman, Class A (Operational Course)

Location: Naval School, Treasure Island, Calif.

Length: *Course 1,* 20 weeks; *Course 2,* 12 weeks.

Objectives: To train personnel to operate radar equipment and to interpret information received from the equipment.

Instruction: *Courses 1 and 2:* Search-radar operation; altitude determining radar; countermeasures equipment; air plotting; maneuvering board; dead reckoning; radar navigation; radiotelephone communications; internal communications. In addition *Course 1* includes DC and AC; power supplies; radar system fundamentals; analysis and maintenance.

Credit recommendation, collegiate level: *Course 1:* 3 semester hours at the freshman or sophomore level as an elective in electricity and electronics, and credit in electrical laboratory on the basis of demonstrated skills and/or institutional examinations. *Course 2:* Credit in electrical laboratory on the basis of demonstrated skills and/or institutional examinations.

Radarman, Class B (Maintenance Phase)
(Radarman, Class B)

Location: Naval Schools, Treasure Island, Calif.

Length: 33 and 42 weeks.

Objectives: To train radarmen to analyze, isolate, and repair electronic equipment and systems.

Instruction: Pulsed radar systems; power supplies; timer and signal circuits; transmitters and receivers; antennas and transmission lines; radar systems analysis; ECM systems and maintenance; AEW systems.

Credit recommendation, collegiate level: 1 semester hour in basic electricity and 9 semester hours at the freshman or sophomore level as a technical elective in the general areas of radio and electronics.

Radarman Preventive Maintenance and Operator

Locations: Radarman Schools, Great Lakes, Ill., and Norfolk, Va.

Length: 24 weeks.

Objectives: To train radarmen in basic preventive maintenance and operational duties.

Instruction: Fundamentals of electricity and electronics; batteries; motors, generators, and starters; safety precautions; tools; test equipment; troubleshooting and repair; radar equipment; surface search radar; air search radar; radar repeater.

Credit recommendation, collegiate level: Credit in electricity and electrical laboratory on the basis of demonstrated skills and/or institutional examinations.

Radio Aids Unit (Device 1-D-5), Class C

Location: Naval Air Technical Training Center, Memphis, Tenn.

Length: 5 weeks.

Objectives: To train tradevmen in radio aids unit maintenance and prepare them to instruct pilots and other tradevmen in such maintenance.

Instruction: Operation of radio aids unit, including navigational terminology, radio and navigational aids, general trainer description, controls and indicators, preoperational preparation, operational procedures, and facilities utilization; maintenance of radio aids unit, including review of positioning and computer circuits and theory of operation.

Credit recommendation, collegiate level: Credit in electrical laboratory on the basis of demonstrated skills and/or institutional examinations.

Radioactive Isotope Technic

Locations: Naval Medical School, Bethesda, Md., and Naval Hospital, San Diego, Calif.

Length: 24–32 weeks.

Objectives: To train personnel to operate and maintain radioactive isotope therapy apparatus and to assist medical officers in preparing and conducting radioactive isotope therapy.

Instruction: Mathematics involved in radioisotope work; general chemistry; clinical practices; laboratory procedures; radiochemistry; nuclear physics; health physics.

Credit recommendation, collegiate level: 3 semester hours at the freshman level in general chemistry, and credit in radioactive isotope therapy technician training on the basis of demonstrated skills and/or institutional examinations.

1. Radioman, Class A
2. Radiomen, Class A

Locations: Naval Schools, Radioman, Class A, Bainbridge, Md., and San Diego, Calif.

Length: *Course 1,* 24 weeks; *Course 2,* 14 weeks.

Objectives: To train personnel to operate and to perform preventive maintenance on radio receiving and transmitting equipment.

Instruction: *Course 1:* Basic mathematics; fundamentals of AC and DC; AC and DC circuits; power supplies; amplifiers and oscillators; transmitters and receivers; superheterodyne receiver; UHF equipment; FSK equipment. *Course 2:* Defense communications; naval communication system; communication security; message and telegraph procedures; teletypewriter procedures; voice procedures; maintenance and material management systems; frequency theory; communication equipment and systems.

Credit recommendation, collegiate level: CAUTION: *These courses vary slightly in title, length, and recommendation. Require exact identification of the course by title and length. Course 1:* 2 semester hours at the freshman or sophomore level as an elective in electricity and electronics, and credit in electrical laboratory on the basis of demonstrated skills and/or institutional examinations. *Course 2:* Credit in electrical laboratory on the basis of demonstrated skills and/or institutional examinations.

Radioman, Class B
(Radiomen School, Class B)

Locations: Radioman Schools, Class B, Bainbridge, Md. and San Diego, Calif.

Length: 30–37 weeks.

Objectives: To train personnel in the theory of electronics and communications systems.

Instruction: DC fundamentals; DC analysis series circuits; parallel circuits; series-parallel and voltage divider circuits; electrical measuring devices; AC fundamentals; inductance, capacitance, and resonance; circuits; power supplies; vacuum tubes; oscillators and amplifiers; modulation; wave propagation; receivers; superheterodyne receivers; troubleshooting and test equipment; transistors; terminal equipment systems; single-side-band equipment.

Credit recommendation, collegiate level: 6 semester hours at the freshman or sophomore level as an elective in electricity and electronics, and credit in electrical laboratory on the basis of demonstrated skills and/or institutional examinations.

1. Rawin-Radiosonde Set Operator, Class C
2. Rawin Set Operator, Class C
3. Radiosonde (SMQ) Set Operator, Class C
   (Radiosonde (FMQ/SMQ) Set Operator, Class C)
   (Radiosonde Set Operator, Class C)

Location: Naval Air Technical Training Unit, Lakehurst, N.J.

Length: 3–6 weeks.

Objectives: To train aerographer's mates and other personnel to evaluate meteorological data and operate the specified equipment.

Instruction: Rawin and/or radiosonde equipment and components operation, alignment, calibration, and preventive maintenance; flight equipment; evaluation of upper air data–chart preparation and aerological records; atmospheric soundings, including release and in-flight procedures and record evaluation.

Credit recommendation, collegiate level: For each course, credit in weather forecasting techniques on the basis of institutional examination.

Recruiters Journalism, Class C

Location: Naval School, Great Lakes, Ill.
Length: 4 weeks.
Objectives: To provide advanced training for personnel in the principles, practices, and tools of recruiting publicity.
Instruction: Public relations; service relations; publicity techniques; publicity media; newswriting; radio and television; photography; comprehensive group problems.
Credit recommendation, collegiate level: 2 semester hours in journalism.

Reserve Officer Candidate Program
(Naval Reserve Officer Candidate Program)
(ROC Program)

Location: Officer Candidate School, Newport, R.I.

The Reserve Officer Candidate (ROC) Program is one of a number of officer procurement programs currently utilized by the Navy to give students who are enrolled in an accredited college, junior college, or university an opportunity to qualify for a commission in the Naval Reserve. Students enroll in the ROC Program through the naval district commandant or the offices of Naval Officer Procurement, both of which are located throughout the country. Students may also enroll through the Chief of Naval Air Reserve Training, Naval Air Station, Glenview, Illinois.

The training consists of two eight-week summer training periods, taken during different summers, at the Officer Candidate School, Newport, Rhode Island. These training periods are known as the Basic (ROC Two) and the Advanced (ROC One) Courses and stress indoctrination in essential naval subjects. The academic curriculum consists of navigation, gunnery, leadership, communications, seamanship, and naval orientation. During the academic year ROC personnel must participate in their local Reserve unit and must be in good standing academically to remain in the program.

Candidates who successfully complete the two eight-week summer courses, receive a baccalaureate degree, and meet other qualificatons, are commissioned ensigns, U.S. Naval Reserve.

Credit recommendation, collegiate level: 3 semester hours in advanced naval science for each course.

School Administration, Course G, Class C

Locations: Naval Schools, Great Lakes, Ill., Norfolk, Va., and San Diego, Calif.
Length: 4 weeks.
Objectives: To train personnel in the instructional procedures and techniques of the administration of Navy schools.

Instruction: The school administrator; management; supervision; evaluation; curriculum preparation and revision; training aids; training equipment.
Credit recommendation, collegiate level: 2 semester hours in instructional methods.

School of Naval Command and Staff
(Command and Staff Course)

Location: Naval War College, Newport, R.I.
Length: 1 academic year.
Objectives: To provide students with an opportunity to further their understanding of the fundamentals of warfare with emphasis upon the operational functions of command. This includes operational planning and command decision, the organization, functions, and procedures of operational staffs, and participation in joint and combined committee work.
Instruction: Operational planning and elements of command decision; nuclear weapons planning; international law; military organization study; weapons systems study; introduction to logistics and logistics planning; interservice operations; exercises in command decision in the solution of operational problems; strategic area studies.
Credit recommendation, collegiate level: 9 semester hours in business administration, and credit in international law and credit in political science, including international relations, on the basis of institutional examinations.

1. **School of Naval Warfare**
2. **Naval Warfare Course**
3. **Naval Warfare Course**

Location: Naval War College, Newport, R. I.
Length: *Courses 1 and 2:* 1 academic year; *Course 3,* 1 or 2 academic years.
Objectives: To train officers in the fundamentals of warfare, international relations, and interservice operations to prepare them for higher command.
Instruction: The course from 1965 to 1968 was *School of Naval Warfare.* The course from 1954 to 1965 was *Naval Warfare Course. Course 1:* Sea power and national strategy; international law; international relations; Soviet Union and Red China; United States; regional associations; developing areas; formulation of national strategies; counterinsurgency; strategic planning and naval warfare; management activities of the Navy Department; operational planning. *Course 2— Given from 1958 to 1965:* General studies; international law; national strategy, counterinsurgency; fundamentals of warfare and maritime strategy; strategic planning study; naval warfare study including organization and planning exercises; global strategy. *Course 3—From 1954 until 1958, the Naval Warfare Course was offered in two parts, each one year in length. A student could take either or both years of the course. First year:* Strategy studies; operations problems and tactics; logistic principles; communications systems; intelligence and international relations; interservice operations. *Second year:* National security; area studies; functions of the Navy and other armed services; strategy; national objectives; interservice operations; planning systems.
Credit recommendation, collegiate level: *Courses 1 and 2:* 9 semester hours in business administration, 6

semester hours in political science, including international relations, and credit in international law on the basis of institutional examinations. *Course 3:* For each year, 9 semester hours in business organization and management, and credit in political science and international law on the basis of institutional examinations.

Scuba Diver

Location: Naval School, Underwater Swimmers, Key West, Fla.

Length: 4 weeks.

Objectives: To train personnel in the knowledge and skills necessary to become a scuba diver.

Instruction: Physics of diving; medical aspects of diving; swimming; underwater swimming; buoyant ascent training; underwater search and inspection; related subjects for diving; demolition orientation.

Credit recommendation, collegiate level: This course is technical and vocational in nature. Credit in deep sea diving on the basis of demonstrated skills and/or institutional examinations.

Senior Officer Orientation
(Senior Officer Helicopter Training)

Location: Naval Air Station, Pensacola, Fla.

Length: 5 weeks.

Objectives: To provide officers with the basic knowledge of the flight characteristics of helicopters.

Instruction: Helicopter orientation and area checkout; basic instruments; radio instruments; flight training.

Credit recommendation, collegiate level: No credit because of the specialized nature of the course.

Shipfitters (Metalsmith or Pipefitter) Class A

Location: Naval Training Center, San Diego, Calif.

Length: 12 weeks, if only one speciality is taken; 15 weeks, if both specialities are taken.

Objectives: To train personnel as metalsmiths and/or pipefitters.

Instruction: For both specialities: Responsibilities and work of the shipfitter; mathematics, blueprint reading, working drawings and symbols; basic tools and materials; basic metallurgy; oxyacetylene welding; torch brazing and soldering; coppersmithing; arc welding processes. In addition metalsmithing and pipefitting in the respective specialities.

Credit recommendation, collegiate level: This course is technical and vocational in nature. Credit in metalsmithing and/or pipefitting on the basis of demonstrated skills and/or institutional examinations.

Shore Fire Control Party Enlisted

Location: Naval Amphibious School, Coronado, San Diego, Calif.

Length: 3-4 weeks.

Objectives: To train enlisted personnel in naval gunfire liaison and spotting team gunfire support procedures.

Instruction: Map reading; conduct of fire; tactics; supporting arms evaluator.

Credit recommendation, collegiate level: No credit as the course is military in nature.

Solid State Fundamentals, Class C

Location: Naval School, Treasure Island, Calif.

Length: 3 weeks.

Objectives: To train electronics technicians in the maintenance of electronic equipment and electronic systems utilizing semiconductor devices.

Instruction: Physics of semiconductors; DC analysis of transistor circuits; transistor switching circuits; transistor and diode logic circuits.

Credit recommendation, collegiate level: Credit in electrical laboratory on the basis of demonstrated skills and/or institutional examinations.

Sonarman, Class A
(Basic Sonarman, 560)

Locations: Sonar School, Key West, Fla., and San Diego, Calif.

Length: 24 weeks.

Objectives: To train personnel to perform preventive and corrective maintenance on sonar and allied equipment.

Instruction: Fundamentals of DC and AC; DC series circuits; DC parallel circuits; DC generators and motors; AC circuits; inductance and capacitance; transformers and alternators; power supplies; rectifiers; amplifiers; vacuum tubes; oscillators; transmitters; receivers; synchros; multivibrators; sonar and auxiliary equipment.

Credit recommendation, collegiate level: 2 semester hours in electricity and electronics, and credit in electrical laboratory on the basis of demonstrated skills and/or institutional examinations.

Sonobuoy Trainer, Class C

Location: Naval Air Technical Training Center, Memphis, Tenn.

Length: 14 weeks.

Objectives: To train tradevmen and other enlisted personnel to operate and maintain sonobuoy trainers.

Instruction: Application of DC, AC, DC and AC circuits, vacuum tubes, and vacuum tube circuits in advanced training; servosystems; navigation; operation of the sonobuoy trainer; target course generator device; power distribution; sonobuoy control and control circuits; multiplexer; display and sound systems; adjustment and calibration of the trainer; trainer maintenance.

Credit recommendation, collegiate level: 3 semester hours at the freshman or sophomore level as an elective in electricity and electronics, and credit in electrical laboratory on the basis of demonstrated skills and/or institutional examinations.

Special Photographic Course for Non-Photographic Personnel, Class C

Location: Naval Air Technical Training Unit, Pensacola, Fla.

Length: 6 weeks.

Objectives: To train non-photographic personnel to operate selected cameras and produce finished photography to quality specifications.

Instruction: Principles of 35 mm photography; laboratory procedures; administration; general and specialized photographic techniques; color films; stereo photography; principles of aerial photography; aerial reconnaissance.

Credit recommendation, collegiate level: 3 semester hours in photography.

Staff Embarkation (LFTU-4)

Location: Naval Amphibious Base, Little Creek, Norfolk, Va.

Length: 3 weeks.

Objectives: To train U.S., Allied, and noncommissioned officers of any service in the special staff duties, tasks, and responsibilities of embarkation personnel assigned at regimental, brigade, or higher staff level.

Instruction: Development of lift requirements from organization and equipping documents; shipping requirements to support a given landing plan; allocation of troops, equipment, and supplies; function and operation of the tactical logistical group.

Credit recommendation, collegiate level: No credit because of the specialized nature of the course.

1. Steelworkers, Class A
2. Steelworkers, Class B

Locations: Naval Schools, Construction, Davisville, R.I., and Port Hueneme, Calif.

Length: *Course 1,* 12 weeks; *Course 2,* 14–15 weeks.

Objectives: To provide basic and advanced training to enlisted personnel in the erection of steel structures.

Instruction: *Course 1:* Mathematics; blueprint reading and sketching; sheet metal; hand tools and materials; gas welding and cutting; electric arc welding; rigging; steel erection. *Course 2:* Foremanship; applied mathematics; sheet metal; materials of structural steelwork; oxyacetylene welding and cutting; electric arc welding; inert gas shielded metal and welding; rigging; steel erection; planning and stenciling.

Credit recommendation, collegiate level: These courses are technical and vocational in nature. Credit in heavy construction work and welding on the basis of demonstrated skills and/or institutional examinations.

Stenography

Location: Naval School, Bainbridge, Md.

Length: 6 weeks.

Objectives: To train petty officers as stenographers capable of high-speed shorthand and typewriting.

Instruction: Stenography; practical secretarial duties; typing; vocabulary building; mechanics of English.

Credit recommendation, collegiate level: Credit in stenography and typing on the basis of institutional examination.

1. Storekeepers (Repair Parts) Class C (Supply Storekeepers School (Repair Parts) Class C)
2. Storekeepers (Independent Duty) Class C School
3. Shop Stores Procedures, Class C

Locations: Naval Schools, Newport, R.I., San Diego, Calif., and Port Hueneme, Calif.

Length: 3–5 weeks.

Objectives: To train personnel for afloat and ashore billets of storekeeper in repair parts supply.

Instruction: Various storerooms; receiving, storing, and issuing items; inventory taking; preparation of requisitions; contacting suppliers; disbursing functions.

Credit recommendation, collegiate level: This course is technical and vocational in nature. Credit in stockroom accounting procedures on the basis of demonstrated skills and/or institutional examinations.

Storekeepers School, Class A

Locations: Naval Training Centers, Newport, R.I. and San Diego, Calif.

Length: 12 weeks.

Objectives: To train personnel for afloat and ashore billets of storekeeper.

Instruction: General store supply afloat; ship's store; commissary; yards and docks and submarine reactor repair parts; ship's machinery repair parts; electronics repair parts; ordnance repair parts; records and reports; typewriting.

Credit recommendation, collegiate level: Credit in typing on the basis of institutional examination. At the technical level, credit in merchandising on the basis of demonstrated skills and/or institutional examinations.

Strategic Photographic Interpretation

Location: Naval Receiving Station, Washington, D.C.

Length: 10 weeks.

Objectives: To train personnel in advanced photographic interpretation.

Instruction: Elementary optics; lens and camera calibration; basic photo geometrics and measurement; stereocomparagraph; industrial target analysis; harbor analysis; damage assessment; underground installations.

Credit recommendation, collegiate level: 3 semester hours in photographic interpretation.

Submarine Medicine Technician, Class C (Submarine Medicine Technic)

Location: Submarine Base, New London, Conn.

Length: 20 weeks.

Objectives: To train personnel to render medical care aboard submarines.

Instruction: Physical qualification, indoctrination, and matriculation; property and accounting and administration in submarines; medical diagnostic and treatment procedures; laboratory procedures; anatomy and physiology; pharmaceutical procedures and pharmacology; minor surgery and first aid; hygiene and sanitation.

Credit recommendation, collegiate level: 3 semester hours in first aid and hygiene.

SWIFT Boat Crew Training

Location: Naval Amphibious School, Coronado, San Diego, Calif.

Length: 9 weeks.

Objectives: To train SWIFT personnel in boat operations, emergency repair, and survival.

Instruction: Counterinsurgency; self protection; survival; boat navigation; radar/radio operation and maintenance; engineering/electrical maintenance; ordnance pyrotechnics; hull and ordnance maintenance; visual communications; physical fitness; air and gunfire support; boat operations.

Credit recommendation, collegiate level: No credit as the course is military in nature.

Tactical Air Control Party

Location: Naval Amphibious School, Coronado, San Diego, Calif.

Length: 3 weeks.

Objectives: To train officers in the basic principles of tactical air support planning.

Instruction: Introduction to tactical air support training; air support in the amphibious operation; tactical air observation; map reading; communications; aircraft weapons and planning; organization; supporting arms; testing; helicopters.

Credit recommendation, collegiate level: No credit as the course is military in nature.

Tactical Photographic Interpretation

Location: Naval Receiving Station, Washington, D.C.

Length: 11 weeks.

Objectives: To train personnel in the fundamentals of photographic interpretation.

Instruction: Photographic process; aerial cameras; types of photos; introduction to intelligence; map reading; flight plan and photo specifications; tactical analysis of terrain; photometrics; night photography; tactical damage assessment; industry interpretation.

Credit recommendation, collegiate level: 3 semester hours in photographic interpretation.

Target Drone, Class C

Location: Naval Air Technical Training Unit, El Centro, Calif.

Length: 9 weeks.

Objectives: To train officers and enlisted personnel in the operation, maintenance, and repair of target pilotless aircraft and associated equipment.

Instruction: Administration; overhaul, maintenance, and preparation; unit flight operations; advanced-type target pilotless aircraft maintenance and overhaul; electronics and electrical systems overhaul; parachutes and fueling.

Credit recommendation, collegiate level: This course is technical and vocational in nature. Credit in aircraft repair shop on the basis of demonstrated skills and/or institutional examinations.

Teletypewriter System (Afloat) Maintenance Models TT-70A/UG and AN/UGC-5 TT-252/UG Typing Perforator

Location: Fleet Training Group, Pearl Harbor, Hawaii.

Length: 6 weeks.

Objectives: To train personnel in the operation and maintenance of the teletypewriter TT-70A and AN/UGC-5 perforator.

Instruction: Nomenclature, theory of operation, and adjustments of the keyboard; nomenclature, theory of operation, disassembly, and preventive maintenance on the automatic typer; adjustments to the automatic typer; troubleshooting the TT-70A; theory of operation of the typing perforator.

Credit recommendation, collegiate level: This course is technical and vocational in nature. Credit in teletypewriter repair on the basis of demonstrated skills and/or institutional examinations.

Test Pilot Training Course

Location: Naval Air Test Center, Patuxent River, Md.

Length: 22 weeks.

Objectives: To train Navy and Marine aviators for test pilot duty.

Instruction: Slide rule; trigonometry; fundamental engineering mathematics; calculus; physics; aircraft power plants, including thermodynamics of heat engines, reciprocating aircraft engines, jet propulsion engines; aerodynamics, including the atmosphere, fundamental dynamics and thermodynamics of air, types of fluid flow, airfoil and wing theory, drag, the basic performance problem, propellers, and maneuvers; airplane stability and control, including theory and design of control surfaces, introduction to stability and control, and longitudinal, lateral and directional stability and control; airplane-engine performance testing; test instrumentation; armament testing; flight performance and handling qualities testing.

Credit recommendation, collegiate level: 3 semester hours in aerodynamics, and credit in mathematics and physics on the basis of institutional examination.

Tissue Bank Technic

Location: Naval Medical School, Bethesda, Md.

Length: 12–26 weeks.

Objectives: To train personnel as tissue bank technicians.

Instruction: Anatomy; physiology; histology; bacteriology; chemistry; genetics; tissue bank preservation; grafting principles and techniques; tissue culture.

Credit recommendation, collegiate level: This course is technical and vocational in nature. Credit in training as technician for tissue bank operations on the basis of demonstrated skills and/or institutional examinations.

Tissue Culture Technic, Class C

Location: Naval Medical Center, Bethesda, Md.

Length: 16 weeks.

Objectives: To train personnel to assist in research investigations in the biological fields related to the growth and maintenance of living cells.

Instruction: Preparing nutrient fluids; preparing, transferring, and maintaining cells; biology; chemistry; glassware and apparatus; short and long term tissue culture; replicate culture technique; photomicroscopy.

Credit recommendation, collegiate level: This course is technical and vocational in nature. Credit in tissue culture technician training on the basis of demonstrated skills and/or institutional examination.

1. Tradevman, Class A
2. Tradevman, Class A

Location: Naval Air Technical Training Center, Memphis, Tenn.

Length: *Course 1*, 20 weeks; *Course 2*, 7–10 weeks.

Objectives: *Course 1:* To provide enlisted personnel with electricity, electronics, and special equipment training which will enable them to operate, maintain, and repair training aids and devices. *Course 2:* To provide graduates of the Aviation Electronics (or Avionics) Fundamentals courses with training in the operation and maintenance of training aids and devices.

Instruction: *Course 1:* Practical and applied mathematics; physics; basic teaching principles, including instructional methods, aids, and management; job analysis, training plans, and testing and grading; electronic fundamentals, including DC and AC theory and circuits, Ohm's law, magnetism, DC and AC generators and motors, transformers, synchros, capacitance, impedance resonance, vacuum tube theory, power supply and amplification circuit theory, coupling, decoupling, and filtering, and test equipment; special devices; basic instrument flight trainer. *Course 2* covers only special equipment training, including radar simulation, ground instruction on instrument trainer, flight simulation, and simulator maintenance.

Credit recommendation, collegiate level: CAUTION: *These courses vary in length and recommendation. Require exact identification by title and length. Course 1:* 6 semester hours at the freshman or sophomore level as an elective in electricity and electronics, and credit in instructional methods on the basis of institutional examination. *Course 2:* Credit in electrical laboratory on the basis of demonstrated skills and/or institutional examinations.

Tradevman, Class B

Location: Naval Air Technical Training Center, Memphis, Tenn.

Length: 35–36 weeks.

Objectives: To provide selected tradevmen with advanced training in the installation, operation, and maintenance of training aids and devices.

Instruction: Mathematics and electricity; amplifier fundamentals, circuits, and power supplies; magnetic amplifiers and test equipment; transmitter circuits; receivers; special circuits; avionics physics; digital and analog computer systems familiarization; administration; flight and tactical simulation; special technology, including computer tie-in, air conditioning, tape recorders, and closed circuit television.

Credit recommendation, collegiate level: 6 semester

hours at the freshman or sophomore level as an elective in electricity and electronics, and credit in electrical laboratory on the basis of demonstrated skills and/or institutional examinations.

Tradevman I (Instructor), Class A

Location: Naval Air Technical Training Center, Memphis, Tenn.

Length: 14 weeks.

Objectives: To train enlisted personnel as instructors in the use and maintenance of training aids and devices.

Instruction: Fundamentals of electricity and physics; special audio, optical, and electromechanical devices; link trainer operation, including operational procedures for instrument flight and flight planning; teaching principles, including planning instruction, teaching methods, training aids, instructional management, testing and grading, and supervised practice teaching.

Credit recommendation, collegiate level: 2 semester hours in instructional methods, and credit in electricity on the basis of institutional examination.

Tradevman R (Repairman), Class A

Location: Naval Air Technical Training Center, Memphis, Tenn.

Length: 17 weeks.

Objectives: To train enlisted personnel in the installation, repair, and maintenance of training aids and devices.

Instruction: Electronics fundamentals, including AC electricity, resonant circuit and vacuum tubes characteristics, audio amplification, radio receiver theory, and receiver troubleshooting and alignment; radar fundamentals, including time constants, pulse-shaping circuits and square-wave generators, and pulse circuits and counters; audio, optical, and electromechanical devices; synchros and servomechanisms; basic instrument trainer, 1-CA-1—vacuum and mechanical theory and adjustments and principles of radio and electrical systems.

Credit recommendation, collegiate level: 6 semester hours at the freshman or sophomore level as an elective in electricity and electronics.

Transportation Management
(Freight Transportation and Traffic Management)

Location: Naval School, Transportation Management, Oakland, Calif.

Length: 22–36 weeks.

Objectives: To train officers for assignment to supervisory billets in material distribution.

Instruction: Transportation regulation and economics; military transportation management; industrial traffic management; carrier modes and surfaces; railroad transportation; motor transportation; air traffic management; on the job observation and training; theory and practice of classificaton, rates, and ratemaking; management techniques for distribution officers; warehouse operations.

Credit recommendation, collegiate level: 10 semester hours in traffic operation and management.

1. **U.S. Naval School, Officer, Women (Reserve)**
2. **Officer Candidate Program, Women**

Location: Naval Women Officer School, Newport, R.I.

Length: *Course 1,* 16 weeks; *Course 2,* 8 weeks.

Objectives: To provide instruction to women ensigns in naval organization, customs and procedures, naval equipment, personnel assignment, and the duties of a naval officer.

Instruction: *Courses 1 and 2:* Personnel administration; Navy orientation; naval publications and correspondence; Department of the Navy; ships, aircraft, and weapons; leadership; naval history. In addition *Course 1* includes communications; uniform code of military justice; training responsibilities.

Credit recommendation, collegiate level: *Course 1:* 4 semester hours in naval organization and history. *Course 2:* 3 semester hours in naval organization and history.

Underwater Demolition Training

Location: Naval Amphibious School, Coronado, San Diego, Calif.

Length: 18 weeks.

Objectives: To train officers and enlisted personnel in the fundamentals of underwater demolition and allied techniques.

Instruction: Physical, mental, and combat conditioning; seamanship; reconnaissance and cartography; communications; explosives and demolitions; land combat techniques; underwater breathing apparatus; first aid.

Credit recommendation, collegiate level: No credit as the course is military in nature.

Underwater Photographer/Scuba Diver

Location: Naval School, Key West, Fla.

Length: 5 weeks.

Objectives: To provide special training for photographer's mates and strikers.

Instruction: Physics of diving; medical aspects of diving; swimming; buoyant ascent training; underwater search and inspection; underwater photography; underwater repair; underwater motion picture cameras and exposure meters; underwater still cameras; film processing.

Credit recommendation, collegiate level: Credit in underwater photography on the basis of demonstrated skills and/or institutional examinations.

Urological Technician, Class C
(Urological Technic)

Locations: Naval Hospitals, Bethesda, Md., Oakland, Calif., Portsmouth, Va., and San Diego, Calif.

Length: 26 weeks.

Objectives: To train technicians to assist the medical officer in examination and treatment of urological patients.

Instruction: Anatomy and physiology; urological operating room technique; cystoscopic room technique; special procedures.

Credit recommendation, collegiate level: This course is technical and vocational in nature. Credit in urological technician training on the basis of demonstrated skills and/or institutional examinations.

1. **Utilities Men, Class A**
2. **Utilities Men, Class B**

Locations: Naval Schools, Construction, Port Hueneme, Calif., and Davisville, R.I.

Length: *Course 1,* 12–14 weeks; *Course 2,* 14–15 weeks.

Objectives: To train personnel to maintain and repair various appliances and utilities.

Instruction: *Course 1:* Basic plumbing; pumps and compressors; sewage disposal; refrigeration; boilers; water treatment. *Course 2:* Mathematics; advanced plumbing; sewage systems; blueprint reading and drawing; air conditioning; advanced studies in boilers, pumps and compressors, and refrigeration; water treatment.

Credit recommendation, collegiate level: *Course 1:* 2 semester hours in theory of water purification. At the technical level, credit in plumbing on the basis of demonstrated skills and/or institutional examinations. *Course 2:* This course is technical and vocational in nature. Credit in refrigeration and air conditioning maintenance on the basis of demonstrated skills and/or institutional examinations.

1. **VP CRAG Pilot ASW Indoctrination, Equipments, and Tactics**
   (VP CRAG Pilot ASW)
2. **VS CRAG Pilot ASW Indoctrination, Equipments, and Tactics S-2D Aircraft**
   (VS CRAG Pilot ASW-2D)
3. **VS CRAG Pilot ASW Indoctrination, Equipments, and Tactics, S-2E Aircraft**
   (VS CRAG Pilot ASW-2E)

Location: Fleet Airborne Electronics Training Unit, Atlantic, Norfolk, Va.

Length: 3–5 weeks.

Objectives: To indoctrinate pilots in the fundamental concepts of ASW and to train them in the operation, capabilities, and tactical applications of the weapon systems indicated in the titles.

Instruction: Submarine operating characteristics; search planning and execution; localization phase; weapons system phase.

Credit recommendation, collegiate level: No credit as the courses are military in nature.

VP CRAG Tactical Coordinator ASW Indoctrination, Equipment and Tactics
(VP CRAG Tactical Coordinator ASW)

Location: Fleet Airborne Electronics Training Unit, Atlantic, Norfolk, Va.

Length: 7 weeks.

Objectives: To train VP CRAG Tactical Coordinators in the operation, capabilities, limitation, and tactical application of the VP aircraft weapons system.

Instruction: Submarine operating characteristics; theory of detection; characteristics, equipment, and tactics; search planning and execution; localization; submarine evasion; weapons system.

Credit recommendation, collegiate level: No credit as the course is military in nature.

1. **VS CRAG Aircrewman ASW**
   (VS CRAG Enlisted Aircrewman ASW
   Indoctrination and Equipments Course)
2. **VP CRAG Aircrewman ASW**
   (VP CRAG Enlisted Aircrewman ASW
   Indoctrination and Equipment Course)

Location: Fleet Airborne Electronic Training Unit, Atlantic, Norfolk, Va.

Length: 5–6 weeks.

Objectives: To train prospective enlisted VP aircrew members in the fundamental concepts of antisubmarine warfare.

Instruction: Introduction; submarine characteristics and operating procedures; radar, ECM, Jezebel, and Exhaust Trail Detection operator techniques and duties; MAD, AQA-1, and Julie operator techniques and duties; introduction to tactical navigational and tactical display equipment.

Credit recommendation, collegiate level: No credit as the course is military in nature.

Water Well Drilling and Development, Class C

Location: Naval Schools, Construction, Port Hueneme, Calif.

Length: 4 weeks.

Objectives: To train enlisted personnel to drill water wells using both percussion and rotary-type drilling rigs.

Instruction: Well drilling and development; ground water supply; rotary and percussion drilling machines; pumps; testing wells for yield and drawdown and chlorine residual.

Credit recommendation, collegiate level: This course is technical and vocational in nature. Credit in diesel engine maintenance and repair on the basis of demonstrated skills and/or institutional examinations.

1. **Welding Certification Course, Class C-1**
2. **Intermediate Welding (Welding Course 1)**
3. **Advanced Welding (Welding Course II)**
4. **Welding for Nuclear Power Plant Operators**
   (Course V)
5. **Stainless Steel Welding Requalification, Phase I,**
   Enlisted
6. **Stainless Steel Welding Requalification, Phase II,**
   Enlisted

Locations: *Course 1,* Naval School, Construction, Port Hueneme, Calif.; *Courses 2, 3, and 4,* Naval School, Welding, San Diego, Calif.; *Courses 5 and 6,* Naval Submarine School, Groton, Conn.

Length: *Course 1,* 4 weeks; *Course 2,* 12 weeks; *Course 3,* 8 weeks; *Course 4,* 16 weeks; *Courses 5 and 6,* 3 weeks.

Objectives: To train personnel in the operation and maintenance of welding equipment as indicated in the title.

Instruction: Electric arc and acetylene welding; joint welds; testing methods; machinable and nonmachinable welds; identifying metals; manual and machine cutting.

Credit recommendation, collegiate level: These courses are technical and vocational in nature. Credit in the specialized welding indicated in the title on the basis of demonstrated skills and/or institutional examinations.

X-Ray Technic, Class C

Locations: Naval Medical School, Bethesda, Md.; Naval Hospitals, Camp Pendleton, Calif., Chelsea, Mass., Great Lakes, Ill., Oakland, Calif., Philadelphia, Pa., Portsmouth, Va., San Diego, Calif., and St. Albans, N.Y.

Length: 52 weeks.

Objectives: To provide instruction in the basic knowledge and skills required to operate medical X-ray equipment in the production of roentgenograms, in the application of X-ray therapy, and in examination by fluoroscope.

Instruction: Mathematics and electricity; roentgenology and radiographic technique; film, screen, and darkroom procedures; special procedures; therapy; photofluorography; photodosimetry.

Credit recommendation, collegiate level: This course is technical and vocational in nature. Credit in X-ray technician training on the basis of demonstrated skills and/or institutional examinations.

Yeoman, Class A

Locations: Naval Schools, Bainbridge, Md., and San Diego, Calif.

Length: 5 and 8 weeks.

Objectives: To train personnel in the duties and skills of yeoman.

Instruction: Clerical duties; filing; operation of duplicating equipment; general office work; records for courts-martial. In addition, the longer course includes typing.

Credit recommendation, collegiate level: Credit in typing on the basis of institutional examination.

Yeoman School, Class B

Locations: Naval Schools, Bainbridge, Md., and San Diego, Calif.

Length: 13–14 weeks.

Objectives: To train enlisted personnel in the requirements of the ratings of yeoman first class and yeoman chief.

Instruction: Advanced training in clerical duties; typing; naval correspondence; all phases of naval court procedure and court reporting; stenography.

Credit recommendation, collegiate level: Credit in typing and stenography on the basis of institutional examination.

DEPARTMENT
OF
DEFENSE

DEPARTMENT OF DEFENSE

Armed Forces Staff College

Location: Norfolk, Va.

Length: 5 months.

Objectives: To prepare selected military officers for duty in all echelons of joint and combined commands through a course of study in joint and combined organization, planning, and operations, and in related aspects of national and international security.

Instruction: Characteristics, organization, and employment of the Armed Forces and their relationships to each other; principles of U.S. unified command organization; organization of joint and combined commands and staffs, their responsibilities, and procedures; organization, composition, and functions of joint and combined commands with respect to strategic, tactical, and logistic responsibilities of the commanders; major war conditions and the organization and composition of current major combined commands in which the U.S. participates; aspects of joint and combined operations, including command relationships, organization, and planning; trends of new weapons and scientific developments; military, political, geographic, historical, economic, psychological, ideological, and other factors affecting U.S. national strategy and U.S. allied security, including the threat to that security.

Credit recommendation, collegiate level: For each academic year (1954–68 inclusive), 6 semester hours in business administration, 6 semester hours in political science, including international relations, and 3 semester hours in recent military history.

1. Broadcast Officer
2. Broadcast Officer

Locations: Defense Information Schools, Fort Benjamin Harrison, Ind., and Fort Slocum, N.Y.

Length: *Course 1*, 4 weeks; *Course 2*, 3 weeks.

Objectives: To train officers in radio-television production and management so that they may plan, coordinate, and supervise operation of an Armed Forces radio or television station.

Instruction: Armed Forces radio and television organization and functions, station management, funding, and logistics; TV fundamentals and studio operations; tape recording; control room operations; radio and TV newswriting and presentation; radio and TV interviews; TV film source material and program schedule preparation; broadcast exercise. In addition to the preceding instruction, *Course 1* includes photojournalism; policy and plans; international relations and government.

Credit recommendation, collegiate level: CAUTION: *These courses vary in length and recommendation. Require exact identification of course by length. Course 1:* 3 semester hours in radio and television programming. *Course 2:* 1 semester hour in radio and television programming.

1. Broadcast Specialist
2. Broadcast Specialist
(Radio and Television Production Specialist)

Locations: Defense Information Schools, Fort Slocum, N.Y., and Fort Benjamin Harrison, Ind.

Length: *Course 1*, 8 weeks; *Course 2*, 3 weeks.

Objectives: To train qualified enlisted men as staff announcers and writers for Armed Forces radio and television overseas.

Instruction: Radio board man and announcer combination operations; announcing techniques, ad-libbing, and sportscasting; documentary writing and production; TV studio operations, camera concepts, telecine operations, and TV film editing; TV newswriting and newscast preparation and production; broadcast exercise. In addition to the preceding instruction, *Course 1* includes public affairs policy and plans; applied journalism; research and oral communications.

Credit recommendation, collegiate level: CAUTION: *These courses vary in title, length, and recommendation. Require exact identification of course by title and length. Course 1:* 3 semester hours in radio and television programming. *Course 2:* 1 semester hour in radio and television programming.

Defense Intelligence Course

Location: Defense Intelligence School, Washington, D.C.

Length: 38 weeks.

Objectives: To train officers in the fundamentals of intelligence which will serve as a foundation for progressive career development and future assignments to intelligence billets.

Instruction: Relationship of size, shape, location, topography, weather, and climate to national action capabilities; impact of physical environment, economic activity, and technology on national social groupings; functions of economic activity in national life; analysis of the political institutions found in sovereign nation-states; description and analysis of the international environment; organization for national security; the intelligence process; foreign intelligence, including elements of national strength, military geography, economics, transportation, technical, sociological, armed forces, and political intelligence factors; power politics, geopolitics, economic warfare, geoeconomics, international law, political warfare, nationalism, control of international conflict, and national political action; intelligence of the Communist bloc; the world Communist threat; United States and world relationships; staff aspects of planning; military, political, and economic aspects of national strategies; strategic intelligence estimate; United States and Union of Soviet Socialist Republics military capabilities.

Credit recommendation, collegiate level: 6 semester hours in modern history, 6 semester hours in political science, and 3 semester hours in geography.

Credit recommendation, graduate level: In 1963 the Executive Committee of the Council of Graduate Schools in the United States requested the Commission on Accreditation of Service Experiences of the American Council on Education to evaluate high-level training programs of the Armed Forces to determine what, if any, aspects of these programs might be regarded as being of graduate-level caliber.

Upon invitation of the commandant of the Defense Intelligence School, the Commission secured the services of professors, nominated by the president of the Council of Graduate Schools in the United States, from three graduate schools, to serve as consultants. They visited the Defense Intelligence School in June, 1965, to study and appraise the library facilities, the instructional program, faculty qualifications, examination program, and the research work required of the students.

As a result of the consultants' evaluations, the Commission on Accreditation recommends that a graduate of the Defense Intelligence Course be allowed a transfer of credit up to 6 hours in the field of international relations or political science. If the transferee's field of work in graduate school is in the area of economics or political geography, the Commission recommends that 4 hours of transfer credit be allowed. This would be a total of either 6 hours or 4 hours of credit, depending upon the field of study.

Industrial College of the Armed Forces

Location: Fort McNair, Washington, D.C.
Length: 10 months.
Objectives: To prepare selected military officers for important command, staff, and policy-making positions in the national and international security structure.
Instruction: United States position today; comparative political thought and government; review of economics; national security policies, programs, and budgets; resources; materiel management; economic stabilization; contemporary international politics in the world economy; economic capability for international conflict; international field studies; plans and readiness; science and security; civil defense; public opinion and morale; legal and legislative problems; public speaking.
Credit recommendation, collegiate level: CAUTION: *These courses contain similar academic material but vary in content emphasis for each academic year. Require exact identification of course by academic year attended.*
For each academic year from 1954–55 through 1962–63: 15 semester hours in political science, including international relations, 3 semester hours in business organization and management, 3 semester hours in speech, and 9 semester hours in recent and contemporary history.
1963–64: 12 semester hours in political science, including international relations, 6 semester hours in business administration, 3 semester hours in speech, 6 semester hours in recent history, and 3 semester hours in economics.
1964–65: 12 semester hours in political science, including international relations, 6 semester hours in business administration, 3 semester hours in recent history, 3 semester hours in economics, and 3 semester hours in geography.
1965–66: 12 semester hours in political science, 9 semester hours in business administration, 3 semester hours in recent history, 3 semester hours in economics, 3 semester hours in geography, 3 semester hours in general physics, and 3 semester hours in mathematics.
For academic years 1966–67 and 1967–68: 12 semester hours in political science, including international

relations, 12 semester hours in business administration, 3 semester hours in recent history, 6 semester hours in economics, 3 semester hours in geography, 3 semester hours in general physics, and 3 semester hours in mathematics.

National War College

Location: Washington, D.C.
Length: 10 months.
Objectives: To prepare selected officers of the rank of permanent colonel and lieutenant colonel of the Armed Forces for important command, staff, and planning assignments.
Instruction: United States interests in the world today; factors of national power; national security policy making; military capabilities and strategies; defense management; counterinsurgency; Communist states; Free Europe and the western hemisphere; Africa and Free Asia; overseas studies—an appraisal of implementation of national security policy in strategic areas; development of national security policy and plans.
Credit recommendation, collegiate level: CAUTION: *This course varies slightly in recommendation according to academic year attended. Require exact identification of course by year attended. For each academic year 1954–55 and 1955–56:* 15 semester hours in political science, including international relations, 9 semester hours in recent and contemporary history, 3 semester hours in business organization and management, and 3 semester hours in speech. *For each academic year from 1956–57 through 1967–68:* 15 semester hours in political science, including international relations, 9 semester hours in recent and contemporary history, and 3 semester hours in business administration.

RESIDENT LANGUAGE COURSES
Defense Language Institute

Locations: West Coast Branch, Presidio of Monterey, Calif.; East Coast Branch, Washington, D.C.; Defense Language Institute Support Command, Biggs Field, El Paso, Tex.

The Defense Language Institute (DLI), which exercises technical control over language training for the military establishment, was established in July, 1963. At that time the Army Language School at the Presidio of Monterey, California, became its West Coast Branch, and the Language Department of the Naval Intelligence School in Washington, D.C., was designated as the East Coast Branch. In order to accomplish Vietnamese language training requirements, which exceeded the capacities of existing DLI schools, the Defense Language Institute Support Command (DLISC) was established in August, 1966, at Biggs Field, El Paso, Texas.

These courses have been evaluated by linguistic experts serving as consultants to the Commission. The credit recommendations listed after each course represent the judgment of these consultants for the maximum amount of credit which an institution may consider granting to an enrolled student. The credit recommended for the programs is based not only upon the type of course given, but also upon the relative difficulty of the language studied. The various languages given by the Defense Language Institute are listed in accordance with their level of difficulty as follows:

A. The least difficult languages for the English-speaking learner include: Danish, French, German, Italian, Norwegian, Portuguese, Romanian, Spanish, Swedish, and Swahili.

B. Languages of greater difficulty, but with alphabetical writing systems which may be learned concurrently without appreciably affecting the progress in learning the spoken language, include: Albanian, Bulgarian, Burmese, Czech, Finnish, Greek, Hungarian, Indonesian, Lithuanian, Persian, Polish, Russian, Serbo-Croatian, Slovenian, Thai, Turkish, Ukrainian, and Vietnamese.

C. The more difficult languages where the reading problem is complicated include: Arabic, Chinese, Japanese, and Korean.

It should be noted that seven of the courses also carry a credit recommendation at the graduate level. Six of these courses are given at the West Coast Branch. These are the 74–75 week Extended or Basic-Intermediate courses in Mandarin-Chinese, Japanese, Korean, and Russian, and the 37-week Intermediate courses in Mandarin-Chinese and Korean. The maximum graduate credit recommended is 6 semester hours for each program. A 60-week course in Mandarin-Chinese has been given at the East Coast Branch for which the consultants recommend 3 semester hours of graduate credit. It was the consensus of the consultants that any of the language courses, 16 weeks or more in length, could be accepted by universities as meeting the language requirements placed upon students in their graduate schools.

Students who have completed language instruction given under the technical control of the Defense Language Institute are issued an official certificate. However, institutions considering granting credit should secure an official transcript from the location where the instruction was given. The official transcript will specify the name of the course completed, its length, dates of attendance, and the type of course. Care should be exercised to obtain exact identification of the course(s) completed. The courses are identifiable by the name of the language, and the credit varies with the type of course completed. Courses with the same name and length, but of different types and carrying different recommendations, are noted with an asterisk.

West Coast Branch, Defense Language Institute (Formerly the Army Language School) Presidio of Monterey, California

Basic Courses

The objective of the Basic Courses given at the West Coast Branch is to train military personnel in the interpretation and translation of the designated language and to provide basic military, geographic, economic, historic, and political information about the country, and/or area, in which the language is spoken. (These area studies are taught in the foreign language.) While these courses are listed as Basic, it should be understood that this is the terminology used by the Armed Forces to indicate that the courses are their "regular" programs in the various languages. They are not limited to what most civilian institutions would term beginning or basic courses in a language.

1954—1956

BASIC COURSES	LENGTH— WEEKS	MAXIMUM SEMESTER HOURS RECOMMENDED— BACCALAUREATE
Albanian	46	18
Arabic	46	18
Bulgarian	46	18
Chinese–Cantonese	46	26
Chinese–Mandarin	46	26
Czech	46	18
Danish	23	15
French	23	15
German	23	15
Greek	46	18
Hungarian	46	18
Italian	23	15
Japanese	46	26
Korean	46	18
Norwegian	23	15
Persian	46	18
Polish	46	18
Portuguese	23	15
Romanian	36	18
Russian	46	18
Serbo–Croatian	46	18
Spanish	23	15
Swedish	23	15
Turkish	46	18

1956—1968

Albanian	47	21
Arabic	47	21*
Bulgarian	47	21
Burmese	47	21
Chinese–Cantonese	47	27
Chinese–Fukienese	47	27
Chinese–Toishan	47	27
Chinese–Mandarin	47	27*
Czech	47	21
Danish	24	15
Finnish	47	21
French	24	15*
German	24	15*
German	32	15
Greek	47	21
Hungarian	47	21
Indonesian	47	21
Indonesian–Malay	47	21
Italian	24	15
Italian–Sicilian	37	18
Japanese	47	27
Korean	47	27
Lithuanian	47	21
Norwegian	24	15
Persian	47	21
Polish	47	21
Portuguese	24	15*
Romanian	37	18*

BASIC COURSES	LENGTH— WEEKS	MAXIMUM SEMESTER HOURS RECOMMENDED— BACCALAUREATE
Russian	47	21
Serbo-Croatian	47	21
Slovenian	47	21
Spanish	24	15*
Swahili	37	18
Swedish	24	15
Thai	47	21
Turkish	41	18
Turkish	47	21
Ukrainian	47	21
Vietnamese (Saigon Dialect)	47	21*

* For a course in the same language and of the same length but with a different credit recommendation, see program listed under **Aural Comprehension Courses** and/or **Intermediate Courses.** Applicant's service transcript should indicate if Basic, Aural Comprehension, or Intermediate Course was taken at the West Coast Branch.

Aural Comprehension Courses

The Aural Comprehension Courses were established at the West Coast Branch on July 1, 1964 (except for the courses in Russian, which were offered previously). Although some reading and writing is included in these courses, they are designed primarily to teach students to comprehend the language as spoken by a foreign national. The spoken language is emphasized as a necessary corollary for developing comprehension skill. Since the Aural Comprehension Courses do not place equal stress on the four language skills, they are recommended for less credit than the Basic Courses. It will be noted that the maximum credit recommended for a 37-week Aural Comprehension Course varies from 12 to 18 semester hours. This credit variation is based primarily upon the higher reading and writing content in those courses recommended for 15 and 18 semester hours. The 50-week Russian Stenotype Course includes the regular 37-week Russian Aural Comprehension Course and 13 weeks of stenotype training.

AURAL COMPREHENSION COURSES	LENGTH— WEEKS	MAXIMUM SEMESTER HOURS RECOMMENDED— BACCALAUREATE
Albanian	37	15
Arabic	47	15*
Bulgarian	37	15
Burmese	37	12
Chinese–Mandarin	33	12
Chinese–Mandarin	37	15*
Chinese–Mandarin	47	18*
Special Chinese– Mandarin	32	12
Czech	37	15
French	24	12*
German	24	12*
Hungarian	37	15
Indonesian	37	15
Japanese	37	15
Korean	37	12*
Persian	37	15
Polish	37	15
Portuguese	24	12*
Romanian	37	15*
Russian	23	15

AURAL COMPREHENSION COURSES	LENGTH— WEEKS	MAXIMUM SEMESTER HOURS RECOMMENDED— BACCALAUREATE
Russian	24	15
Russian	37	18
Russian Stenotype	50	18
Serbo-Croatian	37	15
Spanish	24	12*
Thai	37	12
Turkish	37	15
Vietnamese (Hanoi Dialect)	37	15
Vietnamese (Hanoi Dialect)	47	18*

* For a course in the same language and of the same length but with a different credit recommendation, see program listed under **Basic Courses** and/or **Intermediate Courses.** Applicant's service transcript should indicate if Basic, Aural Comprehension, or Intermediate Course was taken at the West Coast Branch.

Short Basic Courses

The Short Basic Courses at the West Coast Branch are abbreviated versions of the Basic Courses, using the same instructional materials. Less credit is recommended for these programs than for the Basic Courses. However, it will be noted that certain Short Basic Courses, although not as long as the Aural Comprehension Courses in the same languages, carry the same or larger credit recommendations. The difference in these recommendations can be attributed to the fact that the Short Basic Courses are "more academically suitable" than the Aural Comprehension Courses (i.e., they have a higher reading and writing content).

BASIC SHORT COURSES	LENGTH— WEEKS	MAXIMUM SEMESTER HOURS RECOMMENDED— BACCALAUREATE
Arabic	12	8
Arabic	24	15
French	12	8
German	12	8
German	16	10
Greek	12	8
Indonesian	12	8
Italian	12	8
Japanese	12	8
Korean	16	8
Korean	24	15
Persian	12	8
Persian	24	15
Portuguese	11	8
Portuguese	12	8
Romanian	12	8
Spanish	11	8
Spanish	12	8
Thai	12	8
Thai	16	10
Thai	24	15
Turkish	12	8
Vietnamese (Saigon Dialect)	6	3
Vietnamese (Saigon Dialect)	8	8
Vietnamese (Saigon Dialect)	12	8
Vietnamese (Saigon Dialect)	16	10
Vietnamese (Saigon Dialect)	32	15

Extended or Basic-Intermediate Courses

The objective of the Extended or Basic-Intermediate Courses at the West Coast Branch is to train military personnel to a higher level of proficiency in the interpretation and translation of the designated language than is provided for in the scope of instruction of the Basic Courses and to provide, in the language, a somewhat wider knowledge of military, geographic, economic, historic, and political information of the country and/or area in which the language is spoken. The designation "basic–intermediate" given by the military to the courses should not be confused with this term as used by civilian educational institutions. The Commission's consultants recommend as much as 40 semester hours for each course because of the material that the students are required to read and (except for Russian) because of the characters to be learned and the level of the syntax. However, it is recognized that most civilian educational institutions would be reluctant to grant the full amount of credit recommended for these courses inasmuch as this would constitute a major in the language. It is further recognized that most colleges and universities would require some resident work in a major. Nevertheless, it was the consensus of the consultants that these four programs correspond to college courses "directed to mastery of the language." In other words, the courses are the equivalent of beginning, intermediate, and advanced courses in the language, plus composition, advanced composition (i.e., learning to write correctly), conversation, and a semester's course in the civilization of the appropriate country or area. It should be noted that no creative writing or literature is given in these programs.

EXTENDED OR BASIC– INTERMEDIATE COURSES	LENGTH– WEEKS	MAXIMUM SEMESTER HOURS RECOMMENDED– BACCALAUREATE	
Chinese–Mandarin	74–75	40	(6 graduate)
Japanese	74–75	40	(6 graduate)
Korean	74–75	40	(6 graduate)
Russian	74–75	40	(6 graduate)

Intermediate Courses

The Intermediate Courses at the West Coast Branch are a continuation of the Basic Courses with the objective of reaching a higher level of general language ability in all four language skills.

INTERMEDIATE COURSES	LENGTH– WEEKS	MAXIMUM SEMESTER HOURS RECOMMENDED– BACCALAUREATE	
Chinese–Mandarin	37	18*	(6 graduate)
German	24	9*	
Korean	37	18*	(6 graduate)

* For a course in the same language and of same length but with different credit recommendations, see program listed under **Aural Comprehension Courses** and/or **Basic Courses.** Applicant's service transcript should indicate if Basic, Aural Comprehension, or Intermediate Course was taken at the West Coast Branch.

Special Courses

The objective of the Special Courses given at the West Coast Branch is to train military personnel to read and translate Russian technical and scientific publications in their fields of technology with the help of dictionaries and to speak and understand conversational Russian to a limited extent. A college degree is a prerequisite for attending these courses. Inasmuch as they appear to be "tool" courses, it is recommended that any credit granted for them be based only upon institutional examination.

SPECIAL COURSES	LENGTH– WEEKS	MAXIMUM SEMESTER HOURS RECOMMENDED– BACCALAUREATE
Scientific Russian	6	By Examination
Scientific Russian	10	By Examination
Scientific Russian	12	By Examination

East Coast Branch, Defense Language Institute (Formerly the Language Department, Naval Intelligence School) Washington, D.C.

The intensive courses at the East Coast Branch vary in length from 19 to 60 weeks. Their objective is to prepare military personnel to be thoroughly at ease in speaking, understanding, reading, and writing a foreign language. Also taught in the designated language are area studies such as geography, history, politics, economics, government, social structure, and military situations pertaining to the country and/or region. The objective of the shorter courses (8 and 12 weeks) of the East Coast Branch is to give military personnel a limited command of the language (i.e., a practical basic speaking ability and a structural foundation).

COURSES	LENGTH– WEEKS	MAXIMUM SEMESTER HOURS RECOMMENDED– BACCALAUREATE	
Arabic	40	18	
Arabic	47	21	
Chinese–Mandarin	47	27	
Chinese–Mandarin	60	30	(3 graduate)
Chinese–Mandarin (Special 9-Month Course)	36–38	18	
French	8	4	
French	12	8	
French	19	12	
French	24	15	
German	8	4	
German	12	8	
German	32	15	
German	36	18	
Italian	8	4	
Italian	12	8	
Italian	24	15	
Portuguese	8	4	
Portuguese	12	8	
Portuguese	21	12	
Portuguese	24	15	
Russian	36	18	
Russian	47	21	
Russian (Special 6-Month Course)	24–25	15	
Spanish	8	4	
Spanish	12	8	
Spanish	19	12	
Spanish	24	15	
Turkish	36	18	
Turkish	47	21	
Vietnamese (Hanoi Dialect)	36	18	
Vietnamese (Saigon Dialect)	36	18	
Vietnamese (Saigon Dialect)	47	21	

Defense Language Institute Support Command
Biggs Field, El Paso, Texas

For an explanation of the Basic, Aural Comprehension, and Short Basic Courses refer to descriptions under the West Coast Branch.

BASIC COURSE	LENGTH— WEEKS	MAXIMUM SEMESTER HOURS RECOMMENDED— BACCALAUREATE
Vietnamese (Saigon Dialect)	47	21
AURAL COMPREHENSION COURSE		
Vietnamese (Hanoi Dialect)	47	18
SHORT BASIC COURSES		
Vietnamese (Saigon Dialect)	12	8
Vietnamese (Saigon Dialect)	32	15

RESIDENT LANGUAGE COURSES
National Cryptologic School

Course 1. Basic Chinese (Refresher)
Course 2. Basic Russian (Refresher)
Course 3. Basic Vietnamese

Location: National Cryptologic School, Ft. Meade, Md.

Length: *Courses 1 and 2,* 12 weeks; *Course 3,* 30 weeks.

Objectives: *Courses 1 and 2:* To enable personnel to regain a basic competence in comprehension of the standard literary language by an accelerated, systematic review of grammar and vocabulary. A basic course in the language is assumed as a prerequisite. *Course 3:* To teach personnel the grammar and vocabulary necessary for a basic comprehension of the standard literary language with emphasis on a thorough understanding of structure.

Instruction: *Courses 1 and 2:* Phonology; writing system; basic vocabulary of economic, political, and military terms. *Course 3:* In addition to the preceding instruction, this course includes grammar (morphology, derivation, and syntax).

Credit recommendation, collegiate level: CAUTION: *These courses vary in title, length, and recommendation. Require exact identification of course by title and length. Course 1:* 6 semester hours. *Course 2:* 3 semester hours. *Course 3:* 15 semester hours.

ADDENDA

AIR FORCE
ARMY
MARINE CORPS
NAVY

The Addenda comprise new courses received by the Commission after the deadline for inclusion in the main sections of the GUIDE and other courses which, subsequent to deadlines, required evaluation by consultants to the Commission or extensive revision of exhibits in light of new materials provided by the respective services.

AIR FORCE

1. Advanced Data Automation Analysis and Design
2. Automated Systems Analyst
    (Management Support Systems)

Location: Sheppard AFB, Tex.

Length: 4–5 weeks.

Objectives: To train officers in the techniques of data systems analysis and design.

Instruction: Capabilities and limitations of electronic data processing equipment; data systems concepts; preparation for a systems study; survey of present systems resources; analysis of the present systems; design of proposed system, including optimum systems design characteristics, cost considerations, internal control considerations, data systems specifications, and presentation and follow-up of new system.

Credit recommendation, collegiate level: 2 semester hours in computer programming and systems analysis in the field of data processing.

Advanced Electrical–Electronics Measurements

Location: Lowry AFB, Colo.

Length: 6 weeks.

Objectives: To train Air Force, Navy, and Marine Corps personnel as advanced precision measuring equipment specialists.

Instruction: Electrical measurements, including metrology, mathematics and DC network analysis, metrology of resistance and resistance measuring systems, direct voltage and current measurement, AC concepts and measurement techniques, ratio measurements, voltmeters, and metrology of capacitance; electronic measurements, including time interval and frequency measurements, wave-form analysis and distortion measurement, amplifiers, oscilloscopes, phase measurement, generation and measurement of low, medium, and high frequencies, and very-high-frequency impedance determination and voltage principles.

Credit recommendation, collegiate level: Credit in electrical and electronic precision measurement on the basis of institutional examination.

Advanced Microwave Measurements

Location: Lowry AFB, Colo.

Length: 4 weeks.

Objectives: To train Air Force, Navy, and Marine Corps personnel as advanced precision measuring equipment specialists.

Instruction: Metrology and microwave mathematical review; transmission line concepts; Smith chart; waveguide theory; microwave signal generation; microwave measurement systems; network analysis; measurement of microwave power; attenuation measurement techniques; noise measurement and principles of spectrum analysis; directional couplers; radar test set.

Credit recommendation, collegiate level: Credit in microwave measurement on the basis of institutional examination.

1. Automatic Tracking Radar Specialist
2. Automatic Tracking Radar Specialist
3. Automatic Tracking Radar Specialist (Shoran)
4. Automatic Tracking Radar Specialist (Radar Systems)
5. Automatic Tracking Radar Specialist (Auto Tracking Radar Equipment)

Location: Keesler AFB, Miss.

Length: *Course 1,* 16 weeks; *Course 2,* 34 weeks; *Course 3,* 22 weeks; *Course 4,* 34–37 weeks; *Course 5,* 43–44 weeks.

Objectives: To train airmen in the operation, maintenance, and repair of automatic tracking radar equipment.

Instruction: *Course 1:* Analysis of transmitting, RF, receiving, synchronizing, range search, range track, and antenna positioning systems; introduction to consoles and servomechanisms; computer analysis; plotting mechanisms; equipment operation. *Courses 2, 3, 4, and 5:* Direct current; alternating current; electron tubes and power supplies; amplifiers and oscillators; special circuits; radar microwave propagation.

Credit recommendation, collegiate level: CAUTION: *These courses vary in title, length, and recommendation. Require exact identification of course by title and length. Course 1:* Credit in electrical laboratory on the basis of demonstrated skills and/or institutional examinations. *Courses 2 and 4:* 4 semester hours at the freshman or sophomore level as an elective in electricity and electronics, and credit in electrical laboratory on the basis of demonstrated skills and/or institutional examinations. *Course 3:* 3 semester hours at the freshman or sophomore level as an elective in electricity and electronics, and credit in electrical laboratory on the basis of demonstrated skills and/or institutional examinations. *Course 5:* 6 semester hours at the freshman or sophomore level as an elective in electricity and electronics, and credit in electrical laboratory on the basis of demonstrated skills and/or institutional examinations.

CEM Materiel Control Procedures (AFCS)

Location: Lowry AFB, Colo.

Length: 4 weeks.

Objectives: To train airmen to perform materiel control duties in the communications service.

Instruction: Research of supply and maintenance publications; issue and turn-in procedures; document control procedures; inventory; repair cycle control; bench stock operation; equipment acquisition control and support; analysis and use of management reports and listings.

Credit recommendation, collegiate level: This course is technical and vocational in nature. Credit in stock control procedures on the basis of institutional examination.

1. Communications and Relay Center Equipment Repairman, Electro-Mechanical
2. Communications and Relay Center Equipment Repairman, Electro-Mechanical
3. Communications and Relay Center Equipment Repairman, Electro-Mechanical (Others)
4. Communications and Relay Center Equipment Repairman, Electro-Mechanical Cryptographic
5. Communications and Relay Center Equipment Repairman, Electro-Mechanical (TSEC/KW-9)
   (Communications and Relay Center Equipment Repairman, (TSEC/KW-9))
6. Communications Machine Repairman

Locations: Sheppard AFB, Tex., Francis E. Warren AFB, Wyo.

Length: *Course 1,* 34 weeks; *Course 2,* 31–33 weeks; *Courses 3 and 4,* 36–40 weeks; *Course 5,* 33 and 37 weeks; *Course 6,* 19 and 25 weeks.

Objectives: To train airmen to install, maintain, and repair facsimile and teletypewriter equipment.

Instruction: *Course 1:* DC and AC circuits; solid state devices; installation, maintenance, and repair of selected equipment. *Courses 2 through 6:* Fundamentals of electricity; installation, maintenance, and repair of selected equipment.

Credit recommendation, collegiate level: CAUTION: *These courses vary slightly in title, length, and recommendation. Require exact identification of course by full title and length. Course 1:* 2 semester hours at the freshman or sophomore level as an elective in electricity and electronics, and credit in electrical laboratory on the basis of demonstrated skills and/or institutional examinations. *Courses 2 through 6:* Credit in electricity and electrical laboratory on the basis of demonstrated skills and/or institutional examinations.

Electric Power Line Specialist

Location: Sheppard AFB, Tex.

Length: 16 weeks.

Objectives: To train airmen in installation, operation, and maintenance of electric power distribution systems.

Instruction: Safety and pole climbing; fundamentals of electricity; work positioning, resuscitation, and rescue; substation maintenance; construction and maintenance of overhead electrical distribution systems; underground distribution systems maintenance; airfield lighting systems.

Credit recommendation, collegiate level: This course is technical and vocational in nature. Credit in electric power line installation and maintenance on the basis of demonstrated skills and/or institutional examinations.

1. Electronic Digital Data Processing Repairman (AN/FST-2B)
   (Electronic Digital Data Processing Equipment Repairman (Data Transmission))
2. Electronic Digital Data Processing Equipment Repairman
   (Aircraft Control and Warning Radar Repairman, AN/FST-2)
3. Electronic Analog Data Processing Equipment Repairman
   (Aircraft Control and Warning Radar Repairman, AN/GPA-37)

Location: Keesler AFB, Miss.

Length: 35–45 weeks.

Objectives: To train airmen in the principles of operation, maintenance, and repair of coordinate data transmitting, and associated, equipment.

Instruction: Fundamentals of DC and AC; reactive circuits; principles of vacuum tubes and transistors; special purpose tubes; amplifiers and oscillators; motors and servomechanisms; multivibrators and sweep circuits; electronic and data processing principles; digital computer techniques; circuit logic; circuit analysis and testing; shop practices and testing.

Credit recommendation, collegiate level: For each course, 3 semester hours at the freshman or sophomore level as an elective in electricity and electronics, and credit in electrical laboratory on the basis of demonstrated skills and/or institutional examinations.

Launch Enable System Specialist, SM-68B

Location: Sheppard AFB, Tex.

Length: 13 weeks.

Objectives: To train maintenance personnel to perform launch-enable-system maintenance and repair.

Instruction: Fundamentals of transistors and logic circuits; analysis of mathematics as applied to electronic switching; launch-enable-system description; complex ACP and WCP operation; ACPM power supplies and transceiver operation; test equipment, trouble analysis, and maintenance.

Credit recommendation, collegiate level: Credit in electrical laboratory on the basis of demonstrated skills and/or institutional examinations.

Maintenance and Control Specialist

Location: Sheppard AFB, Tex.

Length: 10 weeks.

Objectives: To train airmen in the maintenance of Air Force buildings, including onbase family-type housing.

Instruction: Building maintenance, including plumbing systems, and repair of stairways, doors, and windows; electrical maintenance, including wiring diagrams and building electrical circuits and units; appliance repair; maintenance and control management; project approval and control; work authorization; planning procedures; work requirements; program development; service calls and scheduling procedures.

Credit recommendation, collegiate level: 2 semester hours in maintenance management.

Missile Officer (T&A) WS-133A-M

Location: Chanute AFB, Ill.

Length: 3 weeks.

Objectives: To train officers in the operation of the WS-133A-M weapon system.

Instruction: Weapon system orientation; WS-133A-M electronics; equipment hazards and personnel safety; alignment equipment and procedures.

Credit recommendation, collegiate level: No credit because of the brevity and limited technical nature of the course.

Missile Systems Analyst Specialist, WS-133A-M

Location: Chanute AFB, Ill.

Length: 37 weeks.

Objectives: To train airmen in the operation, inspection, checkout, and periodic maintenance of the WS-133A-M system.

Instruction: DC and AC; motors and servomechanisms; reactive circuits; vacuum tubes; transistors; special purpose tubes; amplifiers and oscillators; multivibrators and sweep circuits.

Credit recommendation, collegiate level: 3 semester hours at the freshman and sophomore level as an elective in electricity and electronics, and credit in electrical laboratory on the basis of demonstrated skills and/or institutional examinations.

Missile Systems Analyst Technician (T&A) WS-133A-M

Location: Chanute AFB, Ill.

Length: 7 weeks.

Objectives: To train airmen to operate, inspect, checkout, and maintain the WS-133A-M weapon system and to perform as members of the targeting and alignment team on WS-133A-M equipment.

Instruction: Control and monitor system; guidance and control system; integrated systems; missile alignment procedures; equipment hazards and personnel safety.

Credit recommendation, collegiate level: Credit in electrical laboratory on the basis of demonstrated skills and/or institutional examinations.

Photogrammetric-Cartographic Technician

Location: Aeronautical Chart and Information Center, St. Louis, Mo.

Length: 8–9 weeks.

Objectives: To provide airmen with a study of earth and physical sciences as related to photogrammetry and cartography.

Instruction: Reconnaissance systems and cameras; photogrammetric mathematics; projections; grids; geodetic control; equipment; transfer points; tilt and tip analyses; height analysis; structural characteristics in industrial and urban areas; region physiography; target material reliability determination.

Credit recommendation, collegiate level: 3 semester hours in photogrammetry.

Professional Personnel Management

Location: Maxwell AFB, Ala.

Length: 6 weeks.

Objectives: To provide senior personnel managers with seminar-level training in personnel management.

Instruction: Department of Defense management environment; management processes; human relations; labor-management relations; management systems and quantitative methods; USAF personnel processes.

Credit recommendation, collegiate level: 3 semester hours in personnel management.

Refrigeration and Air Conditioning Controls (Minneapolis-Honeywell)

Location: Sheppard AFB, Tex.

Length: 3 weeks.

Objectives: To train airmen in the operation, adjustment, and servicing of the Minneapolis-Honeywell control system.

Instruction: Operating procedures; servicing and adjusting procedures; pneumatic systems; electric and electronic controls; thermostats; humidistats; relays; switches; damper operators; valves; positioners; pressure regulators.

Credit recommendation, collegiate level: This course is technical and vocational in nature. Credit in refrigeration and air conditioning controls repair on the basis of demonstrated skills and/or institutional examinations.

1. Security Police Officer
2. Security Policeman

Location: Lackland AFB, Tex.

Length: 5–6 weeks.

Objectives: To train officers and airmen to perform the duties required in security and law enforcement programs.

Instruction: *Course 1:* Corrections; military law; investigations; patrol activities; security facilities and equipment; normal and emergency security operations; weapons training. *Course 2:* Military jurisdiction; application of apprehension and restraint; control of prisoners; investigations; patrols; traffic control; weapons training.

Credit recommendation, collegiate level: These courses are technical and vocational in nature. Credit in police methods on the basis of institutional examination.

Supply Operation Analysis/Design

Location: Amarillo AFB, Tex.

Length: 7 weeks.

Objectives: To train system surveillance personnel to interpret, diagnose, and correct hardware, program, and operational problems.

Instruction: Basic programming techniques; computer room operating procedures; USAF application of active routines; problem diagnosis and computer performance.

Credit recommendation, collegiate level: Credit in electrical laboratory on the basis of demonstrated skills and/or institutional examinations.

Television Production Specialist

Location: Lowry AFB, Colo.

Length: 7 weeks.

Objectives: To train enlisted personnel for assignment as television production specialists.

Instruction: Television system; video and audio switching; staging and principles of lighting; directing concepts; recording processes; practical television production; television script.

Credit recommendation, collegiate level: 6 semester hours in television production.

Tropical Weather Analysis and Forecasting

Location: Chanute AFB, Ill.

Length: 6 weeks.

Objectives: To train Air Force weather forecasters in the analysis of tropical weather.

Instruction: Principles of tropical analysis—techniques of kinematic analysis in the tropics; tropical wind fields, systems, and vorticity concepts; climatic controls; physical geography of the tropics; regional synoptic climatology of the tropics; application of climatology to tropical analysis and forecasting; analysis and forecasting in the tropics.

Credit recommendation, collegiate level: Credit in advanced weather forecasting techniques on the basis of institutional examination.

Weapon Control Systems Mechanic (F-111A)

Location: Lowry AFB, Colo.

Length: 25 weeks.

Objectives: To train airmen in the operation and maintenance of attack radar systems and related equipment.

Instruction: Basic electronics, including DC and AC circuits, solid state devices, and vacuum tubes; F-111A weapon control system introduction; AN/APQ-113 attack radar system and support aerospace ground equipment; lead computing optical sight system and dual bomb timer; integrated systems tie-in.

Credit recommendation, collegiate level: 3 semester hours at the freshman or sophomore level as an elective in electricity and electronics, and credit in electrical laboratory on the basis of demonstrated skills and/or institutional examinations.

Welding of High Performance Aircraft and Missile Systems

Location: Chanute AFB, Ill.

Length: 6 weeks.

Objectives: To provide airmen with lateral training in weld repairs of aircraft and missile systems.

Instruction: Welding high- and low-pressure lines, including inert gas shielded welding and metallic arc welding; inert gas shielded welding of aluminum, magnesium, corrosion resistant, refractory, and super alloys; aircraft and jet engine weld repair.

Credit recommendation, collegiate level: This course is technical and vocational in nature. Credit in welding shop on the basis of demonstrated skills and/or institutional examinations.

ADDENDA
ARMY

Army War College

Location: Carlisle Barracks, Pa.

Length: 42–45 weeks.

Objectives: To prepare senior officers for command-and high-level staff duties with emphasis on Army doctrine and operations; to advance interdepartmental and interservice understanding.

Instruction: Bases and evolution of military strategy, including recent concepts and alternatives; military strategies of the principal world powers; survey of the major problems, forces, and trends of the contemporary world in relation to national security conditions; sources of conflict; strategic appraisal of the United States and its alliances; theory and doctrine of Communism; power potential of the principal Communist states, their political and economic organization, military capabilities, sociology, geography, science, and technology; Communist strategy and tactics emphasizing doctrines for the employment of Army and combined forces; foreign policy of the Communist states; strategic implications of developing areas, including the relationship of the political, economic, social, and psychological problems of development; theater and Army capabilities in selected world areas; problem-solving and decision-making techniques and processes of the Department of Defense; examination and analysis of the factors likely to exert a significant influence on the character of future land warfare; role of military services in formulating a national strategy. *Note—*During academic year 1967–68 the area of political science was covered somewhat less extensively than in previous years.

Beginning with academic year 1967–68 a series of electives was added to supplement the core curriculum by providing each student who wants to expand his knowledge in selected areas with an opportunity for detailed individual study of subjects related to or complementing studies in the academic courses and seminars. Students may take one elective along with the prescribed program for 12 weeks each half of the academic year. Elective courses are as follows:

*Communicative Arts—*The art of communication, its purposes and functions, and the cultivation of the specific skills of speaking, writing, reading, and listening.

*Political Systems and National Security—*Political systems, functions, and processes, and comparative political theory.

*Economics of National Security—*Review of basic economics, economic capability of the United States for military preparedness, collective economic capability of the coalitions of nations, and a review of United States foreign economic policy.

*Social Factors and National Security—*Social forces, attitudes, and values which motivate actions of individuals and groups and which affect national power and security.

*International Law and National Security—*Nature and sources of international law, recognition, nationality, jurisdiction, international agreements, and state responsibility, and principles pertaining to the law of war.

*Analytical Techniques of Management—*Analytical techniques employed by the Services, Joint Chiefs of Staff, and the Office of the Secretary of Defense in the formulation, display, and resolution of problems in selecting weapons systems, force structures, and strategies.

*Management Information Systems—*Requirements for information, the design, installation, and operation of management information systems, and the utilization of the products of management information systems.

*Resource Management and Control—*Policies, organizations, methods, and means used to determine military resource requirements, and the allocation, management, and control of resources by the Department of Defense.

Credit recommendation, collegiate level: CAUTION: *This course varies slightly in recommendation. Require exact identification of course by year of attendance.* Prior to academic year 1957–58 the programs of instruction were not evaluated by the Commission because much of the instructional materials carried a military security classification. *Academic years 1957–58 through 1966–67:* 6 semester hours in social science survey, 3 semester hours in recent history, 3 semester hours in economics, 3 semester hours in business administration, and 6 semester hours in political science, including international relations. *Academic year 1967–68:* 6 semester hours in social science survey, 3 semester hours in recent history, 3 semester hours in economics, 3 semester hours in business administration, and 3 semester hours in political science, including international relations.

Additional credit for the electives is recommended on the basis of institutional examination. Next to the title of each elective is listed the area in which credit might be granted and the maximum number of credit hours to be allowed. Credit for these electives should not exceed an aggregate of 6 semester hours.

ELECTIVE TITLE	APPLICABLE AREA	MAXIMUM CREDIT HOURS
Communicative Arts	Speech	3
Political Systems & National Security	Government (or Political Science)	3
Economics of National Security	Economics	3
Social Factors & National Security	Sociology	3
International Law & National Security	International Law	3
Analytical Techniques of Management	Business Administration	3
Management Information Systems	Business Administration	3
Resource Management & Control	Business Administration	3

1. Audio Specialist
2. Audio Specialist

Location: Fort Monmouth, N.J.

Length: *Course 1,* 13 weeks; *Course 2,* 15 weeks.

Objectives: To train enlisted personnel to operate and perform organizational maintenance on motion-picture sound recording, magnetic tape recording, and television audio equipment.

Instruction: *Courses 1 and 2:* Sound theory, principles of audio recording and reproduction; tape recording; microphones; studio consoles; remote amplifiers; magnetic recordings; optical recordings of sound on film; studio practices. In addition to the preceding instruction, *Course 2* includes television cameras and transmitters; television studio practices; remote amplifiers; sound on film recording.

Credit recommendation, collegiate level: CAUTION: *These courses vary in length and recommendation. Require exact identification of course by length. Course 1* is technical and vocational in nature. Credit in motion-picture sound recording, magnetic tape recording, and television audio equipment repair on the basis of demonstrated skills and/or institutional examinations. *Course 2* is technical and vocational in nature. Credit in motion-picture sound recording on the basis of demonstrated skills and/or institutional examinations.

CH-54 Automatic Flight Control Equipment Repair

Location: Southeastern Signal School, Fort Gordon, Ga.

Length: 3 weeks.

Objectives: To train enlisted personnel in the performance of direct and general support maintenance of CH-54 helicopter automatic flight control equipment.

Instruction: Procedures for testing, and recognition of, malfunctions in the automatic flight control system; use of special test equipment; circuit analysis of the servo loop, pitch, roll, altitude, and yaw channels; troubleshooting, testing, adjustment, and repair of the amplifier, control panel, channel monitor panel, dual channel lag amplifier, stick sensor, and remote stick assembly; direct and general support maintenance on the supervisory panel.

Credit recommendation, collegiate level: Credit in electrical laboratory on the basis of demonstrated skills and/or institutional examinations.

Construction Surveyor Noncommissioned Officer Candidate

Location: Fort Belvoir, Va.

Length: 14 weeks.

Objectives: To train enlisted personnel in the principles and techniques of leadership and construction surveying.

Instruction: Surveying principles and procedures; construction layout; supply and administration; combat operations, leadership, and counterinsurgency; combat support operations; protective mine warfare, booby trapping, and field fortifications; command indoctrination; map reading and land navigation.

Credit recommendation, collegiate level: 3 semester hours in construction surveying.

Conventional/Precise Power Generation

Location: Fort Belvoir, Va.

Length: 9 weeks.

Objectives: To provide enlisted personnel with a working knowledge of the installation, operation, and organizational maintenance of gasoline and diesel driven portable generating equipment and precise power generation.

Instruction: Internal combustion engine systems maintenance; diesel engine maintenance; electrical fundamentals including magnetism, series-parallel circuits; direct and alternating current generators; conventional generator sets; precise power generation.

Credit recommendation, collegiate level: This course is technical and vocational in nature. Credit in conventional and precise power generator repair on the basis of demonstrated skills and/or institutional examinations.

Crime Laboratory Photography

Location: Criminal Investigation Laboratory, Fort Gordon, Ga.

Length: 104 weeks.

Objectives: To train warrant officers and enlisted personnel as crime photographers to qualify them as expert witnesses in crime photography before courts-martial and/or other judicial proceedings.

Instruction: Principles of photography; history of photography; photography in law enforcement; optics of photography; light and its management; the camera and its management; theory of the photographic process; photographic sensitometry; photographic chemistry; the negative process; the positive process; color photography; infrared photography; ultraviolet photography; photomicroscopy and macrophotography; cinematography in laboratory work; surveillance support photography; questioned documents examination procedures; firearms support procedures; chemistry support procedures; legal photography; courtroom procedures; the expert witness; record forms and supply procedures required in the operation of the photographic section.

Credit recommendation, collegiate level: 3 semester hours in police photography, and, on the basis of institutional examination, 3 semester hours in Criminalistics I (introductory), provided applicant has completed baccalaureate courses in chemistry and physics or can demonstrate proficiency in these two subjects by institutional examinations.

Defense Against Methods of Entry

Location: Intelligence School, Fort Holabird, Md.

Length: 6 weeks.

Objectives: To train intelligence personnel in the fundamentals of locking devices and technical protective measures pertaining to these devices.

Instruction: Theory, application, and methods of neutralizing warded locks, disc tumbler locks, pin tumbler locks, lever locks, foreign locking devices, and combination padlocks; disassembly and assembly of pin tumbler locks; methods and techniques of vehicle entry; methods of manipulating high-security safelocks; government standards, theory application, neutralization, and repair of security containers; intrusion detection system.

Credit recommendation, collegiate level: This course is technical and vocational in nature. Credit in locksmithing on the basis of demonstrated skills and/or institutional examinations.

Dental Fixed Prosthetic Specialist

Location: Medical Field Service School, Fort Sam Houston, Tex.

Length: 10 weeks.

Objectives: To train enlisted personnel in fixed partial denture techniques.

Instruction: Use, composition, and physical properties of dental laboratory materials used in fixed prosthodontics; techniques for inlay, crown, and fixed partial denture construction; occlusion of teeth in normal and abnormal situations; dental laboratory equipment; anatomy of the oral cavity and surrounding structures.

Credit recommendation, collegiate level: Credit in dental laboratory technology on the basis of institutional examination.

Dental Removable Prosthetic Specialist

Location: Medical Field Service School, Fort Sam Houston, Tex.

Length: 10 weeks.

Objectives: To train enlisted personnel in advanced removable dental laboratory techniques.

Instruction: Anatomy of the oral cavity; use, composition, and physical properties of dental laboratory materials; procedures employed in the construction of complete dentures; removable partial denture design and function; construction of wrought and cast removable partial dentures and repair procedures; laboratory techniques associated with surgical and orthodontic appliances; dental laboratory equipment.

Credit recommendation, collegiate level: Credit in dental laboratory technology on the basis of institutional examination.

Document Examination

Location: Criminal Investigation Laboratory, Fort Gordon, Ga.

Length: 104 weeks.

Objectives: To train warrant officers and enlisted personnel as document examination technicians to qualify them as expert witnesses in questioned document examination before courts-martial and/or other judicial proceedings.

Instruction: Handwriting identification; operational familiarization with mechanical aids; handwriting systems; general and special factors; analytical reasoning; typewriting identification; parts nomenclature and operational functions; collecting, indexing, and filing typewriting standards; classification of standards; comparison microscope; Nichols measuring plates; general and special factors; counterfeiting; recognition factors; methods of counterfeiting; Armed Forces documents; commercial printing methods; photographic procedures and camera techniques; paper examinations; ink examinations; firearms identification familiarization; fingerprint identification familiarization; courtroom procedures; research and compendium; ethics of the document examiner; the expert witness; records and forms used in the operation of the document section.

Credit recommendation, collegiate level: 3 semester hours in questioned documents, 3 semester hours in police photography, and, on the basis of institutional examination, 3 semester hours in Criminalistics I (introductory), provided applicant has completed baccalaureate courses in chemistry and physics or can demonstrate proficiency in these two subjects by institutional examinations.

Engineer Officer Candidate

Location: Army Engineer School, Fort Belvoir, Va.

Length: 23 weeks.

Objectives: To provide selected personnel with a working knowledge of the duties of platoon leaders in engineer combat battalions.

Instruction: Command indoctrination; company administration; effective writing; military justice; combat service support; leadership and weapons control; map and aerial photo reading; methods of instruction; combat operations; combat support operations; nuclear, biological, and chemical warfare; field fortifications; engineer reconnaissance; tools and rigging; floating equipage; demolition and mine warfare; roads and airfields; T/O construction and job management; fixed bridges and bridge classification; maintenance management and equipment utilization.

Credit recommendation, collegiate level: Credit in advanced military at institutions which regularly offer such credit.

Enlisted Air Defense Electronic Warfare

Location: Army Air Defense School, Fort Bliss, Tex.

Length: 3 weeks.

Objectives: To train enlisted personnel in electronic countermeasures, use of the air defense radars in an ECM environment, and in electronic warfare training devices and techniques.

Instruction: Enemy threat; jamming; target detection; familiarization with the programming of target simulators; preparation and conduct of operator training programs.

Credit recommendation, collegiate level: No credit because of the brevity and limited technical nature of the course.

Equipment Storage Specialist

Location: Quartermaster School, Fort Lee, Va.

Length: 8 weeks.

Objectives: To train enlisted personnel in the Federal supply system, storage operations, packaging and packing, and materials-handling equipment.

Instruction: Familiarization with the flow and distribution of supplies, supply economy, and property accountability and responsibility; receipt, storage, and issue of supplies; planning and computing storage space; stock locator systems; inspection of stored supplies; handling and shipping procedures; inventory procedures; principles and procedures of packaging and packing; use, operation, and maintenance of materials-handling equipment.

Credit recommendation, collegiate level: This course is technical and vocational in nature. Credit in stockroom procedures on the basis of demonstrated skill and/or institutional examinations.

Eye, Ear, Nose, and Throat Specialist

Location: Medical Field Service School, Fort Sam Houston, Texas.

Length: 12 weeks.

Objectives: To train enlisted personnel as nursing assistants to the medical officer or the professional nurse in the care and treatment of eye, ear, nose, and throat patients.

Instruction: Familiarization with the anatomy and physiology of the eye, ear, nose, and throat; pathological conditions peculiar to an otolaryngology clinic; common diseases of the eye; familiarization with the preparation, use, and maintenance of ophthalmologic equipment; applicatory training.

Credit recommendation, collegiate level: This course is technical and vocational in nature. Credit in medical technician training on the basis of demonstrated skills and/or institutional examinations.

Field Artillery Officer Mobilization Advanced

Location: Artillery and Missile School, Fort Sill, Okla.

Length: 8 weeks.

Objectives: To train field artillery officers of the Reserve components during peacetime, and all components during mobilization, for branch command and staff duties at battalion through brigade or comparable levels in divisional and nondivisional units.

Instruction: *Note*—This course is given in three phases. Reserve officers complete *Phase I* through service extension courses provided by the Department of the Army. These extension courses are not evaluated by the Commission. *Phases II and III:* Communication requirements and systems; observed fire procedures; firing battery techniques and procedures; fire direction operations; characteristics, functioning, maintenance, and inspection of cannon materiel ammunition and fuses; principles and techniques of fire support coordination; target acquisition; characteristics, capabilities, and operations of the Sergeant, Pershing, and Lance missile systems; free rocket gunnery procedures.

Credit recommendation, collegiate level: No credit as *Phases II and III* are military in nature.

Finance Officer Mobilization Basic

Location: Finance School, Fort Benjamin Harrison, Ind.

Length: 6–7 weeks.

Objectives: To train Finance Corps officers of the Reserve components during peacetime, and of all components during mobilization, for duty assignments at the company level.

Instruction: *Note*—This course is given in two phases. Reserve officers complete *Phase I* through service extension courses provided by the Department of the Army. These extension courses are not evaluated by the Commission. *Phase II:* Fundamentals of automatic data processing as applied to financial operations; orientation in the control of appropriated funds; military pay; travel allowances; disbursing operations; fiscal code; commercial accounts; civilian pay.

Credit recommendation, collegiate level: 3 semester hours in finance and disbursing.

Fingerprint Examination

Location: Criminal Investigation Laboratory, Fort Gordon, Ga.

Length: 104 weeks.

Objectives: To train warrant officers and enlisted personnel as fingerprint technicians to qualify them as expert witnesses in fingerprint examinations before courts-martial and/or other judicial proceedings.

Instruction: Introduction to, and history of, fingerprint identification and Bertillon system; pattern interpretation; classification of fingerprints; taking of fingerprints; postmortem prints; preserving, marking, and packaging fingerprint evidence; development and comparison of latent fingerprints; casts and molds; report writing and preparation of courtroom charts; courtroom procedures for the fingerprint technician; expert witness observation; chemistry familiarization; document and firearms familiarization; photographic procedures and camera techniques.

Credit recommendation, collegiate level: 3 semester hours in the science of fingerprinting, 3 semester hours in police photography, and, on the basis of institutional examination, 3 semester hours in Criminalistics I (introductory), provided applicant has completed baccalaureate courses in chemistry and physics or can demonstrate proficiency in these two subjects by institutional examinations.

Firearms Examination

Location: Criminal Investigation Laboratory, Fort Gordon, Ga.

Length: 104 weeks.

Objectives: To train warrant officers and enlisted personnel as firearms examination technicians to qualify them as expert witnesses in firearms examination before courts-martial and/or other judicial proceedings.

Instruction: Principles of firearms and ammunition identification; history of early firearms; cartridge development; modern firearms; weapons manufacture; ballistics; history of identification; laboratory handling of evidence; test firing; instruments; bullet comparison; cartridge case comparison; tool mark comparison; numbers restoration; criminal investigation laboratory, including examinations made by the chemistry, photography, fingerprint, and document sections of the criminal investigation laboratory, to include administrative and reporting procedures; familiarization with firearms and powder facilities.

Credit recommendation, collegiate level: 3 semester hours in forensic ballistics, 3 semester hours in police photography, and, provided the applicant has completed baccalaureate courses in chemistry and physics (or can demonstrate equivalent proficiency in these two fields by institutional examinations), he may be granted, on the basis of institutional examination, 3 semester hours in Criminalistics I (introductory), 3 semester hours in Criminalistics II (intermediate), and 3 semester hours in Criminalistics III (advanced).

Fixed Plant Carrier Equipment Repair

Location: Signal School, Fort Monmouth, N.J.

Length: 29 weeks.

Objectives: To train enlisted personnel in the techniques required to install, operate, and perform organizational, field, and depot maintenance on fixed-plant carrier and fixed-station radio terminal equipment.

Instruction: Care and use of multimeter; resistors; series and parallel circuits; induction; capacitive reactance; impedance; series and parallel resonance; diodes and triodes; amplifiers; oscillators; receiver alignment; transistor circuits and amplifiers; communications fundamentals; telephone carrier fundamentals; telegraph fundamentals and loop circuits; installation, maintenance, and repair of telegraph carrier terminals, telegraph terminals, multiplex sets and equipment, alarm systems, integrated communication systems, and transportable communications equipment.

Credit recommendation, collegiate level: CAUTION: *Courses in fixed-plant carrier equipment vary in title, length, and recommendation. Require exact identification of course by title and length. (See also page 175.)* 2 semester hours at the freshman or sophomore level as an elective in electricity and electronics. At the technical level, credit in telegraph, telephone, and radio repair on the basis of demonstrated skills and/or institutional examinations.

---

1. **Fixed Station Technical Controller**
2. **Fixed Station Technical Controller (Fixed Station Facilities Controller)**

Location: Signal School, Fort Monmouth, N.J.

Length: *Course 1,* 18 weeks; *Course 2,* 10 weeks.

Objectives: To train enlisted personnel in the concepts, procedures, and equipment necessary for the control of fixed-station facilities.

Instruction: *Courses 1 and 2:* Telephony, telegraph, and teletypewriter principles; terminal equipment; special transmission systems; transmitter equipment; receiver equipment; records, reports, and procedures; system control and coordination. In addition to the preceding instruction, *Course 1* includes care and use of a multimeter; series-parallel circuits; induction; AC and DC powers; inductive and capacitive reactance; impedance; series and parallel resonance; triode tubes; voltage amplifications; pentode and beam power tubes; oscillators, voltage regulators; receiver and transmitter circuitry; semi-conductor fundamentals.

Credit recommendation, collegiate level: CAUTION: *These courses vary in title, length, and recommendation. Require exact identification by title and length. Course 1:* Credit at the freshman or sophomore level as an elective in electricity and electronics on the basis of institutional examination, and, at the technical level, credit in fixed-station facilities control on the basis of demonstrated skills and/or institutional examinations. *Course 2:* This course is technical and vocational in nature. Credit in fixed-station facilities control on the basis of demonstrated skills and/or institutional examinations.

Hawk Missile and Launcher Repair

Location: Missile and Munitions School, Redstone Arsenal, Ala.

Length: 32 weeks.

Objectives: To train enlisted personnel to inspect, test, troubleshoot, and repair the electronic, hydraulic, and mechanical systems of a Hawk missile, launcher, and associated test equipment.

Instruction: Care and use of a multimeter; series-parallel circuits; alternating current; inductance; trans-

formers; capacitance; series and parallel resonance; transients in RC and LR circuits; amplifiers; microwave measurements; frequency measurements; microwave receivers; transmitters; multivibrators; missile transistor amplifiers; multistage transistor circuits; operator and user maintenance of the CW/pulse console; target and fuze Doppler amplifier; Hawk oriented troubleshooting techniques; AFC and decoder; speedgate; antenna control; autopilot circuits; signal generator and signal generator modulator; servo test set; missile maintenance analysis and application; abbreviated missile test station; launcher test equipment; launcher system troubleshooting; hydraulic console; system analysis; shop operations.

Credit recommendation, collegiate level: 3 semester hours at the freshman or sophomore level as an elective in electricity and electronics, and credit in electrical laboratory on the basis of demonstrated skills and/or institutional examinations.

Image Interpreter Noncommissioned Officer Candidate

Location: Army Intelligence School, Fort Holabird, Md.

Length: 12–13 weeks.

Objectives: To qualify enlisted personnel for assignment in the Republic of Vietnam and for performance of duties as junior NCO leaders.

Instruction: Intelligence; aerial surveillance operations and organization; image interpretation; metrics; terrain; leadership.

Credit recommendation, collegiate level: 2 semester hours in imagery interpretation.

Intelligence Analyst (Intelligence Analysis)

Location: Intelligence School, Fort Holabird, Md.

Length: 9–13 weeks.

Objectives: To train enlisted personnel to assist intelligence staff officers in the collection and processing of military information and the production and dissemination of military intelligence.

Instruction: Combat intelligence organization; enemy capabilities; collection, evaluation, and interpretation of information; dissemination of intelligence; analysis of area operations; production of combat intelligence; order of battle intelligence; techniques of interrogation; aerial surveillance and reconnaissance; organization and functions in the field of counterintelligence and security.

Credit recommendation, collegiate level: 3 semester hours in intelligence methods.

Intelligence Analyst (Special Forces)

Location: Intelligence School, Fort Holabird, Md.

Length: 6–8 weeks.

Objectives: To train Special Forces enlisted personnel to assist in the production of military intelligence, in the preparation and supervision of intelligence training programs, and in the application of counterintelligence principles to the environmental situations which may be encountered by Special Forces in the field.

Instruction: Intelligence reports and format; combat intelligence organization; tactical interrogations; collection, evaluation, interpretation, and dissemination of intelligence; area intelligence; order of battle; counterintelligence principles, methods, and techniques; environmental and security factors in internal attack.

Credit recommendation, collegiate level: 2 semester hours in intelligence methods.

Intelligence Photography
(Investigative Photography)

Location: Intelligence School, Fort Holabird, Md.
Length: 8 weeks.
Objectives: To train intelligence personnel in the techniques, theory, and application of photography in the intelligence field.
Instruction: Basic theory of photography; sensitized photomaterial; press camera operation; action and depth of field; exposure methods; motion picture photography; portrait photography; Polaroid photography; special lenses; Leica camera; principles of intelligence ground photography; microfilm equipment; subminiature photography; film development; photographic print processing; maintenance of equipment; special photographic techniques and equipment; color photography.
Credit recommendation, collegiate level: 4 semester hours in photography.

Intelligence Research Officer Transition

Location: Intelligence School, Fort Holabird, Md.
Length: 7 weeks.
Objectives: To train commissioned officers in counterintelligence procedures and techniques.
Instruction: Investigative legal principles; investigative procedures; purpose, types, sources, techniques, and methods of reporting information; report writing; interrogations; counterinsurgency survey and inspections; physical security; special weapons security; subversion-countersubversion, espionage-counterespionage, and sabotage-countersabotage.
Credit recommendation, collegiate level: 2 semester hours in intelligence methods.

Light and Medium Towed Field Artillery Mechanic

Location: Artillery and Missile School, Fort Sill, Okla.
Length: 4 weeks.
Objectives: To train enlisted personnel to perform organizational maintenance on light and medium towed field artillery weapons.
Instruction: Familiarization with the Army maintenance system, associated supply procedures, and maintenance publications; fundamentals of cannon artillery; adjustment and maintenance of carriage and components, recoil mechanisms, and barrel and breech; nomenclature and functioning of sighting and laying equipment; lubrication and inspection.
Credit recommendation, collegiate level: This course is technical and vocational in nature. Credit in heavy weapons repair shop on the basis of demonstrated skills and/or institutional examinations.

Military Assistance Training Advisor Psychological Operations Orientation

Location: Special Warfare School, Fort Bragg, N.C.
Length: 5–6 weeks.
Objectives: To train officers to serve as psychological operations advisers in the Republic of Vietnam.
Instruction: Insurgent movement, Indochina; history and government of Vietnam; religion, customs, and taboos in the Republic of Vietnam; theory and practice of Communism; the adviser and his counterpart; historical perspective; psychological operations; human factors—the individual, the group, communication, and the attitude formation and change process; economics in society; structure and organization of groups; the role of belief, expression, and education in society; group dynamics; man and society; counterinsurgency operations.
Credit recommendation, collegiate level: 2 semester hours in social psychology.

Military Comptrollership

Location: Finance School, Fort Benjamin Harrison, Ind.
Length: 10 weeks.
Objectives: To train commissioned officers in the comptroller aspects of managing resources, general staff relationships, and the functions of comptrollership with emphasis on the operating level.
Instruction: Economic concepts for managing resources; quantitative aids to decision making, including statistics, operations research, and systems analysis/cost effectiveness; management theory and functions; relationship of money and banking to military financial operations; relationship of defense functions and international balance of payments; activity programming/budgeting; project management; program evaluation and review techniques; management and automatic data processing; managerial accounting; role of the comptroller as an adviser to the commander and other staff officers; functions of comptrollership at the operating level, including programming and budgeting, finance and accounting, management analysis, review and analysis, and internal review.
Credit recommendation, collegiate level: 5 semester hours in business organization and management, and credit in general accounting on the basis of institutional examination. CAUTION: *See* page 201 for 5–6 week course.

Nuclear Power Plant Operator

Location: Fort Belvoir, Va.
Length: 42–48 weeks.
Objectives: To train enlisted personnel to operate and maintain nuclear power reactors.
Instruction: *Note*—Instruction is divided into three phases: *academic phase, operations training phase,* and one of four specialties, *health physics, electrical, mechanical,* or *instrumentation.* All students complete the academic and operations training phases before beginning their specialty training.

The *academic phase* provides instruction in basic mathematical operations required for solution of applied problems; a basic understanding of classical and nuclear physics necessary for a detailed study of nuclear reactor engineering and health physics; an understanding of basic nuclear reactor theory and related fundamental procedures; an understanding of electric circuits and machines as applied to power and power conversion equipment found in electrical power generating stations; an understanding of fluid flow, rest transfer, thermodynamics, vapors, power plant cycles, and components as found in nuclear power plants; and a background in the principles and purpose of health physics and water chemistry.

The *operations training phase* provides the student with a working knowledge in the performance of operator duties at a nuclear power plant.

The *health physics specialty training phase* provides instruction in the theory and practice of water chemistry and health physics in military nuclear power plants.

The *electrical specialty training phase* provides instruction in the operation and maintenance of electrical components of military nuclear power plants.

The *mechanical specialty training phase* provides instruction in the operation and maintenance of mechanical equipment utilized in military nuclear power plants.

The *instrumentation specialty training phase* provides instruction in the theory of instrumentation and controls for the maintenance of instrumentation and control equipment used in military nuclear power plants.

Credit recommendation, collegiate level: CAUTION: *Credit recommendations for this course vary according to year of attendance, the specialty completed, and the major field of study in which credit may be applied. Require exact identification of course by year of attendance and the specialty completed.*

Prior to 1964:

For major field of study in *mathematics or science:* 3 semester hours in general mathematics and science, and credit in laboratory courses in chemistry, physics, or electronics on the basis of institutional examination for completion of any specialty.

For major field of study in *health physics:* 3 semester hours in health physics (radiological safety), and credit in radiation detection laboratory and introductory nuclear engineering on the basis of institutional examination for completion of the health physics specialty.

For major field of study in *electrical engineering* (power): Credit in electrical engineering or instrumentation laboratory, and in introductory circuit theory or power on the basis of institutional examination for completion of the electrical specialty.

For major field of study in *mechanical engineering:* Credit in mechanical engineering laboratory, and in specific physics or power or instrumentation laboratory on the basis of institutional examination for completion of the mechanical specialty.

For major field of study in *instrumentation:* 3 semester hours in nuclear engineering, and credit in electronics and electronic instrumentation laboratory on the basis of institutional examination for completion of the instrumentation specialty.

For major field of study in *nuclear engineering:* 3 semester hours in nuclear engineering, and credit in radiation detection, reactor technology, or reactor operation on the basis of institutional examination for completion of any specialty.

After 1963:

For major field of study in *mathematics or science:* 6 semester hours in general mathematics and science, and credit in laboratory courses in chemistry, physics, or electronics on the basis of institutional examination for completion of any specialty.

For major field of study in *health physics:* 6 semester hours in health physics (radiological safety), and credit in radiation detection laboratory and introductory nuclear engineering on the basis of institutional examination for completion of the health physics specialty.

For major field of study in *electrical engineering* (power): 3 semester hours in electrical engineering or instrumentation laboratory, and credit in introductory circuit theory or power on the basis of institutional examination for completion of the electrical specialty.

For major field of study in *mechanical engineering:* 3 semester hours in mechanical engineering laboratory, and credit in specific physics or power or instrumentation laboratory on the basis of institutional examination for completion of the mechanical specialty.

For major field of study in *instrumentation:* 6 semester hours in nuclear engineering, and credit in electronic and electronic instrumentation laboratory on the basis of institutional examination for completion of the instrumentation specialty.

For major field of study in *nuclear engineering:* 6 semester hours in nuclear engineering, and credit in radiation detection, reactor technology, or reactor operation on the basis of institutional examination for completion of any specialty.

Operations Research/Systems Analysis Executive

Location: U.S. Army Management School, Fort Belvoir, Va.

Length: 4–5 weeks.

Objectives: To train commissioned officers in the use of operations research/systems analysis techniques and in the critical review of operations research/systems analysis studies.

Instruction: Qualitative background of OR/SA; algebra; probability; statistics; computer programming; models; mathematical programming; simulation and war games; relative cost effectiveness; application of models; human factors; social and political aspects of military decision making.

Credit recommendation, collegiate level: 3 semester hours in operations research in the field of computing science.

---

1. Photographic Unit Commander
2. Pictorial Unit Commander

Location: Fort Monmouth, N.J.

Length: 10 weeks.

Objectives: To familiarize officers with the supervision of photographic, film distribution, and television activities at the staff or unit level.

Instruction: Photographic units supply and maintenance procedures; organization and mission of combat arms; photographic coverage and use; still photography; laboratory techniques and procedures; motion-picture photography; film exchange operations; tactical aerial and ground photography; military television.

Credit recommendation, collegiate level: *Course 1:* 1 semester hour in photography. *Course 2:* No credit because of the limited technical nature of the course.

Physical Therapy Aide

Location: Medical Field Service School, Fort Sam Houston, Tex.

Length: 4 weeks.

Objectives: To train enlisted personnel in selected physical therapy procedures.

Instruction: Familiarization with the functioning of a physical therapy clinic, commonly performed duties, and physical therapy procedures; fundamentals of skeletal and muscular anatomy and the physiology of the circulatory, respiratory, and nervous systems; application of physical agents for therapeutic purposes, including electricity, heat, light, hot packs, infrared, diathermy, ultrasound, hydrotherapeutic measures, ultraviolet, electrical stimulation, massage techniques, exercise routines, bandaging, physical reconditioning, and traction; handling and positioning of patients; physical therapy applied to medical and surgical conditions.

Credit recommendation, collegiate level: Credit in physical therapy techniques on the basis of institutional examination.

Pictorial Unit Commander and Motion Picture and Television Director

Location: Signal School, Fort Monmouth, N.J.

Length: 9 weeks.

Objectives: To train commissioned officers to plan and supervise photographic, audio-visual, and television activities at staff or unit level.

Instruction: Maintenance procedures, organization and control of photographic activities; still photography; laboratory practices and supervision; motion-picture photography practices and supervision; television and audio practices and supervision.

Credit recommendation, collegiate level: 12 semester hours in photography.

Power Pack Specialist Noncommissioned Officer Candidate

Location: Fort Belvoir, Va.

Length: 17 weeks.

Objectives: To qualify selected enlisted personnel in the principles and techniques of leadership and to train them in the operation, maintenance, and troubleshooting procedures for gas turbine engines and multi-output package equipment including the MUST utility element.

Instruction: Precise power generation (gas turbine engines); multi-output package units; MUST utility element, fundamentals of refrigeration; troubleshooting and repair of utility element; air-conditioning system; supply and administration; combat operations, leadership, and counterinsurgency; combat support operations; protective mine warfare, booby trapping, and field fortifications; command indoctrination; methods of instruction; map reading and land navigation.

Credit recommendation, collegiate level: This course is technical and vocational in nature. Credit in power station equipment repair on the basis of demonstrated skills and/or institutional examinations.

Psychological Operations Officer

Location: Special Warfare School, Fort Bragg, N.C.

Length: 9–10 weeks.

Objectives: To train officers for assignment in psychological operations staffs and units.

Instruction: World problems; developing nations; insurgency; world politics; human factors—the individual, the group, communication, and attitude formation and change process; structure and organization of groups; belief, expression, and education in society; group dynamics; politics and economics in society; propaganda development and media; psychological operations; counterinsurgency operations; organization and employment of Special Forces; psychological operations planning; Communism and Communistic propaganda.

Credit recommendation, collegiate level: 3 semester hours in social psychology, and credit in political science on the basis of institutional examination.

Radio Set AN/FRC-109 Repair

Location: Signal School, Fort Monmouth, N.J.

Length: 6–7 weeks.

Objectives: To train enlisted personnel in the techniques required to install and perform all levels of maintenance on radio set AN/FRC-109.

Instruction: Operation and organizational maintenance of voice and teletype multiplexing equipment used with the AN/FRC-109 radio set; operation, testing, adjustment, troubleshooting, and repair of the transmit and receive sections; operation, adjustment, and repair of the order-wire, supervisory, and alarm equipment used in the Integrated Wideband Communications System; installation, operation, adjustment, and maintenance of a radio communications system.

Credit recommendation, collegiate level: Credit in electrical laboratory on the basis of demonstrated skills and/or institutional examinations.

Satellite Communications Fundamentals (Satellite Communications Pre Net Training)

Location: Fort Monmouth, N.J.

Length: 8–10 weeks.

Objectives: To train officers and enlisted personnel in the concepts, techniques, and devices employed in the field of satellite communications.

Instruction: Satellite communications; semiconductor diodes; transistor oscillators and multivibrators; power supplies; digital data processing; gating circuits; counters, decoders, and encoders; communications processing equipments; modulator and transmitter analysis; klystrons; RF systems components; antennas and feed techniques; FM receivers; parametric amplifiers and diplexers; receiver parameters; range equipment; synchros and servo circuits; conical scan tracking; monopulse tracking; acquisition and tracking procedures; system performance measurements and GFE equipments; satellite communications link terminal; spread spectrum and measurement interpretation.

Credit recommendation, collegiate level: 2 semester hours at the freshman or sophomore level as an elective in electronics, and credit in electrical laboratory on the basis of demonstrated skills and/or institutional examinations.

Soils Analyst Noncommissioned Officer Candidate

Location: Fort Belvoir, Va.

Length: 12 weeks.

Objectives: To train enlisted personnel in the principles and techniques of leadership and soils analysis.

Instruction: Soils; geology; bituminous materials; drainage; roads and airfields; supervision and performance of soil exploration; soils testing; inspection and design of district projects; supply and administration; combat operations, leadership, and counterinsurgency; combat support operations; protective mine warfare, booby trapping, and field fortifications; command indoctrination; map reading and land navigation.

Credit recommendation, collegiate level: Credit in soils analysis laboratory on the basis of institutional examination.

Sound Recording

Location: Signal School, Fort Monmouth, N.J.
Length: 13 weeks.
Objectives: To train enlisted personnel to operate and perform organizational maintenance on sound recording equipment.

Instruction: Sound recording electronics; basic photography and motion-picture cameras; recording set-ups and practices; recording with motion-picture set AN/TFH-3; newsreel recording assignments and screening; recording equipment maintenance and screening.

Credit recommendation, collegiate level: This course is technical and vocational in nature. Credit in sound recording equipment operation and maintenance on the basis of demonstrated skills and/or institutional examinations.

Stock Control and Accounting Specialist

Location: Quartermaster School, Fort Lee, Va.
Length: 5 weeks.
Objectives: To provide enlisted personnel with a working knowledge in catalogs and authorization media, DSU/GSU and ICC stock control and accounting, and special accounting procedures.

Instruction: Flow and distribution of supplies; basic mathematics; catalog and authorization media; DSU/GSU stock control and accounting; stock management; ICC accounting procedures; inventory management; special accounting procedures.

Credit recommendation, collegiate level: This course is technical and vocational in nature. Credit in stock accounting procedures on the basis of institutional examination.

1. Summer Operations and Mountaineering Instructor
(Cold Weather and Mountain—Summer)
2. Winter Operations and Ski Instructor
(Cold Weather and Mountain—Winter)
3. Mountain and Cold Weather Instructor Training

Locations: Mountain and Cold Weather Training Command, Camp Carson, Colo.; Mountain and Cold Weather Training School, Greely, Alaska.
Length: 4–9 weeks.
Objectives: To train commissioned and noncommissioned officers to perform duties as commanders, staff members, and instructors of units in northern and mountainous regions.

Instruction: Familiarization with northern and mountainous regions of the world, their geographic characteristics, climate conditions, and military significance; special tactical and logistical techniques; employment of standard equipment; techniques of living and operating in the field; instructional techniques of military mountaineering and/or military skiing.

Credit recommendation, collegiate level: For each course, 2 semester hours in camping and survival training.

Supervisory Microwave Radio Maintenance

Location: Signal School, Fort Monmouth, N.J.
Length: 25 weeks.
Objectives: To train enlisted personnel to supervise, coordinate, and participate in the maintenance of a microwave communication system.

Instruction: Fundamentals of maintenance operations; repair parts supply management; supervision of a direct and general support maintenance shop, including employment and flow of maintenance requests; work simplification programs, principles of layout, production control, budgeting, and personnel requirements; depot maintenance operations; field Army and communications zone supply and maintenance operations; methods and techniques of training personnel; basic electronic concepts; wave-shaping circuits, wave form generators, gating, switching, and steering circuits; advanced concepts of amplitude and frequency modulation; principles of multiplexing and microwave concepts; installation, operational adjustments, and maintenance of medium traffic capacity pulse code modulation equipment; adjustment and maintenance of transportable microwave radio systems, line-of-sight and tropospheric scatter communication equipment; multiplexing equipment and pulse code modulation equipment; communication system requirements; special microwave systems.

Credit recommendation, collegiate level: 3 semester hours in maintenance management, 2 semester hours at the freshman or sophomore level as an elective in electronics, and credit in electrical laboratory on the basis of demonstrated skills and/or institutional examinations.

Supply and Service Officer

Location: Quartermaster School, Fort Lee, Va.
Length: 9 weeks.
Objectives: To train commissioned officers in the policies, principles and procedures of supply and service support and organization, capabilities, and employment of supply and service support units.

Instruction: Unit and organization supply; field supply management and accounting procedures; property disposal operations; automatic data processing equipment and automated supply systems; financial management; combat service support, supply operations, and logistical support operations in a theater of operations; depot operations; maintenance and field services; procurement; military management; Army supply systems.

Credit recommendation, collegiate level: 3 semester hours in supply management.

Supply Management Officer

Location: Quartermaster School, Fort Lee, Va.

Length: 9 weeks.

Objectives: To train commissioned officers and warrant officers in the policies, principles, procedures, and developments applicable to all classes of supply and to assignments in continental United States installations.

Instruction: Unit and organization supply; field supply management and accounting procedures; automatic data processing equipment and systems; automated supply systems; financial management; depot operation; supply and service operations in a theater of operations; logistical support operations; maintenance; procurement; general management; Army supply system.

Credit recommendation, collegiate level: 3 semester hours in supply management.

Surface-to-Air Missile Unit Commander
(Guided Missile Unit Commander, SAM)

Location: Artillery and Guided Missile School, Fort Bliss, Tex.

Length: 15 weeks.

Objectives: To train commissioned officers in the duties and responsibilities appropriate to battery-grade officers in surface-to-air guided missile unit.

Instruction: Communications and staff procedures; combined arms; SAM tactics; motors and generators; Nike computer; Nike radars; missile electronics and launcher area equipment; mechanics; handling and battery operation; map reading and survey; basic electronics.

Credit recommendation, collegiate level: 2 semester hours at the freshman or sophomore level as an elective in electricity and electronics, and credit in electrical laboratory on the basis of demonstrated skills and/or institutional examinations.

Topographic Engineer Officer

Location: Engineer School, Fort Belvoir, Va.

Length: 12 weeks.

Objectives: To train commissioned officers in the specialized command and staff duties and responsibilities of the Corps of Engineers topographic officers.

Instruction: Mathematics review; cartometric evaluation; geodetic surveying; measurement of time; triangulation; azimuth by any hour angle; traverse angle problems, third order; electronic distance-measuring problems; gravity computations; third order spirit leveling; cartography; photogrammetric compilation; radial triangulation; planimetric compilation; mosaics; photographic printing; interior and relative orientation of multiplex projectors; multiplex triangulation; map reproduction and distribution; line copying; magenta contact screen; multiple color layout; offset press operations.

Credit recommendation, collegiate level: 3 semester hours in geodetic surveying and 3 semester hours in cartography.

Tropospheric Scatter Terminal REL-2600 Repair

Location: Signal School, Fort Monmouth, N.J.

Length: 7 weeks.

Objectives: To train enlisted personnel in the techniques required to install and perform all levels of-maintenance on tropospheric scatter terminal REL-2600.

Instruction: Operation and organizational maintenance of voice and teletype multiplexing equipment; REL-2600 transmitters and receivers; order-wire, supervisory and alarm system; tropospheric scatter communication system.

Credit recommendation, collegiate level: This course is technical and vocational in nature. Credit in operation and repair of tropospheric scatter communications equipment on the basis of demonstrated skills and/or institutional examinations.

Unit and Organization Supply Specialist
and Armorer

Location: Quartermaster School, Fort Lee, Va.

Length: 7 weeks.

Objectives: To train enlisted personnel in the responsibilities of unit and organizational supply operations and small arms maintenance to enable them to perform general unit supply duties, assist in general supply logistics operations, and serve as unit armorers.

Instruction: Mathematics used at unit and organization level; touch typewriting; supply publications; unit and organization supply; surveillance, storage, and preparation for unit movement; organizational maintenance of small arms.

Credit recommendation, collegiate level: Credit in typing on the basis of institutional examination, and, at the technical level, credit in supply accounting procedures on the basis of institutional examination.

Advanced Electrician

Location: Camp Lejeune, N.C.

Length: 8–9 weeks.

Objectives: To train enlisted personnel in the analysis, testing, and repair of electrical generators and motors and in advanced electrical theory.

Instruction: Mathematics review; electricity, including batteries, the electric circuit, DC series and parallel circuits, DC compound and bridge circuits, electrical conductors and wiring techniques, electromagnetism and magnetic circuits, AC electricity, inductance and capacitance, and AC circuit theory; electrical indicating instruments; AC generators, transformers, and motors; DC generators and motors; AC instruments; magnetic amplifiers; electrical drawings; thermionic emission; vacuum diode elements; gas diode elements; triodes; tetrodes; AC operated power supplies; rectifiers; filters; voltage regulation; amplifiers; relay and control circuits; semiconductors; power supply requirements; servicing transistor circuits; operational testing of engine generators.

Credit recommendation, collegiate level: 2 semester hours at the freshman or sophomore level as an elective in electricity and electronics, and credit in electrical laboratory on the basis of demonstrated skills and/or institutional examinations.

Airborne Radio Operators

Location: Cherry Point, N.C.

Length: 16 weeks.

Objectives: To train enlisted men as airborne radio operators.

Instruction: International Morse code reception, transmission, and telegraphic typing; general operating procedure; radiotelephone message; radiotelegraphy message using correct Navy procedure and International Civil Aviation Organization procedures; airborne electronics; flight training.

Credit recommendation, collegiate level: Credit in typing on the basis of institutional examination, and, at the technical level, credit in radio operation on the basis of demonstrated skills and/or institutional examinations.

Basic Freight Operation

Location: Camp Lejeune, N.C.

Length: 4 weeks.

Objectives: To train enlisted personnel without prior experience in the transportation field for duty as basic freight operations personnel.

Instruction: Capabilities and limitations of the transportation system; regulatory bodies; rules and regulations; documentation; reporting requirements; freight classification; types of equipment available, both military and commercial; household goods movements; fundamentals of shipping and receiving operations.

Credit recommendation, collegiate level: No credit because of the brevity and limited technical nature of the course.

High Intensity Language Training (HILT)—Vietnamese

Location: Quantico, Va.

Length: 6 weeks.

Objectives: To provide instruction in the Vietnamese language to Marine Corps Educational Center graduates which will meet the Fleet Marine Force qualifications in an area where the primary or secondary language is Vietnamese.

Instruction: Language patterns, lexical units, and fluency necessary to communicate effectively with a native speaker; background information on culture, history, and geography; development of a vocabulary for interaction in civic action programs and liaison.

Credit recommendation, collegiate level: 4 semester hours in Vietnamese.

MTDS Fundamentals
(Marine Tactical Data Systems Fundamentals)

Locations: San Diego and Twentynine Palms, Calif.

Length: 11 weeks.

Objectives: To train personnel in the maintenance of the Marine Tactical Data System (MTDS).

Instruction: Basic theory of special purpose semiconductor and electronic circuits utilized in digital data handling equipments; introduction to mathematics applicable to digital systems; basic concepts of logic and logic circuitry utilized in digital systems; arithmetic operations of complex logic and the input-output and storage devices required for these operations; techniques of servicing MTDS equipments and essential fundamentals of the peripheral equipment; functional description of the integral units and their interfacing within the MTDS; timing control elements of the Tactical Air Operations Central (TAOC) of the MTDS.

Credit recommendation, collegiate level: Credit in electrical laboratory on the basis of demonstrated skills and/or institutional examinations.

Redeye Gunner—Platoon
(Redeye Gunners/Platoon Training)
(Redeye Gunner Operator)
(Redeye Gunner/Operator)

Locations: Twentynine Palms, Calif., El Toro, Calif., Camp Pendleton, Calif.

Length: 9 weeks (Full Course); 3–4 weeks (Abbreviated Course).

Objectives: To train selected Marine Corps personnel of designated military occupational specialities and ranks to be Redeye gunners.

Instruction: *Abbreviated Course:* Redeye system; firing sequence; Redeye trainer XM-42 and 49; principles of operation; ranging; hazards and safety measures; launch envelopes and engagement of targets; IR acquisition; maintenance; employment and site selection; aircraft identification; firing exercises. *Full Course:* In addition to the preceding instruction, *Twentynine Palms*—Map reading; magnetic and grid system; scale distances; contour lines; relief maps; aerial photo interpretation; compass operation; aircraft identification; communication briefing. *El Toro*—LAAM, MACS, and MASS units; AAW control facilities and procedures; communications procedures; section control; aircraft identification. *Camp Pendleton*—Deployment of Redeye at division level.

Credit recommendation, collegiate level: *Full or Abbreviated Course:* No credit as the courses are military in nature.

———————

Special AAW Batteryman

Location: Twentynine Palms, Calif.

Length: 7 weeks.

Objectives: To train enlisted personnel having military occupational specialties in the organization of a Hawk battery and in the operation of the Hawk guided missile system as employed by Marine Corps light antiaircraft missile battalions.

Instruction: Hawk missile system; operating procedures associated with the launcher, loader, missile test shop, generator, and missile handling; operating procedures applicable to pulse acquisition radar, range-only radar, continuous-wave radar, high-power illuminator radar, and continuous-wave acquisition radar; battery control central; assault fire command console; basic electronics and radar theory; battery orientation and alignment.

Credit recommendation, collegiate level: No credit as the course is military in nature.

1. AN/SPS-52 Radar Set
2. Talos Radar AN/SPG-49B, Class C
3. Talos Radar AN/SPW-2B, Class C
4. Tartar Radar AN/SPG-51B, Class C
   (Radar AN/SPG-51C, Class C)
5. AN/SPS-48 Radar Set
6. Terrier Radar AN/SPG-55B
7. Terrier Radar AN/SPQ-5A
8. AN/SPS-39 Radar Set
   (AN/SPS-39A Radar Set)

Locations: Naval Schools, Mare Island, Vallejo, Calif., Great Lakes, Ill., and San Diego, Calif.; Guided Missile School, Dam Neck, Va.

Length: *Course 1*, 28 weeks; *Courses 2, 4, and 7*, 24 weeks; *Course 3*, 16 weeks; *Courses 5 and 6*, 30–31 weeks; *Course 8*, 20 weeks.

Objectives: To train enlisted personnel in the knowledge and skills necessary to operate and maintain radar sets.

Instruction: Weapons system; radar system; weapons direction system; guided missile and launching systems; mathematics; radar set operation and maintenance; power distribution system; digital computer procedures and maintenance.

Credit recommendation, collegiate level: Credit in electrical laboratory on the basis of demonstrated skills and/or institutional examinations.

AN/SQS-23, 23A, 23B, 23C Maintenance and Aspect

Locations: Fleet Sonar Schools, Key West, Fla., and San Diego, Calif.

Length: 12 weeks.

Objectives: To train personnel in preventive and corrective maintenance on the AN/SQS-23 series and Aspect equipment.

Instruction: Introduction to AN/SQS series sonar set; use of test equipment; AC and DC power supply; principles of DC generators and AN/SQS motor generators; range detector circuits; amplifier and amplitude control; range scale switching and range power amplifier circuits; sawtooth sweep generator circuits; sweep DC amplifiers, generators, cathode followers, feedback rectifiers, and clamp circuits; cathode-ray tube and blinking circuits; ship's center display, cursor deflection circuits; cursor brightening circuit and scale change indicator; target center display deflection circuits; 2000-cycle oscillator, power amplifier, and transmit scanner; transmit sector gate and sweep relay gate circuits; transmission oscillator, frequency deviation, output switching circuits, and transmit scanners; transmit depression circuits; transmitter power amplifier circuits; audio and video receiver circuits; bearing control circuits; sonar test sets TS-1222 and 1778; test set DC power supplier and VTVM circuits; target signal simulator SM/170; transistors; range and bearing test set AC summary power and DC power supplies; gating multivibrator; preformed beam receiver; Aspect operation; transmit beam control circuits; target angle projection; range and azimuth repeater circuits.

Credit recommendation, collegiate level: Credit in electrical laboratory on the basis of demonstrated skills and/or institutional examinations.

Advanced Flight Training (Advanced Jet) (Advanced Pilot Training (CV Jet)) (CV (Jet) Advanced)

Location: Naval Air Station, Corpus Christi, Tex.

Length: 20–23 weeks.

Objectives: To prepare student naval aviators, who have completed basic flight training, for duties as qualified naval aviators in CV (jet) type aircraft.

Instruction: Engineering; aerodynamics; navigation; meteorology; flight rules and regulations; weapons and warfare; radar fundamentals; carrier air traffic control, aviation safety.

Credit recommendation, collegiate level: 1 semester hour in aeronautics, 1 semester hour in navigation, 1 semester hour in engineering (airplane engines), and credit in meteorology on the basis of institutional examination.

Advanced Pilot Training (Helicopter) (VH)

Location: Naval Air Station, Pensacola, Fla.

Length: 17–23 weeks.

Objectives: To qualify student naval aviators, who have completed basic phase (propeller) pilot training, to fly helicopters.

Instruction: Aerodynamics; aeronautics; carrier air traffic control; instrument navigation; helicopter operations; recognition.

Credit recommendation, collegiate level: The areas of instruction included in the program from 1954 until 1968 have remained the same, but the emphasis has shifted throughout the period. *Note*—Credit recommendations vary for specific years. *From 1965 through 1968* helicopter training is divided into two phases, pre-helicopter instrument and helicopter. In the following recommendation, the two phases will be treated as one unit. *From 1956 to 1965:* 1 semester hour in aeronautics, 1 semester hour in navigation, 2 semester hours in engineering (airplane engines), and credit in meteorology on the basis of institutional examination. *From 1965 through 1968:* 2 semester hours in aeronautics, 1 semester hour in navigation, and credit in meteorology on the basis of institutional examination.

1. Advanced Pilot Training, Multi-Engine Prop.
2. Advanced Pilot Training, VA Prop.
3. Advanced Pilot Training, VS Prop.
4. Advanced Pilot Training, VP Prop.

Location: Naval Air Station, Corpus Christi, Tex.

Length: 18–23 weeks.

Objectives: To prepare student naval aviators who

have completed basic flight training for duties as qualified naval aviators in multi-engine or single-engine propeller type aircraft.

Instruction: *The general areas of instruction in Courses 1 through 4 remain the same, but vary in depth and emphasis.* Aerodynamics; antisubmarine warfare; carrier air traffic control; code and blinker; engineering; flight rules and regulations; instrument navigation; meteorology; dead reckoning navigation; radar navigation.

Credit recommendation, collegiate level: *Course 1:* 5 semester hours in navigation, 1 semester hour in aeronautics, 1 semester hour in engineering (airplane engines), and credit in meteorology on the basis of institutional examination. *Courses 2 and 3:* For each course, 2 semester hours in navigation, 1 semester hour in aeronautics, 1 semester hour in engineering (airplane engines), and credit in meteorology on the basis of institutional examination. *Course 4:* 4 semester hours in navigation, 1 semester hour in aeronautics, 1 semester hour in engineering (airplane engines), and credit in meteorology on the basis of institutional examination.

Airborne Navigator
(Aviation Officer, Navigator)

Location: Naval Air Station, Corpus Christi, Tex.
Length: 10 weeks.
Objectives: To prepare student naval flight officers who have completed Basic Naval Flight Officer School for duties as qualified airborne navigators.
Instruction: Code and blinker; leadership; meteorology; operational navigation (dead reckoning); operational navigation (celestial); operational navigation (radar).
Credit recommendation, collegiate level: 5 semester hours in navigation.

1. Aviation Officer Candidate Program
2. Aviation Reserve Officer Candidate Program

Location: Naval Aviation Schools Command, Pensacola, Fla.
Length: *Course 1,* 11–14 weeks; *Course 2,* 6–8 weeks for each of two summer sessions.
Objectives: To prepare prospective student naval aviators and aviation officers for careers as commissioned officers and for entrance into the Naval School, Flight Preparation.
Instruction: Military training and applied leadership; naval history and world affairs; naval orientation; naval justice; naval leadership; effective communication; prenavigation/seamanship; physical fitness.
Credit recommendation, collegiate level: *Course 1:* 6 semester hours in advanced naval science. *Course 2:* 3 semester hours in advanced naval science for each of the two summer sessions.

Basic Naval Aviation Officers School

Location: Naval Air Station, Pensacola, Fla.
Length: 8–16 weeks.
Objectives: To provide basic academic training and

flight indoctrination for non-pilot aviation officers to prepare them for advanced and technical training leading to eventual designation as naval flight officers.

Instruction: The contents of the Basic Naval Aviation Officers School have been revised continually to keep the program current. The general areas of instruction have been changed in emphasis through the years. Electricity and electronics; radar fundamentals; electronic warfare; flight preparation navigation; airways navigation; code and blinker; dead reckoning navigation; relative motion navigation; training device problems; fleet air operations; meteorology; air intelligence and recognition; aviation flight physiology.

Credit recommendation, collegiate level: CAUTION: *This course varies in recommendation according to year attended. Require exact identification by title and dates of attendance. Note*—In 1962 and 1963 a short NAO course was offered to students who had completed the Basic Flight Training Program. No credit is granted for the short course. *1961–63:* 1 semester hour in navigation and 1 semester hour in communications. *1964–66:* 3 semester hours in navigation, 1 semester hour in communications, and credit in electrical laboratory on the basis of demonstrated skills and/or institutional examinations. *1967–68:* 4 semester hours in navigation and credit in electrical laboratory on the basis of demonstrated skills and/or institutional examinations.

Basic Phase (Jet) Pilot Training, Including Carrier Qualification
(Basic Phase (Jet) Pilot Training)

Location: Naval Air Stations, Meridian, Miss., Memphis, Tenn., and Pensacola, Fla.
Length: 24–26 weeks.
Objectives: To introduce student aviators to a high-performance jet training aircraft, and to instruct them in precision aerobatics, basic instruments, radio instruments, and formation.
Instruction: Aeronautics; communications; meteorology; navigation; physiology; recognition; weapons systems fundamentals.
Credit recommendation, collegiate level: CAUTION: The areas of instruction included in this program from 1959 until 1968 have remained the same, but the scope of instruction has varied throughout the period. *Note* —Credit recommendations vary for specific years. *From 1959 to November 1963:* 1 semester hour in aeronautics, 2 semester hours in navigation, 1 semester hour in engineering (airplane engines), and 1 semester hour in communications. *From November 1963 through 1968:* 1 semester hour in aeronautics and 2 semester hours in navigation.

Basic Phase (Propeller) Pilot Training, Including Carrier Qualification
(Basic Phase (Propeller) Pilot Training)

Location: Naval Air Station, Pensacola, Fla.
Length: 23–32 weeks.
Objectives: To introduce student aviators to a high-performance aircraft and to instruct them in precision aerobatics, basic instruments, radio instruments, and formation.
Instruction: Aerodynamics; communications; engi-

neering; jet engines; meteorology; navigation; weapons systems fundamentals.

Credit recommendation, collegiate level: CAUTION: From 1954 until 1959 the Basic Phase Pilot Training included training that was later given in the primary course. The areas of instruction included in the program from 1954 until 1968 have remained the same, but the scope of instruction has varied throughout the period. *Note*—Credit recommendations vary for specific years. *From 1954 through 1959:* 2 semester hours in aeronautics, 3 semester hours in navigation, 2 semester hours in engineering (airplane engines), and 2 semester hours in communications. *From 1960 through 1962:* 1 semester hour in aeronautics, 2 semester hours in navigation, 1 semester hour in engineering (airplane engines), and 1 semester hour in communications. *From 1962 through 1968:* 1 semester hour in aeronautics, 1 semester hour in engineering (airplane engines), and 2 semester hours in navigation.

C-2A AN/ARN-81 Loran Intermediate Maintenance

Location: Naval Air Station, North Island, Calif.
Length: 4 weeks.
Objectives: To train maintenance personnel in the latest maintenance procedures for the AN/ARN-81 Loran.
Instruction: Overall system theory; timing circuits; display circuits; troubleshooting and aligning the AN/ARN-81.
Credit recommendation, collegiate level: No credit because of the brevity and limited technical nature of the course.

Electricity, Electronics, and Hydraulics, Class P

Location: Service Schools Command, Great Lakes, Ill.
Length: 14 weeks.
Objectives: To train personnel for advanced training on missile launching and gun systems.
Instruction: Hydraulics; properties, identification, and uses of fluids; electricity; electron theory; DC and AC theory and circuits; synchro-servo systems; vacuum tubes and solid state circuitry; magnetic amplifiers; circuit analysis.
Credit recommendation, collegiate level: 3 semester hours at the freshman or sophomore level as an elective in electricity and electronics, and credit in electrical laboratory on the basis of demonstrated skills and/or institutional examinations.

1. **Fire Control Technician, Class A, Phase I**
2. **Fire Control Technician, Class A, Phase II**
3. **Fire Control Technician, Class B**

   Locations: Naval Schools Command, Mare Island, Calif., Bainbridge, Md., and Great Lakes, Ill.
   Length: *Course 1,* 18 weeks; *Course 2,* 14 weeks; *Course 3,* 29 weeks.
   Objectives: To train personnel to operate and maintain complex weapons guidance and control systems.
   Instruction: *Course 1:* Weapons control; electricity; electronics; magnetic amplifiers; electrical machinery; servocontrol systems; gyroscopes and maintenance management. *Course 2:* Advanced electronics; test equip-

ment; computer theory; programming methods and troubleshooting; radar; radar principles and systems. *Course 3:* Mathematics; electricity; electronics; RF theory; test equipment; transistors; magnetic amplifiers; synchros; computer theory; alignment and maintenance management.

Credit recommendation, collegiate level: *Course 1:* 3 semester hours at the freshman or sophomore level as an elective in electricity and electronics, and credit in electrical laboratory on the basis of demonstrated skills and/or institutional examinations. *Course 2:* Credit in electricity, electronics, and electrical laboratory on the basis of demonstrated skills and/or institutional examinations. *Course 3:* 4 semester hours at the freshman or sophomore level as an elective in electricity and electronics, and credit in electrical laboratory on the basis of demonstrated skills and/or institutional examinations.

1. **Fire Control Technician, Class C, Gun Fire Control System Mk 37**
2. **Fire Control Technician, Class C, Gun Fire Control System Mk 56**
3. **Fire Control Technician, Class C, Gun Fire Control System Mk 68**
4. **Fire Control Technician, Class C, Gun Fire Control System Mk 37 and Target Destination System Mk 5**
5. **Fire Control Technician, Class C, Gun Fire Control System Mk 56 and Target Destination System Mk 5**

   Locations: Naval Schools, Bainbridge, Md., and Great Lakes, Ill.
   Length: *Course 1,* 15 weeks; *Course 2,* 12 weeks; *Course 3,* 23 weeks; *Course 4,* 25 weeks; *Course 5,* 20 weeks.
   Objectives: To train personnel to operate, maintain, and repair gun fire control systems and associated equipment.
   Instruction: *Courses 1 through 5:* Theory, construction, operation, and maintenance of amplidyne electric driver; AC and DC power supplies and distribution, control circuits and mode switching, synchro circuits, and optical devices; gyroscopes; radar components; operation, maintenance, adjustment, and repair of analog computers; dynamic testing, calibration, adjustment, casualty analysis, and repair procedures. In addition to the preceding instruction, *Course 3* contains weapons direction equipment and *Courses 4 and 5* contain operation and maintenance of the designation indicator, video generator, and coordinate converter.
   Credit recommendation, collegiate level: For each course, credit in electrical laboratory on the basis of demonstrated skills and/or institutional examinations.

1. **Fire Control Technician, Class C, Target Designation System Mk 5**
2. **Fire Control Technician, Class C, Target Designation System Mk 6**

   Locations: *Course 1,* Naval School, Bainbridge, Md.; *Course 2,* Naval School, Great Lakes, Ill.
   Length: *Course 1,* 12 weeks; *Course 2,* 6 weeks.
   Objectives: To train personnel in the knowledge and skills necessary to operate, maintain, and repair the target designation system specified.

Instruction: Theory, construction, and shop practice of complex circuitry used in radar and television; mathematical analysis of electronic circuits; designation indicator, video generator, and coordinate converter; alignment and maintenance management.

Credit recommendation, collegiate level: Credit in electrical laboratory on the basis of demonstrated skills and/or institutional examinations.

1. **Flight Preparation, Naval Aviation Cadet and Aviation Officer Candidate**
   (Pre-Flight, Naval Aviation Cadet and Aviation Officer Candidate)
2. **Flight Preparation, Officer**
   (Pre-Flight, Officer)

Location: Naval Air Station, Pensacola, Fla.

Length: *Course 1,* 14–16 weeks; *Course 2,* 4–10 weeks.

Objectives: To train personnel in the fundamentals of ground school instruction and aircraft familiarization to prepare them for the Navy pilot training program or Basic Naval Aviation Officers School.

Instruction: *Courses 1 and 2:* From 1956 to 1962—Aviation science; engineering; leadership; naval orientation; navigation; navigation instruments; time, speed, distance problems; wind vectors. From 1962 through 1967—Basic aerodynamics; elementary air navigation; aviation physiology; naval air operations.

Credit recommendation, collegiate level: *Courses 1 and 2:* From 1956 to 1962—1 semester hour in navigation, for each course. From 1963 through 1967—1 semester hour in navigation and 1 semester hour in aeronautics for each course.

1. **Gunner's Mate, Class A, Phase I**
2. **Gunner's Mate, Class A, Phase II**

Location: Naval School, Great Lakes, Ill.

Length: *Course 1,* 16 weeks; *Course 2,* 7 weeks.

Objectives: To train enlisted personnel to operate and maintain gun mounts and missile launching systems.

Instruction: *Course 1:* Construction, operation, and maintenance of gun mounts; surface-to-air missile launching systems; fire-fighting equipment; controlling systems for gun mounts and launching systems; use of standard and digital computers; use and care of mechanical and electrical hand tools; shop practice and operation of small arms; explosives; hydraulics; synchro-servo systems; elements, matter, and magnetism through evaluation of electron theory; DC and AC theory and circuitry. *Course 2:* Shop practice and theory of vacuum tubes and solid state circuitry; magnetic amplifiers; circuit analysis; weapons department organization.

Credit recommendation, collegiate level: *Course 1:* Credit in electricity and electrical laboratory on the basis of demonstrated skills and/or institutional examinations. *Course 2:* 2 semester hours at the freshman or sophomore level as an elective in electricity.

Gunner's Mate, Class C, 5″/54 Rapid Fire Gun and Mount Mk 42 Mods 7 and 8

Location: Naval Schools, Great Lakes, Ill.

Length: 19 weeks.

Objectives: To train gunner's mates in the skills and technology required to maintain an advanced gun system.

Instruction: Construction, operation, and capabilities of rapid-fire gun mount and controlling system; power supplies; electronic and hydraulic circuits; test equipment; vacuum tube voltmeters; frequency generators; synchro and vacuum tube testers; maintenance management; logistics.

Credit recommendation, collegiate level: Credit in electrical laboratory on the basis of demonstrated skills and/or institutional examinations.

1. **Gunner's Mate, Class C, Guided Missile Launching System**
2. **Gunner's Mate, Class C, ASROC Launching Group**

Location: Naval School, Great Lakes, Ill.

Length: *Course 1,* 24 weeks; *Course 2,* 15 weeks.

Objectives: To train gunner's mates to operate, maintain, and repair guided missile, and/or advanced rocket, launching systems.

Instruction: Construction, operation, and capabilities of launching systems; operation, overhaul, repair, and static and dynamic testing of power drives; power supplies; electronic and hydraulic circuits; missile checkout and handling; maintenance management; logistics.

Credit recommendation, collegiate level: Credit in electrical laboratory on the basis of demonstrated skills and/or institutional examinations.

Gunner's Mate, Class C, Rocket Launcher Mk 108

Location: Naval School, Great Lakes, Ill.

Length: 8 weeks.

Objectives: To train personnel to operate, maintain, and repair the rocket launcher Mk 108 and its associated components.

Instruction: Construction, operation, and maintenance of the rocket launcher, power driver, and associated equipment, including loading equipment, handling equipment, maintenance procedures, pneumatic power drives, electrohydraulic power drives, electric and electronic circuits, casualty analysis, and adjustments of equipment; fundamentals and types of hydraulic controlling systems including electrical control units, stroke control systems, solid state amplifiers, vacuum tube amplifers, and components of each amplifier circuit; types and uses of synchronous circuits; use and maintenance of test equipment; subassemblies of 12.75 rockets; rocket-firing circuits; rocket assembly and disassembly procedures; test equipment.

Credit recommendation, collegiate level: Credit in electrical laboratory on the basis of demonstrated skills and/or institutional examinations.

Mark 105 Under Water Fire Control System (UWFCS) Mod 28

Locations: Fleet Sonar Schools, Key West, Fla., and San Diego, Calif.

Length: 16 weeks.

Objectives: To train personnel in the maintenance of the Mark 105 Mod 11–23 UWFCS.

Instruction: Introduction to the weapon system; function of the attack director; description, mechanical components, and electromechanical components and circuits of the Mark 5 Mod 5; solution of horizontal sonar range; target analysis; fixed ballistics; Mark 5 Mod 5 operating procedures; Mark 5 Mod 5 testing, trouble analysis, and adjustments; Mark 17 Mod 2 testing and checkout; Mark 68 Mod 0 and Mark 59 Mod 8 basic circuits, computer fire control problem, instrumentation and control, and maintenance; Mark 108 Mod 1 description and operation; hedgehog, pocket, and torpedo control equipment.

Credit recommendation, collegiate level: Credit in electrical laboratory on the basis of demonstrated skills and/or institutional examinations.

NAVY PILOT TRAINING PROGRAM
(Navy Flight Training Program)

A student may complete the total flight training program or various stages of the program. The specific courses which a student may complete will be found in separate exhibits and are listed in the index alphabetically and under *Navy Pilot Training Program.*

The course lengths given are the minimum lengths of time in attendance. Course lengths may be longer depending upon the availability of flight instructors, weather conditions, and the condition of the training aircraft. *Credit recommendations for pilot courses are not affected by these conditions but are based upon classroom instruction.*

CAUTION: A student may take only *one* of the Flight Preparation courses or Pre-flight courses, *one* of the Basic Phases, and *one* of the Advanced Pilot Training courses. For purposes of identification and verification, students should present the accrediting authority with an official Navy transcript which gives a detailed listing of the completed courses.

Opticalman, Class A

Location: Naval School, Great Lakes, Ill.
Length: 17 weeks.
Objectives: To provide personnel with the technical knowledge and skills involved in maintaining, repairing, and overhauling binoculars, alidades, azimuth and bearing circles, sextants, telescopes, turret and submarine periscopes, range finders, magnetic compasses, and optical gunsights.
Instruction: Use and care of hand tools and measuring instruments; drills and drilling machines; grinder operation; basic lathe operation; operation, maintenance, and adjustment of milling machines; fundamentals of optics; optical instrument components; care, handling, and cleaning of optical equipment; disassembly, repair, assembly, and inspection of optical instruments; sealing, drying, charging, and testing optical instruments; basic requirements and collimation steps for gunsight telescopes; collimation of fixed prisms and straight-line telescopes; auxiliary repair equipment; lens cementing and painting; primary telescopes; navigational instruments.
Credit recommendation, collegiate level: This course is technical and vocational in nature. Credit in preci-

sion instrument repair on the basis of demonstrated skills and/or institutional examinations.

Primary Phase, Basic Pilot Training

Location: Naval Air Station, Pensacola, Fla.
Length: 8–9 weeks.
Objectives: To provide student aviators who have completed preflight training with primary flight training, including academic, flight support, and flight instruction. Upon completion of the primary course, students are qualified for soloing and are competent in precision and fundamental acrobatic maneuvers.
Instruction: Aerodynamics; communications; engineering; flight rules and regulations; meteorology; navigation; aircraft recognition; indoctrination; flight support.
Credit recommendation, collegiate level: CAUTION: The primary phase of the pilot training program has been given as a separate phase since 1959. From 1954 until 1959 it was contained in the basic phase of the pilot training program. The areas of instruction included in the program from 1959 until 1968 have remained the same, but the emphasis has shifted throughout the period. *Note*—Credit recommendations vary for specific years. *From 1959 until 1962:* 1 semester hour in aeronautics, 1 semester hour in navigation, 1 semester hour in engineering, and 1 semester hour in communications. *From 1962 until 1968:* 1 semester hour in aeronautics and 1 semester hour in communications.

Prospective ME (Prop) Flight Instructor
(TS-2A Type Aircraft)
(Prospective ASW Flight Instructor
(S-2 Type Aircraft))

Location: Naval Air Advanced Training Command, Corpus Christi, Tex.
Length: 9 weeks.
Objectives: To train naval aviators as instructors for the specified phases of advanced flight training.
Instruction: Flight training phase: instruments, night familiarization, over-water navigation, tactics, and carrier qualification. Academic training phase: aerodynamics, engineering, flight rules and regulations, instrument navigation, meteorology, and operational navigation. Flight support phase: flight procedures, procedures trainer, and synthetic instrument trainer.
Credit recommendation, collegiate level: No credit as the course is military in nature.

1. **Prospective VA (Prop) Tactical Flight Instructor**
2. **Prospective Phase I CV (Jet) (FF/AF-9J)**
    Tactical Flight Instructor
3. **Prospective Phase II CV (Jet) (F11A)**
    Tactical Flight Instructor
4. **Prospective Advanced Navigation**
    Flight Instructor

Location: Naval Air Advanced Training Command, Corpus Christi, Tex.
Length: 10–16 weeks.
Objectives: To train naval aviators as instructors for the specified phases of advanced flight training.
Instruction: Basic instruments; radio instruments; flight procedures; synthetic instrument trainer; flight

briefing; flight rules and regulations; meteorology; instrument navigation; tactics; maneuvers; weapons; night flight; navigation; carrier qualification; engineering; advanced flight procedures; operational navigation; weapons/warfare orientation.

Credit recommendation, collegiate level: No credit as the courses are military in nature.

RA-5C AN/ALQ-61 Countermeasure Set Shop Maintenance

Location: Naval Air Station, Sanford, Fla.
Length: 11 weeks.
Objectives: To train maintenance personnel in servicing procedures applicable to the AN/ALQ passive electronic countermeasures set.
Instruction: Receivers; frequency encoder; direction encoder; programmer; coded pulse detector; signal data recorder.
Credit recommendation, collegiate level: Credit in electrical laboratory on the basis of demonstrated skills and/or institutional examinations.

RA-5C AN/AYA-1 Signal Data Converter Group Intermediate Maintenance

Location: Naval Air Station, Sanford, Fla.
Length: 5 weeks.
Objectives: To train maintenance personnel in servicing procedures applicable to the RA-5C signal data converter group.
Instruction: Signal data converter, CV-1408/AYA-1, data translator, and timing; data processing-photo channel; translator tape channel; recording head amplifier and optical viewfinder.
Credit recommendation, collegiate level: No credit because of the limited technical nature of the course.

RA-5C Armament Intermediate Maintenance

Location: Naval Air Station, Sanford, Fla.
Length: 3 weeks.
Objectives: To train maintenance personnel in the function and intermediate maintenance of the RA-5C armament system.
Instruction: Controls and indicators; external pylon and related equipment; electrical system; delivery modes; bomb control monitor system.
Credit recommendation, collegiate level: No credit as the course is military in nature.

RA-5C Panoramic Camera Shop Maintenance

Location: Naval Air Station, Sanford, Fla.
Length: 6 weeks.
Objectives: To train maintenance personnel in servicing procedures for the RA-5C panoramic camera system.
Instruction: Introduction to panoramic camera; test equipment; control electronics and automatic exposure control; 3- and 18-inch cameras and camera electronics; mounts and mount electronics; panoramic camera environmental system.

Credit recommendation, collegiate level: No credit because of the limited technical nature of the course.

RA-5C Plane Captain's Organizational Maintenance

Location: Naval Air Station, Sanford, Fla.
Length: 4 weeks.
Objectives: To provide fleet maintenance personnel with instruction in RA-5C aircraft organizational maintenance.
Instruction: Aircraft systems familiarization; structure and corrosion control; electrical and indicating systems; hydraulic power systems; flight and inlet duct airflow-control system; survival and environmental systems; power plants and related systems.
Credit recommendation, collegiate level: No credit because of the brevity and specialized nature of the course.

RA-5C Power Plants and Related Systems

Location: Naval Air Station, Sanford, Fla.
Length: 4 weeks.
Objectives: To provide fleet maintenance personnel with maintenance training on RA-5C power plants and related systems.
Instruction: RA-5C fuel system description and operation; RA-5C power plants and component systems; applied maintenance procedures, including engine test equipment and rigging.
Credit recommendation, collegiate level: No credit because of the brevity and specialized nature of the course.

RA-5C Signal Data Converter Group Test Equipment Intermediate Maintenance

Location: Naval Air Station, Sanford, Fla.
Length: 3 weeks.
Objectives: To train maintenance personnel in servicing procedures applicable to test equipment for the RA-5C signal data converter group.
Instruction: Data converter and viewfinder test equipment and digital data system test equipment description, theory of operation, and maintenance.
Credit recommendation, collegiate level: No credit because of the brevity and limited technical nature of the course.

RA-5C Structures and Hydraulic Sub-Systems

Location: Naval Air Station, Sanford, Fla.
Length: 7 weeks.
Objectives: To provide maintenance personnel with an overall knowledge of the RA-5C aircraft structure and hydraulic systems.
Instruction: Structural repair, including airframes, wing and honeycomb repair, and corrosion removal and treatment; hydraulic power systems operation and maintenance; landing gear and wheel brake systems maintenance; arresting gear; wing and tail fold and

pneumatic systems; high-lift control systems; air refueling probe and primary airflow systems.

Credit recommendation, collegiate level: This course is technical and vocational in nature. Credit in aircraft hydraulic systems repair on the basis of demonstrated skills and/or institutional examinations.

RA-5C Survival and Environmental Systems

Location: Naval Air Station, Sanford, Fla.

Length: 5 weeks.

Objectives: To provide maintenance personnel with training in servicing procedures for the RA-5C aircraft survival and environmental systems.

Instruction: Pneumatics and canopy systems; ejection seat system; oxygen system; heat and vent systems.

Credit recommendation, collegiate level: No credit because of the brevity and specialized nature of the course.

Surface Missile Systems, Officer

Locations: Guided Missile School, Dam Neck, Va.; Naval School, Mare Island, Vallejo, Calif.

Length: 11 weeks.

Objectives: To train officers in the duties of surface missile weapons systems, fire control and missile battery.

Instruction: Missile fire control problems and symbology; synchros; servo systems; gyros; analog computing devices; missiles propulsion and control systems, and ordnance components; specific weapon and weapons direction systems; operation of computing elements; launching systems; telemetering equipment; troubleshooting and analysis; logistics; planning and coordinating missile firing; administration and security.

Credit recommendation, collegiate level: Credit in electrical laboratory on the basis of demonstrated skills and/or institutional examinations.

1. Talos Computer Mk 111 Mod 1, Class C
2. Tartar Computer Mk 118
3. Terrier Computer Mk 100 Mod 2
4. Terrier Computer Mk 119 Mods 3 and 4

Locations: Naval Guided Missile School, Dam Neck, Va.; Naval Schools, Great Lakes, Ill., and Mare Island, Calif.

Length: 14–20 weeks.

Objectives: To provide personnel with the technical knowledge and skills required in the maintenance of the computers specified.

Instruction: *Course 1:* Basics of analog computers; basic computing elements; computer Mk 111 Mod 1 components and circuitry; computer system functioning; weapon system target detection and designation; weapon system intercept prediction; generation of capture angles; dead zone evaluation; generation of aimpoint angles; guidance programming; ground aided acquisition; Q phasing and auxiliary modes; system maintenance and testing. *Course 2:* Tartar missile fire control problem; analog and digital computers; introduction to computer Mk 118; computing elements and loops of analog computers; modes of operation; computer Mk 118 computation and mechanization; instrumentation and mechanization of special circuits; computer and system test, maintenance, and casualty analysis. *Course 3:* Modes of operation, power distribution circuits, computer amplifiers, and operating procedures of controls and indicator; use of test equipment; functions and theory of electromechanical, electrical, and electronic computing elements; designate, Normal AA, surface, and shore modes; computer static tests and dynamic tests; computer checkout. *Course 4:* Introduction to computer Mk 119 Mods 3 and 4; function and adjustment of mechanical, electromechanical, electrical, and electronic elements; basic analog configurations; basic digital theory; test equipment; operation, alignment, and casualty analysis of the AC and DC power supplies; track modes; launcher and missile orders; special modes and circuits; system testing and maintenance.

Credit recommendation, collegiate level: For each course, credit in electrical laboratory on the basis of demonstrated skills and/or institutional examinations.

1. Talos Guided Missile and Guided Missile Test Set Maintenance
2. Terrier/Tartar Guided Missile and Guided Missile Test Set Maintenance

Locations: Naval Guided Missile School, Dam Neck, Va.; Naval School, Mare Island, Calif.

Length: 23 weeks.

Objectives: To train personnel to test and maintain Talos, Terrier or Tartar guided missiles and to operate and maintain guided missile test sets and associated equipment.

Instruction: Description and capabilities of the missile control function, auxiliary power supplies, timing system, steering system, flight termination system, and the airborne flight evaluation system; calibration, alignment, adjustment, and repairs of guided missile test sets; signal comparator; fuse test set; radar test set; combined unit telemeter ground station, including antenna system, pre-amplifier, power supplier, radio receiver, tape transport and motor drive assembly, reproducer, demultiplexer and oscillograph recorder; familiarization with the Talos, Terrier or Tartar weapons systems.

Credit recommendation, collegiate level: For each course, credit in electrical laboratory on the basis of demonstrated skills and/or institutional examinations.

1. Talos Gunner's (Missile) Handling
2. Terrier/Tartar Gunner's Mate (Missile Handling)

Locations: Naval Guided Missile School, Dam Neck, Va.; Naval Schools, Great Lakes, Ill., and Mare Island, Calif.

Length: 3 weeks.

Objectives: To train enlisted personnel to assemble, disassemble, and replace faulty modules within Talos or Terrier and Tartar guided missiles.

Instruction: *Course 1:* Missile receiving, pretest, wing, and fin inspections; hydraulic, fuel, nitrogen, and battery servicing; preventive maintenance; component handling; use of Talos tactical test equipment. *Course 2:* Homing principles and flight sequence, illuminating guidance radar characteristics, internal configuration, ordnance components, and containers; radar beam characteristics; beam-riding principles and flight sequence; special tools and handling equipment; hydraulic test stand operation; pneumatic test unit operation; missile assembly; operation of guided missile test sets.

Credit recommendation, collegiate level: For each course, credit in electrical laboratory on the basis of demonstrated skills and/or institutional examinations.

1. Talos Telemetering Data Reduction
2. Terrier Telemetering Data Reduction

Locations: Guided Missile School, Dam Neck, Va.; Naval School, Mare Island, Vallejo, Calif.

Length: 3 weeks.

Objectives: To train officers and enlisted personnel to perform data reduction and to analyze guided missile telemetered flight records by converting a graphic display into quantitative values.

Instruction: Weapon system characteristics; SMS telemetering system; airborne telemetering equipment; combined unit telemeter ground station; associated equipment; data reduction and flight analysis.

Credit recommendation, collegiate level: No credit because of the limited technical nature of the course.

1. Talos Weapon Direction System Mk 6
   (WDE Mk 2), Class C
2. Tartar Weapon Direction System Mk 4, Class C
3. Terrier Weapon Direction System Mk 7
   (WDE Mk 8)
4. Terrier Weapon Direction System Mk 3
   (DE Mk 9)

Locations: *Courses 1, 2, and 3,* Naval Guided Missile School, Dam Neck, Va.; Naval School, Mare Island, Vallejo, Calif. *Course 4,* Naval School, Great Lakes, Ill.

Length: *Course 1,* 24 weeks; *Course 2,* 14 weeks; *Courses 3 and 4,* 20 weeks.

Objectives: To train personnel in the technical knowledge and skills required in the maintenance and repair of the weapon direction system.

Instruction: *Courses 1 through 4:* Weapon system; associated radars and weapons; weapon direction system; designation equipment; input power indicators and metering circuits; circuit analysis, distribution, and alignment of power supplies; simulating system; sweep generation and deflection systems; video and tracking systems; symbol generation and display systems; target evaluation and display systems; target evaluation and designation data converting systems; weapon assignment system; system adjustments and maintenance; related equipment, computer, and system operability tests.

Credit recommendation, collegiate level: Credit in electrical laboratory on the basis of demonstrated skills and/or institutional examinations.

Tartar Weapons Control System

Locations: Guided Missile School, Dam Neck, Va.; Naval School, Mare Island, Vallejo, Calif.

Length: 10 weeks.

Objectives: To train officers and enlisted personnel to operate, perform preventive maintenance, isolate and correct casualties, adjust, align, and preserve the Tartar weapon system.

Instruction: Tartar weapon control system; missile and launcher; data flow block diagrams; missile fire control system; weapon direction equipment; weapon control system maintenance.

Credit recommendation, collegiate level: Credit in electrical laboratory on the basis of demonstrated skills and/or institutional examinations.

1. Terrier Weapons System MFCS Mk 73
2. Terrier Weapons System MFCS Mk 76
3. Talos Weapon System Mk 77 Mod 2, Class C

Locations: Naval Guided Missile School, Dam Neck, Va.; Naval Schools, Great Lakes, Ill., and Mare Island, Calif.

Length: 6–10 weeks.

Objectives: To train personnel for Terrier or Talos missile weapons systems technical leadership.

Instruction: Introduction to Terrier or Talos weapons control systems; operation of target detection, selection, and tracking equipment; operation of displays of the director assignment console; designation modes of weapons control systems; operation and circuitry of radar sets; computation of missile and launcher orders; weapons control systems maintenance; system test equipment.

Credit recommendation, collegiate level: For each course, credit in electrical laboratory on the basis of demonstrated skills and/or institutional examinations.

Transceiver AN/URC-32 Maintenance (Enlisted)

Locations: Naval Submarine Bases, New London and Groton, Conn.

Length: 3 weeks.

Objectives: To train qualified enlisted men to operate, maintain, and repair the AN/URC-32.

Instruction: Introduction to single-side-band theory; RF tuner basic block; SSB transmit functions; primary power distribution and power supplies; handset and handset adapter-circuit analysis; troubleshooting; antenna coupler circuit operation; frequency generator circuit analysis; oscillator circuit analysis; transceiver malfunctions.

Credit recommendation, collegiate level: No credit because of the brevity and limited nature of the course.

UH-1E Airframe and Related Systems
    Intermediate Maintenance

Location: Camp Pendleton, Calif.

Length: 4 weeks.

Objectives: To provide maintenance personnel with an overall knowledge of the UH-1E aircraft and maintenance of its various systems at the intermediate level.

Instruction: Aircraft general; power plant and fuel supply systems; rotor and power train systems; avionics familiarization.

Credit recommendation, collegiate level: No credit because of the brevity and specialized nature of the course.

Warrant Officer Aviation Indoctrination
(Limited Duty Officer Aviation Indoctrination)
(Limited Duty Officer Pre-Flight School)

Location: Naval Air Basic Training Command, Pensacola, Fla.

Length: 8–13 weeks.

Objectives: To indoctrinate new warrant officers in the customs, traditions, and duties of officership in the aviation service of the Navy.

Instruction: Human relations; naval justice; naval officer orientation; world affairs; study skills; oral and written communications; military; physical fitness.

Credit recommendation, collegiate level: 3 semester hours in naval science.

PART II

CREDIT AND ADVANCED STANDING BY EXAMINATION

GENERAL EDUCATIONAL DEVELOPMENT TESTING PROGRAM

AND

COLLEGE-LEVEL EXAMINATION PROGRAM

CREDIT AND ADVANCED STANDING
BY EXAMINATION

This section of the 1968 GUIDE describes two national testing programs: the General Educational Development (GED) Testing Program, sponsored by the American Council on Education through its Commission on Accreditation of Service Experiences, and the College-Level Examination Program (CLEP), sponsored by the College Entrance Examination Board. These programs can be of assistance to college and university admission officials in their selection and placement of prospective students and to employers in their selection of prospective employees. These tests were established for the purpose of providing an opportunity to qualified adults—military personnel on active duty, veterans, and civilians—to demonstrate their educational competence and to encourage them to seek better educational and vocational opportunities and goals.

A basic national concern of our times is the unrealized potential of millions of our citizens. The great majority of the adults in this country have left school—for one reason or another—before they were graduated from high school. Others have not continued their education after high school graduation. These persons are handicapped when seeking job opportunities and in pursuing higher educational goals. There is a great need to develop their productive abilities as well as to raise their educational levels so that they may contribute to our society to the maximum of their capabilities. Many need instruction to reach the twelfth-grade level of achievement, but there are many others who, through a combination of formal and informal educational experiences, have acquired a level of education at or above that of the high school graduate.

The GED tests provide adults with a means by which they may earn a high school equivalency certificate or qualify for admission to higher education. The CLEP examinations provide an opportunity to persons (who qualify for admission to college through graduation from high school or through successful achievement on the GED tests) to earn credit and advanced standing. Others who cannot pursue full-time or part-time college programs may wish to take the examinations to satisfy educational qualifications for employment.

GENERAL EDUCATIONAL DEVELOPMENT (GED) TESTING PROGRAM

Brief History

The first forms of the tests were developed in 1942 by the Examination Staff of the United States Armed Forces Institute. The Examination Staff, a group of civilian testing experts, worked under the direction of the USAFI's Advisory Committee. This Committee, composed primarily of civilian educators, was established with the cooperation and support of the American Council on Education, the National Association of Secondary-School Principals, and the regional accrediting associations. The tests, as developed, were designed to measure the major outcomes and concepts of four years of high school instruction, thereby providing a means for the veterans of World War II to readjust themselves to civilian life as they resumed their educational and vocational plans.

In August 1945, the American Council on Education established the Veterans' Testing Service so that the tests could be made available to civilian educational institutions for administration to veterans who desired to earn a high school equivalency certificate for vocational purposes or to qualify for admission to higher educational opportunities.

In January 1946, the Commission on Accreditation of Service Experiences became responsible for the policy direction and supervision of the Veterans' Testing Service. The use of the tests with World War II veterans proved so successful that state departments of education and colleges extended the use of the tests to all adult citizens. In 1959, for the first time, the number of nonveteran adults tested exceeded the number of veterans tested.

The Commission on Accreditation, at its May 1963 meeting, officially changed the name of the Veterans' Testing Service (VTS) to the General Educational Development (GED) Testing Service.

The civilian restricted forms of the tests are administered at Official GED Centers located in the fifty states, the District of Columbia, American Samoa, the Canal Zone, Guam, and Puerto Rico. Other comparable forms, called the military restricted forms, are administered through the United States Armed Forces Institute to military personnel on active duty stationed throughout the world. National standardizations were made—1943, 1955, and 1967—at which times national and regional norms were established.

Responsibility for Operation

The operation and the security of the testing program is a joint responsibility of each state department of education and the Commission on Accreditation of Service Experiences.

Each state department of education determines the policies and procedures through which adult residents may earn a high school credential on the basis of the GED tests. The departments have the responsibility to see that the tests are properly administered and safeguarded and that the testing is conducted in accordance with the policies of the state and the Commission.

The Commission is responsible for establishing and making available current national and regional norms through periodic administration of the tests to high school seniors. Each time new forms of the tests are constructed, and when it is necessary to re-standardize the tests nationally, the Commission appoints curriculum specialists (nominated by the National Association of Secondary-School Principals) as consultants to review the tests and determine whether or not the tests measure the major objectives of current high school programs of instruction.

Limitations on Use of the Tests

The civilian restricted forms of the GED tests may be administered only to adult residents who have a serious reason for taking the tests.

The term "adult residents" is defined as (1) those individuals whose school class, of which they would have been a member had they continued, has been graduated from high school; or (2) individuals at least eighteen years of age whose last attendance as regularly enrolled students in a full-time high school program of instruction was at least one year prior to the date of taking the tests.

The term "serious reason" is defined as the desire (1) to earn a high school credential; (2) to qualify for admission to college or, in general, for admission to higher educational opportunities; (3) to meet educational requirements for employment or promotion in a job; (4) to meet induction requirements of the Armed Forces of the United States; (5) to meet requirements of state and local boards of licensing examiners for those occupations where the educational requirements for admission to licensing examinations may be at ninth, tenth, or eleventh grade levels of achievement; or (6) for personal satisfaction.

The GED tests may not be administered (1) for diagnostic purposes; (2) to determine grade levels of achievement for placement in adult education programs; (3) as a measure of student progress; or (4) for the purpose of establishing local normative data.

Where the Tests May Be Administered

The determination of locations and conditions under which the GED tests may be administered is a joint responsibility of each state department of education and the Commission on Accreditation. The civilian restricted forms of the GED tests may be administered only at the following locations.

Official GED Centers

As stated earlier, each state department of education determines where within a state an Official GED Center may be located and the number of such Centers. However, the Commission on Accreditation places restrictions on the selection of locations for Official GED Centers in accordance with the following policy:

> The GED Testing Service shall establish by annual contract an Official GED Center at (1) high schools and institutions of higher education accredited by the appropriate regional accrediting

association or by the state department of education; and (2) at adult schools, boards of education, community colleges, and adult education centers authorized by appropriate state educational agencies and operating under the jurisdiction of state or local school authorities.

State Correctional and Health Institutions

In 1955, at the request of state departments of education, the Commission adopted a policy whereby citizens confined in the state correctional and health institutions could be administered the civilian restricted forms of the GED tests as a part of their rehabilitation. Most states have now extended the opportunity of earning a high school credential on the basis of the GED tests to citizens confined in state correctional and health institutions. In accordance with the policy of the Commission, the state establishes an Official GED Center within its department of education. Through special authorization, the department sends the tests by secure methods to state institutions for administration.

Federal Correctional and Health Institutions

In 1957, at the request of the United States Department of Justice, the Commission established, with the approval of state departments of education, a policy so that individuals confined in federal correctional and health institutions might be administered the GED tests as a part of their rehabilitation program. The Commission administers the testing at federal institutions in the same manner as state departments of education administer their programs at state institutions.

Veterans Administration Hospitals.

The Commission in 1961, at the request of the Veterans Administration and with the approval of state departments of education, granted authorization to Veterans Administration hospitals to administer the GED tests to patients undergoing treatment. This authorization applies only to those hospitals conducting educational therapy programs with an educational therapist as a regular member of the hospital staff.

Visually Handicapped

The Commission has two special editions of the GED tests—one on magnetic tape for administration to completely blind individuals and one in large type for administration to the partially sighted. Both editions have specially prepared answer sheets so that the examinees may record their answers. These editions are sent only to officials within a state who have been approved by the state department of education to administer the tests to the visually handicapped.

American Civilian Citizens
Overseas and Foreign Nationals

In 1966, in response to an increasing demand for the opportunity of taking the GED tests from American civilian citizens overseas and foreign nationals, the Commission established a policy, approved by state departments of education, for the administration of the tests. The American civilian citizens overseas have wished to qualify for an equivalency certificate from their home states or for admission to institutions of higher education overseas. Foreign nationals have requested to take the tests so that they may qualify for further education and training in this country.

Characteristics of Tests

The GED tests are a battery of five tests in the areas of English composition, social studies, natural sciences, literature, and mathematics.

Since primary use of the tests is to appraise the educational development of adults who have not completed their formal high school education, the tests have been constructed somewhat differently from the usual school achievement tests which are designed to measure immediate objectives of instruction. It is recognized that persons can make considerable educational progress through a variety of educative experiences, both in school and in other situations. The educational progress of persons not in school is likely to be the result of firsthand observation, direct experience, self-directed reading and study, conversations and informal group discussions, and other experiences with problems, ideas, and people. In contrast to this is the educational development of students who learn largely by vicarious experiences through the use of textbook and formal pedagogical procedures presented in a sequential arrangement. In the schools there is likely to be a more complete and detailed coverage of specific facts and ideas than is true of the great variety of arrangements of subject matter and problems encountered in out-of-school learning experiences.

In consideration of these differences, the GED tests have been designed to measure as directly as possible the attainment of some of the major objectives of the secondary school program of general education. The emphasis is placed on intellectual power rather than detailed content; on the demonstration of competence in using major generalizations, concepts, and ideas; and on the ability to comprehend exactly, evaluate critically, and to think clearly in terms of concepts and ideas.

In measuring the outcomes of formal instruction, it may be necessary to place stress on detailed descriptive facts in order to be certain that the student thoroughly grasps the generalizations and concepts based on these facts. It is, however, expected that once the generalizations are firmly established, many of the substantiating details and the organization in which they have been learned will be forgotten. In school examinations, it is regarded as desirable to test for these details because of the recency of their acquisition and because they must be retained temporarily. In examinations intended for adults with varied experiences, the emphasis in the testing should properly be on the major generalizations, ideas, and intellectual skills which are the long-term outcome of a sound education.

Evaluation of Test Results

The Commission on Accreditation recommends that state departments of education establish minimum critical scores for the purpose of issuing high school equivalency certificates at the point which approximately 20% of those high school seniors tested failed to achieve. On the basis of national data, approximately 20% of high school seniors tested in 1943, 1955, and 1967 failed to achieve a standard score of 35 or above on each test *or* an average standard score of 45 or above on all five tests. The Commission also recommends that these critical scores be consistent with the educational standards of each state. For this reason, most departments of education now require that examinees achieve a standard score of 35 or above on each test *and* an average standard score of 45 or above on all five tests. For admission to college, the Commission recommends that the applicants be required to achieve scores consistent with the usual practices in the admission of high school graduates. That is, if a college admits only those students graduating in the upper half of the class, then similar standards should be demanded of GED applicants.

Publications

The Commission distributes without charge several publications relating to the GED Testing Program. Copies of the following publications, or further information, may be obtained by writing to the Director, Commission on Accreditation of Service Experiences, 1785 Massachusetts Avenue, N.W., Washington, D.C. 20036.

State Department of Education Policies: Issuance of High School Certificates Based on GED Test Results; Granting of High School Credit for Military Educational Experiences

Opportunities for Educational and Vocational Advancement: GED Testing Program; Comprehensive College Testing Program; USAFI Courses and Tests

Examiner's Manual for the Tests of General Educational Development

Official GED Centers

Handbook for Official GED Centers

Newsletter

COLLEGE-LEVEL EXAMINATION PROGRAM (CLEP)

Background and Goals

The College-Level Examination Program of the College Entrance Examination Board has the broad purpose of improving access to higher education through the development of a national system of placement and credit by examinations. Prior to 1965, this activity was known as the Comprehensive College Test Program and was sponsored by the Educational Testing Service. The Program has five major objectives: to provide a national program of examinations that can be used to evaluate nontraditional college-level education, specifically including independent study and correspondence work; to stimulate colleges and universities to become more aware of the need for and the possibilities and problems of credit by examination; to enable colleges and universities to develop appropriate procedures for placement, accreditation, and admission of transfer students; to provide colleges and universities with means by which to evaluate their program and their students' achievement; to assist adults who wish to continue their education in order to meet licensing requirements or to qualify for higher positions in business and industry.

Basic to the Program is the idea that the diversity of American education is one of its strengths and that there is a value in the overall harmony of the system that must not be vitiated. It is another basic assumption of the Program that truly to treasure learning is to transmit it and to see it used. Individuals differ in their aspirations and abilities; to insure that each person has the opportunity to work in his own style and up to his own capacity, it is essential that higher education should recognize and reward the educational achievement of people regardless of how they have learned. As individual achievement is given concrete support through the granting of credit and placement to those who demonstrate their proficiency through examination, to that extent will CLEP have been a worthy

endeavor. It is estimated that thirty million people are now taking advantage of the wide variety of educational opportunities offered by correspondence courses, university extension, educational television, and the adult education programs operated by public schools, the universities, industry, labor organizations, the Service, churches, museums, libraries, professional societies, welfare associations, fraternal groups, community service groups, and the like. A list and description of some of the ways in which collegiate and noncollegiate institutions have found the examinations useful will be found on pages 400 and 401.

The College-Level Examination Program is a new activity of the College Board. As it develops, the Program will react to the changing needs of the colleges, individuals, and noncollegiate institutions it serves. Higher education has long needed a flexible system of credit by examination. This Program can serve that need. The following discussion should be read with the thought that the Program is dedicated to access, not denial. Questions or requests for further information regarding CLEP should be sent to the appropriate College Board regional office. Publications about the Program may be obtained by writing to:

Program Director, CLEP
Box 592
Princeton, New Jersey 08540

Services Offered by CLEP

The examinations—General and Subject

Two types of examinations are offered in the College-Level Examination Program, General Examinations and Subject Examinations. The former are intended to provide a comprehensive measure of undergraduate achievement in the five basic liberal arts areas (English composition, humanities, mathematics, natural sciences, social sciences–history) . They are not designed to measure advanced training in any specific discipline, but rather to assess a student's knowledge of fundamental facts and concepts, his ability to perceive relationships, and his understanding of the basic principles and concepts. The General Examinations are designed to be particularly relevant to the kinds of general education experiences students can be expected to have had by the end of their first two years of college. They are not based on a particular curriculum or course of study, but sample widely the content of the major disciplines with which each is concerned. With the exception of the test in English composition, which requires 60 minutes, each of the General Examinations is 75 minutes in length. Scores are reported on a standard score scale ranging from 200 to 800 with a mean of 500 and a standard deviation of 100. Two sub-scores are also reported in four of the five tests, not including English composition. The sub-scores are reported on a scale of 20 to 80 with a mean of 50 and a standard deviation of 10. Further information about the General Examinations may be found in the booklet, *A Description of the General Examinations.*

The Subject Examinations, on the other hand, measure achievement in a specific subject and, therefore, bear some similarity to end-of-course tests. They measure the ability to apply the knowledge of basic facts and concepts to the solution of problems and the interpretation of materials as well as the understanding of the facts and concepts themselves. Each of the Subject Examinations is a 90-minute objective test. Most of the examinations also include an optional essay section. The essay section requires an additional 90 minutes and is designed to provide further evidence of a student's competence. Scores on the test are reported on a 20 to 80 standard score scale with a mean of 50 and a standard deviation of 10. The optional essay section is retained by the college for grading. The Subject Examinations differ from the General Examinations in that the former are more closely tied to course content and are intended to cover material that is typical of college courses in these subjects.

It is expected that ultimately more than 100 Subject Examinations in all fields will be produced. At this writing, Subject Examinations are available in American Government, Analysis and Interpretation of Literature, English Composition, General Chemistry, General Psychology, Geology, Introductory Calculus, Introductory Economics, Introductory Sociology, Money and Banking, Statistics, Tests and Measurements, and Western Civilization. Under development are examinations in History of American Education, Educational Psychology, Marketing, Algebra, Computer–Data Processing, American History, Trigonometry, and Algebra-Trigonometry. Details concerning these examinations may be found in the booklet, *A Description of the Subject Examinations.*

Access to the Examinations

This section will discuss the ways in which it is possible to secure access to the examinations for different purposes and applications.

Inspection of the examinations

Most general inquiries about the nature and scope of the College-Level Examinations can be answered by referring to the two descriptive booklets cited above. Those interested in the examinations should obtain and study these booklets as a basis for making a preliminary judgment about the appropriateness of the examinations for the purposes they are contemplating.

College-Level Examinations are loaned for limited periods for inspection by faculty and staff members of colleges and universities contemplating using the Program's services. Confidential test inspection request forms, which outline the security precautions which must be taken and which list the tests, are available from the College Board regional offices.

Under certain conditions, businesses, industrial firms, and licensing agencies may also arrange to inspect the examinations as a precondition to their decision to use or to accept the examination results. As with the colleges and universities, it is necessary that the security of inspection tests be guaranteed. Inspection request forms for use by noncollege potential users are available from College Board regional offices.

Trial test administration

The free trial administration program is subject to annual review and is designed to allow collegiate institutions to gain some experience with the tests and to develop institutional norms. This service is not limited to a single examination. An institution may arrange for a trial administration of one or several tests. Trial administrations of all examinations used need not be held at the same time. An institution may find it more suitable to conduct a trial administration of one examination in one semester and of a different examination in a subsequent semester. Obviously, this service is intended to encourage the use of the examinations where the objectives and the purposes of the college or university and those of the Program seem to be compatible in the long run. The tests are not available under this arrangement to support individual research projects or such institutional research projects or those not intended to lead to continuing use of the Program. These restrictions are necessary because eventually the College-Level Examination Program will depend on test fees. Therefore, requests for trial administrations will be considered in light of the institution's plans to make continuing use of the tests if the data from the trial administration demonstrate to the college that the tests are appropriate to the use intended. No institution need commit itself to long-range use of the tests in advance of a trial administration period, but an institution should consider how it would plan to participate in the Program and how this participation would be financed in the future, whether by candidate fees or through its own resources.

Assuming that the plans of a college or university for a trial administration are in keeping with the circumstances described above, the Board's requirements for participation are minimal. The institution must arrange to protect the security of the examinations during the entire period that the test booklets are in its custody. Data derived from a trial administration should be shared with the College Board to permit further study of the examinations or to supplement the normative data available if such use seems appropriate. Should the College Board use the data in this way, the scores for individual students or for institutions will not be published. An institution wishing to conduct a free trial administration should communicate with the director of the College Board regional office in its area (see page 401). Arrangements should be made with the regional director and concluded at least

five weeks before the anticipated test date.

Regular institutional test administration

Colleges and universities that wish to test their own students (individuals, classes, or other groups of enrolled students) may arrange to rent the College-Level Examinations for administration on dates to suit their convenience.

Order forms for the tests may be obtained from:

> Program Director
> College-Level Examination Program
> Box 592
> Princeton, New Jersey 08540

Even if an institutional purchase order is required, a Program test order form should be used to eliminate errors in specific tests to be supplied, to ensure that packages will be properly addressed, and to indicate consent to the conditions under which the Program makes the examinations available.

It is particularly important that test orders reach the above address at least one month in advance of the test date so that testing materials (test booklets, answer sheets, and supervisor's manuals) may be supplied in accordance with the test order before the intended administration date.

At the present time, the test rental fee for the battery of five General Examinations is $5.00 per student tested. While the General Examinations are designed to be used as a complete battery, there may be special situations in which an institution may find it desirable to use less than a full battery. Arrangements can be made to use any number or combination of the individual tests of the General Examinations at a charge of $1.00 per test administered. The test rental fee for the Subject Examinations is presently $5.00 per student tested for each Subject Examination.

The test rental fee includes scoring and reporting services. As mentioned earlier, institutional administrations apply only to regularly enrolled students, and scores are reported only to the college which is encouraged, though not obligated, to discuss the results with the students tested. The College Board scores all tests with the exception of the optional essay section of the Subject Examinations which is retained by the college for scoring. Scores for multiple-choice Subject Examinations are reported to the institution by alphabetical roster. For the General Examinations battery, thirteen scores are reported to the institution for each student tested (five total scores and eight sub-scores). Score reports are sent only to the institution administering the tests and are presented by both alphabetical roster and by an interpreted tabulating card for each student. The cards may be used for student records for reporting scores to students and for research purposes. Ordinarily, score reports are mailed to colleges approximately two weeks after their answer sheets have been received at the Educational Testing Service.

CLEP testing centers

Since October 1967, all College-Level Examinations have been available to any individual who wishes to take them at testing centers located in or near major cities in the United States. At this writing, there are approximately 55 such centers. The tests are administered during the third week of each month; this procedure, as well as the number of test centers, may change as the Program grows. The cost to the candidate is $15.00 for one or more of the General Examinations and $15.00 for each of the Subject Examinations. The fee schedule, like the number of CLEP centers and the testing procedure, may be altered as the Program matures. Candidates wishing to take the examinations submit their registration forms and fees directly to the test center administrators. A *Bulletin of Information for Candidates* is furnished to anyone requesting it. The *Bulletin* provides detailed information about registration procedures, test fees, center locations, and so forth.

Colleges and universities, employers, licensing agencies, and others, may, of course, refer any individual to College-Level Examinations via CLEP testing centers. Scores earned on CLEP center administered examinations are reported directly to the individual candidate along with an interpretative leaflet, "What Your Scores Mean," and to any institution, employer, or agency as directed by the candidate. Institutions wishing scores should request the candidate to release them. Candidate *Bulletins* and registration forms are available from CLEP, Box 592, Princeton, New Jersey 08540.

The Program is prepared to establish additional centers when sufficient candidate volume is reasonably assured. The Program arranges for special administrations of the examinations for individuals who would be required to travel more than 100 miles to a regular center.

Publications and information services

The following publications are presently available, and most are revised periodically. Other publications will be developed as the need arises and may also be obtained by writing to:

Program Director
College-Level Examination Program
Box 592
Princeton, New Jersey 08540

A Description of the General Examinations
A Description of the Subject Examinations
Bulletin of Information for Candidates
College-Level Examination Program: Description and Uses
Credit by Examination for College-Level Study: An Annotated Bibliography
Progress Report
Score Interpretation Guide
What Your Score Means

Score Interpretation

The *Score Interpretation Guide* contains a great deal of information intended to help institutions evaluate student performance. These statistical data cover such areas as freshman, sophomore, and senior norms. For example—norms for sophomore students intending to major in broad areas—the social sciences, business, and education; correlations between Subject Examinations and end-of-course grades in the subject; and so forth. (See TABLE 1.) As mentioned earlier, the *Score Interpretation Guide* may be obtained by writing to the Program Director, College-Level Examination Program, Box 592, Princeton, New Jersey 08540.

Other sources that may be consulted to help in the interpretation of CLEP scores include the CLEP representative in the nearest College Board regional office, institutions now using the examinations, and normative data on 43,877 USAFI candidates who took the General Examinations. The latter will be discussed in the following section.

TABLE 1
GENERAL EXAMINATIONS
Percentile Ranks
College Sophomores—Spring 1963

Scaled score	ENGLISH			HUMANITIES			MATHEMATICS			NATURAL SCIENCES			SOCIAL SCIENCES—HISTORY			Scaled score
	Men	Women	Total	Men	Women	Total	Men	Women	Total	Men	Women	Total	Men	Women	Total	
800																800
780																780
760					99	99	99						99			760
740		99		99	98	98	98		99	99			98		99	740
720		98	99	98	96	97	97		98	98		99	97		98	720
700	99	97	98	97	95	96	96		98	96		97	96		97	700
680	98	96	97	96	93	95	93	99	96	94	99	96	94	99	96	680
660	95	94	95	94	92	93	89	98	93	92	97	94	90	98	94	660
640	93	91	92	93	90	92	85	96	90	88	94	91	85	95	90	640
620	90	86	88	91	85	88	79	95	86	82	93	87	82	93	87	620
600	86	79	83	88	79	84	75	93	83	77	89	83	77	89	83	600
580	82	73	78	85	74	80	68	91	79	70	86	77	72	85	78	580
560	78	66	73	78	67	73	61	87	73	64	82	73	66	80	73	560
540	74	57	66	73	60	67	53	83	67	59	78	68	63	73	68	540
520	67	50	59	69	51	61	46	77	60	49	72	60	56	67	61	520
500	60	43	52	63	43	54	41	72	55	43	66	54	49	59	54	500
480	51	35	44	57	36	47	33	65	47	39	58	47	41	53	47	480
460	43	28	36	48	28	39	28	57	41	32	46	39	34	44	39	460
440	35	22	29	39	24	32	23	48	34	25	38	31	26	34	30	440
420	27	16	22	29	18	24	18	38	27	19	29	24	20	27	24	420
400	21	12	17	20	13	16	14	28	21	15	22	18	15	19	17	400
380	15	9	12	12	9	11	8	15	11	9	13	11	10	14	12	380
360	10	6	8	7	5	6	2	4	3	5	9	7	6	10	8	360
340	6	4	5	4	1	3				3	6	4	3	5	4	340
320	4	3	4	1						1	3	2	1	3	2	320
300	2	2	2								2	1		1	1	300
280	1	1	1													280
Mean	482	516	498	483	518	499	529	461	498	518	474	498	514	481	498	Mean
Standard deviation	98	98	99	97	99	99	102	80	99	102	90	99	104	91	99	Standard deviation
No. of sophomores	1375	1207	2582	361	317	678	360	303	663	343	290	633	310	297	607	No. of sophomores

Scaled Scores for Selected Percentiles

Percentile																Percentile
75	545	585	570	549	582	564	600	513	566	595	528	571	594	550	568	75
50	477	520	494	463	516	489	530	444	487	523	465	489	505	473	488	50
25	413	451	428	414	444	422	448	394	413	440	408	424	433	413	423	25

CLEP–USAFI and CASE

Procedures in applying for CLEP testing

Under a special arrangement between the College-Level Examination Program and the United States Armed Forces Institute (USAFI), the General Examinations of CLEP are available for administration to members of the Armed Forces. Service personnel interested in taking the examinations should consult with the education officer of the nearest military base, or write to USAFI, Madison, Wisconsin.

Military personnel on active duty should make arrangements through the USAFI Testing Section at the installation or base. If no USAFI Testing Section is available, applications should be made to USAFI, Madison, Wisconsin, or the appropriate USAFI center overseas, for the application form (DD Form 179, Application for USAFI Test or Examination). The completed form must be certified by a duly appointed USAFI Test Control Officer at the base or installation. Upon approval of the test application by the appropriate USAFI office, testing materials are forwarded to the USAFI Test Control Officer through the commanding officer. The applicant is notified when the test materials have been forwarded to the USAFI Test Control Officer. Arrangements should then be made with the Test Control Officer for administration of the tests.

*Recommendations for use of
CLEP results—25th percentile*

Each college or university determines its own policy with regard to admission and placement. However, to assist institutions, and at the request of regional and national accrediting associations and other national organizations and with their cooperation, the Commission on Accreditation of Service Experiences has prepared the following recommendations on the use of the General Examinations and the Subject Examinations:

GENERAL EXAMINATIONS

1. That the examinee achieve a score at or above the 25th percentile on each test. This measure of achievement is based upon the data collected in the national normative study. However, institutions are urged to administer the tests to their own students and to establish a minimum score consistent with the standards of the institution.

2. That six semester hours of credit be granted for each test or the amount of credit the institution normally grants in the areas covered by the tests.

3. That the total amount of credit granted for all five tests not exceed 30 semester hours of credit, or the equivalent of one academic year. However, the Commission suggests that credit might be assigned at either the freshman or sophomore level according to institutional policy in providing instructional programs in the area of the test.

SUBJECT EXAMINATIONS

1. That the examinee achieve a score at or above the 25th percentile of those students in the norming group who achieved a final course grade of C or better in their college class. Institutions are urged to administer the tests to their own students and to establish a minimum score consistent with the standards of the institution.

2. That the credit hours granted for each examination be the same amount normally assigned for the completion of a similar course given at the institution.

*Evaluation studies on CLEP General
Examinations and Subject Examinations*

The use of the College-Level Examinations by colleges and universities has been the subject of a study by national and regional commissions of higher education and by the Commission on Accreditation of Service Experiences of the American Council on Education. A study by the Federation of Regional Accrediting Commissions on Higher Education resulted in the adoption of a resolution at its March 4, 1964, meeting. In part, the resolution reads as follows:

Resolved, That the Federation of Regional Accrediting Commissions recommend to its constituent commissions, and through them to the institutions of higher education, responsible experimentation with these tests in connection with the increasing need for a program of continuing higher education for adult citizens and particularly as a basis for granting advanced standing or academic credit or both to qualified students.

Shortly after, the Commission appointed a special committee to give further study to the College-Level Examination Program. The committee was composed of representatives of national and regional commissions of higher education and other agencies interested in such a program. At its meeting on June 30, 1964, the committee reaffirmed the resolution cited above. Finally, at the meeting of the Federation of Regional Accrediting Commissions of Higher Education in October 1966, the following endorsement was approved:

COUNCIL ACTION:

The Council approved the action taken by the Executive Secretaries' Conference that the Federation approves the principle that students whose education has been gained in unconventional ways might be permitted to validate it through tests prepared and administered by such agencies as the College Entrance Examination Board.

There is no doubt that education outside college is growing. This increase puts a great responsibility on registrars and admissions officers. Nontraditional work must be evaluated, individual competencies must be measured, and standards must be maintained. The College-Level Examination Program provides a sound, adjustable way to perform these functions.

USAFI candidate performance

Through the cooperation of USAFI, the College Board has been furnished with score distributions of all USAFI candidates who took the complete battery of five General Examinations during the period July 1965—December 1966. A total of 43,877 candidates were tested. We have here, perhaps for the first time, some indication of the college-level achievement of a substantial number of American adults most of whom have not formally attended college.

The three tables which follow indicate some of the data that are now available. *Table A* shows percentile ranks for the total group of USAFI candidates. *Table B* shows percentile ranks for those USAFI candidates whose highest level of formal education completed was high school twelfth grade. *Table C* shows per-

TABLE A
GENERAL EXAMINATIONS
Percentile Ranks
All USAFI Candidates Taking Full Battery—July, 1965—December, 1966

Scaled score	ENGLISH COMPOSITION	HUMANITIES	MATHEMATICS	NATURAL SCIENCES	SOCIAL SCIENCES– HISTORY	Scaled score
800						800
780						780
760						760
740				99.7		740
720			99.6	99.3		720
700			99.3	99	99.5	700
680	99.6	99.6	99	98	99.1	680
660	99.3	99.3	98	97	99	660
640	99	99	97	96	98	640
620	98	98	96	92	97	620
600	97	98	93	92	95	600
580	96	97	91	88	93	580
560	94	95	88	85	90	560
540	92	93	84	80	87	540
520	88	89	80	74	82	520
500	85	85	73	68	77	500
480	79	79	69	61	69	480
460	74	71	63	53	62	460
440	67	63	55	45	54	440
420	59	51	47	38	45	420
400	51	41	38	29	36	400
380	42	29	29	22	26	380
360	33	19	19	16	18	360
340	25	11	10	10	11	340
320	17	3	3	6	5	320
300	11			3	1.7	300
280	3			1		280
260	2					260
240	0.06					240
220						220
200						200
Mean	407.	425.	443.	459.	441.	Mean
Standard deviation	88.	73.	90.	95.	85.	Standard deviation
Number tested	43,877	43,877	43,877	43,877	43,877	Number tested

TABLE B
GENERAL EXAMINATIONS
Percentile Ranks
USAFI Candidates—Highest Grade Completed—12th Grade

Scaled score	ENGLISH COMPOSITION	HUMANITIES	MATHEMATICS	NATURAL SCIENCES	SOCIAL SCIENCES– HISTORY	Scaled score
800		99.9+		99.9+	99.9+	800
780		99.9+	99.9+	99.9+	99.9+	780
760	99.9+	99.9+	99.9+	99.9+	99.9+	760
740	99.9+	99.9+	99.9+	99.9	99.9+	740
720	99.9+	99.9+	99.9	99.7	99.9	720
700	99.9+	99.9	99.8	99.5	99.8	700
680	99.8	99.8	99.6	99.2	99.6	680
660	99.7	99.7	99.3	99	99.3	660
640	99.4	99.5	99	97	99	640
620	99	99.3	98	96	98	620
600	98	99	96	94	97	600
580	97	98	94	91	95	580
560	96	97	92	88	93	560
540	94	95	89	84	90	540
520	91	92	85	79	87	520
500	88	88	80	73	82	500
480	84	83	75	66	75	480
460	78	76	68	57	68	460
440	72	68	61	50	59	440
420	64	58	52	42	50	420
400	55	45	42	33	40	400
380	46	32	32	24	30	380
360	37	21	21	18	20	360
340	27	12	12	11	12	340
320	19	4	4	7	6	320
300	11			4	2	300
280	4			1		280
260	2					260
240	0.6					240
220						220
200						200
Mean	396.	415.	430.	447.	429.	Mean
Standard deviation	83.	67.	80.	90.	78.	Standard deviation
Number tested	30,368	30,368	30,368	30,368	30,368	Number tested

centile ranks for those USAFI candidates who had had one year of college.

Here are some of the observations based not only on the tables but on all of the data obtained from USAFI.

a. Among candidates tested by USAFI there is evidence of thousands of people whose achievement would qualify them for consideration for college credit on the basis of recommendations made by the Commission on Accreditation of Service Experi-

ences* (CASE) of the American Council on Education. CASE recommends that credit and advanced standing be awarded to adults, both military and civilian, for scores at or above the 25th percentile of the national college norming groups.

---

* *Opportunities for Educational and Vocational Advancement*, Bulletin No. 10, June 1965. Commission on Accreditation of Service Experiences, American Council on Education, Washington, D.C.

TABLE C
GENERAL EXAMINATIONS
Percentile Ranks
USAFI Candidates—Highest Grade Completed—13th Grade

Scaled score	ENGLISH COMPOSITION	HUMANITIES	MATHEMATICS	NATURAL SCIENCES	SOCIAL SCIENCES– HISTORY	Scaled score
800		99.9+	99.9	99.9+		800
780	99.9+	99.9+	99.8	99.8	99.9+	780
760	99.9+	99.9+	99.7	99.6	99.9	760
740	99.9+	99.9+	99.4	99.1	99.8	740
720	99.8	99.9	99	99	99.5	720
700	99.5	99.7	98	98	99	700
680	99	99.4	97	96	98	680
660	98	99	95	94	97	660
640	98	98	93	92	95	640
620	96	97	90	88	93	620
600	94	95	85	84	90	600
580	92	93	80	78	86	580
560	88	90	74	73	81	560
540	84	85	67	66	75	540
520	78	79	60	58	68	520
500	72	72	53	50	60	500
480	64	64	46	42	50	480
460	55	54	39	34	42	460
440	47	44	32	27	33	440
420	38	34	26	21	25	420
400	30	23	19	15	18	400
380	22	14	13	10	11	380
360	16	8	8	7	7	360
340	11	4	4	4	3	340
320	6	1	1	2	1	320
300	3			1	0.5	300
280	2			0.4		280
260	0.6					260
240	0.1					240
220						220
200						200
Mean	451.	458.	493.	502.	483.	Mean
Standard deviation	89.	76.	96.	96.	86.	Standard deviation
Number tested	4902	4902	4902	4902	4902	Number tested

b. The average USAFI candidate exceeded the score levels recommended by CASE for consideration for college credit in three of the five tests, and in the other two, for all practical purposes, equalled the level recommended.

c. Although the total USAFI candidate group had average scores on each of the examinations lower than regularly matriculated students tested at the end of their sophomore year in college, it should be emphasized that only 20 out of 100 USAFI candidates have attended college at all.

d. The data reveal that there were thousands of adults who had not attended college whose scores exceeded those of the average college-taught sophomores.

e. The USAFI data substantiate the

CLEP premise that educational achievement among American adults is substantial and beyond that which might be indicated solely on the basis of records of formal college attendance. For instance, among the approximately 44,000 candidates tested, only 4200 claimed completion of formal college work beyond the freshman year. As measured by the General Examinations and following standards recommended by CASE, the number of individuals whose achievement was beyond freshman year varies from test to test but ranges from 18 to 24 thousand.

f. The USAFI data, of course, also show that thousands of candidates were not able to demonstrate achievement at the college level. The Program points to this aspect of the results only to indicate that the examinations are rigorous and do discriminate among candidates and that all who take them do not necessarily succeed.

g. The USAFI data add to the store of validity information for the General Examinations. All other things being equal, one would expect General Examinations scores to increase with the amount of formal education completed. This was observed with the USAFI data. There is a steady progression of scores on all tests when mean scores are tabulated according to formal education completed from high school twelfth grade to four years of college. In fact, the data suggest, as a rough rule, that for the USAFI group four years of college added approximately 100 points to General Examinations scores.

h. USAFI also furnished score data by age of candidate tested. These data offer no encouragement to the idea that CLEP General Examinations are biased against the older candidate. For two examinations the oldest candidate group (those over 40 years of age) had the highest mean scores. For the remaining examinations, the lowest mean scores were attained by candidates of ages somewhere between the youngest and the oldest groups tested.

Veterans in increasing numbers are seeking college admission; and because more and more adults, who have acquired their learning through nontraditional ways, are seeking recognition for their work, it seems advisable that institutions participating in CLEP should publish definitive policy statements in their catalogs and elsewhere to encourage all candidates to submit their CLEP scores. For veterans, the opportunity to obtain credit through CLEP means their government educational benefits can be used more effectively. For an educationally ambitious individual the opportunity to move forward and to obtain recognition for previous learning provides incentive and encouragement.

CLEP and the Colleges

A large number of two- and four-year colleges have indicated their support of the Program. A list of these institutions may be obtained by writing to the nearest College Board regional office. Some of the ways in which colleges have determined to use the General Examinations and the Subject Examinations are discussed below. Their uses by businesses and industrial firms are contained later in this report. It should be emphasized that additional and new uses of the examinations will occur after this writing. For details relative to the multiple uses of the examinations, write to the appropriate regional office of the College Entrance Examination Board or to the College-Level Examination Program, Box 592, Princeton, New Jersey 08540.

Multiple use by the colleges

1. To provide alternate channels for meeting General Education requirements (University of Iowa, Iowa City, Iowa).

2. To assist transfer and all continuing students in the transition to upper-class study (Florida Southern College, Lakeland, Florida).

3. To help in the assessment of all transfer applicants (University of Pittsburgh, Pittsburgh, Pennsylvania).

4. To allow a junior college to compare its graduating sophomores with the national norms and to provide a counseling tool for working with graduates (Montgomery Junior College, Takoma Park, Maryland).

5. To provide alternate means of satisfying specific course requirements (Boston University, Boston, Massachusetts).

6. To provide information for use in the

admission and placement of adults in a special beginning college program (Queens College of the City University of New York, Flushing, New York).

7. To provide an alternate means by which persons without a degree may qualify for admission to graduate programs (Graduate School of Business, University of Chicago, Chicago, Illinois; and the Advanced Management Program, Michigan State University, East Lansing, Michigan).

8. To provide information for the educational counseling of enrolled students (New College, Sarasota, Florida).

9. To recognize the continued growth and development of individuals in the military service (United States Armed Forces Institute, Madison, Wisconsin).

10. To recognize superior preparation and accomplishment of high school students at the point of entrance (The American University, Washington, D.C.).

11. To ensure basic levels of achievement in liberal arts areas of students in secondary education programs who seek to enroll for student teaching (San Diego State College, San Diego, California).

12. To assist in the evaluation and placement of foreign students (Pratt Institute, Brooklyn, New York).

CLEP–Business and Industry

During the past two decades, business and industry have developed educational and training programs that match in size the entire university and college systems. More than 32,000 such programs are presently operating.

A number of business and industrial organizations and other agencies have therefore made use of the College-Level Examination Program. These include a quasi-governmental agency, such as The Port of New York Authority, and a business organization, such as Pitney-Bowes, Inc., which used the General Examinations to determine college equivalency to meet promotion requirements. The Georgia State Board of Bar Examiners requires the General Examinations of all applicants for the State Bar Examination who

do not have a college degree. Graduates of two-year, post-high school, technical training programs in Georgia may take the General Examinations and have the results used by the State to indicate on their records that they have the equivalent of two years of college training in certain areas.

In all these cases the agency or organization involved makes its own judgment about the standards it will establish. However, this judgment is usually based on the normative information provided and in many cases on some use of the Commission on Accreditation of Service Experiences' recommendation.

For Further Information about CLEP

Institutions, collegiate and noncollegiate, wishing further information about the College-Level Examination Program may obtain printed materials heretofore cited by writing to:

Program Director
College-Level Examination Program
Box 592
Princeton, New Jersey 08540

Staff members in each of the College Board regional offices are also available to discuss CLEP. The addresses of the regional offices are as follows:

Midwest: 625 Colfax Street
Evanston, Illinois 60201
Telephone: 312 UNiversity 9-1840

Northeast: 475 Riverside Drive
New York, New York 10027
Telephone: 212 866-4400

South: Sewanee, Tennessee 37375
Telephone: 615 598-5668

Southwest: 2813 Rio Grande Street
Box 7276
Austin, Texas 78712
Telephone: 512 GReenwood 6-7641

West: 800 Welch Road
Palo Alto, California 94304
Telephone: 415 DAvenport 1-5211

INDEX
AIR FORCE

INDEX
ARMY

INDEX
COAST GUARD

INDEX
MARINE CORPS

INDEX
NAVY

INDEX
DEPARTMENT OF DEFENSE

AMERICAN COUNCIL ON EDUCATION

LOGAN WILSON, *President*

The American Council on Education, founded in 1918, is a *council* of educational organizations and institutions. Its purpose is to advance education and educational methods through comprehensive voluntary and cooperative action on the part of American educational associations, organizations, and institutions.

The Commission on Accreditation of Service Experiences, established in 1945, serves as an agency concerned with the evaluation of educational experiences of service personnel, cooperating with educational institutions, national, regional, and state educational organizations, the Armed Forces of the United States, and the Veterans Administration. The Commission is also responsible for the policy direction and supervision of the GED Testing Service of the American Council on Education.